The Good Food Guide *1989*

The Good Food Guide *1989*

Edited by Drew Smith

Published by Consumers' Association
and Hodder & Stoughton

Which? Books are commissioned and researched by
The Association for Consumer Research and published by
Consumers' Association,
2 Marylebone Road, London NW1 4DX and
Hodder and Stoughton,
47 Bedford Square, London WC1B 3DP

Special thanks for this year's *Guide* to John Crawford Fraser
for the cover illustration, Mon Mohan for the cover design,
Tim Higgins for the typography. The maps are by
Cartographic Services (Cirencester) Ltd

British Library Cataloguing in Publication Data
Smith, Drew
The good food guide
1989
I. Restaurants, lunch rooms, etc. –
Great Britain – Directories
I. Title II. Consumers' Association
647'.9541'05 TX 10.G7
ISBN 0 340 430656

Photoset in Linotron Meridien Medium
by Tradespools Ltd, Frome, Somerset
Printed and bound in The Netherlands
by Rotatie Boekendruk B.V., Krommenie

Contents

The year of the tigers p7
Further warning to restaurateurs: the good food certificates business p11
How to use this guide p14
The best of the year p19
Restaurants of the decade p21

Restaurants

London p23
England p157
Scotland p481
Wales p537
Isle of Man p579
Northern Ireland p581
Channel Islands p587

International

French Channel Ports p591
Paris: *Lucas Carton* p593
Lyon: *Paul Bocuse* p596
Nice: *Chantecler* p596
Bruges p598
Brussels p602
Milan: *Gualtiero Marchesi* p602
Venice p604
Leningrad: *Metropol* p607
Bangkok p610
Tokyo p613
Manila: *Seafood Market Restaurant* p615
Indonesia p617
New York: *Lutèce* p620
Philadelphia: *Susanna Foo* p623
West-Coast Chinatowns p627
Republic of Ireland p629
Travelling hopefully: the view from the dining car p631

Home thoughts

The search for flavour Tom Jaine p637
The plight of the northern restaurateur Peter Bramley p643
The last frontiersman Victor Sassie p645
The rise and rise of industrial bread Jill Norman p650
Cheese p655

Wines

Sweet things Kathryn McWhirter p673
What to drink in 1989 Roger Voss p678

General Lists p687
The Good Food Club 1988 p692
Alphabetical list of entries p709
Maps p719 Report forms p747

The year of the tigers

This is the year young British chefs have broken through. The established order among the top restaurants, which has been accepted for the last five to ten years, is under threat. The change is being brought about by the passionate commitment of a growing number of young chefs to whom the reputation for British cooking is passing. Quite how they will shape it in the coming years remains an open question, but for the moment it is plain that a great number of them are offering menus of much greater imagination and quality than their peers. Revolution is in the air.

The extraordinary aspect is just how young some of these chefs are – Marco Pierre White (*Harvey's*, London) 26; Garry Hollihead (*Sutherlands*, London) 28; Philip Britten (*Capital Hotel*, London) 30; Chris Chown (*Plas Bodegroes*, Pwhelli, Wales) 31; Aidan McCormack (as we go to press leaving *19 Grape Lane*, York, to set up his own restaurant) 30; David Cavalier (*Cavaliers*, London) 26; Simon Hopkinson (*Bibendum*, London) 34; Alastair Little (*Alastair Little*, London) 38; John Burton-Race (*L'Ortolan*, Shinfield) 31; Rowley Leigh (*Kensington Place*, London) 38.

These chefs are hungry to make a name and are cooking night after night, often to a very high level. They are re-defining ideas on what is good food and what are good restaurants. This irresistible surge has shown up some big reputations in a harsh light. Some –though not all – lack the all-round restaurant polish of their seniors, but judged strictly by what is on the plate they are making their way through the ratings at an electric pace.

It might be said that restaurants like *Alastair Little* or *Harvey's* should wait for their high ratings until their reputation has earned them enough money to move on to castles or manors or whatever. But this is firstly a food guide and who is to say that if the décor gets more comfortable, the cooking will improve? It would be wrong to saddle these young talents with the accepted baggage of restaurateuring when they are so obviously prepared to redefine the profession.

Take the example of Rowley Leigh, who has given up the Roux brothers' conservative City bastion, *Le Poulbot*, in favour of running a hi-tech brasserie at *Kensington Place*, which has been jam-packed since opening. 'I want people to come out to eat rather than to dine,' he says.

On the cooking front itself it has been a fascinating year. At *Bibendum*, Simon Hopkinson's bold decision to eschew so-called *nouvelle cuisine* and go back to some classical bourgeois cooking has put down a marker for the 1990s.

Equally, at the very top level there are signs of the logical development from the two-dimensional sauce and garnish cooking that has been in vogue for two decades. Alain Senderens is perhaps the best example of a new flavour dynamism – see the report on *Lucas Carton* in the International section. The same ambition might be seen in Raymond Blanc, John Burton-Race and perhaps a few others. The style is to create three and four dimensions of tastes and textures on the same plate, which in the eating produce a certain rhythm. This may sound fairly rarified and in a way it is, but it has a certain logic. If modern cooking is led by its respect for ingredients, then the kitchen must eventually choose between recreating classical dishes, as does Hopkinson, and concentrating on their interplay. Modern British cooking is just a stage in the process.

Money, money, money

The financing of these ambitious restaurants remains a problem. The ripple effect of London property prices has seen many of the younger chefs opening in the provinces. But Ian McAndrew has sold *Restaurant 74* in Canterbury and is heading back to Knightsbridge –too late for this edition – in the hope of finding a more solid customer base. David Adlard at Wymondham is looking for a restaurant with rooms to put his cooking on a firmer financial footing. The Fischers of Bakewell are doing much the same in moving to *Baslow Hall,* and hope to be open by the time the *Guide* is published. Two other founding fathers of the British Culinary Institute, Stephen Bull and René Gaté are both out of this year's *Guide* looking for new premises.

These moves underline the fragility of restaurateuring as an industry. It takes time to build a loyal clientele. The Gavroche after all began in 1963, so too the *Walnut Tree Inn* at Llandewi Skirrid. *Sharrow Bay* opened in 1949. Looking back, these seem the great restaurants maintained by chefs not prepared to leave the stove to someone else. But they are the exceptions.

Successful restaurants rarely last ten years. Only 70 have survived the *Guide*'s scrutiny every year since 1980; these are highlighted in the text with a rosette, and listed on page 21. All the rest have changed owners, changed chefs, changed premises, changed style, changed something which has led to their exclusion.

Of course the *Guide* entries represent only the tip of a hotel and catering industry currently employing just under 2.5 million people. Figures from the Hotel and Catering Training Board paint a picture of a fair rough and tumble of economic life: staff turnover running at 26 per cent a year; 93 per cent of people in the industry unskilled.

At the same time, the industry is doubling its size every four years. Fifty restaurants are said to be opening in Greater London every month.

Restaurants have to ride out this economic maelstrom. At their best they are part of the economy of their area, acting as the hub of the local food economy and establishing a reputation for local produce. The Lake District, Devon and now Gwynedd provide cogent example of how this can and does work in rural areas going over to tourism. In other counties the picture is less encouraging, with restaurants happy to bus their ingredients in from London or Paris markets and drawing very little from the surrounding area. For instance in Surrey, most of the restaurants are French. One might interpret that single fact as a sign that the local food economy has collapsed. The other explanation is that Surrey's French restaurants are a mark of its affluence. This is a depressing conclusion for anyone interested in the future of food in this country.

The root strength of French cooking is not the flamboyant displays of luxury in the current three-star *Michelin* and 19.5 *Gault Millau* restaurants in France or their would-be imitators in Surrey. The strength is in the numerous small, family-owned dining-rooms which support the local food producers, be they growers, grocers, bakers or butchers. It is the stability that comes from a series of interconnecting, interdependent businesses that creates the climate for these restaurants to flourish. The majority of the top restaurants open in France at the end of the 1970s are still in business.

There is a very fundamental difference here in thinking. Whereas in France small food producers are encouraged and supported, in this country we have tried to industrialise our foods and supported bigger and bigger companies. At the back of the *Guide* there are reports on bread and cheese. In this country, four companies dominate the production of these two staples. This has surely reduced the choice for the customer. And in both cases the picture in terms of quality is depressing.

The starkest contrast is between wine and beer. France has developed a worldwide industry based on small farms that can sell their wines for enormous premiums. We, on the other hand, have virtually given up making real ales and gone over to factory-produced lagers instead. Can we really afford to give up such a basic industry as brewing?

Service inc.

As the *Guide* goes to press, those working on the Consumer Protection Bill are drawing up code of practice guidelines specifically to cover the thorny question of service charges in restaurants. This will mark a victory for a long-running *Guide* campaign. The Bill is expected to recommend that all non-optional charges be included in the total price. This means service should be inclusive and no longer that grey area of yes-it-is-included-but-gratuities-are-at-your-discretion. It should also stop owners and senior staff snaffling the tips from younger staff. The guidelines are expected to come into force in 1989.

Another piece of legislation is likely to have a dramatic impact over the coming year. The extension of the licensing hours has finally brought the big breweries back into the food arena. There is going to be much activity as a result, which has already begun. On the one hand, some pubs are being done up as outlets for an international fast-food industry. But it has also been encouraging to see a number of pubs bucking the trend and giving food a good name again. The *Angel* at Hetton, and the *Rising Sun* at St Mawes present an alternative philosophy, a sort of English bistro for which there is obviously an enormous demand. It might be that the pub could provide the sort of stability that many chefs are struggling to find in specialist restaurants.

The ability of the discerning consumer to insist on standards by writing to guides like this may well play an important role. As a system it is proven. To everyone who has written in over the last year, many thanks . . . and also a small pat on the back for discovering good restaurants. In 1988 *Morels* at Haslemere got its *Michelin* star and picked up the restaurant of the year award from Egon Ronay. *Good Food Guide* readers had already discovered it four years ago, when it was rated 15/20. Another of Ronay's runners-up as restaurant of the year was *Restaurant 19* in Bradford, first discovered by *Guide* readers in January 1985 and listed ever since. Other recent successes that have gone on to be recognised belatedly elsewhere are John Burton-Race, rated 15/20 in 1985; *Altnaharrie Inn*, lauded on *Take Six Cooks* on TV and in Roy Ackerman's guide, was already 14/20 in the 1985 *Good Food Guide*. *Caterer and Hotelkeeper* predicted Bruno Loubet would make the very top in four years time. He was the *Good Food Guide* young chef of the year in 1984.

And while we are on the subject of raising our own soufflé, a rare chance arises to congratulate one of the usually anonymous inspectors who double-check restaurants recommended by readers. Marion Cooper won the *Observer*/Mouton Cadet Dinner Party Menu Competition. The judges said she had the equivalent of perfect pitch. Well done to her, and to everyone else who has worked so hard putting this edition together.

May this *Guide* lead you to many places to which you will want to return and will be inspired to report on. Good eating.

Drew Smith

Further warning to restaurateurs: the good food certificates business

The Association for Consumer Research and Consumers' Association, as publishers of *The Good Food Guide*, have been systematically protecting *The Good Food Guide*'s name through the courts. Anyone using the words 'good food guide' is trading illegitimately on our name.

We are aware of some 14 seemingly separate operations trading in the twilight world of selling certificates and the promise of advertising to restaurants and hotels. Some of these certificates suggest that restaurants have been inspected and reached a standard. Many restaurants have handed over substantial sums of money to acquire these pieces of paper. There are three different types of approach:

The bogus guide book

Restaurants are invited by letter to buy inclusion in a publication bearing a title which suggests association with a well-known guide book. They are asked to complete a questionnaire, sometimes similar in design to *The Good Food Guide*'s, and to return it with payment. What the restaurant gets for its money in the short term is a certificate. One letter from a 'guide' promoter said, 'Our sales target for '88 is expected to exceed all previous records.' Not difficult when there has not been a guide from the same source before.

The certificate

Some operations simply offer certificates of merit to restaurants prepared to pay. The wording on some certificates is designed to suggest that some inspection has taken place. One restaurant told us that it had been closed over the time the inspection was supposedly conducted. One certificate states: 'The XXXX restaurant has been seen to be a place of refreshment where the quality and style of the cuisine being offered meets the required standard'. Seeing is not quite the same as inspecting; nor is there any indication of the meaning of 'required standard'. The names that appear on the certificates have not always been those of the people behind the business of issuing them. They have been difficult or impossible to contact using the telephone and telex numbers given.

The TV link

Restaurants are invited to advertise on an electronic on-screen service, in one case asking £569.25. Restaurants are shown examples of how their advertisement might look, and are asked to fill in the details they wish to display. Access to these systems is via a special telephone number, using a modem to link the telephone to a computer or TV screen.

These are some of the operations:

THE GOOD FOOD GUIDE (INTERNATIONAL) based in the West Midlands, was produced by S. J. Ryan and his sister, Mrs. S. A. Stewart. Consumers' Association obtained an injunction in June 1987, preventing them from using the name THE GOOD FOOD GUIDE INTERNATIONAL, 'or any other name confusingly similar to *The Good Food Guide*' as a guide title. Shortly after, Mr Ryan and another partner, called Constantino, set up a second operation, called RAC PUBLISHING, which announced 'the forthcoming edition of our handbook.' The Royal Automobile Club took proceedings, which resulted in the two being committed for contempt of court. They were sent to jail.

THE GOOD FOOD GUIDE (UNITED KINGDOM), also based in the West Midlands, started up within months, using a virtually identical circular and similar certificates to the operation above. This operation is the subject of proceedings pending in the High Court. Undertakings have been given by the promoters of THE GOOD FOOD GUIDE (UNITED KINGDOM) that they will not trade again under this name until the matter comes to trial.

THE EUROPEAN GOOD FOOD GUIDE (UK) used an address in the West Midlands to canvass registration fees for inclusion in the '88/89 EUROPEAN GOOD FOOD GUIDE (UK). They were traced by a private investigator to a house in Inverness and subsequently to a tandoori restaurant in Forres. Consumers' Association has obtained an interdict in the Scottish Court of Session, equivalent to a permanent injunction in England.

THE TELEWORLD GOOD FOOD AND WINE GUIDE, based in Manchester and Cheltenham, sells electronic advertising. Teleworld offer certificates using typography very similar to that which we use for the title of *The Good Food Guide.*

TELEVISION INTERNATIONAL NETWORK (TIN) which operates from North-West London, sells electronic advertising for £569.25 (including VAT).

CONSUMER GUIDE is based in Milton Keynes and sells certificates for £37.57.

MASTER CHEF (THE ASSOCIATION OF HIGH CLASS FOOD ESTABLISHMENTS), based in Regent Street, London, sells certificates which have been seen in restaurants in Sheffield.

TDF ENTERPRISES LTD, based in Bishop's Stortford, sells a Chef's Golden Scroll of Excellence for £22.50.

EUROPEAN HOTELS DIRECTORY, working from Bristol, sells registration for a fee of £17, supposedly to prepare restaurants for the trade barriers with Europe coming down in 1992.

SELECTED RESTAURANT AND TAKE AWAY FOOD GUIDE, based in Soho, was asking in 1988 for 'a small remittance' of £84 for inclusion in the 1988 edition, to meet rising publishing costs, but in May was offering free inclusion. The publication has not been seen as the *Guide* goes to press.

NATIONAL GOOD CHEF'S GUIDE, based in Stowmarket, has been asking for £20 for inclusion.

GOOD FOOD CIRCLE, based in West London, sells framed certificates for £87.50.

THE GOOD FOOD AND RESTAURANT GUIDE, from a PO box number in London, asked for a payment of £78 for inclusion.

THE GOOD HOTEL GUIDE, using an address in London, and using exactly the title of *The Good Food Guide*'s sister publication, circulated letters asking for £39.50 for inclusion in a guide to be published in October. Consumers' Association immediately obtained an interim injunction.

What can be done?

Readers can help by informing us when and where you come across these certificates on display. Anyone seeing a certificate displayed from – in England and Wales:

THE GOOD FOOD GUIDE (INTERNATIONAL)

THE GOOD FOOD GUIDE (UNITED KINGDOM)

– or in Scotland:

THE EUROPEAN GOOD FOOD GUIDE (UK)

should draw the restaurant's attention to the fact that injunctions have been obtained against the above operations, and that their restaurant could be held to be in contempt of court if, having been notified of the injunction, it nevertheless continues to display certificates from these operations. Restaurateurs and hoteliers can help by telling us if they are approached.

Our advice is that such certificates, unless backed by bona fide research, are not worth the paper they are printed on. We undertake to protect the *Guide*'s good name and goodwill, taking legal proceedings as and where appropriate. Any letters that genuinely come out of this office carry the *Guide*'s address of 2 Marylebone Road, London NW1 4DX.

How to use this *Guide*

All the entries in this year's *Guide* have been rewritten between March and August. The information on which they are based is from reports sent in by readers over the last year and confirmed by anonymous inspection. No entry is based on a single nomination. In every case there has been a majority of readers and inspectors prepared to endorse the quality of the cooking, the dining-room and the value for money.

Prices quoted are for an average three-course meal with half a bottle of house wine and all extras included, as at summer 1988. Some may prove an approximation, because pricing policies change, but please let the office know of any steep rises.

The restaurants are rated out of a maximum of 20 points. All serve good food or they would not be included. The points are a measure of their success at what they set out to achieve.

Restaurants rated **9/20** will be small cafés, fish and chip shops, wine bars and almost always inexpensive.

Restaurants rated **10/20** and **11/20** will provide the best service in the area, but will not normally be overly expensive. In this category are also found restaurants offering good examples of a style of cooking.

Restaurants rated **12/20** and **13/20** will provide some of the best cooking in the county and will have convinced over a period of time that standards of both food and service are consistent.

Restaurants rated **14/20** and **15/20** will excel in at least one department over and above the usual expected good shopping, sensitive handling and good organisation.

Restaurants rated **16/20** and over will provide some of the best cooking currently to be found in this country.

New restaurants or restaurants which have recently undergone a change of chef or ownership are zero rated for one year if it has not been possible to assess them fully. Readers' reports are particularly useful on such places to help establish a firm view as to their quality. Usually they will be restaurants with the ambition to rate **12/20** or higher.

New this year are **County Round-ups**, mostly, but not always, listed under county towns (to find a County Round-up, check the maps at the back; towns listing a Round-up are underlined). This is a response to readers' requests for more information on an area, especially where the number of main entries is not large. Each address is listed for a particular reason and may be useful to a visitor with special requirements, offering for instance vegetarian foods, rooms to stay, afternoon teas or inexpensive light meals. These are not restaurants that have failed at inspection, but places that have not for one reason or another graduated to the main listings.

Up date As an annual guide the information will date through the year. It is always wise to book ahead and confirm that there have been no changes. For more up-to-date information, see the *Guide* column in *The Guardian* on Saturdays. All reports sent in to the *Guide* are acknowledged with brief notes on the latest changes.

How to read a *Guide* entry

CANTERBURY Kent 1 map 3 2

▲ *Mary's Kitchen* 3 [12/20] 4

16 Elwood Avenue, Canterbury CT41 4RX 5
CANTERBURY (0227) 7770666 6
behind Scala Cinema 7 8 £11–£19 9

(main text) 10 CELLARMAN'S CHOICE 11

CHEF: Mary Smith PROPRIETORS: Mary and David Smith 12
OPEN: Mon to Sat 13
CLOSED: Aug 14
MEALS: 12 to 2, 7 to 9 15
PRICES: £13 (£19). Set D £10.50 (£15). Snacks from £1.50. 16 Service 10% 17
CARDS: Access, Amex, Diners, Visa 18
SEATS: 72. 4 tables outside. Private parties: 26 main room, 10 private room. 19 Car-park. 40 places. Vegetarian meals. 20 Children's helpings. No children under 10. 21 Jacket and tie preferred. 22 No-smoking area. 23 Wheelchair access (2 steps; also WC). 24 Music. 25 One sitting. 26
ACCOMMODATION: 14 rooms, all with bath/shower. B&B £20 to £40. 27 No pets. 28 Afternoon teas. 29 Garden. Swimming-pool. Tennis (GHG)

1 The town and county (in the London section, restaurants are listed alphabetically by name rather than geographically).

2 The map number. The maps are at the end of the *Guide*.

3 The name of the restaurant. ▲ by the name denotes that it offers accommodation too.

4 The *Guide* rating out of 20 (see page 14).

5 The restaurant's address, with post code whenever possible.

6 The restaurant's telephone number, including its STD code.

7 Any special directions in case the restaurant is difficult to find.

8 This symbol is awarded only to restaurants with outstanding wine cellars, not disproportionately priced.

9 This is the price range for three-course meals including half a bottle of house wine, coffee, service and any hidden extras, such as a cover charge, as calculated by the *Guide.*

10 The text is based on reports sent in by readers during the last *Guide* year, confirmed by commissioned, anonymous inspections.

11 Most entries conclude with a CELLARMAN'S CHOICE. This is a wine, usually more expensive than the hosue wine, that the restaurateur assures us will be in stock during 1989, and that we recommend as suitable for the kind of food served, if you do not want to order the house wine.

12 The names of the chef and the owner, so that any change in management will be instantly detectable.

13 The days of the week the restaurant is open.

14 Annual closures.

15 The times of first and last orders for meals. It is always advisable to book before going to a restaurant. If you book and then cannot go, please remember to phone the restaurant to cancel.

16 These are typical prices for three-course meals, giving the à la carte price and variations for set lunch (L) and dinner (D) where applicable. The initial price represents the prices on the main menu; the second price, in brackets, is the real cost when the extras of wine, coffee and service (at 10% unless otherwise specified) have been added.

17 This indicates that a fixed service charge will be added to the bill. Where service is included in the menu prices this is specified. When service is not mentioned, it is at the discretion of the customer.

18 The credit cards accepted by the restaurant.

19 Not all restaurants will take private parties. The maximum number of people in a party is given.

20 Many restaurants claim to cater for vegetarians but do not include suitable dishes on their menus as a matter of course. It is always advisable to explain, when booking, if you do not eat meat.

21 Many restaurants and hotels are not keen on children. Where it says children welcome or children's helpings it indicates that they don't mind. Any limitations on age are specified.

22 Jackets and ties are compulsory in very few restaurants and this is specified; otherwise it means the proprietor prefers smart dress.

23 Any no-smoking arrangements as given to us by the restaurants.

24 Wheelchair access means that the entrance is 33 inches wide and the passages four feet across. Where there are steps it will say so. If it says 'also WC', then the toilet facilities are suitable for disabled people.

25 If a restaurant plays music, this is indicated.

26 The restaurant serves a single sitting at a specific time.

27 The price for rooms as given to us by the hotels. The first price is for one person in a single room, the second price is for two people in a double room.

28 Some hotels will not take pets; others prefer to be asked. It is best to check.

29 Teas are served to non-residents.

30 [GHG] denotes that this establishment is also listed in the 1989 edition of our sister guide, *The Good Hotel Guide*.

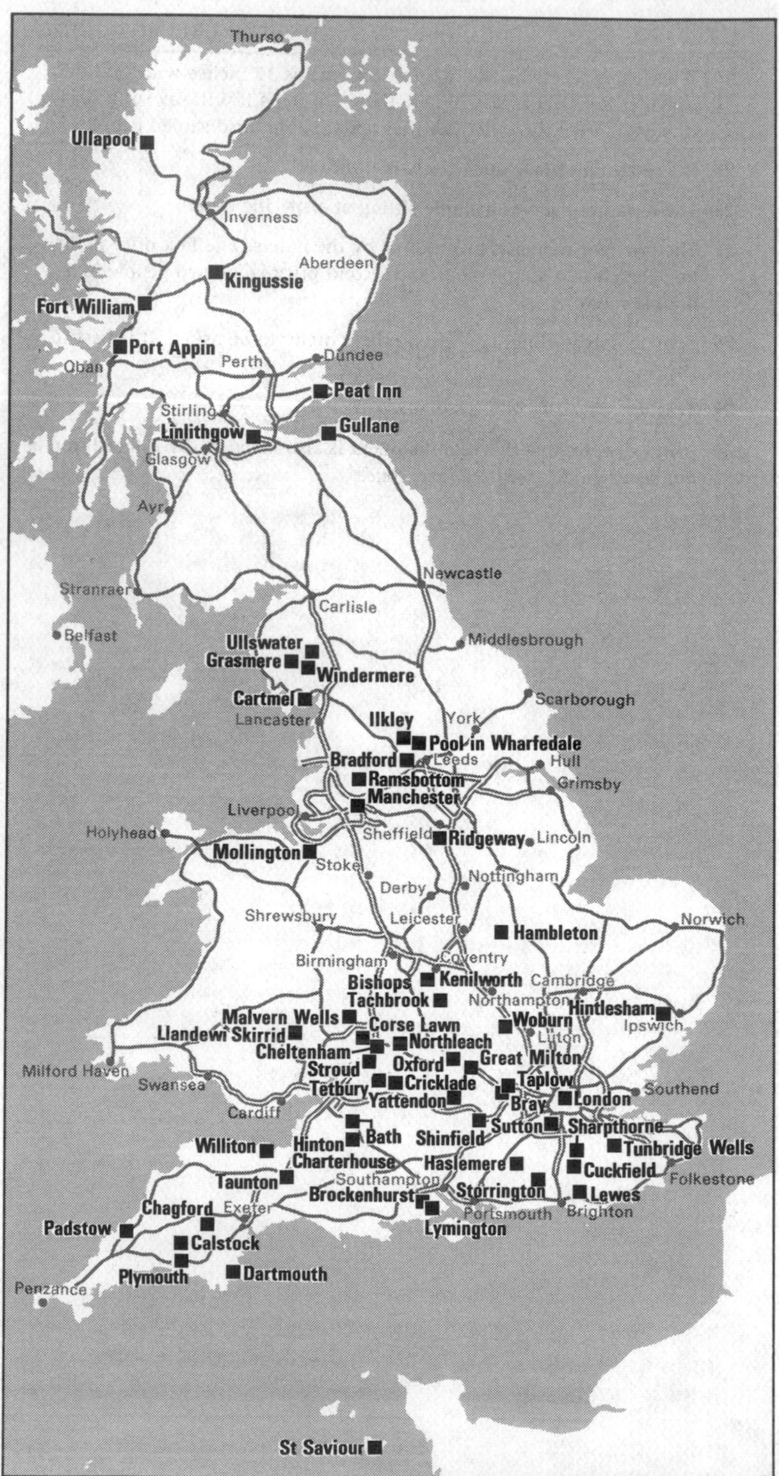

Cartographic Services (Cirencester) Ltd.

The best of the year

18/20

Le Gavroche, London
Le Manoir aux Quat' Saisons, Great Milton
Tante Claire, London

17/20

Alastair Little, London
Carved Angel, Dartmouth
Connaught, London
Harvey's, London
L'Ortolan, Shinfield
Simply Nico, London

16/20

L'Arlequin, London
Bibendum, London
Croque-en-Bouche, Malvern Wells
Gidleigh Park, Chagford
Inigo Jones, London
Oakes, Stroud
Le Petit Blanc, Oxford

15/20A

Airds Hotel, Port Appin
Altnaharrie Inn, Ullapool
Capital Hotel, London
Castle Hotel, Taunton
Gravetye Manor, Sharpthorne
Le Mazarin, London
Miller Howe, Windermere
Morels, Haslemere
Peat Inn, Peat Inn
La Potinière, Gullane
Le Poussin, Brockenhurst
Provence, Lymington
Rue St Jacques, London
Seafood Restaurant, Padstow
Sharrow Bay, Ullswater
Sutherlands, London
Turners, London
Walnut Tree Inn, Llandewi Skirrid
Waterside Inn, Bray
Whites, Cricklade
Yang Sing, Manchester

14/20

Auberge de Provence, St James's Court Hotel, London
Bistro 33, Dartmouth
Bombay Brasserie, London
Box Tree, Ilkley
Calcot Manor, Tetbury
Cavaliers, London
Champany Inn, Linlithgow
Chez Nous, Plymouth
Clarke's, London
Cliveden, Taplow
Clos du Roy, Bath
Corse Lawn House, Corse Lawn
Crabwall Manor, Mollington
Cross, Kingussie
Danescombe Valley Hotel, Calstock
Hambleton Hall, Hambleton
Hintlesham Hall, Hintlesham
Homewood Park, Hinton Charterhouse

Inverlochy Castle, Fort William
Kensington Place, London
Kenwards, Lewes
King's Head, Cuckfield
Langan's Brasserie, London
Longueville Manor, St Saviour
Mallory Court, Bishops Tachbrook
Manleys, Storrington
Mijanou, London
Neal Street Restaurant, London
Old Vicarage, Ridgeway
Old Woolhouse, Northleach
Paris House, Woburn
Partners 23, Sutton
Pool Court, Pool in Wharfedale
Redmond's, Cheltenham
Restaurant Bosquet, Kenilworth
Restaurant 19, Belvedere Hotel, Bradford
Royal Oak, Yattendon
Teignworthy Hotel, Chagford
Thackeray's Tunbridge Wells
Uplands, Cartmel
Village Restaurant, Ramsbottom
White House Hotel, Williton
White Moss House, Grasmere

Anglesey restaurant of the year Bull's Head, Beaumaris
Birmingham newcomer of the year Chung Ying Garden
Brasserie debut of the year Kensington Place, London
Buckinghamshire newcomer of the year Pebbles, Aylesbury
Chelsea restaurant of the year Bibendum, London
Chinese newcomer of the year Dragon's Nest, London
Cornish newcomer of the year Rising Sun, St Mawes
Derbyshire restaurant of the year Old Vicarage, Ridgeway
Glasgow newcomer of the year October, Glasgow
Grampian newcomer of the year Silver Darling, Aberdeen
Grampian restaurant of the year The Oaks, Craigendarroch Hotel and Country Club, Ballater
Gwynedd bistro of the year Bakestone, Caernarfon
Gwynedd newcomer of the year Plas Bodegroes, Pwhelli
Highland luxury of the year Inverlochy Castle, Fort William
Highland restaurant of the year Cross, Kingussie
London hotel debut of the year Capital Hotel
Soho newcomer of the year Sutherland's, London
Strathclyde café of the year Loch Fyne Oyster Bar, Cairndow
Surrey newcomer of the year Lichfields, Richmond
Tayside café of the year But 'n' Ben, Auchmithie

Restaurants of the decade

The following restaurants, marked in the text with a rosette, have had ten successive entries in the *Guide*, since the 1980 edition, under the same kitchen and management.

London

Anna's Place
Beotys
Blooms
Le Chef
Chez Moi
Chuen Cheng Ku
Connaught
Efes Kebab House
Le Gavroche
La Giralda
Hard Rock Café
Justin de Blank
Langan's Brasserie
M'sieur Frog
Poons
Le Suquet
Tante Claire
Tate Gallery

England

At the Sign of the Angel, Lacock
La Belle Epoque,Knutsford
Berties Bistro, Elland
Black Bull, Moulton
Blostin's, Shepton Mallet
Box Tree, Ilkley
Butley-Orford Oysterage, Orford
Byrons, Eastbourne
Carved Angel, Dartmouth
Cleeveway House, Bishop's Cleeve
Corse Lawn House, Corse Lawn
Croque-en-Bouche, Malvern Wells
Dundas Arms, Kintbury
Farlam Hall, Brampton
French Partridge, Horton
Gravetye Manor, Sharpthorne
Horn of Plenty, Gulworthy
Lantern, East Molesey
Lanterna, Scarborough
Manleys, Storrington
Le Manoir Aux Quat' Saisons, Great Milton
Miller Howe, Windermere
Munchy Munchy, Oxford
Old Fire Engine House, Ely
Old Parsonage, Farrington Gurney
Old Woolhouse, Northleach
Pool Court, Pool in Wharfedale
Plumber Manor, Sturminster Newton
Rothay Manor, Ambleside
Sharrow Bay Hotel, Ullswater
Splinters, Christchurch
Stane Street Hollow, Pulborough
Sundial, Herstmonceux
Waterside inn, Bray
White House Hotel, Williton
White Moss House, Grasmere
Yang Sing, Manchester

Scotland

Airds Hotel, Port Appin
Cringletie House, Peebles
Isle of Eriska Hotel, Eriska
Kinloch Lodge, Sleat
Peat Inn, Peat Inn
La Potinière, Gullane
Summer Isles Hotel, Achiltibuie
Timothy's, Perth
Ubiquitous Chip, Glasgow

Wales

Druidstone Hotel, Broad Haven
Meadowsweet Hotel, Llanrwst
Porth Tocyn Hotel, Abersoch
Walnut Tree Inn, Llandewi Skirrid

London

Alastair Little [17/20] map 14

49 Frith Street, W1V 5TE
01-734 5183 £29

Alastair Little's small, office-like Soho operation is the finest café in the country. It feels good that he should provide the first entry in the *Guide*; he is one of the young tigers who are re-defining British cooking. Little's contribution is simple and dramatic. He threw away a standard menu and changes his repertoire of ten starters, eight main courses, five sweets plus cheese, twice a day. The décor is modern, simple, noisy, functional, as is the service. The cooking is spontaneous and cosmopolitan, drawing nobly on all that the London markets can provide. Consommé, sashimi, pot roasts, truffle vinaigrette, couscous, Pavlova and tarte Tatin appear side by side. Examples of different cuisines shuffle across the tables: Chinese – sea-bass steak with soy; Italian – breast of chicken wrapped in Parma ham and leeks with truffle sauce; Greek – sauté of cuttlefish in its own ink. But it is all brought together with a skill and dedication that gives it a discernible personality and identity. Interesting touches make dishes memorable – the pickled cucumber with the gravlax; the onion marmalade with the terrine; the morels and chives with the pot-roast veal; the raspberry sauce on the passion-fruit mousse. For all its seeming lack of veneer this is cooking that is already dealing in the kind of combinations of flavours found only among the élite. The high rating reflects this cooking, even if, as a restaurant, it is stripped down to its essentials. Some readers, albeit impressed by the food, may find it hard to agree with 17. There are no pretensions here. But if high ratings can only go to restaurants with luxurious settings, then eating out will go on being expensive and elitist. 'The best table that I can afford in London,' is another view. The crucial point is that you eat *with* a chef, not just a collection of dishes, which also means that standards drop if the chef is away. In six months there have been recommendations for no fewer than 46 different dishes. The 35-bottle wine list is divided into whites, reds and champagnes, starting at £7.50. CELLARMAN'S CHOICE: Ch. du Grand Moulas '86, £11; Stratford Chardonnay '85, £14; Tinto Pesquera '85, £18.

CHEFS: Alastair Little and Juliet Peston PROPRIETORS: Mercedes Andre-Vega, Kirsten Pedersen and Alastair Little
OPEN: Mon to Fri
CLOSED: bank hols, last 3 weeks Aug
MEALS: 12.30 to 3, 7.30 to 11.30
PRICES: £21 (£29)
SEATS: 35. Children's helpings

Al Hamra [13/20] map 13

31–33 Shepherd Market, W1Y 7RJ
01-493 1954 and 6934 £20–£24

The cool, blue, expensive elegance of London's top Lebanese restaurant and its dazzling food pull in the crowds. Sunday lunch is the prime occasion for Middle Eastern families; at other times the clientele is multi-cultural. Tables are set with a basket of top-quality raw vegetables and a plate of superb olives. The strength of the cooking is in the daunting and brilliant selection of hot and cold starters: hummus; rich, lemony ful medames; stuffed vine leaves; pickled baby aubergines stuffed with rice and walnuts; filo pastries filled with spinach and onion; a meatless moussaka with aubergines, chickpeas and tomatoes. Main courses are primarily barbecued and grilled meats – chicken served with hot sauce and lemon; ground meat grilled with bulgur wheat and walnuts. Other details show the class of the restaurant –very light pitta bread, honeyed sweets baked on the premises, first-rate Turkish coffee. Service has become increasingly uncomprehending of late, more's the pity. House French on a short list is £7.50, or drink arak, from £15 the half-bottle.

CHEF: Hassan Mardani PROPRIETORS: R. Nabulsi and H. Fansa
OPEN: all week
CLOSED: 25 Dec, 1 Jan
MEALS: noon to midnight
PRICES: £11 (£24), Set L and D from £10 (£20). Cover £1. Minimum £7
CARDS: Access, Amex, Diners, Visa
SEATS: 73. 4 tables outside. Private parties: 80 main room. Vegetarian meals. Children's helpings. Wheelchair access. Music

Andrew Edmunds [9/20] map 13

46 Lexington Street, W1R 3LH
01-437 5708 £18

Owned by the next-door print-shop, this handy wine bar has the feel of some of the 1960s Soho coffee-bars and night-clubs – Les Enfants Terribles or La Poubelle – but has a 1980s persuasion in food. A sensible short menu buys cleverly in the area – pasta from Lina's in Brewer Street, cheeses from Camisa's in Old Compton Street – and stays within the realms of tomato and Mozzarella salad; charred duck breast with walnut salad; smoked ham with mustard sauce; Greek yoghurt with honey and fresh fruit. 'It is almost an anti-restaurant – no name over the door, no décor, no service but honest food.' House Spanish and French on a 60-bottle list, £6. CELLARMAN'S CHOICE: Rioja Contino, Gran Reserva '80, £8.50.

CHEF: John Quigley PROPRIETORS: Andrew and Bryony Edmunds
OPEN: Mon to Fri
MEALS: 12.30 to 3, 5.30 to 10.30
PRICES: £12 (£18). Cover 35p at L
CARDS: Access, Visa
SEATS: 48. 2 tables outside. Private parties: 20 main room, 20 private room. Vegetarian meals. Children welcome. No pipes in dining-room. Wheelchair access

Anna's Place [12/20]

map 11

90 Mildmay Park, N1 4PR
01-249 9379 £18

If the mood among London chefs has been to return to one's roots, then once again Anna Hegarty finds herself in front. While for others it has been a pilgrimage back to Elizabeth David and the Mediterranean, Anna has gone the other way, north to Scandinavia. No more tapénade, no more pasta salad. The only signs of Frenchness, a technique that she and Redmond Hayward (now at Redmond's, Cheltenham, see entry) accomplished with more than a little success in the mid '80s, are now a slurp of calvados for the pheasant and the deep fried Camembert. For the rest, a fickle patriotism is emerging, almost to the point that the menu has become a homage to Swedish cooking – two kinds of marinated herring, the exemplary gravlax, turbot with brown butter and horseradish, waffles with blueberry conserve, applecake with vanilla. 'Honest unfussed cooking,' is how Anna Hegarty explains it in one of her famous monologues. When ordering, it is wise to be careful not to double up on the sweet tangy seasonings, most obviously from the mustards and anchovies, which otherwise tend to take over. The atmosphere is café-like and always lively. Schnapps and Swedish beer, both at £1.15, seem most appropriate, though the wine list is compiled with acumen. House red and white £5.25.

CHEFS: James McCarthy and Roz Mason PROPRIETOR: Anna Hegarty
OPEN: Tue to Sat
CLOSED: 2 weeks at Christmas and Easter; Aug
MEALS: 12.30 to 2.30, 7.15 to 10.45
PRICES: £13 (£18). Service 10%
SEATS: 52. 5 tables outside. Private parties: 10 main room. Vegetarian meals. Children's helpings. Smart dress preferred. Wheelchair access. Music

L'Arlequin [16/20]

map 10

123 Queenstown Road, SW8 3RH
01-622 0555 £22–£40

Christian Delteil has been a smouldering talent for a number of years. Premature recognition did not perhaps help him. He is a technician comfortably at ease with modern cooking – an ink sauce for brill; ravioli with fennel and scallops; Challans duck served as two courses, first the breast, then (quite a long time after) the crisped legs. Mixed with the pretty visuals is a bourgeois theme that appears particularly among main dishes – a tapénade with lamb, pigeonneau fermier 'comme en vessie'; crépinette de ris de veau aux lentilles. The cooking has progressed. When he first opened, a chaud-froid of fruits was just a plate of fruits and sabayon placed under the grill. By last year this dish had become an ice-cold plate set with a feather fruit purée around a centre of vanilla ice-cream on to which was set cream and fruit flashed under the grill to get an effect of hot and cold. The style is French and international with *Michelin* pretensions, but the prices also bring some interesting producers on to the menu – for instance the liver of monkfish served in a feuilleté as a starter. M. Delteil complains that we always mention his sorbets, but they are very good; not so the crème brûlée which on two inspections had curdled. Sometimes the cooking lacks real vigour and zeal as if the kitchen has been distracted, and slips occur. Presumably it is only the quality of the saucing which has held off the second *Michelin* star, that and a certain lack of fusion of ideas. The menu offers more choice of cooking techniques than most hotels – in June sweets offered feuilleté, marquise, tulipe, sablé, the chaud froid, gratiné, soufflé. The wine list is typically badly balanced, with an over-preponderance in the £50-plus range. House wines open at £9.

CHEFS/PROPRIETORS: Mr and Mrs C. Delteil
OPEN: Mon to Fri
CLOSED: 1 week in winter, 3 weeks Aug
MEALS: 12.30 to 2, 7.30 to 11
PRICES: £33 (£40), Set L £14.50 (£22). Cover £1. Service inc
CARDS: Access, Amex, Diners, Visa
SEATS: 45. Children welcome. Jacket and tie. No pipes in dining-room. Wheelchair access (also WC). Music. Air-conditioned

Au Bois St Jean [10/20] map 11

122 St John's Wood High Street, NW8 7SG
01-722 0400 £23

The High Street has become as recherché as South Kensington, with galleries and the sort of village gentrification that took hold in outer Chelsea. The Bois, though, is a basement selling its Frenchness by the kilo – the waiters with their difficulty with English, the *chansons*, the menu that should be a good evocative rendition, but sometimes a bit cut-price – thin gruelly sétoise soup, thin-cut salmon in two sauces – but a body of readers point to sauté duck with cream sauce; chicken with mustard sauce; veal stuffed with chicken liver; carré d'agneau with garlic; very rich wood-pigeon; the cheeses and the brochette de fruit as being good enough, were it in France. House French £6. CELLARMAN'S CHOICE: Côtes du Ventoux Rouge '85, £7; Côtes de Bourg, Ch. Cazelles '83, £10.50.

CHEF: Jean-Claude Broussly PROPRIETORS: Cellier du Midi Ltd
OPEN: all week, exc Sat L
CLOSED: 25 and 26 Dec
MEALS: 12 to 2.30, 7 to 11.30
PRICES: Set L and D £16.50 (£23)
CARDS: Access, Amex, Diners, Visa,
SEATS: 65. Private parties: 20 main room, 20 private room. Vegetarian meals. Children's helpings (L only). Smart dress preferred. Music

Auberge [11/20] map 10

44 Forest Hill Road, SE22 ORR
01-299 2211 £11–£21

Sami Youssef has carved himself a good local reputation for his little corner of France. Sunday lunch is very much a family occasion. He cooks with authority – a generous cassoulet of duck; proper chocolate mousse and crème brûlée. There is no truck with anything beyond bourgeois cooking – moules marinière; gratin of seafood – and no embarrassment at offering egg mayonnaise. Good coffee, plenty of refills. House French £5.45.

CHEF.PROPRIETOR: Sami Youssef
OPEN: Mon to Sat D, and Sun L
CLOSED: 3 weeks end Aug
MEALS: 12 to 3, 7 to 10.30
PRICES: Set Sun L £6.95 (£11), Set D £16.50 (£21). Service 10%. Licensed, also bring your own: corkage £2
CARDS: Access, Visa
SEATS: 38. Private parties: 30 main room. Vegetarian meals. Children's helpings (L only). Wheelchair access (1 step; also WC). Music

▲ *Auberge de Provence, St James's Court Hotel* [14/20]

map 11

51 Buckingham Gate, SW1E 6AF
01-834 6655

£25–£42

The least pretentious of the franchises to three-star *Michelin* restaurants in France. Raymond Thuilier, founder and inspiration of the beautiful gardened L'Oustau de Baumanière (thirty years a three-star restaurant) at Les Baux de Provence, has handed control over to his grandson, Jean-André Charial. This London end of the operation is supported by TAJ International Hotels' investment in the luxurious St James's Court Hotel. Three stars it is not, more like a junior three stars, yet the menu has character. But at the end of 1987 Yves Gravelier joined as head chef, after training at Frères Troisgros at Roanne, and the dining-room moved down the road to number 51. At once, the tenor of reports picked up. The dishes are those of an accomplished kitchen: lobster served with a red and yellow pepper cream sauce; sea-bass steamed plainly and served on tomato and basil; John Dory poached in crab liquor with sliced olive; scallops cooked as a fricassee with cabbage and a sauce of tarragon; salmon with red wine. Such sophistication is balanced by an earthy regional representation of navarin of lamb; daube des mariniers du Rhône; ratatouille; gratin dauphinois. Olive oil and wines are from Les Baux, the latter alas expensive, but of fine pedigree as much in the Rhône and Provence sections as the Bordelais. House Côtes du Ventoux £9. CELLARMAN'S CHOICE: Châteauneuf-du-Pape blanc, Domaine du Mont Redon '86, £7.50 for a half-bottle.

CHEF: Yves Gravelier PROPRIETORS: TAJ International Hotels
OPEN: Mon to Sat, exc Sat L
MEALS: 12.30 to 2.30, 7.30 to 11
PRICES: £29 (£42), Set L £17.50 (£25). Licensed, also bring your own: corkage £8
CARDS: Access, Amex, Diners, Visa
SEATS: 90. Private parties: 8 main room. Vegetarian meals. Air-conditioned
ACCOMMODATION: 390 rooms and 90 apartments, all with bath/shower. Rooms for disabled. Lift. B&B £110. Baby facilities. Afternoon teas. Garden. Sauna. Air-conditioning. TV. Phone

Auntie's [11/20] map 13

126 Cleveland Street, W1P 5DN
01-387 3226 £22

There are still echoes of the tea-room in this small narrow dining-room with an Edwardian-style frontage, intense green walls and black upholstered sofas. Shaun Thomson has left, but the kitchen still delivers a convincing version of English home cooking, with some *nouvelle* touches in the presentation. There are plenty of recommendations for crab pâté, Cornish spiced shrimps and beef and mushroom pie with Guinness. Grilled Barnsley chop is good, well-hung meat; trout is baked in paper with mushrooms. Fish generally has been particularly well handled. Tipsy fruit trifle, Nanny Campbell's lemon fluff and bread-and-butter pudding are typical of the old-fashioned sweets. The wine list has some English bottles, but house wine is from Duboeuf at £7.

CHEF: Ian Tozer PROPRIETORS: Auntie's Brasserie Ltd
OPEN: Mon to Sat, exc Sat L
CLOSED: 2 weeks Aug
MEALS: 12 to 2.45, 6 to 10.45
PRICES: Set L and D £15 (£22). Service 12.5%
CARDS: Access, Amex, Diners, Visa
SEATS: 27. 2 tables outside. Private parties: 30 main room. Vegetarian meals. Children welcome. Wheelchair access (1 step). Music

Aventure [11/20] map 11

3 Blenheim Terrace, NW8 4JS
01-624 6232 £17–£22

Catherine Parisot runs a proper French restaurant. The menu takes an attractive middle course between bistro and *nouvelle* – mixing moules marinière or crudités with a sole stuffed with spinach, or nougatine parfait. The cooking is precise – crêpes filled with smoked salmon with a cream sauce garnished with chervil; lamb en croûte. Some reporters seem bedevilled by silly niggles, but no one complaint is repeated and they seem to have merely had bad luck. Prices are not extortionate and it is in its way a genuine place. House French is £6.25.

CHEF: Christian Breteche PROPRIETORS: Catherine Parisot and Chris Mitas
OPEN: all week, exc Sat L
MEALS: 12.30 to 2.30, 7 to 11
PRICES: Set L and D £16.50 (£22), Set Sun L and D £12.50 (£17)
CARDS: Access, Amex, Visa
SEATS: 38. 6 tables outside. Private parties: 40 main room. Vegetarian meals. Children's helpings. No cigars/pipes in dining-room. Music

'Since the waiter pointed out the misprint of suprême of chicken listed under "vegetarian", I presume that smoked salmon over whiskey cask chippings was not all that one might have expected.' On eating in Scotland

Bahn Thai [13/20] map 14

21A Frith Street, W1V 5TS
01-437 8504 **£28**

One of the most evolved of Thai restaurants, run by an Englishman, Philip Harris (who trained as a chef), and his Thai wife. The black tablecloths and dark upholstery make the downstairs look narrow, with pot plants hanging from the ceiling, while upstairs is more spacious, better for parties. As ever, Thai cuisine seems to enchant with its mixes of last-minute cooking and exotic, surprising herbs and seasonings. The hot-and-sour mixed seafood soup served in a steamboat is a strong stock containing large pieces of chilli, mussels in the shell, crab claws and long stems of green coriander, very hot and very sour. Sea-bass is poached over mixed vegetables and served in a terracotta fish-shaped bowl over glowing charcoal, with spiced lemon-grass and ginger, accompanied by steamed rice. Recommendations include the six dim-sum dumpling starter for £2.70 – 'ever-so-delicate pasta encasing pork and crunchy bean sprouts in a soy, chilli and garlic sauce, this was class, – marinated roasted duck, and vegetables coated with coconut cream. Mr Harris has reintroduced a 75p cover charge, because, he says, 'too many customers were coming in for noodles, free crackers and tea.' He is also organising gastronomic tours of Thailand. There is guidance on how to combine the different dishes, but look especially for spare ribs in honey sauce; boned stuffed chicken wings; and the jungle curry chicken with straw mushrooms. There is a large selection of ice-cream, including excellent coconut to finish, and sometimes durian. Chrysanthemum tea helps keep the temperature down. Seventy wines range from house French at £6.45 to CELLARMAN'S CHOICE: Gewürztraminer, Alto Adige '85, one of ten Gewürztraminers, including New Zealand, California and Washington State versions. The Marloes Road branch – the original – has closed.

CHEF: Penn Squires PROPRIETOR: Philip Harris
OPEN: all week
CLOSED: Christmas and Easter
MEALS: 12 to 2.45, 6 to 11.15 (12.30 to 2.30, 6.30 to 10.30 Sun)
PRICES: £16 (£28). Cover 75p. Service 12.5%
CARDS: Access, Amex, Carte Blanche, Visa
SEATS: 100. Private parties: 25 main room, 35 and 50 private rooms. Vegetarian meals. Children welcome. No cigars/pipes in dining-room. Wheelchair access (also WC). Music. Air-conditioned

La Baita Da Piero [10/20] map 10

98 Station Road, North Chingford, E4 7BA
01-529 8311 **£21**

The jolly atmosphere of this colourful slice of Italy is helped along by ebullient Mr Pieropan. The food is a cut above the trattoria average. Excellent pasta is cooked al dente; also look for the daily specials, which feature fresh fish and game in season. Good dishes have included pollo valdostana covered with ham and Fontina cheese sauce, and liver with onions and red wine; liqueur-soaked tiramisu and profiteroles are home made. A typical trattoria list of around 35 wines, almost all from Italy, starts at £5.

CHEF: Apuzzo Martino PROPRIETOR: F.S. Pieropan
OPEN: Tue to Sun, exc Sun L
CLOSED: 3 weeks Aug
MEALS: 12 to 2.30, 6.30 to 11.30
PRICES: £14 (£21). Cover 65p
CARDS: Access, Amex, Diners, Visa
SEATS: 48. Private parties: 10 main room. Children welcome. No cigars/pipes in dining-room. Wheelchair access. Music. Air-conditioned

Bambaya [12/20] map 10

1 Park Road, Crouch End, N8 8TE
01-348 5609 £17

Bambaya is not strictly a Caribbean restaurant since there are equal proportions of African and black American dishes on the menu as well. This is skilful cookery – not oily, not heavy, but delicate, interesting flavours, subtly spiced. The national dish of Jamaica, salt cod with ackee, is peppery hot and a memorable contrast of textures. Also authentic are phoulom balls, made of ground lentils with a green mango sauce, similar to those served at Jamaican roadside stalls. Appetisers include peanut soup; seafood dishes take in Afro-disiac – fish steak in a Latin American-style fish sauce; and there are yams, green bananas, rice and peas. Meats are served Indian style, with several dishes coming together and plates being warmed beforehand. The restaurant is untypically spacious and upmarket, a light, split-level room with colourful paintings on whitewashed walls. There is a non-alcoholic drink of the day and cocktails that go well with the food.

CHEFS: Rosamund Grant and Jenny Agada PROPRIETORS: Bambaya Restaurant Ltd
OPEN: Tue to Sat D, and Sun L
MEALS: 6.30 to 11 (11.30 to 4 Sun)
PRICES: £10 (£17). Cover 50p. Licensed, also bring your own: corkage £2.50
CARDS: Access, Visa
SEATS: 45. Private parties: 45 main room. Vegetarian meals. Children's helpings. Wheelchair access. Music

La Bastide [12/20] map 14

50 Greek Street, W1V 5LQ
01-734 3300 £21–£25

In the culinary revival of Soho, La Bastide is still searching for an identity within the trendy scene. The kitchen has a weakness for the traditional French provincial style, but just to hedge its bets there are three menus: a provincially-inclined set choice that changes monthly – in a month dedicated to the Auvergne there was chestnut soup, aligot, deep-fried frogs' legs and wild boar – a posher *carte* and a brasserie-type 'Soho menu'. The décor comes down firmly if not effectively in favour of the *carte* with yellow tablecloths, small chandeliers, super-realist prints and slightly bordello-looking thick velvet curtains. (The exterior has been done with more polish and more completely than the interior.) Certainly the slightly swanky style seems at odds if you are selecting the Soho menu. Also, why describe the very British salmon on the *carte* as 'Saumon sauvage Ecossais avec sauce oseille' and then have a Soho menu next to it with 'melon', 'smoked salmon' and so on in English? It may seem petty to point to these deficiencies but they are reflected in the food. The kitchen is being stretched, the schizophrenia making it difficult to hit a consistent quality – witness an undercooked yet drooping globe artichoke that had been waiting around too long. Good cooking there no doubt is – recommendations include a 'workmanlike filet et rognons d'agneau' and iced soufflé – but after two years the situation is still developing. The solid provincial menu shows the good wine list at its best. It has plenty of wines well below £10, as well as finer bottles. There are some excellent clarets, ranging from simple wines to second growths, although some of the younger wines are too fine to be drinkable yet, and some of the oldest are surprisingly modest to have kept so long. The 'off' vintages, such as '72 and '77, are best avoided. Red Burgundies are from Burgundian merchants as opposed to growers, but there are some excellent domaine wines among the dozen whites. The rest of the list is sound to very good. Sweet wines are mostly from Barsac, but there's also Jurançon Vendange Tardive '82, £13.50, £7.50 per half-bottle, and Monbazillac '85, Château Theulet, £9.50. Armagnac merits a mini-list of its own, with a host of vintages back to '35 of armagnacs from both big firms and single properties. CELLARMAN'S CHOICE: Tokay d'Alsace '85, £9.90.

CHEF: Nicolas Blacklock PROPRIETORS: Nicolas Blacklock and Susan Warwick
OPEN: Mon to Sat, exc Sat L
CLOSED: bank hols
MEALS: 12.30 to 2.30, 6 to 11.30
PRICES: £17 (£25), Set L and D £14.50 (£21) to £16.50 (£23)
CARDS: Access, Amex, Diners, Visa
SEATS: 45. 3 tables outside. Private parties: 60 main room, 75 private room. No children under 11. Air-conditioned

Bayleaf Tandoori [11/20]

map 10

2 North Hill, N6 4PU
01-340 1719 and 0245

£12–£15

The menu looks and reads like an out-of-town clone of Lal Qila (see entry), although prices are lower, service is only 10 per cent and the atmosphere is less frenetic. Tandooris, rogan josh, karahi murgh and chana masala set the style, backed up by specialities with a bias towards seafood: ruhi johl is 'large Indian river fish' marinated and cooked in herbs; the Bengali fish curry boasts 'seasonal fish' including red and grey mullet, eel, trout and pomfret. Buffet lunches are very good value. To drink there are cocktails, Kingfisher beer and some basic wines.

It is helpful if restaurants keep the office up to date with any changes.

CHEF: Hamid Ali PROPRIETORS: A.A. Khan and B.U. Ahmed
OPEN: all week
MEALS: 12 to 2.30, 6 to 11.30
PRICES: £8 (£15), Set L £6.95 (£12). Service 10%
CARDS: Access, Amex, Diners, Visa
SEATS: 80. 4 tables outside. Private parties: 22 main room, 22 private room. Vegetarian meals. Children's helpings. Wheelchair access. Music. Air-conditioned

Beau-Rivage [11/20] map 11

228 Belsize Road, NW6 4BT
01-328 9992 £15–£22

Fish is the strength of this basement Mauritian restaurant and portions are so generous that you might dispense with one of the courses. The atmosphere – fans, a birdcage, stained glass, textured wallpaper – provides a colourful backdrop to a starter of fish soup which, with a pot of garlic sauce and garlic bread, is a meal in itself. The brouillade du fish consists of half a lobster, a jumbo prawn, two crab claws, mussels, salmon, mackerel and halibut in a saffron sauce. The monster plate of exotic fruits is the best of a limited sweets menu. House wine is £6.25.

CHEF/PROPRIETOR: George Ng Yn Tin
OPEN: Mon to Sat, exc Sat L
MEALS: 12 to 2.30, 6.30 to 11.30
PRICES: £14 (£22), Set L £9.25 (£15), Set D £13 (£19). Cover 75p. Service 10%
CARDS: Access, Visa
SEATS: 54. Private parties: 35 main room, 18 private room. Vegetarian meals. Children's helpings. No-smoking area. Music. Air-conditioned

Bengal Lancer [10/20] map 11

253 Kentish Town Road, NW5 2JT
01-485 6688 £9–£16

Still a good bet for a stylish Indian meal in the unpromising streets of Kentish Town. The menu is strong on tandooris, tikkas and birianis, with one or two unusual specialities, such as kaleja masala – marinated lamb's liver cooked in a spicy sauce – and kidneys pukkan, a survivor from the days of the Raj. Otherwise there are fresh-tasting vegetables, decent breads and saffron-flavoured Basmati rice. Seasonal fresh mangoes and Indian sweets to finish. Drink lager, or house wine by the glass.

CHEF: Stanley Krett PROPRIETORS: Stanley Krett and Akram Ali
OPEN: all week
MEALS: 12 to 3, 6 to 12 (12.30 Fri and Sat)
PRICES: £10 (£16), Set L £3.50 (£9). Cover £1
CARDS: Access, Amex, Diners, Visa
SEATS: 70. Private parties: 8 main room, 40 private room. Vegetarian meals. Children's helpings. Jacket and tie. No-smoking area. Wheelchair access. Music. Air-conditioned

Beotys [10/20]

map 14

79 St Martin's Lane, WC2N 4AA
01-836 8768 and 8548

£28

A dinosaur of the old school. Theodore Frangos began in 1945 and retired at the end of 1987, handing on to his son Michael; chef Stelius Sparsis started in 1952 and now takes more of an executive role in the kitchen. The Greek theme dominates a Continental steak and vanilla ice-cream repertoire that does not change. Over and above the steak Artemis – sirloin cooked at the table with chervil sauce, flavoured with brandy – there is superlative squid cooked in squid ink and red wine. The run of generous entrées and entremets provides as good an example of Greek dishes as anywhere in London – kleftiko, moussaka, souvlaki, stifado, stuffed aubergines, halouva, baklava, logmades. Opening at 5.30pm, with last orders at 11.30pm, accommodates theatre-goers. The splendour of the décor may be starting to fade, but not the warmth of the service. 'Same as fourteen years ago.' House French is £7.50. CELLARMAN'S CHOICE: Greek Cambas '81, £9.70; Cypriot D'Ahera '75, £12.70.

CHEF: Stelius Sparsis PROPRIETORS: The Frangos family
OPEN: Mon to Sat
MEALS: 12.15 to 2.30, 5.30 to 11.30
PRICES: £20 (£28). Cover 90p. Service 12.5%
CARDS: Access, Amex, Diners, Visa
SEATS: 80. Private parties: 14 main room, 40 private room. Vegetarian meals. Children's helpings. No children under 9. Smart dress preferred. No pipes in dining-room. Wheelchair access (also WC). Air-conditioned

Bibendum [16/20]

map 12

Michelin House, 81 Fulham Road, SW3 6RD
01-581 5817

£29–£36

Here we have a great restaurant, designed by a great designer. The cooking has not, over the first year, settled into any comfortable rhythm of perfection, nevertheless this is first division. Simon Hopkinson has set himself firmly against professional and *nouvelle* style and stayed with *cuisine bourgeoise* and all credit to him for breaking the mould. Specialities are listed as tête de veau; steak au poivre; roast poulet de Bresse; scallops beurre blanc. It is a brave course to follow because audiences are more familiar with Elizabeth David than Michel Guérard. In *Italian Food* David suggests that pimentos piemontese should be al dente, but here the red pepper is collapsed in its oil and its filling of tomato, garlic and anchovy still warm, when David says cold. The key is whether or not a team can be moulded to cope with as many as 74 covers at a sitting. Stylistically, in terms of London, it is a revamped model of Langan's Brasserie for the 1990s – down to the chef being one of the proprietors. The décor is an awesome statement of light and space above the dining level. The front of the house is controlled by John Davey, 15 years with Girardet at Crissier. He reinvents the role of maître d'hôtel, chatting amiably, dismantling the formalities, and setting people at ease while staying vigilant. The menu is deceptive in its simplicity. It offers choice: three soups; twenty starters; five fish; four roasts for two; eleven main dishes. The loyalty is firmly to good-quality ingredients. But look also at the quality of the pastrywork in the tarts. The long list of recommended dishes says much about the affection for this style of cooking: endive au gratin; risotto; crab mayonnaise; Toulouse sausage with lentils; truffle omelette; grilled aubergine with pesto; carré d'agneau persillé; grilled wild mallard with orange sauce; onglet with shallots; grilled turbot with beurre blanc. There is always a hot pudding of the day to complement the good chocolate sweets and the crème brûlées. Trimmings, from coffee to olives, are impeccable. All told it is refreshingly lacking in fuss and pretension. The downstairs oyster bar is small, less expensive, but similar food with an emphasis on shellfish. The wine list is excellent, though quite expensive, and nothing comes under £9.50, but there is a good representation of half-bottles. Clarets and Burgundies make the heaviest weights: a long list of clarets includes plenty of '70s, several '66s, and others back to '47, and there are some excellent Burgundies, many of them from fine domaines – though be wary of ancient bottles. Selections from the Loire, Alsace, Rhône, Italy and Spain are limited but excellent. A handful of German wines are all from fine estates. California and Australian wines are more extensive, but all from good producers. Choice of sweet wines is wide ranging, expensive and unusual. From California, there's a rare Mondavi Sauvignon Blanc Botrytis '81, £24 per half-bottle, as well as Phelps Late Harvest Riesling '83, at £32.50 per half, and an Australian Late Harvest Botrytis Semillon from De Bortoli, at £19.75 per half. Or there are several sweet Germans, young and mature, two expensive Alsace Vendange Tardive and eight Sauternes, including the '48 and '76 vintages of Yquem – £170 and £287.50. House French is £9.95.

CHEF: Simon Hopkinson PROPRIETORS: Paul Hamlyn, Sir Terence Conran and Simon Hopkinson
OPEN: Mon to Sat, exc Sat D
MEALS: 12.30 to 2.30 (3.30 Sat), 7 to 11.30
PRICES: £23 (£36), Set L £18.50 (£29). Service 15%
CARDS: Access, Amex, Diners, Visa
SEATS: 74. Children's helpings. No children under 5. Wheelchair access (lift; also WC). Air-conditioned

▲ *Blakes Hotel* [13/20] map 12

33 Roland Gardens, SW7 3PF
01-370 6701 £44

Mystery and foreboding lurk beneath the dark green paint covering the exterior of Blakes. No other signs are evident, in order to enhance the discreetness and exclusiveness of the hotel. The way down into the basement restaurant is via an open staircase, short and quite ordinary, that provides an essential prop for making an entrance. The descent leads you straight into the centre of the room where, for an instant, all eyes converge to study each new arrival. There always seems to be a moment of silence as conversations momentarily pause and pairs of eyes dart across for a lightning assessment. The dining-room is a gleaming black, which helps to dramatise the *objets d'art* featured on the walls. There is careful use of spotlighting, which focuses on each item like a museum piece aided by a ceiling covered with whirling low-voltage lights that resemble flying saucers. The central glass case comprises a full set of samurai armour with metal studs that gleam and sparkle; round another wall may be an oriental costume or a gold-lacquered silk folding screen, or perhaps majestic wooden peacocks and horses. The occupants, both plant and human, are equally theatrical. Each table has two huge onion plants that are four inches in diameter and have miniature spiky violet flowers. Sometimes enormous globe artichokes are paired with them, their bases covered with gigantic triffid-like cabbage leaves. The women at the dining-tables appear like tear-outs from pages of Condé Nast publications: flowing blonde hair and gaunt thin bodies wearing strapless numbers in black. They tend to wear minimal jewellery, offset by expensive watches and smart, cosmopolitan male companions. The menu comprises eleven starters, four intermediate dishes and a dozen main courses, eclectic dishes from all over the world written in a tone that has no clichéd intentions. In some ways, this is Alastair Little's menu, but in a setting equal to the shops down in Brompton Cross. Richard Sparrow, another Connaught trainee and previously in the *Guide* at the Swan at Streatley, has taken on the kitchens. Standards yoyo, but the thought behind the cooking has more substance than the designer dining-room might suggest. There are good breads – black, brown malt and fruit. Canapés of five small spring rolls echo the Eastern aspect of the signature dish of Szechuan duck with roasted salt and pepper: three slices of breast cut lengthwise and fanned out, together with a duck leg on a large black plate accompanied by a mound of chopped spring onions, a good quality char siu bun and a cluster of fiercely hot pickled ginger. Also notable are the massive soufflés suissesses; the wild mushroom sauce with its ravioli; the wild rice, ordered separately from the vegetable menu. Service is prim and efficient. The wine list is impenetrable as too much starts at £20 plus, although the house wines at £11 are serviceable and the champagne has plenty of fruit. CELLARMAN'S CHOICE: Ch. Tayac '83 at £19.50.

CHEF: Richard Sparrow PROPRIETOR: Anouska Hempel Weinberg
OPEN: all week
CLOSED: 25 and 26 Dec
MEALS: 12.30 to 2.30, 7.30 to 11.30
PRICES: £28 (£44). Service 15%
CARDS: Access, Amex, Diners, Visa
SEATS: 45. Private parties: 10 main room. Vegetarian meals. Children's helpings. Smart dress preferred. No pipes in dining-room. Music. Air-conditioned
ACCOMMODATION: 50 rooms, all with bath/shower. Lift. B&B. £106.90 to £168.80. Children welcome. Baby facilities. Afternoon teas. Air-conditioning. TV. Phone. Confirm by 6 [GHG]

The 1990 Guide *will appear before Christmas 1989. Reports are particularly helpful in the spring. Report forms are at the back of this book, but just write a letter if you prefer. Address to The Good Food Guide,* FREEPOST, *2 Marylebone Road, London NW1 1YN. No stamp is necessary if you post it in the UK.*

Bloom's [9/20]

map 11

90 Whitechapel High Street, E1 7RA
01-247 6001 £14

Bloom's is the classic place for Sunday lunch after a visit to Brick Lane or the Columbia Road flower market and before a walk around the Whitechapel Art Gallery, just a few doors down. The waiters make the atmosphere, in turn glowering or grinning. The famous Ashkenazi cooking seems to have become tired of fame. Borshches – cabbage and beetroot – are still praised, as is the chopped liver and the salt-beef plate. Portions do not get any smaller. House Israeli Cabernet Sauvignon is £6.50.

CHEF: Peter Nicholas PROPRIETORS: The Bloom family
OPEN: Sun to Fri, exc Fri D
MEALS: 11.30am to 9.30pm (3pm Fri, 2pm Fri in winter)
PRICES: £8 (£14), Snacks from £3.50
CARDS: Access, Visa
SEATS: 160. Private parties: 160 main room. Car-park, 100 places. Vegetarian meals. Children's helpings. Wheelchair access (1 step). Air-conditioned

Blue Elephant [11/20]

map 10

4–5 Fulham Broadway, SW6 1AA
01-385 6595 £31

The blue neon lights of the Broadway frontage give way to a jungle of house plants, tropical flowers and staff in Thai dress. The atmosphere is quite special, though the pedantic view is that as part of an hotel chain the cooking lacks some of the *esprit* found in smaller, chef/owner venues. The glossy menu reaffirms the ambitions with cocktails and over 70 dishes. Five soups include a Floating Market, featuring seafood flavoured with lemon-grass and curried with nam prik pao and served for two in a beaten brass bowl. There is a good choice of fish, plus the popular westernised Thai dishes like satay and sliced duck with coriander. Rice dishes also confirm the quality. Branches in Brussels and the Chao Khun in Bangkok. House wine £6.95.

CHEFS: Thaviseuth Phouthavong and Rungsan Mulijan PROPRIETORS: Blue Elephant Ltd
OPEN: all week, exc Sat L
CLOSED: 25 and 26 Dec
MEALS: 12 to 2.30, 7 to 11.30
PRICES: £16 (£31). Cover £1.50. Service 15%
CARDS: Access, Amex, Diners, Visa
SEATS: 150. Private parties: 150 main room. Vegetarian meals. Children welcome. Smart dress preferred. Wheelchair access (2 steps; also WC). Music. Air-conditioned

Blue Nile [10/20]

map 11

341A Harrow Road, W9 3RA
01-286 5129 £14–£15

Of the three Ethiopian restaurants to open in London in recent years, the Blue Nile emerges as the most credible. It is well supported by expatriates.

The décor is appropriate, with its Ethiopian airline posters, maps and old drawings of explorers, and also music. Meals are built round large flat loaves of injerah bread on to which small quantities of stews are placed – lentils, chicken, meat with peppers – and eaten with the fingers. Other dishes include a starter of sweet potatoes with a peanut sauce served on a banana leaf, and sorbets to finish. The interesting range of teas and coffees is worth pursuing as is the mead-like Tej (£5 a bottle, £1 a glass), a honey wine that offsets the spicier dishes well.

CHEF/PROPRIETOR: Elsa Wubneh
OPEN: all week, D only
MEALS: 7 to 11.30
PRICES: £11 (£15), Set D £21 (£28) for two, Snacks from £3.50
CARDS: Access, Visa
SEATS: 50. 2 tables outside. Private parties: 70 main room, 70 private room. Vegetarian meals. Children's helpings. Wheelchair access. Music

Bombay Bicycle Club [10/20]

map 10

95 Nightingale Lane, SW12 8NX
01-673 6850 £12-£24

The décor is deliberately fashionable, with batik-style prints and potted palms. Like many comparable new-wave Indian 'brasseries' this place hasn't quite lived up to its early promise, but the menu has some good things: lahore machi (fish in batter), sizzling tandoori prawns with fenugreek and ginger, and a good showing of lamb specialities, including pasanda and biriani. The buffet Sunday lunch is well reported. Drink Tiger beer.

CHEF: Ismail Gulam Mamad Mussa PROPRIETORS: Perry and Amanda de Samarkandi
OPEN: all week D only, and Sun L
CLOSED: Christmas
MEALS: 12 to 3, 7 to 11.30
PRICES: £14 (£24), Set Sun L £7.50 (£12). Cover £1. Minimum £9
CARDS: Access, Visa
SEATS: 60. Vegetarian meals. Children's helpings (Sun L only). Wheelchair access (2 steps)

Bombay Brasserie [14/20]

map 12

140 Gloucester Road, SW7 4QH
01-370 4040 £18–£26

The most remarkable Indian restaurant in the country now has some imitators, but few equals. Only Amin Ali's Jamdani (see entry) seems truly in the same league, although its style and intentions are different, and it is badly erratic. The Bombay Brasserie is classic Raj-chic, a spacious room full of palms and fans, with a lady sitting and singing at a white piano; the overall effect is impressive, startling but not intimidating. Signs of success, like the dog-eared menu and the pressed service, seem to fit into the era. This was the first restaurant to devote its menu to Indian regional cooking: here are tandooris from the North-West frontier; Bombay roadside snacks and Gujerati savouries; fish and coconut specialities from Goa; dishes from

Kashmir and Kerala. Sev batata puri is an outstanding vegetarian starter, along with Malabar crab sauté with coconut and fresh curry leaves. Among the main courses, chicken tikka makhani comes in a rich butter sauce and masala prawns are four enormous specimens in a classic Goan sauce. The finer details of the cuisine are equally memorable: chaas, diluted and spiced yoghurt, to start; home-made relish with vegetables in a fresh mint and yoghurt sauce; excellent breads and rice, good authentic dhals as accompaniments. The choice of vegetable dishes includes a mix of mushrooms, potatoes stuffed with cottage cheese and a purée of mustard leaves. Thalis are a good introduction to the full menu; the buffet lunch is renowned. Service stays calm despite the restaurant being full most evenings. To drink, the house French is £6.95, or there is Indian Kingfisher beer, exotic cocktails, or cherry and pear juices.

CHEFS: S. Rao and Udit Sarkhel PROPRIETORS: TAJ International Hotels
OPEN: all week
MEALS: 12.30 to 3, 7.30 to 12
PRICES: £15 (£26), Set L £11.50 (£18). Service 12.5%
CARDS: Access, Amex, Diners, Visa
SEATS: 175. Vegetarian meals. Children's helpings. Wheelchair access (4 steps; also WC). Music

Le Bonheur [11/20]

35 High Street, Hampton Wick, Kingston upon Thames, KT1 4DA
01-977 4895 £18

Right on Hampton Wick High Street near Kingston Bridge in a conservation area of Georgian/Victorian houses, this is a simply converted shop-front restaurant with white crockery, flowers and candles. The short menu changes periodically, dishes consistently well executed: pastry for a salmon croissant is light and flaky; loin of pork comes in a sweet caramel and cream sauce. Calf's liver in Pernod is fresh and good. *Nouvelle*-ish in style, but portions are satisfyingly hearty. Meats are of especially good quality. House French is £5.65.

CHEFS: Steve Hardman and Julie Lever PROPRIETOR: Steve Hardman and Robert Falana
OPEN: Mon to Sat, exc Sat L
MEALS: 12 to 2.30, 7 to 10.30
PRICES: £12 (£18)
CARDS: Access, Visa
SEATS: 36. Private parties: 36 main room. Vegetarian meals. Children welcome. Smart dress preferred. Wheelchair access (1 step). Music

Bouillabaisse [13/20] map 11

116 Finborough Road, SW10 9ED
01-370 4183 £27–£42

To all intents and purposes this is the renamed L'Olivier, the meat restaurant to Pierre Martin's fish chain, identical but for the added attraction of bouillabaisse. The quasi-nautical basement is run by mostly male staff who barely have a word of English between them, but who tone well with the blue carpet and burgundy-red – decorator's, not Pinot Noir – tablecloths. The bouillabaisse, which arrives in a bowl with half a dozen white fish fillets already in it and a side plate of some viciously garlicky aïoli, round toasts and grated cheese, lacks the zingy, spicy edge of a great Mediterranean version, but is probably as good as any in London. It is a subtle, rustic blend with a taste of Pastis/fennel coming through and uses potato rather than flashy trimmings like langoustine. The rest of the menu also deserves attention. For the same price as the small serving of bouillabaisse, the set menu of crudités, charcuterie, ravioli, soupe au pistou, grilled meat or fish, salad and cheese or dessert is a bargain. There are also seven kinds of oyster, foie gras at £9, shellfish and pasta. Service is disjointed. If you know what you want, it is possible to eat very well. The wine list is short, well spread in price and on the expensive side. The house wine, £3 for a small pichet, is ordinaire.

CHEF: Phillippe Moron PROPRIETOR: Pierre Martin
OPEN: Mon to Sat, D only
CLOSED: 2 weeks at Christmas
MEALS: 7.30 to 1.30 (last orders 11.30 Set D)
PRICES: £27 (£42), Set D £16 (£27). Service 15%
CARDS: Access, Amex, Diners, Visa
SEATS: 50. Children welcome. Music

Boulestin [13/20]

map 14

1A Henrietta Street, WC2E 8PS
01-836 7061

£22–£37

'This is how restaurants were in my youth.' Boulestin has many of the virtues that the French most admire in London eating: a sense of history; a marvellously grand, unfusty dining-room; oil paintings of quaint old strains of cattle; service in the grand English dinner-suited manner; a wine list, cheapish by French standards, of 280 entries; a menu of ambitious proportions written in French without translation; finally, and all important, execution that will satisfy, but not threaten France's dominance of European restaurant cuisine. Choice abounds. There are three starters, three fish, five grills, six meat dishes plus at least three dishes of the day and a good value lunch for £15. There are long descriptions – for instance, 'filet de porc fumé à la maison au genièvre, sauce raifort japonnaise' – but plenty on this menu to give enormous pleasure, not least the application of classical techniques, properly done, as in a consommé with langoustines or a brioche with scrambled eggs and sevruga caviare. Sauces based on stock reduction are beautifully intense for, say, a saddle of hare with rösti potatoes covered with a slice of foie gras or poached turbot with hollandaise. Cheeses are from Androuët. The grand scale offers a proper choice among the sweets: a brûlée, a soupe, a soufflé, a tulipe, a mousse. Some say the rating is too low, others that the restaurant is pretentious. Either way it sails on calmly, unruffled by fashion and comment. The wine list is very expensive, but the choice is on the whole very interesting, except in Burgundy, where most of the wines are merchants' blends rather than individual growers' wines. Clarets are the really strong point of the list, with a variety of good vintages of the first growths back to the '20s and plenty of lesser growths. There's a good cross-section from the rest of France, a few good German and California wines, and '71 and '76 vintages of Torres Gran Coronas Black Label from Spain, £34 and £26. Vintage armagnacs come by the glass, peaking at 1900 Castarade, £40 per *large* measure. For sweet wines, choose from expensive *premier cru* Sauternes, including old vintages and '71, '75 and '76 Ch. d'Yquem (between £95 and £120), two sweet '76 Alsace wines at £38 and £47, and Muscat de Beaumes de Venise, Domaine de Coyeux, at £3 per glass. House French from £9.

CHEF: Kevin Kennedy PROPRIETORS: Grand Metropolitan
OPEN: Mon to Sat, exc Sat L
CLOSED: 3 weeks Aug, 1 week at Christmas
MEALS: 12.30 to 2.30, 7.30 to 11.15
PRICES: £26 (£37), Set L £15 (£22). Minimum £30 at D. Service 15%
CARDS: Access, Amex, Diners, Visa
SEATS: 70. Private parties: 25 main room. Vegetarian meals. No children under 5. Jacket and tie

Boyd's Glass Garden [13/20] map 11

135 Kensington Church Street, W8 7LP
01-727 5452 £16–£30

Kensington Church Street has blossomed into one of the most interesting restaurant streets of London. In Boyd's a small dining area (once a wine bar) is given a surprising sense of space through glass, mirrors, white tiles, living greenery and rattan furniture. The sense of balance in the evening meal and the genuine choices between dishes cooked in different manners – sauté venison; ragoût; stuffed scrolls of sole; roast lamb wrapped in filo; are the mark of a very serious kitchen. Set-price menus are classy and unpretentious and draw an unusually long list of recommendations including brioche filled with soft-boiled quail's eggs with a butter sauce garnished with caviare; fillet of beef in filo pastry with a madeira sauce; ragoût of scallops with ginger and mange-tout; venison with red wine, and another night with pickled walnuts; chocolate marquise with a Grand Marnier sauce; hot glazed pancakes with winter fruits. 'Care had been taken at every stage'. Service has suffered from a high staff turnover. The wine list is limited but quite well chosen and includes more than a dozen half-bottles. House French and Spanish £7.50; CELLARMAN'S CHOICE: Médoc, Ch. Sigognac '81, £15.

CHEF/PROPRIETOR: Boyd Gilmour
OPEN: Tue to Sat, exc Sat L
CLOSED: bank hols, 1 week at Christmas
MEALS: 12.30 to 2.30, 7.30 to 10.30
PRICES: Set L £12 (£16) to £14 (£18), Set D £21 (£25) to £26 (£30). Service inc
CARDS: Access, Amex, Visa
SEATS: 40. Private parties: 40 main room. Vegetarian meals. Children welcome

Brewer Street Buttery [9/20] map 13

56 Brewer Street, W1R 3FA
01-437 7695 £7

For the last six years this lunchtime venue has provided some of the best-value European cooking in Soho. 'Continental cuisine with a Polish flavour' is how Ania Czeremska describes the short menu. The bigos, the cheese piroshki, the stuffed cabbage and the goulash offer the most interest. 'Roast sausage and veg. was divine.' Good pastries and coffee. Takeaways.

CHEF/PROPRIETOR: Ania Czeremska
OPEN: Mon to Fri L
MEALS: noon to 3.30pm
PRICES: £5 (£7). Unlicensed
SEATS: 32. Private parties: 10 main room. Vegetarian meals. Children's helpings. No-smoking area. Wheelchair access (1 step). Music

Brilliant [9/20]

72–74 Western Road, Southall UB2 5DZ
01-574 1928 £8–£15

The best-known of Southall's many cafés, offering North Indian cooking. The butter chicken and jeera chicken are specialities. Good samosas, too. Drink Kenyan or Kingfisher beer, otherwise stay with lassi.

CHEF: D.K. Anand PROPRIETORS: K.K. and D.K. Anand
OPEN: Tue to Sun D, exc Sat L and Sun L
CLOSED: Aug
MEALS: 12 to 3, 6 to 11.30 (12 Fri and Sat)
PRICES: £8 (£15), Set L £5 (£8) to £7 (£10), Set D £7 (£10) to £10 (£13), Snacks from 40p. Service 10%
CARDS: Access, Amex, Diners, Visa
SEATS: 120. Private parties: 80 main room, 40 private room. Vegetarian meals. Children's helpings. Wheelchair access (also WC). Music. Air-conditioned

Brinkley's Champagne Bar [9/20] map 13

17C Curzon Street, W1Y 7FE
01-493 4490 £19

Previously the Champagne Exchange. The stylish grey and smoked-glass dining-room has responded well to the takeover by Brinkleys, who have a well-established restaurant in Hollywood Road and four smaller wine-bar offshoots (see Wine Gallery, London and Oxford). The menu stays with the simple, or whatever can be finished at the last minute – caviare, crudités, asparagus, crab salad, gravlax – with sub themes of Frenchness in cassoulet and Englishness in steak and kidney pie, and salamagundy salad. Original paintings of food and kitchens reinforce the sense of elegance and style. 'At once romantic and practical,' is one verdict. Around 20 champagnes run from house non-vintage at £16 (£3.50 per glass) to Taittinger Blanc de Blancs '81 at £60, including a choice of three pink ones. The humbler NVs – Moët and Chandon, Louis Roederer – rub shoulders with their prestige counterparts: Dom Perignon '80 and Roederer Cristal '82. Given their compatability with most of the dishes it seems almost churlish to drink from the short wine list of still wines, all French bar a brace of Australians and a Spanish rosé.

CHEF: Co-operative PROPRIETORS: Brinkley's Restaurants Ltd
OPEN: Mon to Sat, exc Sat L
MEALS: 11.30 to 3, 5.30 to 12
PRICES: £13 (£19), Snacks from £3. Service 12.5%
CARDS: Access, Amex, Diners, Visa
SEATS: 80. 2 tables outside. Private parties: 100 main room. Vegetarian meals. Children's helpings. Music. Air-conditioned

▲ *Britannia Intercontinental Hotel* [new entry, zero rated]

map 13

Grosvenor Square, W1A 3AN
01-629 9400 £24–£35

The Adams Gourmet restaurant bids to break away from the Best of Both Worlds – UK and USA – image of before, but in the long shadow of the American Embassy the Britannia remains the most overtly Americanised of the big hotels. David Nicholls has fought hard to give the cooking an identity. He is armed with some fine ingredients from either side of the Atlantic and lavishly combines them into something of a hybrid of French cooking – scallops of chicken with scallops; monkfish with lobster; cassolette of lobster, scallops and asparagus; salmon en papillote with chervil sauce. Sauces power the cooking through and often something as humble as pigeon with Savoy and a few truffles for luxury can be as successful as anything. Coffee is hot and strong. The wine list is long and intercontinental, with a predictably strong American influence. Over 200 wines start with house Médoc at £9.95. CELLARMAN'S CHOICE: Ch. Giscours '81, £31; Pouilly-Fuissé '83, £30. More reports, please.

CHEF: David Nicholls PROPRIETOR: Intercontinental Hotels
OPEN: Mon to Sat, exc Sat L
MEALS: 12.30 to 2.30, 6.30 to 10.30
PRICES: £26 (£35), Set L £21.50 (£24), Set D £22.50 (£30)
CARDS: Access, Amex, Carte Blanche, Diners, Visa
SEATS: 44. Private parties: 30, 80 and 120 private rooms. Vegetarian meals on request. Smart dress preferred. No-smoking area. Wheelchair access. Air-conditioned
ACCOMMODATION: 354 rooms, all with bath/shower. Rooms for disabled. Lift. B&B £114 to £161. Children welcome. Baby facilities. Guide dogs welcome. Afternoon teas. Air -conditioning. TV. Phone. Confirm by 6

Café Bistro [10/20]

map 10

107 Humber Road, SE3 7LW
01-858 7577 £16

The décor is bistro with a striped awning, half curtains at the windows and French posters on the walls, but the cooking centres on Italy. Spaghetti with tomato, black olives and Parmesan, Italian vegetable torta and calf's liver with sage and white wine are typical. Casserole of duck with red wine and capers is served with polenta, and there is an excellent sweet of tiramisu with layers of cream cheese, chocolate and coffee. Away from Italy, the menu also has marinated herring fillets with apple and potato salad, and steamed salmon with watercress sauce. Good espresso. A dozen basic Italian wines, starting with house at £6. Snacks and tapas are served in the cellar.

CHEF: Sarah Halse PROPRIETORS: Domenico Lo Vecchio and Sarah Halse
OPEN: Tue to Sat, D only
CLOSED: last week Aug, first week Sept, Christmas
MEALS: 7 to 11
PRICES: Set D £10.50 (£16), Snacks from £2 (£6)
SEATS: 38. 2 tables outside. Private parties: 20 main room, 12 private room. Vegetarian meals. Children welcome. Music

Le Café du Marché [12/20] map 11

22 Charterhouse Square, Smithfield Market, EC1M 6AH
01-608 1609 £15–£23

Tucked away in a mews off the quiet oasis of Charterhouse Square (approaching past the Fox & Anchor, the iron gates are beyond the alley; if coming from Charterhouse Square, the alley is beyond the gates), and announced only by a discreet sign at the top of the mews and a blackboard with choices. The success in this barren area by Smithfield, close to the Barbican and the western half of the city, has led to an expansion, with a grill room upstairs and even pre-theatre menus. The atmosphere is more of a French country restaurant than of a city market bistro – a lot of wood, brick, lace curtains and general Francophile paraphernalia. In the centre are cheeseboards and desserts; liqueurs are perched on the piano. Any sense of tweeness is saved by the roomy proportions and general restraint on too much design. All meals are set menus. The scope is wide-ranging, from clam chowder to salmon tartare, though oddly the meat dishes seem more conservative – veal milanese, for instance – than the fish. Of many recommended dishes are: provençal fish soup; fricassee of mushrooms; chicken à l'américaine with crab and cream; monkfish with red and yellow peppers; a casserole of lamb. Charcuterie and cheeses are served already plated. The bourgeois accent is countered by a cosmopolitan London influence with the occasional dish such as satay. Characteristically, the wine list is short, ten white, ten red, all French. The house wines set the right note, starting at £5.50.

CHEFS: Stephen Bullock, Rupert Pitt and Ewan Yapp PROPRIETOR: C.K. Graham-Wood
OPEN: Mon to Sat, exc Sat L
MEALS: 12 to 2.30, 6 to 10
PRICES: Set L and D £9 (£15) to £15.50 (£23). Service 15%
CARDS: Access, Visa
SEATS: 50. Private parties: 50 main room. Vegetarian meals. Children's helpings. No children under 2. No pipes in dining-room. Music

Café Flo [9/20]

map 11

205 Haverstock Hill, NW3 4QG
01-435 6744 £9–£17

The cheapest set meal at £5.25 is excellent value at this bright, popular brasserie-ette, offshoot of Camden Town's Bistroquet. The cooking can be patchy, but is based on sound ingredients mostly cooked to order, and is set within a framework of good salads, such as frisée with lardons and soft poached egg; tarte à l'oignon; brochette of monkfish; and grills. House Rhône is £5.50.

CHEF: Tommy Man PROPRIETOR: Russel Joffe
OPEN: all week
MEALS: 12 to 3 (3.30 Sat, 3.45 Sun), 6 (6.30 Sat, 6.45 Sun) to 11.30 (11 Sun)
PRICES: £11 (£17), Set L and D £5.25 (£9) to £7.25 (£11). Minimum £5. Service 12.5%
CARDS: Access, Visa
SEATS: 38. 9 tables outside. Private parties: 8 main room. Vegetarian meals. Children welcome. Wheelchair access. Music

▲ *Capital Hotel* [15/20]

map 12

Basil Street, SW3 1AT
01-589 5171 £25–£41

Chef Philip Britten's arrival at the Capital has swept more than half a breath of fresh air into the dining-room. The food and menu are now that of a top small chef/proprietor restaurant. Gone is the ponderous hotel *carte* written all in French. This is replaced with a set menu in English with no supplements, even for foie gras or lobster. Britten earned Chez Nico 14/20 in the 1987 *Guide* and has also worked at the Dorchester. His cooking has the confidence to offer simple combinations without overembellishment; he is not worried that some diners may not be sufficiently impressed by the complexity of a dish. Take the simplicity of the following. A simple breast of 'French farm chicken' with part of the skin still intact and more than sufficient firm texture and full flavour to justify its billing, sits unsliced in the centre of the plate. This is topped with tiny cubes of firm vegetables and surrounded by a delicate Riesling cream sauce. Around the edge of the plate are brilliant-coloured rough ovoids of different carved vegetables – one striking orange piece of carrot, a cucumber piece in a beautiful shade of pale green, a round white crisp onion. Some of these are a little too crisp, making it hard to get a fork into them in some cases; when the potatoes are similarly undercooked something has gone a bit awry. The crisp onions are most successful, however, and the freshness of the crisp vegetables is a good clean foil to the chicken and cream sauce. Not many chefs at this level have the confidence to serve the lightest of orange mousses with a straightforward, slightly sweet, light sauce made from the zest of the oranges, but no other complication is necessary.

The physical and organisational structure of the dining-room remains largely unchanged. It is still a narrow, formal, high-ceilinged, awkwardly shaped room, quite small for a London hotel dining-room. It is hung with chandeliers and rust curtains hiked up over the tall windows like a row of satin ball-gowns. Some diners get a view of the serving hatch to the downstairs small kitchen where last-minute preparations are done. The dinner menu offers six starters and seven main dishes for an all-inclusive price, with dessert as an extra (£5.50 on top of the £27.50). The debt to the Ladenises is plain, but on balance, Britten's fish soup at inspection was thicker and rounder, verging on the sweet, than the one at Simply Nico (see entry). The execution is vital – a cèpe butter for a pastry box filled with scallops and asparagus; a great swathe of tomato concasse with olive oil for a ragout of sweetbreads, slightly caramelised on one side and flavoured with basil and black olives. Smoked salmon is arranged around the plate with a little frisée salad in the centre covering a relish-like mound of cream cheese and leek. In its way, this is just a development of the salmon roulade of the 1970s, but with uncanny vision of its strengths – here it is a dish in which the seasoning alters fractionally with each mouthful, with none of the single-minded and relentless monotony of the old-fashioned Swiss roll approach. Terrine of foie gras is a small slab, just marginally overlapping julienne of celery dotted with parsley for change in texture, with hazelnut oil to cut the delicious sweet terrine. A baby lobster fricassee with a sauce infused with ginger and a hint of orange improves in flavour as the dish is eaten, the tiny julienne of ginger and the orange just subtle enough not to spoil but just lift the orange-coloured lobster sauce.

Sweets seem less developed, but are classic examples of the two-dimensional cooking of late *nouvelle cuisine*, except in armagnac parfait with caramel sauce and almond cake, which is a little smooth frozen ice in the shape of a fez, surrounded by a remarkably thin but flavourful caramel sauced laced also with armagnac. The tiny almond biscuit/cake is a little dry, but makes a good combination with the other two ingredients. Chocolate marquise is a square slab in its custard. 'In producing food of this quality Britten seems to have achieved that elusive balance between traditional and *nouvelle cuisine* and despite the visual impact on the plate creates a triumph of real food over pseud food. He has made complicated drudgery in the kitchen appear as simple elegance on the plate. You cannot ask for more.' The wine list is a travesty, disdainfully opening with Bordeaux at £21 and offering a handful of bottles between £10 and £20. It is an insult to London customers, who may be put off by such high prices.

CHEF: Philip Britten PROPRIETOR: David Levin
OPEN: all week
MEALS: 12.30 to 2.30, 6.30 to 10.30 (10 Sun)
PRICES: Set L £16.50 (£25), Set D £27.50 (£41)
CARDS: Access, Amex, Carte Blanche, Diners, Visa
SEATS: 35. Private parties: 10 main room, 4 and 24 private rooms. Car-park, 12 places. Vegetarian meals. Children's helpings. No children under 4. Smart dress preferred. No pipes in dining-room. Wheelchair access (3 steps; also WC). Air-conditioned
ACCOMMODATION: 54 rooms, all with bath/shower. Rooms for disabled. Lift. B&B £131.50 to £163. Children welcome. Baby facilities. Pets welcome (by arrangement). Afternoon teas. Air-conditioning. TV. Phone. Confirm by previous day [GHG]

Places rating 9 may not be restaurants at all, but still serve good food; expect to find pubs, cafés, small hotels and wine bars.

Caprice [10/20]

map 13

Arlington House, Arlington Street, SW1A 1RT
01-629 2239 £23

Despite its name, the Caprice has become one of the longer-running success stories of London brasseries; the slick, monochromatic dining-room, enhanced by a black canopy in this discreet Mayfair dead-end, is well booked ahead. The menu provides a pragmatic choice between grills and fashionable assemblages like bang bang chicken or Caesar salad. More than 30 dishes are offered for starter or main course. 'Original food at sensible prices.' Recommended dishes have been: calf's liver with sauté potatoes; large portions of smoked salmon; grilled veal steak. Sunday brunch is among the most fashionable in London. Service is attentive and professional. The wine list is modern and challenging with interesting choices from minor regions and the New World, as well as some showy vintages. Four sweet wines are offered in half-bottles, from Château Monbazillac '81, £5.75, upwards. House wine is £5.50.

CHEF: Charles Fontaine PROPRIETORS: C.J. Corbin and J.R.B. King
OPEN: all week
MEALS: 12 to 3, 6 to 12
PRICES: £15 (£23). Cover £1
CARDS: Access, Amex, Diners, Visa
SEATS: 70. Vegetarian meals. No children under 5. Wheelchair access. Music. Air-conditioned

Cavaliers [14/20]

map 10

129 Queenstown Road, SW8 3RH
01-720 6960 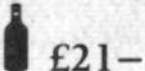 £21–£29

Ten years ago, cooking of this calibre might have collected a series of gongs. Such is the pace at which cooking and restaurateuring have moved since then, that David Cavalier's brave move to South London, half a mile from Chelsea Bridge, enters only at 14/20. He has absorbed two of the major influences of the decade, the visuals of Anton Mosimann and some of the gustatory impact of Nico Ladenis, and has progressed perceptibly since the *Guide* discovered him at Pebbles in Aylesbury, now giving his dishes far greater cohesion. The dining-room has been successfully expanded since the days when this was Chez Nico; rather like L'Arlequin, a few doors up, this is a mark of the ambition. Perfect floral plates, tiny pre-meal snacks, petits fours, young waiters in black all help create a top-drawer French restaurant style. The cooking has a rich earthiness to it – a slice of salmon roulade before the meal, a tiny artichoke base overloaded with chicken livers and finished with a madeira sauce. But it is complex and artful: salmon with a parcel of fish mousse wrapped in spinach, like Chinese sticky rice in a lotus leaf, served with a dark brown mix of lobster and thyme garnished with a spray of asparagus tips. Visually it can be stunning. Witness also a sweet: a slab of chocolate marquise on a rum-flavoured caramel cream sauce, topped with a slightly smaller, creamier pistachio terrine, topped in its turn with a thumb of water-ice. The approach is intricate, with many packages: pigeon wrapped in cabbage in filo and mushrooms, lobster in pastry. Little remains as it is: everything is transformed and raw ingredients are barely recognisable, occasionally lost in the complexities. As a result, some tastes do not fuse as successfully as the visuals. The restaurant is almost Yorkshire in its showiness, and very un-London in its sense of occasion, but clearly a style is emerging and the evident dedication makes dishes bristle. The menu is commendably, defiantly English in tone – caramel cream, not crème caramel. Some 20 fine English cheeses. There is a small and almost perfectly formed wine list. The clarets are well chosen and many of them both delicious and affordable, the Burgundies rather patchier but with good wines from properties such as Domaine Sauzet, Domaine de la Folie, Dujac and Domaine de la Pousse d'Or. The Rhônes include wines from Paul Jaboulet Aîné, Château de Beaucastel, Guigal, and even the renowned (and overpriced) Château Grillet '84, £45. But the Loire section is remarkable. Whites are carefully listed as dry, medium and medium sweet and include 11 different Vouvrays from the top properties of the area, going back to '21. The red Loires include five Chinons, three vintages of the famous Clos de l'Echo and three different Bourgeuils. Alsace wines are from Trimbach and Deiss, there are three English wines and a good mixed section of eight wines from the rest of the world. For sweet wines, as well as one German Beerenauslese, there is a choice of three different Sauternes, a Muscat de Beaumes de Venise, £18.95 or £2.60 per glass, or an impressive pick of mature Vouvray. CELLARMAN'S CHOICE: Australian Chardonnay, Château Reynella '86, £12.85; Graves, Ch. Roquetaillade, La Grange '79, £15.20.

CHEF: David Cavalier PROPRIETORS: David and Susan Cavalier
OPEN: Tue to Sat
MEALS: 12.15 to 2, 7.15 to 10.30 (11 on busy Saturdays)
PRICES: Set L and D £15.50 (£21) and £23.50 (£29). Service inc
CARDS: Access, Amex, Diners, Visa
SEATS: 50. Private parties: 50 main room. No children under 10. Smart dress preferred. Air-conditioned

Chanterelle [11/20]

map 12

119 Old Brompton Road, SW7 3RN
01-373 5522 and 7390

£12–£18

The set meals at this well-established French restaurant are notably good value – £8 for lunch and £9.50 for supper after 10pm. The dining-room is filled with wood and mirrors, and service is uncommonly proficient. The menu has a sense of enjoying some old bistro ideas – mussels served on a crumpet with dill hollandaise, salt beef with herb dumplings. Unusual fish and game are listed as specialities. Recommended dishes: ox-tail soup, duck breast with green peppercorns, tomato and basil soup, lamb cutlets with rosemary, veal and lamb casserole, raspberry vacherin, apple and sultana crumble. The wine list is equally cannily assembled and is not overpriced. Some 30 bottles, from £5.40. Muscat de Beaumes de Venise at £2.20 a glass or Château Doisy Vedrines at £8.50 a half-bottle complement the sweets. CELLARMAN'S CHOICE: Ch. Cana '83, £9.20.

CHEF/PROPRIETOR: Fergus Provan
OPEN: all week
CLOSED: 4 days at Christmas
MEALS: 12 to 2.30, 7 to 11.30
PRICES: Set L £8 (£12), Set D £13.50 (£18), from 10pm £9.50 (£14)
CARDS: Access, Amex, Diners, Visa
SEATS: 45. 3 tables outside. Private parties: 15 main room. Children welcome. Wheelchair access

Le Chef [10/20]

10 YEARS

map 11

41 Connaught Street, W2 2BB
01-262 5945

£15–£22

The resilience of Le Chef is a recommendation for its formula, even if the gingham table-cloth imagery of the 1960s bistro now seems dated. Alan King's cooking remains firmly on the right rails after eighteen years and, given the location near Marble Arch and Hyde Park, the menu is good value. Le Chef excels at wonderful French bourgeois clichés – generous helpings of fish soup with grated cheese, rouille and plenty of bread; a piquant sauce of cream and mushroom for pork; tomatoes provençal, stuffed with breadcrumbs, onion and garlic. Good straightforward French desserts and cheeses. House wine is £4.95.

CHEF/PROPRIETOR: Alan King
OPEN: Mon to Sat, exc Sat L
CLOSED: 2 weeks Aug
MEALS: 12.30 to 2.30, 7 to 11.30 (11 Sat)
PRICES: £14 (£18), Set L £15.25, Set Sat D £18.50 (£22). Cover 50p. Service inc
CARDS: Access, Visa
SEATS: 50. 5 tables outside. Private parties: 20 main room; 20 private room. Vegetarian meals. Children's helpings. Wheelchair access. Music

Cherry Orchard [9/20]

map 10

241–245 Globe Road, E2 0JD
01-980 6678

£7–£10

The Orchard has blossomed from the old café into a light, more sophisticated dining-room, and more ambitious changes are planned. The value remains excellent, even for the candlelight dinners with thoughtful waitress service. It is still run by a women's co-operative, next to a Buddhist centre. The repertoire is a familiar one: salads, hummus, crumbles, raviolis, mousselines and soups, with fresh pasta recently added. Sweets are notably good. Take your own wine, or choose from the wide selection of juices and teas.

CHEFS: Rachel Birkett and Harriet Lintott PROPRIETORS: Pure Land Co-operative
OPEN: Tue to Sat
CLOSED: 1 week at Christmas, 1 week in summer
MEALS: 12 to 3, 6 to 10.30
PRICES: L £4 (£7), D £7 (£10). Unlicensed, but bring your own: corkage 80p
CARDS: Access, Visa
SEATS: 54. 5 tables outside. Private parties: 25 main room. Vegetarian meals. Children's helpings. No smoking. Wheelchair access (1 step). Music

Chez Liline [10/20] map 10

101 Stroud Green Road, Finsbury Park, N4 3PX
01-263 6550 £23

The generosity of the portions and the excellent value for money help this small French/Mauritian fish restaurant in the listings. The décor is a spread of Mauritian posters, maps and pictures. Fish is from the shop next door and can include interesting tropical varieties. Bouillabaisse is a speciality. Plateau Sétoise is an array of shellfish in a cream sauce. Other parts of the meal, such as rice, vegetables and fruit sweets are handled with equal care. Wines from £5.25.

CHEF: Sylvain Ho-Wing-Cheong PROPRIETOR: Liline Ng-Yu-Tin
OPEN: Mon to Sat
CLOSED: 2 weeks Aug
MEALS: 12 to 2.30, 6.30 to 11
PRICES: £16 (£23)
SEATS: 44. 2 tables outside. Private parties: 40 main room. Vegetarian meals. Children's helpings. Music

Chez Moi [13/20] 10 YEARS map 10

1 Addison Avenue, W11 4QS
01-603 8267 £19–£26

The average life of a successful restaurant is often said to be seven years, which makes this twenty-one-year-old a very grandfatherly figure. But the deeply ingrained and disciplined French techniques of the kitchen continue to show up in a good light and the menu has aged gracefully. There is, for example, a fashionable salmon tartare which has been on the menu for over 15 years. Richard Walton explains: 'We stayed with a family in the Loire valley at Easter 1970. On the Monday, the mother produced a mammoth lunch that lasted six hours, one of the dishes being salmon tartare.' The chopped raw salmon is bound, as in a mayonnaise, with raw egg yolks, capers and olive oil – a solidly French dish in comparison to modern marinated versions bound with sour cream, as inspired by Raymond Blanc. The printed menu is a traditional assembly of five cold and four hot starters; three fish; three lamb – the house speciality being grilled with apricots, the others rack, either stuffed with garlic and meat or smeared with French mustard, breadcrumbs, shallots and herbs; four other meats; eight vegetables. It is supplemented with up to ten dishes of the moment, which are more provincial: calves' brains with black butter and capers, then quenelles or boned quail stuffed with foie gras baked in pastry and served with a white port and grape sauce. Other recommendations include spinach salad with chicken livers, the saddle of hare, a fish soup, Arbroath smokies, chocolate truffle cake. A couple of token Germans are the only concessions to the non-French winemaking world. Clarets, from *petit château* level to Rausan Gassies '59, £57.50, are good, and reasonably priced for London. Burgundies, both red and white, are patchier, but there are some good wines from lesser-known domaines. Hugel Alsace, Domaine du Père Caboche Châteauneuf-du-Pape and Domaine du Raifault Chinon are also reliable. Sweet wine drinkers have to be content with the almondy Muscat de Beaumes de Venise, Domaine de Coyeux '85, £7.60 per half, and Château de Malle '81, £11.75 per half, from Sauternes. House French £6.

CHEF: Richard Walton PROPRIETORS: Richard Walton and Colin Smith
OPEN: Mon to Sat, exc Sat L
CLOSED: 2 weeks Aug, 2 weeks at Christmas, bank hols
MEALS: 12.30 to 2, 7 to 11
PRICES: £18 (£26), Set L £12.50 (£19)
CARDS: Access, Amex, Diners, Visa
SEATS: 45. Children's helpings. No pipes in dining-room. Wheelchair access. Air-conditioned

Chiang Mai [10/20]

map 14

48 Frith Street, W1V 5TE
01-437 7444

£15–£19

Chiang Mai describes its menu as concentrating on Northern Thai cooking. The 110-dish list takes a slow journey through more than 30 piquant starters, 13 soups, 30 main dishes built strongly around prawns, imported fish, and an array of meats (introduced to an otherwise vegetarian cuisine by the Muslims), six rice dishes, a vegetarian section, finally reaching coffee at 75p and iced coffee at 95p. Teak pillars and traditional costume reinforce the atmosphere. Recommendations specifically for: fried beef meatballs in batter with a sweet sauce; seafood salad in spiced chilli sauce; chicken, coconut and galanga soup; whole fried fish in a glaze. Set meals for four provide an easy introduction. House Blanc de Blancs £6.25.

CHEF/PROPRIETOR: Vatcharin Bhumichitr
OPEN: Mon to Sat
MEALS: 12 to 3, 6 to 11.30
PRICES: £10 (£15), Set L and D from £27.20 (£37) for two. Service 10%
CARDS: Access, Amex, Visa
SEATS: 60. Private parties: 12 main room, 20 and 25 private rooms. Vegetarian meals. Children welcome. Music

China China [10/20]

map 14

3 Gerrard Street, W1V 7LJ
01-437 3864

£12–£18

On the principle that the newest restaurant in Chinatown is often the best, this corner-site café earns a clear entry. It opened in April 1988 – a clean, smart, three-floor establishment but no different in its ethic from some of the long-standing, scruffier cafés of this street. The window kitchen specialises in roast meats, freshly wok-fried vegetables, and soup and noodle dishes. It offers essentially fast food with the emphasis on one-plate meals, though the menu extends to hot-pots, good fish such as scallops (£1.25 each), and generous plates of crab with ginger and spring onion. House wine £5.50.

CHEFS: S.K. Tang and Mr Man PROPRIETORS: Ten Express Ltd
OPEN: all week
MEALS: noon to 4am
PRICES: £10 (£18), Set L and D £7 (£12) to £10 (£15), Snacks from £2.80. Service 10%
SEATS: 150. Private parties: 60 main room. Vegetarian meals. Children welcome. Music. Air-conditioned

Chinon [12/20] map 10

25 Richmond Way, W14 OAS
01-602 5968 £24

Following on from A Taste of Honey and then the Perfumed Conservatory in Wandsworth, Barbara Deane and Jonathan Hayes have firmly established their third venture. With each move, the food and the décor have become more sophisticated, reaching now a smallish room with a hippy-esque elegance of trappings – paintings, plants and screens. The food is always described as English, but like the décor, is eclectic. The menu has shrunk sensibly to a short set meal with three choices at each stage, a deliberate seasonality, and also a fad for filo. There is no shortage of imagination or flair in presentation, for instance just-cooked skate wing is folded over a few prawns and something mousse-like, steamed, dusted with paprika and set in a sea of raspberry vinegar. Fish, from snapper to salmon, has been consistently well timed. Seasoning is heavy – ginger for duck breast with noodles; fennel and Pernod for perch; prunes and chestnut for quail – and sometimes unbalances dishes. Sweets are on the lines of chocolate parfait with a Grand Marnier sauce and a spun-sugar dome, and bread-and-butter pudding with fresh fruits. Other details lift meals: a choice of breads; excellent cheese; the short, interesting wine list with a French preference. House French at £6.50 is from Georges Duboeuf.

CHEFS/PROPRIETORS: Barbara Deane and Jonathan Hayes
OPEN: Tue to Sat, exc Sat L
CLOSED: bank hols
MEALS: 12 to 2, 7 to 10 (11 Fri and Sat)
PRICES: £15 (£24). Service 15%
CARDS: Access, Amex
SEATS: 21. Private parties: 30 main room. Vegetarian meals. Children welcome. Smart dress preferred

Christian's [11/20] map 10

1 Station Parade, Burlington Lane, W4 3HD
01-995 0382 and 0208 £20

Christian Gustin's cooking has grown and evolved since the restaurant opened in December 1982. It remains a slow-paced personal restaurant, but the attention to detail without pretension is commendable. The monthly-changing menu has shaped into a modern British variation on French. He cooks a fine beurre blanc and is sensitive with fish and meats. Soufflés and salads are very good. The kitchen is less open-plan than before but is visible from the bar; cooking smells are still pervasive. 'Good value, nicely cooked, interesting and plenty of it.' The wines match, only a dozen or so, but carefully chosen and most under £10. 'A good local restaurant.'

CHEF/PROPRIETOR: Christian Gustin
OPEN: Tue to Sat, D only
MEALS: 7.30 to 10.15
PRICES: £15 (£20). Service 12%
SEATS: 32. 4 tables outside. Private parties: 8 main room. Vegetarian meals. Children's helpings. No cigars/pipes in dining-room

Chuen Cheng Ku [10/20]

10 YEARS

map 14

17 Wardour Street, W1 3HD
01-437 1398

£9–£20

The rivalry between Chuen Cheng Ku and New World as Chinatown's premier dim-sum house runs deep. Chuen Cheng Ku has the advantage of more recent decoration and also perhaps now of coming to the competition in the role of underdog. Service has had the edge here lately; certainly it has better English. In truth there seems very little to choose between the dim-sum, though the range of cold meats is wider and the main menu has drifted into more fundamental Cantonese dishes – hot pots, casseroles, ducks' feet, chicken blood – as well as offering the westernised renditions.

CHEF: Yat Au PROPRIETORS: Choi and Kam Au
OPEN: all week
MEALS: 11 to midnight (11.30pm Sun)
PRICES: £10 (£20), Set L £4.50 (£9), Set D from £7 (£11). Service 10%
CARDS: Access, Amex, Diners, Visa
SEATS: 400. Private parties: 150 main room, 80 and 50 private rooms. Vegetarian meals. Children welcome. Wheelchair access. Music

Ciboure [12/20]

map 11

21 Eccleston Street, SW1 9LX
01-730 2505

£20–£25

The food is French, but the neat, business-like décor is more Tokyo, being minimal and all black and white, down to the waiters' and manager's clothes. The set lunch is exceptional value for cooking which is workmanlike but with interesting ideas evident both in the plain dishes, as in asparagus vinaigrette or roast leg of lamb stuffed with apricots and sage, and the more elaborate, as in a timbale of leeks and mushrooms with rosemary butter. Visuals are strong: wavy lines across the butter in a pot; five slices of pale mauve poached pear on a thick, luscious, purple, sharp, not too sweet blackcurrant sauce feathered in cream. A short wine list has house French at £7.50. 'Most appropriate for business dining.' CELLARMAN'S CHOICE: Bourgogne Passetoutgrain, Domaine de Galius '86, £10.50.

CHEF: Richard Price PROPRIETOR: Jean Louis Journade
OPEN: Mon to Sat, exc Sat L
CLOSED: 1 week Aug
MEALS: 12 to 2.30, 7 to 11.15
PRICES: £17 (£25), Set L and D £13.50 (£20). Service 15%
CARDS: Access, Amex, Diners, Visa
SEATS: 36. Children welcome. No cigars/pipes. Wheelchair access. Air-conditioned

Clarke's [14/20]

map 11

124 Kensington Church Street, W8 4BH
01-221 9225

£18–£29

Sally Clarke answered the hesitations in last year's *Guide* with a dramatic re-launch, transforming her small, personal restaurant. Now there are two levels, with a basement below the original restaurant, and a shop and coffee bar next door. As at Orso and Bibendum, there is a refreshingly stimulating new accent on London atmosphere. The downstairs, with its wooden floor, low ceiling and open-plan kitchen, fizzes noisily. The cooking has also taken a deep breath and forged ahead. The formula – daily changing menus which offer no choice, except at lunch, and then only from three dishes a course, and all led by the market – allows Clarke's to compete at the top level, and the striking combinations are at front of modern cookery. Visits to Japan and California have influenced her style, but she is firstly someone who exploits the contrasting flavours. A lunch in February offered lemon soup with wild rice, a pork and pork kidney sausage grilled and served with tomato and coriander relish, superb caramelised apple tart. Ideas may be borrowed, but they are always developed personally. Tempura-style deep-fried vegetables are served with a mustard mayonnaise; char-grilled salmon is on rösti potatoes, with a chive dressing on top of a salad of more than ten leaves and tubers. Other recommendations are for roast duck with beetroot and carrot purée, monkfish with pineapple relish, sea-bream baked with fennel and hot soup of roast peppers with dill and sour cream. 'The food suits me better for lunch than dinner.' Breads have become a major new venture and are quite magnificent, baked in house and sold next door in the delicatessen. Cheeses, in both the restaurant and the shop, are from Neal's Yard. Clarke's has a wine list pared down to the essentials in France and California. Almost all are of high quality, and even the 'French Country Wines' are interesting. The Burgundy section has some illustrious names: Rion, Durup, Vincent, Leflaive, Roulot and Lafon. The seven-strong claret section includes, of course, Ch. Clarke '79, £24, and the most expensive wine is Ch. Montrose '70, at £50. Alsace wines are from the excellent Ostertag estate and California wines are from Mondavi, Joseph Phelps, Edna Valley, Acacia, Heitz and Trefethen. With the exception of Quady's Essencia '86, £16, from California and Robert Mondavi Sauvignon Blanc Botrytis '81, £18 per half-bottle, all the sweet wines come from Bordeaux, ranging from a Cadillac, £10, to Château Coutet premier cru Barsac '80, £22. House white and red are £7.

CHEF/PROPRIETOR: Sally Clarke
OPEN: Mon to Fri
CLOSED: 2 weeks Aug, 1 week Christmas, 4 days Easter; bank hols
MEALS: 12.30 to 2, 7.30 to 11
PRICES: Set L from £14 (£18), Set D £25 (£29). Service inc
CARDS: Access, Visa
SEATS: 90. Private parties: 10 main room. Vegetarian meals. Children welcome. Wheelchair access (also WC). Air-conditioned

College Farm [9/20] map 10

45 Fitzallen Road, Finchley, N3 3PG
01-349 0690 £2

The old tea-room has been lavishly restored on this farm with rare breeds and opens on Sundays and bank holidays (sometimes Saturdays too, best to check first). What it does – scones, tea, cream and jam, all served on blue and white china – it does impeccably. Entry to the farm is an extra 75p.

CHEF/PROPRIETOR: Sue Russell
OPEN: Sun and bank hols
MEALS: 2 to 6
PRICES: Set tea £1.95 (£2)
SEATS: 35. 4 tables outside. Private parties: 60 main room. Children welcome. Wheelchair access

▲ *Connaught* [17/20] 10 YEARS map 13

Carlos Place, W1Y 6AZ
01-499 7070 £30–£55

The Connaught is genuinely from another world, another era, an oasis of Edwardian civility. Everything gleams, from the mirrors to the endless expanse of wood panelling, the silver serving trolley containing the daily roast, the immaculate marble floors in possibly the world's most perfect loos and even the tops of the chocolate creams. This is one of the few bastions of true English tradition which should disappoint neither the tourist nor the Old Etonian. The surface formula is much like other grand hotels, but unlike most of these and like a truly great performer, the Connaught plays it straight. Every guest is treated as a gentleman or lady. Nor will anyone in search of good food be disappointed. It is straight down the line, very expensive but not a rip-off. Hotel clichés are properly done. A gentleman may sup on a meal of cold turkey and ham. Kidney and bacon sit unashamedly on the menu beside a Galette Connaught aux 'Diamants Noirs', Salade Aphrodite. The set-price menu, with meals priced by the main dish, ranges from Edwardian splendour – petite marmite, homard en gelée Connaught, medaillons de cailles 'belle epoque' – to Edwardian simplicity – chicken pie, kipper paté, cold ox tongue – with a list of luxurious 'extras', starters with supplements on the main menu price. During the time a labour-intensive course is being served it seems that the staff-to-guest ratio is 10 to 1. A waiter will arrive four or five times with hot toast for the foie gras, each time just as you are running out. Young trainees dressed in simple white aprons serve coffee. Others can be singled out by the colour of their bow ties, visible around the outside of starched collars on pristine formalblack attire: more lowly waiters wear white, the head waiters black, the wine waiter red. Before dessert is served the reverse of the pulling-the-tablecloth-off-the-table trick is practised. A waiter carefully rolls a new starched white cloth over the old one as a second waiter lifts the condiments, cutlery and glassware. Is French cooking 'better' than Chinese? Is classical cooking 'superior' to modern? These are idle speculations, especially since the Connaught is so different to more modern *nouvelle cuisine* restaurants that direct comparison is not possible. One observation is striking, however. When serving a fairly conventional duck à l'orange, foie gras or fish nantaise, it is not possible to depend on modern saucing or garnishing techniques or the novelty of the dish; both the flavour and integrity of the ingredients must be excellent, which is really what cooking should be about. This is sometimes forgotten in modern cooking. The flavours in a salmis de canard du Norfolk à l'orange et au citron avec pommes abricotines, for example, grow in the eating: the duck is mostly large, skinless fillets, pot roasted pink to red, tender and wonderfully flavourful; the rich, faintly orange sauce is quite unsweet, a very deep brown colour, with skinless slices of orange, but then also lemon, to lift the dish with the shock of tart acidity; tiny curls of separately crisped duck skin add another texture and slightly candied orange juliennes add just enough sweetness. Perhaps the accompanying grated potato dressed up as an apricot is fun, but it is not necessary. The foie gras, off the trolley, has also been very fine: a thin sliver at one end of the long terrine loaf removed and discarded before serving; two generous slabs each studded with an indulgently large nugget of black truffle and surrounded by brilliant port jelly cubes and slivers of more truffle. Finally, the rendezvous du pêcheur sauce legère Nantaise proves the same point: a side soup bowl filled with pieces of lobster, sole, scallops, langoustine, salmon and crab, served with a classical but light sauce with wonderfully old-fashioned flavours of cream, wine and fish stock and sharpened with a little lemon, it is really excellent. Vegetables have varied. Pommes soufflées are perfect pillows of extreme lightness; pommes vapeurs, slightly salty but up to the standards of good Breton fish restaurants. Other vegetables can be too old-fashioned – soft and buttery – for their good. Crème brûlée has a rough crispy top and classical creamy interior containing fraises de bois; an autumn surprise was fraises des bois between the thinnest crisp biscuits with an amazingly intense berry coulis.

The setting for all this is hard to fault, from the yellow glass canopy and wrought-iron entrance to the long dining-room entrance corridor lined with black suited waiters and stocked with superb looking cheeses, a colourful array of cold hors d'oeuvres, half a cold lobster and other perfectly presented wonders. The lounges have old-fashioned, but fine, carpets and paintings. One picture of a gent writing a letter at his desk hangs discreetly above a writing desk, its writing light turned on for the evening to mimick the painting. One could make good cases for different ratings for the Connaught in the 13 to 17 range, as some readers have. But while all the headlines and column inches go to the younger, newer places it is also important to recognise the established places that have moved on and ahead. Michel Bourdin's achievement is not only to have trained a dynasty of young chefs, but also to have defined and maintained a great, some say *the* great, discipline of classical cooking. The wine list is pompous. There are some splendid wines, certainly, just look at claret: great vintages, wonderful châteaux, but under £15 what is offered? Mouton Cadet. Nothing else, just Mouton Cadet. There are a few wines elsewhere under £15 (Muscadet, Fleurie etcetera), but they are hardly exciting. It is a lazy list and doesn't care about money. Whereas it is good to see wines like dry German Rieslings, just look at the only Portuguese wine – Mateus. Consider other mark-ups, for instance the Italians: Orvieto Classico Secco '86 Antinori is under £4 retail, yet here it is £17. House French is £8.50.

CHEF: Michel Bourdin PROPRIETORS: Savoy Hotel Plc
OPEN: all week
CLOSED: weekends and bank hols (Grill Room)
MEALS: 12.30 to 2, 6 to 10.15
PRICES: £36 (£55), Set L from £19.50 (£30), Set D from £20 (£31). Minimum £18. Service 15%
CARD: Access
SEATS: 80 main restaurant, 35 Grill Room. Private parties: 20 in each of 2 private rooms. No children under 6. Jacket and tie. No pipes. Wheelchair access (also WC). Air-conditioned
ACCOMMODATION: 90 rooms, all with bath/shower. Rooms for disabled. Lift. Rates on application only. Afternoon teas (priority to residents). TV. Phone

F. Cooke [9/20] map 11

41 Kingsland High Street, E8 2JS
01-254 2878 £3

Fred Cooke and his brother Chris operate one of London's most traditional pie and eel shops and also trade in eels, selling to Chinatown. The shop has occupied its present site at 41 Kingsland High Street since 1910 (though the business goes back to 1862), and it can barely have changed: marble table-tops, wooden benches, mirrors, stained glass and beautiful late-Victorian tiles depicting early Dutch eel barges. Last winter Ostlers wine merchants put on a wine tasting to match the Cockney fare with Loire wines. It opened with a glass of Saumur Rosé, Château Langlois Cremant, followed by Muscadet, Château des Gautronnières '86; then, with jellied eels, Sancerre, Les Crilles '86; with steak and kidney pie, Chinon, Caves du Petit Columbier '86; with apple and damson pie with custard, Coteaux du Layon, Domaine de Mihoudy '82 – all for £15. The eel cooking can be blunt, but the liquor 'sings of fresh parsley and the mash might reconvert anyone put off at school.' The pies are of a standard, too, and are baked at the back. Take-away eels are sold jellied or hot in four sizes of container. Tea is strong. No licence.

CHEFS/PROPRIETORS: F. S. and C. R. Cooke
OPEN: Mon to Sat
CLOSED: bank hols
MEALS: 10 to 6 (to 8 Mon and Thur, 10 Fri and Sat)
PRICES: £3. Unlicensed. Bring your own: no corkage
SEATS: 70. Private parties: 28 main room, 40 private room. Children welcome. Wheelchair access (1 step; also WC). Music. Self-service

Cork & Bottle [9/20]

map 14

44–46 Cranbourn Street, WC2H 7AN
01-734 7807

£14

The basement cellar, dark and full of talk, provides an inexpensive bolthole in the heart of the West End. Salads are more imaginative than usual – flageolets, kidney beans, green and red peppers, celery, French beans and Feta, for instance. The wine list provides stimulating drinking under £10 – a spread of Alsace wines, 17 Australians and samples from other good-value regions world wide, including Chile. Related to Shampers in Kingly Street, W1 which also gets very crowded, and Methuselah's in Victoria Street, SW1. House French £5.95.

CHEF: Gronia O'Neil PROPRIETOR: Don Hewitson
OPEN: all week, exc Sun D
MEALS: 11 to 3, 5.30 to 11 (7 to 10.30 Sun)
PRICES: £8 (£14)
CARDS: Access, Amex, Diners, Visa
SEATS: 60. Private parties: 20 main room, 20 private room. Vegetarian meals. Music. Air-conditioned. Self-service

Corney & Barrow [12/20]

map 11

118 Moorgate, EC2M 6UR
01-628 2898

£34

Of the wine merchant's three City venues, it is this middle-range venture – both in terms of ambition and price – that has survived in the listings (the Cannon Street branch is cheaper and more youthful, Broad Street more expensive and mature), though it is frustrating to compare the investment and the result. The restaurant is expensive, though eating at the bar is less so. But enough, we carp. The New York-style split-level décor, which once seemed rather flashy, has now aged into a fairly restrained dining-room in comparison to the inventions of the late 1980s. In the same way it seems almost to have shrunk – as it fills up, the frenetic City atmosphere grabs the décor by the lapels. Staff are pushed to keep up. A new bread oven has been installed and provides rolls still hot for early lunchers. The menu seems to have calmed down some and now provides a better marriage with the extensive range of wines. Good terrines, such as smoked salmon with a lemon-flavoured butter sauce, casserole of fish, and an unmarinated version of vitello tonnato offset plainer dishes like asparagus or grilled kidneys and bacon. There is a wide choice of sweets, which can outshine other courses, plus English and French farmhouse cheeses. Strangely, though it is a heavily male dining place, women inspectors and readers are the most impressed. The wine selection is excellent, if expensive. Fine wines are better value than the 'cheaper' offerings – even vin de pays costs £10.50. Most impressive is the list of top clarets, but red and white Burgundies are serious, mostly

Report forms are at the back of the book.

single domaine wines, and there are short but very interesting selections from elsewhere in the world. Marqués de Grinon Cabernet Sauvignon '84 is unusually good value at £13. Muscat de Beaumes de Venise, though, is a hefty £2.95 a glass. CELLARMAN'S CHOICE: Montagny *premier cru* '86, £13.50.

CHEF: Robin Stewart PROPRIETORS: Corney & Barrow Restaurants Ltd
OPEN: Mon to Fri, L only
MEALS: 11.30 to 3
PRICES: £21 (£34), Snacks from £2.95. Service 12.5%
CARDS: Access, Amex, Diners, Visa
SEATS: 100. No children under 6. Air-conditioned

La Coupée [10/20] map 10

17 Half Moon Lane, Herne Hill, SE24 9JU
01-737 1556 £12–£20

Two minutes on foot from Herne Hill station is this small, essentially French restaurant. Good salads, such as duck, avocado, bacon and ginger, followed by chicken in tarragon sauce or duck with sage and onion sauce and side plates of vegetables are the style. 'Quick.' 'Informal.' 'Plenty of service.' 'Quite a beacon in the area.' House wine is £4.95. CELLARMAN'S CHOICE: New Zealand Sauvignon, Hawkes Bay '87, £9.95.

CHEF: Dermot Jones PROPRIETORS: Dermot Jones and Cyril McCandless
OPEN: Tue to Sat, exc Sat L
CLOSED: 2 weeks Sept; Feb to Mar; 2 weeks at Easter
MEALS: 12 to 2.30, 6.30 to 9.30
PRICES: £15 (£20), Set L £7.95 (£12), Set D from £8.95 (£13)
CARDS: Access, Visa
SEATS: 32. 6 tables outside. Private parties: 40 main room. Vegetarian meals. Children welcome. No pipes in dining-room. Wheelchair access

La Croisette [12/20] map 11

168 Ifield Road, SW10 9AF
01-373 3694 £27

As La Croisette gets older, the founding basement of Pierre Martin's fish flotilla becomes seemingly more of an ethnic restaurant. Staff offer little English beyond 'yes' and 'no' and again there are reports of total misunderstandings. When the waiter's role is reduced to that of plate carrier, all too often he or she becomes the only person not there for the food (see Victor Sassie's article in the features section). Their great achievement here is to be able to stack quite so many platters of shellfish side by side on tables which are in fact nearly the same size, in so cramped an area. The difference from others in the group is that the meal is set, based on very fine fish for the most part served simply. The platters of shellfish are spectacular; fillets of white fish are served in herb sauces, such as monkfish with basil; and sorbets to finish provide a hard core of quality matched with good wines. Nor is the price currently rapacious. House French is £7.80.

CHEF: Robert Lanoé PROPRIETOR: Pierre Martin
OPEN: Tue to Sun, exc Tue L
CLOSED: 2 weeks at Christmas
MEALS: 12.30 to 2.30, 7.30 to 11.30
PRICES: Set L and D £20 (£27)
CARDS: Access, Amex, Diners, Visa
SEATS: 50. 3 tables outside. Private parties: 10 main room. Children welcome. Smart dress preferred. No smoking in dining-room. Music

Crowthers [13/20] map 10

481 Upper Richmond Road West, East Sheen SW14 7PU
01-876 6372 £21–£32

The Crowthers have been joined by Andrew and Nicola Eastick, who both impressed at Michael's Nook at Grasmere; his particular skill is saucing, hers is pastry, both of which are featured here on a menu of emerging stature. Everything is home made and the atmosphere is personal. The menu, set-price with half a dozen choices per course, moves along with the market. Typical of quite excellent dishes have been a feuilleté of sweetbreads and prawns with spinach and a tarragon cream sauce, and a salmon strudel served in rounds like a roulade, filled with fresh mint in the centre and offset by lime sauce garnished with dill. Or there may be something more down to earth, such as rack of lamb with whole cloves of garlic and a ratatouille. Sweets give full rein to the pastry-work – lemon tart, mille-feuille. The wine list is modest in size but well thought out and, like the cooking, up to date. House French £8.50. CELLARMAN'S CHOICE: Bandol Mas de la Rouvière '82, £12.50.

CHEFS: Philip Crowther, Andrew Eastick and Nicola Eastick PROPRIETORS: Philip and Shirley Crowther
OPEN: all week, exc Sat L
MEALS: 12 to 2 (Sun 2.30), 7 to 10.30
PRICES: Set L £15 (£21), Set D £25 (£32)
CARD: Access
SEATS: 32. Private parties: 32 main room. Vegetarian meals. Children welcome. Wheelchair access. Air-conditioned

Daphne [10/20] map 11

83 Bayham Street, NW1 0AG
01-267 7322 £15

On the fringes of the fragmented Greek quarter of Camden Town is this smartly appointed taverna in a terraced house. It is still well supported, despite the occasional shaky patch. Meze is exceptional value at £6.25; the rest of the menu stays with tried and tested avgolemono soup, stifado, afelia and charcoal grills. Greek coffee comes with Turkish delight. There are plenty of Greek-Cypriot wines, although the house wine is a Beaujolais at £6.30 a litre.

CHEFS: L. Georgiou and A. Georgiou PROPRIETORS: Anthony Evangelou and Mrs. A. Lymbouri
OPEN: Mon to Sat
MEALS: 12 to 2.30, 6 to 11.30
PRICES: £9 (£15)
CARD: Access
SEATS: 85. 10 tables outside. Private parties: 30 main room. Vegetarian meals. Children welcome. Wheelchair access (also WC). Music

Deals [9/20]

map 10

Chelsea Harbour, Harbour Yard, SW10
01-376 3232 £18

The hot place for much of the summer, though it takes some finding: 'down Lots Road, across a building site, through a Docklands landscape and finally on to the marina, surrounded by what will be expensive flats. Harbour Yard is a white hi-tech complex with an atrium and see-through lifts.' Deals has a ranch-style, old American frontage along one wall. Despite the hype of the ownership – Viscount Linley, Patrick Lichfield and Eddy Lim of Tai Pan – this is a pragmatic late 1980s version of fast-ish food. The décor is big and western, the menu ecletic and global offering Thai curries, steak sandwiches, DIY dishes to cook at tables, Eddy's king prawns, a memorable chocolate mud pie. Fairly simple, fairly basic, but good ingredients on the whole and served up with verve. House Californian £5.95.

CHEF: Jacqueline Brown PROPRIETORS: Latchmede Group PLC
OPEN: all week, exc Sun D
MEALS: 12 to 3, 6.30 to 10.30
PRICES: £12 (£18). Service 12.5%
CARDS: Amex, Access, Visa, Diners
SEATS: 160. Private parties: 16 main room. Children's helpings. Smart dress preferred. Wheelchair access (also WC). Music. Air-conditioned

Diana's Diner [9/20]

map 13

39 Endell Street, WC2H 9BA
01-240 0272 £7

A happy hybrid between an English caff and an American diner. In the winter it's hot and steamy, crowded at peak times, but in the summer the tables outside allow a bit more elbow room. The atmosphere gains from the locale: 'far enough from the tourists and the glitzy piazza to draw in bike couriers, sales reps, grannies and other unfashionably normal people.' Décor remains like a 1950s milk bar, with theatre posters stuck up on wooden walls and a couple of very bad paintings, plus odd notices about lunchtime specials. There is steak with one of four chef's sauces, or chilli con carne, but the traditional steak pies or steak and kidney puds are the real winners among the dishes on the standard menu. All the potatoes – bubble and squeak, deep-fried coins for chips, boiled in or out of their skins – are good, too. The more adventurous daily specials – turkey nuggets with cheese and garlic filling or vegetable stuffed marrow – can be erratic, although poached plaice with parsley sauce (a wine-based béchamel) is well cooked and the fish very fresh. Service is characterised by motherliness and native wit; occasionally plates get muddled, but everything seems to get sorted out in the end. Portions are very large by any standards and prices especially low for Covent Garden, with most platefuls under £5. Few people seem to get to the puds, which are apple crumble and the like. There's real tea or watery coffee, plus orange juice.

CHEF: Roger Denman PROPRIETORS: Paul Denman and Melvyn Shaer
OPEN: Mon to Sat
MEALS: 9 to 7
PRICES: £5 (£7), Snacks from 75p. Minimum £2.45. Unlicensed, but bring your own: no corkage
SEATS: 38. 5 tables outside. Private parties: 45 main room. Vegetarian meals. Children's helpings. Wheelchair access

Dining Room [9/20] map 11

1 Cathedral Street, SE1 9DE
01-407 0337 £13

This basement vegetarian restaurant in the shadow of Borough fruit and vegetable market is almost Dickensian in its setting. The cooking though is forward-looking, with imaginative ideas incorporating Japanese and American influences. Portions are generous; flavours are distinct. The range might be sweetcorn served on a bed of basil mayonnaise; couscous; avocado salad. The fruit salad of raspberries, blueberries, and pineapple arrives decorated with honey. Look also for melon jelly with plum. First-class fruit juices.

CHEF: Sandra Cross PROPRIETORS: William English and Sandra Cross
OPEN: Tue to Fri
MEALS: 12.30 to 2.30, 7 to 10
PRICES: £9 (£13). Service 10%
SEATS: 32. Private parties: 35 main room. Vegetarian meals. Children's helpings. Music

La Dordogne [12/20] map 10

5 Devonshire Road, Chiswick, W4 2EU
01-747 1836 £25

The fortunes of this deeply French restaurant rise along with the area. The cooking continues to be bourgeois – moules marinière; fillet of beef with forestière sauce – and, in deference to the restaurant's name, there are a variety of dishes local to the Dordogne region, with an emphasis on duck, and local wine – turbot in a Cahors sauce for instance. Eight sweets range from hot praline pancakes with apricot liqueur to île flottante and apple tart. The restaurant is busy, staff pressed. A short wine list takes in some French country wines, for instance Jurançon '86 and Cahors, Pelvillain '83, both £7.50.

CHEF: Pierre Vincent PROPRIETOR: Rachel Bitton
OPEN: Mon to Sat, exc Sat L
MEALS: 12 to 2.30, 7 to 11
PRICES: £16 (£25). Cover £1. Service 10%
CARDS: Access, Amex, Diners, Visa
SEATS: 64. 6 tables outside. Private parties: 64 main room, 38 private room. Smart dress preferred. Wheelchair access. Music

Dragon's Nest [13/20]

map 14

58–60 Shaftesbury Avenue, W1V 7DE
01-437 3119 £9–£21

A rare phenomenon – a restaurant which transcends all other London Chinese by the expedient of a kitchen team arriving direct from Taiwan complete with three chefs. How long will it continue? Who knows, but without doubt this restaurant has bowled everyone over in the months going up to press. The cooking is northern Chinese – Szechuan influenced, but with a style and ferocity that is frankly unparalleled. The Taiwan décor is up to western standards and the service is slick and understanding. The point of departure is where the Dragon's Gate began. But here, in a little Chairman Mao-size booklet, is a long read with some dishes throughout that are not usually found – squab in green peppers, for instance. And there is a long wait while dishes are prepared. Listen to this: 'Sweet-and-sour fish was just sensational, as it sat on the table there was a waft of garlic and ginger. It had little Chinese mushrooms, and a red sauce, but not dyed.... Little white ravioli-style dumplings were twisted like a packet of salt for crisps, filled with prawn, boiled and set on a red soup of chilli and soy and oil with chopped spring onion.... The squid was another winner, carved into rolls with whole dried chilli, red peppers and a gravy with a meat essence. Rice was excellent.' Another testimony: 'Schezuan aubergine with hot garlic sauce was the best I can recall, tasting wonderfully freshly cooked, nicely judged as to chillies, the skin still pretty purple, the coriander flecks and spring onion bright green, the chillies bright red.' Another meal: 'A succession of stunning dishes: tripe sections with hot sauce in fire-pot; squid in sizzling plate, in a short, sticky, garlicky, spicy sauce with peppers; dry cooked beans, probably steamed first and then fried with garlic and spices and possibly nuts, with a very crunchy semi-caramelised coating; ox tendon in fire pot, an extraordinary dish of tenderised cartilages in a rich brown sauce.' On occasion there has been garoupa fish. Flaws have tended to appear in the more Londonised dishes, like smoked quail or shredded beef with carrot, so it pays to be adventurous. A good Chardonnay from the adequate wine list might cope with the range of hot flavours, or drink tea.

CHEF: C.F. Chang PROPRIETOR: N.L. Yeh
OPEN: all week
MEALS: noon to 11.30pm
PRICES: £11.50 (£21), Set L from £4.50 (£9), Set D (minimum 2 persons) from £12 (£17). Service 12.5%
CARDS: Access, Amex, Diners, Visa
SEATS: 150. Private parties: 100 main room, 40 private room. Children's helpings on request. Music. Air-conditioned

▲ *Dukes Hotel* [11/20] map 13

St James's Place, SW1A 1NY
01-491 4840 £25–£45

This small luxury hotel, rightly discovered and used by Americans, is one of the less sung, almost as if its proximity to Buckingham Palace has lent it an aristocratic self-effacement. Bedrooms are lavish and private suites for small parties and receptions are a feature. Tony Marshall's kitchen has managed to assimilate the best habits of classical hotel cooking without losing its way. It is expensive but in return there are turbot, Dover sole, Scotch fillet, and a genuine choice down to a vegetarian main course of a kohlrabi and carrot timbale with an Emmental and chive sauce. The use of cheese to sauce is a frequent device – Shropshire Blue for a fillet of veal; Stilton for chicken. Saucing of fish has been elegant – brill with horseradish sauce one lunch, with lemon sauce garnished with candied lemon and chervil another. Recommended sweets include the chocolate mousse and bread-and-butter pudding. Service is old-school but sharpened from dealing with visitors who expect a high standard. The wine list shows little regard under £20. House claret from Berry Bros creeps on to the list at £9.50; a glass of Ch. Lafaurie-Peyraguey '82 for dessert is £4.50. CELLARMAN'S CHOICE: Saint Aubin '85, £22.

CHEF: Tony Marshall PROPRIETORS: Dukes Hotel Ltd
OPEN: all week
MEALS: 12.30 to 2.30, 6 (7 Sun) to 10
PRICES: £28 (£44), Set L from £15 (£25)
CARDS: Access, Amex, Diners, Visa
SEATS: 50. Private parties: 45 main room, 12 private room. Vegetarian meals. No children under 5. Smart dress preferred. Wheelchair access (also WC)
ACCOMMODATION: 58 rooms, all with bath/shower. Lift. B&B £134 to £168. Deposit: one night's stay. Afternoon teas. TV. Phone. Confirm 2 days prior to arrival [GHG]

Efes Kebab House [11/20] 10 YEARS map 13

80 Great Titchfield Street, W1P 7AF
01-636 1953 £16–£18

The bustling atmosphere is a tribute to the success of Kazim and Ibrahim's kebab house (the back of their business card reads: 'any complaints phone 08366 11169'). No fewer than 19 variations on kebabs, including a fine liver and aubergine, are augmented by very good meze. Efes (Ephesus) is one of the places the Virgin Mary is supposed to have died. Takeaways. Wines from £5.90.

CHEFS/PROPRIETORS: K. Akkus and I. Akbas
OPEN: Mon to Sat
MEALS: noon to 11.30
PRICES: £9 (£16), Set L and D £13 (£18). Cover 50p. Minimum £5. Service 10%
CARDS: Access, Amex, Visa
SEATS: 100. Private parties: 50 main room. Vegetarian meals. Children welcome. Music. Air-conditioned

Elgin [9/20] map 11

239 Elgin Avenue, W9 1NJ
01-328 6400 £12–£14

A smart little Turkish place with a thriving take-away trade; useful as it stays open all day Sunday. The cooking is consistent. Recommended are the pathian tara – hot fried aubergine slices with yoghurt and tomato sauce – and sis baste – marinated lamb on rice with salad. Honey cake and native coffee with Turkish delight to finish. House white and red £5.95.

CHEF: Cemal Usta PROPRIETOR: Z. Ince
OPEN: all week
MEALS: noon to midnight
PRICES: £9 (£14), Set L and D £8 (£12). Cover £1.50. Service inc
CARDS: Access, Amex, Diners, Visa
SEATS: 50. 3 tables outside. Private parties: 30 main room. Vegetarian meals. Children's helpings. Wheelchair access

Faulkner's [9/20] map 11

424–426 Kingsland Road, E8 4AA
01-254 6152 £15

The only thing to change round here in recent years has been the name over the door, from Seashell to Faulkner's after John Faulkner sold his famous Lisson Grove branch. He has set out to do for Dalston what he did for Marylebone – unpretentious, no-nonsense, good-quality fish and properly fried chips. 'Staff are harassed, charming and overworked. Sometimes food is slow to come when the takeaway next door is on warp factor. They cope. Nobody minds waiting for food like this.' Basic wines start at £3.80, or bring your own (corkage £1.50).

CHEF: Michael Webber PROPRIETORS: John Faulkner and Mark Farrell
OPEN: Mon to Sat
CLOSED: bank hol Mons, 1 week Christmas to New Year
MEALS: 12 to 2, 5 (4.30 Fri) to 10 (11.30am to 10pm Sat)
PRICES: £8 (£15). Cover £1.75. Minimum £1.75. Licensed, also bring your own: corkage £1.50
SEATS: 65. Children welcome. Music. Air-conditioned

Fifty One Fifty One [12/20] map 12

Chelsea Cloisters, Sloane Avenue, SW3 3DW
01-730 5151 £31

A slick restaurant on the scale of a car showroom, on the ground floor of Chelsea Cloisters. It is back to back with Zen and previous to Zen something of a restaurant graveyard in an area that otherwise thrived. Greys, mirrors, space and some very cool design-work give an air of class, reinforced by some American trappings – hat-check girl, valet parking, and young, on-the-ball staff. The cooking is Cajun. The menu is attractively novel for London, with mesquite grilling and seared dishes adding an extra dimension to a spread of extravagant dishes based on the sort of luxuries that London has previously regarded as sacred. Oysters and artichokes are casseroled together; crawfish is made into a bisque; catfish is rolled and stuffed. The style was laid down by Beany Macgregor of the Royal Orleans Restaurant in Orlando. In effect it is fast food gourmet style – good ideas executed with ranging levels of skill. At its best there is pecan pie, served still warm and presented as a triangle with decorative feathered sauce. The wines include Texans, but Dixie Beer fits the bill.

CHEF: David Wilby PROPRIETORS: President Entertainments
OPEN: all week
MEALS: 12 to 3 (4 Sun), 6.30 to 11.30 (7 to 10.30 Sun)
PRICES: £20 (£31). Cover £1. Service 15%
CARDS: Access, Amex, Diners, Visa
SEATS: 160. Private parties: 10 main room. Car-park, 15 places. Vegetarian meals. Children's helpings (L only). Wheelchair access (4 steps; also WC). Music. Air-conditioned

Fleet Tandoori [10/20] map 11

104 Fleet Road, NW3 2QX
01-485 6402 £11–£12

More reliable and more popular than most of its competitors in the area. There is no red flock in the décor, although the menu is in the mould of well-tried curry-house cooking, from rogan josh and chicken dhansak to tandooris. Vegetable dishes, such as muttar paneer and channa masaladar are consistently good. Drink lassi or lager. Useful, all-day opening on Sunday. There is a branch at 346 Muswell Hill Broadway, London N10.

CHEF/PROPRIETOR: Abdur Rahman Khan
OPEN: all week
MEALS: 12 to 2.30, 6 to 11.30 (12 to 11.30 Sun)
PRICES: £6 (£11), Set L and D £7.80 (£11) to £9 (£12). Service 10%
CARDS: Access, Amex, Diners, Visa
SEATS: 52. Private parties: 52 main room. Vegetarian meals. Children's helpings. Wheelchair access

Forum Court [10/20] map 10

7A–8 High Street, South Norwood, SE25 6EP
01-653 0295 £14–£16

This clean, smart Chinese restaurant provides a valuable service in the area. A familiar repertoire of aromatic duck, sweet-and-sour dishes, chow mein and toffee bananas served with ice-cream is well handled. A clutch of spicier dishes has recently been added to the menu. Service is unusually accommodating. Chinese beers.

The Guide *is independent, accepts no advertising and survives solely on the number of copies sold.*

PROPRIETOR: Joseph Kwok Ying Loh
OPEN: all week
CLOSED: 25 and 26 Dec
MEALS: 12 to 2.15, 6 to 11.15 (11.45 Fri and Sat)
PRICES: £9 (£16), Set D from £9.90 (£14). Minimum £6.50. Service 10%
CARDS: Access, Amex, Diners, Visa
SEATS: 80. Private parties: 80 private room. Vegetarian meals. Children's helpings (Sun L only). Music. Air-conditioned

Frith's [12/20] map 14

14 Frith Street, W1V 5TS
01-439 3370 £29

The interesting point about Frith's is its creative menu. The sense of quest and adventure in the ideas and combinations lifts it above the usual: coriander pesto for pasta made with duck egg and served with fresh, small asparagus tips; pan-fried squid, lightly undercooked with baby leeks. After an unhappy sojourn with *haute cuisine* in Mayfair, Carla Tomasi is back in control producing these explosive combinations but backed by a professional and solid restaurant frame – good service, wines, décor. Nor is it beyond the kitchen to produce the occasional blistering success, such as a clear fish soup flavoured with lemon-grass and served with ravioli, or chocolate truffles, served with coffee, which are among the finest in London. The dining-room has had the designer touch applied and shows a commitment to food, even in the prints. The vegetarian option is strong on the menu, as is the confident, unapologetic modernism. Twenty-five wines, from house French at £8.50. CELLARMAN'S CHOICE: Hawkes Bay Sauvignon Blanc '87, £11; Dry Creek Fumé Blanc, Sonoma County '86, £13. The garden is open in good weather.

CHEF/PROPRIETOR: Carla Tomasi
OPEN: Mon to Sat, exc Sat L
CLOSED: bank hols
MEALS: 12.30 to 2.30, 7.30 to 11.15
PRICES: £19 (£29). Licensed, also bring your own: no corkage
CARDS: Access, Visa,
SEATS: 80. 4 tables outside. Private parties: 40 main room. Vegetarian meals. Children's helpings. No cigars/pipes in dining-room. Wheelchair access. Air-conditioned

Fung Shing [13/20] map 14

15 Lisle Street, WC2H 7BE
01-437 1539 £13–£21

Fung Shing retains its composure while the rest of Chinatown yo-yos around, thereby striking an unusual balance, satisfying both Chinese and European; similarly the décor comes smart enough in the restaurant stakes but has kept much of the fizz of a smaller, first-generation Canton restaurant. The restaurant has become the blueprint (actually green) for Lisle Street. Even the Diamond, reopened since the fire, has modelled itself on Fung Shing in both style and menu. Beyond the usual Cantonese repertoire there are, by arrangement, intriguing specialities: winter melon soup, the whole centre hollowed out and filled with a meat/fish and vegetable broth, served with slivers of crab, which would make an inexpensive feast for a large party; or else lacquered pigeons, deep fried, still with their heads on; broccoli with chicken consommé sauce; pork and salted fish sausages with green vegetables; or a whole sea-bass, stuffed and reformed and sliced across, tasting not unlike Middle European quenelles; even an amazing whole duck stuffed with glutinous rice and deep fried. Finally, as a last course of a banquet, a perfect noodle soup. Many of these need advance notice and depend on the seasons, but the regular repertoire spans admirably the one-dish meal and more complicated dishes. The main menu is *circa* 160 dishes long: 15 soups; 8 starters; 45 fish dishes, including abalone, crab, fine squid fried with chilli, plenty of eel dishes (always a good test of a Chinese restaurant), 16 chicken dishes, 12 duck, 10 beef, 15 pork – from stir-fries to home-made stewed belly-pork in a pot – 8 bean curds and as many as 20 one-plate meals, rice and noodle dishes. New dishes in 1988 include baked lobster with superior sauce, braised whole abalone with oyster sauce, double boiled fluffy supreme sharks fin. House French £6.80.

CHEF: Fu Kwun PROPRIETORS: Traceflow Ltd
OPEN: all week
MEALS: noon to 11.45
PRICES: £15 (£21), Set L and D from £8 (£13). Minimum £7. Service 10%
CARDS: Access, Amex, Diners, Visa
SEATS: 85. Private parties: 50 main room, 30 private room. Vegetarian meals. Children welcome. Music. Air-conditioned

Ganpath [9/20] map 11

372 Grays Inn Road, WC1X 8BB
01-278 1938 £6–£9

The sign saying South Indian Brasserie has disappeared, otherwise little has changed at this no-frills Indian restaurant not far from Kings Cross station. The décor is spartan, the service benignly friendly and the food is excellent value. The menu is on a laminated board and divides up between curry house stalwarts, such as sag gosht and prawn bhuna, and South Indian vegetarian specialities: bhajias, idlis, fresh masala dosa with coconut relish and thick sambar for dipping. Interesting vegetables and good breads. Drink lassi or lager.

CHEF: P.G. Ramalingam PROPRIETORS: R. Sivananthan and P.G. Ramalingam
OPEN: all week, exc Sun L
CLOSED: bank hols, 24 to 26 Dec
MEALS: 12 to 3, 6 to 12
PRICES: £5 (£9), Set L £4.95 (£6), Set D £8 (£9). Minimum £4. Service 10%
CARDS: Access, Visa
SEATS: 50. Private parties: 60 main room. Vegetarian meals. Children's helpings. No-smoking area. Wheelchair access. Music

Garbo's [10/20]

map 11

42 Crawford Street, W1H 1HA
01-262 6582 £18

This Swedish restaurant is well placed between the Swedish Embassy and the Swedish church. The food is plain Swedish home cooking – fine pickled herring and gravlax; smoked fish; meatballs; stuffed cabbage leaves. The dining-room is small and warm, with almost a log-cabin effect, presided over by pictures of Carl Gustav and Queen Silvia. Of special interest are the eels cooked in beer and served with scrambled eggs and chives, and Janson's Temptation, a bake of anchovies, potatoes, onions and cream. Twenty wines, plus a range of Schnapps and Swedish lager. House French £5.45.

CHEF: John-Pierre Cattiaux PROPRIETOR: Ake Lindholm
OPEN: all week, exc Sat L and Sun L
MEALS: 12 to 3, 6 to 12
PRICES: £11 (£18). Cover £1
CARDS: Access, Amex, Diners, Visa
SEATS: 50. Private parties: 50 main room, 50 private room. Children's helpings. Wheelchair access. Music. Air-conditioned

Le Gavroche [18/20]

map 13

43 Upper Brook Street, W1Y 1PF
01-408 0881 £26–£56

'We ate at the old Gavroche twice and were disappointed each time. This occasion was impressive.' Such testaments underline the fact that Le Gavroche is not a static Mayfair monument to its reputation, but a constantly developing kitchen. If Hopkinson at Bibendum and Little in Soho are going back to provincial, bourgeois ideas and being fêted for it, Albert Roux has never given up that ground, always retaining a pot au feu or a ragout, even at the stark height of so-called *nouvelle cuisine*. Like a general, he marshalls his growing business interests to provide an infrastructure for excellence at this basement show-piece. He has set up in butchery and charcuterie, organised van-runs to Rungis market in Paris and developed vacuum-cooking. No surprise, then, that Gavroche is the most obvious heir to the great London hotel kitchens of the turn of the century, far more of a restaurant in the round than any of its current peers. The size of the menu is awesome and the humbler dishes should not be scorned. Soups, of which there are invariably three – perhaps a cream, a velouté and a consommé – are magnificent. The backbone of the *carte* consists of 25 dishes familiar in their use of luxuries: mousseline de homard au champagne; ballotine de foie gras à l'ancienne; suprême de bar rôti aux échalotes au porto; caneton Gavroche; poulet fermier sauté en cocotte aux lentilles et au thym. Beyond these are usually at least half a dozen specialities of the day – perhaps a gratin of shellfish spiked with morels, or a master craftsman's dish, such as the pigeon and fois gras tourte 'et sa salade de laitue aux noix'. A *menu exceptionnel* (for two) offers a further half-dozen dishes and the back page of the menu can also hide a few seasonal specialities before the list of a dozen *entremets*. There are no translations because this is, forcefully, a French restaurant. All is in the grand style: three trays of cheese; trays of petits fours and boxes of chocolates; main dishes presented from under silver salvers. The service, under the brilliant supervision of Silvano Giraldin, has held the reputation intact under the kind of pressure that would have broken many restaurants. Of course there are criticisms. Three bad reports came in a run last winter, suggesting that the menu had suddenly run off the tracks. A March diner makes the point: 'the fat content of all the sauces was too high. Somehow the separate dishes were insufficiently delineated; their richness makes them run together in the mind; old-style cooking, not frightfully exciting and of variable finish, with too much cream and butter.' The Achilles heel of the Roux style is the accumulation of richness, and in ordering it is a good idea to bear this possibility in mind. Perhaps this is why non-dairy dishes, such as the ragout of new season lamb in May, stand out in reports: 'a superb blend of chunks of sublimely tender and pink lamb with a light, gorgeous sauce surrounded by two or three morsels of six or seven vegetables, each and every one tasting quite separately. One of the finest dishes I've ever eaten.' Much of the richness is in the early stages, while sweets seem modern and light; they feature the outstanding pastry. The economics are madness. The set lunch at £19.50 is one of the bargains of London; a bottle of wine costs the same; at night, bills of £100 per person are not uncommon. The wine list is largely French, with a few good wines from elsewhere. Most come from the major areas and there is an emphasis on champagne, red and white Burgundies (from both merchants and growers, including a few old vintages) and claret, a long list including many older wines of top properties. Half-bottles of sweet wines are limited to a few Barsacs and Sauternes (here there are some dodgy vintages), but there are full bottles of excellent sweet Loires, a few extraordinarily expensive sweet Germans (mostly minus their producers' names) and a couple of dozen sweet Bordeaux, with six vintages of Yquem back to '69. House French starts at £12.80.

CHEF: A.H. Roux PROPRIETORS: Le Gavroche Ltd
OPEN: Mon to Fri
CLOSED: 23 Dec to 2 Jan
MEALS: 12 to 2, 7 to 11
PRICES: £46 (£56), Set L £19.50 (£26), Set D £42.50 (£52). Minimum £40 at D. Service inc
CARDS: Access, Amex, Carte Blanche, Diners, Visa
SEATS: 60. Private parties: 10 main room, No children under 5. Jacket and tie. No pipes in dining-room. Air-conditioned

Gavvers [12/20] map 12

61–63 Lower Sloane Street, SW1W 8DH
01-730 5983 £18–£23

The newly revamped Gavvers is a reflection of the muted tones of the late 1980s. The quaint little corner block with its horizontal white shuttering has been brought up to date by a discreet awning with white letters in fashionable designer grey. The inside is a calming green with hessian grey walls and a chequered green carpet sporting a sharp geometric pattern. The atmosphere is classy, French and slightly chaotic compared to the more rustic air of the Rouxs' new Les Trois Plats (see entry). There are interesting similarities and differences between Gavvers and Les Trois Plats. Both are unashamed bastions of the Roux empire, in danger of being part and parcel of a monolithic chain. Both restaurants have been allocated a theme, for Gavvers it is modern, for Les Trois Plats it is farmhouse. Both kitchens have access to van-runs to Rungis market in Paris, good suppliers, patisserie factories and the clout of the imperial organisation. Compared to Les Trois Plats, the Gavvers menu is longer and more varied, and in the first few weeks more variable in quality, its emphasis on a more modern and light form. The determination here is almost to evoke the possibility of eating the crumbs from under the tables of Le Gavroche. First-class dishes have shone through delicate mousses and fine sauces, for instance a slightly gamey brown sauce bursting through with sweet garlic flavour for the duck with some whole roast cloves set on a potato and onion galette. It is not unusual for a Roux place to start off erratically – it happened at Les Trois Plats and at Le Mazarin. The wine list covers about 40 bottles, showing all the predictable Chablis, Sancerre and Muscadet; and several minor clarets of which the Ch. Millet '82 is the best value at £17.95.

CHEF: Danny Crow PROPRIETORS: Roux Restaurants Ltd
OPEN: Mon to Sat, exc Sat L
CLOSED: bank hols
MEALS: 12 to 2.30, 7 to 11
PRICES: Set L £14.50 (£18), Set D £23. Service inc
CARDS: Access, Amex, Diners, Visa
SEATS: 80. Children welcome. Wheelchair access. Air-conditioned

Gay Hussar [new owners, zero rated] map 14

2 Greek Street, W1V 6NB
01-437 0973 £17–£27

How long can the Hussar fend off the inevitable? Victor Sassie has at last retired and writes in the features section at the back of the *Guide*. The first reports indicate that standards have not entirely gone out the back door. Not a 15/20, but a good ethnic Hungarian nonetheless. This entry is really inspired to encourage owners Messrs Crawley and Wilson (previously of the Dolphin Square Brasserie) and Laslo Holecz in the kitchen to maintain a standard, which in the first six months they have. The style of the menu has not changed: large helpings of chicken paprika; stuffed goose gizzard; jellied borshch; cold cherry soup. Soups, as before, are particularly good. Recent niggles have centred on the service, but that might be unfair; others who may not have been aware of the changes have reported positively. House Hungarian £6.50. More reports, please.

CHEF: Laszlo Holecz PROPRIETORS: Crawley & Wilson Restaurants Ltd
OPEN: Mon to Sat
MEALS: 12.30 to 2.30, 5.30 to 11
PRICES: £17 (£27), Set L £10.50 (£17). Cover £1
SEATS: 90. Private parties: 20 main room, 10 to 12 private room. Children's helpings. Smart dress preferred. Wheelchair access. Air-conditioned

Gilberts [new entry, zero rated] map 12

2 Exhibition Road, South Kensington, SW7 2HF
01-589 8947 £18–£20

Previously this was Champers, a black cave full of white lace, sorcery artefacts and candles oozing with dripping wax. The clean-up is complete: walls coloured Indian red, small cosy tables with floral fabrics and a Cézanne poster framed on the chimney breast. Julia Chalkley from the Ebury Street Wine Bar presides over the cooking downstairs in the basement, while Ann Wregg looks after the front of house, more like a hostess than a waitress. The set menu comprises bistro fare based on five choices per course. The cooking shows flair in the saucing, braising and fast sautéing. And the attention to detail, as in the superb olives left on the table, or the brioches warm from the oven, impresses. Good dishes have included braised rabbit, the pan-juices added to chopped broad beans and garlic for a sauce, and calf's liver with tarragon. Soups tend to be vegetable and herb combinations: leek and parsley or carrot and coriander. There are some fine baked puddings, too, such as hot lemon and walnut tart or rhubarb pie and home-made details like bread, fudge and preserves. The wine list shows the same good value, concentrating on the £6 to £16 range, with short helpful descriptions. More reports, please.

CHEF: Julia Chalkley PROPRIETORS: Julia Chalkley and Ann Wregg
OPEN: all week, exc Sun D
CLOSED: last two weeks Aug
MEALS: 12 to 2.15 (12.30 to 2.45 Sun), 6 to 10.15
PRICES: Set L £12 (£18), Set D £14.50 (£20). Minimum £12 at D
CARDS: Access, Visa
SEATS: 28. 2 tables outside. Children's helpings Sun L. No smoking preferred. Wheelchair access (2 steps). Music. Air-conditioned

Ginnan [10/20] map 11

5 Cathedral Place, EC4M 7EA
01-236 4120 and 5150 £12–£19

The Ginnan has been going for a number of years and has a captive clientele of Japanese businessmen, who regard it, correctly, as one of the more economical restaurants. Its lunchtime set meals give some of the best value in the City area. A few years ago, the cooking was for a while exceptional, but it has now fallen back into producing a comfortable, range of standard dishes, all very acceptable without being outstanding. Neither does the low-key décor lift expectations too high, rather it reinforces the sense of competence and practicality of the cooking. Fine dishes have been whole baby squid cooked in soy, dashi and mirin; deep-fried tofu with grated ginger and finely shredded spring onion; aubergine sliced in half lengthwise and spread with a rich salty-sweet miso sauce, made with plenty of mirin, topped with sesame seeds, served on an oblong pottery dish on a paper napkin. All these emphasise the point that this is a kitchen that is firstly about cooking. The Japanese menu conceals many interesting dishes, such as noodles cooked at the table or salt-grilled flounder. There are decoratively sliced fruits to finish. A choice of two sakés plus whisky, beer or free tea.

CHEF: Mr Goto PROPRIETORS: Ninjin Ltd
OPEN: Mon to Sat, exc Sat D
CLOSED: Christmas and New Year
MEALS: 12.30 to 2, 6 to 9.30
PRICES: £10 (£17), Set L from £8 (£12), Set D from £15 (£19). Service inc
CARDS: Access, Amex, Diners, Visa
SEATS: 70. Private parties: 8 main room. Vegetarian meals. Children welcome. Music. Air-conditioned

La Giralda [10/20]

66 Pinner Green, Pinner, HA5 2AB
01-868 3429 £12–£16

The menu has been trimmed back to bring in more dishes of the day and there is the promise of more regional Spanish dishes rather than the international tenor of recent years, which would be welcome. Wines remains the glory – the list is unswervingly Spanish, modestly priced, and especially good value at the expensive end, since there is a fixed rather than percentage mark-up. It is quite extraordinary to omit so many vintages from the list. Vintages abound, however, in the long Rioja section, where mature wines are a speciality (back to '34). Torres Gran Coronas Black Label also comes in three vintages, '79, '76 and '71, from £9.60 to £23.20, and there are various vintages of the expensive Valbuena and Vega Sicilia. A few wines from other areas include a good, inexpensive Valdepeñas, an uninspiring Navarra section, and a sprinkling from the Penedés. Many other areas and new producers of fine wines that have been emerging over the last few years have not yet made it to the list – with the exception of an interesting Rioja, from the single estate of Remélluri. House Spanish £5.75.

CHEFS: David Brown and Derek Knight PROPRIETOR: David Brown
OPEN: Tue to Sat
MEALS: 12 to 2.30, 6.30 to 10.30
PRICES: Set L £7 (£12), Set D £10.50 (£16)
CARDS: Access, Amex, Diners, Visa
SEATS: 120. Private parties: 50 main room,; 16 and 35 private rooms. Vegetarian meals. Children's helpings. Wheelchair access (also WC). Air-conditioned

Good Food [10/20] map 14

8 Little Newport Street, WC2H 7JJ
01-734 2130 £7–£19

One of the more comfortable Chinatown venues for inexpensive one-plate meals. Good dishes here have been crispy fried noodles with beef, shrimps and bean curd, hot-and-sour soup. Fish is also a major strength. Crocodile is a curiosity, served in a broth with scallops. Wines from £5.

CHEFS: C. K. Yip and S. Y. Wong PROPRIETORS: Haylin Ltd
OPEN: all week, D only
MEALS: 4.30pm to 4.30am
PRICES: £11 (£19), Set D from £3 (£7). Service 10%. Licensed, also bring your own: corkage £1
CARDS: Access, Amex, Visa
SEATS: 70. Private parties: 30 main room, 30 private room. Vegetarian meals. Music. Air-conditioned

Good Friends [9/20] map 10

139–141 Salmon Lane, E14 7PG
01-987 5541 and 5498 £16

Currently the best of a trio of staunch East-End Cantonese restaurants – the Good, the New and the Old – that were among the first to put this cuisine on the map in London in the 1950s. The Good still lives up to its name. Billingsgate is close by, so fish is fresh and reliable. Otherwise look for the soups and bean curd dishes. Best to book at peak times.

CHEFS: Wah Moon Cheung and Wah Tong Cheung PROPRIETORS: Cheung Brothers Co. Ltd
OPEN: all week
MEALS: 12 to 3.30, 5 to 11.30
PRICES: £9 (£16). Service 10%. Licensed, also bring your own: corkage 60p per person
CARDS: Access, Amex, Diners, Visa
SEATS: 110. Private parties: 80 main room. Vegetarian meals. Children welcome. Wheelchair access (also WC). Music. Air-conditioned

Grafton [12/20] map 10

45 Old Town, Clapham, SW4 0JL
01-627 1048 and 8231 £19–£28

Reputedly the oldest building in Clapham, and one that has housed a number of restaurants over the years. Currently it feels like a bistro, with green woodwork outside, pine floors, wooden chairs and wreaths of dried flowers on the walls inside. But its aspirations are those of a serious French hotel restaurant, with dinner-jacketed waiters, expensive china and ornate food. Fish draws recommendations, from scallops on a bed of baby vegetables to halibut topped with chopped artichoke hearts. Offal is also good: excellent veal kidneys with mushrooms and sherry sauce; lightly cooked sweetbreads; lambs' brains accompanying pink fillet of lamb. Meals end well with chunky fruit terrine or bitter chocolate mille-feuilles, and home-made petits fours are outstanding. The comprehensive, well-chosen wine list begins with house French at £7.70.

The entries are compiled from the views of readers who have eaten at the restaurant in the last year, backed up by anonymous inspections and by information supplied and facts verified by the restaurants.

CHEF: Eric Alloush PROPRIETOR: M.W. Gabr
OPEN: Tue to Sun, exc Sat L and Sun D
CLOSED: 3 weeks Aug, 1 week at Christmas
MEALS: 12.30 to 3, 7 to 11.30
PRICES: Set L £11.50 (£19) to £12.50 (£20), Set D £20 (£28). Minimum £11.50
CARDS: Access, Amex, Carte Blanche, Diners, Visa
SEATS: 74. Private parties: 22 main room, 24 and 28 private rooms. Vegetarian meals. Children welcome. Smart dress preferred. No-smoking area. Music

Grahame's Seafare [10/20] map 13

38 Poland Street, W1V 3DA
01-437 3788 and 0975 £19

A loyal clientele keep Grahame's thriving. The dining-room hardly seems to have changed since the 1950s – dark brown varnished woodwork, green padded seating, old prints of fish on the walls. The quality of the fish and the generosity of the portions are marked. The restaurant being Jewish, batter is light matzo. Fish is offered grilled, stewed or cooked in milk and butter (extra). Massive fillets of haddock are cut from the meaty head end; plaice comes three ways – whole, middle or fillet. Smoked salmon is excellent; there's also chopped herring. Shot-sized balls of gefilte fish are a favourite and there are cheese blintzes to finish. The waitresses are 'the kind that no-one could object to be called darling by.' Cold borshch or lemon tea to drink. House Muscadet, Frascati and Chablis start at £5.30.

CHEF/PROPRIETOR: Robert Dehaan
OPEN: Mon to Sat, exc Mon D
MEALS: 12 to 2.45, 5.30 to 8.45 (7.45 Fri)
PRICES: £13 (£19). Cover 50p. Service 10%
CARD: Visa
SEATS: 90. Children's helpings. Wheelchair access. Air-conditioned

Great Nepalese [9/20] map 11

48 Eversholt Street, NW1 1DA
01-388 6737 £11–£15

Still one of the most genuine and bold Nepalese restaurants in London. Unlike most comparable places it moves straight into top gear from the moment it opens; there's no recycling or reheating. Spicing is pungent rather than subtle and the kitchen shows its Nepalese roots with fresh herbs, pulses, vegetable dishes and accompaniments. The waiters will happily devise a balanced meal. Vegetarians have plenty of choice. Look for the masco bara (deep-fried black lentil cakes), kerauko achar (a cold dish of potatoes with sesame seeds) and aloo bodi tama. Roughly shredded, barely cooked spinach tastes like something from the wild; excellent boiled Basmati rice is a better bet than pilau. Finish with a shot of Nepalese Coronation rum or masala tea. House Italian £4.35. No smoking at the front five tables.

CHEF: Mr Masuk PROPRIETOR: Gopal Manandhar
OPEN: all week
CLOSED: Christmas Day and Boxing Day
MEALS: 12 to 2.45, 6 to 11.45
PRICES: £9 (£15), Set D £7.25 (£11). Minimum £4.25. Service 10%
CARDS: Access, Amex, Carte Blanche, Diners, Visa
SEATS: 48. Private parties: 34 main room. Vegetarian meals. Children's helpings. No-smoking area. Music

Green's [11/20]

map 13

36 Duke Street, St James's, SW1Y 6BR
01-930 4566 and 1376

£37

Green's is so old school that it seems churlish to recall that it is hardly into the sixth form as yet, having only opened four years ago. Champagne bar, oyster bar, restaurant with private rooms and wine merchant, this haunt of the racing fraternity is most things to most gentlemen. The cut of the menu fits the image precisely – good raw materials, for the most part plainly served, plus some nanny-ish dishes like fish cakes and treacle tart. Oysters, steaks, lobsters are the main lines. Chief seafood preparer Peter Manzi is a regular contestant in the world oyster opening championships. The cooking is less authentic in the sense that it is quite capable of producing finely flavoured mousse of salmon and not overcooking the vegetables, though the odd fishcake reverts to type. Extras lift the bill. A dozen and a half champagnes start at £17 a bottle (£4 a glass) and run through Crémant de Cramant to luxury cuvées and vintages. From under the reassuring blanket of well-known clarets and white Burgundies, at West End prices, peep a few interesting bottles, such as Iron Horse Chardonnay and a Spätlesetrocken from the Mosel.

CHEF: Beth Coventry PROPRIETOR: Simon Parker Bowles
OPEN: all week, exc Sun D
MEALS: 12.30 to 2.45 (12 to 4 Sun), 6 to 11
PRICES: £24 (£37). Cover £1
CARDS: Access, Amex, Diners, Visa
SEATS: 60. Private parties: 40 private room. Children's helpings (Sun L only). No babies. Smart dress preferred. Air-conditioned

Guernica [new entry, zero rated]

map 13

21A Foley St, W1P 7LA
01-580 0623

£19–£26

The windows open out on to the pavement with an optimistic expectation of hot Madrid-style nights. Plants tumble from the ceiling; tables are covered with pink cloths; staff are traditionally dressed; a reproduction of Picasso's *Guernica* on the wall – 'very post *movida,* as much a symbol of the optimism that has surged since Franco's death and of the return of the painting to the country, as of the conflict and shame of the past.' The menu is at its best when Basque oriented. The emphasis is strongly on fish. Some of the best choices are dishes of the day, as in 'rascasse or besugo (bream) and we could cook it for you with wine, peppers and garlic.' Traditional dishes – which include a fine squid in its ink – mark it out. There is no paella. But there are deep-fried-hake throats, excellent stuffed pimentos with garlic sauce, and reddish-brown fish soup. The more international dishes and the sweets have been markedly less succesful. Look also for patcharan – sloe liqueur – among the finos and Rioja. More reports, please.

CHEF: Benat Arroave PROPRIETORS: Foley 21 Ltd
OPEN: Mon to Sat, exc Sat L
MEALS: 12 to 3, 7 to 11
PRICES: £18.50 (£26), Set L £12 (£19)
CARDS: Access, Amex, Diners, Visa
SEATS: 40. Private parties: 10 private room. Children welcome. Music. Air-conditioned

▲ *Halcyon Hotel, Kingfisher Restaurant* [13/20] map 11

81–82 Holland Park, W11 2RZ
01-221 5411 £22–£32

Presiding over a corner in the middle of tree-lined Holland Park, the Halcyon stands shoulder to shoulder with embassies, expensive apartments and opulent double-fronted town houses sporting wrought-iron and glass canopies. The hotel boasts no name plaques or signs to its identity. The only clue lies in the particular shade of pink that the exterior is painted, the colour of strawberry fondant, which makes the house look like a giant birthday cake. Despite expensive conversion of the house, the route down to the basement restaurant is misleading and tortuous, recalling the cheap communal breakfast rooms in seedy hotels on the fringes of Paddington. The entrance is (or, with luck, *was* by the time you read this) one of the four doors marked 'Fire doors, keep shut'. Restaurant and bar, by contrast, look out on to patios and are filled with white timber trellises and cleverly hung mirrors, all very pink and a shade impersonal. James Robins promises a lot with his fixed, unseasonal *carte*, Italianate theme and liking for unconventional combinations. For instance, wild rice accompanies medallions of beef; ravioli is stuffed with crab and ricotta. Some of the details, like the gorgeous black bread and the hollandaise, lift the kitchen several notches. Plain dishes, for instance a salad of langoustine, are classic, while the black tagliatelle, 'deliciously mushroomy and dense, dyed black with octopus ink' and served with scallops pan-fried on one side only, gives a measure of the creative possibilities. Sweets range from sorbets – champagne, mango or blackcurrant – to 'a composition of three chocolates'; alternatively, there are French, Italian and English cheeses. On a test meal marked out of 10, no dish scored less than 8, and that despite some mistakes. Apart from house wines at £8.75, nothing is under £10 on the wine list, and mark-ups are high. However, some good clarets include '70 second, third and fourth growths, and Burgundies are from repected growers. Well-chosen, young wines from the other main French regions make up most of the rest of the list, but there are good limited selections from Italy, Spain, California and Australia, and German wines (producers not listed). Sweet wines are restricted to expensive bottles or half-bottles of first and second growth

Sauternes, and Muscat de Beaumes de Venise, La Vieille Ferme, at £21.75 per bottle, £12.25 per half. CELLARMAN'S CHOICE: Château du Clos Renon '82, £18; Sancerre, Domaine des Chasseignes '86, £16; Chardonnay, Wyndham Estates, Hunter Valley '85, £15.75.

CHEF: James Robins PROPRIETORS: Halcyon Hotel Corporation
OPEN: all week
MEALS: 12.30 to 2.30, 7.30 to 11.30
PRICES: £25 (£32), Set L from £15.50 (£22). Service inc
CARDS: Access, Amex, Carte Blanche, Diners, Visa
SEATS: 66. 6 tables outside. Private parties: 60 main room. Children's helpings. Jacket and tie. Wheelchair access. Music. Air-conditioned
ACCOMMODATION: 44 rooms, all with bath/shower. Rooms for disabled. Lift. B&B £123 to £143. Deposit: £103. Baby facilities. Afternoon teas. Sauna. Air-conditioning. TV. Phone. Scenic. Confirm by 6

Hard Rock Café [10/20] 10 YEARS map 13

150 Old Park Lane, W1Y 3LN
01-629 0382 £15

Not even a fire in the basement kitchen could stop the Hard Rock trading. Plans are now in place for a new dining-room downstairs, which may reduce the queues (will this be a teeny-bopper section to counter the onset of middle-age for 'the greatest rock'n'roll collection in the world'?). American restaurants have tried hard to establish a foot in London in the last year, but if anything, the Hard Rock looks even better in comparison to the newcomers. It offers straight down the line American food of the 1960s –large portions, good quality, not overpriced, with loud music. The burgers, char-grilled and served in sesame seed buns, come with or without melted cheese (three kinds), bacon, BBQ sauce, plus crisp fries and salad. An alternative is the Southern-style pig sandwich, using smoked pork pulled, rather than carved, off the bone and served with fresh coleslaw. There are sweets from the soda fountain, alternatively, try the good pecan pie. Many of the staff have been here since the early 1970s, another pointer to the quality of the management principles. It has outlasted the groups and the era to which it is dedicated, although the Casino group Pleasurama who last year bought the Seashell in Lisson Grove have taken a controlling interest for £63 million worldwide, but founder Isaac Tigrett remains on the board. To drink there are American beers, Cona coffee, Coke floats, shakes or house French at £5.75.

CHEF: Dermot Lehane PROPRIETORS: Hard Rock Café (London) Ltd
OPEN: all week
MEALS: noon to 12.30am (1am Fri and Sat)
PRICES: £11 (£15). Minimum £3.75. Service 12.5% on bills of £16 and over
SEATS: 100. 4 tables outside. Vegetarian meals. Children welcome. Smart dress preferred. Wheelchair access. Music. Air-conditioned

Restaurants that we have not been able to assess as fully as we would like are given a zero rating this year. We are particularly keen to have reports on these places.

Harvey's [17/20] map 10

2 Bellevue Road, SW17 7EG
01-672 0114/0115 £19–£31

Who is cooking better? Others have their reputations and their experience, but Marco Pierre White has forged his reputation where it matters – on the plate. Believe the hype. The volume of reports confirms last year's award of South London restaurant of the year, and inspectors who have eaten at the best restaurants here and in France would not say that there have been better dishes than here on a good night. Of course, as a restaurant it is still in a formative stage, reopening as the *Guide* appears after a three-month revamp. The average age of the staff is 20. Marco Pierre White is 26. But this is a meteor hurtling through the restaurant firmament, powered by the extraordinary passion of one young man. The cooking demonstrates a flair that leaves others still bewildered at the starting line. Already there is evidence of an understanding that far outstrips anything usual. Take a plate and on one side place a row of pan-fried scallops, down the centre a lattice of shredded carrots and on the other an oval piece of roast foie gras. The sauce is a magisterial veal stock sweetened with Sauternes. But this is not sauce cooking as such, plates are just washed with infusions to show off main features. The tone of the dining-room is that of all truly great eating places, a quiet hum of people enjoying and discovering. There is a constant buzz, not dissimilar to the excitement in Frith Street when Alastair Little first opened the doors to his restaurant in December 1986.

Where to start on the cooking itself? The saucing is impeccable. The herb sauce to go with the salmon is no more than a beurre blanc generously sprinkled with chopped parsley, chives and basil; the perfume of the basil, excessively sweet by itself, is balanced perfectly when combined with the rich buttery texture of the fish. The veal stock for sweetbreads is not over-reduced, thus allowing the madeira or port, together with the juices of the cèpes, also to shine through. On the other hand the fish fumet to go with ravioli is understated, not light, but just sufficient to coat the envelopes of langoustines and let the shellfish flavours develop. The meats and fish are not delicate in the vein of *nouvelle*: the fillet of salmon, for example, is a generous rectangular mass that has been baked, bearing more affinity to cucina rustica. The seasoning appears heavy handed as items are viciously salted, but somehow the dishes do not end up being over-salty. There are few fussy garnishes: the citron tart comes as a solitary triangular wedge, entirely naked, with a light lemony frothy texture, slightly biting on the tongue, not harsh, but entirely sensuous. The list of endorsed dishes is a long one: shellfish soup with coriander, lobster ravioli, sole mousseline with a beurre blanc, lamb sweetbreads with tagliatelle, potage of scallops, pig's trotter stuffed with sweetbreads (after Pierre Koffmann), baron of rabbit. And then there are the signatures, such as the leek and langoustine terrine or the oysters with tagliatelle, a dish that redefines the mood of cooking – served on a tray of ice, the shell wiped clean, filled with a swirl of pasta in a little butter, topped with the warmed oyster and a little acidulated cucumber or a few drops of caviare. Peripheral items have not always come up to scratch, reflecting the pressure in the kitchen. The famous fettuccine swirls to accompany main courses have been watery and bland; the tuile basket soggy and dull; bread might be more interesting. A steadier dining-room is needed – a good front-of-house person would be a sound improvement. But the central features are of such calibre and executed with such flair that they overshadow all else. The bargain loss-leader menus have been replaced by more appropriate prices, alas, but that is hardly surprising. 'I believe that Harvey's is at the moment the best restaurant in Great Britain,' is not an isolated view. The wines match – 50 taking in claret, Burgundy and the New World, mostly in the range of £7 to £25. CELLARMAN'S CHOICE: Coonawarra Chardonnay '86, £19.50; Pouilly-Fuissé '84, £23.

CHEF/PROPRIETOR: Marco Pierre White
OPEN: Mon to Sat, exc Sat L
MEALS: 12.30 to 2, 7.30 to 11.15
PRICES: Set L £15 (£19), Set D £26 (£31)
CARDS: Access, Visa
SEATS: 45. No children under 16. No pipes in dining-room. Air-conditioned

Heal's [new entry, zero rated] map 13

196 Tottenham Court Road, W1P 9LD
01-636 1666 £15–£25

The bright, modernistic dining-room on the first floor of the department store makes a comfortable retreat from heavy-duty shopping. The kitchen, now under Justin de Blank's wing, offers a menu a sight more interesting and up to date than at other stores. There are half a dozen choices at each course: leeks with quails' eggs on a beetroot sauce; and fillet of sea-bass on julienne of fennel in a mustard sauce are successful examples. Sauces tend to be creamy although there are lighter alternatives. Other details, such as excellent crisp vegetables, bread rolls and the range of teas and coffees, lift full lunches. House Cabernet Sauvignon £7.50. More reports, please.

CHEF: Virginia Clayton PROPRIETORS: de Blank Restaurants Ltd
OPEN: Mon to Sat, L only
CLOSED: bank hols
MEALS: 12 to 2.30
PRICES: £17 (£25), Set L £10 (£15). Minimum £6
CARDS: Access, Amex, Diners, Visa
SEATS: 75. Private parties: 100 main room. Vegetarian meals. Children's helpings on request. Wheelchair access (also WC). Music. Air-conditioned

L'Hérisson [11/20] map 10

8 High Street, Wimbledon, SW19 5DX
01-947 6477 £19–£26

The hedgehog's pale green walls are hung with prints and paintings by artists associated with the Francis Kyle Gallery. David Healey's menu is an English rendition of mostly modern French ideas and it changes regularly. Fish shows up well: pâté of lobster, salmon and sole with chives; fricassee of monkfish and scallops in lobster sauce; poached halibut with Pommery mustard sauce. Medallions of lamb are glazed with garlic hollandaise; the loin is served in pastry with tomato and basil. Sweets, though, can fade. Some have found the sometimes pontificating style of management intrusive and prickly. Wines are well spread, with a strong showing from Alsace and plenty of drinking round the £10 mark. CELLARMAN'S CHOICE: Tokay, Cuvée Jean Baptiste '83, £12.50; Côtes du Rhône, Domaine St Esteve Rosé '86, £8.25.

CHEF: David Healey PROPRIETORS: G. Thomson, I. Thomson, and A. Wood
OPEN: Mon to Sat, exc Sat L
CLOSED: 1 week at Christmas, bank hols
MEALS: 12 to 3, 7 to 11
PRICES: £17 (£26), Set L £12.95 (£19). Licensed, also bring your own: no corkage
CARDS: Access, Amex, Diners, Visa
SEATS: 50. Private parties: 12 main room. Vegetarian meals. Children's helpings on request. No pipes in dining-room. Wheelchair access (also WC). Air-conditioned

Hiders [12/20]

map 10

755 Fulham Road, SW6 5UU
01-736 2331 £16–£20

There is no shortage of imagination in the cooking at this smart, well-established split-level restaurant with its heavy drapes, padded banquettes and superb chandelier. Sausage and mash features at lunch, though more characteristic is pigeon breasts with a sauce of fennel, bitter chocolate, red wine and fruit jelly. If the food on the plate sometimes lacks the final touch to pull the dish together, it is modern without being over-fussy – gravlax with two sauces; hot scallops and Jerusalem artichoke salad; salad topped with fried quail's egg; wing of skate in a brown butter sauce; poussin with herbs and garlic. The gratin dauphinois with sticky threads of Gruyère stands out. Also, exotically garnished crème – someone has a nice free hand with the swirls of fruit coulis and the loquats. At night menus are sensibly set by all-inclusive price, only service at 12 per cent – 'optional' – confuses. Twenty-six wines, mostly from Burgundy, Bordeaux and Champagne, are in the £10 to £20 range. House Blanc de Blancs is £5.95.

CHEFS: Paul Duvall and Andrew George PROPRIETORS: Richard and Hilary Griggs
OPEN: Mon to Sat, exc Sat L
CLOSED: bank hols
MEALS: 12.30 to 2.30, 7.30 to 11.30
PRICES: L £13 (£18), Set L from £11.50 (£16), Set D from £14.50 (£20). Service 12.5%
CARDS: Access, Amex, Visa
SEATS: 70. Private parties: 40 main room. Children welcome. Wheelchair access

Hilaire [13/20]

map 12

68 Old Brompton Road, SW7 3LQ
01-584 8993 £20–£29

The cut of a serious restaurant lingers, from when the Kennedy Brooks chain (Wheelers, Mario and Franco, Braganza etcetera) was set up by Simon Hopkinson – now at Bibendum – and PR svengali Alan Crompton-Batt, although ownership has now passed to Trusthouse Forte. The sensible set-price menu is in the same style, but now with the accent more modern

British than Hopkinson's bourgeois cooking. It is a good read, with plenty of provocative combinations: oysters with laverbread and Stilton; pigeon breast with a ravioli of wild mushroom. The sauces are Bryan Webb's forte and have power and vibrancy; the dishes that play on them are far and away the most successful. But there seems to be a consensus view that his cooking has consolidated and developed. Alpha dishes in summer were a grilled baby lobster, sauce vièrge; a plate split between, on one side, scallops on a purée of potato and, on the other, grilled scallops on a sabayon decorated with samphire; best end of lamb with aubergine and pesto. 'Fresh, original, imaginative, inventive – it felt like the touch of one chef, not endless sous chefs.' There is a substantial choice too, as many as a dozen dishes per course at night, half the choice at lunch for half the price. Wines inflate the bill, contributing £20 plus with some very fine vintage claret and Burgundies. The wine list tries to be all things to all people, and gets pretty close. A quarter of a century of claret doesn't come cheap, any more than prestigious Burgundy, but balance is provided by Chateau Vignelaure from Provence, Marqués de Murrieta Rioja, a sound contingent from the new world, and a more than generous collection of over 40 half-bottles, including a Recioto della Valpolicella, Italy's unfortified answer to port.

CHEF: Bryan Webb PROPRIETORS: Kennedy Brooks plc
OPEN: Mon to Sat, exc Sat L
MEALS: 12.30 to 2.30, 7.30 to 11
PRICES: Set L £14.50 (£20), Set D £23 (£29)
CARDS: Access, Amex, Carte Blanche, Diners, Visa
SEATS: 50. Private parties: 8 main room. Children's helpings. Air-conditioned

Ho-Ho [10/20] map 10

20 High Road, South Woodford, E18 2QL
01-989 8021 and 1041 £18–£24

The expansion into next door means this second-generation Peking/Szechuan restaurant no longer looks like a trattoria but has taken on a modern, tinted-glass aspect. Popular dishes on an inter-regional menu are done well, notably crispy duck, crispy beef with carrots, Manchurian lamb, Singapore noodles, bang bang chicken. Service is a cut above the usual, as is the musak. House claret is £6.50.

CHEF: Lok Sing Yuen PROPRIETOR: Steve Man
OPEN: all week, exc Sat L
MEALS: 12 to 2.30, 6 to 11 (11.30 Fri and Sat)
PRICES: £11 (£20), Set L and D £11.50 (£18) to £17 (£24). Service 10%
CARDS: Access, Amex, Diners, Visa
SEATS: 100. Private parties: 100 main room, 12 private room. Vegetarian meals. Children welcome. Jacket and tie. Music. Air-conditioned

'Am I correct in assuming that the average customer's manners are getting worse? We have a high proportion of non-arrivals, parties arriving as a different number to that booked (generally fewer, of course) and promptness seems to have flown out of the window.' Gloucestershire restaurateur

Hung Toa [9/20]

map 11

54 Queensway, W2 3RY
01-727 6017 £10–£42

The Chinese community uses Hung Toa as a lunch canteen. This is *the* place in town to eat barbecued roast pork and succulent roast duck. For a quick meal there is no need to spend more than £3.20 (including service) – simply have a plate of rice with an assortment of roast meats and a pot of tea. The turnover is fast and the main à la carte features predictable standard fare. If there is no chef at the window chopping board, the prime meats are not on.

CHEFS: Mr Wong and Mr Leong PROPRIETORS: Jeromglen Ltd
OPEN: all week
MEALS: noon to 11pm
PRICES: £5 (£10), Set L and D £14 (£20) to £34 (£42), Snacks from £1.20. Service 10%
CARD: Access
SEATS: 66. Private parties: 30 main room. Vegetarian meals. Children welcome. Wheelchair access (3 steps)

Ikeda [10/20]

map 13

30 Brook Street, W1Y 1AG
01-499 7145 £18–£40

More authentically Japanese and more relaxed than its sister, One, Two, Three (see entry). The menus are the same, but the open-plan scheme here affords a view from the bar of dishes being assembled. There is also a small sushi bar. Prices are Mayfair, not helped by cover charge and 15 per cent service.

CHEF/PROPRIETOR: S. Ikeda
OPEN: Mon to Fri
MEALS: 12.30 to 2.30, 6.30 to 10.30
PRICES: £22 (£38), Set L £9.50 (£18) to £12 (£21), Set D £23 (£34) to £30 (£40). Cover 50p at L, £1 at D. Service 15%
CARDS: Access, Amex, Diners, Visa
SEATS: 25. Private parties: 30 main room. Vegetarian meals. No children under 10. Wheelchair access. Music. Air-conditioned

Ikkyu [10/20]

map 13

Basement, 67 Tottenham Court Road, W1P 9PA
01-636 9280 £9–£18

At lunch-time, this busy crowded basement a few doors from Goodge Street Tube station continues to offer some of the best-value Japanese food in the West End. There's not much décor and the pace can be hectic, but the mood is casual. The food is in keeping: more robust, more substantial and less artfully presented than in most other Japanese restaurants in the capital. Lunches centre on set meals with rice, pickles and miso soup. Sushi and sashimi show the excellent quality of the raw fish. The menu is wide ranging,

especially interesting being yakitori of hearts and tongues; tofu in a pot; sea-urchin sashimi; five-coloured fermented soy bean; all of which are prepared to order. Drink green tea, saké, Kirin beer or whisky.

CHEF: M. Suzuki PROPRIETOR: M. Kawaguchi
OPEN: Mon to Fri, and Sun D
MEALS: 12.30 to 2.30, 6 to 10.30
PRICES: £12 (£18), Set L £4 (£9) to £7 (£12). Service 10%
CARDS: Access, Amex, Diners, Visa
SEATS: 65. Private parties: 70 main room. Vegetarian meals. Children welcome. Music. Air-conditioned

L'Incontro [new entry, zero rated] map 12

87 Pimlico Road, SW1W 8PH
01-730 6327 £21–£34

The address may be Pimlico Road, five minutes' walk from Sloane Square, but it is also lower Belgravia, as the surrounding antique dens and florists demonstrate. This is a sister to Santini (see entry), sparse and elegant, decorated mainly with grandiose flowers and in the same vein as Le Caprice. The specials of the week add considerable interest to a static trattoria menu – cuttlefish in its ink with polenta; lamb with a prune and pine kernel sauce. The regionality is Venice with adaptations for London, as per Orso (also see entry), with an accent on the charcoal grill. Also good has been freshly made tagliatelle with wild mushrooms. Prices match the area, with house Soave opening at £8 on a predominantly Italian list. More reports, please.

CHEF: D. Minuzzo PROPRIETOR: G. Santin
OPEN: all week
MEALS: 12.30 to 2.30 (12 to 3.30 Sun), 7 to 11.30 (10.30 Sun)
PRICES: £24 (£34), Set L £12.50 (£21). Cover £1.50. Service 12%
CARDS: Access, Amex, Diners, Visa
SEATS: 65. Private parties: 30 private room. Vegetarian meals. Children's helpings. Wheelchair access. Music. Air-conditioned

Inigo Jones [16/20] map 14

14 Garrick Street, WC2E 9BJ
01-836 6456 and 3223  £28–£52

The stark financial contrast between the good-value set-price menu at £18.25 served at lunch and pre-theatre from 5.30 and the serious implications of a *carte* with outmoded traits of pricing – as in a cover charge of £2, service of 15 per cent and coffee at £2.75 – which can work out as expensive as anywhere, has tended to work against Inigo's reputation. How to compare virtually the same meal at £25 at lunch with £50 at night? But Paul Gayler has established the supreme restaurant virtue of consistent quality – and he has achieved it in an area of cooking which is still only developing. The commendable vegetarian menu, which we praised last year, goes from strength to strength. Gayler was one of the first to give the style proper consideration. Courses might include a soup of spinach and truffle and then a mousse of aubergine with a tomato and caraway sauce. The cooking is decorative, intuitive, not overstated. Neat English translations on the various menus underline that the teaching is French-inspired and modern. The lunch and pre-theatre menu has five dishes to start and five main courses; the *carte* offers seven dishes per course, plus dishes of the day. There are some neat tricks, like three pastry cones filled with langoustine, sweetbreads and asparagus, and a fondness for flavour combinations, as in a loin of lamb roasted with thyme and served with goats' cheese raviolis. Similarly, raviolis have been filled with smoked haddock and served with a coriander and pepper butter sauce before a tart of baked rabbit with a mushroom and chestnut stuffing as part of the set meal. Cheeses are from Androuët in Paris. The sweets menu, also built around flavour contrasts, runs from a baked compote of apples, pears and prunes with cider sabayon to a fashionable terrine truffée aux deux chocolats. A scaled-down choice of 20 wines in the £10 to £20 bracket is offered as a pragmatic foretaste of the main list, which is expensive, exclusively French and extremely well chosen. Loires, Rhônes, Burgundies and Alsace wines are from top producers, and clarets include many expensive old vintages. Choice of sweet wines is limited. Mature Vouvray and Bonnezeaux seem overpriced in comparison with low prices elsewhere, and Sauternes of the '70s are offer for prices between £35 and £150. A handful of half-bottles includes a Tokay d'Alsace, Sélection de Grains Nobles '83 from Muré, £29.30. House French £10.95. CELLARMAN'S CHOICE: St Emilion, Ch. Franc-Grâce-Dieu *grand cru* '81, £16.40. As we go to press the building is under threat of redevelopment.

CHEF: Paul Gayler PROPRIETORS: Peter Ward, Jean Kaeser, William Chalmers and Paul Gayler
OPEN: Mon to Sat, exc Sat L
MEALS: 12.30 to 2.30, 5.30 to 11.30
PRICES: £36 (£52), Set L £18.25 (£28), Set D £18.25 (£32), vegetarian menu £25.50 (£37). Cover £2 after 7pm. Service 15%
CARDS: Access, Amex, Diners, Visa
SEATS: 70. Private parties: 35 main room. Vegetarian meals. Children welcome. Smart dress preferred. Air-conditioned

Interlude [new chef, zero rated] map 14

7–8 Bow Street, WC2E 7AH
01-379 6859 £22–£37

The interlude at the Interlude is of a succession of chefs coming and going and with each arrival the system becomes a shade more fragile and further away from the good-value format established so successfully by Jean-Louis Taillebaud. Not that the cooking has dipped badly. Each chef seems to bring a new treatment for salmon: David Lawrence – a mousse stuffed inside smoked salmon; Claude Esprabens – poached with apple and green peppercorn sauce; Bussy Nicolas – with cream and ginger (not successful). Overall, the style remains the same, with set meals offering much better value than the creamy *carte*, more in keeping with the possibilities of a kitchen geared to this number of covers. Feuilletés, magrets, gratins are the pitch and there is much emphasis on saucing. The dining-room has an executive-style elegance and if it is the proximity to the Opera House that sustains the restaurant, that is partly due to the lack of serious alternatives in the Covent Garden area. Wine is included in the lunch price, but not that of dinner, when a massive wine list, very strong in Burgundy, is available, albeit at mark-ups higher than usual. More reports on comings and goings, please.

CHEF: Bussy Nicolas PROPRIETORS: Interlude Restaurants Ltd
OPEN: Mon to Sat, exc Sat L
CLOSED: Aug
MEALS: 12.15 to 2.15, 6 to 11.30
PRICES: £31 (£37), Set L £19.50 (£22), Set D £24 (£31). Minimum £22
CARDS: Access, Amex, Diners, Visa
SEATS: 50. Private parties: 24 main room. Vegetarian meals. Children welcome. Air-conditioned

Jade Garden [new entry, zero rated] map 14

15 Wardour Street, W1V 3HA
01-437 5065 £12–£23

One of the old stagers, dating from the early 1970s, before Chinatown was established in quite such density, but given a facelift last spring and now decorated in gold and blues. The balcony at the back is the favoured place to sit. The mood has also picked up: less MSG, better service and better dishes on the main menu, not just good dim-sum. The cooking is Cantonese, combining sophisticated, family and rustic dishes – stir-fries, clay pots, steams, roasts. The very Eastern dishes stand out and these are what bring the Garden back to the listings – shredded jelly fish with shredded duck; duck's feet with fish lips. Look also on the Chinese menu for roast quails with garlic and spiced salt. The wok dishes have improved noticeably too. Tea is jasmine and, as is the habit in Chinatown, meals end with segments of orange. More reports, please.

CHEF: Kwai Yueng PROPRIETOR: P.W. Man
OPEN: all week
CLOSED: 25 and 26 Dec
MEALS: noon to 11
PRICES: £18 (£23), Set D £7.50 (£12). Minimum £6. Service 10%. Licensed, also bring your own: corkage £2
CARDS: Access, Amex, Diners, Visa
SEATS: 150. Private parties: 150 main room. Vegetarian meals. Children welcome. Wheelchair access (also WC). Air-conditioned

Jamdani [new entry, zero rated] map 13

34 Charlotte Street, W1P 1HJ
01-631 0417 and 636 1178 £25

The area around Charlotte Street has been transformed and revitalised by Channel Four and an influx of media set-ups. Amin Ali has shrewdly placed his most ambitious venture at the heart of this activity, and plays to a guaranteed audience. The cool, deliberately civilised dining-room has been planned to the last detail. Every feature fits, from the rough-cast walls that look like 'designer neolithic' with strange invented hieroglyphic figures all around them, to the hi-tech metallic chairs with woven fabric seats (Jamdani is the name of the highly prized Bangladesh muslin), to the menu, which is written on strips of waxed paper between wooden boards. When the kitchen is in full swing – particularly at lunch-time – it can deliver excellent food: thalis artfully arranged on a square black tray; murgh hariyali cooked with fresh spinach, mint and coriander; also methi flavoured with fresh fenugreek. Early evening can be a very different story. Despite the high prices, high profile and 15 per cent service charge, customers who arrive before eight o'clock have found an unsure kitchen, off-hand waiters and reheated lunchtime leftovers. Erratic standards may be explainable in a tandoori house, but at these high prices they are unforgiveable. The concise wine list has house French at £6.50 and CELLARMAN'S CHOICE: Le Bourgogne Bichot-Chardonnay '86, £10.50, and St Emilion, Ch. La Roque *grand cru* '83, £15.95. More reports, please.

CHEF: Naresh Matta PROPRIETOR: Amin Ali
OPEN: all week
MEALS: 12 to 3, 6 to 11.30
PRICES: £12 (£25). Minimum £15. Service 15%
CARDS: Access, Amex, Diners, Visa
SEATS: 90. Private parties: 30 private room. Vegetarian meals. Children's helpings. Smart dress preferred. Weelchair access (2 steps). Music. Air-conditioned

Jams [11/20] map 13

42 Albemarle Street, W1X 3FE
01-499 8293 £29

Jams gets itself into a bit of a jam every now and then. Rumours of change of ownership and backstage fallings out overshadow conversations about the food. The style is set and determined, though it is plain that when Jonathan Waxman is here rather than in New York (where he still runs the first branch), the cooking finds its identity again. Signatures are the red pepper pancakes with a sweetcorn sauce, smoked salmon, salmon caviare, crème fraîche and chives – a sort of western answer to caviare, blinis, cream and vodka – and the scattering of large numbers of vegetables across the main dishes. The gravies and stock sauces are heavily flavoured – garlic for Barbary duck; ginger for veal with an apple and pear compote; vodka in a game stock for fillet of beef. Much is pre-assembled and then wood grilled. 'It is stylish in a transient way'; not cheap; the atmosphere is of noise and clatter from the terracotta-style flagged floors, offset by the activity in the kitchen at one end, the street the other, and some large modern abstracts in between. Downstairs is more trattoria-like. Service is pressing at lunch, as if it feels obliged to be seen and felt. House French and California are £7.50 and £9.

CHEF: Jonathan Waxman PROPRIETORS: My Kinda Town
OPEN: Mon to Sat, exc Sat L
MEALS: 12 to 3, 7 to 11
PRICES: £20 (£29). Service 12.5%
CARDS: Access, Amex, Visa
SEATS: 90. Private parties: 75 main room. Vegetarian meals. Children welcome. Wheelchair access. Music. Air-conditioned

Julius's [new entry, zero rated]

map 11

39 Upper Street, N1 OPN
01-226 4380 £23

There are a few tables out front and a narrow corridor leading past the kitchen, visible behind a glass wall, to the flowery green dining-room at the back. The cooking relies on good-quality meat and fish, which appear in dishes such as fillet steak with mushroom, pepper and red wine sauce; fresh sardines with light mustard sauce; monkfish in cream and champagne sauce. Meat is well cooked to individual tastes. The sweets trolley is less imaginative, but rounds off adequately. A short list of around 20 wines, strong on Burgundies, is supplemented by changing specials; house French £6.35. More reports, please.

CHEF/PROPRIETOR: Julius Oberegger
OPEN: Mon to Sat, exc Sat L
MEALS: 12.30 to 2.30, 7.15 to 11.15
PRICES: £14 (£23). Cover £1
CARDS: Access, Amex, Diners, Visa
SEATS: 60. Private parties: 50 main room. Vegetarian meals. Children welcome. No-smoking area. Air-conditioned

Justin de Blank [9/20]

10 YEARS

map 13

54 Duke Street, W1M 5DS
01-629 3174 £13

Justin de Blank's self-service canteen uses real foods, intelligently cooked to modern British tenets to which, after all, de Blank has contributed a good deal. The bustle and throughput can take its toll on dishes through the day, but the theme of quality runs through the bakes, gratins and casseroles. Breads and cakes are equally good. House Bulgarian is £5.

CHEFS: Catherine Hawkins and Joe Bloomfield PROPRIETOR: Justin de Blank
OPEN: Mon to Sat, exc Sat D
CLOSED: bank hols
MEALS: 8.30am to 9pm
PRICES: £8 (£13)
CARDS: Access, Visa
SEATS: 50. Vegetarian meals. Children welcome. No-smoking area. Wheelchair access (1 step). Air-conditioned. Self-service

Kalamaras [11/20]

map 11

76–78 Inverness Mews, W2 3JQ
01-727 9122 £17–£27

One of the few, perhaps the only, truly Greek restaurant in London, strictly, the others are Cypriot. The era captured in the basement atmosphere is the late 1960s, as the islands opened up to the first wave of young holidaymakers. The meze, as ever in this cuisine, provides a good choice from 20 or so starters on any given night. Main dishes get away from the usual moussakas with, say, suckling pig. There is always a speciality of the day. Wines are Greek, from £5.80.

CHEF: Antonio Jiminez and Zannis Casanove PROPRIETOR: Stelios Platonos
OPEN: Mon to Sat, D only
CLOSED: bank hols
MEALS: 7 to 12
PRICES: £10 (£17), Set D £15 (£22) to £20 (£27). Cover £1. Service 10% on parties of 6 or over
CARDS: Access, Amex, Diners, Visa
SEATS: 96. Private parties: 12 main room, 16 and 28 private rooms. Vegetarian meals. Children's helpings. Wheelchair access. Music. Air-conditioned

Kanishka [new entry, zero rated] map 13

14 Warren Street, W1P 5DA
01-388 0860 and 0862 £11–£22

Kanishka – the Great Emperor – was a vegetarian who allowed his courtiers to eat meat. This miniature new-wave Indian restaurant follows suit. The short menu reads well, avoiding most traces of curry-house language and style, although dishes are bedevilled by hyped-up descriptions that don't always match the food on the plate. Half the menu is vegetarian, and vegetarian dishes are cooked in a separate kitchen. Otherwise there's a strong regional bias: here are Goan fish dishes – including crab and scallops – tandooris from the North-West frontier, and a speciality of mutton with apricots that has Persian and Parsee overtones. Mustard leaves appear among the vegetables and Basmati rice is done four ways. Lunch is an eight-dish buffet for £6.95. More reports, please.

CHEF: Mr Mohamed PROPRIETOR: Mr J. Vitish
OPEN: all week, exc Sat L
MEALS: 12 to 3, 6 to 11.30 (12 Thur, Fri and Sat, 1 to 10 Sun)
PRICES: £13 (£22), Set L £6.95 (£11), Set D £7.25 (£12) to £10.50 (£16). Service 10%
CARDS: Access, Amex, Diners, Visa
SEATS: 120. Private parties: 30 main room. Vegetarian meals. Children's helpings on request. Smart dress preferred. No-smoking area. Wheelchair access. Music. Air-conditioned

Keats [12/20] map 11

3A Devonshire Hill, NW3 1NR
01-435 3544 £19–£31

This long-standing fixture of the NW3 restaurant world has picked up of late. Its virtue is that it is a proper French restaurant. Much is made of the Keats link – not a man known for his love of food – but stops short of 'entrecôte à l'urne grecque'. The menu offers a dozen dishes to start and for main course, with fish promiscuously mixed in with meat. Cold puddings are on a tray, supplemented by hot dishes, such as tarte Tatin. The style is both classical, as in fine quenelles, and more modern as in nage of fish fillets. At its best the cooking offers stuffed quail in filo with a warm port sauce, mousserons and a side plate of perfect gratin dauphinoise. The short French list concentrates on Burgundy, mostly from négociants rather than domaines, and there is a second list of forbiddingly expensive clarets. House French is £12.

CHEF: David Legg PROPRIETOR: Aaron Misan
OPEN: Mon to Sat, exc Sat L
MEALS: 12 to 2.30, 7 to 11
PRICES: £22 (£31), Set L £13 (£19), Set D £21 (£27)
CARDS: Access, Amex, Diners, Visa
SEATS: 60. Private parties: 50 main room, 16 and 34 private rooms. Vegetarian meals. Children's helpings. No children under 6. Smart dress preferred. Wheelchair access (2 steps)

Kensington Place [14/20]

BRASSERIE DEBUT GFG '89 OF THE YEAR

map 11

201 Kensington Church Street, W8 7LX
01-727 3184

£25

In its own way, Rowley Leigh's decision to forsake high-class perfectionist business cooking for the Roux brothers at Le Poulbot and throw in his lot with the popularising team from Launceston Place, might be seen as just as important as Simon Hopkinson's and Bibendum's stance against *nouvelle cuisine* and sauce cookery in particular. Leigh – like Sally Clarke over the road – offers high-class cooking but at affordable prices and via a developing menu. This style of operating is far better suited to most kitchens in this country anyway, if for no better reason than that the customers are prepared to give it support. The volume of throughput also gives this sort of cooking a new edge. The setting is a hi-tech, open-windowed ground floor, decorated in modernistic Warhol style, with a vast expanse of white wall and a menu that tantalises and promises all that it ought. Slowly the choice has grown over the year and it might now be termed a new version of the menu at Langan's Brasserie: fine consommés, for instance beef with oysters or of lobster; good buying, evident in the carpaccio and the foie gras, which is grilled and served on a sweetcorn pancake; steamed saddle of lamb with mint; duck and sweetbread stew with chanterelles. Leigh describes his approach as, 'Honest treatment of the best possible ingredients – not necessarily the most expensive – without unnecessary garnishing and saucing.' The quality evokes comparisons with places like La Coupole in Paris, but fish shows up rather better: scallops with creamed endive; grilled swordfish with sesame seeds; poached brill with shallots and tomato. Saddle of rabbit wrapped round with salty pork on a bed of lentils is a good example of peasant cooking, while delicate beurre blanc with chopped herbs under a barely lukewarm slice of turbot aspires to something higher. Sweets might include 'chocolate indulgence', wild strawberry pudding, and prunes and custard. Given a steady team and better service this welcome addition could quickly climb the ratings. A short, sensible wine list has house claret at £6.95. CELLARMAN'S CHOICE: Moulin à Vent, Domaine Couibes '85, £9.95, and Condrieu '86, £25.

CHEF: Rowley Leigh PROPRIETORS: N. Smallwood and S. Slater
OPEN: all week
MEALS: 12 to 11.45 (10.30 Sun)
PRICES: £16 (£25)
CARDS: Access, Visa
SEATS: 90. Private parties: 90 main room. Children's helpings. Music. Air-conditioned

Kettners [10/20] map 14

29 Romilly Street, W1V 5TQ
01-437 6437 £18

The splendid surroundings of this hundred-year-old Soho dining-room provide a restaurant setting for this element of the Pizza Express chain. The thin-based pizzas – the best still of all the chains' pizzas – with a selection of generous toppings are generally reliable, although one or two reports say recent examples have been soggily under par. King Edward – four cheeses on a potato base – stands out among recommendations. Plenty of alternatives along the lines of BLTs, burgers and grills and also in atmospheres – the champagne bar, black and white hi-tech back room, piano bar with pianist. House Italian is £6.25.

CHEF: Michael Brazza PROPRIETOR: Peter Boizot
OPEN: all week
CLOSED: 25 Dec
MEALS: 11am to midnight
PRICES: £12 (£18)
CARDS: Access, Amex, Diners, Visa
SEATS: 250. Private parties: 25 private room. Vegetarian meals. Children welcome. Wheelchair access. Music

Korea House [10/20] map 13

10 Lancashire Court, 122–123 New Bond Street, W1Y 9AD
01-493 1340 £12–£33

There is a superb patio garden for eating outside in summer at this Korean restaurant tucked up a tiny alley off Bond Street – just down from Fenwicks on the opposite side, round the corner from the inexpensive Japanese Kitchen Yakitori. The basement dining-room is well spaced and set with a clash of different décors, but a largely faithful menu stays in the orbit of kim chee; piquant stuffed cucumbers; bulgogi; Korean pizzas. There are variations on steak tartare and raw skate. Seasoning takes the shape of diced anchovies and sesame seeds. To drink there is ginseng brandy or vodka. House French is £6.50.

CHEF: Mr Lee PROPRIETOR: Y.S. Rhee
OPEN: all week, exc Sun L
MEALS: 12 to 3, 6 to 11
PRICES: £23 (£33), Set L £6.50 (£12) to £8.50 (£15), Set D £17 (£24) to £24 (£32). Service 12.5%
CARDS: Access, Amex, Diners, Visa
SEATS: 100. Private parties: 72 main room, 30 private room. Vegetarian meals. Children's helpings. Smart dress preferred. Music. Air-conditioned

Lal Qila [12/20]

map 13

117 Tottenham Court Road, W1P 9HL
01-387 4570

£18

Until recently, Lal Qila was the only new-wave Indian on the fringes of the curry house territory around Whitfield Street and Warren Street. Now it has some rivals. This is still a very consistent, serious restaurant dealing in a short menu of skilfully prepared North Indian dishes. Highlights are the excellent tikkas, tandooris, and subtly spice curries, such as a murgh makhani enriched with yoghurt and ground almonds. Vegetables include little potatoes cooked in their skins with fenngreek and ginger. Basmati rice is fragrant and delicately coloured with saffron. The décor is all low-key luxury, service is youthful, extremely diligent and swift, and there are flashy cocktails to drink.

CHEF: Ayub Ali PROPRIETORS: Enamul Haque, Abul Kalam and Ayub Ali
OPEN: all week
MEALS: 12 to 3, 6 to 1115
PRICES: £10 (£18), Set L and D from £12 (£17). Service 12.5%
CARDS: Access, Amex, Diners, Visa
SEATS: 80. Private parties: 40 main room. Vegetarian meals. Children's helpings. Smart dress preferred. Music. Wheelchair access (1 step). Air-conditioned

Langan's Bistro [10/20]

map 13

26 Devonshire Street, W1N 1RJ
01-935 4531

£21

'There is every reason to keep this historic place in the book – with due warning. Without being modern in presentation, the food is well bought and well cooked.' The warnings centre on the service, which has been unusually shambolic. 'The wine was neither offered for taste nor poured at all – is this a record in a medium-expensive place?' On the credit side, the décor of upside-down parasols sets a relaxing tone. The menu is a sensible evolution of the traditional – melon and mint; gratin of Arbroath smokies; steak béarnaise. Fifteen pedigree wines, up to Ch. Millet '82 at £16.

CHEF: David King PROPRIETORS: Peter Langan, Michael Caine and Richard Shepherd
OPEN: Mon to Sat, exc Sat L
MEALS: 12.30 to 2.30, 7 to 11.30
PRICES: £12 (£21). Cover 75p. Service 10%
CARDS: Access, Amex, Diners, Visa
SEATS: 38. Private parties: 8 main room. Vegetarian meals. Children welcome. Wheelchair access. Air-conditioned

Langan's Brasserie [14/20]

10 YEARS

map 13

Stratton Street, W1X 5SD
01-493 6437

£25

The story so far: Michael is threatening to leave, but rumours that Peter has banned Michael are not what they seem. Michael has been seen at his old table again. Richard has a new place in the Algarve but is still trying to keep the show on the road, along with Langan's other restaurants, and is chairing the Académie Culinaire; back-stage is just soap opera. But the history of what is probably London's greatest restaurant of the 1980s has always been liberally speckled with reports of outrage. With 600 or so covers a day and a pack of papparazzi outside the door, it is inevitable that there will be news, all of this fuelling the buzzing atmosphere with which Langan's is, in any case, well endowed. The food is, in the words of a March visitor, 'surprisingly good'. In fact, it has got better after a bad patch. Shepherd has taken a more directorial role and let a new generation through, though Roy Smith and Dennis Mynot have been here as long as him. And if, in 1987, some questioned the rating being pitched as high as 14/20, there was a consensus to keep it that high. After all, preciousness is no virtue and if a few dishes are bland, they are rarely unacceptable, while in most meals there are very good dishes. The range of the menu is a monument to the organisational skills of the kitchen. Recommended dishes this year have included croustade d'oeufs de caille, grilled fillet of beef with a béarnaise sauce, pan-fried salmon with tarragon and basil, fried hare with mushrooms, creamed spinach, treacle tart, crème brûlée, meringue glacée. 'It is serious cooking in a lovely atmosphere.' The restaurant is in its way as classical as the Connaught, yet it has surely persuaded more people to the cause of good food than any other. Thirty wines, from house at £5.95 to Krug Grand Cuvée at £43.

CHEF: Richard Shepherd PROPRIETORS: Peter Langan, Michael Caine and Richard Shepherd
OPEN: Mon to Sat, exc Sat L
MEALS: 12.30 to 2.45, 7 to 11.45 (8 to 12.45 Sat)
PRICES: £17 (£25). Service 12.5%
CARDS: Access, Amex, Diners, Visa
SEATS: 200. Private parties: 12 main room. Vegetarian meals. Children's helpings. Wheelchair access (1 step). Air-conditioned

Last Days of the Empire [11/20] map 14

42–43 Dean Street, W1V 5AP
01-439 0972 £14–£22

The name has changed from the Last Days of the Raj and the menu is slightly different, otherwise the mood and the cooking are much as before. The dining-room is full of the opulent trappings of the new wave, with lots of mirrors and smoked glass. A strong showing of tandooris back up a range of creditable curries, from lamb pasanda and rogan josh to murgh korai. Meat and vegetarian thalis offer plenty of variety. To drink there's lassi, as well as cocktails, Kingfisher beef and house wine at £5.95 a bottle.

CHEF: Masuk Miah PROPRIETORS: Last Days of the Empire Ltd
OPEN: all week
MEALS: 12 to 3, 6 to 11.30
PRICES: £9 (£17), Set L £8 (£14) to £12 (£18), Set D £10 (£16) to £15 (£22). Service 15%
CARDS: Access, Amex, Carte Blanche, Diners, Visa
SEATS: 80. Private parties: 80 main room. Vegetarian meals. Children's helpings. Wheelchair access (also WC). Music. Air-conditioned

Launceston Place [11/20] map 12

1A Launceston Place, W8 5RL
01-937 6912 £15–£23

The strain of launching a fashionable sister restaurant, Kensington Place (see entry), and of being open seven days a week has shown on standards for a while, but a local following keeps the friendly dining-room full and in the *Guide.* The former Casa Porrelli has acquired a deep Englishness in its décor, as old-school as Kensington is new. 'It exudes a constant feeling of wholesome English Sunday lunches.' Rice pudding is 'as good as at school'. The *carte* is oddly up to date with interesting combinations, though its strength is in ingredients and ideas rather than execution. Recommended dishes have included warm salad of goats' cheese with coarse honey; lettuce and clam soup; lamb with aubergine and coriander; king snapper in broth with scallops and radish; monkfish wrapped in leeks and carrots. There is always a vegetarian choice. The wine list is similarly clever in its selection, opening with claret at £7.20 and dealing intelligently with quality French wines, with their escalating prices, and the New World. CELLARMAN'S CHOICE: Pinot Blanc, Réserve '86, from Théo Faller, £12.

CHEF: Philip McMullen PROPRIETORS: Nick Smallwood and Simon Slater
OPEN: all week, exc Sat L and Sun D
MEALS: 12.30 to 2.30, 7 to 11.30
PRICES: £15 (£23), Set L and D (until 8pm) £8.50 (£15) and £10.50 (£17)
CARDS: Access, Visa
SEATS: 55. Private parties: 25 main room, 14 private room. Vegetarian meals. Children's helpings (L only). No pipes in dining-room. Wheelchair access. Air-conditioned

Leek's Fish Bar [10/20] map 10

23 Lavender Hill, SW11 5QW
01-228 9460 £14

Leek's is one of the few outstanding fish and chip shops in London. The kitchen is sensitive to detail. Fish is fried or steamed and elevated from the norm by home-made tomato sauce, parsley garnishes, flavoured batters and daily specials away from the usual run – say a gratin of crab or cucumber and mint soup. The prawn cocktail is a good version. Sweets tend to stickiness. The setting is bistro-esque with a bar for speedy and single diners. House wine £5.50. CELLARMAN'S CHOICE: Gros Plant, Domaine du Parc, £6. Other good fish and chip shops not listed are Geales and Costas at Notting Hill; Nautilus at Finchley; the North Sea in WC1.

CHEF: H. Reyes PROPRIETOR: Rita Leek
OPEN: Mon to Sat, D only
MEALS: 5.30 to 11
PRICES: £9 (£14)
SEATS: 55. Private parties: 20 main room. Children's helpings. Wheelchair access (1 step)

This symbol is awarded only to restaurants with outstanding wine cellars.

Left Bank [new entry, zero rated]

map 11

88 Ifield Road, SW10 9AD
01-352 0970 £13–£25

Once Nick's Diner, then Martin's (now transferred to Baker Street) and now a young French restaurant with a conservatory added to the back; the pink and grey rag-rolling and the mock gas wall-lights create the same smart look as that of its predecessor. The good-value menu of the day, inclusive of wine, has half a dozen dishes per course, very much in the modern idiom: herb vinaigrette for asparagus, raw marinated salmon, calf's liver with sage, fashionable lettuces for garnish. Good dishes have been: scallops in a saffron sauce; a salad of mange-touts and warm bacon dressed in a good vinaigrette; precisely cooked fillets of fish – salmon in a rich lemon butter sauce, monk with a cream sauce garnished with limes; nougat glacé surrounded by a raspberry coulis. The *carte* changes monthly, but there are new specials and changes to the set menu every day. Prompt, cheerful service. House wine on a predominantly French list is £6.50. CELLARMAN'S CHOICE: Ch. Haut Brisson '82, £14; Chablis *grand cru* '85, £13.75. More reports, please.

CHEF: Roger Houart PROPRIETORS: Fernando Peire and Keith Wormleighton
OPEN: all week, exc Sun L
MEALS: 12 to 2.30, 7 to 11.30
PRICES: £17 (£25), Set L £8.50 (£13), Set D £12.50 (£17)
CARDS: Access, Amex, Visa
SEATS: 95. 2 tables outside. Private parties: 14 main room, 30 private room. Children's helpings. Wheelchair access. Music. Air-conditioned

Leith's [13/20]

map 11

92 Kensington Park Road, W11 2PN
01-229 4481 £29–£38

Prue Leith has spent £150,000 relaunching her restaurant and has done it in the best possible way, reaffirming her own values and stance. The trolleys survive, both before and after the main course. So too does duck. But the whole effort seems to have fused the rest of the operation and given it an electricity it had lost. This is again a serious restaurant, not in the style of a single chef/patron, but professionals are engaged and things run smoothly. The same level of interest is evident in the menu – no market cooking here. The seasonal changes are limited to every three months. The style of cooking is almost that of a grand hotel, for instance a terrine of foie gras served with breast of quail and cube of madeira-flavoured jelly. Also, the excellent cuts of meat, far from being left to themselves, are enhanced: fillet of lamb in filo pastry with lentils, bacon and tarragon; fillet steak garnished with bone-marrow sauced with watercress and a little side pastry of wild mushrooms. The opening trolley also shows signs of coming back to life: 'wonderful artichoke and olive pie'; sweet-and-sour monkfish; 'excellent' venison pâté. The sweets trolley is greeted with in-drawn breath for chocolate cake, fresh mango and papaya slices, caramelised oranges, tropical fruit mousse. Hot bread-and-butter pudding involves a 20-minute wait. Vegetables are a weak point, so too pastry, but in return the restaurant is open seven nights a week and there is a wide choice. Clarets are the high point on a wine list that is mostly French, with the exception of four token German wines, some vintage port and a handful of good Italian, Spanish, New World, Chilean and Lebanese bottles. Clarets range from '78s (some of the cheaper ones must be tasting rather elderly) back to '52 first growths. Burgundies are predominantly from merchants, and brief selections from elsewhere in France are sound to very good. House Gamay and Chardonnay are £9.75; CELLARMAN'S CHOICE: Navarra, Chivite Anniversario '81, £18.75, and Alsace Riesling '83, from Gisselbrecht, £12.

CHEF: Thomas Alf PROPRIETOR: Prue Leith
OPEN: all week, D only
CLOSED: 3 or 4 days at Christmas, 2 days at Aug bank hol
MEALS: 7.30 to 11.30
PRICES: Set D £23.50 (£29) to £32.50 (£38). Service inc
CARDS: Access, Amex, Diners, Visa
SEATS: 85. Private parties: 24 main room, 10, 24 and 36 private rooms. Vegetarian meals. Children welcome. No-smoking area. Wheelchair access (3 steps). Air-conditioned

Lemonia [10/20] map 11

154 Regent's Park Road, NW1 8XN
01-586 7454 £14

For 10 years Lemonia has provided reliable Greek/Cypriot food in a dining-room which is a cut above the Camden High Street tavernas. Interesting points on the menu include a Cypriot soup of milk and wheat, served only in winter; grilled aubergines chopped with onion, oil and herbs; and some simmered dishes of squid and also sweetbreads. The meze is £6.25 a head. Othello, Afames, Aphrodite and Arsinoe are under £6; ouzo £1.10 a shot.

CHEF: George Ioannou PROPRIETOR: Anthony Evangelou
OPEN: Mon to Sat, D only
CLOSED: first 2 weeks Aug
MEALS: 6 to 11.30
PRICES: £7 (£14)
SEATS: 85. Private parties: 12 main room. Vegetarian meals. Children welcome. Wheelchair access (also WC). Music. Air-conditioned

Liaison [12/20] map 10

11 Alma Road, SW18 1AA
01-870 4588 £24–£29

The name fits: off the main road, plenty of space between tables, a leisurely pace, luxurious in a small way, and with unusually welcoming staff, it's a good place for a tryst. The six-weekly menu is distractingly entertaining with some sophisticated combinations, decorative without being fey. The kitchen has the technical ability to pull them off. Veal sweetbreads have been served in good pastry with a green pepper sauce; shellfish ravioli with a laverbread and cream sauce. Even a difficult meat like guinea-fowl has been a success: marinated, boned, stuffed, rolled and sauced with its herb and wine marinade and cream, then combined with leeks inside more pastry. The offer is there to have dishes plainly cooked instead, but this is a kitchen that is thinking and taking care. Potatoes are sliced on the mandolin and grilled; canapés and petits fours are homemade and good. Supplements on the set menu for lobster, foie gras and the like would lift the bill substantially. Sweets escape predictable fruit and ices with soufflés, bavarois, mille-feuilles and mousses, including a good example of dark and light chocolates. A detailed list of 35 wines puts the emphasis on quality, which can put the bill up, but the loyalty is to the cooking. House French is £8.50.

CHEF: Paul Harvey PROPRIETORS: H.T. Salez and I.M. Perinton-Powell
OPEN: Tue to Sat, exc Sat L
CLOSED: 25 Dec, 1 Jan, bank hols
MEALS: 12 to 2.30, 7.30 to 10.30
PRICES: £16 (£24). Set D £19.95 (£29). Service 12.5%
CARDS: Access, Amex, Diners, Visa
SEATS: 30. 2 tables outside. Private parties: 24 main room. Vegetarian meals. No children under 12. Smart dress preferred. No pipes in dining-room. Music

Lilly's [11/20] map 11

6 Clarendon Road, Holland Park, W11 3AA
01-727 9359 £18–£26

This relaxed wine bar has evolved into a restaurant. A short, eclectic menu is taken from table to table on a portable blackboard. It is ferociously *cuisine naturelle* in style with everything freshly bought daily, the accent on expensive fish and poultry. There are some challenging ideas, often held up by some effective sauces, for instance a basil sauce for a lobster thermidor served inside a brioche, or chicken with a morel sauce. There is a sparing use of cream, salt and alcohol. Lettuce and scallop soup is served on an octagonal black dish, topped with a sprig of green coriander and a pile of red caviare. Breast of mallard with leek purée and roast boned quail with sage and onion stuffing follow the modern British theme, while salmon teriyaki and lobster Peking show the oriental influence. Meals have variously ended with Stilton matured with port or a plate of different goat's cheeses, a plate of fruits with coffee or chocolates undoing the healthy theme. A capable French list with some good Loire bottles. House French £6.50.

CHEF: J. Roger Jones PROPRIETORS: Dr Peter and Mrs C. Lillywhite
OPEN: Mon to Sat
CLOSED: Aug
MEALS: 12 to 2.45, 7 to 11.15
PRICES: £17 (£26), Set L £11.95 (£18)
CARDS: Access, Amex, Diners, Visa
SEATS: 32. 3 tables outside. Private parties: 40 main room. Children welcome. Music

The Guide *recruits new inspectors from readers who write in regularly. If you would like to apply, write to the Editor with (a) a detailed report on a restaurant where you have eaten and (b) a comparative study of restaurants known to you.*

Lou Pescadou [10/20]

map 11

241 Old Brompton Road, SW5 9HP
01-370 1057 £23

There is no booking at this fish restaurant, part of Pierre Martin's flotilla, the cheapest and most café-like. The décor is time-warp 1960s, a Côte d'Azur fishing village, almost deliberately tatty, evoking the same spirit as the Troubadour a few doors down. The menu is a list of omelettes and pizzas supplemented by cuts of fish at not unreasonable prices – £5 for cod Provençale; £6 for turbot. The small bouillabaisse at £6.50 compares with £14 at its smarter sister La Bouillabaisse a few blocks south. Good grills and soupe de poissons; sweets less so. Keep it simple. Ten wines, three champagnes, house pichet £2, but that's only 25 cls.

CHEF: Laurent David PROPRIETORS: Oakhelm Ltd
OPEN: all week
MEALS: 12 to 3, 7 to 12
PRICES: £15 (£23). Cover 90p.
CARDS: Access, Amex, Diners, Visa
SEATS: 60. 7 tables outside. Vegetarian meals. Children welcome. Wheelchair access (1 step)

Lowiczanka [9/20]

map 10

238–246 King Street, W6 OR5
01-741 3225 £9–£15

On the second floor of the Polish centre is a huge institutional dining-room. The atmosphere is generated entirely by waitresses in national costume and the customers, almost exclusively Polish. Everyone knows the menu inside out. It is what used to be described as an international restaurant with Polish specialities – relegated to the back of the menu with the drinks. The soups; the dumplings; meatballs; excellent cream cheese pancakes (nalesniki: 'eat with a shot of krupnik vodka') are all worth the visit. It is essentially winter food. The set lunch at £4.50 is formidable value. Drink the beer for the stodge; and take occasional nips of the different flavoured vodkas served in little sherry glasses.

CHEF/PROPRIETOR: H. Mizaniak
OPEN: all week, exc Tue D
MEALS: 12.30 to 3.30, 6 to 10 (10.30am to 11.30pm Fri, 11am to midnight Sat)
PRICES: £10 (£15), Set L £4.50 (£9). Minimum £8 Fri D and Sat D
CARDS: Access, Amex, Diners, Visa
SEATS: 80. 4 tables outside. Private parties: 50 private room. Vegetarian meals. Children welcome. Jacket and tie Fri D and Sat D. Wheelchair access (also WC). Music

Ma Cuisine [new owners, zero rated]

map 12

113 Walton Street, SW3 2HP
01-584 7585 £17–£25

At last, after three years of rumour and attempted deals, Guy Mouilleron sold his little Chelsea dining-room in March. You might be forgiven for not noticing at first, as the style is identical, only the master's consistent, diligent care is missing, but not by that much. First meals suggest the kitchen can still turn out quality dishes. Main dishes have been characteristically gutsy, as in kidneys and sweetbreads in a classy thin cream sauce, monk and scallop on a potato galette and an intense pesto, and individual apple tart. Other dishes slip up in the execution, and service lacks Madame Mouilleron's stern attention. Wines are main-line claret and Burgundies. More reports, please.

CHEF: Stephane Landwerlin PROPRIETOR: Lucien Celentino
OPEN: Mon to Sat, exc Sat L
MEALS: 12.30 to 2, 7 to 11
PRICES: £16 (£25), Set L and D £10 (£17) to £15 (£23). Cover £1. Service 12.5%
CARDS: Amex, Diners, Visa
SEATS: 37. Jacket and tie. Wheelchair access (1 step; also WC). Air -conditioned.

Magno's [12/20]

map 13

65A Long Acre, WC2E 9JH
01-836 6077

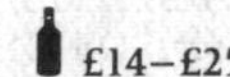

£14–£25

Magno's goes up in the world with more sophisticated food, a tidier ambience and higher prices than its equivalents such as, say, Mon Plaisir or Café du Marché. It has its ups and downs but over a period keeps up a standard. First reports of new chef Gilbert Rousset do not suggest any radical rethinking of policy. The appeal is the Frenchness. Set meals, notably pre-theatre, and dishes of the day supplement the *carte* of eight dishes per course, solidly in the vein of bouillabaisse; Roquefort profiteroles; carré d'agneau. The seasoning illuminates – smoked bacon and tomato for calf's liver; raisins in the onion compote for pan-fried veal. Fish has also come in unusual sauces, such as brill with celery, and classically, as in turbot on the bone with a béarnaise. The wine list rams home the Frenchness – even the one English wine is listed under 'Angleterre'. It's a traditional list, with the weight of numbers in Bordeaux and Burgundy. The Burgundy section is particularly well chosen, crammed with good domaine wines from the likes of Vincent, Leflaive, Bonneau du Martray, Lejeune, Trapet and Hubert de Montille. Prices are not greedy for the clarets, although the mature Bordeaux are not cheap. For those on a budget, the Côtes du Rhône '83 from Guigal, £10.50, is glorious red Rhône on a small scale, and the trio of '80 sweet Bordeaux wines from Monsieur Meslier, the winemaker at Château d'Yquem, is noteworthy. House French is £6.45.

CHEF: Gilbert Rousset PROPRIETORS: E. Coliadis and A. Wastell
OPEN: Mon to Sat, exc Sat L
CLOSED: 24 Dec to 2 Jan
MEALS: 12 to 2.30, 6 to 11.30
PRICES: £16 (£25), Set D (6 to 7pm) £8.45 (£14), Cover 75p. Service 12.5% alc, inc Set
CARDS: Access, Amex, Diners, Visa
SEATS: 50. Private parties: 60 main room. Vegetarian meals. Children welcome. Wheelchair access. Music

Magnum's Wine Bar [9/20] map 11

4–6 Fleet Road, NW3 2QS
01-485 3615 £18

The popularity of this wine bar lends a positive atmosphere. The 60 mostly French wines are backed by an adventurous menu by wine bar standards. Fruits are used in profusion, and there is always a vegetarian dish, such as pancakes stuffed with leeks. House wine £5.50. CELLARMAN'S CHOICE: Coonawarra Shiraz '84, £8.95; Mâcon-Lugny '87, £7.50.

CHEF: Simon Rapkin PROPRIETOR: Michel Lallai
OPEN: all week, exc Mon L
CLOSED: 25 Dec
MEALS: 11.30 to 3, 6 to 11 (12 Fri and Sat)
PRICES: £11 (£18), Snacks from £1.50. Service 10%
CARDS: Access, Amex, Carte Blanche, Visa
SEATS: 100. Private parties: 40 main room, 20 private room. Vegetarian meals. No children after 9. No pipes in dining-room. Wheelchair access (1 step; also WC). Music

Malabar [10/20] map 11

27 Uxbridge Street, W8 7TQ
01-727 8800 £15–£18

Jo Chalmers and Anil Bist call their style Indian home cooking, and the description suits the bustling atmosphere in their distinctive restaurant. The short menu has a few dishes seldom found elsewhere – such as charcoal-grilled chicken livers in yoghurt and spices, and deep-fried prawns in lentil batter. Otherwise there are half a dozen specialities each of lamb, poultry and seafood, from karahi gosht to murgh makhni. There are bananas and pumpkin among the vegetables. On Fridays there's a curry of seasonal fish such as grey mullet, tuna and monkfish; Sunday lunch is a buffet for £5.25. Drink lassi or Kingfisher beer.

CHEF: Anil Bist PROPRIETORS: Jo Chalmers and Anil Bist
OPEN: all week
CLOSED: 1 week Aug, 4 days at Christmas
MEALS: 12 to 3, 6 to 11.30
PRICES: £10 (£18), Set L and D £20 (£30) for two, Set Sun L £5.95 (10). Cover 50p. Service 12.5%
CARDS: Access, Visa
SEATS: 56. Private parties: 12 main room. Vegetarian meals. Children welcome

Mandalay [10/20] map 10

100 Greenwich South Street, SE10 8UN
01-691 0443 £8–£21

Probably still the only insistently Burmese restaurant in the country. Gerald Andrews has re-asserted himself, bringing in extra help in the kitchen, and so returns to the ratings. The menu straddles the cuisine, from mohinga (rice noodles in a fish-based soup served with fried onions in batter and coriander) to a range of curries. Set meals are designed to initiate; some recipes have been handed down through his family. Fish features strongly and has been of good quality. Sweets are unusual – semolina-based cakes; a seaweed and coconut concoction; a sweet golden rice cooked with palm jarrery. There are also ice-creams, including durian. The white wines fit best with the spicy heat, or there is Spanish beer. 'Service is excluded.'

CHEFS: Gerald Andrews and Alastair Shea PROPRIETOR: Gerald Andrews
OPEN: all week D, and Sun L
MEALS: 12.30 to 3.30, 7 to 10.30
PRICES: £14 (£21), Set Sun L £7.50 (£8)
CARDS: Access, Visa
SEATS: 58. Private parties: 26 main room, 26 private room. Vegetarian meals. Children welcome. Music

Mandarin Kitchen [11/20] map 11

14 Queensway, W2 3RX
01-727 9012 £17

The Mandarin Kitchen has been around for the decade, slowly moving towards becoming a Cantonese seafood restaurant. For a while, there was a tank with live lobsters in front of the bar. In the last couple of years, under the ownership of Mr and Mrs Cheung, it has become immeasurably better. The grotto-like dining-room is filled with gold and, when full, bubbles like an emporium. The booklet menu is divided into categories, such as lobster, prawn, fish, duck, chicken and so on, and contains plenty of interest, including fine Peking duck; steamed sea-bass in the ancient way with shredded pork; stir-fried monk. It impresses with its variety and regionalism, particularly in the rice and noodle section with lotus leaf, salted fish and diced chicken fried rice. Notably good dishes are lemon chicken; stewed pork with preserved cabbage, correctly fatty; stir-fried Chinese broccoli with ginger and ginger juice. 'More comfortable than Hung Toa, the other major Chinese restaurant in Bayswater.' Jasmine tea.

CHEFS: T. K. Tsui, F. Ho, K. W. Man PROPRIETORS: Stephen and Helen Cheung
OPEN: all week
MEALS: 12.30 to 11.30pm
PRICES: £10 (£17). Minimum £6. Service 12.5%
CARDS: Access, Amex, Diners, Visa
SEATS: 110. Private parties: 100 main room. Vegetarian meals. Children welcome. Music. Air-conditioned

Mandeer [10/20] map 13

21 Hanway Place, W1P 9DG
01-323 0660 £11–£13

A really serious Indian vegetarian restaurant just a few minutes from Tottenham Court Road Tube station, up a dark alley. The thalis cater for all vegetarian tastes – dairy-free vegan or jaini, which contains no garlic or onion. A Wednesday special offers khichadi (rice and mung dahl), kadhi, three puris, stuffed vegetables, raita, chutney, a poppadum and dessert of gulab jamun, all for £6.50. Try the wide range of fried starters as an option; bhajias and samosas are good but don't overlook the more unusual dishes made from pulses, for instance kachori, patra and dahi vada. House Italian £5.25.

CHEF: Mr Daudbhai PROPRIETORS: Mr and Mrs Patel
OPEN: Mon to Sat
CLOSED: bank hols and New Year
MEALS: 12 to 2, 6 to 10.15 (10.30 Fri and Sat)
PRICES: £7 (£11), Set L and D £5.75 (£10) to £8.50 (13). Minimum £5. Service 10%
CARDS: Access, Amex, Diners, Visa
SEATS: 75. Private parties: 100 main room. Vegetarian meals. Children's helpings. No-smoking area. Music. Self-service

▲ *Manzi's* [10/20] map 14

1–2 Leicester Street, WC2H 7BL
01-734 0024 £29

'Not fair to drop good old Manzi's – it's still a proper restaurant with proper waiters and good plain food (provided you stick with it) and decent white wine. It is no longer cheap, but the downstairs restaurant has an easy conviviality and the grilled scallops with bacon are excellent.' This is not an uncommon refrain from readers and ushers back London's oldest fish restaurant after an absence of some years from the listings. Devotees point out that Manzi's uses large fish and hence the flavour is more developed. Smoked fish, too, is excellent. As are the chips. Service is prompt and unobtrusive. House French £5.95.

CHEF: V. Frappola PROPRIETORS: The Manzi family
OPEN: all week, exc Sun L
MEALS: 12 to 2.30, 5.30 to 11.30 (6 to 10.30 Sun)
PRICES: £20 (£29). Cover £1
CARDS: Access, Amex, Diners, Visa
SEATS: 75. No children under 5. Wheelchair access (2 steps). Music
ACCOMMODATION: 15 rooms, all with bath/shower. Lift. B&B £25 to £45. Deposit: £10. Confirm by 12

Maroush I [11/20] map 11

21 Edgware Road, W2 2JH
01-723 0773 £14

Through the day and into the small hours this cracking, atmospheric Lebanese restaurant dispenses fine meze, robust stews and strong coffee to a stream of mostly Middle Eastern customers. At the front it is part café – with old men sitting at little square tables – and part family eating place that is friendly to children. At the back there is more style, with plush wall seating and lots of greenery. A bowl of luxuriant raw vegetables comes first, with a dish of olives. The real highlight is the list of 20 hot and cold starters, fresh, authentic and colourfully presented. This is healthy stuff, with lots of herbs, pulses and grains. Everything impresses: soupy ful medames, tabouleh green with parsley, montabal, grilled chicken wings with garlic and lemon sauce. There are excellent pickles, brains and tongues delivered daily, and other classic such an kibbeh and bastourma. Main courses centre on a handful of grills, stews and stuffed cabbage backed up by a few Continental stalwarts. Warm, puffed-up bread is replenished automatically. Lebanese house red is a no-nonsense accompaniment, and there is ksarak too.

CHEF: W. C. Abouzaki PROPRIETOR: M. C. Abouzaki
OPEN: all week
MEALS: noon to 2am
PRICES: £8 (£14)
CARDS: Access, Amex, Diners, Visa
SEATS: 80. Private parties: 60 main room, 60 private room. Vegetarian meals. Children's helpings. Smart dress preferred. Music. Air-conditioned

Maroush II [10/20] map 12

38 Beauchamp Place, SW3 1NV
01-581 5434 £22

The extras in some Lebanese restaurants are like the meze – a glory of accounting, add on the cover charge, the service, and as for wines, best forgotten. Armed with this essential fact of life, it is nevertheless possible to eat reasonably if one chooses carefully from the menu. The 39 starters provide a wealth of small dishes. Recommended have been ful mesdames, montabal, kibbeh, sujuk, spicy sausages with most around £2. Workmanlike kebabs provide the centrepieces. 'Sound Middle-Eastern cooking.' Upstairs is a bar and downstairs an opulent room of mirrors and fountains.

CHEF: A. Sawass PROPRIETOR: Mr Abouzaki
OPEN: all week
MEALS: noon to 5am
PRICES: £13 (£22)
CARDS: Access, Amex, Diners, Visa
SEATS: 80. Private parties: 50 main room, 30 private room. Vegetarian meals. Children's helpings. Smart dress preferred. Music. Air-conditioned

Martin's [13/20] map 11

239 Baker Street, NW1 6XE
01-935 3130 and 0997 £19–£29

A smart, modern, thoroughly metropolitan place, where the boudoir-style apricot walls and drapery are lifted by the conservatory glass roof. It is a good place for business entertaining. The *carte* is sensibly separated into plain grills – Dover sole; calf's liver; steak – and richer main courses – salmon with spinach in filo; chicken breast stuffed with foie gras. The food is interesting without being pretentious. Lime-pickled salmon is moist and flavoursome with a bright green edge from the lime and parsley; jugged hare is decently high; chunky game terrine comes with a rather strident fruit jelly; grilled halved kidneys are served in a sticky, boozy, garlicky sauce with whole baked garlic cloves. Half a dozen sweets have a strong leaning to fruit – three fruit sorbets in a biscuit tulip; mixed fruit pudding; gratin of fresh fruit – with the likes of coconut soufflé and chocolate marquise completing the list. Good cheeses. A shortish wine list has a sensible selection at the front in three different price bands. House French is £6.75; CELLARMAN'S CHOICE: South Australian Chardonnay '86, from Brown Bros, £12.75, and St Julien, Ch. Haut-Beychevelle-Gloria '82, £16.

CHEF: Brendon McGee PROPRIETOR: Martin Coldicott
OPEN: all week, exc Sat L
MEALS: 12 to 2.30, 6 to 11 (7 to 10 Sun)
PRICES: £22 (£29), Set L from £13.50 (£19). Service 15%
CARDS: Access, Amex, Diners, Visa
SEATS: 60. Private parties: 16 private room. Children welcome. Smart dress preferred. Wheelchair access (1 step). Music. Air-conditioned

La Mascotte [10/20] map 10

54 Cricklewood Lane, NW2 1HG
01-452 1299 £15–£18

There are several too many tables so there is barely enough room for the waiters' and the clients' comings and goings, but in terms of value, atmosphere and honest simple French cooking the Mascotte rates well. Most people return. The set-price menus offer a good choice: typical of endorsements are gratin of fish, petite marmite de poissons, celery soup, magret of duck, poached salmon, and fruit salad. Specialities are escargots, chicken liver pâté and suprême de poulet aux crevettes. Service prefers unrushed meals. House Côte de Buzet £6.25. CELLARMAN'S CHOICE: Mont Louis, Domaine des Liards, '85, £10.75.

CHEF: Phillip Kanoun PROPRIETORS: Rachid and Phillip Kanoun
OPEN: Tue to Sun D, and Sun L
MEALS: 12 to 2.30, 7 to 11
PRICES: Set D £9.50 (£15) and £12.75 (£18). Cover 80p. Minimum £12
CARDS: Access, Visa
SEATS: 40. Private parties: 40 main room. Vegetarian meals. No children under 5. Wheelchair access (1 step). Music

Mayflower [10/20] map 14

68–70 Shaftesbury Avenue, W1V 7DF
01-734 9207 £16–£19

A good all-round Cantonese restaurant with very fine duck dishes and a good edge to the cooking of hot-and-sour soup or a winter melon soup. Alas, the service can let it down, otherwise it would rate among the best in Chinatown. House Portuguese wine is a pricey £7.

CHEF: F. Chung PROPRIETOR: Patrick Tsang
OPEN: all week
CLOSED: 25 and 26 Dec
MEALS: noon to 3.30am
PRICES: £9 (£19), Set D from £10 (£16). Service 10%
CARDS: Access, Amex, Diners, Visa
SEATS: 140. Private parties: 40 main room, 20, 30 and 40 private rooms. Vegetarian meals. Children welcome. Music. Air-conditioned

Le Mazarin [15/20]

map 11

30 Winchester Street, SW1V 4NZ
01-828 3366 £26

The high rating reflects the enthusiasm for René Bajard's catacomb. He is the most assertive and assured of the second generation of the Roux brothers' graduates, coming out of the Gavroche side of the stable, where he was head chef. This is a serious restaurant, with décor, service, good-quality ingredients and a popular all-inclusive price that is not, by London standards, expensive. In the urban manner it is tightly packed, which lends atmosphere or crush, depending on your perspective, and the service can be disjointed at peak times. The menu is arranged exclusively in French as seven starters, four fish, five meats, cheeses or seven sweets. Looking down the right-hand side of the menu, the seasonings read like the description of a potager – 'au parfum de menthe', 'aux basilic', 'aux baies roses', 'persillées', 'à l'oseille', 'duxelle de champignons'. This is sauce cooking of the highest calibre, but there is also texture and choice. Bajard shares Albert Roux's taste for provincial cooking – a plain saucisson de Lyon, albeit with a little truffle, served with potatoes; onglet steak with shallots. He might even be seen in the context of the new mood of returning to one's roots, like Little and Hopkinson. But in this case the cooking style is tinged with luxuries, as in 'chevreuil aux airelles et sa fondue de choux au champagne'; also, given his background, Bajard's return to roots means to classic tradition, such as 'médallions de homard sauce Nantua'. As with all Roux cookery, dishes are based on good clear stocks. Of many recommended dishes are a warm salad of smoked salmon with a Martini sauce, fillet of beef with fresh noodles and morels, turbot with a saffron and champagne sauce, roast magret of duck with green peppers. Sweets are beautiful to look at, for instance a croustade of strawberries with a passion-fruit sauce. Petits fours are equally excellent. The trimmings, like coffee, wines – other than the house Rhône or Muscadet at £9.90 – and the house cocktail of fresh raspberry cream and champagne, all lift the bill substantially. Nonetheless, meals of this calibre are relative bargains at around £25 a head. CELLARMAN'S CHOICE: St Emilion, Roc de Lussac '85, £17.30; Mâcon-Clessé '85, £16.40.

CHEF/PROPRIETOR: René Bajard
OPEN: Mon to Sat, D only
CLOSED: bank hols, 2 weeks at Christmas
MEALS: 7 to 11.30
PRICES: Set D from £19.50 (£26). Service inc
CARDS: Access, Amex, Diners, Visa
SEATS: 55. Private parties: 10 main room. Vegetarian meals. Children's helpings. Music. Air-conditioned

Melati [10/20]

map 14

21 Great Windmill Street, W1V 7PH
01-437 2745 £18

The ever-busy Melati seems to span the Soho decades, having something of the 1950s coffee bar in the décor, but some slick, fast foods that suit the

1980s' love affair with exotic cuisines. The Malay/Indonesian menu moves through satays, soups such as soto madura (chicken, rice, vermicelli and egg), excellent laksa, nasigoreng and dalca daging (Malayan beef curry), to a wide selection of vegetarian dishes. Specialities include a fish-head curry and ikan pangek, fish cooked in a hot-sour sauce. Sam's triple – tricoloured and flavoured with sweet avocado, mango and pineapple – is recommended among the sweets, as are the ice-creams. House French £5.75.

CHEFS: S. Alamsjah and H. Hasyem PROPRIETORS: Mrs M.C.W. Ong and S. Alamsjah
OPEN: all week
MEALS: 12 to 11.30 (12.30am Fri and Sat)
PRICES: £9 (£18), Set L and D £32 (£35) for two. Service 10%
CARDS: Access, Amex, Diners, Visa
SEATS: 80. Private parties: 30 main room. Children welcome. Wheelchair access. Music

Le Mesurier [new entry, zero rated] map 11

113 Old Street, EC1V 9JR
01-251 8117 £22

Le Mesurier is west of Old Street Tube station, by St Luke's Church and opposite Whitecross Street, where there is a small daily food market. Upstairs in the Victorian terraced house Mr Enthoven runs an architect's office; downstairs Mrs Enthoven cooks. There is one door and one buzzer for both. Inside, the décor is in fact 1980s architect-restrained. There are only seven tables and it is a fairly tight squeeze; flowers and ashtrays have to be removed before the only, very obliging waiter can fit the plates on the table. The food has a strong bias towards very good pastry, and is Elizabeth David in style. The menu is short, with a choice of three for each course, changing every two weeks, and preceded by *bonnes bouches* – home-made Scotch egg with quail egg; a miniature cheese croissant. A March menu offered four king prawns in fresh tomato sauce with a little cream and diced green pepper; filo pastry with Feta cheese mashed with coriander and cumin and garnished with grilled pine kernels; straight-down-the-line main courses – veal with lime, salmon in pastry with hollandaise, steak with artichoke and béarnaise sauce; a stodgy almond tartlet; then the cheeseboard – Boulette, ewes'-milk cheese in leaves, Roquefort. 'It's a lot nicer than the menu suggests, due to the care and quality of the cooking.' Popular dishes, says Mrs Enthoven, are hot oysters with Gruyère and cream, and plum soufflé. A short, well-thought-out wine list has house French from Corney & Barrow at £5.20; CELLARMAN'S CHOICE: Côtes du Rhône, St Joseph '83, from Jaboulet Aîné, £10.30; Australian Pokolbin Chardonnay, Hunter Valley '86, £11.40. Muscat de Beaumes de Venise is £2.50 a glass. More reports, please.

CHEF/PROPRIETOR: Gillian Enthoven
OPEN: Mon to Fri
CLOSED: 3 weeks Aug, 1 week after Christmas
MEALS: 12 to 3, 6 to 11
PRICES: £16 (£22)
CARDS: Access, Visa
SEATS: 24. Private parties: 24 main room. Vegetarian meals. Children's helpings. No children under 5. Wheelchair access

▲ *Le Metro Wine Bar* [9/20] map 12

28 Basil Street, SW3 1AS
01-589 6286 £15

In the basement of the Capital Hotel, virtually next door to Harrods; the style is designer-bistro with bentwood chairs, bare floorboards and marble-topped tables. Value for money is exceptional: prices are in line with basic pub grub, but the quality of the food, which comes from the hotel kitchens, is almost that of a serious restaurant. Typically good have been fat home-made tortellini stuffed with chunks of sweetbread, and salad of cold pink lamb with salad leaves and vegetables in a good nut oil vinaigrette. Excellent espresso coffee. The only drawback is, it has been well discovered. A hundred wines, almostly exclusively French, with bottles from the lesser-known regions. A Cruover machine allows wine to be tasted by the glass. House French £5.95; CELLARMAN'S CHOICE: Saumur '86, £7.20 and Ch. Rauzan-Gassies '73, £13.

CHEFS: John Elliot and Jacques Abdou PROPRIETOR: David Levin
OPEN: Mon to Sat, exc Sat D
CLOSED: Christmas and bank hols
MEALS: 12 to 2.30, 5.30 to 10
PRICES: £10 (£15)
CARDS: Amex, Visa
SEATS: 60. Private parties: 15 main room. Vegetarian meals. Children's helpings. Wheelchair access. Air-conditioned
ACCOMMODATION: 12 rooms, all with bath/shower. Rooms for disabled. Lift. B&B £90 for single or twin. Baby facilities. TV. Phone. Doors close at 11

Mijanou [14/20] map 12

143 Ebury Street, SW1W 9QN
01-730 4099 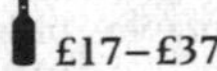 £17–£37

There is always a hard-core following for Sonia and Neville Blech's small restaurant – ring the bell to get in. He is to wine what she is to cooking and the décor is perhaps somewhere in between, starting to look a trifle dated but that is also a testimony to how long they have been here. The menu is French translated into English, with a note that says no menu is new, but interpretations are original. Meals open with excellent cake/bread before almost *nouvelle*-style decorative, very good mousselines and bavaroises. Flavour contrasts are vivid: lemongrass in a lobster terrine, for instance. Fish features strongly as a main course. Marmite des Pecheurs has included tagliatelle, asparagus, broccoli, turnips, beans and carrots in a clear consommé with salmon, white fillets, prawns and scallops. Sweets return to the picturesque, often variations on classical ideas, for example peach Melba, the fruit covered with crème anglaise, raspberry purée and set on meringue, or a sort of Swiss-roll of mint ice-cream, delicate sponge and vanilla ice-cream in a chocolate coating. There is also a tasting menu and supplementary dishes. The wines are a tour de force, and the list is effectively a summary of the world's best winemaking: Mondavi and Stag's Leap from

California; Petaluma and Moss Wood from Australia; Sassicaia and Gaja's Barbaresco from Italy; Jean Léon Chardonnay, Vega Sicilia and Torres Black Label from Spain, quite apart from an impeccable selection from France that includes Ott from Provence and Faller from Alsace. At the same time, it doesn't take a snooty attitude to pricing, so there is extremely good drinking under £12: Chilean Cabernet Sauvignon, Cousiño Macul '81 is £8.95; from Portugal, Joao Pires Dry Muscat '86 is £7.85, and J.M. da Fonseca's Periquita Reserva '75 is £8. Then there are over 40 half-bottles. CELLARMAN'S CHOICE: Chenin Blanc, Wildflower Ridge '87, £8.45; Chevalier Montrachet '82, from Leflaive, £52.50.

CHEF: Sonia Blech PROPRIETORS: Neville and Sonia Blech
OPEN: Mon to Fri
MEALS: 12.30 to 2, 7.30 to 11
PRICES: Set L £11.50 (£17) to £23.50 (£30), Set D £19.50 (£26) to £29.50 (£37)
SEATS: 30. 4 tables outside. Private parties: 24 main room. Children welcome. No-smoking area

Ming [10/20] map 14

35–36 Greek Street, W1V 5LN
01-734 2721 £13–£19

The smart, green-painted corner building has big windows looking out onto the Soho action. This is one of the few genuine Pekingese restaurants in the West End, although the menu roams around. Hot and cold appetisers stand out: smoked shredded chicken, Peking-style dumplings, squid in batter, barbecued spare ribs. Staples such as Peking or aromatic crispy duck are well reported, but the menu also moves into the territory of Szechuan-style aubergines and Tibetan garlic lamb with peanuts and dried chillies. Also look for the bean curd dishes and the fat, worm-like hand-made noodles. Drink Jasmine tea, otherwise there is decent house wine at £5.90 a bottle.

CHEF: Mr Wu Bun PROPRIETORS: Christine Yau and May Yau
OPEN: all week
MEALS: noon to midnight
PRICES: £10 (£19), Set L and D £7.80 (£13) to £11.50 (£17). Minimum £5. Service 10%
CARDS: Access, Amex, Diners, Visa
SEATS: 80. Private parties: 56 main room, 24 private room. Vegetarian meals. Children welcome. Wheelchair access. Music. Air-conditioned

Miyama [13/20] map 13

38 Clarges Street, W1Y 7PJ
01-499 2443 £17–£35

Of all the London Japanese, Miyama has adapted most comfortably to its surroundings. The staff have unusually good English and the menu has been adapted to make the more interesting avenues accessible to Westerners. The charm of the pale room is enhanced by the intricate origami pictures. Beyond the familiar lines of impeccably fried tempura, stacks of sashimi or miso soup it is in the chef's specials, usually taken as starters, that the menu outstrips its rivals: abalone with saké or soy; the rare delicacy of liver of monkfish; raw, paper-thin strips of beef to roll around spring onions and dip in a sweet garlic soy. Bean curd is a stanchion: deep fried and griddled, steamed with a garlic paste or chilled with more spring onion and soy. Drink the soup at the end of the meal. The set lunches are good value (as in nearly all London's Japanese restaurants), while the alcohols are not.

CHEF/PROPRIETOR: Mr Miyama
OPEN: Mon to Sat, exc Sat L
MEALS: 12.30 to 2.30, 6.30 to 10.30
PRICES: £20 (£35), Set L from £7 (£17), Set D from £23 (£35). Cover £1.50. Service 15%
CARDS: Access, Amex, Diners, Visa
SEATS: 70. Private parties: 18 main room. Children welcome. Smart dress preferred. Wheelchair access (also WC). Music. Air-conditioned

Miyama [12/20] map 11

17 Godliman Street, EC4V 4PN
01-489 1937 £19–£34

This younger, City branch of the entry above is a cut more expensive. The emphasis is on teppanyaki and sushi, built on set meals around the £30 mark. The sushi menu itself can offer as many as 21 different varieties of fish. There are set lunches for a third of the price and the menu details the chef's specials in English, which is helpful. The beef fillet cooked on the teppanyaki counter is as good quality as to be found anywhere in the City.

CHEFS: Y. Ishibashi and T. Miura PROPRIETORS: T. Miura, F. Miyama and Y. Ishibashi
OPEN: Mon to Fri
MEALS: 12 to 3, 6 to 10
PRICES: £18 (£34), Set L £7.50 (£19) to £10.50 (£22). Cover £1.50. Service 15%. Licensed, also bring your own: corkage £1
CARDS: Access, Amex, Diners, Visa
SEATS: 80. Private parties: 30 main room, 8 and 12 private rooms. Vegetarian meals. Children's helpings (L only). Music. Air-conditioned

Mon Plaisir [10/20] map 14

21 Monmouth Street, WC2H 9DD
01-836 7243 £12–£22

'Mon plaisir est le vôtre.' This is so much a bistro that it might have invented the genre. A dozen choices at each course supplement a blackboard menu. The selection is as if from a text-book: gratinée à l'oignon; escargots à l'ail; sole meunière ou grillé; pot au feu; carbonnade; steak tartare; entrecôte béarnaise. Helpings are generous and the humble details, from a choice of three styles of potato and an equal choice of salads, to the wide selection of cheese, lift it well above the competition in Covent Garden. Fifty wines listed on the reverse of the menu include house French at £6.50.

Many of the more expensive restaurants offer bargain lunches for half the price of a meal in the evening. Details are given in the text.

CHEF: Michel Dubarbier PROPRIETOR: A. Lhermitte
OPEN: Mon to Sat, exc Sat L
MEALS: 12 to 2.30, 6 to 11.15
PRICES: £15 (£22), Set L £10.95 (£17), Set pre-theatre D (6 to 7.15) £10.95 (£12). Service 12.5%
CARDS: Access, Amex, Visa
SEATS: 75. Private parties: 26 main room, 30 private room. Vegetarian meals. Children's helpings. Wheelchair access. Music

Monkeys [11/20]

map 11

1 Cale Street, Chelsea Green, SW3 3QT
01-352 4711 £19–£23

Given the pace of change in London restaurants, anything that stands still for more than five minutes begins to look dated. What may once have been a romantic's idea of a Parisian brasserie, now – with Bibendum only a five-minute walk away – looks more in need of a new carpet and a lick of paint to brighten up the milk chocolate walls. But the food still delivers. Ignoring fashion in this too, it models itself successfully on the kind of functional no-nonsense everyday restaurant with which France, its inspiration, is littered. Galantine of duck, fish terrine, or a salad are followed by grills, from Dover sole to liver to steak. Steamed trout comes in a shellfishy soup-cum-sauce with strips of scallop, and sauté saddle of lamb with tarragon is equally simple and impressive, all the more so for its clump of glistening samphire. Cheeses, mostly French, are wheeled around on a trolley, and puddings are largely old favourites, from crème brûlée to chocolate mousse to crêpes with Cointreau. The pity is that it all rather shoots itself in the foot with an out-moded, unnecessary, and probably counter-productive minimum food and drink spend at dinner amounting to £20.50, which is stated on the menu, 'but employed at our discretion.' Good food should attract custom, not frighten it away, and the food here is quite able to stand up for itself. The wine list is perfectly sound, if unbalanced; all five German gems are from the '76 vintage, four of them Auslesen, and the seven Spanish wines are all from Torres.

CHEF: Tom Benham PROPRIETORS: Tom and Brigitte Benham
OPEN: all week
CLOSED: first week Feb, 3 weeks Aug, 25 and 26 Dec
MEALS: 12.30 to 2.30 (1.15 to 3 Sun), 7.30 to 11.30 (10.30 Sun)
PRICES: £17 (£23), Set L £13.50 (£19), Set D £17.50 (£23)
SEATS: 50. Private parties: 20 main room, 12 private room. Children's helpings (Sun L only). No pipes in dining-room. Wheelchair access (3 steps). Air-conditioned

M'sieur Frog [12/20]

map 11

31A Essex Road, N1 2SE
01-226 3495 £15–£24

If there is a single style of cooking favoured above all others by London restaurant-goers, then it is surely provincial French, not overly expensive, served in busy, noisy surroundings. Over the decade it is this kind of restaurant which has consistently picked up the bulk of reader support. Different parts of the city have their own exponents: Le Chef in Marble Arch, the Ark in Notting Hill, Magno's Brasserie in Covent Garden, La Poule au Pot in Pimlico and Mustoe Bistro in Primrose Hill trade on, while rivals go to the wall. M'sieur Frog is perhaps the supreme example. Lively and crowded, with small tables, plain wood chairs and wooden walls, it has a seasonally changing menu which, although aware of changes and progress, stays within a bourgeois framework. The recommendations capture it neatly: pheasant and chestnut soup, terrine of Roquefort and pistachio, choucroûte, roast goose with wild rice and kumquats, roast capon, sticky toffee pudding, chocolate and raisin cake. 'Was always good and now improvements in food and service make it among the best.' Fifty wines, with a commendable sprinkling of half-bottles. House French £5.95.

CHEF: Jean Luc Guiral PROPRIETORS: Howard Rawlinson and Tina Rawlinson
OPEN: Mon to Sat, exc Sat L
CLOSED: 1 week at Christmas, 10 days Aug
MEALS: 12.30 to 2.30, 7 to 11.30
PRICES: £16 (£24), Set L £9.95 (£15). Cover 75p. Service 10%
CARDS: Access, Visa
SEATS: 63. Private parties: 14 main room. Vegetarian meals. Children's helpings. Wheelchair access

Nanten Yakitori Bar [9/20] map 13

6 Blandford Street, W1H 3HA
01-935 6319 £9–£16

The departing Japan Economic Trade Organisation has left a number of Japanese restaurants stranded in its wake. This yakitori bar has found a solid English lunchtime clientele to support it instead. The full range of yakitori, strictly either salt-grilled or served with a sauce, is only available at night, but at lunch there has been fine sashimi. By Japanese standards it is cheap and portions are generous; décor and muzak are functional. A sign reads: 'Cold Japanese saké – no hangover even if you drink a whole bottle – guaranteed.' Service is, as ever in Japanese restaurants, prompt. House French £7.

CHEF: Kinya Deguchi PROPRIETORS: Ninjin Ltd
OPEN: Mon to Sat, exc Sat L
MEALS: 12.30 to 2, 6 to 9.30
PRICES: £10 (£15), Set L from £5.80 (£9), Set D from £12 (£16). Service inc
CARDS: Access, Amex, Diners, Visa
SEATS: 30. Private parties: 8 main room, 12 and 8 private rooms. Vegetarian meals. Children welcome. Music. Air-conditioned

Neal Street Restaurant [14/20] map 14

26 Neal Street, WC2H 9PH
01-836 8368 £29

Despite entering the TV superstar stakes with his films for BBC2's *Food and Drink*, Antonio Carluccio is to be found most days in his neat restaurant cajoling the kitchen and encouraging customers into his enthusiasms. Wild mushrooms are a passion; there are freezers full of them in the basement. They provide a soup, a sauce for game ravioli, arrive with the baccala and appear through the menu. The style is an uncommonly long look at different European cookings on an arc from somewhere in Italy through France and Denmark about as far as Cornwall – for a parcel of crab or scrambled eggs with smoked salmon. In October and November there are white truffles from Alba. Recommended dishes: marinated herring; salmon quenelles with horn of plenty sauce; calf's kidney, liver and sweetbreads in breadcrumbs; gravlax; calf's liver Venice; crème brûlée; crêpe noisette. The Hockneys are originals. House wines from Sicily open at £7.80 on a sophisticated list.

CHEF: M. Santiago Gonzalez PROPRIETOR: Sir Terence Conran
OPEN: Mon to Fri
CLOSED: Christmas to New Year
MEALS: 12.30 to 2.30, 7.30 to 11
PRICES: £21 (£29). Cover £1.10. Service 15%
CARDS: Access, Amex, Diners, Visa
SEATS: 65. Private parties: 65 main room, 20 private room. Vegetarian meals. Children's helpings. Wheelchair access. Air-conditioned

Neal's Lodge [new entry, zero rated] map 10

Wandsworth Common, SW18
01-870 7484 £16–£20

Set in the middle of the Common; park in Baskerville Road, from where it is a three-minute walk to the well-lit Lodge. A conservatory extension for the dining-room makes it less like a pavilion than its previous incarnations. By day an upmarket menu of snack lunches and teas operates, but in the evening there is a short modern menu of four dishes per course cooked by Phil Mears, who has trained at the Savoy and at Inigo Jones. First meals have produced fine feuilleté of sweetbreads; a salad of bean sprouts, fennel, red pepper, artichoke coriander and fennel leaves with monkfish; roasted pigeon supreme with the cooking juices enhanced with a little tomato concasse. Some of the mousses have been over-firm and there is a tendency to fussiness. Cheeses have included Brie, goats', mature Cheddar and a French blue, and are served with the warm rolls offered through the evening, or biscuits. The wine list leans heavily to France with a few examples from Spain, Italy and Australia. Muscat de Beaumes de Venise is £2.95 a glass, £14.50 a bottle. House claret, currently an '85, is £6.95. More reports, please.

CHEF: Phil Mears PROPRIETORS: Vicki MacCallum and Alex Campbell
OPEN: Tue to Sat, and Sun L
MEALS: 12 to 3, 7 to 10
PRICES: £9 (£16), Set L £9.50 (£16), Set D from £13.50 (£20). Service 10% alc, 12.5% Set L, 15% Set D
CARDS: Amex, Visa
SEATS: 90. 12 tables outside. Private parties: 90 main room, 40 and 50 private rooms. Vegetarian meals on request. Children's helpings (L only). No-smoking area. Wheelchair access. Music

New World [11/20] map 14

Gerrard Place, W1V 7LL
01-734 0677 and 0396 £9–£13

How far does a dim-sum trolley girl walk in a day? This cavernous restaurant on three floors can seat six hundred at a time and through the day the steel prams are pushed round and round the gloriously garish surroundings. On the frying trolley there are excellent stuffed peppers warmed through at the table; on the cold meats trolley are roasts of duck, chicken, suckling pig complete with crackling; white chicken. There are two trolleys stacked with bamboo baskets: one is noticeably angled to the more purist Eastern tastes of chicken feet and whelks with chilli, and bean curd, while the other has more approachable dumplings of prawn, pork, and vegetables. Dumpling is perhaps not the right word, for the pork is in fact held in a small case of yellow pasta; the prawn in white, almost transparent rice flour. The rest of the menu is not of the same calibre, but is worthwhile for a few inexpensive dishes – lobster with black-bean sauce is £7.80, steamed scallops in the shell 90p each. Pots of tea are automatically refilled when the lid is flipped upside down.

CHEFS: K. Tang and C. Poon PROPRIETORS: New World Restaurant Ltd
OPEN: all week
MEALS: 11am to 11.45pm (11pm Sun)
PRICES: £8 (£13), Set L and D £5.30 (£9). Snacks from £1.10
CARDS: Access, Amex, Diners, Visa
SEATS: 600. Private parties: 200 main room, 20, 80, and 100 private rooms. Vegetarian meals. Children welcome. Wheelchair access (also WC). Music. Air-conditioned

▲ *Ninety Park Lane, Grosvenor House* [13/20] map 13

90 Park Lane, W1A 3AA
01-499 6363 £32–£49

The opulence at the THF shrine is coated in layers, just in case you miss it. In the bar there is wallpaper like fine Italian marbled bookbinding paper. The décor hedges all bets as an old French clock competes with a horse racing print, an ancient portrait in oils and a very modern painting. The dining-room settles into a more classical mode with more old oil paintings, mostly of dour, eighteenth-century aristocrats. A large painting which looks like a Canaletto from a distance turns out to be an oriental harbour scene (Kowloon?). About half the dining-room seating is on opulent sofas. In addition there is carved wood panelling, a spectacular five-foot display of lilies and giant white tulips, fine white damask tablecloths, five-tiered polished wooden sweets trolleys and a blazing fireplace, even in April. The large, pretty, flower-decorated menus seem just off the presses and match the tableware which has been made for the restaurant. The cooking can approach 16/20, especially if Outhier is cooking, but equally there is very safe and fashionable, almost impersonal, execution with, naturally, a litany of luxuries. Take one lunch: 'foie gras slightly overcooked, even burned, on a salad of good leaves and some over-sharp citrus fruits; a very fine rabbit terrine with a pile of cabbage and pomegranate and currants; good halibut sandwiching a mix of wild and less wild and rather undercooked mushrooms on a watercress sauce, in which the taste of stock and wine was superior; and roast monk with a similar sauce slightly caramelised and served with truffle.' The sweet table remains an impressive feature, with a variety of gateaux, charlottes, délices and bavarois (but no flans, no tarts, no pots, nothing hot, nothing without alcohol). 'It is all fine, just a little pricey and not quite the edge you might expect for the money – good for a business lunch.' 'I was thinking how some of the claret prices were quite reasonable until I realised I was looking at the half-bottles.' The rest of the choice is impressive if money is no constraint – Hermitage '61; Ch. Latour '45. House Santenay or Pinot Blanc is £14.

CHEF: Stephen Goodlad PROPRIETORS: Trusthouse Forte Ltd
OPEN: Mon to Sat, exc Sat L
MEALS: 12 to 2.30, 7 to 10.30
PRICES: £39 (£49), Set L £25 (£32), Set D £33 (£40). Service inc
CARDS: Access, Amex, Carte Blanche, Diners, Visa
SEATS: 70. Private parties: 80 main room. Vegetarian meals. No children under 6. Jacket and tie. No-smoking area. Wheelchair access (2 steps; also WC). Music. Air-conditioned
ACCOMMODATION: 468 rooms, all with bath/shower. Rooms for disabled. B&B £165 to £190. Lift. Pets welcome. Afternoon teas. Swimming-pool. Sauna. Air-conditioning. TV. Phone

Ninjin [10/20] map 13

244 Great Portland Street, W1N 5MF
01-388 4657 £8–£22

The basement restaurant, beneath its supermarket, goes some way to prove that Japanese food need not always be expensive. Set meals are excellent value, especially at lunch-time. Prices are all inclusive of pickles, rice, soup, oranges – only the main dish changes. Tempura of freshly fried king prawns, ornate boxes of sushi and nori rolls, and mixed grilled meats on salads have all been generous choices. Green tea is refilled happily. Service is acclimatised to westernised perceptions. Beer is Japanese and puts the bill up at £1 a bottle. Otherwise excellent value.

CHEF: Mr Yuki PROPRIETORS: Ninjin Ltd
OPEN: Mon to Sat, exc Sat D
MEALS: 12 to 2.30, 6 to 10.30
PRICES: £12 (£17), Set L £5 (£8) to £8 (£11), Set D £16 (£20) to £18 (£22)
CARDS: Access, Amex, Carte Blanche, Diners, Visa
SEATS: 66. Private parties: 10 main room. No children under 5. Music. Air-conditioned

▲ *Nontas* [10/20] map 11

16 Camden High Street, NW1 0JH
01 387 4579 £11

Camden Town's adoption of café society has extended this far down the High Street. An 'Ouzerie' extension to this established Greek restaurant offers light meals through the day though the restaurant itself runs at a more leisured pace. It is the meze that is usually recommended, but there are individual dishes worth pursuing – moussaka; afelia; kleftiko; rosewater sorbet. Aromatic coffee. Greek wine from £4.80. CELLARMAN'S CHOICE: Boutari, £6.30.

CHEF: Nontas Vassilakas PROPRIETORS: Helen and Nontas Vassilakas
OPEN: Mon to Sat
MEALS: 12 to 2.45, 6 to 11.30
PRICES: £6 (£11), Snacks from 90p
CARDS: Access, Amex, Diners
SEATS: 50. Private parties: 25 main room. Children welcome. Wheelchair access. Music
ACCOMMODATION: 12 rooms, 11 with bath/shower. B&B £25 to £38. No children under 12. Afternoon teas. TV. Phone. Doors close at 12.30

▲ *Oak Room, Le Meridien Hotel* [15/20] map 13

Piccadilly, W1V 0BH
01-734 8000 £26–£46

The concerted attempt to turn this modern hotel into one of the landmarks of London's luxury constellation has finally been a disarming success. The loss-leader business lunch at £18.50 is one of the bargains of the West End. The voluptuous chandeliers, tall, scrubbed panelling, and burgeoning pot plants speak of the *nouveau riche,* while the menu speaks of current fashionable things in France. There is serious cooking, albeit at a price, on the *carte.* David Chamberlain has also given dishes a depth of taste and flavour uncommon in hotels, and his own personality to the grand scheme as laid down in a franchise by Michel Lorain, of Côtes St Jacques at Joigny (three rosettes in *Michelin*). The sheer generosity with expensive ingredients, and also the waiting crew who have matured into a skilled team, set it apart. The sense of pretension and the erratic cooking that dogged the early days of the collaboration have vanished. Flambé service is replaced at sweet stage with the waiters creaming and feathering plates for items from the excellent and cream-laden trolley: pralines, sponge gateau, and picturesque confiserie. The kitchen is comfortable with extravagance: a circle of poached lobster and monk is set on a coulis of tomato and surrounded by a spread of asparagus and sweetcorn on a vegetable stock; lavish slices of Gressingham duck are interlaced with proper, thickly sliced foie gras and thinner slices of apple; a superlative langoustine sauce accompanies char-grilled fillets of sole. This is a hotel kitchen out to make its mark. The Terrace Garden Conservatory offers lighter meals. The wines, like the food, don't stint on quality or variety – there is an attractive spread from California – but at a price; it must be hard to shut the till on account of all the arms and legs. Who gets the prize for London's most expensive bottle of restaurant wine? The Oak Room makes a bid with Ch. Petrus '70 at £430. Even humble English wine (Wootton Seyval Blanc '86) is £17. House wine starts at £9.50.

All inspections are carried out anonymously.

CHEF: David Chambers PROPRIETORS: Meridien Hotels
OPEN: Mon to Sat, exc Sat L
MEALS: 12 to 2, 7 to 10.30
PRICES: Set L £18.50 (£26), Set D £27 (£35) to £37 (£46)
CARDS: Access, Amex, Carte Blanche, Diners, Visa
SEATS: 45. Vegetarian meals on request. Children restricted. Jacket and tie. No cigars/pipes in dining-room. Wheelchair access (also WC). Music. Air-conditioned
ACCOMMODATION: 284 rooms, all with bath/shower. Rooms for disabled. Lift. B&B £150 to £180. Baby facilities. Afternoon teas. Swimming-pool. Sauna. Tennis. Snooker. Air-conditioning. TV. Phone. Confirm by 6

Odette's [13/20] map 11

130 Regent's Park Road, NW1
01-586 5486 £24

There is a choice between the formal front room and the conservatory, with its white painted walls, photographs, and plants in hanging baskets. Excellent service helps and the overall feel is of a well-run, first-class restaurant. The handwritten menu gives a daily choice of nine or ten dishes at each course: ballotine of duck with foie gras, redcurrant sauce and warm brioche – a dish of concentric circles working outwards from a pistachio-stuffed olive; a salad of garden vegetables with sweetcorn and courgettes; grilled calf's liver with a compote of apple and onion; sea-bass, red mullet, sea-bream, squid and poached salmon, with, somewhat unusually, a carrot beurre blanc; then a mousse of white chocolate and passion fruit, or a hot pear feuilleté with caramel sauce. The cheeses are French and farmhouse English, and come with apples and Bath Olivers; there is a choice of tisanes as well as coffee. The 50-strong wine list includes a handful of half-bottles and two Sauternes for dessert. House French is £6.50; CELLARMAN'S CHOICE: Margaux, Ch. Notton '82, £13.50; St Véran '86, £10.75; and Chardonnay, Orlando '86, £8.25.

CHEF: John Armstrong PROPRIETOR: Simone Green
OPEN: Mon to Sat, exc Sat L
MEALS: 12.30 to 2.30, 7.30 to 11
PRICES: £17 (£24). Service 12.5%
SEATS: 55. Private parties: 28 private room. Children welcome

Oh Boy [10/20] map 10

843 Garratt Lane, SW17 0PG
01-947 9760 £17–£19

This flamboyant French-Thai restaurant was a forerunner of the current wave of Thai openings, but none the worse for it. The French influence comes in terms of brandy and wine used in the cooking. Specialities include Samuri Seafood; muan phan din; King and I, being fillet steak, seafood and vegetables grilled and served with a choice of sauces. A second branch has opened at 18 South End, Croydon (tel. 01-760 0278). House wine from £5.25.

CHEF/PROPRIETOR: Paranee Pokavanit
OPEN: Mon to Sat, D only
CLOSED: 2 weeks Aug
MEALS: 7 to 10.30 (10.45 Fri and Sat)
PRICES: £12 (£18), Set D £12 (£17) to £14 (£19). Service 12.5%. Licensed, also bring your own: corkage £5
CARDS: Access, Amex, Diners, Visa
SEATS: 55. Private parties: 40 main room; 15 private room. Vegetarian meals. Children welcome. Music. Air-conditioned.

One Two Three [11/20]

map 13

27 Davies Street, W1Y 1LN
01-409 0750 £17–£36

The discreet frontage suggests a select travel agent, but downstairs there is an atmosphere of supreme calm. Set lunches are more expensive than at other Japanese venues, but are served in formal stages, one course after the other. The specials of the day – often as many as 15 dishes – contain much of real interest. The main menu takes on board, in some depth, the major avenues of the cooking: simmered; grilled; fried rice and noodles. To drink there is green tea, Chivas, Glenlivet, Suntory and Bells whisky, or saké. House French £9.

CHEF: K. Soda PROPRIETOR: S. Ikeda
OPEN: Mon to Fri
MEALS: 12 to 2.30, 6.30 to 10.30
PRICES: £22 (£36), Set L from £9.50 (£17), Set D from £23 (£31). Cover £1. Service 15%
CARDS: Access, Amex, Diners, Visa
SEATS: 50. Private parties: 50 main room. Vegetarian meals. No children under 10. Music. Air-conditioned

Orso [12/20]

map 14

27 Wellington Street, WC2E 7DA
01-240 5269 £28

The point about Orso is that it redefines the notion of Italian food in London (as the Bombay Brasserie has done for Indian food). It is not to everyone's taste, but it challenges both the classic old-style trattoria image and the new wave of pizza/pasta places. The discreet entrance is close to Covent Garden Opera House; the open-plan dining-room has polished wooden floors and there is chunky, hand-painted peasant crockery on the tables. The kitchen shows its aspirations with fried Mozzarella with anchovies and capers, grilled swordfish with roasted peppers, ravioli stuffed with wild mushrooms and sweetbreads with roasted shallots. In more familiar territory it also delivers good versions of tomato and basil soup, osso buco and steak in Barolo and pepper sauce. Service is nearer English public school than Italian café. Good coffee. Fifty Italian wines, starting at house for £7.50 a litre.

It is always advisable to book a restaurant in advance.

CHEF: Martin Wilson PROPRIETORS: Orso Restaurants Ltd
OPEN: all week
CLOSED: 24 and 25 Dec
MEALS: noon to midnight
PRICES: £19 (£28). Snacks from £4.50
SEATS: 110. Vegetarian meals. Children welcome

Otters [new entry, zero rated] map 11

271 New Kings Road, SW6 4RD
01-371 0434 £13–£20

Close to Parsons Green, in a prime site surrounded by estate agents, this long, narrow, plum and terracotta room combines above-average dishes with reasonable value. The menu offers half a dozen starters and ten main dishes all with a suggested wine. The style is modern and cosmopolitan, for instance parrot fish on a sweet pepper sauce and a mandatory vegetarian main dish of, say, Caerphilly and walnuts wrapped in vine leaves. Some of the flavours are more than direct – limes and Dubonnet with veal; Dijon mustard with golden syrup and ground hazelnuts for rack of lamb; mango and mint compote with rose-water ice-cream. Coffee is espresso, cappuccino or decaffeinated. Service is adept. The 32 wines move quickly into double figures which can make the pairings with dishes expensive. Classicists might raise an eyebrow at smoked venison with vegetables à la grecque with Ch. Mouton Baron Philippe '80 at £18.50 – smoked foods and claret are not natural allies, let alone marinated vegetables. But otherwise there are interesting bottles including a quartet of Australians around 10. More reports, please.

CHEF: Neil Stott PROPRIETOR: Julian Sowerbutts
OPEN: all week, exc Sun D
MEALS: 12 to 3, 7 to 11
PRICES: £14 (£20), Set L £6.95 (£13)
CARDS: Access, Amex, Diners, Visa
SEATS: 56. Private parties: 12 main room. Vegetarian meals. Children's helpings (weekends only). Wheelchair access (also WC). Music. Air-conditioned

Le P'tit Normand [new entry, zero rated] map 10

185 Merton Road, Southfields, SW18 5EF
01-871 0233 £14–£17

There is a concentrated effort to be Norman – timbers, candles, gingham, posters of Norman towns, Norman cheeses, a show of calvados, brass pots and pans on the ceiling. The menu follows up with veal normande, tarte Tatin but also roams around favourite bistro dishes. The fish soup is brought to the table in a large pot and served with rouille, grated cheese and garlic croûtons. Specials of the day have been prawns provençale; gigot with flageolets. There is an interesting cheese tray or apple sorbet with calvados, tarts, and crème brûlée. Service is French, but the maître d' has good English and a deft skill in dealing with the crowds who have quickly found this place. Thirty French wines from house at £5.80. More reports, please.

CHEF/PROPRIETOR: Philipe Herrard
OPEN: all week, exc Sat L
MEALS: 12 to 2.30 (2 Sun), 7 to 11 (10 Sun)
PRICES: £12 (£17), Set Sun L £8.75 (£14). Service 12.5%
CARDS: Access, Amex, Visa
SEATS: 35 to 40. Private parties: 25 private rooms. Vegetarian meals on request. Children's helpings. No pipes in dining-room. Wheelchair access (3 steps). Music

Il Passetto [10/20] map 13

230 Shaftesbury Avenue, WC2H 8EG
01-836 9391 £20

At the very top end of Shaftesbury Avenue, close to the Shaftesbury Theatre, is this old-school, all-purpose trattoria with a small corridor of a dining-room. Two rows of tables are packed into every square inch, and the narrow aisle is barely wide enough for the sweets trolley. It pays to stay with the food that is visible from the table: the daily selection of antipasti – seafood salad, globe artichokes, stuffed fresh mussels – and the fresh fish specials which are paraded round in their raw state. Skate comes as a mighty wing perfectly cooked with butter and capers, alternatively there might be salmon, lemon sole or halibut. The short, printed menu is old-style trattoria with Continental overtones – duck with cherries and chicken Kiev, as well as baby chicken with rosemary, and good fillet of beef with red wine, mushroom and brandy sauce. Sweets are variations on fruit, alcohol, cream and meringues. Standards fluctuate; some readers report poor meals, others rely on the place regularly. The predominantly Italian wine list is 50 bottles strong, with house Soave and Valpolicella at £4.95.

CHEF: Jesus Sanchez PROPRIETORS: Lindown Ltd
OPEN: Mon to Sat, exc Sat L
MEALS: 12 to 3, 6 to 11.30
PRICES: £12 (£20). Cover 95p
CARDS: Access, Amex, Diners, Visa
SEATS: 42. Private parties: 20 main room. Vegetarian meals. Children welcome. Wheelchair access. Air-conditioned

Pearl of Siam [10/20] map 10

107 Roman Road, E2 OQN
01-980 1676 £15

The gentrification of the East End has not as yet given rise to the expected regeneration of restaurateuring. This small converted shop is one exception. The cooking is Thai and first reports indicate that it is providing a valuable service. The signature dishes have been well executed – a chicken and coconut soup with a strong sour edge; fresh, airy tofu, deep-fried into golden cubes; well garlicked wok-fried squid. Portions are typically small – a growing fault in Thai restaurants – which puts the bill up. As does Singha beer at £1.85.

CHEF: Mrs Ek-Une PROPRIETORS: Mr and Mrs Mitchell
OPEN: Mon to Sat
MEALS: 12 to 3, 6 to 11
PRICES: £8 (£15). Service 10%. Licensed, also bring your own: corkage £1
CARDS: Access, Diners, Visa
SEATS: 66. Private parties: 25 main room, 25 private room. Vegetarian meals. Children welcome. Wheelchair access. Music. Air-conditioned

Phoenicia [10/20] map 11

11–13 Abingdon Road, W8 6AH
01-937 0120 £12–£20

A hard core of devotees maintain that the Phoenicia is one of London's premier Lebanese restaurants. Certainly it is among the most accessible, having come to terms more fully with European ideas of service and style. The meze extends to 36 dishes, half hot and half cold, which contain the main glory of the cuisine. Set meals are arranged either as a meze or with a main-dish kebab. Beyond hummus and tabouleh are aubergine moutabal, goats' cheese in thyme, basturma, smoked beef flavoured with chilli and paprika, ful medames. Lunch is now a buffet – eat as much as you want for £7, Monday to Saturday. Three kinds of arak – house, Musar, Ksarak – and two Château Musar are appropriate.

CHEF: Chaoki Serhal PROPRIETOR: Hani Khalife
OPEN: all week
MEALS: noon to midnight
PRICES: £11 (£20), Set L (exc Sun) £7 (£12), Set D from £10.55 (£15). Cover £1.25. Minimum £10.55. Service inc Set, 15% alc
CARDS: Access, Amex, Diners, Visa
SEATS: 80. Private parties: 80 main room, 15, 25 and 40 private rooms. Vegetarian meals. Children's helpings. Wheelchair access. Music. Air-conditioned

Pizzeria Castello [9/20] map 11

20 Walworth Road, SE1 6SP
01-703 2556 £10

Some of the best pizzas in the capital are served in this buzzy place on the Newington Butts roundabout. There's not much décor – just a few photographs of American footballers on the yellow walls – but the cooking is excellent. Pizzas are freshly made, piled high with toppings and baked the traditional way in big ovens by the entrance. Good fresh minestrone, garlic bread, well-dressed salads and strong espresso make up the rest of the picture. Better than average house Chianti at £4.50 a bottle.

CHEF: Cicero Calogero PROPRIETORS: Renzo Meda and Antonio Proietti
OPEN: Mon to Sat, exc Sat L
MEALS: noon (5 Sat) to 11
PRICES: £6 (£10)
CARDS: Access, Visa
SEATS: 180. Private parties: 40 main room. Vegetarian meals. Children's helpings. Wheelchair access (also WC). Music. Air-conditioned

Pollo [9/20]

map 14

20 Old Compton Street, W1V SPE
01-734 5917 £10

The modest frontage of this family-run Continental café hides an old-school Soho coffee-bar with basement dining-room. Its reputation for serving some of the best pasta in London is well established and can lead to queues up the stairs. The menu is a handwritten dictionary of pasta shapes and a map of Italy for the sauces. For pasta it is A1. Other dishes are more trencherman. Good espresso.

CHEF: Zazi Adermo PROPRIETOR: M. Mansini
OPEN: Mon to Sat
CLOSED: bank hols
MEALS: 12 to 3, 6 to 11
PRICES: £6 (£10)
SEATS: 80. Vegetarian meals. Children's helpings. Wheelchair access

Poons [11/20]

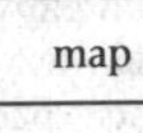

map 14

4 Leicester Street, WC2H 7BL
01-437 1528 £10–£19

'We are hoping to expand, taking the 100 covers to 200 possibly, by converting the upper flat to a restaurant area.' The most consistent and consistently well-liked of the many Chinatown old guard specialises in wind-dried foods, as shown in the window display. Duck, two kinds of sausage, hard black-bellied bacon, and offal provide a dramatic start to an otherwise mainstream Cantonese menu. A plate of meats with rice makes an inexpensive meal, or there are Original Rice Hot Pots. Eel dishes are good. Staples are reliable, though standards elsewhere on the menu tend to go up and down. Some say it is always advisable to book, but others say it is usually necessary to wait anyway. The original premises in Lisle Street have reopened – without redecoration.

CHEF/PROPRIETOR: W. N. Poon
OPEN: Mon to Sat
CLOSED: Christmas Day
MEALS: noon to 11.30
PRICES: £11 (£19), Set L £5.80 (£10) to £9.50 (£14), Set D £6.50 (£11) to £9.50 (£14). Licensed, also bring your own: corkage £1
SEATS: 100. Private parties: 30 main room. Children welcome. Air-conditioned

Ports [11/20]

map 12

11 Beauchamp Place, SW3 1NQ
01-581 3837 £15–£27

Although Portuguese hotel cooking can plumb the depths, the restaurant cooking can often by contrast be excellent. Since opening in 1984, Ports has had the reputation of being the best place in London to eat the cuisine. The emphasis is firmly on a wide choice of fish. Good reports extend to the bacalhau – four ways – and the braised octopus, among others. There is the mandatory caldo verde – green cabbage soup – and much char-grilling. Sweets, such as chilled walnut nougat parfait with green fig sauce, are not to be dismissed lightly. Equally underrated can be the wines, which open at £6.90 with a Serradayres from the Ribatejo region. CELLARMAN'S CHOICE: Quinta de Abrigada '76, from the Alenquer region, £11.50.

CHEF: Elio de Andrade PROPRIETORS: A. Valerio and Luis Pimentel
OPEN: Mon to Sat
CLOSED: Christmas, Easter, bank hols
MEALS: 12 to 2.30, 7 to 11.30
PRICES: £18 (£27), Set L £8.75 (£15). Service 12.5%
CARDS: Access, Amex, Diners, Visa
SEATS: 45. Private parties: 45 main room, 45 private room. Children welcome. No pipes in dining-room. Music. Air-conditioned

Le Poulbot [13/20] map 11

45 Cheapside, EC2V 6AR
01-236 4379 £31

Next to Next is the unlikely frontage – red, white and blue stripes in the doorway and the name emblazoned in simple plastic letters above the front window. The suggestion is of a tobacconist, travel agent or a dress shop, anything but the Roux brothers' long-standing City bastion of their distinctive style of French cooking. The upstairs cheap lunch area is brightly furnished with bentwood chairs. Despite one wall of French posters when you turn the corner of the stairs, the faded and soiled carpet leading to the basement restaurant suggests anything but a French restaurant – perhaps a below-stairs Cantonese or cheap Italian eating place. It is a dramatic contrast to arrive at the reception with its pictures of Napoleon and the dining-room with its decadent red plush booths. The cooking is sound, relying on solid technical skills learned in Roux brothers' kitchens. The menu is similarly unexciting but sensible. Standbys like soupe de poisson, 'a perfectly respectable upmarket version' compensate for excessive richness for this day and age. The new chef is Philippe Vandewalle, who took over from Rowley Leigh, who has gone to Kensington Place, but the style is faithful to the Roux idiom: cold cucumber soup; warm goats' cheese salad; crescents of puff pastry garnishing crab with a lightly curried sauce. Sauces dominate – an early-1970s-style cream sauce flavoured with horseradish for veal; a tomato butter sauce for a pastry package with salmon and langoustines; a rich sabayon for a hot raspberry gratin. Trimmings of petits fours and canapés are as the City expects. The booth tables are preferable to the trio by the kitchen door. All proper and correct, but it is salutary to note that the set lunch at Le Gavroche is cheaper. Twenty-eight wines assist the upward price spiral, all of good quality, all at a price, the lowest, a Côtes de Provence, being £13.

CHEF: Philippe H. Vandewalle PROPRIETORS: Roux Restaurants Ltd
OPEN: Mon to Fri, L only
MEALS: 12 to 3
PRICES: Set L £24.50 (£31). Service inc
CARDS: Access, Amex, Carte Blanche, Diners, Visa
SEATS: 50. Private parties: 50 to 60 main room. Children welcome. Jacket and tie. No pipes in dining-room. Air-conditioned

Le Quai St Pierre [10/20] map 11

7 Stratford Road, W8 6RF
01-937 6388 £29

This French restaurant, part of Pierre Martin's group, is chiefly notable for the quality of its fish. The shellfish platter is among the best in London, there is a wide choice of oysters, and other fish are offered on the same lines as at the senior restaurants in the chain, for instance Le Suquet (see entry). Cooking and service have been variable, which is a shame because the essentials for a very good restaurant are here. CELLARMAN'S CHOICE: Muscadet '85 from Métaireau, £13.50.

CHEF: Alain Patrat PROPRIETORS: La Francine Ltd
OPEN: Mon to Sat, exc Mon L
CLOSED: 2 weeks at Christmas
MEALS: 12.30 to 2.30, 7 to 11.30
PRICES: £21 (£29). Cover £1
CARDS: Access, Amex, Diners, Visa
SEATS: 55. 3 tables outside. Vegetarian meals. Children welcome. Wheelchair access. Music

Quincy's [12/20] map 11

675 Finchley Road, NW2 2JP
01-794 8499 £20–£22

Just north of the turn-off for the A1 on a surprisingly scruffy stretch of the Finchley Road, Quincy's looks an archetypal bistro with its bottle-green walls and ceiling, small rickety stripped pine tables, wicker lampshades and polished wood floors. It rises a notch above that stereotype, however, with candles in silver holders rather than bottles, framed nineteenth-century etchings and the full panoply of nibbles and petits fours that might characterise a 'proper' restaurant. The details are good. Cheesy toasts and anchovy and tomato hors d'oeuvre are tasty. There are very good wholemeal bread slices; excellent butter; chocolate truffles; decaffeinated coffee. The move to a seven-days-a-week operation has not helped the precision of the kitchen, and the more delicate dishes have tended to suffer. But the menu, augmented by half a dozen specials of the day, remains an attractive, innovative read: timbale of asparagus with a beurre blanc; roast veal kidneys on a purée of shallots. And there are good wines to match, on a list also selected with a serious restaurant in mind. House French £7; CELLARMAN'S CHOICE: Pouilly Fumé '86, from Dagueneau, £14.50.

CHEF: Sandy Anderson PROPRIETORS: D.J.C. Wardle and Sandy Anderson
OPEN: all week D only, and Sun L
MEALS: 12 to 2, 7 to 10.30 (9.30 Sun)
PRICES: Set Sun L £14.50 (£20), Set D £16.50 (£22)
CARDS: Access, Visa
SEATS: 30. Private parties: 30 main room. Vegetarian meals. Children's helpings. Wheelchair access. Music. Air-conditioned

Ragam [10/20] map 13

57 Cleveland Street, W1P 5PQ
01-636 9098 £7–£11

A short way from Goodge Street Tube station, this unpretentious South Indian restaurant puts the emphasis on food rather than décor. Its specialities are from the Kerala coast – kaallan, a curry with mango, yoghurt and coconuts, and avial, which is vegetables flavoured with curry leaves –and there is a selection of vegetarian dishes such as masala dosai. The choice is greatly extended for the non-vegetarian, with chicken kormas, bhunas, dopiazas; methi gosht with mixed lamb and beef; and the meat or seafood curries. Drink fruit juice, lassi or Kingfisher lager, or bring your own wine (corkage £1).

CHEFS: J. Dharmaseelan and Mojid Ullah PROPRIETORS: J. Dharmaseelan, T. Haridas and S.Pillai
OPEN: all week
MEALS: 12 to 3, 6 to 12
PRICES: £6 (£11), Set L and D £3 (£7). Minimum £3. Service 10%. Licensed, plus bring your own: corkage £1
CARDS: Access, Amex, Diners, Visa
SEATS: 34. Private parties: 34 main room, 25 private room. Vegetarian meals. Children's helpings. Wheelchair access (also WC). Music

Rajdoot [10/20] map 10

291 King Street, W6 9NH
01-748 7345 £11

The new brick and plate-glass frontage stands out in this run-down end of King Street, past Ravenscourt Park. Inside, the décor is in tune with the times – pink linen napkins, carnations on the tables, prints on the pale beige walls – but the menu is stuck fast in the early 1970s. A mere handful of tandooris are outflanked by a heavy contingent of curries: rogan josh, chicken biriani, murderously hot bangalore phal. The style is familiar, but dishes are carefully done – finely chopped fresh herbs are mixed in, not simply used as a garnish for chicken dhansak; brinjal bhaji is given a hint of coconut. Half a dozen pickles, good fresh breads and Basmati rice are well above average. This is the kind of place that gives curry houses a good name and it is excellent value: it may not be as cheap as the cafés in Southall or Bradford, but it knocks spots off most provincial Indians. Service is affable. Drink lager.

CHEF/PROPRIETOR: M. Rafique
OPEN: all week
MEALS: 12 to 2.30, 6 to 12
PRICES: £7 (£11). Service 10%
CARDS: Access, Amex, Carte Blanche, Diners, Visa
SEATS: 120. Private parties: 50 main room, 40 private room. Vegetarian meals. Children welcome. Wheelchair access (also WC). Music. Air-conditioned

Rani [11/20] map 10

3–5 Long Lane, Finchley, N3 2PR
01-349 4386 and 2636 £7–£15

The Pattni family are planning to expand their modest converted tea-shop into two neighbouring premises. Their red and white dining-room is still informal, not at all luxurious, but comfortable. Against a setting of stylised prints, sitar and drum music, they produce a short menu of Indian vegetarian food that is as good as any in the capital. The secret is in the fresh, delicate spicing and individual flavours of dishes that have echoes of genuine Indian home-cooking. Curries, such as aubergine and lima bean, are distinctive, and there are excellent bhajias, samosas, and aloo dhai poori. Thalis are good value; there are special daily starters and curries; chutneys are based on coriander, dates, and coconut. Sweets include kulfi, shrikhand and falooda, as well as English ice-creams from Loseley Park Farm. Drink lassi or Kingfisher lager.

CHEFS: Kundan and Sheila Pattni PROPRIETOR: Jyotindra Pattni
OPEN: Tue to Sun, exc Tue L
CLOSED: 25 Dec
MEALS: 12.30 to 2, 6 to 10.30
PRICES: £9 (£15), Set L from £3 (£7), Set D from £9 (£13). Minimum £6 at D. Service inc Set, 10% alc
CARDS: Access, Visa
SEATS: 34. Vegetarian meals. Children's helpings. No children under 6. No cigars in dining-room. Music

Rasa Sayang [new entry, zero rated] map 11

Kinswell Shopping Centre, Heath Street, NW3 1EN
01-435 6508 £16

North London has suddenly produced a new generation of Indonesian restaurants each with hi-tech décor and quite similar menus. This one is related to the original in Soho, but takes its cue from Zen W3 (see entry) nearly opposite – a snazzy, slick, spacious black, white and pink theme with chrome tube and black leatherette directors' chairs and black marble tables. The menu is clearly laid out with offers of set-price meals arranged for two around two starters, five main dishes, house wine, coffee and brandy inclusive. Satays, both chicken and vegetarian (using soya protein), noodle dishes and the colourful sweets have been good. 'Inexpensive but stylish.' Above average wine list.

CHEF: P. Wong PROPRIETOR: S. Kee
OPEN: Tue to Sun
MEALS: 12 to 3, 6 to 10.45 (all day Sat and Sun)
PRICES: £8 (£16), Set L and D £29.50 (£32) for two. Service 10%
CARDS: Amex, Diners, Visa
SEATS: 70. Private parties: 100 main room. Vegetarian meals. Children's helpings, on request. Wheelchair access. Music. Air-conditioned

Rebato's [12/20]

map 10

169 South Lambeth Road, SW8 1XW
01-735 6388 £14

Probably the best Spanish restaurant in London, but also an amazing success in its own area. The dining-room is split between an inexpensive tapas bar and a grander dining-room well favoured by family/birthday/business/office parties. Waiters have been known to do a quick flamenco, taking over half the restaurant. Tapas laid out in trays by the bar are sardines, octopus, spicy sausage, baby eels, anchovies. Especially good are tripe, tortilla, chicken livers and freshly cooked battered calamares. Bacalhau is served in a little Le Creuset-type dish in a rich, silky tomato sauce. The main room excels at the grills of fish and meat, large portions, and a few specials like a dark red fish bisque or halibut meunière, rather than Spanish or quasi-French dishes. Birthdays are quite an occasion. A personalised cake arrives to dimmed lights, with sparklers and Sambuca, and everyone sings and claps. Book ahead five or six weeks for Saturday, three or four for weekdays. The 50-strong wine list is almost exclusively Spanish, with Torres house wines £4.95.

CHEF: Eduardo Carvalho PROPRIETORS: Tino and Marco Rebato
OPEN: Mon to Sat, exc Sat L
CLOSED: bank hols, 24 Dec
MEALS: 12 to 2.30, 7 to 11.15
PRICES: Set L and D £9.75 (£14), Snacks from £1.25
CARDS: Access, Amex, Diners, Visa
SEATS: 60. Children welcome. No pipes in dining-room. Wheelchair access. Music. Air-conditioned

Red Fort [13/20]

map 14

77 Dean Street, W1V 5HA
01-437 2525 and 2115 £18

Amin Ali's most recent London venture, Jamdani (see entry), may have temporarily eclipsed his other star in the publicity stakes, but on its day, this restaurant can still deliver some of the classiest Indian food in the West End. The cool, elegant dining-room, the ladies in saris at the door and the air, heavy with perfume, all combine to create a world far away from the clichés of the curry house. Yet the menu moves in familiar territory, with impeccable tandooris – including duck – rogan josh, chicken jalfrezi and lamb biriani. But here, too, are less common dishes: momo (Indian dumplings); masha (spicy beans stuffed into a hollowed-out onion); Goan-style fish; occasionally brains. Spicing is fresh and subtle, and the accompaniments – from vegetables to breads – are notably good. The range of drinks includes alcoholic and non-alcoholic cocktails, and no fewer than seven champagnes. As the *Guide* goes on sale, Ali plans to open yet another restaurant, in the Tobacco Docks complex at Wapping, and also one in Moscow. Drink Kingfisher lager, house French at £6.95, or CELLARMAN'S CHOICE: Gewürztraminer '86 at £10.95.

CHEF: Azad Ullah PROPRIETOR: Amin Ali
OPEN: all week
MEALS: 12 to 3, 6 to 11.30
PRICES: £10 (£18). Service 15%
CARDS: Access, Amex, Diners, Visa
SEATS: 160. Private parties: 100 private room. Vegetarian meals. Children's helpings. Smart dress preferred. 1 step to rest. Wheelchair access (1 step, also WC). Music. Air-conditioned

Red Sea [9/20] map 11

51 Kilburn High Road, NW6 5SB
01-624 5289 £10–£14

One of the very few Ethopian restaurants in the capital. It has precious little décor, apart from a few ethnic musical instruments and some authentic paintings on the walls. The cooking may lack variety, but it packs a punch with hot spiced lamb stews and dero wot, a curry-like dish of chicken with hard-boiled egg. Shiro, mild, creamy ground chickpeas, and classic injera bread help to alleviate the heat. Good coffee and tea spiced with cardamom seeds. To drink try Tej – Ethopian honey wine – or the house French.

CHEF: Tse Hay Taye PROPRIETOR: Mr Maalo
OPEN: all week, D only
MEALS: 6 (6.30 Fri and Sat) to 11 (11.30 Fri and Sat)
PRICES: £6 (£13), Set D £6.50 (£10) to £10 (£14).
CARDS: Access, Amex, Diners, Visa
SEATS: 42. Private parties: 42 main room. Vegetarian meals. Children's helpings on request. Smart dress preferred. Wheelchair access (1 step; also WC). Music

Rêves des Seychelles [new entry, zero rated] map 10

160 Woolwich Road, SE10 0LS
01-305 1745 £28

Greenwich, says the menu, is a poor substitute for the Seychelles. The troughs of flowers and parasols brighten up a drab stretch of road. Inside is in aquatic greens and blues, with a menu based essentially on fish from the Seychelles and half a dozen meat curries. The cooking has spicy elements – a well-judged chilli oil for cold, deep-fried fish balls, or a sauce of onion, peppers, thyme, parsley, garlic and ginger for a meaty slice of garoupa fish cut across the bone into a steak. Sweets are ice-creams and fruits. Service and atmosphere are relaxed. House French is £6.50. More reports, please.

CHEF: Yvon Françoise PROPRIETORS: Mr & Mrs Domingue
OPEN: Mon to Sat
MEALS: 12 to 2.30, 7 to 11 (11.30 Sat)
PRICES: £22 (£28). Service inc
CARDS: Access, Visa
SEATS: 30. Private parties: 30 main room. Car-park, 4 places. Vegetarian meals. Children welcome. Wheelchair access (also WC). Music. Air-conditioned

La Rive Gauche [11/20]

map 11

61 The Cut, SE1 8LL
01-928 8645

£16–£24

Almost directly opposite the Young Vic, from which it takes much of its evening trade (also the Old Vic and the National Theatre), in otherwise old-fashioned corner-shop company. The Cut has not yet smartened itself out of existence; nevertheless, Rive Gauche could, from its restrained and smart façade, be picked up and put down in Covent Garden. Inside is an atmosphere of quiet formality. Wedding-style sprays sprout from pale creamy yellow walls. After an unsure opening few months, the kitchen has settled into a vein of traditional French cooking, incorporating some *nouvelle* influences – mostly in the seasonings and combinations, rather than the playing down of the richness, for instance a cream and mussel sauce for sea-bass; more cream is blended with eggs in a seafood terrine, served with a lemon-flavoured sauce with more single cream. Similarly good have been the duck-liver pâté and the salmon terrine. Other recommendations extend to the fish soup and salads, both of smoked fish. Game dishes feature much fruit: wild duck with sultanas and orange; red-legged partridge with juniper. Sweets hark back to bourgeois traditions: pears in red wine with cinnamon; a savarin coated in rum and served with Chantilly cream. Fifty wines, with house red and white from Georges Duboeuf at £7.

CHEF: Alain Cahour PROPRIETORS: Alain Cahour, W. Pettit and M. McMahon
OPEN: Mon to Sat, exc Sat L
MEALS: 12 to 2.30, 6 to 11
PRICES: £19 (£24), Set L and D from £12.50 (£16)
CARDS: Access, Amex, Diners, Visa
SEATS: 40. Private parties: 40 main room. Vegetarian meals. Children's helpings. Smart dress preferred. Wheelchair access (1 step). Music

River Café [11/20]

map 10

Thames Wharf, Rainville Road, W6 9HA
01-385 3344

£21

Opposite the mammoth grey bulk of Charing Cross hospital is a hinterland of two-storey terraced houses. This once working-class heartland is now suburbia, sandwiched between the flats and warehouses fronting the river and the furore of Fulham Palace Road, but it remains time-warped. Richard Rogers, guru of hi-tech architecture, occupies two of the warehouses fronting the river, and has transformed them; through the entrance gap is a gigantic steel-panelled staircase painted white, and in the middle of the three-sided terrace stands a revolving sculpture of blue pencils that whirl incessantly. Ruthie Rogers runs the vaulted restaurant that was originally the canteen for the Thames Wharf Studios. It still offers lunch only, but is a genuine attempt to produce unfussy *cucina rustica*, Italian farmhouse cooking, in a fashionable outpost of the capital. The power of the food shows in excellent farfalline with sun-dried tomatoes and basil, and grilled calf's liver with polenta and wild mushrooms. Roast leg of lamb comes stuffed with herbs and garlic, accompanied by lentils and white bean purée. The short menu can also take in roasted red and yellow peppers with tapénade, grilled fillet of red mullet with courgette salad, pan-fried scallops with fennel purée. To finish there is good apricot tart or fromage frais with strawberry purée. House wine is Montepulciano d'Abruzzo at £5; CELLARMAN'S CHOICE: Soave Classico, Monte Carbonara '86, £10.

CHEFS: Rose Gray and Ruthie Rogers PROPRIETORS: Richard and Ruthie Rogers and Rose Gray
OPEN: Mon to Fri, L only
CLOSED: 2 weeks Aug
MEALS: 12.30 to 3.30
PRICES: £16 (£21)
CARDS: Access, Amex, Visa
SEATS: 58. 6 tables outside. Private parties: 60 main room. Vegetarian meals. Children's helpings. Wheelchair access (also WC). Air-conditioned

Rotisserie [10/20] map 10

56 Uxbridge Road, Shepherd's Bush Green, W12 8LT
01-743 3028 £17

The smell of the rotisserie permeates this large eau de nil dining-room at the Tube station end of the Bush green, close by the 'awful bridge with a train on it'. The menu is short, fashionable and sensible, built round the spit-roasts served with either shoestring chips or dauphinois. It is a well executed formula. Three breads arrive automatically. Other dishes have been well handled – a salad of jambon de Bayonne with rocket and Parmesan; a salmon en papillote; sorbets. The ribs of beef at £14 for two come with generous amounts of vegetables. The wine list is fashionable with an international section and some French country wines. House French is £5.50. Like the menu, the emphasis is strongly on good value.

CHEFS: Mohammed Hassanin and Donovan Stewart PROPRIETOR: Karen Doherty
OPEN: all week, exc Sat and Sun L
MEALS: 12 to 3, 6.30 to 11 (10.30 Sun)
PRICES: £11 (£17)
CARD: Visa
SEATS: 76. Private parties: 20 main room. Vegetarian meals. Children welcome. Wheelchair access. Music

Royal Thai Orchids [10/20] map 10

141 Upper Richmond Road, SW15 2TX
01-789 4304 £20

An unassuming Thai restaurant run with good humour by a family from Bangkok. The menu is short and accessible, but the kitchen has not sold out to the mass-market or toned down its flavours (nor unfortunately the MSG-level). Classics such as tom yam gung – hot-and-sour prawn soup with chillies and lemon-grass – are well handled. Otherwise the choice ranges from dim-sum and spring rolls to chicken with sweet basil and chillies. Good-value business lunches, also take-aways from the fast-food bar in the basement.

CHEFS: B Suwankumpoo and S Panrod PROPRIETORS: The Suwankumpoo family
OPEN: Mon to Sat
CLOSED: 2 weeks Aug
MEALS: 12 to 2.30, 6.30 to 11 (11.30 Fri and Sat)
PRICES: £14 (£20)
SEATS: 110. Private parties: 65 main room, 45 private room. Vegetarian meals. Children's helpings. Music

RSJ [12/20]

map 11

13A Coin Street, SE1 8YQ
01-928 4554

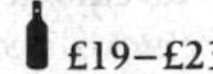 £19–£23

Gone are the days when the ultra-casual dress of the staff set the tone. Now they are more formal and things a little less relaxed. Nigel Wilkinson's upward mobility from brasserie to restaurant in his corner building among the hoardings has been effected with style. This remains one of the most popular restaurants in the listings, being close to the theatres and galleries of the South Bank. Recommended dishes that set the style are: tomato soup; escallops in filo pastry; salmon mousse; confit of duck; breast of pigeon in a port sauce; chocolate fudge cake; rhubarb tart. 'A fine establishment doing its job.' The wines are remarkable and include a better selection of Loire wines than you will find almost anywhere, France included. Nigel Wilkinson has been an evangelist for the best Loire wines for several years, and it would be sad to forgo the opportunity of tasting the splendours of Savennières, Sancerre, Vouvray, Chinon, Bourgueil, St Nicholas de Bourgueil, Anjou and Saumur Champigny at extremely reasonable prices. There is an enticing clutch of dry whites from the famous Clos de la Coulée de Serrant estate, and a couple of pages of Loire 'sweeties' to round off the meal. There are also Burgundies and clarets far better than on most restaurant wine lists, from producers such as Vincent, Ponsot, Pothier-Rieusset and Potel in Burgundy, and Ch. Cantemerle, Ch. Cissac and Ch. La Lagune in Bordeaux. House French is £7.85. RSJ does not stand for reinforced steel joist, as we have said, but rolled steel joist, which secures the building. Steel is not reinforced, concrete is.

CHEF: Ian Stabler PROPRIETOR: Nigel Wilkinson
OPEN: Mon to Sat exc Sat L
CLOSED: 3 days at Christmas
MEALS: 12 to 2, 6 to 11
PRICES: £16 (£23), Set L and D £11.95 (£19) to £12.95 (£20). Service 10%
CARDS: Access, Amex, Visa
SEATS: 60. Private parties: 40 main room, 20 private room. Children's helpings. Smart dress preferred. Music. Air-conditioned

The Guide *is independent, accepts no advertising and survives solely on the number of copies sold.*

Rue St Jacques [15/20] map 13

5 Charlotte Street, W1P 1HD
01-637 0222 £28–£44

The refurbishment has created a series of interlinked small dining-rooms, ideal for small business parties, being smart and yet affording some privacy. The menu offers as long a *carte* as is sensible in London, backed up by menus of the day. It is verdant in fashionable luxuries, as in fresh noodles with kidneys and tongue, red mullet in a sauce of saffron and superior fish stock, or lamb with the freshest and youngest of broad beans. Günther Schlender is above all a chef of sauces – deep, intense, piquant puddles that grace all dishes, not in swamps but little smears here, a full plate of demi-glace there. The final spark of electricity is sometimes missing because of the artifice involved, but counter this with a simple carrot and cucumber soup, followed by thick sliced beef fillet on rösti potatoes and a pyramid of layered chocolate mousse in a summer meal. Cheeses are French, a healthy selection of soft varieties with an extra dimension lent by goats'. Staff behave suitably like aspiring executives, always on hand to fill a glass or check a detail or two. The wines are universally pricey, upwards of £12 and moving from £20 very quickly.

CHEF: Günther Schlender PROPRIETOR: Donald McTaggart
OPEN: Mon to Sat, exc Sat L
CLOSED: Christmas, Easter, bank hols
MEALS: 12.30 to 2.30, 7.30 to 11.15
PRICES: £31 (£44), Set L £16.50 (£28). Minimum £25 at D. Service 15%
CARDS: Access, Amex, Diners, Visa
SEATS: 70. Private parties: 25 main room, 12, 25 and 30 private rooms. Children's helpings. Jacket and tie. No pipes in dining-room. Wheelchair access (1 step). Music. Air-conditioned

La Rueda [10/20] map 10

68 Clapham High Street, SW4 7UL
01-627 2173 £5–£16

Clapham High Street is like a catering fruit machine. There are any number of different eating places, some doing much better than others; La Rueda is one of the lucky ones whose number has come up. It is a shade less pretentious than the other good Spanish restaurant south of the river, Rebato, with traditonal tiles and posters of Spanish towns, and less discovered, although you still need to book to be sure of a table in the evening. People linger. Tapas are served at the bar or as a starter. There is a goodly range, from chorizo, tortilla, whitebait, anchovies and artichoke hearts to sardines and deep-fried squids. The paella comes in a large black pan with ladles either side and generous amounts of chicken and shellfish. Otherwise fish predominates, often prime cuts of monk or hake, plus a few predictable dishes like kidneys al Jerez or trout a la plancha. Sweets are more international but there is a good Manchega, with a taste akin to mature Cheddar. Espresso coffee. Very good choice of Spanish wines, with some more unusual ones from Galicia, from £5.50 to £75.

CHEF: Tino Sanchez PROPRIETORS: Gino Harcas and L Garrido
OPEN: Mon to Sat, exc Sat L
MEALS: 12 to 3, 6 (6.30 Sat) to 11
PRICES: £11 (£16), Snacks from £1.50
CARDS: Access, Visa
SEATS: 50. Private parties: 55 main room. Music. Air-conditioned

Ryoma [new entry, zero rated] map 13

14 Hanway Street, W1P 9DD
01-637 7720 £15–£29

Ryoma, on the site of Rasoi – a promising Indian that bit the dust – is evidence of a new phase in Japanese restaurants. It is deliberately trying to appeal to western ideas of restaurants. The only concessions to Japan in the décor are a devilish Noh mask spotlit on one wall and some fine porcelain on a shelf. The menu is printed in Japanese and English and includes kaiseki. The food is expensive but the quality of the ingredients is high. The traditional order of dishes is maintained – small-bowl dishes including eel and cucumber salad; hors d'oeuvre such as grilled scallops; various sashimi; teriyaki, such as salmon and beef; grilled/fried dishes; tempura; rice dishes; assorted sushi, of very high standard served on lacquered fan-shaped plates and making use of rare fish like ahagi (a red shellfish)as well as red tuna and cod roe. Soups are delicate, though the lobster is overpowered in the miso. Desserts are mostly fruits. Twenty wines from £8. More reports, please.

CHEF: Mori Moto PROPRIETORS: Echomoon Ltd
OPEN: Mon to Sat, exc Sat L
CLOSED: bank hols
MEALS: 12 to 2.30, 6 to 10.30
PRICES: £13 (£27), Set L £8 (£15) to £12 (£20), Set D £20 (£29). Service 15%
CARDS: Access, Amex, Diners, Visa
SEATS: 38. Private parties: 12 private room. Vegetarian meals. Children's helpings, Sat D, 6 to 7. Children welcome. Music. Air-conditioned

Sabras [12/20] map 10

263 Willesden High Road, NW10 2RX
01-459 0340 £7–£11

The décor has had a facelift, with a new porch jutting out on to the pavement, new colour schemes in the Indian national colours of orange, green and white, Hindu pictures on the walls and more greenery in the hessian-walled dining- room. The Desais still serve the best Indian vegetarian food in the capital and the menu covers a lot of territory: farshan snacks with mint chutney; cold puris in the style of Bombay chowpaty; Gujerati specialities, all kinds of pulses and vegetable curries. Ragada patish (grilled potato cake topped with yellow peas, tamarind chutney and onions) and Kashmiri kofta in nutty lentil sauce are still highlights. Ravaiya – vegetables stuffed with spices – is a speciality. Some sections of the menu are now available only on certain days. Good-value thalis, and buffet-style lunches. The restaurant is still unlicensed, although you can bring your own wine.

CHEFS/PROPRIETORS: Hemant and Nalinee Desai
OPEN: Tue to Sun
MEALS: 12.30 to 3, 6 to 9.30
PRICES: £7 (£11), Set L £5.75 (£7), Set D £8 (£10), Snacks from £1.75. Service 10%. Unlicensed, but bring your own: corkage 75p
CARDS: Access, Visa
SEATS: 32. Private parties: 32 main room. Vegetarian meals. Children's helpings. No-smoking area. Wheelchair access (also WC). Music

Saigon [11/20]

map 14

45 Frith Street, W1V 5TE
01-437 7109

£16–£20

Arguably London's best Vietnamese restaurant. 'We don't mix with another cuisine.' An agreeably jungly atmosphere pervades the inside, with tables lit by flickering, floating candles. From a 40-dish menu written in pragmatic detail, crab with garlic, bamboo and water-chestnuts comes with shell and claws in a rich sauce served in an earthenware pot. Barbecued beef is DIY, cooked at the table; Vietnamese duck is rolled into rice paper pancakes stuffed with cucumber, mint and coriander. Good squid, either deep fried in balls or rolled into cakes served with spicy sauce. House French is £5.20.

CHEF: C.H. Lin PROPRIETOR: E.C.L. Man
OPEN: Mon to Sat
CLOSED: bank hols
MEALS: noon to 11.30
PRICES: £11 (£20), Set L and D from £11.15 (£16). Service 10%
CARDS: Access, Amex, Diners, Visa
SEATS: 80. Private parties: 40 main room, 50 private room. Children welcome. Music

St Quentin [12/20]

map 12

243 Brompton Road, SW3 2EP
01-581 5131 and 589 8005

£18–£30

The 1980s style of slick, imported French brasserie seems to have been characterised by a dish of kidneys with a sauce of grain mustards and cream. And even if St Quentin no longer calls itself brasserie, the kidneys remain on the *carte* of nine starters, four fish, seven meats. The upgrading has brought with it lavish touches – fresh foie gras with country bread; vin jaune to sauce brill; crayfish sauce for veal fillet – but at heart this is an efficiently run restaurant that stays with its formula. Much of its achievement derives from its supplier, the related and excellent Specialités St Quentin nearby, which also sells some of the best French tarts and bakery in the area, plus foie gras and cheeses from Olivier in Boulogne. The atmosphere is deliberately that of a brasserie in miniature – a sort of reduced Langan's or La Coupole. Having only 85 covers it can serve well, but stops short of the kind of quality a chef/patron system might offer. The good-value set meals quickly move up into Knightsbridge prices when extras are put on top. Service is self-consciously French. The third arm of the business, Grill St Quentin across the road at 136, does good steaks and has a similar spread of good wines.

The restaurant's wine list has some good bottles, but incomplete information on the list makes selection difficult. All the wines are French, with Bordeaux the main area: two dozen range from a generic Bordeaux St Quentin, at £8.90, to '75s and '78s of middle-range and a few top châteaux. Burgundies are mostly village wines from Burgundian merchants. Sweet wines are limited to three Sauternes of varying qualities and unspecified vintages, and a Muscat of undetermined origin, £8.90. House Burgundy £6.90.

CHEF: C. Christian PROPRIETOR: Hugh O'Neill
OPEN: all week
MEALS: 12 to 3 (4 Sat), 7 to 12 (11.30 Sun)
PRICES: £19 (£30), Set L £10.50 (£18), Set D £13.90 (£22). Cover £1.20. Service 12.5%
CARDS: Access, Amex, Diners, Visa
SEATS: 85. Private parties: 25 private room. Children's helpings. Wheelchair access. Air-conditioned

San Martino [10/20] map 12

103 Walton Street, SW3 2HP
01-589 3833 and 1356 £24

In the twilight of the big Chelsea trattorias – San Frediano, sold on (one of its founders shot dead in Rimini) and Meridiana, sold on twice now – this small, slightly kitsch but long-established, family-run Italian restaurant enjoys a small revival. The heavy reliance on veal and cheese recipes has been superseded by a taste for some regional dishes, mostly Tuscan, for example a pappardelle with a sauce based on hare stock flavoured with cinnamon. There has also been fine kid cooked with artichokes, and also braised with white wine and oil, flavoured with bay and juniper and served with a purée of potatoes. They make great claims for the bresaola too. Sweets revert to the standard clichés, alas. Owner Constanzo Martinucci enjoys some notoriety as a campaigner for consumer rights. He was arrested for trying to stop police towing his customers' cars away! Tuscan wines, like Pomino and Frescobaldi, are the best value. House Italian £6.80. Sunday opening planned.

CHEFS: Constanzo Martinucci, Fernando Lima, Roberto Buratti and Alfonso Cestaro
PROPRIETOR: Constanzo Martinucci
OPEN: Mon to Sat
CLOSED: 25 Dec, Easter
MEALS: 12 to 2.45, 7 to 11.30
PRICES: £14 (£24). Cover £1.15. Minimum £6.50. Service 15%
CARDS: Access, Amex, Diners, Visa
SEATS: 48. Private parties: 24 private room. Vegetarian meals. Children's helpings. Wheelchair access (1 step)

Santini [12/20] map 11

29 Ebury Street, SW1W 0NX
01-730 4094 and 8275 £21–£31

Santini has taken some criticism on its prices and service (possibly due to the opening of a second branch L'Incontro, see entry), but on balance it earns its inclusion. The setting is elegant in black and white with photos of Venice, the atmosphere less personal than some, and the menu is a well balanced break from the usual. The pasta is excellent and can be sauced with aubergines and olives or with mushrooms. There is a regional bias in the shape of polenta to offset the tomato sauce for squid. Other good dishes mentioned include vitello tonnato; Parma ham and melon; fish soup (except the night the bones were left in); sea-bass; veal with orange sauce. The fruits seem to have the edge on the sweets. The wine list is confusingly split between the everyday drinking around the £10 to £12 area and rarities up in the £25-plus range, with 11 Barolos and the emphasis strongly on Italy.

CHEFS: Mr Santin and Mr G. Rosselli PROPRIETOR: Mr Santin
OPEN: all week, exc Sat L and Sun L
CLOSED: bank hols
MEALS: 12.30 to 2.30, 7 to 11.30
PRICES: £21 (£31), Set L £12.50 (£21). Cover £1.50. Service 12%
CARDS: Access, Amex, Diners, Visa
SEATS: 65. Private parties: 25 main room. Vegetarian meals. Children's helpings. Wheelchair access. Air-conditioned

▲ *Savoy* [13/20] map 14

Grill Room, Strand, WC2R 0EU
01-836 4343 £35

The cartoonist Jak penned a sketch for the London *Evening Standard* after publication of last year's *Guide*. It showed a team of Savoy waiters and the maître d' saying: 'Block all the exits, men, we're ready to give table five the bill!' It now hangs in pride of place in the Grill Room, which shows that this great hotel has not lost its sense of humour. It is the Grill, a low-slung, impeccable aristocrat of a dining-room, that has taken the initiative from the River Restaurant. Its re-emergence after some dour years has been a gradual ascendancy, not just due to Alan Hill, now in charge, formerly at the Caledonian in Edinburgh, but also to Keith Stanley, gone to the Ritz, and of course Anton Edelmann. Now that Mosimann has left the Dorchester, his former colleagues Edelmann and Hill are bidding to regain the reputation as the premier hotel dining arena. Not that its loyal following of powerful customers deserted – its kudos stayed intact – but the cooking is now once again of a significant standard. The world is to rights, the Savoy is back, and if power is an aphrodisiac, the Grill is the most seductive of London restaurants. Expensive? Of course, but not in fact as expensive as the cut of the dining-room or the penguin suits or the smell of cigars might lead one to suspect. There has been a sensible pruning of the menu, and business tastes are catered for by the roasts trolley and daily dishes: sausage and mash on Mondays are three, served with duchess potatoes and lyonnaise onions. Beyond the simple, excellent plates of smoked salmon and grills are other dishes – a salad of chicken and langoustines; a worked trellis of sole with a salmon mousse, set on a cream sauce browned with wild mushroom. The sweets trolley is equally correct. As you might expect, France rules the expensive wine list, with a choice of thoroughly reliable clarets back to '70.

Red Burgundies are less interesting, mostly from Burgundian merchants, but whites are sound, with several good domaine wines. The rest of France is rather briefly covered but there are bright spots in most sections; Alsace has good wines from Rolly Gassman and Hugel, and the Rhône has Guigal and Domaine du Grand Tinel Châteauneuf-du-Pape. The champagne selection is very good, if extremely expensive. There are some good estate wines from Germany, as well as, strangely, two Liebfraumilch, and very brief selections from the rest of the world, including occasional stars. Sweet wines are in short supply, but include four good Sauternes châteaux, from Château Filhot '81 by the glass, at £3.40, to Yquem '76 at £150, and one German Beerenauslese. House French £7.70.

CHEF: Anton Edelmann; Grill Room: Alan Hill PROPRIETORS: The Savoy Hotel plc
OPEN: Mon to Sat, exc Sat L
CLOSED: Grill Room: Aug
MEALS: 12.30 to 2.30, 6 to 11.15
PRICES: £27 (£35). Service inc. Licensed, also bring your own: corkage £8.50
CARDS: Access, Amex, Diners, Visa
SEATS: 80. Private parties: 10 main room. Car-park, 58 places. No children under 12. Jacket and tie. Wheelchair access. Music. Air-conditioned
ACCOMMODATION: 202 rooms, all with bath/shower. Rooms for disabled. Lift. B&B £126.50 to £173. Baby facilities. Afternoon teas. Air-conditioning. TV. Phone

Seafresh Fish Restaurant [9/20]

map 11

80–81 Wilton Road, SW1V 1DL
01-828 0747 £15

Anastasis Leonidou opened his traditional fish and chip shop round the corner in Vauxhall Bridge Road in 1945, and moved here in 1965. The principles do not change. Fish comes down on ice (not frozen) from Aberdeen and Peterhead; frying is in groundnut oil; the chips are handcut. Well used by cab drivers, and the odd Mercedes and Rolls-Royce. Also offers take-aways. 'We own our own freehold which allows us to keep costs down.' House wine is £4.95. CELLARMAN'S CHOICE: Pouilly Fumé '86, £10.95.

CHEFS: Jose Tajes and Nicos Constantinou PROPRIETORS: George and Marios Leonidou
OPEN: Mon to Sat
CLOSED: 10 days Christmas and New Year
MEALS: 12 to 3, 5 to 10.45 (12 to 10.45 Sat)
PRICES: £11 (£15)
SEATS: 120. Private parties: 60 main room. Children's helpings. Wheelchair access. Air-conditioned

Seashell [9/20]

map 11

49–51 Lisson Grove, NW1 6UH
01-723 8703 £9–£15

Business is as usual. The new owners – casino group Pleasurama who also acquired the Hard Rock Café – have left North-West London's most famous fish and chip shop as it was. The take-away still does a roaring trade. Next door, up a few steps, is the grand period dining-room on two floors, connected by a metal spiral staircase. Dark varnished woodwork, glass partitions etched with scenes of the defunct Billingsgate fish market, and the bevy of waitresses all provide a Cockney atmosphere. The quality of the fish is outstanding – halibut, Dover sole, skate, haddock, plaice are offered on or off the bone, grilled or fried, in matzo meal or ordinary batter. Chips are thick cut and freshly fried. The size of the portions justifies the relatively high prices. House wine £5.50.

CHEF: Gerald Tiernan PROPRIETORS: Pleasurama plc
OPEN: Tue to Sat
MEALS: 12 to 2, 5.15 to 10.30
PRICES: £11 (£15), Set L £6 (£9). Minimum £2.50. Licensed, also bring your own: corkage £2.50
CARDS: Access, Visa
SEATS: 170. Private parties: 90 main room. Children's helpings. No-smoking area. Music. Air-conditioned

La Seppia [new entry, zero rated] map 13

8A Mount Street, W1Y 5AD
01-499 3385 £24–£30

Mount Street represents old-school Mayfair – the Connaught, Scotts, art galleries, high-class butchers. In that context La Seppia seems almost good value, a basement Italian restaurant specialising in fish and going some way to break the mould of the London trattoria. The menu reads well within printed boundaries – squid and broccoli salad with a coriander dressing; gnocchi sauced with Dublin Bay prawns, wild mushrooms and aubergines; a fine dish of fillet of brill on lentils. There is ambition for a high level of cooking – a meat stock reduction for sea-bass, squid ink used to colour the spaghetti – but also a these-you-have-loved conservatism, as in tiramisu. The décor is reassuringly coffee bar but the service equipped to deal with an international clientele. The tasting menu is good value against the *carte*. A printed list of wines concentrates on Italy, mostly in the £8 to £13 bracket with a few sops to France. More reports, please.

CHEF: Antonio Fiori PROPRIETOR: Serafino Fiori
OPEN: Mon to Sat, exc Sat L
CLOSED: bank hols
MEALS: 12 to 2.45, 6.30 to 11
PRICES: £22 (£30), Set L £17 (£24), Set D £19.50 (£27)
CARDS: Access, Amex, Diners, Visa
SEATS: 60. Private parties: 18 main room. Vegetarian meals on request. Children welcome. Air-conditioned

Shapla Tandoori Restaurant [10/20] map 10

380 Brixton Road, SW9 7AW
01-733 7053 £5–£17

Well-judged cooking puts this slightly upmarket tandoori restaurant ahead of its local rivals. The menu holds few surprises, taking in the usual range of tandooris, curries, karahi and masala dishes. The old trappings of the converted shoe-shop have been replaced by fashionable white Doric columns and tubs of flowers on the pavement. Drink lager.

CHEF: M. Miah PROPRIETOR: Ranu Miah
OPEN: all week
MEALS: 12 to 3, 6 to 12
PRICES: £8 (£12), Set L £3.55 (£5) to £6 (£8), Set D from £5.50 (£7) to £15 (£17). Service inc
CARDS: Access, Amex, Visa
SEATS: 80. Private parties: 80 main room. Vegetarian meals. Children's helpings. Wheelchair access (also WC). Music

Si Chuen [11/20] map 14

56 Old Compton Street, W1V 5PN
01-437 2069 £10–£33

The twisting trail of London's most influential Szechuan restaurant leads here to a designer cream and pale green dining-room across from Chinatown on the fringe of the Soho European restaurant heartland. Yet another change of ownership may mean the ends are getting frayed, but two inspection meals affirm the quality that has kept this team in the *Guide* for the best part of the decade. (For historians, the owners are the original ones who stayed at Dragon Gate after the splinter group went off to open one restaurant after the other, like a nuclear reaction: Shu Shan, I Ching, Shu Shan 2, Loy Loy Inn, Zen, Zen Too, Zen W3, Pun, Zen Central and soon in Hong Kong). Chef Tso now increasingly takes a consultant's role and the menu is not without concessions – none of the tripe dishes that made Dragon Gate famous; as many Cantonese as Szechuan dishes on the menu; very lean pork used for the double-cooked pork, doubtless as a sop to healthy eating. Nevertheless, there are dishes here rarely found elsewhere and the cooking has continued to demonstrate flair. Look especially for Pelmeni with red spicy sauce; special Szechuan soup noodles; stir-fried Szechuan shrimps; fish fragrant aubergine; ants climbing the tree; tea-smoked duck – which can get dry in quarters, so is best ordered as a whole. Chilli can be liberally scattered through dishes. Chinese wine is £9.50 and £12.50, or drink saké at £2.80.

CHEF: Kwong Cheung PROPRIETORS: A.Y.C. Cheung and C.M. Liew
OPEN: all week
MEALS: noon to midnight
PRICES: £11 (£21), Set L £4 (£10) to £10 (£16), Set D £7.50 (£13) to £25 (£33). Cover 50p. Service 12.5%. Licensed, also bring your own: corkage £2
CARDS: Access, Amex, Diners, Visa
SEATS: 80. Private parties: 30 main room, 30 private room. Vegetarian meals. Children's helpings. Wheelchair access (3 steps). Music

'Great things have happened at last on the supply scene, particularly for fruit and vegetables. The varieties of different lettuce seem to be constant now and varieties of vegetables are extensive. Twelve months ago they were not.' Yorkshire restaurateur

Simply Nico [17/20] map 11

48A Rochester Row, SW1P 1JU
01-630 8061 £45

Through sheer force of personality Nico Ladenis has again created a restaurant of rare calibre. The constellation seems dotted with his abandoned prototypes: Shinfield, Queenstown Road. Gone are the pretensions of genteel suburbia from his Dulwich or Battersea days, and a great deal of thought, care and attention has gone into the design. His, and Dinah-Jane's single-minded commitment and passion disarm criticism. On a good night there are few restaurants in Europe who can equal Nico in full flow. 'It was the precise and absolute balance of these sauces – a beurre blanc for sea-bass; a tomato coulis with cream and butter for salmon – which made the restaurant score so highly for me.' But is he a greater chef than he is a self-publicist? When columnists are reduced to talking about his lovely silky skin, one starts to wonder what sort of spell is being cast. Nico writes: 'There is an enormous picture of the proprietor at the entrance and each guest is required to kiss it three times, then bow before entering.' The faith brooks no faint hearts. Dissenters are severely admonished. 'Sweet bondage' is how Christopher Driver once described eating at his Battersea restaurant. There is another view, of course: 'boorish bad manners'; 'miserable atmosphere'; 'you are doing your readers a disservice by recommending this place.' But equally: 'Food and service are impeccable.'

The cooking has considered new styles, sometimes quite surprisingly, for instance: a salad of red cabbage, shredded into spaghetti lengths (as per Marco Pierre White) and dressed with chilli, sugar and ginger (as per a Chinese restaurant), is served with the famous livers enriched with port. The precision can be remarkable – a duck breast served with a fumet of cèpes, not more than a puddle but of sufficient intensity to balance the meat and its little pot of mange-tout. These triumphs are tempered by other thoughts. 'Some dishes are ridiculously complicated combinations or contain overly strong muddy flavours. The pintadeau au choux avec confits de fruits citrus was complicated by numerous distractions on the plate. The mustard sauce for the rognons de veau tasted unbelievably strongly of raw mustard, chillies, who knows what, but was overpowering to the point of bitterness. An excellent apple tart was somewhat spoiled by the triple combination of buttery rather than tart apples, buttery pastry and a rich and buttery caramel sauce. A fish soup was unmistakeably Mediterranean in flavour, but perhaps lacked a roundness of flavour found in more humble versions by having a too intense flavour of strong fish like red mullet and perhaps too much anis.' 'Among the starters was salade de cailles beurre de cèpes and included as a main fish course was turbot saveur de cèpes.... On the subject of quail, another salad of quail (legs only) was part of the main course of quail (breast as it turned out). "Fraisier" had an orange-flavoured sauce similar to the one with the chocolate marquise.' Put that against an escalope of salmon with a topping of grated horseradish mustard and breadcrumbs grilled to make a crunchy top set on a bed of shredded celeriac and a butter sauce flavoured with chives. The white tableclothes and crisp décor make it more formal and less soft than many places today. The German expressionist prints lend a splash of decadent colour to the front of the restaurant and there are attractive sketches of wartime Parisian restaurants in the skylit rear section with its dubious vertical view of scruffy apartment blocks. The assertive brass rail going around the room is in some contrast to the subdued checked wallpaper. The money-making has become rather obvious. Tables, which require strict confirmation a day ahead, are closely packed. Dishes arrive disconcertingly fast, and there is insistence on some customers being out at a set time to let in a second sitting. Lunch remains the bargain. Recommendations for the rating span 14 to 18. As with everything else, controversy seems to be the key point. The wine waiter is helpful and doesn't just recommend the more expensive wines, although there are precious few really cheap ones. The pricing on the dearer wines is not terrible for a place of this stature, but one would like a few bargains lower down the scale.

CHEF/PROPRIETOR: Nico Ladenis
OPEN: Mon to Fri
MEALS: 12 to 2, 7.30 to 11
PRICES: £34 (£45)
SEATS: 35

Singapore Garden Restaurant [10/20] map 10

83–83A Fairfax Road, NW6 4DY
01-328 5314 £14–£23

This much glassed and mirrored family-run restaurant specialises in a hybrid of Far Eastern cooking; the Singapore food is notable. Ingredients, especially fish, are first class, witness scallops steamed in their shells with garlic and ginger or steamed turbot with fresh ginger, garlic and spring onions. Look also for oyster omelette. Some of the Chinese crossovers, like ma po bean curd, have been well done. Steamboats are £22 per person.

CHEF: Mrs Lim PROPRIETORS: The Lim Family
OPEN: all week
MEALS: 12 to 2.45, 6 to 10.45 (11.15 Fri and Sat)
PRICES: £12 (£23), Set L from £10 (£14), Set D from £15 (£20). Minimum £6.50. Service 10%
CARDS: Access, Amex, Diners, Visa
SEATS: 100. 4 tables outside. Private parties: 80 main room, 60 private room. Vegetarian meals. Children welcome. Music. Air-conditioned

Soho Brasserie [10/20] map 14

23–25 Old Compton Street, W1V 5PJ
01-439 9301 £22

The Brasserie, done out in blues and whites, with tables on either side of a central screen, is reminiscent of the old Bertorelli's in Charlotte Street. It bristles noisily with the banging of plates, the espresso machine and the clatter of cutlery. In that sense it is definitely new-wave, and although brewery-owned, has managed to recognise and play to its strengths – a good French fish soup, one-plate meals of salads and saucissons, steak sandwich, grilled turbot with a dribble of good oil. The menu has immense variety and fine buying – pain poîlane with shrimps cooked in cider; rocket in the French bean and lentil salad with an anchovy dressing; fromage blanc with fresh fruit. Portions tend to be small. The iced soufflés and ice-creams do not seem to be of the same calibre. Happy Hour is 5.30 to 7.30. Forty wines, though undetailed, suggest sensible buying too. House French £6.50. CELLARMAN'S CHOICE: Ch. de Beauregard '86, £9.95.

CHEF: David Schwartz PROPRIETORS: Ind Coope Ltd
OPEN: Mon to Sat
MEALS: 10am to 11.30pm (L 12 to 3, D 6 to 11.30)
PRICES: £14 (£22). Snacks from £2.95. Cover 85p
CARDS: Access, Amex, Diners, Visa
SEATS: 75. 5 tables outside. Private parties: 20 main room. Vegetarian meals. Children welcome. Wheelchair access. Music. Air-conditioned

Sonny's [10/20] map 10

94 Church Road, SW13 0DQ
01-748 0393 £14–£20

At heart this is a bistro transformed into something more modish, with minimalist grey and white décor and a pretty patio garden through French doors. The menu is a lively, eclectic mix of familiar and exotic ideas with unusual twists: steamed chicken with watercress sauce, salmon with pesto sauce, English ham with split pea purée. Navarin of lamb has been a cut above average. Sweets are a high point, as in espresso ice-cream with chocolate sauce, or sticky toffee sponge pudding. Popularity and demand can stretch the kitchen beyond its capabilities. The wine list includes a decent choice of half-bottles. House French is £5.75. CELLARMAN'S CHOICE: Hardy's Bird Series Cabernet Shiraz, £7.75.

CHEF: Kath Lynch PROPRIETOR: Rebecca Mascarenhas
OPEN: all week, exc Sat L and Sun D
MEALS: 12.30 to 2.30 (3 Sun), 7.30 to 11
PRICES: £13 (£20), Set L and D £9.50 (£14)
CARDS: Access, Visa
SEATS: 60. Private parties: 60 main room. Vegetarian meals. Children welcome. Wheelchair access. Air-conditioned

▲ *Le Soufflé, Inter-Continental Hotel* [13/20] map 12

1 Hamilton Place, W1V 0QY
01-409 3131 £30–£44

It is a surprise to discover that the restaurant is still in the same room, so great is the transformation. Arrival is via the airport lounge-style bar with its pianist playing Irving Berlin. Entrance reveals a cross between a pre-war Odeon and the dining-room of a cruise ship where creams leaning to sand and grey offset the greens. The effect is light and fresh but nondescript. The menu retains its character, and a big brigade in the kitchen makes many things possible. Without desperately seeking to be innovative, the kitchen is capable of producing familiar dishes very well, within an international context of langoustines, salmon, lobster, cèpes and garnishes of caviare.

The soufflé remains a fixture (order in advance for dessert) and has seen a novelty in the shape of potato – baked, scooped out, filled with quails' egg and smoked salmon, on to which the waiter spoons sour cream and caviare. The sauces earn the most distinctions – for instance, for a sea-bass fillet there is a dark meaty sauce filled with mushrooms for depth, cooked spring onions for sweetness, vinegar for sharpness, and the sweetness of reduction which can be much more effective with fish than meat. Sweets are now on a trolley, and waiters do much preparation at the table, feathering and saucing. There is a little Mayfair game going on here – Ninety Park Lane was the first to re-introduce the stylish trolley, and the Oak Room at the Meridien also feathers the plates at table. All told, there is much service. The big Rolls-Royce wine list has some six cylinders on it, offering some mitigation under £15, but not under £10. House French is £10.40. CELLARMAN'S CHOICE: Pouilly Fuissé, Château de Pouilly '85, £42; Pauillac, Ch. Lynch-Bages '75, £60.

CHEF: Peter Kromberg PROPRIETORS: Inter-Continental Hotels Corp
OPEN: all week, exc Sat L
MEALS: 12.30 to 3, 7 to 11.30
PRICES: £27 (£39), Set L £21.50 (£30), Set D £34.50 (£44)
CARDS: Access, Amex, Carte Blanche, Diners, Visa
SEATS: 72. Private parties: 14 main room, 700 private room. Car-park, 100 places. Vegetarian meals. Children's helpings. Jacket and tie. No-smoking area. Wheelchair access (also WC). Air-conditioned
ACCOMMODATION: 490 rooms, all with bath/shower. Rooms for disabled. Lift. B&B £151 to £176. Children welcome. Baby facilities. Afternoon teas. Sauna. Air-conditioning. TV. Phone

Spices [9/20] map 10

30 Stoke Newington Church Street, N16 8BJ
LONDON 01-254 0528 £7–£19

The best-looking building in a street that is fast becoming populated with restaurants. This family-run Indian vegetarian restaurant has been through two refurbishments since 1984 and looks attractive, with pale ochre walls, cushioned low seating at the back and pinkish tables. Many of the South Indian specialities are well reported: deep-fried paneer cutlets, cashew nut pakoras, corn kurma and dahi vada have all been subtly spiced and neatly presented. Also look for aloo kashi (a cold dish of potatoes with lemon, cumin, chillies and coriander leaves) and specials such as soya curry with pilau rice. Excellent gulab jamun to finish. Drink lassi.

CHEF: Khaleda Choudhury PROPRIETORS: Spices Ltd
OPEN: all week, exc Fri L
CLOSED: Christmas
MEALS: 12.30pm to 11.30pm
PRICES: £7 (£10), Set L £3.50 (£7), Set D £7.45 (£19). Service 10%
CARDS: Access, Amex, Diners, Visa
SEATS: 90. Private parties: 25 private room. Vegetarian meals. Children's helpings. No-smoking area. Wheelchair access (also WC). Music. Air-conditioned

Sree Krishna [10/20]

map 10

194 Tooting High Street, SW17 0SF
01-672 4250

£9

The South Indian vegetarian dishes here compare with the best of their kind in London. Masala dosais, dahi vada (lentil doughnuts in yoghurt), all kinds of bhajias and vegetables are delicately and freshly prepared. Birianis have properly spiced rice, and there is kulfi to finish. Otherwise there are standard curry-house meat and prawn dishes, such as methi gosht and prawn korma. Low prices, charming service. Useful for families with children. Drink lager.

CHEF/PROPRIETOR: R. Ramanarayan
OPEN: all week
MEALS: 12 to 2.45, 6 to 10.45 (11.45 Fri and Sat)
PRICES: £4 (£9). Minimum £2.50. Service 10%
SEATS: 120. Vegetarian meals. Children welcome. Wheelchair access (also WC). Music. Air-conditioned

Suntory [12/20]

map 13

72 St James's Street, SW1A 1PH
01-409 0201

£22–£65

Highly regarded in terms of status, Suntory is the Japanese equivalent of some of the lesser grand hotels, relying heavily on its presence for its charm. It is a very good restaurant in every respect except possibly the food itself; despite using high-class ingredients it does not make the most of them. The hollow section in each of the lacquered tables is appropriate. In essence this is no more than a shabu-shabu house or sukiyaki bar – two of the dullest arms of a fascinating cuisine. Downstairs the teppanyaki rooms deal in lobster and fillet steak. There is little distraction from the superbly Japanese atmosphere or from the bill, which rises like the yen against the £. It is wise to stick to the *carte* and dishes like the soups and the Suntory salad, where the quality of the ingredients is shown off to best effect. There is even foie gras at £11.80. Wines begin at £10. Service is a thumping 15 per cent on top.

CHEF: K. Miura PROPRIETORS: Suntory Ltd
OPEN: Mon to Sat
MEALS: 12 to 1.30, 7 to 9.30
PRICES: £34 (£54), Set L £12 (£22), Set D £23 (£34) to £50 (£65). Cover £1.60. Service 15%
CARDS: Access, Amex, Diners, Visa
SEATS: 130

Le Suquet [13/20]

map 12

104 Draycott Avenue, SW3 3AE
01-581 1785 and 225 0838

£37

The most genuinely French atmosphere since Mon Plaisir in the 1970s. This is not just because of French pictures, French-speaking staff, gleaming, seaweed-strewn plateaux of fruits de mer, the crowded dining-room and an awful giant photo of a French town on the stairs. At a busy restaurant in Brittany or Paris, one receives the odd plate of slightly overcooked fish or rough-looking but good-tasting sauce. The composite result in still usually a good meal where the ingredients stand out. Le Suquet, foremost of Pierre Martin's fish restaurants, is comparable. Its virtues are its simplicity and even its aggressive Frenchness. Tables are the size of chessboards, dwarfed by the platters on metal struts. But the atmospherics are allied to a menu rooted in mostly good-quality fish, about which there is little debate, set in sauces that are erratic, with little mitigation from either vegetables or sweets. Against that, there is a run of different oysters, langoustines four ways and scallops four ways, all best at their plainest. The plateau de fruits de mers is £12.50 and extensive. All told, a mixed bag, but on its own terms able to excel. The short wine list reaffirms the ambition. House French is £7.80. CELLARMAN'S CHOICE: Pouilly Fumé '87, £12.

CHEF: Jean Yves Darcel PROPRIETOR: Pierre Martin
OPEN: all week
MEALS: 12.30 to 2.30, 7 to 11.30
PRICES: £28 (£37). Cover £1
CARDS: Access, Amex, Diners, Visa
SEATS: 50. 4 tables outside. Private parties: 16 private room. Vegetarian meals. Children welcome. Smart dress preferred. Wheelchair access. Music. Air-conditioned

Surucchi [10/20] map 11

18 Theberton Street, Islington Green, N1 0QX
01-359 8033 £5–£9

Typical of the new face of Indian vegetarian food in the capital. Gone is the old image of the stripped pine café. Instead, there is an airy green décor with bamboo blinds, and subdued classical music. The short menu has the full range of South Indian snacks, specialities and thalis. Khati (vegetable kebabs) are long, cigar-shaped fritters; house dosa comes with light steamed iddly and a sambar sauce. Spicing is light and subtle. Unlicensed, but drink passion-fruit juice or bring your own wine.

CHEF: Azad Miah PROPRIETORS: Suruchi Partnership
OPEN: all week
MEALS: 12 to 2.30, 6 to 10.45
PRICES: £6 (£9), Set L and D £4 (£5) to £6 (£7). Service inc. Unlicensed, but bring your own: no corkage
CARDS: Amex, Visa
SEATS: 40. Vegetarian meals. Children welcome. Music

Sutherlands [15/20] map 13

45 Lexington Street, W1R 3LG
01-434 3401 £29–£35

Far and away the best restaurant to open in Soho since Alastair Little and, in many ways, seems to have the makings to outstrip Little – proper décor, high-class service, a chef trained in the best modern professional kitchen but free to create, lack of pretension. 'There is no place for egotistical food and wine snobbery,' writes Siân Sutherland-Dodd, who controls the front of house with a professionalism which belies her years and who may yet become one of London's great hostesses. The north-west frontier of Soho has traditionally struggled to bring customers at night, being that bit further from the West End, but those inspectors and friends sent by the *Guide* have been returning four and five times. The street is narrow and discreet, as is the frontage, with lower-case typography for the name. It was a café but has been rejuvenated into a long, elegant room with space between tables and a stained-glass panel ceiling at the back. Staff are in neat uniforms. The menu, two set meals at lunch and one at dinner, deals comfortably with fashionable luxuries. From the moment the breads arrive – superb Parmesan, lemon and thyme, or walnut and raisin rolls with unsalted butter – it is clear that this is a serious operation. Garry Hollihead was schooled with Mosimann, Outhier and Edelmann at the Savoy. His saucing is light, largely using chicken stocks. Soups are exceptional and a trademark: for white radish soup the plate is presented dry, with mushroom and diced meat garnish at the bottom, and the soup poured from a copper pan. There is a liking for unusual soup combinations, as in carrot and kohlrabi poured over ravioli; in summer a white plate is scattered with passion-fruit seeds, mango, peach, strawberries and a hawthorn flower on to which, from a white jug, is poured a chilled claret and grenadine version. There is genuine thought: bavarois of lobster is laid on some root vegetables; sliced duck breasts surround a central mound of dauphinois potatoes and a little tartlet of mushrooms on one side of the plate, while on the other a deep caramelised cream sauce with lentils and cabbage, ringed with asparagus – so far so brilliant – is topped needlessly with scallops and a pastry hat. There would be no harm in having a few plainer dishes to show off the subtleties and colours of the rest of the menu or to let one or two aspects ring out clearly. Another signature is the hot cheese course – always on offer and making intelligent use of different flavours. The sweets are immaculately decorative: nage of spring fruit in a warm Bordeaux essence is encased within a pulled sugar cage; a white chocolate mousse, interleaved with marinated pears and served in crème anglaise flavoured with poire William eau de vie is garnished by a wing of pastry finished with a little drop of chocolate to look like a butterfly.

'This was a thoroughly interesting meal, very good in parts, not disastrous even when it fell. Little still rules, and Gavroche and Tante Claire, but this is pushing up.' We are talking first division. Service is mature and behaves as if everyone is on the same side. 'No fuss but quiet human consideration.' The stylishly minimalist wine list (just over 50 wines) is actually more reliable outside France than in. But there are some extremely fine wines. Of the French bottles, Château de Fleurie '86, Pommard from Parent and Pouilly-Fuissé from Vincent are all excellent and several others are very acceptable. Wines from Italy, Germany, Spain, California, Australia, New Zealand and England are all recommendable. Prices are fair. Sweet wines come on a separate little list opposite the desserts, and include Robert Mondavi Moscato d'Oro '85, £2.95 per glass, Brown Bros Orange Muscat and Flora, £2.75 per glass, and two wines by the half-bottle – the exceptional Sauternes, Château Rabaud-Promis '83, £13.25, and a German Eiswein of unmentioned vintage for £40.50. House French is £8.

CHEF: Garry Hollihead PROPRIETORS: Siân Sutherland-Dodd, Garry Hollihead and Christian Arden
OPEN: Mon to Sat, exc Sat L
MEALS: 12.15 to 2.15, 6.15 to 11.15
PRICES: Set L from £16.80 (£29), Set D £21.50 (£35). Service 12.5%
CARDS: Access, Amex, Carte Blanche, Visa
SEATS: 55. Private parties: 40 main room, 20 private room. Vegetarian meals. Children's helpings on request. No cigars or pipes in dining-room. Wheelchair access. Air-conditioned

Tante Claire [18/20] 10 YEARS map 12

68–69 Royal Hospital Road, SW3 4HP
01-352 6045 £23–£50

For all its reputation, Tante Claire remains a restaurant free of the ostentation that bedevils its contemporaries, especially on the Continent. Some of the panels on the side walls have been left unpainted as if even now, some two/three years after the redecoration, there is something that is deliberately being left unsaid. There is no *menu gastronomique*, just a simple *carte* and a short, excellent-value lunch. There are no waves of petits fours, no sorbets between courses, no rattling of the liqueur trolley round the room, no going round of the tables to shake hands. Pierre Koffmann is rarely seen in the dining-room. Instead, the style is more of an old-fashioned French provincial restaurant, with boundaries between kitchen and front of house clearly drawn. The front of house is ably patrolled by Christophe Laurent and sommelier Batrice Jégat, no plate lifters these but serious men whose camaraderie and team-work offset the creeping internationalism that status has brought. In most meals there is at least one, usually two dishes that demonstrate why this kitchen is so highly regarded. Nothing showy, no Matisse-style pictures on the plate, just precision and confidence. Luxuries there are, but they are subjected to the kitchen's will along with humbler items – a little foie gras mousse is served with lentils poached in stock as an appetiser. The exactness is what singles it out, rather in the same way as Joël Robuchon in Paris.

Description does not do justice to the sheer technique: one fat ravioli is filled with half a dozen langoustines poached in an asparagus bouillon and garnished with the same, the sauce sweetened with a little butter. A croustade of duck arrives, the pastry neatly browned; the waiter breaks the surface, as he might to a soufflé, and pours in a little stock sauce to moisten the farce of duck meat and liver. Sauces have a subtlety that is at first deceptive, so too the combinations, for instance a whole raspberry for each medallion of pink venison in a sauce sweetened with chocolate. The menu of seven starters, five fish and seven meats also offers: a large piece of foie gras, sauté until pink, served on a crisp galette of grated potato and surrounded by a Sauternes sauce, and then perhaps the famous pig's trotter with morels; or maybe a pigeon, the breast taken off the bone and pink, the leg meat sliced and made into a tiny hamburger topped by a fried quails egg, a small heap of tiny French fried potatoes, and a superb, light but intense stock reduction and pan juice sauce – 'à la Macdonalds'. Some combinations are illuminating: terrine of foie gras with veal tongue and grilled country bread; scallops with spinach and lardons; turbot with lentils; hare or venison with chocolate and raspberry vinegar. Vegetables might be no more than a plate of stir-fried wild mushrooms. The display of fruits and sorbets provides a refreshing break or, for something richer and heavier, there might be a weighty croustade de pommes. The single plate of petits fours is scattered with perfect tuiles, tiny choux swans, each a little masterpiece. For its class, and particularly for London compared to France, it represents very good value and prices. Paying top prices for food, expect to pay generously for the wine, too. The base price of £10 buys a selection of well-made Vins de Pays des Sables du Golfe de Lyon, listed more romantically as 'Camargue', and half as much again would net some reasonable Loire and Alsace whites, a Bourgogne Rouge or a Beaujolais, but the 'cheaper' selection is very limited, and prices soon shoot up. The bulk of the list is fine Burgundy and claret. Strangely, there is much more 'affordable' Burgundy than claret, where few bottles cost less than £45. There's a commendably wide selection of half-bottles.

CHEF: Pierre Koffmann PROPRIETORS: Mr and Mrs Pierre Koffmann
OPEN: Mon to Fri
MEALS: 12.30 to 2, 7 to 11
PRICES: £43 (£50), Set L £18.50 (£23). Minimum £30 at D. Service inc
CARDS: Access, Amex, Diners, Visa
SEATS: 38. Children welcome. Jacket and tie. Wheelchair access

Tate Gallery [10/20]

map 11

Millbank, SW1P 4RG
01-834 6754

£18

Galleries are supposed to preserve standards, but the dining-room standard, despite the splendid Whistler, is slowly, inexorably, showing signs of decline. There are red meats and cheeses and some gesturing to history, but these are the bridgehead and mast; the hull is holed and taking in water. Action is needed or the still fine – though not as good as it was – wine list will become disenfranchised from its restaurant and float off somewhere. For the moment, the list's life-raft keeps the Tate in the *Guide*. There's a fine run of mature clarets and shorter selections of fine, mature Germans, Sauternes, vintage ports, even California reds of the mid-'70s. Burgundies are less exciting – younger wines, largely from merchants. Rare vintage malts, fine cognacs, armagnac and eaux-de-vie come by the glass.

CHEF: Michael Driver PROPRIETORS: Trustees of the Tate Gallery
OPEN: Mon to Sat, L only
CLOSED: Christmas and most bank hols
MEALS: 12 to 3
PRICES: £12 (£18), Snacks from 45p. Minimum £5
SEATS: 120. Private parties: 15 main room. Vegetarian meals. Children's helpings. No-smoking area. Wheelchair access (also WC). Air-conditioned

Report forms are at the back of the book.

Topkapi [11/20] map 13

25 Marylebone High Street, W1M 3PE
01-486 1872 £15

The back of the dining-room has a high domed ceiling, recalling the moment in the film of the same name where the thief comes down on a wire to steal the dagger. The restaurant rates well because it stays within the confines of proper Turkish cooking. Its strengths are simple: a dozen fine kebabs and an array of good mezeler, including imam bayildi, taramosalata, cacik, muska böregi, which make a substantial, very good-value set meal. There are also a few dishes of note: kuzu firin – roast lamb with green peppers, onions, leeks and rice – and chicken marinated in fresh cream with garlic, lemon and wine, plus char-grilled. Its popularity provides a lively atmosphere. Wines start at £5.50, Turkish at £7 and there is imported Turkish beer, Efés. CELLARMAN'S CHOICE: Villa Doluca £7.50.

CHEF: R. Kalayci PROPRIETOR: U. Fahri
OPEN: all week
MEALS: noon to midnight
PRICES: £9 (£15), Set L and D £10.50 (£15). Service 10%
CARDS: Access, Amex, Diners, Visa
SEATS: 50. Private parties: 20 main room. Vegetarian meals. Children's helpings. Wheelchair access (also WC). Music

Les Trois Plats [13/20] map 12

4 Sydney Street, SW3 6PP
01-352 3433 £16–£23

This little T-junction off the Fulham Road has always maintained its exclusivity. The cluster of elegant shops and restaurants, dominated by the Spanish villa frontage and first-floor conservatory of the Meridiana restaurant, recalls the glamorous Chelsea style of living in the 1960s. Les Trois Plats – previously Chelsea Rendezvous, Sails and Rouxl Britannia – occupies the first of a row of handsome brick and stucco terraced houses. The déjà vu experience on entering is immediately striking: this is an unashamed outpost of the Roux Empire with familiar photos and cartoons of the brothers, well-thought-out colour schemes and a slightly rustic theme to the dining-room. Everything from the colourful chinaware showing peasant boys and girls in Breton clothes to the pink table-cloths, the white tiling on the walls and to the floral carpet seem to be house colours, house styles or house details. The upstairs café is extremely good value; it is ideal for one course, perhaps steak frites, and a glass of the Duboeuf wine. Downstairs a set price all-inclusive menu offering four or five dishes per course, plus coffee and a half-bottle of house wine, operates. There is such a strong support system (for example, frequent delivery runs to Rungis market in Paris, a pâtisserie factory and a constant flow of enthusiastic young staff) that it has a generous head start over comparable London restaurants. Ironically some of the small details, like the dull canapés and tired petits fours, show the chinks in the armour. Notwithstanding, the cooking for the main courses shows immense flair for accurate saucing and straightforward matching of flavours. It is refreshing *cuisine bourgeoise* devoid of pretension. A sauce provençal is a medium-strength garlic and tomato affair with hints of herbs and plenty of onions for slices of monkfish; 'it speaks more about farmhouse cooking than all the whimsical country chinaware on the dining-room walls.' Look also for the fish soup, the grenadins de veau Maintenant, the exemplary small cheeseboard, the two chocolate mousses. Half a bottle of wine is included in the set dinner price in the restaurant, otherwise bottles start at £5.70.

CHEF: Robert Couzens PROPRIETORS: Roux Restaurants Ltd
OPEN: Mon to Sat (D only in Restaurant)
CLOSED: bank hols
MEALS: Café noon (7pm Sat) to 11; Restaurant 7 to 11
PRICES: Café L £11 (£16), D £14 (£19); Restaurant Set D £23 (£23). Service inc Set
CARDS: Access, Amex, Diners, Visa
SEATS: Café 30, Restaurant 50. Children welcome

Tuk Tuk [10/20] map 11

330 Upper Street, N1 2XQ
01-226 0837 £13

Hunt the chef. Stephen Binns leaves a trail of good reports behind him each time he opens a new venture. The latest, said to be the first of a series of Thai fast-food restaurants, is named after the three-wheel taxis of Bangkok, half of one of which bursts through the wall at the end of the room. Regulars have left the parent, Lakorn Thai, frustrated at what seems to be a gradual but serious decline, in favour of the extra few minutes' walk from Sadler's Wells to the Green. Apart from the trimmings of lettuce and tomato, the cooking is fast and well spiced. Especially notable on a menu of 25 dishes are the noodle dishes and the clay-pots of pork or beef. Service is speedy. Drink Thai or Singapore beer.

CHEF: Mr Phongphongsavat PROPRIETOR: Stephen Binns
OPEN: Mon to Sat
MEALS: 12 to 3, 6 to 11.15
PRICES: £10 (£13). Service 10%
CARDS: Access, Amex, Visa
SEATS: 36. 2 tables outside. Private parties: 16 main room. Vegetarian meals. Children's helpings. Wheelchair access (1 step). Music

Turner's [15/20] map 12

87–89 Walton Street, SW3 2HP
01-584 6711 £20–£29

Walton Street is one of London's most fashionable pieces of real estate. Although dominated by the rejuvenated Michelin building, and the series of razor-sharp clothes shops, it still maintains a human scale and, despite the glitzy image, remains a terraced-house street of three-storey-high façades, mainly residential and retaining a sense of history. Not everything is short-lived, as one can see; Ma Cuisine and Waltons are still trading. The deep green interior of the old Bewicks restaurant has been transformed into soothing shades of magnolia cream and powder blue. The classy subtleness which is part and parcel of the street has been retained, but the introduction of Venetian micro-blinds and low-voltage lighting convey more the feel of an executive lounge. Discreet, but a bit clever. The atmosphere is a touch bland, despite the trim brass fittings and tall balloon vases that hold giant white lilies, their leaves sprouting provocatively forward. A small opening affords a glimpse, swing-doors permitting, into the kitchen. The scene is highly animated, full of roaring fires and steam bellowing from three-feet-high aluminium stock-pots bubbling furiously. Figures in white swerve in and out of view accompanied by the clanging and banging noises of pots and pans. Brian Turner himself is barely seen at his stock-pots these days and acts as telephonist, cloak hanger, meeter/greeter, menu explainer, menu taker, wine list explainer, server and general entertainer. The four-course, fixed-price menu is surprisingly cheap at £22.50 with VAT and service included. The à la carte covers nine starters and nine entrées. Dishes appear like mini classics and betray Turner's background in the nearby luxury of the Capital Hotel. There are no visible signs of experimental combinations of ingredients, nor a particularly fashion oriented repertoire, considering its location. Given the benefit of the doubt, there is a level of sustained consistency that runs through the courses. Alpha dishes include lobster, monk and scallops in a sweet sauce made with the shells of crab; fine salmon quenelles; fillet of lamb encircled by mounds of red and green vegetables and given a heady veal-stock-based sauce infused with alcohol; and, best of all, an apple and bilberry tart – a three-inch circle of light pastry set with thin strips of apple that have risen in the baking and blossom like flower petals, adorned with a cluster of berries soaked in liqueur and a cloud of icing sugar. The purely French wine list of 80 bottles follows the French habit of power lunching, with extremely well chosen Burgundies, red and white, from properties such as Domaine de la Maldière, Domaine de la Folle, Clos de Condemine, Château Fuissé, Domaine Tollot-Beaut and Domaine Mongeard-Mugneret. The clarets are good and affordable, the most expensive being Château Cos d'Estournel '78, £63, although, in the French style, they are all quite young. Alsace and Rhône wines are dependable, and in the Loire, the Sancerre of Dezat and the Chinon of Domaine du Raifault should be excellent. Sweet wines include three from the Loire, Coteaux du Layon, Quarts du Chaume and Vouvray, all in their infancy, and a Sauternes, Monbazillac from Château de la Peyrade Muscat de Frontignan, £18.50 or £3.50 per glass.

CHEFS: Brian J. Turner and Mark Clayton PROPRIETOR: Brian J. Turner
OPEN: all week, exc Sat L
MEALS: 12.30 to 2.45, 7.30 to 11
PRICES: £23 (£29), Set L from £14.25 (£20), Set D from £19.75 (£25). Service inc
CARDS: Access, Amex, Diners, Visa
SEATS: 52. Private parties: 16 main room. Children's helpings. Wheelchair access (2 steps). Music. Air-conditioned

Restaurants are checked every year and their entries rewritten. The restaurant scene changes very rapidly. Don't trust an out-of-date Guide.

Upper Street Fish Shop [9/20] map 11

324 Upper Street, N1 2XQ
01-359 1401 £7–£11

Still rated as one of the best fish and chip shops in London, with a bustling atmosphere that feels like a French café. Alan Conway cooks, while Olga chats to the queues. Top-drawer fish and chips is the main business, with occasional specials, ranging from halibut fried in egg to poached salmon salad. The deep-fried onion rings are good, as are the fish soup and the old-fashioned English puddings such as treacle tart or jam roly-poly. Unlicensed but bring your own.

CHEF: Alan Conway PROPRIETORS: Alan and Olga Conway
OPEN: Mon to Sat, exc Mon L
CLOSED: bank hols
MEALS: 12 to 2 (3 Sat), 5.30 to 10
PRICES: £8 (£11), Set L and D from £5.50 (£7). Unlicensed, but bring your own: no corkage
SEATS: 50. Children's helpings. Wheelchair access. Air-conditioned

Wakaba [11/20] map 11

122A Finchley Road, NW3 5LG
01-722 3854 £12–£31

The sparkling, minimalist, all-white dining-room matches the designer simplicity of the dishes. The menu deals in the main avenues of Japanese cooking: tempura, yakitori, sukiyaki, sashimi, grills. The quality of the ingredients, notably the fish and bean curd, is exemplary. Service is friendly. Drink green tea, or saké at £2.50.

CHEF/PROPRIETOR: Minoru Yoshihara
OPEN: Mon to Sat
CLOSED: 5 days at Christmas, 4 days at Easter
MEALS: 12 to 2.30, 6.30 to 11
PRICES: £20 (£31), Set L from £6.90 (£12), Set D from £17.80 (£24). Service 12.5%
CARDS: Access, Amex, Diners, Visa
SEATS: 60. Private parties: 40 main room, 20 private room. Children welcome. Wheelchair access (also WC). Air-conditioned

Waltons [12/20] map 12

121 Walton Street, SW3 2HP
01-584 0204 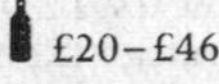 £20–£46

Walton's is long established as somewhere to spend a lot of money. It deals in luxuries, rather like the bijou art galleries clustered around it on the street of the same name. The dining-room is dramatic, with drapes, canopied ceilings, fine French Bergère chairs – all rather extravagant, as is the menu. There are two schools of thought about the cooking, which has stayed stylistically the same through a series of chefs. One says that it is fine haute cuisine and worth its *Michelin* star, the other that it is pretentious. Certainly, it is the more robust meat dishes, rather than fish, which excel, such as a roast duck with ginger and honey, as well as the picturesque sweets. The set-lunch and post-theatre menus provide the best-value eating. The wine list is mostly French, the specialities being a long list of excellent estate-bottled Burgundies and single-vineyard Beaujolais, and a fine selection of clarets, from *crus bourgeois* at the perfect stage for drinking (not too old) to various good vintages of a wide range of classed châteaux. A few good Germans and the odd Californian and Australian wine make up the weights. Roederer house champagne is only £18 per bottle, or £4.50 per glass. Choice of sweet wines is limited: a small selection of Bordeaux includes Loupiac and Ste-Croix du Mont as well as a few Sauternes; there are also Muscat de Beaumes de Venise, Domaine de Durban '86, £13.50, and Alsace Gewürztraminer Vendange Tardive '83, £22, and a German Auslese '76, excellent value at £9.50. House French is £8; CELLARMAN'S CHOICE: Pouilly Fumé '86, £11.50; Ch. Gruaud Larose '79, £24.

CHEF: Tony Cameron PROPRIETORS: Waltons Restaurants Ltd
OPEN: all week
CLOSED: Easter and Christmas
MEALS: 12.30 to 2.30 (2 Sun), 7.30 to 11.30 (10.30 Sun)
PRICES: £32 (£46), Set L £13 (£20), £15.15 (£22) Sun. Set D £19.50 (£27). Service 15%
CARDS: Access, Amex, Carte Blanche, Diners, Visa
SEATS: 65. Private parties: 33 main room, 24, 12 private rooms. Vegetarian meals. Children welcome. Smart dress preferred. No pipes in dining-room. Wheelchair access. Air-conditioned

White Tower [12/20] map 13

1 Percy Street, W1P 0ET
01-636 8141 £28

Perhaps the only old-style London restaurant left that still keeps up a standard. 'Traditionally popular with illuminati. Today was no exception with David Frost and George Cole as the most prominent and others, particularly media folk, to be seen.' With formal waiters and white cloths, the White Tower's enduring virtues are a literary menu, plentiful meze, excellent duck, proper Stroganoff. There is a charcoal grill for meats and fish. The wine list shambles around the £20 to £30 range, with only the Demestica, Aphrodite and a few others at £7 easing the financial burden. CELLARMAN'S CHOICE: Deutz and Gelderman NV Champagne, £23.75.

CHEF: Luigi Contini PROPRIETOR: E. Stais
OPEN: Mon to Fri
CLOSED: 1 week at Christmas, 3 weeks Aug
MEALS: 12.30 to 2.30, 6.30 to 10.30
PRICES: £20 (£28). Cover £1.50
CARDS: Access, Amex, Diners, Visa
SEATS: 80. Private parties: 10 main room, 16 private room. Children welcome. Air-conditioned

Wiltons [11/20]

map 13

55 Jermyn Street, SW1Y 6LX
01-629 9955 £37

Wiltons has managed to preserve the slightly censorious atmosphere of 1940s and 1950s dining-out better than anywhere else. The slavish fidelity to the old values extends into the cooking. 'Plain cooking, and plainer than it should be,' comments an expense-account diner. Apart from a few omelettes and the mandatory lobster thermidor, there is barely any cooking at all, even the saucing is abbreviated on the menu to 'dill sce' or 'hol'. There is a fierce chauvinism in the produce, displayed along the oyster bar; there is no truck with fashion. Oysters are only available when there is an 'r' in the month. It is a place to eat grouse, properly hung, with its trimmings and somewhere where the tables are sufficiently far apart to hold a private conversation. It is also somewhere that offers hot asparagus – '15 minute wait'. Respectable house wine is £9.50.

CHEF: Ross Hayden PROPRIETORS: Wiltons Ltd
OPEN: Mon to Sat, exc Sat L
CLOSED: 3 weeks a year
MEALS: 12.30 to 2.30, 6.30 to 10.30
PRICES: £28 (£37). Cover £1. Minimum £12.50. Service inc
CARDS: Access, Amex, Diners, Visa
SEATS: 90. Private parties: 20 main room, 18 private room. Children welcome. Jacket and tie. Wheelchair access. Air-conditioned

Wine Gallery [9/20]

map 12

49 Hollywood Road, SW10 9HX
01-352 7572 £15

The wine bar is the offshoot of the more expensive Brinkleys next door, and parent now to four similar operations including one at Oxford and Brinkleys Champagne Exchange, both listed. It is good value for an inventive menu and on occasion surprisingly competent execution of dishes, by wine bar standards. Wines show the same depth of thought.

CHEF: Sami Robinson PROPRIETOR: John Brinkley
OPEN: all week
MEALS: 12 to 3.30, 6.30 to 12
PRICES: £10 (£15)
CARDS: Access, Visa
SEATS: 75. 10 tables outside (L only). Private parties: 25 main room, 28 private room. Children welcome. Wheelchair access (1 step). Music

Wing Ki [10/20]

29 Burnt Oak Broadway HA8 5LD
01-205 0904 £10–£23

Wing Ki Yueng and his Irish wife Hannah moved from the very well-supported Wings in Barnet to this restaurant in Edgware. His low-key,

80-item Peking/Szechuan menu plays to the local trade (even avoiding pork to cater for the high Jewish presence in the area). The strength of the kitchen is in the well-reported starters: bang-bang chicken, crispy lamb with spicy sauce, and spiced smoked chicken have all been good. Only one duck dish appears, in the form of crispy duck with pancakes. Sizzling beef, Szechuan prawns with sea-spice sauce and Singapore noodles have been recommended. Mr Yueng also promises a good variety of vegetarian dishes, though they are not on the menu. Friendly, helpful service. House wine £5.50.

CHEF: Wing Ki Yueng PROPRIETORS: Wing Ki and Hannah Yueng
OPEN: all week
MEALS: 12 to 2.30, 6 to 11.30
PRICES: £13 (£23), Set L from £6.50 (£10), Set D £13.50 (£18). Service 12.5%
CARDS: Access, Amex, Diners, Visa
SEATS: 56. Private parties: 60 main room. Vegetarian meals. Children's helpings. Smart dress preferred. Wheelchair access (also WC). Music

Wong Kei [9/20]

map 14

41–43 Wardour Street, W1V 3HA
01-437 3071 and 6833 £6–£9

The Chinese have a great respect for value for money which may explain the 20-yard queues outside this multi-tiered, 550-seater, fast-food operation. It is perhaps the cheapest place to eat in Chinatown – excellent one-plate meals; soups of noodle, wun-tun, pork and pickled vegetable; roast meats. The style is somewhere midway between carry-out and sit-down, ideally suited to lone diners or large groups rather than twos or threes. The service is brusque, but usually in Cantonese rather than English. Drink tea.

CHEF: T.F. Tang PROPRIETORS: E. Liu and M.H. Lo
OPEN: all week
MEALS: noon to 11.30pm
PRICES: £7 (£9), Set L and D £3.90 (£6). Service inc alc only
SEATS: 550. Private parties: 80 main room, 80 private room. Vegetarian meals. Children welcome. Wheelchair access (also WC)

Yung's [11/20]

map 14

23 Wardour Street, W1V 3HD
01-734 4566 £11–£21

In spite of the three levels, elbow room is at a premium and the food takes somewhat longer to arrive than is usual in Soho. Cooking is basically Cantonese, with sizzling and wind-dried prominent, marginally more succesful than excursions to Peking and Szechuan. It is a restaurant for serious Chinese eaters – the mixed meat soup, or the pork and salted cabbage soup, are almost a meal in their own right, and the casserole dishes, such as duck's web or bean curd and fish-head, are equally fine. The main strength is fish: grilled turbot, or steamed sea-bass with ginger and spring onion. Orange segments are served automatically. Stays open and keeps the standards up until 4am.

CHEF: Mr Ng PROPRIETORS: Mr Wokiuliu and Mr Ng
OPEN: all week
MEALS: 4pm to 4am
PRICES: £11 (£21), Set D £6.50 (£11) to £11 (£16). Minimum £6.50. Service 10%
CARDS: Access, Amex, Diners, Visa
SEATS: 100. Private parties: 20 main room. Vegetarian meals. Children welcome. Air-conditioned

Zamoyski [9/20] map 11

85 Fleet Road, NW3 2QY
01-794 4792 £13

One of the best-value East European eating places in the capital. The wine bar is downstairs; the restaurant is up a spiral staircase. It gets very jolly and warm once customers arrive. Dishes are wholesome and substantial and the flavours are authentic: exemplary borshch with cubes of potato, cabbage and a dollop of sour cream; potato and walnut latkes; zrazy – fillet of beef wrapped round dill cucumbers and mushrooms, served on wild rice. Cheesecakes, pastries and semifreddo – a superior European trifle – to finish. Vodkas, Polish beers and basic wines to drink.

CHEF: Richard Slomka PROPRIETORS: Richard Slomka, Kathy Witkowska and Christopher Witkowski
OPEN: Mon to Sat
MEALS: 12 to 3, 6.30 to 10.30
PRICES: £9 (£13), Snacks from £1. Service 10% for parties over 6
SEATS: 72. Private parties: 38 to 40 main room. Vegetarian meals. Children's helpings. Smart dress preferred. No-smoking area. Music. Air-conditioned

Zazou [10/20] map 13

74 Charlotte Street, W1P 1LB
01-436 5133 £28

Sandwiched between Saatchi and Saatchi and Channel 4, this media brasserie has the sassy image its name implies. The design is almost an imitation of the fashionable Zanzibar Club in Covent Garden. The menu is abrupt and deals quite sensibly with some good fish and cheeses. It is an off-shoot of the Chez Gerard steak and chips trio and follows the same minimum-choice format. The shellfish platter is generous, though with crabs rather than lobster, enormous decorative whelks, langoustines, winkles, shrimps, etcetera. Other fish are simply grilled. Muscadet is £8.90.

CHEF: Patrick Girard PROPRIETOR: Chez Gerard Ltd
OPEN: Mon to Sat
CLOSED: Christmas
MEALS: 12.40 to 2.40, 7 to 11.30
PRICES: £20.50 (£28). Cover £1.60. Service 12.5%
CARDS: Access, Amex, Diners, Visa
SEATS: 50. Private parties: 50 main room. Vegetarian meals. Children welcome. Music. Air-conditioned

Zen [12/20]

map 12

Chelsea Cloisters, Sloane Avenue, SW3 3DN
01-589 1781 £16–£24

The original of Lawrence Leung's trio of Chinese restaurants still thrives in opulent surroundings beneath Chelsea Cloisters. It was one of the first to have a deliberate 'no MSG' policy, to give full weight to vegetarian dishes and to incorporate specialities from all regions of China. And all of this in a setting that is consciously European, with mirrors in the ceiling, a fountain and chairs with pin-stripe upholstery. The centrepieces are classics – Peking and Szechuan duck, Kwantang-style roast whole suckling pig, braised whole abalone with oyster sauce, lobster steamed or baked in chilli oil. Hot and cold appetisers take in not only minced quail in lettuce leaves, and sesame prawn fingers, but dry tangerine-flavoured beef slices, Peking ravioli in hot pepper sauce and duck's tongue Szechuan style. Also look for the sea-bass soup with chopped coriander, baked pomfret with garlic, wrapped in banana leaves, and shredded mooli with rice vermicelli and grated dried seafood. The wine list is an intelligent choice that would do credit to many a Western restaurant in the capital. House French is £8.

CHEF: K.S. Leung PROPRIETOR: Lawrence Leung
OPEN: all week
CLOSED: 25 to 27 Dec
MEALS: 12 to 3, 6 to 11.30 (11 Sun)
PRICES: £12 (£24), Set L £9 (£16). Cover £1. Minimum £8. Service 15%
CARDS: Access, Amex, Diners, Visa
SEATS: 120. Private parties: 100 main room, 20 private room. Vegetarian meals. No cigars/pipes in dining-room. Music. Air-conditioned

Zen Central [12/20]

map 13

20–22 Queen Street, W1X 7PJ
01-629 8103 £30

The inside of the latest of the Zen inspirations has the look of a 1930s white and black ocean liner, being quite stark, with the only blush of colour coming from the covers of the menus and the garish cocktails in long glasses. The trimmings are Mayfair – inscribed chopstick rests and silver plates and napkins in the French manner, because this is one of the foremost adaptations of high-class Cantonese cooking to western notions of restaurateuring. The menu is built round centrepieces, for instance lobster and Dover sole, with a choice of six ways of cooking – perhaps the sole steamed with tangerine peel or else served deep-fried with a sweet-and-sour sauce. Around these are found some superlative smaller dishes – Szechuan salad of sliced meats with jelly-fish; some fine Peking ravioli; succulent smoked chicken imbued with spices; sea-spiced aubergines. Standards are frustratingly erratic for the prices. Some dishes are as good as anywhere, but in others there is a rather lazy, let-the-chilli-oil-take-the-strain approach, which, given a menu that does not change, is not really good enough. The range of vegetarian dishes includes mixed vegetables cooked in a clay pot, rich in species of mushrooms.

Rice is cooked in a lotus leaf; fruit sorbets are first-class. Service is swift and skilled. Plans are afoot to open a branch in Hong Kong which may account for an element of distraction in the management, but which could equally result in some useful cross-fertilisation. House Côtes de Provence is £8.50.

CHEF: Michael Leung PROPRIETOR: Lawrence Leung
OPEN: all week
CLOSED: 25 Dec
MEALS: 12 to 2.45, 6 to 11.45 (11.15 Sun)
PRICES: £15 (£30). Cover £1. Service 15%
CARDS: Access, Amex, Diners, Visa
SEATS: 110. Private parties: 80 main room, 20 private room. Vegetarian meals. Children welcome. Jacket and tie. Music. Air-conditioned

Zen W3 [11/20] map 11

83 Hampstead High Street, NW3 1RE
01-794 7863 and 7864 £12–£27

The second of Lawrence Leung's trio stays with the formula of cool, designer décor, excellent service and a menu that moves with the times. The dining-room is dominated by glass – in the roof panels, on some of the table tops – with a fountain along the staircase and a chopstick-patterned carpet. No MSG is used in the cooking, although sugar levels can be noticeably high. Ingredients are very good and the menu spans the Chinese regions, with some eclectic ideas such as steamed prawns with fennel seeds. Red bean sauce features with chicken and chilli, as well as with aubergines and garlic. House French is £5.50.

CHEF: Michael Leung PROPRIETOR: Lawrence Leung
OPEN: all week
CLOSED: 25 to 27 Dec
MEALS: noon to 11.30pm
PRICES: £18 (£27), Set L £6.80 (£12). Service 12.5%
CARDS: Access, Amex, Diners, Visa

England

ALDBOROUGH Norfolk map 6

Old Red Lion [10/20]

The Village Green, Aldborough NR11 7AA
CROMER (0263) 761451 £12–£20

Overlooking the village green, this has been a pub twice in its history and still bears the name. Bruno Diluzio cooks a simple, fixed-price menu with a Franco-Italian bent – pâté, egg mayonnaise, lasagne, followed by a choice of nine main courses ranging from goujonettes of sole and veal pizzaiola to more English steak and kidney pie. Scampi in cream sauce is well reported. Good value with a friendly welcome. House French is £4.50.

CHEF: Bruno Diluzio PROPRIETORS: Mr and Mrs Eyles, Mr and Mrs Diluzio
OPEN: Tue to Sun, exc Sun D
MEALS: 12 to 2.30, 7 to 10.30
PRICES: £14 (£20), Set L £8.85 (£12), Set D £9.95 (£13). Licensed, also bring your own: no corkage
CARDS: Access, Visa
SEATS: 40. Private parties: 60 main room. Car-park, 12 places. Children's helpings. Music

ALDBOURNE Wiltshire map 2

Raffles [10/20]

1 The Green, Aldbourne, Nr Marlborough SN8 2BW
ALDBOURNE (0672) 40700 £20

The dandyish name might suggest the worst foppish elements of *nouvelle cuisine,* but James Hannan's inclinations are more bourgeois. Only the cluttered décor and the prints aspire to Victoriana. Sole bonne femme – here, fillets poached for two minutes in stock with shallots, mushrooms and white wine, the fish taken out, the stock reduced with double cream and glazed with butter – is listed as a speciality. The menu stays within tight confines of five starters and five main courses with an emphasis on classic cream and butter sauces. Pasta is home made. Fifty well-spread wines from Berry Bros, house claret at £5.35.

An index of restaurants by name appears at the back of the Guide.

CHEF: James Hannan PROPRIETORS: James and Mary Hannan
OPEN: Tue to Fri L, Mon to Sat D
CLOSED: last 2 weeks Aug, 25 to 30 Dec
MEALS: 12.30 to 2.15, 7 to 10.30
PRICES: £14 (£20)
CARDS: Access, Amex, Diners, Visa
SEATS: 36. 3 tables outside. Private parties: 36 main room. Children's helpings (L only). Smart dress preferred. Wheelchair access. Music

ALFRISTON East Sussex map 3

Moonrakers [10/20]

High Street, Alfriston BN26 5TD
ALFRISTON (0323) 870472  £21

The Wilkinsons stick to their formula in their pretty sixteenth-century cottage in the High Street. Some dishes are hardy perennials: Sussex smokie, flaked, served in béchamel sauce, browned with Parmesan under a grill; Southdown terrine – coarse chicken liver with ham, pork, bacon, cream, herbs and brandy; duck with, for example, satsumas, though apricots and grapes have also been used. Other dishes look across the Channel for inspiration – sole and prawn in filo pastry with a herb sauce – and there have been good reports of the vegetarian dishes, mushroom pie for example, and nut rissoles. The home-made desserts come in large portions; profiteroles are recommended. The wine list is not an attempt to dazzle by sheer volume, but a discerning selection of about a hundred bottles. For lovers of fine German wines there is an unusually strong section, with sonorous names like Steinberger, Bürklin-Wolf, von Schubert, Hohe Domkirche and Dr Thanisch. Other regions are well represented, too, and it would be hard to choose between Domaine de Chevalier '81, £24 and Puligny-Montrachet, Domaine Leflaive, '84 £26.10, at the top end of the quality and price range for dry whites. Clarets are sensibly and affordably chosen, mostly from up-and-coming châteaux, although there is an 'off-vintage' '73 Ch. Latour, £38, thrown in for those who like a famous name on their table. Red Burgundies include wines from the redoubtable Trapet, Dujac and Tollot-Beaut domaines; Rhônes take in wines from Jaboulet and Guigal. The Spanish and Italian selections are exemplary. Australia is mainly from the trustworthy Penfold's stable, and a pair of Californias are from Château St Jean and Heitz. Highlights of a short sweet white Bordeaux section are '71/'76 Ch. Coutet, £20.60 per bottle, £10.60 per half, and '75 Ch. d'Yquem, £38 per half bottle.

CHEF: Elaine Wilkinson PROPRIETORS: Elaine and Barry Wilkinson
OPEN: Tue to Sat, D only
MEALS: 7 to 9.15 (6.45 to 9.45 Sat)
PRICES: Set D £15.90 (£21)
SEATS: 32. 2 tables outside. Private parties: 32 main room. Vegetarian meals. Children's helpings

'Potato soufflé – is this the 1001st use for a potato? I'm surprised they didn't call it cuisine Irlandaise.' On eating in a grand hotel

ALTRINCHAM Greater Manchester map 5

French [11/20]

25 The Downs, Altrincham WA14 2QD
061-941 3355 £13–£19

The French is upwardly mobile – starting up function rooms next door, opening a brasserie opposite, generally upgrading the décor. It is what it says, down to 'le garlic bread'. There are many recommendations: fish soup; smoked meats salad with orange vinaigrette; vegetable cassoulet; lamb noisettes served with two sauces, a tangy tomato and a cream-based onion, honey and coriander; strawberry tart. The cooking is not slavishly bistro, for instance a ballotine of duck with pistachios is served with a beetroot and cumin sauce or a tournedos is stuffed with a mixture of Brie and goats' cheese, rolled in black pepper, roasted and served with a red wine glaze. The dining area is dignified, with plenty of space, wood panelling and mirrors. Services too is professional. Eighty per cent of the wines are imported direct by the restaurant's own company. House wine is £5.50. CELLARMAN'S CHOICE: Ch. Haut-Brisson '78, £12.75.

CHEF/PROPRIETOR: Chris Hume
OPEN: all week, exc Sat L
MEALS: 12 to 2.30, 6 to 11.30
PRICES: £14 (£19), Set L £7.50 (£13)
CARDS: Access, Visa
SEATS: 85. Private parties: 80 main room; 15, 25 and 40 private rooms. Vegetarian meals. Children's helpings. Wheelchair access (2 steps). Music. Air-conditioned

Hanni's [10/20]

The Downs, Altrincham WA14 2QG
061-941 2551 £17

Hanni Al-Taraboulsy moved from Church Street during 1988, into this Victorian house formerly an Italian restaurant. A number of rooms have been knocked into one, and although the sum of the parts is not great, a family atmosphere pervades, and the food is broadly Middle-Eastern and Mediterranean in style. Meze can be taken individually or as a group: falafel, fasulya, spicy lamb sausage, stuffed vine leaves, hummus, lemony tabouleh, and a large heap of marinated vegetables. Charcoal-grilled kebabs and impressive couscous (of lamb, chicken or fish, with hot harissa sauce) are the main business, and baklava is home made. Three-dozen bottles of mostly French wines are reasonably priced. The only one from the Middle East is CELLARMAN'S CHOICE: Château Musar Red '80, £11.

CHEF: Minas Gharpetian PROPRIETOR: Mohamed Hanni Al-Taraboulsy
OPEN: Mon to Sat, exc Sat L
MEALS: 12 to 2, 6 to 10.30 (11 Fri and Sat)
PRICES: £12 (£17)
CARDS: Access, Amex, Diners, Visa
SEATS: 70. Private parties: 90 main room, 22 and 35 private rooms. Car-park, 22 places. Vegetarian meals. Children's helpings. Wheelchair access (7 steps). Music

AMBLESIDE Cumbria map 7

▲ *Kirkstone Foot Country House Hotel* [10/20]

Kirkstone Pass Road, Ambleside LA22 9EH
AMBLESIDE (0966) 32232 £19

The Batemans' white manor house is set in acres of gardens beside the Stock Ghyll stream. Outside there's a croquet lawn and displays of heathers, inside is a comfortable, tasteful dining-room for dinner at eight. The main course is always a roast with trimmings and plenty of vegetables, but the real high-spots come before and after: good starters such as cream of beetroot soup or poached pears stuffed with cream cheese; a trolley loaded with fine creamy sweets, and decent English cheeses with grapes. The value for money extends to the wine list, which has house wine at £5 a bottle. CELLARMAN'S CHOICE: Orlando Chardonnay '86 at £7.75.

CHEF: Jane Bateman PROPRIETORS: Jane and Simon Bateman
OPEN: all week, D only
CLOSED: 4 Dec to early Feb
MEALS: 8
PRICES: Set D £14.75 (£19)
CARDS: Access, Visa
SEATS: 50. Private parties: 10 main room. Car-park, 30 places. Vegetarian meals. Children's helpings on request. No children under 7. Jacket and tie. No smoking in dining room. Wheelchair access (also WC). Music. One sitting
ACCOMMODATION: 16 rooms, all with bath/shower. B&B £38 to £76. Deposit: £20. Baby facilities. Pets welcome. Afternoon teas. Garden. Fishing. TV. Phone. Scenic [GHG]

▲ *Rothay Manor* [10/20]

Rothay Bridge, Ambleside LA22 0EH
AMBLESIDE (053 94) 33605 £6–£25

One of the best afternoon teas in the Lake District is found in this long-established hotel: a substantial, help-yourself buffet of sandwiches, vol au vent, sausage rolls, quiche, two kinds of tea bread, treacle tart, Christmas cake, mince pie, apple cake, meringues and scones with butter and jam evoke the cooking of a generation ago. The view over the lawned gardens adds to the cultivated air of Victoriana. Mob-capped serving maids flit silently around a dining-room that is richly clad in browns and gold. The five-course set dinner is at its best a traditional affair, perhaps centred on a roast loin of pork, stuffing, crackling and apple sauce, with a soup or pâté before and a solid English pudding to finish. The reasonably priced wine list is wide ranging. Taking things alpabetically, the first page includes bottles from Alsace, Australia, Brazil and Bulgaria, the second goes on to California, Chile and the Lebanon, before arriving in Bordeaux. Where half-bottles are not available, Rothay Manor offers diners one half of a full bottle for three-fifths of the full price (with certain exceptions) but then sensibly suggests that it would be a better idea to buy the whole bottle and take home whatever is

Restaurants rating 12 or more serve the best food in the region.

not drunk. Clarets range from young Côtes de Castillon to English bottlings of famous properties in older vintages. Red and white Burgundies include good wines from the likes of Durup, Gagnard-Delagrange and Chevillon, and Crémant de Bourgogne Blanc and Rosé make good, inexpensive alternatives to champagne. The list of Loires is longer than usual, and there are two pages of wines from the Rhône and the South of France. Sweet wines are indicated on the list with an 's', and include two Sauternes, a German Beerenauslese and South of France Muscat Cuvée José Sala, £8. House French and Bulgarian are £7.50. CELLARMAN'S CHOICE: Vacqueyras '85, £10.10; California Clos du Bois Merlot '84, £10.50.

CHEF: Jane Binns PROPRIETORS: Nigel Nixon and Stephen Nixon
OPEN: all week
CLOSED: last 3 weeks Jan, first week Feb
MEALS: 12.30 to 2 (12.45 to 1.30 Sun), 8 to 9
PRICES: Set Sun L £10.50 (£16), Set D £19 (£25), L Snacks from £1
CARDS: Access, Amex, Diners, Visa
SEATS: 70. Private parties: 12 main room, 30 private room. Car-park, 30 places. Vegetarian meals. Children's helpings. Smart dress preferred. No smoking in dining room. Wheelchair access (also WC). Air-conditioned
ACCOMMODATION: 18 rooms, all with bath/shower. Rooms for disabled. B&B £53 to £74. Deposit: £50. Children welcome. Baby facilities. Afternoon teas. Garden. TV. Phone. Scenic. Doors close at 12. Confirm by noon [GHG]

Sheila's Cottage [10/20]

The Slack, Ambleside LA22 9DQ
AMBLESIDE (053 94) 33079 £13

The dining-room expands into the cottages next door in 1989, which may help ease the queues at Stewart Greaves' infallibly popular all-day café. The style does not change, nor does the tenor of recommendations. The Alpine influence is appropriate to this fell-dominated climate. There is no contradiction in finding local ham served on a white wine soaked biscotte base with mushrooms and soured cream sauce topped by melted Raclete or in a fine Viennese Sachertorte. At heart the menu is about Real Food and very, very English – for tea muffins made with local stoneground flour, Lakeland lemon bread or Cumberland sugar-baked ham, plus treacle tart. There are real ciders and English wines on a short, inexpensive list of drinks. House red £4.25. CELLARMAN'S CHOICE: Matua Valley Sauvignon Blanc '88, £8.95.

CHEF: Janice Greaves and Jane Sutherland PROPRIETOR: Stewart Greaves
OPEN: Mon to Sat
CLOSED: Jan
MEALS: 12 to 5.30 (L to 2.30)
PRICES: £8 (£13). Minimum £3.50 at L
SEATS: 38. Private parties: 38 main room. Children's helpings (L only). Wheelchair access. Music

All letters to the Guide *are acknowledged.*

ASHBOURNE Derbyshire

map 5

▲ *Callow Hall* [11/20]

Mappleton Road, Ashbourne DE6 2AA
ASHBOURNE (0335) 43403 £13–£30

The Spencer family have been bakers in Ashbourne for the last five generations, and this impressively refurbished manor house has its own bakery and patisserie department. David Spencer buys meat by the carcase, and all hanging and butchery is done on the premises; there are home-made sausages and home-cured bacon too. Trout is out of the River Dove. The menu is French-inspired with a few fashionable touches: casserole of lamb with apples; salmon with cream and dill sauce; marinated venison on a bed of endive; tarte Tatin. There are also good reports of the artichoke soup and jugged hare. Service can be slow. Some 75 wines, including house French bottled for the Hall at £4.95.

CHEF: David Spencer PROPRIETORS: Mr and Mrs David Spencer
OPEN: Tue to Sat D, and Sun L (other days by arrangement)
MEALS: 12.30 to 2.30, 7.30 to 9.30
PRICES: £19 (£26), Set L £8.75 (£13) to £10 (£14), Set D £16.50 (£21) to £24 (£30)
CARDS: Access, Amex, Diners, Visa
SEATS: 80. Private parties: 50 main room, 50 private room. Car-park, 70 places. Vegetarian meals. Children's helpings (Sun L only). Wheelchair access (also WC)
ACCOMMODATION: 11 rooms, 9 with bath/shower. B&B £48 to £70. Deposit: 10%. Baby facilities. Garden. Fishing. Golf. TV. Phone. Scenic. Doors close at 11.30

ASTON CLINTON Buckinghamshire

map 3

▲ *Bell* [13/20]

Aston Clinton HP22 5HP
AYLESBURY (0296) 630252 £19–£38

The Bell has been a *Guide* stalwart since the days of Raymond Postgate, but has moved with the times. Jocelyn Rickards' murals have brought nature and the garden into the famous old dining-room, with its wide aisles for trolleys of classic English roasts, luscious sweets and cheeses. Kevin Cape has given the cooking a new lease of life. His training at the Connaught (see London) shows in the blend of classic French technique with touches of modern invention. Cold terrine of goose liver and sweetbreads is interleaved with seaweed; grilled turbot comes with chicory and walnuts; veal is topped with a sauce of morels and served with braised endive and Parma ham. Classic Bell Inn smokies are still a feature. Vegetables are perfectly crisp. Cottage cheese soufflé with apples and a sabayon of Riesling shows that the kitchen is keeping pace with the times. The wine list is long and tempting, largely French but with a broad, brief spread from elsewhere. German and Italian wines are excellent, and there are a few top Californias and good Australians. Pride of the list, however, are the clarets, very well selected, with plenty of mature vintages. Loire and Provence wines are also excellent.

Burgundies are largely from merchants, with some estate wines, and Rhônes are predominantly from Jaboulet. The Loires offer best value among the sweet wines, especially Anjou Moulin Touchais '59 at £15.40, and Vouvray Moelleux '76, from Foreau, £17.60. There's also a Vouvray '47 from Marc Brédif, at £90, Coteaux du Layon '83, too young to drink, Sauternes of the '70s and '80s, and Lanson Rich Champagne, £25.30.

CHEF: Kevin Cape PROPRIETORS: The Harris family
OPEN: all week
MEALS: 12.30 to 2, 7.30 to 10
PRICES: £25 (£32), Set L £15.50 (£19) to £35 (£38), Set D £19.50 (£23) to £35 (£38). Service inc
CARDS: Access, Visa
SEATS: 100. Private parties: 20 and 200 private rooms. Car-park, 250 places. Children welcome. Wheelchair access (also WC)
ACCOMMODATION: 21 rooms, all with bath/shower. Rooms for disabled. B&B £60 to £83. Children welcome. Baby facilities. Pets welcome. Afternoon teas. Garden. TV. Phone [GHG]

AVENING Gloucestershire map 2

Gibbons [13/20]

Avening GL8 8NF
NAILSWORTH (045 383) 3070 £16–£25

At the foot of the steep hill through Avening which divides the village into old and new. The restaurant is down among the history, on the corner of the bend, prominent but laid back, with parking on the pavement outside. The dining-area is squeezed into the front of the old house and is unmistakably French from the *chansons* to the sauces that run through the set-price menu. Details impress – the stoned olives in the lounge, the hot bread rolls, the power of the cooking right through from the quiches, the cheese straws and the new casserole lunches. The menu is sensibly arranged with an optional fish course in the middle. A kebab of monkfish is alternated with slices of red pepper on a very vinegary beurre blanc – the monkfish cooked to the perfect point where it could be lobster, the peppers adding succulence; lamb is cut two ways and arranged in medallions on a plate of deep brown sauce of immense vigour; small nuggets of duck are set on a bed of red cabbage and Chinese leaves. To finish there are no tricks – a meringue with a tumble of fine fresh raspberries and some Jersey cream, a good St Emilion au chocolat, apple sorbet with calvados. The wine list is interesting with some good bin-ends. House French £5.25.

CHEF: Philip Gibbons PROPRIETORS: The Gibbons family
OPEN: Mon to Sat D, Wed to Fri and Sun L
MEALS: 12.30 to 3.30, 7.30 to 10
PRICES: Set L £12 (£16), Set D £15.80 (£21) to £19.60 (£25). Minimum £12
CARDS: Access, Amex, Diners, Visa
SEATS: 26. Private parties: 26 main room. Car-park, 12 places. Children's helpings. No children under 5. Smart dress preferred. No cigars/pipes in dining-room. Music

It is always advisable to book a restaurant in advance.

AYLESBURY Buckinghamshire map 2

Pebbles [new entry, zero rated]

BUCKINGHAMSHIRE NEWCOMER OF THE YEAR

Pebble Lane, Aylesbury HP20 2JH
AYLESBURY (0296) 86622 £21–£32

Jeremy Blake O'Connor was making quite a reputation at Cannizaro House in Wimbledon before he eschewed large hotel policies in favour of this small seventeeth-century, Grade II dining-room, formerly in the *Guide* under the ownership of the Cavaliers, who are now in London (see entry under Cavaliers). Copies of menus from the prestigious French restaurants where he has trained are framed on the wall. No surprise, then, that there is a strong French accent to the modern British style, as exemplified by a dariole of wild mushrooms in a mousse set on a light sauce, or a grilled fillet of beef in a cognac sauce with onions. Sauces tend to be unthickened or else deliberately rich and buttery. Game features strongly. A signature is a saddle of wild rabbit and jambonette of the leg with wild mushrooms and a Sauternes sauce. Sweets are modern French, in the sense of a fruit soup with sorbets or a pear spiked with pistachios and served with a pistachio ice-cream. The general enthusiasm shines through in care with details. The butter and English cheeses are local; breads are baked each day; the main menu, offering half a dozen choices per stage, is backed up by a set vegetarian menu or an eight-course surprise menu. A hundred wines open at a hefty £11 for the house claret, albeit an '82, but the quality of the list is found a little over this mark, where some exceptional wines are offered at flat-rate mark-ups, for instance, CELLARMAN'S CHOICE: Ch. Millet '78, £14.95. More reports, please.

CHEF/PROPRIETOR: Jeremy Blake O'Connor
OPEN: Tue to Sun, exc Sun D
MEALS: 12 to 2.15, 7.15 to 11
PRICES: Set L from £10.50 (£21), Sun L from £16 (£25), Set D from £18 (£32)
CARDS: Access, Amex, Diners, Visa
SEATS: 32. Private parties: 22 main room. Vegetarian meals. Children's helpings. Smart dress preferred. No cigars/pipes in dining-room. Wheelchair access. Music

Buckinghamshire Round-up

CHINESE: *China Diner*, 7 The Highway, Station Road, Beaconsfield (049 46 3345).
INDIAN: *Tandoori Nite*, 56 High Street, Great Missenden (024 06 5116).
RIVER SETTING: *Compleat Angler*, Marlow (06284 4444).
BAR MEALS: *Kings Head*, Ivinghoe, Nr Leighton Buzzard (0296 668264); *Plough*, Hyde Heath (0494 783163).

Reports on shops, cafés and farms are useful, as well as reports on restaurants.

Restaurants are checked every year and their entries rewritten. The restaurant scene changes very rapidly. Don't trust an out-of-date Guide.

BAKEWELL Derbyshire map 5

Green Apple [9/20]

Diamond Court, Water Street, Bakewell DE4 1EW
BAKEWELL (062 981) 4404 £9–£18

Bakewell is noted for its brownstone buildings, pudding, market and its antique shops; this small all-day restaurant currently represents the best of its cooking, since the Fischers have moved to Baslow. It looks something like a park pavilion, but gives on to a courtyard hung with flowers and reached up a curved, narrow passage. The food is English cooking at its best, with lots of flans, pies, tarts and puddings, and interesting good-value dishes like pork, apricot and raisin casserole, Mrs Beeton's lemon tart, Bakewell pudding, banoffi pie. Inexpensive counter-served lunches and well-reported afternoon teas give way to more formal dinners with loose-leaf, handwritten menus, built around rump and fillet steaks, salmon and local trout. Thirty wines from across the spectrum start at £5.50.

CHEFS: Roger Green, Nick Andrews and Pam Wain PROPRIETOR: Roger Green
OPEN: Winter: L Mon to Sat, D Thu to Sat; Summer: L all week, D Wed to Sat
CLOSED: mid-Jan to mid-Feb
MEALS: 12 to 2, 7 to 10
PRICES: L £5 (£9), D £11 (£18)
CARDS: Access, Diners, Visa
SEATS: 50. 6 tables outside. Private parties: 50 main room. Vegetarian meals. Children's helpings. No smoking. Wheelchair access. Music

BARNSTAPLE Devon map 1

▲ *Lynwood House* [12/20]

Bishops Tawton Road, Barnstaple EX32 9DZ
BARNSTAPLE (0271) 43695
on A377, between Barnstaple and Exeter £17–£19

In the 25 years the Roberts have been here, the hotel has turned full circle. Having converted it from a family hotel into a two-restaurant complex, they have now combined the two menus in the refurbished downstairs restaurant and opened a handful of executive bedrooms. The outside gives little indication of the elegant pink and grey dining-room with its huge ceiling fan, view over the countryside and fine furniture. Ruth Roberts' cooking is pitched deeply in a vein of French provincial ideas. Her chicken liver pâté, slightly pink, heavy on the brandy and cream, is now served (a development, this) with Cumberland sauce; duck is roasted and served inside a crêpe; and meals end with meringues, chocolate orange pot and clotted cream. Fish is always good. Supplies are first-rate, influencing the menu and saving it from from becoming static: a variety of salad includes locally picked leaves of 'wild garlic for shelled prawns turned in butter; a whole langoustine garnishes a pot of sole, salmon, scallops and prawns on rice. The cheeseboard, ever-changing, is usually in good condition and might include Marigold, a cow's-milk cheese flavoured with the flower petals, made locally almost exclusively for the restaurant. A shortish wine list includes ten half-bottles. House French is £5.95; CELLARMAN'S CHOICE: Pouilly Blanc-Fumé, Château des Nozet '85, £17.50 and Ch. Caronne St Gemme '79, £13.

CHEFS: Ruth and Adam Roberts PROPRIETORS: Mr and Mrs J.H. Roberts, Adam and Matthew Roberts
OPEN: all week
MEALS: 12 to 2, 7 to 10
PRICES: £14 (£19), Set L £12.50 (£17), Snacks £1.50
CARDS: Access, Visa
SEATS: 70. Private parties: 70 main room, 24,70 private rooms. Car-park, 25 places. Vegetarian meals. Children's helpings. Wheelchair access (also WC)
ACCOMMODATION: 3 rooms, all with bath/shower. B&B £47.50 to £67.50. No children under 12. Garden. Fishing. Golf. TV. Phone. Scenic. Confirm by 6

BARWICK Somerset map 2

▲ *Little Barwick House* [12/20]

Barwick, Yeovil BA22 9TD
YEOVIL (0935) 23902 £18

The Colleys' dower-house, which underwent a facelift last year, is a splendid hideaway. It could be advertised as, 'a tired businessman's convalescent home'. They combine the friendliness of a family house with a sense of professionalism. The cooking is mid-Channel, slightly old-fashioned, but built on fine ingredients – undyed haddock, fine cheese, good bakery. There is no shyness in offering steaks – with madeira, mushroom and cream sauce; plain; au poivre and with herb butter. Other meats and fish are simply sauced – lemon and parsley butter with sole meunière. Sweets are in the vein of Pavlova and brandy-snaps with caramel oranges. The lounge for drinks and coffee is filled with old, comfortable chairs and in winter there is a log fire. A short wine list has house French at £6.90; CELLARMAN'S CHOICE: St Aubin '85, £14.50; Penedés Torres, Gran Sangredetoro Reserva '82, £9.20.

CHEF: Veronica Colley PROPRIETORS: Mr and Mrs C. Colley
OPEN: Mon to Sat, D only
MEALS: 7 to 9.30
PRICES: Set D from £14.80 (£18). Service inc
CARDS: Access, Amex, Diners, Visa
SEATS: 30. Private parties: 50 main room. Car-park. Children's helpings. Music
ACCOMMODATION: 6 rooms, all with bath/shower. B&B to £57. Pets welcome. Garden. TV. Scenic. Doors close at 11 [GHG]

BATH Avon map 2

Clos du Roy [14/20]

7 Edgar Buildings, George Street, Bath BA1 2EH
BATH (0225) 64356 £17–£22

There is a *menu surprise*, but the *carte* may hold quite enough eye-openers: courgette and aubergine soup with baby squid? Timbale of langoustine and sweetbreads with basil sauce? If not all the extraordinary concoctions work, such as an imbalance in the mille-feuille of salmon, snails and chervil, others are based on sound modern principles, for instance a veal stock sauce slaked with smoked oysters for a mix of steamed turbot, prawns and scallops. Like most modern French cooking, the appeal is firstly to the eye and secondly to the palate, with artistic use of courgette flower and samphire. The approach does not rule out a piece of beef with a Meaux mustard sauce on a good-value lunch menu. Philippe Roy has been buying rare breeds of meat from Ann Petch's farm, hence pork may be from Gloucester Old Spot. The front of the house – a small neat corridor of a dining-room, unembellished except for a big mirror and a few paintings and dominated by the fine windows looking on to George Street – is run with confident ease by Emma Roy. One hundred wines open at £8.50, but it is a pedigree list, especially at the deeper end. CELLARMAN'S CHOICE: Hautes Côtes de Nuits '85, from Yves Chaley, £14.90.

CHEF: Philippe Roy PROPRIETORS: Philippe and Emma Roy
OPEN: Tue to Sat
CLOSED: 2 weeks Aug, 2 weeks Jan to Feb
MEALS: 12 to 2, 7 to 10.15
PRICES: £22 (£31), Set L £9.95 (£17) to £12.50 (£19), Set D £19.95 (£28) to £24.50 (£33). Service 12%
CARDS: Access, Amex, Diners, Visa
SEATS: 30. Private parties: 30 main room. Vegetarian meals

Moon and Sixpence [10/20]

6A Broad Street, Bath BA1 5LJ
BATH (0225) 60962 £9–£24

In a tiny cobbled courtyard off Broad Street on the site of the old Post Office is this light, airy bistro-cum-restaurant built of old yellow Bath stone. A big plus is the attractive conservatory and the courtyard patio with its huge tarpaulin, little fountain and fairy lights. The menu has been shortened to good effect. The cooking is modern, with a healthy emphasis on fish and interesting use of exotic fruits and spices. Marinated scallops are served with fresh asparagus, tomatoes and a ginger dressing; breast of duck appears as a warm salad with mango, or as a main course with lychees and a port and cranberry sauce. The style extends to the sweets which include home-made ice-creams in brandy-snap baskets, and caramel mousse with fresh orange and caramel sauce. At lunch-time, a buffet is served downstairs. Good, locally baked bread and cafetière coffee. The wine list has plenty of excellent drinking for under £10. House French is £5.50. CELLARMAN'S CHOICE: Sauvignon du Haut Poitou '84, £6.75; Ménétou-Salon, Domaine de Chatenoy '86, £9.95.

CHEF: Kevin King PROPRIETOR: Keith Waving
OPEN: all week
MEALS: 12 to 2.30 (2 Sun), 5.30 to 10.30 (11 Fri and Sat)
PRICES: £17 (£24), Set L £3.65 (£9) to £9.75 (£15)
CARDS: Access, Amex, Visa
SEATS: 70. 15 tables outside. Private parties: 25 main room, 25 private room. Vegetarian meals. Children's helpings. Music

Popjoy's [new owners, zero rated]

Beau Nash's House, Sawclose, Bath BA1 1EU
BATH (0225) 460494 £17–£28

Last year a change of ownership at Beau Nash's former home by the theatre led to exclusion from the *Guide*, and there are new owners again, but in practice the kitchen team under Mark Anton Edwards has survived and established a consistent reputation in the city. The menu is three courses, with soup and fish announced on the day. The style is a mix of modern British and *nouvelle* with some traditional touches, such as parsnip soup, and figgy pudding with apricots. There's a fondness for fruit and flowers: red bream comes with orange and avocado, brill is stuffed with pink grapefruit, and sweets, such as lemon sponge with vanilla ice, might be garnished with nasturtium leaves. Like many of the sauced dishes, farm-reared mallard with cassis and blackcurrant sauce has been a good main course. Meals begin with little cheese pastries; good coffee is taken in the upstairs lounge. A hundred and twenty wines extend up to Ch. Palmer '70 at £69, but there is a stimulating choice from the New World at the more affordable end, including no fewer than seven dessert wines, six by the glass, of which the cheapest, Brown Bros late-picked Muscat, looks a snip at £1.60. House Provence is £7.50. More reports, please.

CHEFS: Mark Anton Edwards and John Headley PROPRIETORS: Carrington Hotels
OPEN: Tue to Sat, exc Sat L
MEALS: 12 to 2, 6 to 10.30
PRICES: Set L £10.50 (£17) to £14 (£21), Set D £19.90 (£28). Minimum £10.50. Service 12.5% (parties of 5 and more). Licensed, also bring your own: corkage £7.50
CARDS: Access, Visa
SEATS: 36. Private parties: 36 main room. Vegetarian meals. No children under 10. No cigars/pipes in dining-room. Wheelchair access (1 step; also WC). Music. Air-conditioned

▲ *Priory Hotel* [13/20]

Weston Road, Bath BA1 2XT
BATH (0225) 331922 £18–£29

Before he sold up in the autumn of 1987, John Donnithorne had created a model of a small business hotel. The initiative has been taken on by Select Country Hotels, but Michael Collom has stayed on and has been cooking some excellent dishes. The hotel looks very old, but is Georgian neo-Gothic, built of mellow Bath stone with battlements and window mouldings. Behind is a sloping garden with immaculately cared-for borders and a heated swimming-pool. Inside is thickly carpeted and restful, painted in warm colours, with some semi-master paintings, ceiling friezes, and a variety of fabrics even on the walls. The décor in fact lends the feel of a country-house hotel. The menu offers nine dishes per course and makes a conscious effort to accommodate all tastes, including vegetarian. One can eat comparatively conservatively, such as steak with béarnaise, or gravlax, but on the whole the choice is modern, if non-revolutionary. Mousselines and pastry are much in evidence. But the strong, clear tastes of a kitchen on form are plain. Witness five peeled prawns served on home-made noodles with an aromatic garlic sauce and spiced with green peppercorns. Or, a brilliant modern British variation on an old French theme – plainly roasted guinea-fowl served as two legs and a breast with a grape and tarragon crumble ('halved green and purple grapes, skin on, in a mix of dried coconut, freshly dried breadcrumbs, freshly chopped tarragon') and a sauce of good stock, cream and a measure of calvados. Other dishes show the kind of slickness and polish that might be expected on the international circuit, such as a raspberry charlotte with a raspberry and lime flavoured sauce. Prices on the predominantly French wine list are not cheap. There is a good selection of mature claret, and a well-above-average selection of both red and white Burgundy, a nice clutch of '85 *crus* Beaujolais, good red Rhônes, mainly from Paul Jaboulet Aîné. Wines from the rest of the world are limited in number, but well chosen.

CHEF: Michael Collom PROPRIETORS: Select Country Hotels
OPEN: all week
MEALS: 12.30 to 2, 7 to 9.15
PRICES: £23 (£29), Set L from £12 (£18) to £17 (£23), Set D £20 (£26). Service inc
CARDS: Access, Amex, Carte Blanche, Diners, Visa
SEATS: 64. Private parties: 40 main room, 22 and 40 private rooms. Car-park, 25 places. Vegetarian meals. Children welcome. Smart dress preferred. No smoking in dining-room. Wheelchair access
ACCOMMODATION: 21 rooms, all with bath/shower. Rooms for disabled. B&B £60 to £99. Afternoon teas. Garden. Swimming-pool. TV. Phone. Scenic. Doors close at 12

Supannahong [9/20]

3 John Street, Bath BA1 2JL
BATH (0225) 448108 £10–£15

Suraphon Klinpikuln's Thai café is in a room above the crowded Salamander pub. Thai posters and tinkling music create the mood for some authentic cooking with a bias towards fish. Look for specialities such as gaeng keowan pla – monkfish with bamboo shoots, ginger, green chilli paste and coconut – or Black Tiger king prawns cooked with kaffir lime leaves and chilli-paste sauce. Chicken satay and stir-fried beef are well reported, too. Drink tea or Singha Thai beer.

CHEF/PROPRIETOR: Suraphon Klinpikuln
OPEN: Mon to Sat, exc Mon D and Sat L
CLOSED: 1 week at Christmas, at Easter and in summer; bank hols
MEALS: 12 to 2.30, 7 to 10.30
PRICES: £10 (£15), Set L £5.50 (£10)
CARD: Visa
SEATS: 28. Private parties: 28 main room. Vegetarian meals. Children's helpings. Music. Air-conditioned

CELLARMAN'S CHOICE *This is a wine recommended by the restaurateur which is usually more expensive than the house wine but is good value and fitting for the kind of food served.*

Tarts [10/20]

8 Pierrepont Place, Bath BA1 1JX
BATH (0225) 330280 and 330201 £19

An inconspicuous maze of cellars, with pine tables and Mozart, between the abbey and the station. The menu is bistro in style with an ambitious choice of blackboard specials. Soups are well reported: sorrel and watercress, carrot and orange, Stilton and onion. Some main courses rely on a lot of cream, as in pork Stroganoff or fillets of plaice with Noilly Prat and fennel sauce. Others, like marinated English lamb cutlets or vegetable feuilleté with fresh tomato sauce, bring lighter relief. Vegetables are *nouvelle* in style, but *ancien* in quantity. Half a dozen home-made desserts, notably ice-creams and treacle tart with lemon, to finish. The revamped list of around 50 wines has plenty of bottles under £10, including CELLARMAN'S CHOICE: Côtes de Duras Blanc, Domaine de Laulan '87 £8.60, and house wines by the glass.

CHEFS: Tom Bridgeman and Sue Cullinane PROPRIETOR: John Edwards
OPEN: Mon to Sat
MEALS: 12 to 2.30, 7 to 10.30
PRICES: £13 (£19), Snacks from £2.40
CARDS: Access, Visa
SEATS: 50. Private parties: 25 main room. Vegetarian meals. Children welcome. Music

Avon Round-up

VEGETARIAN: *Huckleberry's*, 34 Broad Street, Bath (0225 64876); *Cherries*, 122 St Michael's Hill, Bristol (0272 293675).
ITALIAN: *Pasta Galore*, 31 Barton Street, Bath (0225 63861).
CHINESE: *Orient Rendezvous*, Queens Road, Bristol (0272 745231).
BRUNCH: *Cafe de Daphne*, 12 York Road, Montpelier, Bristol (0272 426799).
INDIAN: *Rajpoot*, 4 Argyle Street, Bath (0225 66833).
JAPANESE: *Chikako's*, Theatre Royal, Sawclose, Bath (0225 64125).
SETTING: *Pump Room*, Stall Street, Bath (0225 444488).
BISTRO:*Flowers*, 27 Monmouth Street, Bath (0225 313774).
ROOMS: *Bath Lodge Hotel*, Norton St Philip, Bath (022 122 3737.

BEACONSFIELD Buckinghamshire map 3

Leigh House [10/20]

Wycombe End, Beaconsfield HP9 1XL
BEACONSFIELD (049 46) 6348 £17–£20

Generally acknowledged as offering an excellent example of Chinese food for Westerners. The 70-dish menu is based in the Northern tradition – paper-wrapped prawns, bang-bang chicken, Manchurian crispy lamb, crispy aromatic duck – and also has a strong emphasis on seafood – steamed sea-bass, steamed scallops, or lobster in either ginger or black-bean sauce. There are griddle dishes too. The set meal has a good balance. Presentation is keen. Wines start at £6 and are sensibly weighted towards whites, notably Loires and Burgundies.

CHEF/PROPRIETOR: S.W. Tang
OPEN: all week
MEALS: 12 to 2, 6 to 11
PRICES: £10 (£20), Set L and D from £11 (£17): Minimum £9. Service 10%
CARDS: Access, Amex, Diners, Visa
SEATS: 80. Private parties: 25 main room. Car-park, 8 places. Vegetarian meals. Children welcome. Wheelchair access. Music. Air-conditioned

BECKINGHAM Lincolnshire map 6

Black Swan [12/20]

Hillside, Beckingham LN5 0RF
FENTON CLAYPOLE (063 684) 474 £12–£19

That there is a need for good restaurants in this sparsely covered part of the map is borne out by the fact that tables at this four-year-old restaurant have to be booked ahead. Anton and Alison Indan keeps this operation small and buy to order. The set menu is short with two or three starters and main dishes split by a sorbet. Fruit and pastry figure prominently. Recommended dishes: guinea-fowl with an anise sauce; skate salad with bacon and garlic; French onion soup; chocolate Bavarian cream; the soufflés.
House wine £5.75.

CHEF: Anton Indans PROPRIETORS: Anton and Alison Indans
OPEN: Tue to Sat D, and Sun L
MEALS: 12 to 2, 7 to 10
PRICES: Set L £7.50 (£12) to £8.50 (£13), Set D £14.50 (£19)
CARDS: Access, Visa
SEATS: 30. Private parties: 24 main room, 12 and 24 private rooms. Car-park, 9 places. Children's helpings (L only). Wheelchair access (also WC). Music

BEDALE North Yorkshire map 7

Plummers [new entry, zero rated]

7 North End, Bedale DL8 1AF
BEDALE (0677) 23432 £21

The setting is a converted eighteenth-century building near the church in this rather austere Dales village. Downstairs is an informal wine bar with a blackboard menu; upstairs is like a huge raftered barn with well-spaced tables. The net is spread wide, taking in tapas and Thai-style scallops as well as sauté of wild mushrooms and steamed sea-trout with spinach. Wild pigeon terrine is rough, and looks almost like an extra-wholesome brawn; real mushroom soup is laced with madeira; hefty slices of local duckling are stuffed with apricots. Other details are equally impressive: mighty hunks of wholemeal bread, farmhouse cheeses, home-made petits fours, hot strong coffee. The wine list reflects North Country prices and has plenty of good value drinking for less than £10. House wines start at £5.50. CELLARMAN'S CHOICE: Touraine Sauvignon '86, £7.50; Côtes du Buzet '85, £8.90. More reports please.

CHEF: Chris Cope PROPRIETOR: Guy and Audrey Staniland
OPEN: Tue to Sat
MEALS: 12 to 2, 7 to 10
PRICES: £16 (£21)
CARDS: Access, Visa
SEATS: 40. Private parties: 12 main room, 40 private room. Vegetarian meals. No children under 10. Wheelchair access. Music

BERKHAMSTED Hertfordshire map 3

Cook's Delight [9/20]

360–364 High Street, Berkhamsted HP4 1HU
BERKHAMSTED (04427) 3584 £9–£18

A principled wholefood restaurant, part of a bookshop, health food and organic vegetables and wine complex, run by the poetic Tylers. 'Some will never realise and others do not care, but chemical-dependency vineyards are everywhere.' On Saturday nights the restaurant offers gourmet evenings, either South-East Asian vegetarian, seafood or Malaysian cuisine, occasionally involving turkey. Health is uppermost and organic produce used wherever possible. For the rest of the week, cheaper platters in the evenings while lunchtimes see salads, quiches and claypot dishes. No licence, take your own wine; corkage 50p per person.

CHEF: Khai-Eng Tyler PROPRIETORS: Rex and Khai-Eng Tyler
OPEN: Thu to Sun, exc Sun D
CLOSED: 2 weeks Aug
MEALS: 9 to 5, 7.30 to 9 (8 to 11 Sat)
PRICES: £7 (£9), Sat D £15.50 (£18). Unlicensed, but bring your own: corkage 50p
CARDS: Access, Visa
SEATS: 56. 4 tables outside. Private parties: 36 to 40 main room, 16 and 36 to 40 private rooms. Vegetarian meals. Children's helpings. No smoking. Wheelchair access. Music

Hertfordshire Round-up

SETTING: *Redcoats Farmhouse Hotel*, Little Wymondley, Nr Hitchen (0438 729500).
ITALIAN: *La Fiorentina*, 21-23 Lower Kings Road, Berkhamstead (044 27 3003).
GREEK: *Zeus*, 20b High Street, Baldock (0462 893620).
INDIAN: *Alban Tandoori*, 145 Victoria Street, St Albans (0727 62111).
BAR MEALS: *Garibaldi*, 61 Albert Street, St Albans (0727 55046); *George and Dragon*, High Street, Watton-at-Stone (0920 830285).

BERWICK-UPON-TWEED Northumberland map 7

Funnywayt'mekalivin [11/20]

53 West Street, Berwick-upon-Tweed TD15 1AS
BERWICK-UPON-TWEED (0289) 308827 and 86437 £6–£12

In a narrow, dull street between the Market Place and the Tweed, this small, multi-level restaurant still has a put-together feel from its former incarnation as a craft shop, albeit very warm. The furniture is a mixture, from Lloyd Loom chairs to wooden benches, dried flowers and grasses hang from the ceiling, and there are a great many knick-knacks. The whole is overseen by Elizabeth Middlemiss with great energy and enthusiasm, with an emphasis on fresh produce – free-range eggs, home-grown herbs, locally shot pigeon. The set dinner menu, which changes daily and is written on a blackboard, is limited but imaginative, and might take in celery and almond soup; pears and walnut in tarragon cream; smoked salmon in pastry; marinated herring; quail egg salad; fanned steak à la moutarde; Northumbrian roast beef; fish crumble pie. Typical sweets are rhubarb and ginger syllabub and tarte au citron; cheeses include Cotherstone and Bonchester. Strong coffee; hand-made chocolates. Service is swift and smiling. Simpler dishes at lunch-time. Unlicensed, but bring your own wine (corkage £1). In the evening, a no-choice aperitif, perhaps sherry, or a glass of Pineau des Charentes, is included in the set-meal price.

CHEF: Elizabeth Middlemiss PROPRIETORS: Mr and Mrs Middlemiss
OPEN: Mon to Wed L; Fri and Sat D
MEALS: 12 to 2, 8
PRICES: Set L from £5 (£6), Set D £12.50 (£13). Service inc. Unlicensed, but bring your own: corkage £1
SEATS: 25. Private parties: 25 main room. Vegetarian meals. Children restricted. No smoking. Wheelchair access. Music. One sitting at D

Northumberland Round-up

AFTERNOON TEAS: *Seafarers*, Main Street, Seahouses (0665 720931).
WINE BAR: *Scotsgate*, 1 Sidey Court, Berwick-upon-Tweed (0289 302621).
BAR MEALS: *Masons Arms*, Stamford Cott, Stamford, Nr Pennington, Alnwick (0665 77275).
INEXPENSIVE: *Saddle Hotel*, 24-25 Northumberland Street, Alnmouth (0665 830476).

BEXHILL ON SEA East Sussex — map 3

Lychgates [new entry, zero rated]

5A Church Street, Old Town, Bexhill-on-Sea TN40 2HE
BEXHILL (0424) 212193 — £12–£16

In one of the few remaining Sussex Wealden houses in old Bexhill, on the west side of town. Service by Mrs Tyson is relaxed, and the dining-room's rough-papered walls and floral curtains add to the homely feel. John Tyson came from the Dorchester in 1986 and cooks a monthly-changing fixed-price menu, drawing on French, Italian and British sources, avoiding both the classic repertoire and showmanship. Venison is served with celery and walnut sauce, avocado with a blackcurrant and cassis dressing, and monkfish with garlic mayonnaise. The underlying spirit is modern British, and there seems no end to the combinations – duck breast with rhubarb, beetroot and turnip soup, and clementines in ginger – although they rub shoulders with

This symbol is awarded only to restaurants with outstanding wine cellars.

simpler chicken liver pancake, braised ox-tail, lamb with a port sauce. The 30-strong French wine list starts with house wine at £6.50. CELLARMAN'S CHOICE: Pouilly Blanc Fumé, Les Loges '87, £14.25; Beaujolais Villages, Château du Carras '86, £8.50. More reports, please.

CHEF: John Tyson PROPRIETORS: John and Sue Tyson
OPEN: Tue to Sat (Sat L bookings only)
MEALS: 12.30 to 2, 7.15 to 10.30
PRICES: Set L £7.25 (£12), Set D from £11.50 (£16)
CARDS: Access, Visa
SEATS: 26. Private parties: 18 main room. Vegetarian meals. Children's helpings. No children under 8 at D. Wheelchair access

BIDDENDEN Kent map 3

Three Chimneys [9/20]

Biddenden, Ashford TN27 8HA
BIDDENDEN (0580) 291472 £11

One of a dying breed of traditional country pubs that haven't been 'Dralonised'. Lots of rickety wooden chairs and tables, odd corners, nooks and crannies, draughts here and there where the fire doesn't get to. The garden has developed over the years, too. The menu, chalked up on a blackboard, gives four choices for each course, all real food well cooked, for instance spinach and pork terrine, Stilton and mint soup, duck and pheasant casserole, aubergine and tomato pie. Puddings, served with Jersey cream, might be nutty treacle tart, Pavlova, cinnamon cheesecake, and sugar plum flan. House French on a basic list is £4.95, or try one of the real ales from Adnams, Harvey, Marston and Hook Norton. Or Biddenden cider, of course.

CHEFS: Audrey Morris and Janet Croucher PROPRIETORS: Christopher and Pippa Sayers
OPEN: all week
CLOSED: 25 and 26 Dec
MEALS: 11.30 to 2 (12 to 1.30 Sun), 6.30 (7 Sun) to 10
PRICES: £8 (£11), Snacks from £1.55. Service inc
SEATS: 100. 40 tables outside. Private parties: 40 main room. Car-park, 50 places. Vegetarian meals

BILBROUGH North Yorkshire map 5

▲ *Bilbrough Manor* [11/20]

Bilbrough Y02 3PH
TADCASTER (0937) 834002
m off A64, between Tadcaster and York £15–£33

In a hundred acres of farm and woodland, originally built by Guy Thomas Fairfax in 1901, then converted into four houses, and now back as one hotel. The memory of the Fairfax family is perpetuated through the coat of arms which is displayed throughout the house, and on the cover of the menu. The restaurant has dark wood panelling and thick, deep maroon curtains. The china is Wedgwood; the staff are neatly dressed in black and white. Into this environment of calm, enter Idris Caldora, a chef embarked on an odyssey of elaborate flavours and combinations which can sometimes be supremely successful. Little is left alone. Take this starter: three thick slices of a terrine with Dover sole just cooked tender wrapped around king prawn is, seasoned and textured with pistachio nuts and served with a pale-pink thin sauce américaine. This is almost Escoffian in its complexity. Take another dish, this time removed from under a flash of salvers at the table: fillet of beef topped with a slice of foie gras and a mousse of chicken, set in a madeira sauce. The presentation reaches its peak with the sweets, notably the 'assiette d'entremets du Manoir' being five miniature sweets together – a slice of three-chocolate cake; strawberry tart; blackberry mousse; a brandy-snap filled with apricot ice-cream; and sliced fruits – and all of those early in March in defiance of the seasons. Coffee is taken in the library. Breakfasts re-affirm the intention to make this one of the premier country-house hotels in the North of England: brioche, eggs Benedict, omelette Arnold Bennett, kedgeree. On Saturday nights a second, less attractive dining-room is pressed into service and it is worth asking, when booking, for the panelled room. Wines are reliable to very good and predominantly French. Burgundies include some from excellent growers, and there are some very good Germans and four well-chosen English wines. Sweet wines are limited: Pascal's Muscat de Beaumes de Venise at '13.65, a rare Mosel Beerenauslese of the outstanding '76 vintage at £24, and Asti Spumanti Martini at £9.

CHEF: Idris Caldora PROPRIETORS: Mr and Mrs Colin C. Bell
OPEN: all week
MEALS: 12 to 1.45, 7 to 9.30
PRICES: £30 (£40), Set L £10 (£15), Set D from £17.50 (£24) to £26 (£33). Minimum £17.50
CARDS: Access, Amex, Diners, Visa
SEATS: 60. Private parties: 30 main room, 20 private room. Car-park, 50 places. Vegetarian meals. No children under 12. Jacket and tie. No smoking in the dining-room. Wheelchair access (also WC). Music
ACCOMMODATION: 12 rooms, all with bath/shower. B&B £75 to £80. No children under 12. Afternoon teas. Garden. TV. Phone. Scenic [GHG]

BIRDLIP Gloucestershire map 2

▲ *Kingshead House* [10/20]

Birdlip GL4 8JH
GLOUCESTER (0452) 862299 £13–£20

The Knocks' eighteenth-century coaching-inn stands at the top of the hill, almost opposite the Royal George pub in one of the highest villages in Gloucestershire. The building, with its oak beams and log fires, is elegant but informal and service is urbane to match the mood. The *carte* has been dropped in favour of set-price menus only, mixing French and English, from salmon in puff pastry or sea-trout with watercress to roast loin of pork with orange sauce or guinea-fowl in white wine with lemon sauce and asparagus. There is always something for vegetarians, such as the interesting-sounding hot mousse of black and white mushrooms, surrounded by oyster mushrooms. Guards' pudding with raspberry sauce is one of the typically good sweets. Home-made truffles and petits fours. House French £6.25; CELLARMAN'S CHOICE: Soave, Costeggiola '85, £9.25; St Amour cru Beaujolais '85, £10.50.

CHEF: Judy Knock PROPRIETORS: Warren and Judy Knock
OPEN: Tue to Sun, exc Sat L and Sun D
MEALS: 12.15 to 2.15 (1.45 Sun), 7.15 to 10
PRICES: Set L from £8.50 (£13), Set D from £15 (£20), Snacks from £2.25
CARDS: Access, Amex, Diners, Visa
SEATS: 32. 2 tables outside. Private parties: 36 main room. Car-park, 12 places. Vegetarian meals. Children's helpings. Wheelchair access (also WC). Music
ACCOMMODATION: 1 room, with bath/shower. B&B £28 to £35. Garden. Scenic. Doors close at 12. Confirm by 6

BIRKENHEAD Merseyside map 5

Beadles [10/20]

15 Rosemount, Oxton, Birkenhead L43 5SG
051-653 9010 £18

The Gotts' long-standing restaurant still has a strong French accent. For the past eleven years they have been changing their menus every month, using fresh ingredients and making their sauces from reduced stocks thickened with butter. The menu has some interesting, but not overly contrived dishes, such as baked avocado with a quails egg in the centre, home-made gnocchi with pesto, and fillets of brill on a bed of lentils with saffron and ginger sauce. Vegetables are good. Roy Gott talks his way through a short, well selected wine list, including house French at £5 and CELLARMAN'S CHOICE: Morgon, Domaine les Pillets '86, £8.50.

CHEF: Bea Gott PROPRIETORS: Roy and Bea Gott
OPEN: Tue to Sat, D only
CLOSED: Aug
MEALS: 7.30 to 9
PRICES: £12 (£18)
SEATS: 34. Private parties: 30 main room. Vegetarian meals. Children welcome. Wheelchair access (1 step). Music

BIRMINGHAM West Midlands map 5

Adil [9/20]

148–150 Stoney Lane, Sparkbrook, B11 8AJ
021-449 0335 £7

Sparkhill and Sparkbrook have the biggest concentration of Indian cafés and sweet-centres in Birmingham. A few are still as they were 10 years ago – meeting-places for local Asians, with a modest choice of savoury snacks and sweetmeats. Others have moved on and developed as balti houses, specialising in meat, fish and vegetables cooked in cast-iron Kashmiri pans like blackened woks. Like football teams, all have their partisan followers. The Adil now attracts customers from way beyond the neighbourhood and is the fashionable choice for Westerners. Despite this, it has not compromised on flavours or ingredients. By-pass the microwaved starters and tandooris and concentrate on the excellent baltis – particularly those with fresh vegetables, such as mustard leaf and tinda. Huge steaming hot roti are exceptional and massive 'large' nans provide enough bread for four people. Spartan décor, minimal use of cutlery. Unlicensed, but there's an off-licence next door. Adil 2, at 130 Stoney Lane is a smaller off-shoot with a shorter menu.

CHEF: Mr Ashraf PROPRIETOR: Mr Arif
OPEN: all week
MEALS: noon to midnight
PRICES: £4 (£7). Unlicensed, but bring you own: no corkage
CARDS: Access, Visa
SEATS: 70. Private parties: 50 private room. Vegetarian meals. Children welcome

Los Andes [10/20]

806 Bristol Road, Selly Oak B29 6BD
021-471 3577 £12–£15

The most genuine Latin American food in the country is served in this cooperatively run *cantina* opposite a new, red-brick Sainsbury. Inside, the plain dining-room is bedecked with flutes, rugs, tapestries and paintings, and tables are closely packed. The cooking matches the décor, offering authentic, peasant-style dishes prepared with gusto. Ceviche, chilli and tacos are above average, but the menu goes far beyond the clichés. From Ecuador there is pork loin casseroled with orange juice and hot pepper sauce, from Brazil comes fish cooked with wine in a sauce of tomato, prawns, lemon and coconut milk. Asado is Chilean roast beef with chillies and coriander, aji de gallina is Peruvian-style chicken in a tomato and pepper sauce. On Friday and Saturday there's also a South American version of paella. Drink Chilean wine or strong Mexican Bohemia beer. Live music on Tuesdays.

CHEFS: Freddy Aburto, Alejandro Lira and Roque Mella PROPRIETORS: Freddy Aburto, Greg Grandon and Roque Mella
OPEN: all week, exc Sun
MEALS: 12 to 2, 7 to 11.30
PRICES: £10 (£15), Set L and D from £8 (£12)
CARDS: Access, Amex, Diners
SEATS: 66. Private parties: 80 main room. Vegetarian meals. Children's helpings. Music

Le Biarritz [11/20]

148–149 Bromsgrove Street, B5 6RG
021-622 1989 £12–£29

The greeting in this French restaurant, hard by Birmingham's Chinatown, is Eine Kleine Nachtmusik and pink table-cloths and napkins; but in an area where this kind of cooking is at a premium, it stands out. Carl Timms' continuing presence ensures the importance of fish: salmon with sorrel or lime sauce; goujons of sole; lobster Thermidor; monkfish with basil. A *menu dégustation* typically contains a Mediterranean fish soup, with fennel, garlic croûtons and rouille; hot goats' cheese in flaky pastry; a main fish dish that changes daily; and strawberries in a Grand Marnier sabayon. Other dishes mentioned include a 'delicately flavoured' courgette soup; filet de boeuf. Desserts could be profiteroles with ice-cream and hot chocolate, or hazelnut parfait. Eighty wines are almost exclusively French, with house wine from Georges Duboeuf at £6.90. CELLARMAN'S CHOICE: Mâcon-Fuissé '86, £12.90.

CHEF: Carl Timms PROPRIETOR: Andrea Lo Coco
OPEN: Mon to Sat, exc Sat L
CLOSED: 25 Dec to 9 Jan
MEALS: 12 to 2, 7 to 10.30
PRICES: £20 (£29), Set L £7.50 (£12), Set D £19 (£25). Service 10%
CARDS: Access, Amex, Diners, Visa
SEATS: 40. Private parties: 50 main room. Car-park, 10 places. Vegetarian meals. Children's helpings. Smart dress preferred. Wheelchair access. Music. Air-conditioned

Chung Ying [11/20]

16–18 Wrottesley Street, B5 4RT
021-622 5669 and 1793 £10–£21

With the opening of its new branch, the Chung Ying Garden (see entry), the Chung Ying may have lost its pole position on the Midlands grid of Chinese restaurants, but it is nevertheless a serious contender, and not even an aberration with the environmental health offices suggests otherwise. The décor is untypical of Chinese restaurants, having been glamorised, probably with a view to attracting theatre-goers from the nearby Hippodrome. The menu is straight from the shoulder Cantonese – 310 dishes long. Some dim-sum items are better than in Hong Kong. The chef is very generous with prawns and applies them well. Difficult dishes are not shirked: prawn mousse is used as a stuffing for intestines; generally, ducks used for pot roasts are roast ducks, but here fresh ducks are used. One-plate meals of rice and noodles are inexpensive. Sundays are very crowded at lunch. House wine on a 40-strong list is £5.80, or try a Chinese red or white at £6.80.

CHEF/PROPRIETOR: Siu Chung Wong
OPEN: all week
MEALS: noon to midnight
PRICES: £15 (£21), Set L £5 (£10) to £10 (£15), Set D £7 (£12) to £12 (£17). Service 10%
CARDS: Access, Amex, Diners, Visa
SEATS: 200. Private parties: 200 main room, 100 private room. Car-park, 10 places. Vegetarian meals. Children welcome. Smart dress preferred. Music. Air-conditioned

Chung Ying Garden [13/20]

17 Thorp Street, B5 4AT
021-666 6622 £14–£23

The new branch of the Chung Ying is a massive brick warehouse conversion (used as a drill-hall in the war), almost opposite Forbidden City (which has new owners) on the fringes of Chinatown, hard by the Hippodrome. More luxurious and spacious than the original, with thick carpets, huge marbled pillars and murals covering the vast wallspace. The effect is comfortable, accessible, reassuring. The three-hundred dish menu from the original Chung Ying is virtually intact – dim-sum, a daunting choice of one-plate meals, all the Cantonese classics – but there's an extra dimension in extended vegetarian and sizzling dishes, and the page of chef's specialities. From the first months it is plain that both the dim-sum and the roasting are as good as anywhere in the UK. Other dishes might be helped by the use of better stocks, the blandness that creeps in being the more noticeable for the sheer excellence elsewhere. On the plus side, portions are large for the prices, and larger than at London's smarter Chinese equivalents; MSG is used sparingly; there is an unusually wide variety of Chinese vegetables. Some dishes – baked crab with ginger and spring onion, an excellent stir-fry of giant clam with shrimp roe – set high standards, clearly meriting a rating of 14 or 15/20. Other dishes that underwrite the assumption of such pedigree are mixed seafood and bean curd soup; braised noodles with barbecued pork, ginger and spring onion; congee with salted pork and green eggs (Sundays only); steamed scallops stuffed with minced prawn; Chung Ying special rice. But this level has not been reached consistently through the menu; the wok chefs in particular need to attend to details as regards flavour, quality of ingredients and finishing of sauces in order to lift the cuisine to the tradition of the giant Hong Kong and Canton restaurants. Nevertheless, this is a major new restaurant capable of setting standards for Chinese cookery. It has cut its teeth in a tougher restaurant environment than either the Manchester or London Chinese have had to do. In terms of service and décor it scores highly. Forty wines (house French £6.40), free tea.

CHEF/PROPRIETOR: Sui Chung Wong
OPEN: all week
MEALS: noon to 11.45 (11 Sun)
PRICES: £13 (£23), Set L and D from £8.50 (£14). Service 10%
CARDS: Access, Amex, Diners, Visa
SEATS: 300. Private parties: 100 main room; 50, 100 private rooms. Vegetarian meals. Children welcome. Wheelchair access (side entrance; also WC). Music. Air-conditioned

Days of the Raj [11/20]

51 Dale End, B4 7LN
021-236 0445 £11–£16

One of the top three Indian restaurants in Birmingham, tucked away beneath the back of Tesco, not far from the Law Courts. Inside is a tendency towards Raj overkill in the faded photos of tiger hunts and the gents loo labelled 'Officers'. A young team in the kitchen produces an up-market version of North Indian and Punjabi cooking with some original touches. The subtlety and freshness shows in the tandooris and tikkas. Otherwise there are thickly spiced curries such as rogan josh and chicken pasanda. Basmati rice is first-rate and the full range of breads, from rotai to bhatura, are well handled. Colourful Indian sweets include many kinds of barfi. Lunch is an excellent-

All inspections are carried out anonymously.

value hot buffet. The pace is slow and leisurely, service is courteous and civilised. Short, interesting wine list with some bottles from lesser French and German vineyards.

CHEFS: Rashpal Sunner and Jagtar Singh PROPRIETORS: Balbir Singh and P.S. Kulair
OPEN: all week, exc Sat and Sun L
MEALS: 12 to 2.30, 7 to 11.30 (6 Fri and Sat)
PRICES: £11 (£16), Set L £5.95 (£11). Minimum £6.50.
CARDS: Access, Amex, Diners, Visa
SEATS: 120. Private parties: 100 main room, 325 and 30 private rooms. Vegetarian meals. Children's helpings (with prior notice). Smart dress preferred. Wheelchair access (also WC). Music. Air-conditioned

Henry Wong [10/20]

283 High Street, Harborne, B17 9QH
021-427 9799 £10–£16

The former Municipal Bank on Harborne High Street is now one of the most popular Chinese restaurants in Birmingham. The cooking is westernised Cantonese, which appeals, but lacks the pungency and power of the best places in the city's Chinatown. It has all the trappings that Westerners expect from new Chinese restaurants: tables set with beige napkins in wine glasses, polite service and reassuring cleanliness. Dishes come with spectacular horticultural garnishes, designed to impress. Specialities include deep-fried dim-sum to start, and steamed seafood with black-bean sauce. Wine prices start at £5.50.

CHEF: Steven Yeung PROPRIETORS: Henry Wong and Steven Yeung
OPEN: Mon to Sat
MEALS: 12 to 2, 5.30 to 11 (11.30 Fri and Sat)
PRICES: £8 (£16), Set L from £5.50 (£10), Set D from £8.50 (£13). Service 10% set
CARDS: Access, Amex, Diners, Visa
SEATS: 120. Private parties: 100 main room, 20 private room. Vegetarian meals. Wheelchair access (also WC). Music

Henry's [10/20]

27 St Pauls Square, B3 1RB
021-200 1136 £10–£18

The younger brother of Henry Wong's in Harborne, this purpose-built creamy-white restaurant is in a prime site just by the old jewellery quarter of the city. Development is imminent in this area. The décor is fashionably stylish and so is the menu, with satays, sizzling dishes and birds' nests. Starters include excellent stuffed crab claws, and deep-fried dim-sum, while crispy duck – either stuffed or served with plum sauce – is one of the best main dishes. Steamed seafood with black-bean sauce is a speciality. Seems to have the edge on the original branch. House wine is £5.50.

'I've just invented a new rule: if the menu is larger than your table, leave at once.'
On eating in Scotland

CHEF: C.W. Choi PROPRIETORS: H.Y.W. Wong and C.W. Choi
OPEN: Mon to Sat
CLOSED: one week Aug
MEALS: 12 to 2, 6 to 11 (11.30 Sat)
PRICES: £9 (£18), Set L from £5.50 (£10), Set D from £8.50 (£13). Service 10% Set
CARDS: Access, Amex, Diners, Visa
SEATS: 80. Vegetarian meals. Children welcome. Music

Ho Tung [11/20]

308 Bull Ring Centre, B5 4PY
021-643 0033 and 0183 £5–£22

This city-centre Chinese restaurant by the Bull Ring has been through several incarnations since the 1960s. Currently it is one of the most popular in town, drawing both Chinese and Midlanders. Service has improved of late. The kitchen delivers excellent one-plate rice and noodle dishes with good roast meats; there are also authentic Cantonese casseroles and hot-pots. Freshly prepared dim-sum are a better bet than the westernised set lunches. The upstairs dining-room is a collage of flashing fairy lights, lacquered screens and spherical lampshades in wooden lattice-work cages.

CHEF: Winston Cheng PROPRIETOR: Tony Ho
OPEN: all week, exc Sat L and Sun L
MEALS: noon to midnight
PRICES: £14 (£22), Set L £1.50 (£5) to £3 (£7), Set D £4.95 (£9) to £14 (£19). Service 10%
CARDS: Access, Amex, Diners, Visa
SEATS: 160. Private parties: 250 main room, 90 private room. Car-park, 100 places. Vegetarian meals. Children welcome. Wheelchair access (also WC). Music. Air-conditioned

Loon Fung [10/20]

37–41 Pershore Street, B5 4BS
021-622 7395 and 5056 £20

The elegant pink and grey dining-room with its technicolour dragons on one wall and elaborately folded napkins is geared to Westerners, but the long menu of over 200 dishes is nearer to the earthy Cantonese style of the original Chung Ying across the road. There's a good choice of one-plate meals and the list of 30 dim-sum has its own chef, who delivers roast suckling pig on Sundays. From the full menu there are recommendations for lemon chicken, stir-fried beef with ginger, and king prawns with cashews.

CHEF: P. Li and S. Law PROPRIETOR: Y.C. Cheung
OPEN: all week
MEALS: noon to midnight
PRICES: £12 (£20). Service 10%
CARDS: Access, Amex, Diners, Visa
SEATS: 250. Private parties: 100 main room, 100 private room. Car-park, 15 places. Vegetarian meals. Children welcome. Smart dress preferred. Wheelchair access (also WC). Music. Air-conditioned

Maharaja [10/20]

23–25 Hurst Street, B5 4AS
021-622 2641 £10–£15

Still one of the best-loved and most popular Indian restaurants in Birmingham, partly because it is only a few doors from the Hippodrome. It gets busy before and after the shows. This is a curry-house with some aspirations, and the revamped décor is nearer Indian new-wave than English dining-room. The menu is quite short and North Indian in style, steering clear of the clichés. Curries are the kitchen's forte – rogan josh and chicken bhuna masala are thick with freshly ground spices and skilfully handled. Rice and breads are genuine too. Service is as gracious as ever. House French is £5.50, alternatively drink lager.

CHEF: Bhupinder Waraich PROPRIETOR: N.S. Batt
OPEN: Mon to Sat
MEALS: 12 to 2.30, 6 to 11.30
PRICES: £8 (£15), Set L £5.50 (£10) to £7.50 (£13), Set D £6.50 (£11) to £10 (£15). Service 10%
CARDS: Access, Amex, Diners, Visa
SEATS: 65. Private parties: 30 main room. Vegetarian meals. Children welcome. Wheelchair access. Music. Air-conditioned

Plaka [9/20]

204 Lightwoods Road, Warley B67 5AZ
021-429 4862 £17

For many years this was one of the best known tavernas in Birmingham city centre. In 1987 it moved lock, stock and barrel to a converted corner shop in Warley. The new premises are brighter than before, otherwise it is the same familiar mixture of authentic Greek/Cypriot food: good-value meze, dips, kebabs and casseroles such as arni (baked lamb with herbs served with savoury potatoes), stifado, aubergine and potato. House French is £4.50, otherwise drink retsina at £5.25 or Amalia at £5.95.

CHEFS: Gareth Davies and Moosavi-Shendi PROPRIETORS: Judevale Ltd
OPEN: Mon to Sat, D only
MEALS: 6.30 to 12
PRICES: £11 (£17). Cover 25p
CARDS: Access, Visa
SEATS: 50. 5 tables outside. Private parties: 50 main room. Vegetarian meals. Children's helpings. Music. Air-conditioned

Rajdoot [10/20]

12–22 Albert Street, Birmingham B4 7UD
021-643 8805 and 8749 £11–£26

Still one of Birmingham's favourite restaurants, dispensing good North Indian and Punjabi cooking in an ornate extravagant setting of sculpted figurines, carvings, brasswork, hanging bells and finger cymbals. Bowls of roasted chickpeas and sevra are laid out on low brass tables in the dimly lit bar area. The menu has decent tandooris – including fish and kidney – as well as carefully spiced specialities, such as jeera chicken pointed up with cumin seeds and quail makhani cooked with butter, tomatoes and cream. Vegetables include a pulsy brinjal bhaji, and paneer is made on the premises. Good breads. Service is by a team of young men, plus a venerable head waiter complete with full raj turban and sashes. Drink lager or the house wine.

CHEF: B. Mali PROPRIETOR: D.R. Sarda
OPEN: all week, exc Sun L
MEALS: 12 to 2.15, 6.30 to 11.30
PRICES: £13 (£26), Set L £6 (£11), Set D £10.50 (£16) to £12.50 (£18). Cover 50p. Minimum £6.50. Service 12.5%
CARDS: Access, Amex, Carte Blanche, Diners, Visa
SEATS: 80. Private parties: 40 main room. Vegetarian meals. Children welcome. Wheelchair access (2 steps; also WC). Music. Air-conditioned

Sloans [12/20]

27–29 Chad Square, Hawthorne Road, Edgbaston B15 3TQ
021-455 6697 £17–£27

The décor is cool pink and grey with green settees. Chef/proprietor Roger Narbett serves a 'luncheon menu rapide', popular for business entertaining, offering as a starter rillettes of smoked and fresh salmon, or smoked haddock in a white wine and cream sauce, and as main courses the likes of entrecôte of beef in a mustard sauce, or English lamb flavoured with rosemary. Dinners are more complex: rabbit and pork terrine with pistachios and mushrooms in Cumberland sauce; beef fillet pan-fried with artichoke, onion and horseradish. Desserts include fruit sorbets, crème brûlée, and a hot honey and lime soufflé. Cheeses are English and French, though the Reblochon has been hard and the Coulommiers dry. Not so well attended in the evening, even Saturdays. Commendably, the hundred-strong wine list sports over a dozen half-bottles and eight house wines, the latter starting at £8, and all named as CELLARMAN'S CHOICE. There has been a loose approach to vintages, however.

CHEF: Roger Narbett PROPRIETORS: W.J. and Roger Narbett
OPEN: all week, exc Sat L and Sun D
CLOSED: bank hols and 1 week from 1 Jan
MEALS: 12 to 2, 7 to 10
PRICES: £19 (£27), Set L £11.50 (£17)
CARDS: Access, Amex, Diners, Visa
SEATS: 60. Private parties: 30 main room. Car-park, 60 places. Children welcome. Smart dress preferred. Wheelchair access (1 step; also WC). Music. Air-conditioned

'We now think we have a source of pork and bacon which is produced traditionally, so more pork may be used in future. I think it would be a good thing if all chefs took a stand against pork full of hormones and produced from breeding sows that are kept tethered and confined and forced to have litter after litter until they are worn out.' Dorset restaurateur

Thai Paradise [10/20]

31 Paradise Circus B1 2BJ
021-643 5523 £9–£19

Not far from the Town Hall, but it can be difficult to find, not being part of the Paradise Circus complex, but in an arcade of shops and offices further along. Inside is a bright, cheerful oriental-occidental mix, with Thai fabric pictures on the wall, caged exotic birds, and Thai-dressed waitresses. The menu is extremely broad, though there is a way in, via the set menus. A set lunch might include pork satay, Thai chicken curry in coconut milk and bamboo shoots, or stir-fried beef with chillies, followed by ice-cream and lychees. The main menu offers substantial, flavoursome clear soups: chicken with lime leaves and lemon-grass; king prawn with the addition of chilli. The main dishes show the same variety of seasoning – crab claws with basil leaves and chillies; sweet-and-sour Thai fish; pork and noodles in lemon-grass; squid in onion sauce. House wine is £6, or drink Thai Singha beer.

CHEF: Surachet Lathe PROPRIETORS: Preecha and Robert Lathe
OPEN: Mon to Sat, exc Sat L
MEALS: 12 to 3, 6 to 12 (1am Fri and Sat)
PRICES: £11 (£19), Set L £4.95 (£9). Service 10%
CARDS: Access, Amex, Diners, Visa
SEATS: 60. Private parties: 25 main room. Vegetarian meals. Children's helpings. Smart dress preferred. Wheelchair access. Music. Air-conditioned

West Midlands Round-up
INDONESIAN: *Satay House*, 72 Hurst Street, Birmingham (021-622 1313).
SPANISH: *Casa Paco*, 7 Fletchers Walk, Paradise Place, Birmingham (021-233 1533).
VEGETARIAN: *Wild Oats*, 5 Raddlebarn Road, Selly Oak, Birmingham (021-471 2459).
CARIBBEAN: *Rustie's Caribbean*, 69 Hurst Street, Birmingham (021-622 4137).
INDIAN: *Milan* (takeaway), 191 Stoney Lane, Sparkhill Birmingham (021-449 1617); *Milan*(takeaway), 238 Soho Road, Handsworth, Birmingham (021-551 5239); *Indus Tandoori*, 11 Kings Road, Sutton Coldfield (021-355 5089); *Friends Corner*, Foleshill Road, Coventry (0203 686688/689962); *Bilash*, 2 Cheapside, Wolverhampton (0902 27762).
FRENCH: *French Connection* 1 & 3 Coventry Street, Stourbridge, (0384 390940).
FRENCH VEGETARIAN: *La Santé*, 182-184 High Street, Harborne (021-426 4133).

BIRTLE Greater Manchester map 5

▲ *Normandie* [new chef, zero rated]

Elbut Lane, Birtle BL9 6UT
061-764 3869 and 1170
off B6222 Rochdale Old Road £21–£30

Since the Champeau brothers sold up, this extended pub at the top of a hill has had a chequered history, with a succession of chefs and managers. The latest is Pascal Pommier, who, at 22, was listed in the *Guide* at the Mill Hotel in Kingham. He takes on a modern French menu with serious aspirations – pithivier of snails; mille-feuille of salmon and scallops with a herb and horseradish sauce. The good-value *menu gourmand* has a between-course sorbet and salad of tiny Parisian sausages. A hundred wines span the world from Chile to Australia. House French from Duboeuf is £6.75. More reports, please.

CHEF: Pascal Pommier PROPRIETORS: Gillian and Max Moussa
OPEN: Mon to Sat, exc Sat L
CLOSED: 26 Dec to first Sun in Jan, exc New Year's Eve
MEALS: 12 to 2, 7 to 9.30
PRICES: £23 (£30), Set D £16.50 (£21). Service inc Set only
CARDS: Access, Amex, Diners, Visa
SEATS: 60. Private parties: 70 main room. Car-park, 60 places. Vegetarian meals. Children's helpings. Smart dress preferred. No cigars/pipes in dining-room. Wheelchair access (also WC). Music
ACCOMMODATION: 24 rooms, all with bath/shower. Rooms for disabled. Lift. B&B £45 to £55. Baby facilities. Pets welcome. TV. Phone

BISHOPS CLEEVE Gloucestershire map 2

▲ *Cleeveway House* [11/20]

10 YEARS

Bishop's Cleeve GL52 4SA
BISHOP'S CLEEVE (024 267) 2585
3m N of Cheltenham on A435 £21

Twenty years of continuous *Guide* entries testify to the standards at this gracious country-house hotel and restaurant which stands in five acres by the Cheltenham to Evesham road. Chef/patron John Marfell offers an extensive menu of a dozen choices per course, taking in spare ribs with plum sauce, saddle of hare with grapes and madeira, and trout stuffed with walnuts, spinach and shallots served with a lemon sauce. There is also a cold table. Everything, down to the ice-creams and sorbets, is home made. A hundred wines concentrate on France with some early vintages which put up the prices, but the Loire wines open at £5.60 and there is a fair choice under £15.

CHEF/PROPRIETOR: John Marfell
OPEN: Mon to Sat, exc Mon L
CLOSED: 1 week after Christmas, Good Friday and all bank hols
MEALS: 12 to 1.45, 7 to 9.45
PRICES: £14 (£21)
SEATS: 38. Private parties: 10 main room. Car-park, 50 places. Vegetarian meals. Children's helpings. No cigars/pipes in dining-room. Wheelchair access (also WC). Air-conditioned
ACCOMMODATION: 3 rooms, all with bath/shower. B&B £28.50 to £45. Children welcome. Baby facilities. Pets welcome. Afternoon teas. Garden. Air-conditioning. TV. Scenic. Doors close at 1

Report forms are at the back of the book.

BISHOPS TACHBROOK Warwickshire map 2

▲ *Mallory Court* [14/20]

Harbury Lane, Bishops Tachbrook CV33 9QB
LEAMINGTON SPA (0926) 30214
off A452, 2m S of Leamington Spa 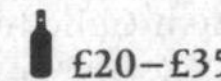 £20–£35

The 1920s' character lingers. The substantial building, set in extensive formal gardens in striking distance of Stratford, has been ambitiously and luxuriously refurbished, and over the decade Allan Holland has kept up a standard. The lunch menu is a dull read at the price – main courses being two roasts, liver and onions or fish – but presentation and execution uplift and dispel fears of a lack of conviction. High-class dishes are to be had: courgette and thyme soup; parfait of chicken livers; goujons of turbot and salmon in mustard, butter and fish stock sauce garnished with lobster coral, for instance, at a late summer meal. Trimmings – petits fours, canapés and table bread – are impeccable, and staff are concerned and knowledgeable. The wine list, largely French, is expensive, and has very little to offer at under £10 – a Saumur Champigny, Domaine Couly-Dutheil '83, £9.50 is perhaps best-value. But there are some unusual *petits châteaux* and *cru bourgeois* clarets as well as classed growths of good years, including some older vintages, good Burgundies from the domaines and Burgundian merchants, interesting single vineyard Beaujolais, good Loires, Alsace and Rhônes and German wines from reliable producers. There are some reasonable Italian wines, Californians from Robert Mondavi and Australians from Brown Brothers. Sweet wines are in fairly short supply: four turn-of-the-eighties Sauternes and Barsac plus Château La Tour-Blanche, Premier Cru Sauternes '66, £43.25, and a German Trockenbeerenauslese '76, £33.50 per half-bottle. House white and red from £6.95.

CHEFS: A.J.G. Holland and A. Wright PROPRIETORS: A.J.G. Holland and J.R. Mort
OPEN: all week
MEALS: 12.30 to 1.30, 7.30 to 9.30 (10 Sat)
PRICES: Set L £17 (£20), Set D £32 (£35). Service inc
CARDS: Access, Amex, Visa, Diners
SEATS: 50. Private parties: 50 main room. Car-park, 50 places. No children under 12. Jacket and tie. No cigars/pipes in dining-room
ACCOMMODATION: 10 rooms, all with bath/shower. B&B £75 to £135. No children under 12. Afternoon teas. Garden. Swimming-pool. Tennis. TV. Phone. Scenic [GHG]

BLANDFORD FORUM Dorset map 2

▲ *La Belle Alliance* [10/20]

Whitecliff Mill Street, Blandford Forum DT11 7BP
BLANDFORD FORUM (0258) 52842 £23

The alliance is between the Davisons themselves. She is one of the county's most charming hosts and his cooking is enterprising and modern. There are five or six choices per course, usually featuring a warm salad and a spread of sauces – sorrel for salmon; tarragon and cream for steak; red wine and grapes for duck. The cheese course is an optional extra or alternative to the terrine, syllabub, roulade and marinated fruits for dessert. House pichet £6.95. CELLARMAN'S CHOICE: St Estèphe, Ch. Andron-Blanquet '82, £13.25.

CHEF: P. Davison PROPRIETORS: Mr and Mrs P. Davison
OPEN: Mon to Sat, and bank hol Suns
MEALS: 7 to 9.30 (10 Sat)
PRICES: Set D £17 (£23)
CARDS: Access, Amex, Diners, Visa
SEATS: 28. Private parties: 36 main room. Car-park, 9 places. No children under 7. Smart dress preferred. No smoking in dining-room. Wheelchair access. Music
ACCOMMODATION: 5 rooms, all with bath/shower. B&B £30 to £540. Children, by arrangement. Pets welcome. TV. Phone. Scenic. Doors close at 12. Confirm by 6. [GHG]

BOLLINGTON Cheshire map 5

Mauro's [11/20]

88 Palmerston Street, Bollington SK10 5PW
BOLLINGTON (0625) 73898 £16

Bollington is an old textile mill village with fine examples of stone terrace housing along the main street. The Mauro family moved here from Enzo's in Penzance where they were also listed. The overwhelming impression is of light and space from the fine double front. Blue and cream motif is repeated on the china. This is a serious Italian restaurant with the emphasis on fresh produce. Baskets of fennel, peppers, aubergines, etcetera are piled high at the back of the dining room. Trolleys carry about a dozen starters and sweets supplemented by dishes of the day. Fish is a feature. Pasta is made in-house. The small details underline the elegance of the kitchen – eight small tomato and garlic croutons with drinks; a jug of chocolate sauce left on the table with the fine profiteroles; a whole pot of cafetière coffee for one. Notable dishes: calves' kidneys in Marsala sauce; chocolate and almond gateau. Service, sometimes from the Mauro's young children, is not included. Forty Italian wines.

CHEF/PROPRIETOR: Mr V. Mauro
OPEN: Tue to Sat
MEALS: 12 to 2.30, 7 to 10
PRICES: £10 (£16)
CARDS: Access, Amex
SEATS: 50. Vegetarian meals. Children's helpings. Wheelchair access (also WC). Music

BOTLEY Hampshire map 2

Cobbett's [11/20]

15 The Square, Botley SO3 2EA
BOTLEY (048 92) 2068 £18–£30

The village square provides a tranquil English setting for a French restaurant that is homely rather than pretentious. The vegetable soup comes in a tureen large enough for second helpings, while the venison that follows is likely to have been bagged by Charles Skipwith and cooked by Lucie or chef Peter Hayes. Mr Skipwith also fetches fresh fish from nearby Portsmouth and marinated the salmon and monkfish have been praised. Autumn menus are putting to good use the bolets and chanterelles which the family have collected in the woods around Botley. House wine is Ch. Peynaud-La Grange '85 at £8, or CELLARMAN'S CHOICE: Lirac, La Fermade '82, £10.85.

CHEFS: Lucie Skipwith and Peter Hayes PROPRIETORS: Charles and Lucie Skipwith
OPEN: Mon to Sat, exc Mon and Sat L
CLOSED: 2 weeks summer, 2 weeks winter
MEALS: 12 to 2, 7.30 (7 Sat) to 10
PRICES: £20 (£30), Set L £10 (£18)
CARDS: Access, Amex, Visa
SEATS: 40. Private parties: 35 main room, 14 private room. Car-park, 15 places. Vegetarian meals. Children's helpings. No cigars/pipes in dining-room. Wheelchair access (also WC)

BOURNEMOUTH Dorset — map 2

Crust [10/20]

Hampshire House, Bourne Avenue,
The Square, Bournemouth BH2 6EA
BOURNEMOUTH (0202) 21430 — £11–£26

Crust has stepped back in time into a 1930s daze of mirrors, palms and marbling, but the cooking stays within its bistro framework, making positive use of local produce, especially fish. The day's specials are listed on the blackboard. Lunch is notably good value. Recommended dishes have been: moules marinière; roast duck; grilled lemon sole; mushrooms in garlic; lobster; sea-bass grilled with 'fines herbes'; the platter of six vegetables. Sweets tend to be more English, like treacle tart or pies. The wine list is extensive and a big asset. House Rhône £5.95. CELLARMAN'S CHOICE: Vacqueyras, Domaine le Sang des Cailloux '85, £8.95.

CHEFS: Paul Harper and Sue Cole PROPRIETORS: Tricia and Paul Harper
OPEN: all week
MEALS: 12 to 2.30, 6.30 to 11 (11.30 Sat)
PRICES: £14 (£22), Set L £6.50 (£11), Set D £12 (£17) to £20 (£26), Snacks from £1.50. Service 10%
CARDS: Access, Diners, Visa
SEATS: 50. Private parties: 30 main room; 50 private room. Vegetarian meals. Children's helpings. Smart dress preferred. Wheelchair access. Music

Sophisticats [10/20]

43 Charminster Road, Bournemouth BH8 8UE
BOURNEMOUTH (0202) 291019 — £20

Steaks and veal dominate the menu in this converted shop. Javanese fillet is marinated in soy and spices; a Yugoslavian baked veal sandwich also contains ham, onion, mushroom, tomatoes and cheese. But fish changes with the market: halibut this week, salmon next, very likely in pastry with ginger, currants and a mousseline sauce. Meals can begin or end with a soufflé, and puddings are on the up. Service is courteous. Four dozen wines include Montana's Sauvignon Blanc from New Zealand. House French £5.60.

CHEF: Bernard Calligan PROPRIETORS: John Knight and Bernard Calligan
OPEN: Tue to Sat, D only
CLOSED: 2 weeks Jan, 1 week May, last 2 weeks Oct
MEALS: 7 to 10
PRICES: £13 (£20)
SEATS: 32. Private parties: 20 main room. Vegetarian meals. Children welcome. Wheelchair access (also WC). Music

Dorset Round-up

ROOMS: *Mansion House,* Thomas Street, Poole (0202 685666).
FISH: *Riverside Restaurant & Café,* West Bay, Bridport (0308 22011); *The Galley,* 9 High Street, Swanage (0929 427299).
VEGETARIAN: *In a Nutshell,* 27 Arndale Centre, Poole (0202 673888).
BAR MEALS: *Castle Inn,* Main Street, West Lulworth (092 941 311).
WINE BAR: *Sibleys,* The Esplanade, Weymouth (0305 782196).
SETTING: *Ship Inn,* West Stour, Nr Gillingham (074 785 640).

BOWNESS-ON-WINDERMERE Cumbria map 7

Porthole Eating House [13/20]

3 Ash Street, Bowness-on-Windermere LA23 3EB
WINDERMERE (096 62) 2793 £23

The individuality of the Porthole sets it apart. It is genuinely old – the beams are so low it can feel as though the people upstairs are standing on top of you. The real cooking and spirit of the menu is found on the list of specialities of the night. Each is matched to two recommendations for wine – a Tokay '85 for spaghetti bolognese – from the stupendous list. This is classical cooking featuring powerful sauces: quail wrapped in bacon, roasted and served with a red wine sauce; pigeon breast with a port and red wine sauce and its leg-meat made into a purée with apricot and leeks and cooked in a mould; salmon baked with dill, Chablis and Campari and served with an hollandaise coloured with red peppers. To finish there is a very rich sticky toffee pudding. Most interesting buys on the extensive wine list are off the usual beat. There are some exceptional wines from Australia and New Zealand, and a long list of very fine German wines, including some affordable older vintages. Italy includes two vintages of Sassicaia and several mature vintages of Biondi Santi's Brunello di Montalcino, while there are several vintages of the very fine Valbuena from Vega Sicilia on the Spanish list. Burgundy, heavy with merchants' wines, and particularly Louis Latour, is not as tempting as the rest of France. There's fine scope for the sweet-toothed, from German Beerenauslesen and Trockenbeerenauslesen, sweet old Loires and variety of Sauternes to the less usual: mature Sélection de Grains Nobles from Alsace, Piccolit from Italy and Sauternes-style, botrytised wines from Australia. Plenty of choice under £10. House Italian £6.60; CELLARMAN'S CHOICE: Pinot Grigio Venegazzù '86 £8; Hermitage Sizeranne '83, from Chapoutier, £19.

CHEF: Michael Metcalfe PROPRIETORS: Judy and Gianni Berton
OPEN: all week D, exc Tue
CLOSED: mid-Dec to mid-Feb
MEALS: 6.30 to 11
PRICES: £15 (£23)
CARDS: Access, Amex, Diners, Visa
SEATS: 40. Private parties: 36 main room, 22 private room. Vegetarian meals. Children's helpings. Music

BRADFORD West Yorkshire map 5

Kashmir [9/20]

27 Morley Street, Bradford BD7 1AG
BRADFORD (0274) 726513 £2–£6

Bradford's daunting contingent of curry houses ranges in style from a bizarre car-park café in a caravan to a flamboyant dining-room in a converted Sikh temple. The Kashmir has been in business for more than 35 years, and has the edge over its neighbours. This Formica-tabled basement has precious little décor and knives and forks are a rarity, but the freshness of the ingredients and the sheer pungency of the food put it in a class of its own. Meat bhuna, chicken masala special and keema dhal laced with cumin have all been excellent. The value for money is brilliant: around £2 will pay for a soup-bowl of curry, three incomparable steaming hot chapatis and yoghurt salad. Unlicensed, but bring your own.

CHEF: F. Hussaien PROPRIETORS: M. Latif and M. Bafhir
OPEN: all week
MEALS: 11am to 3am
PRICES: £4 (£6), Set L £1.50 (£2) to £2.70 (£3), Set D £1.50 (£2) to £3 (£4). Service inc. Unlicensed, but bring your own: no corkage
SEATS: 80. Private parties: 60 main room, 14 private room. Vegetarian meals. Children welcome. Music

▲ *Restaurant 19, Belvedere Hotel* [14/20]

North Park Road, Bradford BD9 4NT
BRADFORD (0274) 492559 £27

It is not possible to talk of Restaurant 19 except in terms of food. It is a serious eating place, run by courteous and serious-minded men. The atmosphere is comfortable, with an Edwardian elegance, although it lacks the grandeur of setting of Yorkshire's old rivals, Pool Court and the Box Tree, and service is personal rather than professional. Since the *Guide* first discovered Stephen Smith and Robert Barbour, they have grown substantially in stature as restaurateurs. The menu is modern British – bold, imaginative and eclectic with vivid mixes of colour, texture and flavour. Relishes, home-made chutneys and jewel-bright jellies are much in evidence, but sauces equally are of the highest calibre. Breads and pastries are made in-house and vegetables (in summer from Robert's father's allotment) are cooked to order. Presentation shows the reverence and dedication in the kitchen – not just art on a plate, but total fusion of creativity. All of this leads to some peerless individual dishes - partridge on braised cabbage; medallions of venison with rowanberry jelly served in a pastry shell; sliced breast of wood-pigeon served with a celery and grape salad to one side, a beetroot and apple relish to the other; pigeon again, this time as a stuffing for spinach ravioli in a wild mushroom sauce; figs poached in red wine and served with fig and cinnamon ice-cream. Some of the final execution still lacks the steely hand of perfection – slightly overcooked fish, an under-saffroned sauce with a beautifully silvery scallop mousse – but the kitchen is transparently getting there. Dishes often use two or three different components from the same base, for instance, a platter of banana desserts, combining a mousse with cream sauce, cheesecake with walnuts, and an ice-cream in a biscuit cup with a butterscotch sauce, which demonstrates a move in the same direction as premier European cooking. Over a hundred wines, though not a great many are under £10. CELLARMAN'S CHOICE: Macon-Clessé '85, £12.55; Fleurie '86, £12.40.

CHEF: Stephen Smith PROPRIETORS: Stephen Smith and Robert Barbour
OPEN: Tue to Sat, D only
MEALS: 7 to 9.30 (10 Sat)
PRICES: Set D £19 (£27) to £21.50 (£30)
CARDS: Amex, Diners, Visa
SEATS: 40. Private parties: 10 main room. Car-park, 16 places. Children welcome. Smart dress preferred. Music
ACCOMMODATION: 13 rooms, 3 with bath/shower. B&B £25 to £35. TV. Doors close at 11.30. Confirm by 6

BRAMPTON Cumbria map 7

▲ *Farlam Hall* [10/20]

10 YEARS

Brampton CA8 2NG
HALLBANKGATE (069 76) 234
on A689, 2m from Brampton (not at Farlam village) £22

The Quinion family's country-house hotel, part of the luxurious Relais et Châteaux grouping, has a beautiful setting, with wide views across the Cumbrian hills. Cordon bleu-style English cooking, written out in lavish italics for a short set dinner of three choices per course, is led by the seasons and local produce. Tomato and fennel soup, or a crab and prawn tartlet might be followed by grilled lemon sole, pasta with cream, cheese and ham, or roast loin of pork. Meats are of good quality. The cheeseboard is English. Service is assiduous. Forty wines with a little from everywhere. House French £5.75.

Places rating 9 may not be restaurants at all, but still serve good food; expect to find pubs, cafés, small hotels and wine bars.

CHEF: Barry Quinion PROPRIETORS: The Quinion family
OPEN: all week, D only
CLOSED: Feb
MEALS: 8
PRICES: Set D £17.50 (£22)
CARDS: Access, Amex, Visa
SEATS: 40. Private parties: 30 main room. Car-park, 30 places. No children under 4. Smart dress preferred. Wheelchair access. One sitting
ACCOMMODATION: 13 rooms, all with bath/shower. B&B £45 to £65. Afternoon teas. Garden. TV. Phone. Scenic. Doors close at 12. Confirm by 2 [GHG]

BRANSCOMBE Devon map 2

▲ *Masons Arms* [9/20]

Branscombe EX12 3DJ
BRANSCOMBE (029 780) 300 £19

Six hundred years of history, a good pub atmosphere and a pebbled beach not far away are the attractions at this old-fashioned inn. New chef Thierry Quiniou has moved the restaurant menus towards French provincial, with dishes such as ballotine of chicken with saffron, magret of duck with forest mushrooms and sauté scallops with calvados and crab sauce. Bar meals are good value and have assumed a new importance in the small scheme of the kitchen. Beers from Hall and Woodhouse, cider from Inchs and a fine wine list with CELLARMAN'S CHOICE: Lirac, Les Roches '83, at £9.50.

CHEFS: Thierry Quiniou and Stephen Tipper PROPRIETORS: J. and M. Inglis
OPEN: all week D, and Sun L
MEALS: 12.30 to 1, 7.15 to 8.30
PRICES: Set L £8 (£13), D £14 (£19), Snacks from £1
CARDS: Access, Visa
SEATS: 46. 11 tables outside. Private parties: 30 main room, 30, 14 private rooms. Car-park, 45 places. Vegetarian meals. Children's helpings. Smart dress preferred. Wheelchair access (also WC)
ACCOMMODATION: 21 rooms, 18 with bath/shower. Rooms for disabled. B&B £30. Baby facilities. Pets welcome. Garden. Fishing. TV. Phone. Scenic. Doors close at 12

BRAY Berkshire map 2

Waterside Inn [15/20]

10 YEARS

Ferry Road, Bray SN6 2AT
BRAY (0628) 20691 and 22941 £24–£45

The setting on the Thames is romantic and charmed. Michel Roux has taken up the role of the statesman, working hard behind the scenes to set up such things as the Meilleur Ouvrier de Grande Bretagne award for young chefs. In the meantime his restaurant remains a mini-rollercoaster of ups and downs, with the young staff both front and back of house not being as sensitive as the master to the nuances of his cooking. This is compounded by the pressure of serving perhaps 80-plus diners in an evening. Reports vary wildly, from those completely enchanted to those who feel the substance of the cooking gets thinner, and the technique more careless. The menu, very much in the French tradition (and why not, this is after all a very French restaurant), stays strictly within the familiar text of the Roux brothers' *New Classic Cuisine,* augmented to an extent by luxuries such as foie gras and caviare. At its best there might be lightly poached scallops and crayfish on a bed of chopped, sweated leeks surrounded by a creamy sauce from a shellfish stock, or a mousse of foie gras and quail breasts. Sauces are often the main points of the meal, the constantly recognisable seal of a Roux kitchen, as is the sheer quality of the ingredients. A plainer strain has been apparent – 'wonderful lamb chops'; 'good' châteaubriand – alongside the rich oeufs brouillés aux oeufs. Strange that this, the more inflexible of the two brothers' flagships, has sent out individualists like Pierre Koffman and Christian Delteil to open their own restaurants, while Gavroche graduates have so far stuck far more closely to the accepted disciplines, as at Paris House, Woburn, or Mazarin in London (see entries). The wine list is resolutely French, strong on good-quality wine, albeit at a price, plus there is a fine selection of digestifs.

CHEF/PROPRIETOR: Michel Roux
OPEN: Tue to Sun
CLOSED: 25 Dec to 15 Feb; Sun D in winter
MEALS: 12 to 2, 7 to 10
PRICES: £32 (£40), Set L £19.50 (£24), Set D £40.50 (£45). Service inc
CARDS: Access, Amex, Carte Blanche, Diners, Visa
SEATS: 75. Car-park, 50 places. Children welcome. Smart dress preferred. No pipes in dining-room. Wheelchair access (also WC). Air-conditioned

Berkshire Round-up

RIVER SETTING AND ROOMS: *Swan Hotel,* Streatley (0491 873737); *Sir Christopher Wrens House,* The Orangerie Restaurant, Windsor (0753 861354); *Monkey Island,* Bray on Thames, Maidenhead (0628 23400).
BAR MEALS: *Bacon Arms,* Oxford Street, Newbury (0635 31822); *King Charles Head,* Goring Heath, Pangbourne (0491 680268).
VEGETARIAN: *Farmers Table,* Stanford Dingley (0734 744369).
WINE BAR: *Wine Butts,* 61 St Mary Butts, Reading (0734 5093663).
ITALIAN: *White Hart,* Hampstead Marshall, Nr Newbury (0488 58201).
ENGLISH: *Ascot Guinea,* Mill Ride Estate, Mill Ride, Ascot (0344 886737); *Conways,* East Garston, Nr Lambourn (048839 275).
CHINESE: *Peking Inn,* 49 High Street, Cookham (0628 520900).
ROOMS: *Royal Berkshire Hotel,* London Road, Sunninghill, Ascot (0990 23322).

BRIGHTON East Sussex map 3

Chilka [10/20]

58 Preston Street, Brighton BN1 2HE
BRIGHTON (0273) 27343 £12–£17

Mr Ghoshal's Bengali eating house is unlike most standard curry houses: there's no music, the waitresses are English and only a few Indian pictures brighten up the walls. The cooking is distinctive, with fish dishes featuring on the short menu – anything from salmon curry and halibut korma to fish cutlets with dahl. Vegetables can take in puris with leeks and aubergines, pumpkin with chickpeas and mushrooms with cashew nuts. Chicken vindaloo is well reported. Rice and breads are good, and to finish there's kulfi or mango soufflé. As we go to press, Mr Ghoshal is planning to move his restaurant to Rye in March 1989.

CHEF/PROPRIETOR: A.K. Ghoshal
OPEN: Wed to Sun, D only
CLOSED: 22 Dex to 1 Jan, last week Feb, first week Mar
MEALS: 6.30 to 11
PRICES: £9 (£17), Set D from £7 (£12). Minimum £7
CARDS: Access, Amex, Diners, Visa
SEATS: 34. Private parties: 36 main room. Vegetarian meals. Children welcome. Smart dress preferred. Wheelchair access (also WC)

Food for Friends [10/20]

17A–18 Prince Albert Street, The Lanes, Brighton BN1 1HF
BRIGHTON (0273) 202310 £6

In a strange town, without advice as to where to eat, the pragmatic choice would be to seek out a vegetarian restaurant. The probability is that the people running it would be committed, the produce genuine, the ideas possibly intriguing and the value excellent. All of these are values close to this book's heart. Food for Friends, among the best of the vegetarians, supports the theory admirably, the more so in this town where décor and service seem to be prized above quality of food. Here soups are home made, salads are inventively dressed with blue cheese and pear or peanut and chilli and the familiar hot-dish bakes are complemented by exotic interventions like tortillas or tempura. Sweets celebrate the English tradition of baking. Much is cooked to order, hence the queues, and the menu changes from day to day. Prices are not inflationary. Organic wines, low-alcohol beers, Ecusson ciders and house French at £3.95.

CHEF: Philip Taylor PROPRIETOR: Simon F. Hope
OPEN: all week
MEALS: 9am (10 Sun) to 10pm (11 Fri and Sat)
PRICES: £4 (£6), Snacks from £1. Service inc
SEATS: 55. Vegetarian meals. Children's helpings. Wheelchair access. Music

French Cellar [12/20]

37 New England Road, Brighton BN1 4GG
BRIGHTON (0273) 603643 £26

The cynical view is that with 350 or so restaurants in Brighton and Hove, the French Cellar is the only one to be relied upon to provide a consistently good upmarket meal. Why else are there more recommendations for Jean-Claude Rozard's refurbished restaurant than for all the others put together? The cooking is French: moules farcies; onion soup; charcuterie; with a marked accent for, say, grilled sea-bream with herb butter. Fish has been conspicuously well prepared. There is a small selection of cheeses. Sweets are in the vein of chocolate mousse with Tia Maria or stuffed pancakes. Mrs

Rozard runs the front of house with élan. Fifty wines, with house French at £7.50. CELLARMAN'S CHOICE: Château les Gravettes '82, £9.50; Pinot Blanc, Medaille d'Or '84, £9.50.

CHEF: Jean-Claude Rozard PROPRIETORS: Mr and Mrs Jean-Claude Rozard
OPEN: Mon to Sat, D only, and L by arrangement
MEALS: 7.15 to 10
PRICES: £16 (£26). Service 12.5%
CARDS: Access, Visa
SEATS: 40. Private parties: 40 main room. Children welcome. Smart dress preferred. No cigars/pipes in dining-room

▲ *The Twenty One* [10/20]

21 Charlotte Street, Brighton BN2 1AG
BRIGHTON (0273) 686450 £23

Dinners are for residents only in this personable Victorian hotel set in fashionable Kemptown. Roger Pryde cooks a four-course set menu which is now nearer modern British than classical French. Tomato and plum soup with mint might be followed by salad of avocado, kiwi, melon and raspberries on a bed of leaves. Main courses, such as poached salmon with ginger and lime sauce, or a roast breast of duck with pear and madeira sauce, come with unadorned fresh vegetables. Sweets veer between lavender sorbet with bilberries and chocolate marquise. Some 50 wines include a good choice of half-bottles, as well as a few indulgent vintages. House French is £5.60.

CHEF: Roger Pryde PROPRIETORS: Simon Ward and Stuart Farquharson
OPEN: Mon to Sat, D only; residents only
CLOSED: Christmas
MEALS: 7 to 8.30
PRICES: Set D £18 (£23). Service 12.5%. Licensed, also bring your own: corkage £1
CARDS: Access, Amex, Diners, Visa
SEATS: 14. Private parties: 12 main room. No children under 12. No cigars/pipes in dining-room. Music
ACCOMMODATION: 7 rooms, 5 with bath/shower. B&B £30 to £55. Deposit: £25. No children under 12. Pets welcome. TV. Phone. Confirm by 5.30 [GHG]

Sussex Round-up

INEXPENSIVE: *Melrose*, 132 Kings Road, Brighton (0723 26520).
AFTERNOON TEA: *Mock Turtle*, 4 Poole Valley, off East Street, Brighton (0273 27380).
ITALIAN: *Cucina*, 13 Station Street, Lewes (0273 476707); *Latin in the Lane*, 10 Kings Road, Brighton (0273 28672).
SETTING: *Coach & Horses*, School Lane, Danehill (082 574 369).
ENGLISH: *Swans*, 21 Norfolk Square, Brighton (0273 721211).
WINE BAR: *Bosworths*, 8 Bolton Road, Eastbourne (0323 23023).
ROOMS: *Little Hemingfold Farmhouse*, Telham, Battle (042 46 4338).
GERMAN: *Lannards*, Okehurst Lane, Five Oaks, Billingshurst (040 381 4626 and 2692).
BAR MEALS: *Shepherd and Dog*, Fulking (079 156 382); *Swan*, Lower High Street, Fittleworth (079 882 429/242; *Coach and Horses*, School Lane, Danehill, Nr Haywards Heath (082 574 369).

BRIMFIELD Hereford & Worcester map 2

Poppies, The Roebuck [12/20]

Brimfield SY8 4WE
BRIMFIELD (058 472) 230
on old A49 between Leominster and Ludlow £26

The designer chic of the café-au-lait walls, bamboo furniture and framed prints contrasts with the much more down-to-earth aspects of the Roebuck pub in the centre of the village. Carole Evans' cooking is equally a cut above the usual and bravely develops more striking combinations – for instance a poppy-seed parfait served with a ragout of dates – many of which work well. They colour a menu that is also determined by the correct cooking of more mainstream dishes: asparagus hollandaise; turbot with Dijon mustard sauce. Classic traditional English dishes are executed with élan – steak and kidney pie or bread-and-butter pudding with apricot sauce – and can outshine the more Frenchified marquises. The saucing is based on sound stocks. The bar benefits from this philosophy, offering exemplary ploughman's – farmhouse cheese, fresh bread, home-made pickles – and home-made pies, such as chicken laced with Dunkerton's cider; pigeon in red wine; cottage. There is a special supplement to the 60-bottle wine list of California and Australian bottles. House Italian, Loire and Liebfraumilch £8; CELLARMAN'S CHOICE: Edna Valley Chardonnay '85, £13.50; Margaux, Ch. La Lagune '82, £30.50. Also Ansells' beers and draught Guinness.

CHEF: Carole Evans PROPRIETORS: John and Carole Evans
OPEN: Tue to Sun, exc Sun D
CLOSED: 2 weeks Feb and Oct, 25 and 26 Dec
MEALS: 12 to 2 (1.45 Sun), 7 to 10 (9.30 Sun)
PRICES: £18 (£26), Snacks from £2.75
CARDS: Access, Visa
SEATS: 32. Private parties: 32 main room. Vegetarian meals. Children welcome. No-smoking area. Wheelchair access (also WC)

BRISTOL Avon map 2

Bistro Twenty One [10/20]

21 Cotham Road South, Kingsdown, Bristol BS6 5TZ
BRISTOL (0272) 421744 £20

It might seem to make commercial sense to take over an existing successful restaurant, but reputations are daunting and the Markwicks enjoyed one of the best. With hindsight, Alain Dubois might have done better to start with a new name and new décor. He is an accomplished cook but lives in the harsh light of someone else's achievements. The décor is virtually unchanged. There's not much light and the wooden seats now have some padding. The new regime sometimes overreaches itself and results can be patchy, but the kitchen can deliver good best end of lamb with honey and ginger, filet mignon with port and banana sauce and chicken breast stuffed with Gruyère and walnuts. Fish arrives nightly from Cornwall for monkfish with shallots and red wine sauce, salmon with turbot mousse, or squid provençale. Ornamental bavarois, flambéed bananas or dark and white chocolate mousse to finish. Clarets and Burgundies dominate the list of around 60 wines. House Rhône is £6.75 a litre.

CHEF/PROPRIETOR: Alain Dubois
OPEN: Mon to Sat, exc Sat L
CLOSED: 1 week at Christmas
MEALS: 12 to 2.30, 6.30 to 11.30
PRICES: £14 (£20)
CARDS: Access, Visa
SEATS: 40. Private parties: 16 private room. Vegetarian meals. Children's helpings. Wheelchair access. Music

China Palace [new entry, zero rated]

18A Baldwin St, Bristol BS1 1SE
BRISTOL (0272) 262719 £14–£20

The West Country isn't noted for its Chinese restaurants, but this upmarket place in a defunct fast-food operation just out of the city centre has made a promising start. The long menu of 188 dishes has Cantonese and Szechuan specialities, with only a few compromises to western tastes. Deep-fried prawns in rice paper, crispy shredded beef and diced chicken with prawns and mushrooms have all been good. Discreet, helpful service. More reports, please.

CHEF: Kwow Wong PROPRIETOR: Kam Wong
OPEN: all week
MEALS: 12 to 2.30, 6 to 11.30
PRICES: £9 (£17), Set D £9.50 (£14) to £15 (£20). Service 10%
CARDS: Access, Amex, Visa
SEATS: 150. Private parties: 150 main room. Vegetarian meals. Children's helpings. Music. Air-conditioned

Edwards [new owner, zero rated]

24 Alma Vale Road, Clifton, Bristol BS8 2HY
BRISTOL (0272) 741533 £12–£16

Ex-film-maker John Selwyn Gilbert has taken over this oak-panelled restaurant tucked away in a narrow street, and runs the front of house. He has kept Gerrard Perry in the kitchen, and the cooking still has its roots in France, with layered terrine of salmon, whiting and spinach; venison casseroled with red wine and brandy; and kidneys in Meaux mustard sauce. Monkfish might be served provençale or with mussels and saffron in puff pastry. Other dishes, such as seventeenth-century English pea soup with mace and spinach, or Irish stew are closer to home. Chocolate mousse or home-made ice-cream to finish. The modest wine list has a few new arrivals, including CELLARMAN'S CHOICE: Lindeman's Cabernet Sauvignon '85, £8.50. More reports, please.

CHEF: Gerrard Perry PROPRIETOR: John Selwyn Gilbert
OPEN: Tue to Sat, exc Sat L
MEALS: 12 to 2.30, 7 to 10.30
PRICES: £11 (£16), Set L £8.50 (£12)
CARDS: Access, Visa
SEATS: 44. Private parties: 40 main room, 2 private room. Vegetarian meals. Children's helpings, on request. Smart dress preferred. Wheelchair access (1 step)

Ganges [10/20]

368 Gloucester Road, Horfield, Bristol BS7 8TP
BRISTOL (0272) 45234 and 428505 £14–£16

The menu in this vividly decorated Indian restaurant tries to follow the course of the sacred river and offers dishes from the regions through which it flows. There are good reports of the chicken tikka and lamb pasanda; also Afghan prawns, cooked with coconut, banana, pineapple and sultanas. The vegetarian thali is £5.75 and there's a wide choice of set meals. Drink Kingfisher beer or try Indian Veena wine.

CHEFS: B. Bista and H. Ali PROPRIETOR: Ahmed Chowdhury
OPEN: all week
MEALS: 12 to 2.15, 6 to 11.30
PRICES: £10 (£15), Set L and D £8.95 (£14) to £11.50 (£16). Service 10%
CARDS: Access, Amex, Diners, Visa
SEATS: 54. Private parties: 30 main room, 24 private room. Vegetarian meals. Children's helpings. Smart dress preferred. Wheelchair access. Music. Air-conditioned

Harvey's [10/20]

12A Denmark Street, Bristol BS1 5DQ
BRISTOL (0272) 277665 £19–£29

The cuisine is overshadowed by the wines, although the bill of fare tries to compete in length – 16 starters, 13 specialities, 11 fish, 6 poultry, 12 meats, 4 seasonal dishes, 4 grills, not to mention the côte de boeuf marchand de vin and 4 other grandiose centrepieces for two, each requiring 30- or 40-minute waits. This is old-school stuff and the discerning usually find something of quality among the panoply. The wine list is exciting for mature claret, patchy for anyone on a tight budget. As part-owners for many years of Ch. Latour, Harvey's can offer vintages back to '17. Vintages of other clarets stop at '52, with impressive lists in all the good post Second World War years. Burgundies are a less interesting selection, almost all from merchants rather than single estates, and though there are vintages back to '34, Burgundies of any year after '78 are for gamblers only. The list concentrates on France, with sparse coverage of the rest of the world, except for the other 'classic' areas: Germany (there are some tempting old sweet wines), sherry and port. Cheaper wines listed without producers' names are Harvey's own brands, and rarely exciting. Mark-ups are usually a generous 100 per cent or more. Mas de Daumas-Gassac '81, a rich, claret-like Vin de Pays de l'Hérault, is excellent value at £10.

CHEF: Thierry Rouvrais PROPRIETORS: John Harvey & Sons Ltd
OPEN: Mon to Sat, exc Sat L
CLOSED: bank hols
MEALS: 12 to 2.15, 7 (6.30 Sat) to 11.15
PRICES: £19 (£29), Set L £12.95 (£19). Cover £1
CARDS: Access, Amex, Diners, Visa
SEATS: 120. Private parties: 60 main room. Jacket and tie. No-smoking area. Music. Air-conditioned

Jameson's [10/20]

30 Upper Maudlin Street, Bristol BS2 8DJ
BRISTOL (0272) 276565 £18

Bristol has developed a history of bistros from the days Keith Floyd ran a string of restaurants. Jameson's is the red building opposite the Royal Infirmary. There is a blackboard menu that roams between extravagant terrines, plus generous salads combining various ingredients, perhaps tuna, chicken and avocado, and stock genre versions of roast Aylesbury duck with port and black cherries, and profiteroles. Presentation is secondary. Some 40 well-spread wines include house Côtes du Frontonnais at £6.50 a litre.

CHEFS: Filali and Carole Jameson PROPRIETORS: Carole and John Holmes
OPEN: Tue to Sat, D only
MEALS: 7 to 11 (11.30 Fri and Sat)
PRICES: £12 (£18)
CARDS: Access, Visa
SEATS: 70. Private parties: 30 main room. Vegetarian meals. Children's helpings. Wheelchair access. Music

Lettonie [new entry, zero rated]

9 Druid Hill, Stoke Bishop, Bristol BS9 1EW
BRISTOL (0272) 686456 £15–£23

Rene Gaté's small neighbourhood restaurant in a half-timbered row by Markwicks Discerning Butcher and Threshers has been sold to Martin Blunos and Siân Williams, formerly at Les Fauves in Battersea. Gaté is rumoured to be taking over a hotel in the north. The inside looks like a set for *Diary of an Edwardian Country Lady*: ruches and stripes, with landscapes on the walls. The short menu of half a dozen dishes, written in French with English subtitles, generates much interest even controversy. One view has it that: 'The food is complex. One is exhausted by the sheer number of visual and olfactory and gustatory impressions by the end of the evening. It is all a little bit of this and a little bit of that. Nothing that one can really get one's teeth into and one's imagination working on. All fleeting and vague. It is not so much that the food doesn't taste of the main ingredient, it is more that there is so little of the main ingredient. And such a lot of other little bits. It is unhealthy food: white bread, lots of little nibbles and petits fours, practically no vegetables. Really city food.' But another puts it: 'The starter of scallops ranged around a three-quarter egg shell filled with scrambled eggs and topped with caviare was 14/20 for sure.' The presentation is unquestioned, also the generosity, which made the amuse-gueules almost a course in themselves. Martin Blunos' Latvian ancestry is evident in the soup of beetroot served with blinis and sour cream, but the main thrust is modern – a cold terrine of fish served with green peppercorns and parsley set in its own jelly with an olive oil and garlic dressing, or the new season lamb roasted and served with aubergines and peppers, a thyme-scented sauce with five fat roast cloves of garlic in their skins. The hesitation is in how well all these fuse together. But the quality of the breads or the chicken with a watercress sauce is first division. Service is conscientious and formal. Coffee comes, predictably by this time, with eight or nine petits fours. Sixty wines concentrate exclusively on France with a choice of four house wines around £8. More reports, please.

CHEFS/PROPRIETORS: Martin Blunos and Siân E. Williams
OPEN: Tue to Sun, exc Sun D
CLOSED: 2 weeks Aug
MEALS: 12.30 to 2, 7 to 10
PRICES: Set L £9.95 (£15), to £16.95 (£23). Set D £16.95 (£23)
CARDS: Access, Visa
SEATS: 24. Private parties: 14 main room. Music

Muset [10/20]

12 Clifton Road, Clifton, Bristol BS8 1AF
BRISTOL (0272) 732920 £18

There have been a few changes in the kitchen of this converted shop on two levels, but the cooking remains sound, mainly French with a few cosmopolitan touches – cottage cheese with peaches in filo pastry with curried yoghurt; roast duck with grapefruit; breast of chicken stuffed with cashew nuts. Best end of lamb comes with a gherkin sauce or mint and lemon butter. Fresh fish specials are from the market. Vegetables are firm and, sweets range from home-made ice-creams to decorative strawberries in a pastry swan. The short wine list has some good Australians, including CELLARMAN'S CHOICE: McWilliams Inheritance Cabernet Shiraz '85, £6.95. Customers can also bring their own wine, no corkage charged.

CHEFS: A. Portlock, C. Portlock, J. Thomas and D. Wheadon
PROPRIETORS: B.Y.O. Holdings
OPEN: Tue to Sat, D only
MEALS: 7 to 10.30
PRICES: £13 (£18). Service 10% (on parties above 4). Licensed, also bring your own: no corkage
CARDS: Access, Visa
SEATS: 70. Private parties: 30 main room. Music

Rajdoot [10/20]

83 Park Street, Bristol BS1 5PJ
BRISTOL (0272) 268033 and 291242 £10–£20

The Bristol branch of the small chain of North Indian restaurants extending to Manchester and Birmingham. The menu is standardised, as is the classy décor – real brass tables and carved stools in the bar area and waiters in formal turbans. Good-quality meat and subtle spicing in tandooris and curries, plus the quality of pickles, nan and rice dishes set it apart, though portions can be modest. Recommended dishes: quail masala with coriander and cardamom; chicken moghlai with herbs and silver foil. House French £5.90.

CHEF: C. and S. Mali PROPRIETOR: D.R. Sarda
OPEN: all week, exc Sun L
MEALS: 12 to 2.30, 6.30 to 11.30
PRICES: £11 (£20), Set L from £6 (£10), Set D from £6.50 (£11). Service 12.5%
CARDS: Access, Amex, Diners, Visa
SEATS: 60. Private parties: 30 main room. Vegetarian meals. Children's helpings. Wheelchair access. Music

BRIXHAM Devon map 1

Elizabethan [10/20]

8 Middle Street, Brixham TQ5 8ER
BRIXHAM (080 45) 3722 £16

Brixham was once a Chapel/Low Church serious fishing port. In recent years it has been definitively ruined by the Torbay effect, though the fishing port survives prosperously. Older *Guide* readers will remember the glories of Randalls, which spent much of its time closing out the environment. The Elizabethan has not yet tried that course. It is a valiant effort at fair cooking of fresh ingredients without breaking the straitjacket of a seaside restaurant in popular taste; the menu includes versions of prawn cocktail and a dozen steak specialities. The decoration is relentlessly mock Elizabethan, inside and out. Short of garish, it has the air of a tea-room that has converted to doing full meals. The menu is worryingly long: eight first courses, eight fishes, eight meats, a dozen steaks, half a dozen desserts. Too many. Yet there are honest dishes: a carrot and fennel soup, not over herbed, with a fine consistency; Dart salmon has a good sauce montée; a fricassee of seafood has red mullet, lemon sole and monkfish; roast poussin arrives with a gravy and chestnuts. Desserts are seafront café in style, but properly done, as in poire belle Hélène or strawberries and clotted cream. The bread is home baked. House wine is £3.50 a half-litre.

CHEF/PROPRIETOR: Kevin Hensby
OPEN: Tue to Sun, exc Sun D
MEALS: 12 to 2, 7 to 9.30
PRICES: £13 (£16). Service inc
CARDS: Amex, Visa
SEATS: 20 to 28. Private parties: 34 main room. Vegetarian meals on request. Children's helpings. Wheelchair access (1 step; also WC). Music. Air-conditioned

'B's is a typical 1980s "dangerous" restaurant. Everything has been carefully designed to give an appearance of suave, fluent elegance in which excellent food is somehow a natural, incidental ingredient. But do not be deceived: it is an expensive con, served with a typical London/Home Counties tinge of arrogance and self-satisfaction!' On eating in London

BROADWAY Hereford & Worcester map 2

▲ *Collin House* [10/20]

Collin Lane, Broadway WR12 7PB
BROADWAY (0386) 858354
on A44, 1m NW of Broadway £14–£17

The old Cotswold stone building stands on a hilltop overlooking Broadway, the valley and its quiet simple gardens. It is all very English. The cooking is too, taking in ancient and modern, from black pudding with mustard sauce, kedgeree and roast fillet of beef with rosemary and red wine sauces to terrine of duck livers with quince and crab-apple relish, and poached salmon with sorrel and horseradish sauce. The plain vegetables stand up well on the whole. Sweets are a strong point – excellent date and butterscotch pudding, home-made damson ice-cream, Queen of puddings. Good bar lunches are served in the lounge or out in the garden. Friendly, knowledgeable service. An enthusiast's wine list has some bin-ends and half-bottles, as well as CELLARMAN'S CHOICE: Rosemount Estate Hunter Valley Chardonnay '87, at £9.85.

CHEF: Judith Mills PROPRIETORS: John and Judith Mills
OPEN: all week
MEALS: 12 to 1.30, 7 to 9
PRICES: Set L £10.50 (£14), Set D from £12.50 (£17), Bar L £7 (£11) weekdays
CARDS: Access, Visa
SEATS: 35. 5 tables outside. Private parties: 30 main room. Car-park, 30 places. Children's helpings. Children under 6 by arrangement only. Wheelchair access (also WC)
ACCOMMODATION: 7 rooms, all with bath/shower. B&B £31 to £57.50. Deposit: £35. No children under 6. Garden. Swimming-pool. Scenic. Doors close at 12

Hunters Lodge [11/20]

High Street, Broadway WR12 7DT
BROADWAY (0386) 853247 £14–£26

The Friedlis' individual little restaurant has become a feature of the *Guide* in recent years, sustained by a loyal local clientele and the many visitors to this picturesque town. The creeper-clad house is old with monastic origins, and lawns and orchard behind. Kurt Friedli cooks, Dottie runs the front of the house with a friendly efficiency. The quality of the cooking is never less than good, as shown by a starter of trout wrapped around mousse of white fish with a sauce of reduced fish stock; herb-stuffed rack of lamb with red wine gravy; or very good roast duck with honey and almonds. Desserts might include lemon mousse in raspberry sauce and almond and apricot meringue. The set menus, available at lunch and dinner, are good value for some careful cooking properly grounded in classical principles. House French is £5.95.

The entries are compiled from the views of readers who have eaten at the restaurant in the last year, backed up by anonymous inspections and by information supplied and facts verified by the restaurants.

CHEF: Kurt Friedli PROPRIETORS: Kurt and Dottie Friedli
OPEN: Tue to Sun, exc Sun D
CLOSED: first 2 weeks Feb, first 2 weeks Aug
MEALS: 12.30 to 2, 7.30 to 9.45
PRICES: £17 (£26), Set L £9 (£14)
CARDS: Access, Amex, Diners, Visa
SEATS: 55. 6 tables outside. Private parties: 35 main room, 22 private room. Car-park, 20 places. Vegetarian meals. Children's helpings. No children under 8 at D. No cigars/pipes in dining-room. Wheelchair access (also WC)

▲ *Lygon Arms* [new chef, zero rated]

Broadway WR12 7DU
BROADWAY (0386) 852255 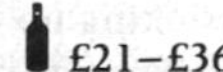 £21–£36

The broad main street of the village is now barely wide enough to cope with the flocks of American tourists who descend on this photogenic corner of the Cotswolds. The Lygon Arms is ancient and famous with its restaurant in the converted Great Hall. The Savoy Group has brought in Clive Howe from Rookery Hall to replace Michael Quinn in the kitchen. Early reports suggest that he is still settling in, but the new regime promises great things. This dish was served in June: fillet of sea-bass on a bed of almost raw julienne of vegetables, surrounded by three fresh ravioli stuffed with crabmeat and coriander leaves, with alternating melon balls and little mounds of chopped tomatoes and dark green samphire, all on a thin, clear sauce, mostly fish juices. Clive Howe is full of ideas and his menus cater for all tastes: there are grills, vegetarian dishes, and variations on classics, such as rack of Cotswold lamb with peppers, lentils and cloves of roasted garlic. Meals can end on a British note, with unpasteurised farmhouse cheeses and traditional puddings – apple charlotte and clotted cream on Thursday, rhubarb amber pudding on Friday. Nibbles and petits fours are excellent. The wine list is as good as the architecture, opening with a dozen cellarman's choices, all well chosen, and then heading off to the stratosphere of vintage champagnes, clarets and Burgundy, but not beyond Mateus Rosé either. A complex Malaga, Scholtz Solera 1885, £12, would make an alternative to port or the few sweet wines. House French £7.25. More reports, please.

CHEF: Clive Howe PROPRIETORS: The Savoy Group of Hotels
OPEN: all week
MEALS: 12.15 to 2, 7 to 9
PRICES: £27 (£36), Set L £14.75 (£21), Set D £22.50 (£29), Snacks from £1.95. Licensed, also bring your own: corkage £5
CARDS: Access, Amex, Carte Blanche, Diners, Visa
SEATS: 120. Private parties: 90 main room, 90 private room. Car-park, 150 places. Vegetarian meals. Children's helpings. Jacket and tie. No cigars/pipes in dining-room. Wheelchair access
ACCOMMODATION: 66 rooms, all with bath/shower. Rooms for disabled. B&B £70 to £105. Deposit: one night's stay. Children welcome. Baby facilities. Pets welcome. Afternoon teas. Garden. Tennis. Snooker. TV. Phone. Scenic. Confirm by 6

'You will have to wait while the wine ('85 white Burgundy) cools, sir, because the cellar is rather warm today.' Berkshire restaurateur

BROCKDISH Norfolk map 6

▲ *Sheriff House* [10/20]

Brockdish, IP21 4JY
HOXNE (037 975) 316 £20

The Pichel Juans' long-established restaurant remains one of the few places still loyal to classical disciplines. The short menu of the night is supplemented by a far wider range of dishes, ordered in advance. It is proudly old school, encompassing paella, bouillabaisse, caviare and a whole girls' school of Véroniques, Jeannettes and Camélias. There is a sensible list of everyday drinking up to around £10, but, as with the menu, on application there are vintage clarets in the cellar.

CHEF: E. Pichel Juan PROPRIETORS: F., E. and A. Pichel Juan
OPEN: all week, exc Wed
MEALS: 12 to 2, 7 to 9
PRICES: £13 (£20)
CARDS: Access, Visa
SEATS: 32. Private parties: 6 main room, 16 private room. Car-park. No children under 14. Jacket and tie. No pipes in dining-room
ACCOMMODATION: 2 rooms, 1 with bath/shower. B&B £7 to £14. No children under 14. Doors close at 12

BROCKENHURST Hampshire map 2

▲ *Poussin* [15/20]

57–59 Brookley Road, Brockenhurst SO42 7RB
LYMINGTON (0590) 23063 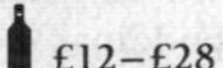 £12–£28

The setting is a small town restaurant by the station, but Alex Aitken's cooking now ranks with the best in southern England. His style is serious, with attention to the finer points and a feeling for aesthetics: home-baked rolls, intense sauces, excellent young vegetables, fresh New Forest chanterelles, pastry cooked to order. Evening meals are served at a slower tempo. On the dinner *menu gastronomique*, dishes are complemented by individually chosen wines: flowering courgette with chicken mousseline with Beaujolais Villages '84; rendezvous of seafood with sorrel with Riesling Kirchberg '79; saddle of venison with onion confit with Côtes du Tricastin '78. The style is more French than his contemporaries, reinforced by French staff. Notable of many recommended dishes have been a poached sea-bass with a butter sauce with wild oyster mushrooms; offal raised to new heights, as in steamed calf's liver marinated with port and truffles and served as a salad; millefeuille of langoustine and asparagus. By contrast, a knock-down £5.95 lunch is simplicity itself: fish soup; coq au vin; chocolate marquise. The fifth birthday celebration menu offered a salad of foie gras, truffles and asparagus; lobster tourte; pink champagne sorbet; squab with wild mushrooms; cheeses from Olivier; and an array of different sweets. Other sweets have included summer fruits spilling out of a puff-pastry shell, or festival of bananas – banana mousse, sorbet and a hot mille-feuille with caramel sauce. Fine cheeses are also sold in the adjoining delicatessen. The new bedrooms over the dining-room show the same attention to details and are inexpensive. Apart from a handful of German wines, the wine list is entirely French, concentrating very much on Bordeaux and Burgundy, backed up by a few good Loires, Rhônes, champagnes and Alsace wines. A large range of good clarets includes many mature vintages, and there are Burgundies from both merchants and growers, though some are listed unhelpfully without producers' names. There's some good value to be found among the sweet wines: eight vintages of Anjou Moulin Touchais from '49 to '78 cost between £16.15 and £34.50, two German Auslesen '76 cost £14.50, or there are half-bottles of Beerenauslesen '71 for less than £17. Young vintages of Sauternes look less exciting.

CHEF: Alexander Aitken PROPRIETORS: Mr A.W. and Mrs C. Aitken
OPEN: Mon to Sat, exc Mon L
MEALS: 12.30 to 2, 7 to 10
PRICES: 20 (£28), Set L £5.95 (£12), Set D £20 (£28).
CARDS: Access, Visa
SEATS: 35. Private parties: 35 main room, 20 private room. Vegetarian meals. Wheelchair access (also WC)
ACCOMMODATION: 4 rooms, all with bath/shower. B&B £20 to £45. Deposit: £20. Baby facilities. Doors close at 12. Confirm by 4

BROMSGROVE Hereford & Worcester map 5

▲ *Grafton Manor* [11/20]

Grafton Lane, Bromsgrove B61 7HA
BROMSGROVE (0527) 31525 and 37247
1m SW of Bromsgrove, on B4091 £16–£28

The Morris family run this beautifully restored sixteenth-century manor in consort. Inside, it is all Regency restoration, with carved plasterwork and ceiling friezes and carved surrounds to the fireplaces. Outside there are extensive grounds with a large lake and a formal herb garden laid out like a chessboard. Over 100 herbs are grown in 144 beds, and they dominate the cooking as flavours and garnishes. In recent years, the kitchen has developed its own blend of traditional and modern British dishes – roast leg of lamb with paloise, and whisky-steamed pudding, alongside hake and laverbread terrine with crab sauce, fillet of pork with lovage, served with honey and mustard sauce, or Norfolk squab stuffed with Worcestershire pear and fresh sage. Cured pig's liver is a curiosity: the meat is salted for 18 days, air-dried for a week, then pan-fried in olive oil with wild mushrooms, asparagus, quails' eggs, radishes and spring onions. Quibbles over the prices, the quality of the finer details and meagre portions have raised questions about the rating. Service is neat, friendly and as civilised as ever. In keeping big names to a minimum, wines stay reasonably priced. Within classic regions, from Beaujolais up to Chablis for instance, good use is made of the négociant skills of Loron, Chanson, Latour; and the Loire, Alsace and Rhône add interest in Quincy, Sancerre rouge, Vendange Tardive Gewürztraminer, Coteaux du Tricastin. House French is £6.75. CELLARMAN'S CHOICE: Mâcon-Lugny les Charmes '85, £13.25.

CHEFS: Nicola, John and Simon Morris PROPRIETORS: John and June Morris
OPEN: all week, exc Sat L
MEALS: 12.30 to 1.30, 7.30 to 9
PRICES: Set L £9.85 (£16) to £16.50 (£24), Set D £21 (£28)
CARDS: Access, Amex, Diners, Visa
SEATS: 50. 2 tables outside. Private parties: 14 main room. Car-park, 55 places. Vegetarian meals. No children under 12. Wheelchair access
ACCOMMODATION: 9 rooms, all with bath/shower. Rooms for disabled. B&B £55 to £77. No children under 12. Pets welcome. Garden. Fishing. TV. Phone. Scenic. Doors close at 12. Confirm two days before arrival [GHG]

BROUGHTON Lancashire map 5

▲ *Courtyard, Broughton Park Hotel* [12/20]

Garstang Road, Broughton PR3 5JB
BROUGHTON (0772) 864087 £35

The feel of this restaurant, one of two in a health club and business-oriented hotel, is pleasantly personal. Beneath a rather thick layer of 'Poisson du jour specialité chef Paul' there are first-class ingredients cooked intelligently with some good, if rather showy, ideas. The said poisson has been a fillet of sea-bass served with five scallops complete with corals, mussels, fennel sprigs and a sauce based on vegetable stock. But look also at the shellfish terrine set in the shellfish juices or the pan-fried fillet of beef with a red wine sauce, served with roast shallots, creamed wild mushrooms and a few grilled flat-tops for garnish. The staff are geared for a high level of professionalism. Dishes are explained as they are put down; tables are equipped with bottles of Buxton still mineral water; intermediary sorbets arrive unannounced. The predominantly French list has house French from £8. CELLARMAN'S CHOICE: Mâcon-Lugny les Genièvres '85, £13.75 and Fleurie, La Madone '86, £12.50.

CHEF: Paul Heathcote PROPRIETOR: Country Club Hotels Ltd
OPEN: Mon to Sat, D only
MEALS: 7 to 10.30
PRICES: £25 (£35)
CARDS: Access, Amex, Diners, Visa
SEATS: 30. Private parties: 30 main room. Car-park, 65 places. Vegetarian meals. Children welcome. Jacket and tie. Smoking after meal only. Wheelchair access (also WC). Music
ACCOMMODATION: 98 rooms, all with bath/shower. Rooms for disabled. Lift. B&B £51 to £60. Baby facilities. Afternoon teas. Garden. Swimming-pool. Sauna. Air-conditioning. TV. Phone. Scenic. Confirm by 6

CELLARMAN'S CHOICE *This is a wine recommended by the restaurateur which is usually more expensive than the house wine but is good value and fitting for the kind of food served.*

BROXTED Essex map 3

▲ *Whitehall* [10/20]

Broxted CM6 2BZ
BISHOPS STORTFORD (0279) 850603 £20–£32

A much under-appreciated part of the country, with fine churches all around, and close for Stanstead Airport. The kitchen of this increasingly hotel-orientated business produces a set evening menu that is not without its ambitions or its individual successes: scallop salad in walnut oil; Dover sole in lime butter and a salmon tranche; rack of lamb. It succeeds mostly by breaking away from the usual idiom and fails when it reaches beyond, as in the chocolate with four sauces - custard, greengage and two plain. Presentation is excellent. House wine at £8 includes a pair of Australians; CELLARMAN'S CHOICE: from a list of 60 is Graves, Ch. la Louvière '80, £16.

CHEF: Paula Keane PROPRIETORS: Mr and Mrs G.M. Keane
OPEN: Tue to Sat D, and Sun L
CLOSED: 3 weeks Jan, to non-residents
MEALS: 12.30 to 1.30, 7.30 to 9.30
PRICES: Set L £14 (£20), Set D £25 (£32)
CARDS: Access, Amex, Visa
SEATS: 40. Private parties: 40 main room, 8 private room. Car-park, 20 places. Vegetarian meals. No children under 5
ACCOMMODATION: 10 rooms, all with bath/shower. Rooms for disabled. B&B £55 to £70. No children under 5. Garden. Swimming-pool. Tennis. Fishing. Golf. TV. Phone. Scenic. Doors close at 1 [GHG]

BRUTON Somerset map 2

Truffles [new entry, zero rated]

95 The High Street, Bruton BA10 OAR
BRUTON (0749) 812 255 £12–£18

This small cottage inspired a host of late nominations in the summer. 'A first class example of *nouvelle cuisine*,' is one comment. The list and variety of recommended dishes is a long one for mousses of avocado or more interesting crab with a gazpacho sauce with mussels, loin of veal in a herb bread jacket, and honey glazed poussin, boned and stuffed with apples. Many people mention the chocolate gateau. House Bulgarian £5.50. CELLARMAN'S CHOICE: St Véran '85, £13.50. More reports, please.

CHEF: Martin Bottrill PROPRIETORS: Mr & Mrs M. Bottrill
OPEN: Tue to Sat, D only (L by arrangement)
MEALS: 7 to 9.30
PRICES: Set L £7.95 (£12), Set D £13.95 (£18)
SEATS: 20. Private parties: 20 main room. Vegetarian meals. Children restricted. Smart dress preferred. 1 step to rest. Wheelchair access. One sitting

'I travelled in the South Pacific and was particularly struck by how healthily people eat there – the food is far less rich, but quite delicious.' Restaurateur

BUCKDEN North Yorkshire map 7

▲ *Low Greenfield* [10/20]

Langstrothdale Chase, Buckden BD23 5JN
KETTLEWELL (075 676) 858 £13

The remoteness of the setting is the main draw to the Sedgleys' farmhouse in a sheltered south-facing spot 1200 feet high at the head of Langstrothdale/Upper Wharfedale. There is a set, no-choice menu of home cooking – soups; pâtés; roast meats; local cheeses. Theakston's beer and Nicolas house wine at £6 a litre.

CHEF: Lindsay Sedgley PROPRIETORS: Austin and Lindsay Sedgley
OPEN: Mon to Sat, D only
CLOSED: Nov to Easter, and Aug
MEALS: 8
PRICES: Set D £9.50 (£13). Service inc
SEATS: 8. Car-park, 6 places. Children welcome. No smoking in dining-room. Music. One sitting
ACCOMMODATION: 3 rooms. B&B £15.50 to £31. Deposit: £20. Children welcome. Baby facilities. Garden. Sauna. Fishing. Scenic. Doors close at 11. Confirm by 10pm previous day [GHG]

BURNHAM MARKET Norfolk map 6

Fishes' [10/20]

Market Place, Burnham Market PE31 8HE
FAKENHAM (0328) 738588 £12–£23

Gillian Cape's smartly informal restaurant on the village green is still one of the best local choices for fresh and home-smoked fish. Like the Butley-Orford Oysterage in Orford (see entry), the mainstays are products from the smokehouse and oysters from the restaurant's own beds. Scallops, sole and sea-trout are from the North Norfolk boats; mussels come from the pollution-free waters around Brancaster. Local crab is made into soup or used as a sauce with salmon fishcakes. Otherwise the menu can range from skate with black butter to baked ham with smoked goose. To finish, there are home-made ice-creams and excellent British farmhouse cheeses from Sue Elston's enterprising provisions shop a few doors away. Lunch is very good value. The wine list has some carefully chosen whites. House French £5.25. CELLARMAN'S CHOICE: Mâcon-Villages, Château de Franclieu '86, £10.60, and Chenin Blanc-Touraine '85, £6.25.

CHEFS: Carole Bird and Gillian Cape PROPRIETOR: Gillian Cape
OPEN: Tue to Sun
CLOSED: Sun D Oct to June, 24 to 27 Dec, 3 weeks Jan
MEALS: 12 to 2, 6.45 to 9.30
PRICES: £14 (£23), Set L from £7.25 (£12)
CARDS: Access, Amex, Diners, Visa
SEATS: 48. Private parties: 30 main room. Children's helpings. No children under 5. Wheelchair access (1 step)

BURNHAM-ON-CROUCH Essex map 3

Polash [9/20]

169 Station Road, Burnham-on-Crouch CM0 8JH
MALDON (0621) 782233 £14–£15

Fish tanks now divide the smoking and no-smoking areas. An extensive menu covers the span of Indian influence, from Kashmir south, with a corresponding variation of heat and spicing. Set menus take their names from films or literature: Kipling's Favourites for two, Far Pavilion for eight. House red and white are £4.95; alternatively, drink lager.

CHEF: Abdul Shofique PROPRIETORS: Faruque Ahmed and Abdul Shofique
OPEN: all week
MEALS: 12.15 to 2.45, 6 to 11.45
PRICES: £10 (£14), Set D £10.75 (£15)
CARDS: Access, Amex, Diners, Visa
SEATS: 68. Private parties: 46 main room. Vegetarian meals. Children's helpings. Wheelchair access (also WC). Music. Air-conditioned

BURY ST EDMUNDS Suffolk map 3

Mortimer's [10/20]

30 Churchgate Street, Bury St Edmunds IP33 IRG
BURY ST EDMUNDS (0284) 60623 £19

This city-centre restaurant near Cathedral Green is named after the nineteenth-century seascapist, Thomas Mortimer. His paintings add interest to the plain white walls, the only decoration apart from some potted greenery. Fish is delivered daily from Grimsby and served with various sauces and boiled potatoes. There's smoked fish too, home-made taramosalata and a lobster-flavoured soup; the daily special, perhaps smoked haddock kedgeree, is inexpensive. There's a second branch at Ipswich (see entry). House French from £5.65.

CHEF: Paul Cox PROPRIETORS: Kenneth Ambler and Michael Gooding
OPEN: Mon to Sat, exc Sat L
CLOSED: 23 Dec to 5 Jan
MEALS: 12 to 2, 7 to 9 (8.30 Mon)
PRICES: £14 (£19)
CARDS: Access, Amex, Diners, Visa
SEATS: 60. Private parties: 8 main room. Children's helpings. Smart dress preferred. No pipes in dining-room. Wheelchair access (1 step)

If you suspect that a restaurant is using processed food, always ask. It would be a contravention of the Trade Description Act for the restaurant to lie.

Please keep the Guide *informed of any changes to the restaurants listed. Report forms are at the back of the book.*

CALDBECK Cumbria map 7

▲ *Park End* [11/20]

nr Caldbeck, Wigton CA7 8HH
CALDBECK (069 98) 494 £12–£22

About two miles west of John Peel's village of Caldbeck on the B5299, this low-ceilinged building was once featured in a novel by Margaret Foster. Judith and Michael Bulger have moved here from Dunain Park at Inverness – *Guide* listed from 1976 to 1986 (and still listed, under new owners). The set-price dinner starts with a choice, perhaps smoked pigeon with home-made beetroot pickle. After soup there's chicken with grapes, venison pie, beef in beer or fish. A simple home-made dessert follows, then three cheeses. Coffee, fudge and mints are included. The handwritten, 40-bottle wine list is almost entirely French, the exceptions being from Germany, Greece and Bulgaria. House Beaujolais £7.95 a litre. CELLARMAN'S CHOICE: Crozes-Hermitage '83, £9.50.

CHEF: Judith Bulger PROPRIETORS: Judith and Michael Bulger
OPEN: Tue to Sun, exc Sun D
CLOSED: last week Oct to first week Mar
MEALS: 12 to 2, 7.30 to 9
PRICES: L £7 (£12), Set D from £16 (£20) to £18 (£22). Service inc
SEATS: 20. 3 tables outside. Private parties: 20 main room. Car-park, 12 places. Children's helpings (L only). No smoking. Wheelchair access
ACCOMMODATION: 3 rooms, all with bath/shower. B&B £40. Deposit: £20. Baby facilities. Pets welcome. Afternoon teas. Garden. TV. Scenic. Doors close at 11. Confirm by 5

CALSTOCK Cornwall map 1

▲ *Danescombe Valley Hotel* [14/20]

Lower Kelly, Calstock PL18 9RY
TAVISTOCK (0822) 832414 £20

In the 1955 *Guide*, Raymond Postgate described this as a prettily situated hotel above the Tamar, comfortable with excellently served food. 'Mostly the food is good plain English, but sometimes it is more adventurous and Tamar salmon en papillote may appear on the menu.' Now Tamar salmon is smoked and served with pink grapefruit, and one summing up is 'good *cuisine bourgeoise* for modern tastes.' The four-course menu offers no choice. Much of its virtue is in Anna Smith's execution and in the quality of her ingredients, most obviously her unpasteurised English cheeses, which are served on a glass plate for you to help yourself. Regular supplies provide, from sheep's milk: Sheviock, marinated in cider; Ladywell, a soft version from Tor Point; Coleford Blue, similar to Roquefort, from Somerset; plus three hard goats' cheeses. From cow's milk there are Exmoor, Devon Garland, smoked Cheddar, Wheatland, and three kinds of Yarg. The style of the rest of the menu is low-key – a chicken liver, bacon and walnut salad; braised scallops in their shells served with fresh vegetables; spring chicken with lemon and herbs; poached chicken breast with mustard sauce; walnut tart. The wordy wine list is divided into grape varieties: Sauvignons and Chardonnays from France and New Zealand for instance. Mark-ups are commendably low and everything is good value. House French £6. CELLARMAN'S CHOICE: St Véran '86, £8.75; Château Méaume '85, £6.25. 'Breakfast was perfect and included local mushrooms and Tamar honey.'

CHEF: Anna Smith PROPRIETORS: Martin and Anna Smith
OPEN: all week, D only
CLOSED: Jan to Mar, Nov and Dec
MEALS: 7 to 8
PRICES: Set D £16.50 (£20). Service inc
SEATS: 12. 2 tables outside. Private parties: 12 main room. No children under 12
ACCOMMODATION: 5 rooms, all with bath/shower. B&B £48 to £55. Deposit: £30. No children under 12. Garden. Golf. Scenic. Doors close at 12. Confirm by 6 [GHG]

CAMBRIDGE Cambridgeshire map 3

Free Press [9/20]

7–9 Prospect Row, Cambridge CB1 1OU
CAMBRIDGE (0223) 68337 £7

There are no pretensions, no muzak and no microwaves in this back-street pub, which continues to serve real ale and honest, unfussy bar food at lunch-time and in the evenings. The style takes in good home-made soups, such as curried parsnip or carrot and coriander, a wholesome hot dish – macaroni cheese, Texas chilli – and plenty of fresh interesting salads. Pies, cold meats and sweets such as treacle tart. Beers from Greene King.

CHEFS: Debbie Lloyd and Kate Willis PROPRIETORS: Chris and Debbie Lloyd
OPEN: all week
MEALS: 12 to 2, 6 to 9
PRICES: £5 (£7)
SEATS: 40. 3 tables outside. Private parties: 12 main room, 6 private room. Vegetarian meals. Children welcome. No-smoking area. Wheelchair access. Self-service

Midsummer House [new entry, zero rated]

Midsummer Common, Cambridge CB4 1HA
CAMBRIDGE (0223) 69299 £16–£33

The latest incarnation of Midsummer House does everything possible to be elegant, fashionable and sophisticated. Whereas the old regime had good honest breads, cheeses, soups, homely but accomplished English desserts, and vegetarian dishes with a sophisticated edge, we now have dishes composed in the modern French idiom out of very many good ingredients variously steamed, sauté, carved, layered, sauced and arranged into patterns. Chef Hans Schweitzer owns a patisserie in Cambridge and has been financed by TV food men Chris Kelly and Michael Smith. The restaurant is now quite large, with dining areas in the large airy sophisticated conservatory, its adjoining dark blue ground level dining-room and upstairs. There are umbrellas in the garden, possibly for dining out on fine days. The setting is all. The serving staff are dressed in severe black. The menu is quite short:

four first courses, two second courses, five or six main courses and four desserts. It reads well – as in ballotine of ox-tail in its own consommé, or salmon in champagne – but the early execution has seemed to be oriented more to showiness than loyalty to flavour and has been let down in some cases by the quality of the ingredients. The wine list is sound but unimaginative, mostly standard clarets and Burgundies. Among a few more reasonable bottles is still very young Gigondas '85, from Jaboulet, at £12, but the Pauillacs concentrate on £50 plus. More reports, please.

CHEF: Hans Schweitzer PROPRIETORS: Chris Kelly, Hans Schweitzer and Michael Smith
OPEN: Tue to Sun, exc Sat L and Sun D
MEALS: 12 to 2, 6.30 to 9.30
PRICES: Set L £9.80 (£16), Set D £17.50 (£25) to £25 (£33)
CARDS: Access, Diners, Visa
SEATS: 30. 2 tables outside. Private parties: 30 main room, 12 private room. Children's helpings, on request. Smart dress preferred. Wheelchair access. Music

Shao Tao [10/20]

72 Regent Street, Cambridge CB2 1DF
CAMBRIDGE (0223) 353942 £14–£20

This example of the multi-regional Chinese restaurant, complete with décor, draws an uncommon amount of support. The menu runs to some 150 dishes, majoring in popular techniques like sizzling, five ways with duck (proper Peking requires 24 hours' notice), some hot and garlic sauces inspired by the Hunan, and, of course, toffee bananas or apples. The chef's specials at the back of the menu include a steam pot (£20 a head, minimum four people) and a range of hotter dishes, often using prawns. The 25p cover charge and 10 per cent service charge put the bill up. Twenty basic wines, from £5.

CHEF/PROPRIETOR: Mr Tao
OPEN: all week
MEALS: 12 to 2.30, 6 to 11 (11.30 Fri and Sat)
PRICES: £12 (£20), Set D from £9.50 (£14). Cover 25p. Service 10%
CARDS: Access, Amex, Diners, Visa
SEATS: 100. Private parties: 100 main room, 30 private room. Vegetarian meals. Children's helpings. Wheelchair access (also WC). Music. Air-conditioned

Twenty Two [new owners, zero rated]

22 Chesterton Road, Cambridge CB4 3AX
CAMBRIDGE (0223) 351880 £20

Michael and Susan Sharpe have taken over this Victorian terraced house near Jesus Green. In the pink-walled dining-room with its stained-glass window, old oak dresser and fresh flowers, they have created an intimate, dinner-party setting for some excellent, serious cooking. The four-course fixed-price menu is modern and eclectic. Soups, such as sorrel or cauliflower and almond, appear alongside prawns in filo pastry with garlic, or beef satay to start; then comes a salad – perhaps a mixture of peppers, tiny tomatoes and flower petals – before roast duck with raspberry sauce or pork tenderloin charcutière. Monkfish is cooked in a thick wedge like osso buco and served with tagliatelle. To finish there are colourful home-made sorbets, brandysnap baskets filled with tiramisu, or orange, carrot and nut cake. The 50-strong wine list supports Spain, Portugal and New Zealand, as well as France. CELLARMAN'S CHOICE: Rioja Imperial Gran Reserva '76 at £9.95. More reports, please.

CHEF: Michael Sharpe PROPRIETORS: Michael and Susan Sharpe
OPEN: Tue to Sat, D only
CLOSED: Christmas to New Year
MEALS: 7.30 to 10
PRICES: Set D £14.50 (£20). Licensed, also bring your own: corkage £3
CARDS: Access, Visa
SEATS: 32. 4 tables outside. Private parties: 28 main room. Vegetarian meals. No children under 12. Music

Upstairs [11/20]

71 Castle Street, Cambridge CB2 3AH
CAMBRIDGE (0223) 312569 £11–£14

Virginia La Charité's cramped upstairs restaurant has a devoted following. The food is authentic Middle Eastern and North African and the dining-room has a slightly eccentric yet discreet mood. Despite the gutsiness of the cooking, this is not the old bazaar in Cairo. Hot sesame seed bread with yoghurt and mint dip is offered before chorba (thick vegetable soup), or gagamp (cabbage leaves stuffed with minced beef and topped with tomatoes and raisins). Couscous is a mighty dish, enough for two, and the quality of the lamb shows in an Armenian speciality with apricots and raisins. Finish with sweet crêpes or haytaliah – pieces of pomegranate and pistachios in rose-water. Moroccan Tarik M'Tir matches the food, though CELLARMAN'S CHOICE: Romeira Garrafeira '76, £6.50, or Hill-Smith Chardonnay '85, £9.

CHEFS: Hywel Evans PROPRIETOR: Virginia La Charité
OPEN: Tue to Sun D
MEALS: 6.30 to 10.30 (9.30 Sun)
PRICES: £9 (£14), Set L from £7 (£11), Set D from £7 (£11)
CARDS: Access, Visa
SEATS: 36. Vegetarian meals. Children's helpings. Smart dress preferred. Music

Cambridgeshire Round-up

SETTING: *King Pantry,* 9 Kings Parade, Cambridge (0223 321551).
CHINESE ON A BOAT: *Grain Barge,* The Quayside, Embankment Road, Peterborough (0733 311967).
ROOMS: *Old Bridge Hotel,* 1 High Street, Huntingdon (0480 52681).
INEXPENSIVE: *Bistro 29,* Bridge Street, Peterborough (0733 61996); *Cambridge Blue,* Gwydir Street, Cambridge (0223 61382).
AFTERNOON TEA: *Café 38,* 38 High Street, Soham, Ely (0353 721055).

The Guide *recruits new inspectors from readers who write in regularly. If you would like to apply, write to the Editor with (a) a detailed report on a restaurant where you have eaten and (b) a comparative study of restaurants known to you.*

CAMPSEA ASH Suffolk map 3

▲ *Old Rectory* [12/20]

Campsea Ash IP13 0PU
WICKHAM MARKET (0728) 746524
on B1078, 1m E of A12 £14–£21

The dining-rooms of Stewart Bassett's large eighteenth-century country house are reminiscent of Dordogne hotels: high-ceilinged, big French-doored, simply decorated with a lot of white. The corridors are those of a small château. There's a feeling of space, restrained opulence and a faintly tatty, relaxed and informal country air. A new blue and yellow conservatory is now operating. The virtues lie in an anti-restaurant stance: little choice, an attempt perhaps to recreate a pre-war country-house dinner party, but some superb dishes and a wine list of unquestionable calibre. Pastry is always a strength. Otherwise the style is exemplified by fish terrines, roast duck, saddle of hare, fine green salads, 'ordinary but delicious' puddings. Breakfast comes with copies of *The Times* and a large dog. The wine list is reasonably priced, ranges around Europe and the New World, though it is brief in its selections from outside France. Clarets range from good, simple wines to many mature vintages back to '45. The short lists of red and white Burgundies include wines from both growers and merchants, and some elderly bottles. Rhônes are excellent, unusually stretching back to '70 in the North. There is a good choice of sweet wines, and the long list of sweet Bordeaux has mature wines back to '61. Among six sweet Loires are four vintages, from '75 to '47, of Anjou Moulin Touchais, £13.45 to £43, and a selection of Tokays begins with Five Putts '76 at £8.90, and peaks at Tokay Aszu Essencia '47, £120. CELLARMAN'S CHOICE: Bourgogne Aligoté '83, £6.90, Chiroubles '83, £8.85; Lebanese Château Musar '79, £8.90.

CHEF/PROPRIETOR: Stewart Bassett
OPEN: Mon to Sat D (L by arrangement)
MEALS: 7.30 to 10
PRICES: Set L from £9.50 (£14), Set D £14 (£19) and £16 (£21)
CARDS: Access, Amex, Diners, Visa
SEATS: 40. Private parties: 18 main room; 20, 6 private rooms. Car-park, 20 places. Vegetarian meals. Children's helpings. No children under 10. Wheelchair access
ACCOMMODATION: 8 rooms, all with bath/shower. B&B £26 to £40. Deposit: 10%. No children under 8. Garden. Doors close at 1 [GHG]

CANTERBURY Kent map 3

George's Brasserie [9/20]

71–72 Castle Street, Canterbury CT1 2QD
CANTERBURY (0227) 65658 £10–£16

This family-run, all-day French brasserie is set in a long upstairs room, the dark-brown walls studded with pictures and posters. Food is fresh and Mediterranean in origin: home-made linguine features next to couscous served with harissa and chickpea salad; a slice of warm onion tart comes before a brochette of pork and prunes soaked in armagnac. A dish of the day appears on the blackboard menu. House Italian and French £5.50. CELLARMAN'S CHOICE: St Véran blanc, £10.75.

CHEFS/PROPRIETORS: Simon Day and Beverly Holmes
OPEN: Mon to Sat
MEALS: 10am to 10pm (10.30 Fri and Sat)
PRICES: £10 (£16), Set L from £5.90 (£10), Set D from £7.45 (£12), Snacks from 85p. Service 10%
CARDS: Access, Amex, Carte Blanche, Visa
SEATS: 100. Private parties: 50 main room; 10, 30 and 50 private rooms. Vegetarian meals. Children's helpings. No-smoking area. Wheelchair access. Music

Tuo e Mio [10/20]

16 The Borough, Canterbury CT1 2DR
CANTERBURY (0227) 61471 £12–£18

The small period house behind the cathedral evokes a corner of Italy. A show of fresh produce lends confidence and the menu seems to avoid the usual clichés. Fish and pasta are the key areas of quality. Also notable are the calf's liver with a rich onion and wine sauce, profiteroles, and chocolate gateau. Family-run and busier at night than at lunch-time, when there is a good-value set meal. House Italian is £5.

CHEFS: Bernardino Lombardo and Tino Guzman PROPRIETORS: Mr and Mrs R.P.M. Greggio
OPEN: Tue to Sun, exc Tue L
MEALS: 12 to 2.30, 7 to 10.45 (10 Sun)
PRICES: £12 (£18), Set L £8 (£12). Cover 50p. Service 10%
CARDS: Access, Amex, Diners, Visa
SEATS: 40. Private parties: 20 main room. Vegetarian meals. Children welcome. No pipes in dining-room. Wheelchair access (1 step; also WC). Music

Kent Round-up

ROOMS: *Howfield Manor*, Chartham Hatch, Canterbury (0227 738495); *Royal Oak Hotel*, Upper High Street, Sevenoaks (0732 451109).
ENGLISH: *Wife of Bath*, 4 Upper Bridge Street, Wye (0233 812540); *Cranes*, 2 Waterloo Road, Cranbrook (0580 712396); *Eastwell Manor*, Eastwell Park, Boughton Lees, Ashford (0233 35751).
VIEW: *Spotted Dog*, Smarts Hill, Penshurst (0892 870158).
BISTRO: *Paul's*, 2A Bouverie Road West, Folkestone (0303 59697).
COFFEE HOUSE: *Sweet Heart of Canterbury*, Old Weavers House, 2-3 Kings Bridge, Canterbury (0227 458626).
SETTING: *Bull Hotel*, Bull Lane, Wrotham, Nr Sevenoaks (0732 883092).
ITALIAN: *Emilio's*, 124A Sandgate Road, Folkestone (0303 55866).
CHINESE: *Mandarin Chef*, 35 Lower Stone Street, Maidstone (0622 55917); *Ming*, London Road, Wrotham Heath, Sevenoaks (0732 883427).

All details are as accurate as possible at the time of going to press. Please notify the Guide *office of any changes.*

CARTMEL Cumbria map 7

▲ *Aynsome Manor* [12/20]

Cartmel LA11 6HH
CARTMEL (044 854) 653 £11–£20

This attractive house is set on the limits of the Lake District proper, and so misses most of the tourist hordes. The manor is Georgian, with typically spacious proportions to the rooms; the dining-room has wood panelling and subtle lighting. The menu changes daily and uses for the most part local ingredients (not, though, the shark in a shallot and white wine sauce). A spring menu offers puff pastry horns with cream cheese and herb pâté with redcurrant purée; asparagus mousse with orange and tomato salad; roast pheasant with sherry and almond sauce. The style is very much in the Lakeland tradition, with plenty of fruit in evidence, adventurous combination soups, such as leek, broccoli and tarragon, and calorific sweets. Of the 90 wines the New World holds the most interest and value. CELLARMAN'S CHOICE: Rosemount Coonawarra Estate, Cabernet Sauvignon Show Reserve '84, £11.50.

CHEFS: Ernest Scott, Tony Varley, Ian Simpson and Ava Hill PROPRIETORS: Tony and Margaret Varley
OPEN: Mon to Sat D, and Sun L
CLOSED: 2 to 27 Jan
MEALS: 1, 7 to 8.15
PRICES: Set L £6.95 (£11), Set D £13.50 (£20)
CARDS: Access, Amex, Visa
SEATS: 35. Private parties: 35 main room. Car-park, 20 places. Children's helpings. No children under 5 at D. Smart dress preferred. No smoking in dining-room. Wheelchair access
ACCOMMODATION: 13 rooms, 12 with bath/shower. B&B £20 to £40. Pets welcome. Garden. Fishing. Golf. TV. Phone. Scenic. Doors close at 11.30

▲ *Uplands* [14/20]

Haggs Lane, Cartmel LA11 6HD
CARTMEL (044 854) 248 and 249 £14–£23

It is a tribute to John Tovey's style of cooking that it is so transferable from one restaurant to another, retaining its vigour and freshness, immediately identifiable as Tovey's and yet also different every night. Tom Peter is an impressive disciple. He has developed the cuisine outside of Miller Howe where he and his wife Diana were before. In terms of value and, increasingly, consistency, the smaller, younger off-shoot competes vigorously with the *grande dame* at Windermere, and is more a restaurant in the round than the new venture, the Bay Horse at Ulverston (see entry). Here there is a short menu, with a choice of two starters and three main courses, usually including one fish, and four sweets. The stage props are the hot loaf of brown bread left with a carving knife on the table to start; the tureen of a Tovey-inspired vegetable-combination soup, again left for DIY, and the fine vegetables around the main course. The cooking wears its seasonings on the outside and they persistently nag and tug at the centrepiece – ginger in parsnip soup; or again with soy, mustard, rosemary and wine in a marinade for lamb eventually served with a piquant sauce. Freshly dressed Filey crab comes with a kiwi-fruit salad; fillet of Scarborough woof is topped with a salmon mousse and served with a tarragon and Chambéry sauce; chicken breast is stuffed with cheese and herb pâté and served with a mustard, honey and cream sauce. These are assertive displays of taste, matched by sweets such as banana, walnut and ginger farmhouse pie with warm butterscotch sauce, or tipsy trifle. Game is from the local estate at Holker Hall. Many of the vegetables are organic. The décor, while less theatrical than Miller Howe, has a certain upward mobility. Rooms are clean, spacious and well furnished. The wine list is limited but tries to offer a choice in most of the major regions. CELLARMAN'S CHOICE: Riesling, Falkensteiner Hofberg '86, £8, Orlando de Chardonnay, Barossa Valley '87, £8.50.

CHEF: Tom Peter PROPRIETORS: John J. Tovey, Tom and Diana Peter
OPEN: Tue to Sun, and Mon bank hols
CLOSED: 4 Jan to 12 Feb
MEALS: 12.30 to 1, 7.30 to 8
PRICES: Set L £9 (£14), Set D £17 (£23). Service 10%
CARDS: Access, Amex
SEATS: 34. Private parties: 34 main room. Car-park, 18 places. Vegetarian meals. No children under 8. No smoking in dining-room. Wheelchair access. Music
ACCOMMODATION: 4 rooms, all with bath/shower. B&B £22 to £56. No children under 8. Pets welcome. Garden. TV. Phone. Scenic. Doors close at 11. Confirm by 3 [GHG]

CHADDESLEY CORBETT Hereford & Worcester map 5

▲ *Brockencote Hall* [12/20]

Chaddesley Corbett DY10 4PY
CHADDESLEY CORBETT (0562) 83876 £16–£31

The magnificent Georgian hall is set in 70 acres of landscaped grounds with a half-timbered dovecote, a two-acre lake and a fine collection of trees from Europe and North America. It has pure classical elegance, yet feels like a luxurious family residence. Serge Demollière's cooking is in the style of modern French hotel food: terrine of monkfish with sauces of red pepper and fennel; home-made 'duck foie gras' in a Bordeaux jelly; mille-feuille of leek whites with a sauce made from the green of the vegetable. Gigot of lamb is carved at the table and served with a sauce of its own juices; pigs' trotters are stuffed with sweetbreads. Fish are luxury items: salmon, turbot, scallops, lobster and the like. Lime soufflé is a good sweet and the cheeseboard is reckoned to be one of the best within striking distance of Birmingham. Bordeaux dominates the list of 70 wines, but CELLARMAN'S CHOICE is Montagny *premier cru*, Domaine Arnoux '85, £16.30.

Restaurants awarded a rosette have had an entry in every Guide *since 1980. See Restaurants of the decade on page 21.*

CHEF: Serge Demollière PROPRIETORS: Mr and Mrs J. Petitjean
OPEN: all week, exc Sat L and Sun D
MEALS: 12.30 to 2, 7.30 to 9.30
PRICES: £26 (£31), Set L £10.50 (£16). Service inc
CARDS: Access, Amex, Diners, Visa
SEATS: 38. 5 tables outside. Private parties: 40 main room, 25 private room. Car-park, 45 places. Vegetarian meals. Children welcome. Smart dress preferred. Wheelchair access (also WC). Music
ACCOMMODATION: 9 rooms, all with bath/shower. B&B £45 to £58. Afternoon teas. Garden. TV. Phone. Scenic. Doors close at 12. confirm by 6 [GHG]

CHAGFORD Devon map 1

▲ *Gidleigh Park* [16/20]

Chagford TQ13 8HH
CHAGFORD (064 73) 2367/8/9 and 2225
from Chagford square, turn R at Lloyds,
then R at first fork for 2m £26–£35

The achievement of Paul and Kay Henderson's isolated country-house hotel is that although its profile is one of luxury, there is an understanding of the finer things of life, unclouded by financial constraints. In all, a rather grown-up approach. The house and grounds, too, have matured and developed over the last 10 years; many rooms have been revamped. Chef Shaun Hill has been made managing director and the Hendersons plan to open a London hotel next year. There is a fusion throughout the operation, but where the hotel prices match the top flight in Europe, eating and drinking at the lower end of the wine list are not that expensive, considering. A set, no-choice, tasting menu changed every day supplements other set-price menus that are surprisingly long by country-house hotel standards but a reflection of the investment in the kitchen. The style is unusually cosmopolitan, bringing together many of the best ideas of recent years. Among the starters are Italian touches, for instance bresaola, pasta in the form of ravioli stuffed with chicken liver and garlic, and again with scallops in the consommé. Luxuries that carry supplements include Tay smoked salmon and beluga caviare. Fish can take up as many as half the main courses – rarely outside of specialist restaurants do monk, sole, turbot and mullet share the same menu, here one night sauced respectively with mussels; mustard and cucumber; a tomato mille-feuille and sorrel; and with rosemary and cream and, respectively, steamed; sauté; grilled; sauté. Other points illustrate a deep understanding of the use of expensive ingredients – lentils with a foie gras essence for grilled guinea-fowl breast; a sensational parade of veal fillet, kidney and sweetbreads arranged with two sauces, one a creamy Meaux mustard and the other a shallot-based stock, divided by a spoonful of brown lentils – and also out-of-the-ordinary techniques, such as beef fillet poached in veal stock and served with a béarnaise sauce. Recommendations include: corn-fed pigeon with grilled baby vegetables; the same with sauté foie gras and red wine sauce; salad of lettuces with roasted rabbit and artichoke with walnut-oil dressing; sauté foie gras on a toasted brioche

(£3 supplement); sauté calf's sweetbreads with roasted shallots and sherry vinegar sauce; sweetbreads again, this time with a very light, crisp, thin batter coating, served with a cassis and stock sauce with mixed lettuce and a sort of rösti potato cake. The cheeseboard has little groups of hard cheeses, double-cream and triple-cream versions, goats' cheeses, superb French examples, and a good selection of walnut bread or biscuits. Sweets take in exemplary caramel and apple tart, cherry Bakewell tart, magnificent tuiles, and 'a mille-feuille made out of a slab each of caramel, white and dark chocolate with a filling of frothy cream mixed with jagged pieces of caramel and hazelnuts.' Breakfasts improve. The usual cereals are offered plus a good home-made meusli; generous glasses of freshly squeezed orange juice; thinly sliced Gouda cheese and cervelat sausage; corned beef hash with poached egg; Loch Fyne kippers; fried egg with Irish potato bread; yoghurt with compote of quince, pear and peach; or a mammoth plate of herb sausage, tomato, mushroom, bacon and eggs (the last is £6 extra). As an American, Paul Henderson is justly proud of his list of American wines, almost all from California, and probably the best selection of mature American wines in Britain. It includes nine examples of Cabernet Sauvignons from Joseph Heitz's top vineyards, Martha's Vineyard and Bella Oaks Vineyard. Three different vintages of Ridge Montebello Cabernet Sauvignon, numerous estates' top Reserve wines, and excellent ranges of American Chardonnay and Riesling wines also make the Gidleigh Park list a delight for homesick Americans and enquiring Europeans alike. However, the list is by no means all American. The £130,000 worth of stock encompasses a truly top-class selection of red and white Burgundies, stretching back to some virtually unobtainable mature vintages, an excellent range of clarets (the grand wines come from the good years, not just the lesser ones for the satisfaction of having famous names on the list), marvellous Rhône from Paul Jaboulet-Aîné, and Alsace wines, mainly from Hugel and Trimbach. Six house wines are available by the glass, including champagne and two dessert wines, and a further and finer eight by the glass from a Cruover machine. Lovers of sweet wines are exceptionally well looked after, with wonderful wines from Alsace – '76 Sélections de Grains Nobles from Hugel, at £8.05 per glass, for instance – some very good Sauternes and California sweeties, mainly sold in half-bottles, and even three German Beerenauslesen, also in half-bottles. Fine port, madeira, cognacs, armagnacs and malt whiskies jostle for post-prandial attention.

CHEF: Shaun Hill PROPRIETORS: Kay and Paul Henderson
OPEN: all week
MEALS: 12.30 to 2, 7 to 9
PRICES: Set L from £18.50 (£26), Set D from £26.50 (£35). Service inc
CARDS: Access, Amex, Diners, Visa
SEATS: 35. Private parties: 18 main room. Car-park, 25 places. Children welcome. Smart dress preferred. No cigars/pipes in dining-room. Wheelchair access
ACCOMMODATION: 14 rooms, all with bath/shower. B&B £55 to £125. Pets by arrangement. Afternoon teas. Garden. Tennis. Fishing. TV. Phone. Scenic [GHG]

This symbol is awarded only to restaurants with outstanding wine cellars.

▲ *Teignworthy Hotel* [14/20]

Frenchbeer, Chagford TQ13 8EX
CHAGFORD (064 73) 3355
3m SW of Chagford. From Chagford Square follow signs to Fernworthy, then Kestor and Thornworthy £19–£31

At the end of a long, winding, narrow lane bordered on both sides by great mossy boulders. The extensive gardens on the edge of the Dartmoor National Park fall away to the River Teign far below. Huge granite fireplaces add to the feeling that Teignworthy was built to hold out against the elements. The Newells marked 10 years in residence with a redecoration of the dining-room, now less rustic in appearance though still, like the rest of the hotel, straightforward and restrained. The menu makes appealing reading, full of colours: avocado and mango salad with raspberry vinegar; saffron sauce; lemon hollandaise; dark chocolate crème brûlée with kumquat salad. There is nothing sissy about the flavours. Each dish makes its point in no uncertain way. Supplies are excellent real foods, down to the farmhouse butter. Fish, vegetarian and pastry are strong themes, witness a baked fillet of red mullet wrapped in filo pastry with basil served on a bed of tomato and fennel – the basil chopped between two fillets, the pastry soft, the sauce just lightened with the fennel; or a sauté of maize-fed guinea-fowl in an armagnac and grape sauce with a hint of honey. Vegetables are plain and excellent – the kitchen garden is coming on line. Sweets feature a fine brandysnap basket filled with praline ice-cream and served on an amaretto sabayon. Bordeaux and Burgundy are the strongest points of the 133-strong wine list, but there are plenty of more basic wines at very affordable prices, starting with red and white house wines at £6.50 per litre, £1.20 per glass. There are several good *cru bourgeois* clarets, and a number of classed growths going back to '70. Burgundies are mostly from highly respected growers, Beaujolais also from single properties. A few good wines from Australia, California, Spain, Germany and Italy top up the list. Apart from two ports, two sweet wines are available by the glass: Muscat de Beaumes de Venise, Domaine de Durban and Australian Brown Bros Orange Muscat and Flora '85, both £2, or there's Sauternes and Barsac by the bottle. CELLARMAN'S CHOICE: Brown Bros Chardonnay '86, £10.90; Rioja, Imperial Reserva '78, £9.90.

CHEF: David Woolfall PROPRIETORS: John and Gillian Newell
OPEN: all week
MEALS: 12 to 2, 7.30 to 9
PRICES: £20 (£24), Set L £14 (£19) to £24 (£29), Set D £14.50 (£23) to £27.50 (£31), Snacks from £1.50
SEATS: 30. 3 tables outside. Private parties: 30 main room. Car-park. Vegetarian meals. No children under 12. No smoking in dining-room. Wheelchair access (also WC)
ACCOMMODATION: 9 rooms, all with bath/shower. B&B £45 to £78. No children under 12. Afternoon teas. Garden. Sauna. Tennis. Fishing. TV. Phone. Scenic [GHG]

'There was a lot of service. I could see people enjoying a quiet threesome – husband, wife and waiter.' On eating in London

CHEAM Surrey map 3

Al San Vincenzo [12/20]

52 Upper Mulgrave Road, Cheam SM2 7AJ
01-661 9763 £24

Vincenzo Borgonzolo describes his cooking as creative Mediterranean. Now shorter, the dozen dish *carte* offers octopus in a chilli-piquant sauce of tomato and oil; steamed razor-fish with marsala, smoked pancetta and onion sauce; monkfish with sea-urchin sauce. Fish now comes direct from Scotland. The style is more in the manner of modern French or British restaurants: small, personal, plenty of opera. Standard Italian dishes like pasta, calf's liver with sage, ice-cream often have a southern accent, but there are also more innovative combinations: warm artichokes with smoked salmon and new potatoes, quail braised with mango sauce. There is usually an interesting choice of Italian cheeses such as Pecorino, Scamerza and Taleggio, over and above Dolcelatte. Ice-creams and sorbets are made in house and move with the markets, providing versions such as pineapple sorbet or almond ice-cream. The wine list is short, exclusively Italian and mostly under £10, with the house wine traded in to allow on to the list a white Sardinian Muraghe Majore '86 which goes particularly well with fish. CELLARMAN'S CHOICE: Dolcetta D'Alba Ceretto '85, £10.75.

CHEF: Vincenzo Borgonzolo PROPRIETORS: Vincenzo and Elaine Borgonzolo
OPEN: Mon to Sat (Sat L by arrangement only)
MEALS: 12 to 2.30, 6.30 to 10.30
PRICES: Set L and D £17.50 (£24)
CARDS: Access, Diners, Visa, Amex
SEATS: 20. Private parties: 22 main room. Children's helpings. No smoking. Wheelchair access

CHEDINGTON Dorset map 2

▲ *Chedington Court* [12/20]

Chedington DT8 3HY
CORSCOMBE (093 589) 265
off A356 4m SE of Crewkerne  £24

The Englishness of the Court, emphasised doubtless for foreigners, is its charm. It is an England where the stunning garden gets more attention than the house, which is left in academic seclusion for much of the day. Guests are left to their own devices and they only come together in the library before dinner. Hilary Chapman's cooking provides a focal point. She is a confident and accomplished technician, a cook's cook and content to understate rather than show off. Fishcake is made from the white meat of a crab and sauced with a bisque from its shell. Her duck is the breast only, the skin crisped almost like crackling, with a sticky orange and lemon sauce scattered with vegetables, sauté potatoes providing a contrast of texture. Typical of the style are grilled red mullet with mustard and dill, rack of lamb with tarragon sauce, filo tart filled with mushroom purée, asparagus and hollandaise, pork escalope sauced with tomato and orange. The sweets trolley is among the finest in the South of England, with Pavlova, mousses, and bombes, all of impeccably judged flavours. Tactfully, the cheeseboard does not try to compete. Bedrooms are sizeable and solid. Philip Chapman has assembled a cellar to match the sweep of house and grounds, with an interesting selection of non-champagne sparkling wines, good wines from less well-known parts of France including Cahors, Bergerac and Vin de Thouasais, a selection from Israel, Greece and Rumania, and a handful of good Australian and Californian wines. Spain is rarely well represented on restaurant wine lists, but this must be one of the best Rioja lists in the country. A long and very well chosen selection includes several wines from Muga, La Rioja Alta, Murrieta, CVNE and several others, and older vintages are remarkably inexpensive. Not all the wines are great: red Italians are better than white, some of the Rhônes are less interesting and Burgundies are mixed in quality, but Beaujolais is good, and a fairly short list of clarets includes a number of very mature vintages. There is a good choice of sweet wines: a fine array of mature German Auslesen, Beerenauslesen, Trockenbeerenauslesen and Eiswein, a few sweet Bordeaux, a choice of half-bottles of Muscat de Beaumes de Venise, Greek Samos Muscat, Vin de Paille from the Jura and from Australia, Brown Bros Late Harvest Orange Muscat and Flora '85, £8.20 per half-bottle. House wines are red and white Mouflon d'Or, at £5.80, and there are two pages of CELLARMAN'S CHOICE: one red, one white.

CHEF: Hilary Chapman PROPRIETORS: Philip and Hilary Chapman
OPEN: all week, D only
MEALS: 7 to 9
PRICES: Set D £21 (£24). Service inc
CARDS: Amex, Visa
SEATS: 30. 2 tables outside. Private parties: 30 main room, 40 private room. Car-park, 20 places. Vegetarian meals. Children's helpings. Smart dress preferred. No cigars/pipes in dining-room. Wheelchair access (also WC). Music
ACCOMMODATION: 10 rooms, all with bath/shower. B&B £30 to £80. Deposit: £30. Baby facilities. Garden. Snooker. TV. Phone. Scenic. Doors close at 12. Confirm by 9pm [GHG]

CHELMSFORD Essex map 3

Melissa [9/20]

21 Broomfield Road, Chelmsford CM1 1SY
CHELMSFORD (0245) 353009 £8–£12

Although many pubs in the town now do quiche for the same price, Melissa, a daughter of Farmhouse Feast at Roxwell (see entry), has the virtue of being vegetarian, a full-time café through the day, with everything made on the premises, often to order. The atmosphere is rather 1960s café with brown patterned plastic tablecloths, wooden chairs and a display/serving counter, not unlike the café in TV's *Last of the Summer Wine*. The basic line is not-over-generous pizzas, but other dishes show more enterprise, for instance a cheese and vegetable charlotte served with brussel sprouts and red cabbage;

three-layered carob gateau; mushroom and nut pie. Dishes are one hundred per cent wholefood and many of the ingredients are organic. Prices are low, with most dishes around £2. The wine list is a triumph of naïveté – from £4.

CHEFS/PROPRIETORS: Rosemary and Melanie Upson
OPEN: Mon to Sat, L only, and D first Fri each month
MEALS: 9 to 4 (L 11.30 to 3)
PRICES: £4 (£9), Set L £5 (£8), Set D £8.50 (£12), Snacks from 85p
SEATS: 24. Private parties: 28 main room. Vegetarian meals. Children's helpings. No smoking in dining-room. Wheelchair access. Self-service (waitress service at D)

CHELTENHAM Gloucestershire map 2

Le Champignon Sauvage [new entry, zero rated]

24–26 Suffolk Road, Cheltenham GL50 2AQ
CHELTENHAM (0242) 573449 £18–£26

Formerly the highly rated Ciboulette, now owned by David and Helen Everitt-Matthias, who have spruced up the décor with salmon pinks and slate greys. He trained at the Inn on the Park and has instantly impressed a number of readers. The menu is short, with half a dozen dishes per course, written (not always accurately) in French with wordy translations which reflect the rather fussy nature of some of the dishes. Ingredients are impeccable, so too the timing and the saucing, but sometimes the ideas are not properly suited to a small kitchen, needing a large hotel brigade to succeed. The fillet of beef in an old-madeira sauce is sufficient in itself without the pickled walnuts, the tomato concasse or the vegetables in the shape of a tasteless roulade. Balancing this criticism is the testament of experienced readers who suggest the rating should be a high one. A style is forming – pike mousse with crayfish; pork with prunes and apricots; fillet of lamb stuffed with kidney and aubergines with another fine sauce of lamb stock. Service from Helen Everitt-Matthias is charming and well informed. Wines are from good, old-fashioned growers like Parisot and Jaboulet-Vercherre, a rather upmarket list with only about 20 per cent under £10, which is in contrast to the good-value menu. House French from £6. CELLARMAN'S CHOICE: Sancerre, Le Chêne Marchand '86, £10.50; Santenay *premier cru*, Clos Rousseau '83, £14; Rully Blanc, La Fontaine '84, £13.50. More reports, please.

CHEFS: David Everitt-Matthias and Adrian Offley PROPRIETORS: David and Helen Everitt-Matthias
OPEN: Mon to Sat, exc Sat L
MEALS: 12.30 to 2, 7.30 to 9.30
PRICES: Set L £10.95 (£18) to £15.95 (£23), Set D £15.95 (£23) to 18.95 (£26)
CARDS: Access, Amex, Visa
SEATS: 34. Private parties: 26 main room. Children welcome. Smart dress preferred. No cigars/pipes in dining-room. Wheelchair access (1 step). Music. Air-conditioned

'Coffee was strong, and good and generous. Petits fours were Smarties.'
On eating in Devon

Number Twelve [10/20]

12 Suffolk Parade, Cheltenham GL50 2AB
CHELTENHAM (0242) 584544 £13–£21

Pink, green, lacy, and comfortably bourgeois, Number Twelve keeps consistent standards in a part of town where there's plenty of competition. The menu changes with the seasons but the *carte* is classic French cooking with a modern touch in the saucing – duck breast with a compote of blackberries, or deep-fried chicken strips with a yoghurt and ginger dressing. Vegetables are plain and perfectly cooked. Results are clear and strong, even when powerful flavourings like ginger and mint are employed. Fifty wines take in some token New World bottles. House French £5.95; CELLARMAN'S CHOICE: Gevrey-Chambertin '81, £18.50; Meursault '84, £22.50.

CHEFS: Norman Young and David Harker PROPRIETOR: Norman Young
OPEN: Tue to Sun, exc Sat L and Sun D
MEALS: 12 to 2, 7.30 to 10 (10.30 Fri and Sat)
PRICES: £15 (£21), Set L £7.95 (£13)
CARDS: Access, Amex, Diners, Visa
SEATS: 40. Private parties: 48 main room. Vegetarian meals. Children's helpings. Music

Redmond's [14/20]

12 Suffolk Road, Cheltenham GL50 2AQ
CHELTENHAM (0242) 580323 £16–£20

'Goes from strength to strength. Redmond Hayward seemingly does everything right. He cooks to order. He never overbooks. He uses fresh, quality ingredients, and has a limited menu which he can handle easily. His wife Pippa controls the front of house with engaging, easy efficiency'. In essence, it is a two-person team that works like a well-oiled machine. The menu changes frequently, has a choice of four dishes for each course, with a choice of two, three or four courses with set prices. Oxfilet Johanna, a rewarding starter of smoked-salmon-thin beef in a mustard-based sauce and gravlax are dishes brought from his days with Anna Hegarty at Anna's Place in London, when together they rated 15/20. Most dishes though, bear his own stamp. Sauces feature strongly – mussels wrapped in salmon are given a mild curry sauce; sirloin steak arrives with a mousse of mushrooms and a port sauce. Hayward's soufflés are exceptional, for example ginger with avocaat cream. Pastry is notable, as is the bread-and-butter pudding laced with rum, which comes with Jersey cream. Late suppers for theatre-goers, by arrangement. Over 30 wines, plus a few half-bottles. Muscat de Beaumes de Venise is £2.25 the glass. Four house wines start at £6.25; CELLARMAN'S CHOICE: Mercurey, Clos l'Evêque '84, £16.30, and Conn Creek Cabernet '81, £15.50.

New this year are County Round-ups, mostly, but not always, listed under the county town. To find a County Round-up, check the maps at the back; towns listing a Round-up are underlined.

CHEF: Redmond Hayward PROPRIETORS: Redmond and Pippa Hayward
OPEN: Tue to Sat D, Sat L and Sun L
CLOSED: first week Jan, 1 week May, 2 weeks Aug to Sept
MEALS: 12.30 to 2, 7.15 to 10
PRICES: Set L £12.50 (£16), Set D from £16.50 (£20). Service inc
CARDS: Access, Visa
SEATS: 22. Private parties: 22 main room. Children's helpings. No children under 5. No cigars/pipes in dining-room. Wheelchair access (1 step). Air-conditioned

CHESTER Cheshire map 5

Abbey Green [10/20]

2 Abbey Green, Northgate Street, Chester CH1 2JH
CHESTER (0244) 313251 £9–£14

'Like the Magi, we trekked back and forth across a wintry landscape, in search of a vegetarian restaurant of the year. Prestwick, York, Cockermouth, Southampton, back up to Chester...and there were times when the voices were ringing in our ears saying that this was all madness.' The Abbey Green won the award with its pleasant atmosphere, artful arrangements on the plate, easily read handwritten menu, some half-dozen starters and half-dozen main courses, a varied provenance for the dishes – starters of mushrooms dijonnaise; potted broccoli with Lymeswold; red pepper and tomato soup (served lukewarm – a surprise, but entirely correct for the flavours). Main courses also show a world-wide inspiration, certainly in titles: Szechuan aubergine and tofu parcels; spanokopita – filo pastry with spinach and Feta cheese; mushrooms korma with turmeric rice and vegetable balls, though it has to be said that the internationalism can be more in the title than in the taste. Non-vegetarians are comfortably converted. A short wine list starts with house French at £5; CELLARMAN'S CHOICE: Tokay d'Alsace '86, £9.90; Marqués de Murrieta '81, £9.70; Mas de Gourgonnier '84, £8.75.

CHEFS: Julia Lochhead, Michael Davies and Christine Scott PROPRIETORS: Julia and Duncan Lochhead
OPEN: all week, exc Sun D and Mon D
MEALS: 11.30 to 3, 6.30 to 10.15
PRICES: L £5 (£9), D £10 (£14)
SEATS: 48. Private parties: 8 main room, 24 private room. Car-park, 20 places. Vegetarian meals. Children's helpings. No-smoking area. Wheelchair access. Music

▲ *La Brasserie, Chester Grosvenor Hotel* [10/20]

Eastgate Street, Chester CH1 1LT
CHESTER (0244) 324024 £16–£27

In excess of ten million pounds has been spent on refurbishing this renowned hotel. Prices in the Arkle Room restaurant tend to gallop away, but the new Brasserie redresses the balance by offering quality and value for money. The menu has a wide range of snacks, and stylish modern bistro dishes: terrine of salmon with sauce grelette, warm salad of smoked duck with oyster mushrooms, cassoulet of scallops with a powerful broth of champagne, basil and saffron. The more simple items, such as char-grilled lamb cutlets, are good too. Blueberry parfait is a typical sweet, and French cheeses come from Philippe Olivier. Smart surroundings, and cheery, knowledgeable service. All wines are available by the glass. House Côtes du Rhône is £7.50. CELLARMAN'S CHOICE: Crustaces Alsace '83, from Dopff & Irion, £10.75.

CHEF: Paul Reid PROPRIETORS: Grosvenor Estate Holdings
OPEN: all week
MEALS: 6.30am to 11.30pm
PRICES: £18 (£27), Set L £8.95 (£16), Set D £12.50 (£20), Snacks from £2.95
CARDS: Access, Amex, Carte Blanche, Diners, Visa
SEATS: 122. Private parties: 12 main room, 18, 60 and 350 private rooms. Vegetarian meals. Children's helpings. Smart dress preferred. Wheelchair access (also WC). Air-conditioned
ACCOMMODATION: 87 rooms, all with bath/shower. Rooms for disabled. Lift. B&B £97 to £144. Baby facilities. Afternoon teas. Sauna. Air-conditioning. TV. Phone [GHG]

Cheshire Round-up

WINE BAR: *Oddfellows*, 20 Rood Hill, Congleton (0260 270243).
VEGETARIAN: *Fourgate's*, 126 Foregate Street, Chester (0244 315046).
ENGLISH: *Randalls*, 22 Old Market Place, High Street, Bollington, Nr Macclesfield (0625 75058).
ROOMS: *Stanneylands Hotel*, Stanneylands Road, Wilmslow (0625 525225).

CHILGROVE West Sussex map 3

White Horse Inn [10/20]

Chilgrove PO18 9HX
EAST MARDEN (024 359) 219 £21–£24

'Every year on holiday I dream of running a restaurant with no menu – just verbal offerings of what is good and fresh,' says Barry Phillips. In fact the menu of seven starters and seven mains is augmented by seven dishes of the day. It is not really market cookery at all, but classically inclined – sauce Nantua for squid, hollandaise for asparagus, thermidor for lobster. As often happens with restaurants with great wine lists, there is a less than neat dovetailing with the menu, some quite complex dishes providing too many distractions to truly complement the quality of the drinking, which is quite spectacular. There are pages of top names and mature vintages on the list as well as fine ready-to-drink young wines at prices that range from the reasonable to the super-bargain. This is surely the best German wine list anyone could hope to find: a vast array of fine estates and fine vintages, including many tempting '71s and '76s, but also vintages back to '59. The Californian section is extensive and includes many vintages, going back to '74. French wines concentrate largely on the classic areas. Burgundies stand out among the outstanding, with a huge list including many top growers and a lot of *grands crus*. Old Burgundies are always a risk, but the curious might be tempted at between £26 and £45 for vintages of the '60s and '40s. The clarets are perhaps more stunning still, stretching back to '19, topped by special collections of the finest wines: there are, for instance, 37 vintages of Latour between '19 and '80. Choose in Alsace from late harvest wines of the '76, '73 or '71 vintages, in champagne from five vintages of Bollinger Vieilles Vignes. There are good sweet wines in abundance, too: many German Beeren- and Trockenbeerenauslesen, sweet Bordeaux including 'fringe' areas such as Loupiac and Cérons (and vintages of Yquem from '42 to '73), mature late harvest Californias, and from the Loire various vintages of Moulin Touchais as well as other sweet wines, such as a Bonnezeaux, Château de Fesles '66 for just £19.95. If, unsurprisingly, you feel you've over-indulged by the time you reach the pudding, there's Solera madeira by the glass for £4.50. Antelope real ales. Bar food is inexpensive.

CHEF: Neal Findley PROPRIETORS: Dorothea and Barry Phillips
OPEN: Tue to Sat, and Sun L
CLOSED: 3 weeks Feb, 1 week Oct
MEALS: 12 to 1.45, 7 to 9.30
PRICES: Set L £12.95 (£21), Set D £15.95 (£24), Snacks from £1.25. Service 12.5%
CARDS: Access, Amex, Diners, Visa
SEATS: 65. 12 tables outside. Private parties: 65 main room. Car-park, 50 places. Vegetarian meals. Children's helpings. Wheelchair access (also WC). Music

CHINNOR Oxfordshire map 2

Sir Charles Napier Inn [10/20]

Sprigg's Alley, nr Chinnor OX9 4BX
RADNAGE (024 026) 3011 £14–£26

From the M40, turn right at Chinnor crossroads and the inn is two miles down the lane, set in its own grounds with fine views from the terrace at the back. Décor and food coincide, being a mix of the plain and sophisticated. 'An extraordinary collection of non-matching old furniture, old photographs, potted plants, disused samovar and a waitress whose habit would appear outlandish in Chelsea, let alone rural Oxfordshire, but whose knowledge of the English cheeses on the splendid cheeseboard is encyclopaedic.' The menu takes in poached mussels, saddle of hare with brandy sauce, duckling with a duck-liver and citrus fruit sauce, salmon with mustard hollandaise, home-made beef sausage. Recommended dishes include fish soup with saffron; loin of boar with prunes and armagnac; braised ox-tail; steak with marrow-bone sauce; bread-and-butter pudding. Extras accelerate the bill. The short wine list doesn't seek to be too ambitious, but almost every single wine is recommendable, as well as being remarkably inexpensive. French wines are in the majority, and the list is particularly good on both red and white Burgundy, the Loire and Alsace. A few wines from California and Germany and some interesting wines from Italy round off the selection. Sweet wines are limited, but there's a good Bonnezeaux, Château de Fesles '79, £8.95, and a Sauternes, Château Rieussec '78, £6.25 per half-bottle.

If you suspect that a restaurant is using processed food, always ask. It would be a contravention of the Trade Description Act for the restaurant to lie.

CHEF: Batiste Tolu PROPRIETORS: The Griffiths family
OPEN: Tue to Sun, exc Sun D
MEALS: 12 to 2 (3 Sun), 7.30 to 10 (10.30 Fri and Sat)
PRICES: £17 (£26), Set L from £8.75 (£14). Service 12.5%
CARDS: Amex, Diners
SEATS: 65. 10 tables outside. Private parties: 45 main room, 45 and 25 private rooms. Car-park, 60 places. Vegetarian meals. Children's helpings (L only). No children under 7 at D. No cigars/pipes in dining-room. Wheelchair access. Music. Air-conditioned

---

CHIPPING CAMPDEN Gloucestershire map 2

▲ *Charingworth Manor* [new entry, zero rated]

Charingworth, nr Chipping Campden, GL55 6NS
PAXFORD (038) 678 555 £22–£36

The latest Cotswold manor house to be turned into a country-house hotel. The many-gabled building of honey-coloured stone has slate roofs and mullioned stone windows with leaded glass panes. It lies in an extensive estate, a mile or two east of Chipping Campden, on the B4035 (which has been moved so that guests can enjoy the facade as they approach; the B4035 used to run along the back of Charingworth). No expense has been spared on the interior. The manor is mentioned in the *Domesday Book*, but the present building dates from the early fourteenth century. Hand-painted chevrons on the oak beams in the library date from medieval times. There are exceptional antiques, including a superb carved chest and magnificent grandfather clock. The dining-room, called the John Greville Room, is serene in atmosphere. The wine list has been composed with some thoroughness and provides plenty of choice under £10. The menu is complicated to a degree, but based on sound ingredients and fine sauces which help alleviate the effect of so many ingredients. For instance: 'Two fine fillets of Cotswold beef enhanced with fresh tarragon, then rolled with smoked bacon, quickly fried with shallots, wine and grain mustard, finished with asparagus and a fine crust of Stilton cheese.' That's the menu, not a report. Vegetables are a 'melody of glazed'. The dishes of the day have been the better bets; there is also a strain of traditional cooking which has produced fine summer pudding. More reports, please.

CHEF: Patrick McDonald PROPRIETORS: Darryl and Nigel Gregory
OPEN: all week
CLOSED: mid-Jan to mid-Feb
MEALS: 12.30 to 2 (2.30 Sun) 7.30 to 9.30 (10 Fri and Sat)
PRICES: £28 (£36), Set L from £15.25 (£22), Set D £19.50 (£27)
CARDS: Access, Amex, Visa, Diners
SEATS: 40. Private parties: 12 main room, 30 and 10 private rooms. Car-park, 50 places. Vegetarian meals. No children under 8. Jacket and tie. Wheelchair access (also WC)
ACCOMMODATION: 19 rooms, all with bath/shower. B&B £60 to £75. Deposit: £50. No children under 12. Pets welcome. Afternoon teas. Garden. TV. Phone. Scenic

---

Restaurants that we have not been able to assess as fully as we would like are given a zero rating this year. We are particularly keen to have reports on these places.

CHIPPING NORTON Oxfordshire map 2

La Madonette [13/20]

7 Horsefair, Chipping Norton OX7 5AL
CHIPPING NORTON (0608) 2320 £26

Chipping Norton lacks the auspicious style of its neighbour, Burford, but it boasts a serious restaurant in Alain Ritter's cosy, low-ceilinged dining-room, reminiscent of a better class of country tea-shop. The young, enthusiastic French service and authentic French cooking lift it out of the 'copper kettle' syndrome. Consistently good meals begin with excellent canapés and end with petits fours. In between, there may be pigeon salad; salmon and prawn mousses; soupe de poissons; pheasant with a red wine sauce and glazed onions; rabbit cooked in pastry with a pile of wild mushrooms sitting on two fresh sage leaves as decoration. To finish there are cheeses from Philippe Olivier of Boulogne and sweets such as sabayon on a Grand Marnier sauce, apples with calvados in puff pastry, exotic fruits in a brandy-snap basket. Wines start with house Côtes du Ventoux and Sauvignon at £6.15; CELLARMAN'S CHOICE: Laupiac, Ch. La Nère '83, £11.20; Chardonnay, Latour '85, £10.95; Médoc, Ch. Les Ormes Sorbet '81, £10.20.

CHEF/PROPRIETOR: Alain Ritter
OPEN: Tue to Sat, D only
MEALS: 7.30 to 10
PRICES: £19 (£26)
CARDS: Access, Visa
SEATS: 32. Private parties: 10 main room. Children's helpings. No cigars in dining-room

CHRISTCHURCH Dorset map 2

Splinters [10/20]

12 Church Street, Christchurch BH23 1BW
CHRISTCHURCH (0202) 483454  £22

'After 24 years we don't anticipate any changes in style,' writes John Carter. The menu stays deeply in French provincial cooking, with much cream and butter in evidence. If anything there is a tendency to under rather than over-cook vegetables and also the poached Christchurch salmon. The true glory of the panelled and beamed dining-room is its wines. Look for the page of Burgundies (mostly red) bought from the auctions at the Hospice de Beaune and Hospice de Nuits; these are rather more interesting than the mainly merchant Burgundies otherwise listed. Clarets are fairly pricy but good, Alsace wines almost all from Kuentz-Bas, and German wines impeccably selected. Sweet wines include three Beerenauslesen and two Trockenbeerenauslesen, seven from Bordeaux and Muscat de Beaumes de Venise, Domaine de Durban, £13.50 per bottle, £7 per half-bottle. House French is £5.95.

CHEFS: Jua Franke and Shelia Scott PROPRIETORS: John Carter and Jua Franke
OPEN: Mon to Sat, D only
MEALS: 6.30 to 10.30
PRICES: £14 (£22). Cover 50p
CARDS: Amex, Diners, Visa
SEATS: 40. Private parties: 20 main room, 8 and 12 private rooms. Vegetarian meals. Children's helpings. No children under 3. Wheelchair access (also WC)

CLANFIELD Oxfordshire map 2

▲ *Plough* [13/20]

Clanfield OX8 2RB
CLANFIELD (036 781) 222
on A4095 between Faringdon and Witney £16–£26

The Plough might be the British Tourist Authority's answer to Ludwig's German castles and Al's Disneyland – a sixteenth-century, mellow stone manor in the centre of an attractive village (opposite a good pub, the Tavern). The large car park and pink silk ruched curtains reaffirm the twentieth century. The cooking is about quality and quantity. Cream abounds. A series of set-price menus are characterised by 'marinated in, wrapped, served with' and then a list follows of herbs/spices/garnishes. Fish is excellent – a fricassee of lobster, turbot, sole and prawns; brill with a garnish of fat langoustines. So too the roast veal kidney wrapped in bacon and served with a sauce of three mustards, Meaux, Dijon, and Urchfont. All through, the impression is one of plenty – large portions; drinks; chairs – backed up by some young, well dressed staff: 'Have a little cheese'; 'Have a little fruit'; 'Have some petits fours'; 'Try a little port, Madame, if you don't like it don't worry, if you do we'll soon top you up'. The sweet course is the crystallisation: rhubarb crumble; fine Bakewell tart; fresh junket; melon balls of five different melons macerated in Muscat de Beaumes de Venise; orange and ugli-fruit soufflé with passion-fruit sauce, and more. Always there are two hot traditional puddings with proper custard. The Plough is part of the Hatton Hotels group which also has hotels at Gloucester, Tetbury, Doncaster and on Jersey, but Paul Barnard has succeeded in giving it a distinct personality. One half-expects a nomination from Billy Bunter saying 'Cripes, jolly super nosh.' Bar meals and teas in the walled garden at the front are very good value. The 160-strong wine list is smattered with half-bottles, which eases the steep rise of the prices into double figures. You could have bought most of a case of Ch. Cissac '83 en primeur a few years ago for the £46.95 a magnum charged here. Seven dessert wines are offered but only one by the glass, £2.95 for Muscat de Beaumes de Venise. House white and red from £8.95; CELLARMAN'S CHOICE: Ch. Guibeau St Emilion '83, £14.

This symbol is awarded only to restaurants with outstanding wine cellars.

Many of the more expensive restaurants offer bargain lunches for half the price of a meal in the evening. Details are given in the text.

CHEF: Paul Barnard PROPRIETORS: Hatton Hotels Ltd
OPEN: all week
MEALS: 12 to 1.45, 7 to 9.45
PRICES: Set L from £10.50 (£16), Set D from £18.95 (£26)
CARDS: Access, Amex, Diners, Visa
SEATS: 45. 6 tables outside. Private parties: 30 main room, 16 and 30 private rooms. Car-park, 40 places. Children's helpings. No smoking in dining-rooms. Wheelchair access (also WC). Music
ACCOMMODATION: 6 rooms, all with bath/shower. B&B £57 to £72. Deposit: £40. Afternoon teas. Garden. TV. Phone. Scenic. Doors close at 12. Confirm by 6 [GHG]

CLEVELEYS Lancashire map 5

Cleveleys Wholefood & Vegetarian Restaurant [9/20]

44 Victoria Road West, Cleveleys FY5 1BU
CLEVELEYS (0253) 865604 £5–£7

Over the healthfood shop in what was obviously the living quarters, is a small, Edwardian-style, vegetarian restaurant. For value, interest and cooking it is probably a cut above the standard of most cafés in the area. The short menu is limited to two starters, three main courses and five sweets. Dishes are busy in their flavourings – for instance, a soup of split peas, parsnips and lemon; tomato stuffed with avocado, beans and cheese; aubergines with almonds, apricots, onions and raisins and served with boulangère potatoes and honeyed carrots. Afternoon teas and morning coffees. House wines by the glass. Absolutely no smoking allowed.

CHEFS: Betty Nuttall and Laura Crossley PROPRIETOR: Sandra Crossley
OPEN: all week L, and Fri D
MEALS: 12 to 4, 6.30 to 9
PRICES: £5 (£8), Set L from £2.50 (£5), Set Fri D from £3.75 (£7), Snacks from 35p. Service inc
SEATS: 40. Private parties: 40 main room, 40 private room. Vegetarian meals. Children's helpings. No smoking. Music

CLUN Shropshire map 4

▲ *Old Post Office* [new owners, zero rated]

9 The Square, Clun SY7 0HG
CLUN (058 84) 687 £23

Martin Pool has moved on, and this little restaurant in the converted post office is now run by ex-*Michelin* inspector Richard Arbuthnot and his wife Anne. The décor remains unchanged: the colour scheme is white and metallic grey with apricot-coloured walls; and the dining-room has a long oval Georgian window looking out on to the tiny garden with the clutter of Clun rooftops and hills beyond. The Arbuthnots have made a good start and the cooking has some fine modern touches: crab and ginger ravioli with grapefruit sauce, vegetable terrine with olive oil vinaigrette, steamed sea-trout on a bed of watercress with chive sauce. They have also inherited good habits. Bread still comes from a local baker and the cheeseboard, served with salad, is still British, with Pencarreg (an unpasteurised Brie, made in Lampeter) and Cerney as well as Single Gloucester, Yarg and Shropshire Blue. Sweets are in the mould of lemon and white rum pie and unusual home made ice-creams. Good canapés and petits fours. The wine list is unusually interesting, led by Rhônes rather than claret and with good choices for quality in less expensive regions. More reports, please.

CHEF: Richard Arbuthnot PROPRIETORS: Anne and Richard Arbuthnot
OPEN: Tue to Sat, exc Tue and Sat L
CLOSED: 1 week after May and Aug bank hols; 17 Dec to 30 Mar for alterations
MEALS: 12.30 to 1.30, 7.15 to 9.30
PRICES: Set D £18 (£23)
SEATS: 30. 1 table outside. Private parties: 25 main room. Vegetarian meals. Children welcome. No cigars/pipes in dining-room. Music
ACCOMMODATION: 4 rooms, all with bath/shower. B&B £20 to £40. Baby facilities. No pets. Scenic. Doors close at 1am

COCKERMOUTH Cumbria map 7

Quince and Medlar [10/20]

13 Castlegate, Cockermouth CA13 9EU
COCKERMOUTH (0900) 823579 £12

One of the most promising vegetarian restaurants in the Lake District. The setting is an attractive Grade II Georgian corner-house close to the castle. Inside is pretty and pink. The Whitehead-Whitings serve excellent-value evening meals blending English wholefood with ethnic influences, using organic produce where possible. Menus change every six weeks. Armenian apricot and lemon soup is a favourite starter, otherwise there might be spinach and pine-nut croûte; Mediterranean vegetable and pasta casserole with red grape sauce; mung beans and spiced rice with poppadums. Most main courses come with baked potato or a good fresh salad. Sweets are the likes of spiced apple cheesecake, sticky toffee pudding and blackcurrant sorbet. Absolutely no smoking. Around 20 basic wines, with house French at £4.50.

CHEFS/PROPRIETORS: Susan and Jonathan Whitehead-Whiting
OPEN: Tue to Sat, D only, and Mon bank hols
CLOSED: 2 to 3 weeks Jan
MEALS: 7 to 9.30
PRICES: £8 (£12)
CARDS: Access, Visa
SEATS: 26. Private parties: 18 main room. Vegetarian meals. Children welcome. Smart dress preferred. No smoking. Music

▲ *This restaurant offers accommodation.*

'But for how long will a leasehold restaurant with 28 seats be able to survive? Having turned away twice the capacity of the restaurant at weekends, how do you persuade customers to eat midweek?' Avon restaurateur

COGGESHALL Essex map 3

Langan's [13/20]

4 6 Stoneham Street, Coggeshall CO6 1TT
COGGESHALL (0376) 61453 £12–£26

Langan's-in-the-country is a small bustling bistro. Some of the cooking has been exceptional. Clever ideas with cheap ingredients keep the costs down – for instance braised ox-heart. Service can be a less polished. 'Out of five visits, three times plates have been dropped.' But counteracting that, dishes like Stilton mousse with Melba toast, skate wing in butter sauce, fine soufflés, breast and leg of duck in a coulis of rhubarb and orange, and good fish of many variations, demonstrate a kitchen of flair. House French is £5.50. CELLARMAN'S CHOICE: Long Flat White '87, at £6.95; Woodstock Cabernet Sauvignon '85, £11.25.

CHEF: Mark Baumann PROPRIETORS: Peter and Susan Langan
OPEN: Tue to Sun, exc Sun D
CLOSED: 2 weeks Jan
MEALS: 12.30 to 2, 7.30 to 10
PRICES: £20 (£26), Set L £6.50 (£12) to £8.50 (£14)
CARDS: Access, Amex, Diners, Visa
SEATS: 75. Children welcome. Wheelchair access (2 steps; also WC)

COLCHESTER Essex map 3

Warehouse Brasserie [10/20]

12 Chapel Street North, Colchester CO2 7AT
COLCHESTER (0206) 65656 £14

From the outside, the restaurant still looks like a warehouse in an obscure side-street, but it's already so popular that it's usually packed inside. Bentwood chairs and tables are on several levels, and walls are decorated in fuchsia pink and dark green; the overall effect is stylish. Service is friendly and efficient. Starters might take in a rich, warm brioche filled with sliced button mushrooms in a cream sauce or smoked prawns in garlic mayonnaise; the main courses straightforward fillet of beef with mushrooms and a green salad, or more adventurous salmon in filo with hollandaise sauce. Vegetables are matched to the main dish. Desserts are at heart French – crème brûlée, chocolate pot and Grand Marnier soufflé – but there's a good ginger sponge with butterscotch sauce. House French is £4.85.

CHEFS: G.C.H. Ford, Larkin Warren and Karen Buffel PROPRIETORS: G.C.H. and J.M. Ford
OPEN: all week, exc Sun
MEALS: 12 to 2, 7 to 10.30
PRICES: £10 (£14)
CARDS: Access, Visa
SEATS: 80. Private parties: 12 main room. Vegetarian meals. Children's helpings. No smoking. Wheelchair access. Air-conditioned

Wings [9/20]

Mercury Theatre, Balkerne Gate, Colchester CO1 1PT
COLCHESTER (0206) 46881 £10–£15

The theatre restaurant has emerged as one of the more interesting places to eat in the area over the last couple of years. It is an irregular-shaped room, with 1970s Habitat-style stripped-pine décor, dominated by a huge bar. There is a two-course set menu for theatre-goers, served from 6pm to 7.30pm (and also after the show) plus, from 7.30pm, an à la carte with four starters and mains, plus a choice of seven desserts, offering the likes of fresh seafood; warm calf's liver salad; entrecôte steak with a black pepper, cream and brandy sauce; duck pie with cranberry and port sauce. Puddings are home made and include brown-bread ice-cream and strawberry tart. At lunch there are pastas, baked potatoes and quiches. Thirty wines. House French £4.50.

CHEFS: V. Baxter and M. Capper PROPRIETOR: Mercury Theatre
OPEN: Tue to Sat
MEALS: 12 to 2, 6 to 10.45
PRICES: £10 (£15), Set L and D £6.50 (£10). Snacks at L from £1.30. Minimum £2 at L
CARDS: Access, Visa
SEATS: 60. 4 tables outside. Private parties: 100 main room. Vegetarian meals. Children's helpings. Wheelchair access (also WC). Music

Essex Round-up

JELLIED EELS: *Osborne Bros*, Billet Wharf, High Street, Leigh-on-Sea (0702 77233).
CHINESE: *Wo Ping*, 60-62 High Road, North Weald Basset (037 882 3815); *Lee Kiang House*, 25 Mill End, Thaxted, Great Dunmow (0371 830101).
ROOMS: *Dedham Vale Hotel*, Terrace Restaurant, Stratford Road, Dedham (0206 322273).
FISH: *Contented Sole*, 80 High Street, Burnham on Crouch (0621 782139); *Oysters*, 22 Coggeshall Road, Braintree (0376 551035); *Fisherman's Wharf*, Western Esplanade, Westcliff-on-Sea (0702 346773).
SETTING: *Talbooth*, Gun Hill, Dedham, Colchester (0206 323150).

COLTISHALL Norfolk map 6

▲ *Norfolk Mead Hotel* [new entry, zero rated]

Church Street, Coltishall NR12 7DN
NORWICH (0603) 737531 £25

There has been a steady trickle of nominations over the last three years for this red-brick country manor. To one side is a walled garden with swimming-pool, to the other a meadow leading down to the river, where the hotel keeps two boats. The inside is full of light and lace. The cooking is modern – wild mushroom tarts; warm salads of duck breast; steamed lemon sole on a shallot and tarragon sauce flavoured with red wine. Game draws endorsements in the form of venison with gin and juniper; hare hot-pot with baby vegetables; partridge with two sauces. Bread and croissants are made in-house as are the ice-creams. A short list of wines. More reports, please.

CHEF/PROPRIETOR: Reginald Blair Davies
OPEN: Mon to Sat D, and Sun L
CLOSED: first 10 days Jan
MEALS: 12 to 2, 7 to 9
PRICES: £19 (£25). Licensed, also bring your own: corkage £2.50
CARDS: Access, Amex, Diners, Visa
SEATS: 35. Private parties: 40 main room, 16 private room. Car-park, 45 places. Children's helpings. No children under 3. Wheelchair access (2 steps; also WC). Music
ACCOMMODATION: 10 rooms, all with bath/shower. B&B £35 to £45. Deposit: £10. No children under 3. Garden. Swimming-pool. Fishing. TV. Phone. Scenic. Doors close at 1. Confirm by 7.30

COOKHAM Berkshire map 2

Alfonso's [10/20]

19–21 Station Hill Parade, Cookham SL6 9BR
BOURNE END (062 85) 25775 £23

In the middle of the shopping centre opposite the station is this small family-run restaurant with a liking for fish. Smoked salmon is served hot with peppers, squid comes with mild curry sauce and grilled sea-bream gets a sauce of wild mushrooms. Décor is all pale green tablecloths and gentle lights, service is warm and friendly. Wines start with house French at £6.50. CELLARMAN'S CHOICE: Rully '86, £12.50.

CHEFS: Manuel Manzano and Richard Manzano PROPRIETORS: Alfonso Baena and Manuel Manzano
OPEN: Mon to Sat, exc Sat L
MEALS: 12.30 to 2, 7 to 10 (11 Fri and Sat)
PRICES: £17 (£23)
CARDS: Access, Amex, Diners, Visa
SEATS: 36. Private parties: 36 main room. Car-park, 50 places. Children's helpings. Smart dress preferred. No pipes in dining-room. Wheelchair access. Music

CORBRIDGE Northumberland map 7

Ramblers Country House [11/20]

Farnley, Corbridge NE45 5RN
CORBRIDGE (043 471) 2424
1m S of Corbridge on Riding Mill road £18–£19

Travelling out of the centre of Corbridge on the Hexham road, turn south over the Tyne bridge, and then straight on south to the station. The restaurant is about a quarter of a mile further along the road beyond the station. This Victorian house, tastefully refurbished, stands isolated on the bank above the Tyne valley. The front room is splendid, with a dark wallpaper and pleasant traditional eighteenth-century-style furniture, with tables attractively set out. Heinrich Herrmann trained in Germany, and his menu reflects the development of his own Swiss/German style, evidenced in dishes like rachmussalat – mange-tout, fennel, Gruyère and peanuts tossed in anchovy dressing and served with tomatoes. Some dishes, like a saddle of venison with mushroom sauce, are served with home-made noodles, others may have fruity accompaniments – lamb sauté with fresh mint and pears is an example. There are four vegetarian dishes on the long *carte*. Fish draws noticeably good reports too. The wine list does not make as much of Germany as it might and has a canny eye to business accounts. House Rhône £5.65. CELLARMAN'S CHOICE: Deinhard Forellenwein '86, £6.85.

CHEF: Heinrich Herrmann PROPRIETORS: Heinrich and Jennifer Herrmann
OPEN: Tue to Sat, D only
MEALS: 7 to 10
PRICES: £14 (£19), Set D £13.25 (£18)
CARDS: Access, Amex, Diners, Visa
SEATS: 80. Private parties: 80 main room; 40 private room. Car-park, 30 places. Children's helpings. Smart dress preferred. Wheelchair access (1 step; also WC)

CORFE CASTLE Dorset map 2

▲ *Mortons House Hotel* [10/20]

East Street, Corfe Castle BH20 5EE
CORFE CASTLE (0929) 480988 £16–£22

The house is an impressive E-shaped Elizabethan manor, enlarged in the seventeenth century with stones pillaged from the Norman castle on the hill. Inside is gaunt and impressive, all gables, mullioned windows and a huge flagstoned floor in the hall. In contrast the dining-room is in delicate pinks with dried flowers. The cooking can have more enthusiasm than flair, but fish and meat are of good quality and there are some useful touches – good walnut bread, superb unsalted butter, decent cafetière coffee and home-made petits fours. Their style is seen in the good reports of warm salmon mousse with chive sauce; medallions of venison with leek feuilleté and reducrrant sauce; and poached salmon on a bed of vegetables; even Tournedos Rossini. The vegetarian menu is worth exploring. More rooms, a second dining-room and bar are being added this winter. The wine list is a carefully chosen selection of around 50 with some good names and plenty under £10. The house red is Fitou, the white is from New Zealand. CELLARMAN'S CHOICE: Chardonnay Rosemount Estate '85 at £11.60.

CHEFS: Janice Timothy and Simon Wright PROPRIETORS: Janice E. Hughes, Gerhard Bockau and Janice Timothy
OPEN: all week
MEALS: 12.30 to 2, 7.30 to 10
PRICES: £11 (£17), Set L £9.50 (£15) to £10.50 (£16), Set D £15 (£21) to £16.50 (£22), Snacks from £2
CARDS: Access, Visa
SEATS: 75. 6 tables outside. Private parties: 35 conference room, 60 private room, 30 hall. Car-park, 30 places. Vegetarian meals. Children's helpings. Wheelchair access
ACCOMMODATION: 17 rooms, all with bath/shower. Rooms for disabled. B&B £30 to £60. Deposit: £20 or 20%. Children welcome. Baby facilities. Pets welcome. Afternoon teas. Fishing. Golf. TV. Phone. Scenic

CORSE LAWN Gloucestershire map 2

▲ *Corse Lawn House* [14/20]

10 YEARS

Corse Lawn GL19 4LZ
TIRLEY (045 278) 479
on B4211, 5m SW of Tewkesbury £16–£28

The extension to the Queen Anne house has given extra rooms. The menu is essentially French, written in English, with an attractive preference for pre-*nouvelle cuisine* country dishes, as might be found in a very fine brasserie – stylistically it is similar to Langan's Brasserie in London. The *carte* offers 17 starters, 10 main dishes covering most of the major meats, plus a sweets trolley, but there are also set lunches and dinners of four or five starters and main courses; a vegetarian menu offers as much choice. Dishes range from fillet of veal with Noilly and a mousseline of chanterelles to pressed duck with orange chutney, red mullet cooked in red wine, hare feuilleté with a port and herb sauce. Guinea-fowl has been dry but saved on occasion by an intense tarragon and saffron sauce. The sweet selection does not seem to change; toffee ice-cream with a butterscotch sauce is as good as in 1983. Passionfruit soufflé and the chocolate mousse are equally of a standard. Cheeses good French, also Stilton and Single Gloucester. 'Excellent' breakfasts offer a majestic choice and include home-made yoghurt, porridge and kippers. Bar snacks include feuilletés, lobster and venison sausages. Votes on the rating vary from 11 to 15, which suggests a certain inconsistency. Bordeaux and Burgundy dominate the wine list though there is a sprinkling of Australian, Californian, New Zealand, Spanish and Italian bottles. House French £6. CELLARMAN'S CHOICE: Châteauneuf du Pape, Domaine du Vieux Télégraphe '83, £14.50.

CHEF: Baba Hine PROPRIETORS: Denis and Baba Hine
OPEN: all week
MEALS: 12.30 to 2, 7 to 10
PRICES: £21 (£28), Set L £11.50 (£16), Set D £17.75 (£21). Service inc
CARDS: Access, Amex, Diners, Visa
SEATS: 45. 8 tables outside. Private parties: 55 main room, 24 private room. Car-park, 50 places. Vegetarian meals. Children's helpings. Wheelchair access (also WC)
ACCOMMODATION: 10 rooms, all with bath/shower. Rooms for disabled. B&B £50 to 65. Baby facilities. Pets welcome. Afternoon teas. Garden. TV. Phone. Scenic. Doors close at 12. Confirm by 6 [GHG]

COUNTESTHORPE Leicestershire map 5

Old Bakery [10/20]

Main Street, Countesthorpe LE8 3QX
LEICESTER (0533) 778777 £12–£18

The Victorian bakery has been comprehensively converted into a modern restaurant that looks like a cross between a hotel dining-room and a pub lounge decked out in shades of blue and grey. The value for money is a big plus – especially at lunch-time – although the style is essentially bistro, with a few home-made dishes balancing out standard restaurant clichés. Plain dishes, such as roast pheasant and steak and kidney pudding, are more successful than mousseline of salmon with watercress sauce or entrecôte Balmoral topped with Scottish Cheddar. Apple and plum pie comes with a separate boat of vanilla-flavoured custard. A demon little wine list has plenty of interesting drinking for under £10. House French is £5.50.

CHEF: R. Gilbertson PROPRIETORS: R. Gilbertson, P. Chivers and G. Turner
OPEN: Tue to Sun, exc Sat L and Sun D
MEALS: 12.15 to 1.45, 7 to 9 (9.45 Fri and Sat)
PRICES: Set L from £7.95 (£12), Set D £13.25 (£18)
CARDS: Access, Visa
SEATS: 50. Private parties: 50 main room. Car-park, 20 places. Vegetarian meals. Children welcome. Jacket and tie. Wheelchair access (also WC). Music

COVENTRY West Midlands map 5

▲ *Herbs, Trinity House Hotel* [10/20]

28 Lower Holyhead Road, Coventry CV1 3AU
COVENTRY (0203) 555654 £13

Now decorated in soothing pinks, Robert Jackson's restaurant has, since 1982, been winning over reluctant nearly-vegetarians. An enterprising menu generally avoids stodginess and makes careful use of combinations, for instance caponata – a mix of aubergines, celery, onions and tomatoes with black olives and capers, or Tibetan roast – barley, mushrooms, walnuts and spinach, roasted and served with a carrot and apricot sauce. Well reported is the parsnip timbale with Dijon mustard vinaigrette and warm wholemeal yoghurt muffins, or a side salad of Edam and fruit bound with yoghurt and mayonnaise. Two daily dishes for non-vegetarians might include seafood and spaghetti gratin and steak, Guinness and mushroom hot-pot. Rich sweets are a strong point, with old favourites banana split and chocolate fudge brownies featuring. Plans are afoot as we go to press to open a new branch in the city. Twenty wines, from house French at £4.60 to CELLARMAN'S CHOICE: Rock's Elderflower, £5.30, and organically produced Bordeaux Blanc, Moulin de Romage '86, £5.40.

CHEF: Robert Jackson PROPRIETORS: Robert and Lesley Jackson, and Charles Davis
OPEN: Mon to Sat, D only
MEALS: 6.30 to 9.30
PRICES: £8 (£13). Service inc
CARDS: Access, Visa
SEATS: 42. 3 tables outside. Private parties: 42 main room. Vegetarian meals. No children under 5. Wheelchair access. Music
ACCOMMODATION: 7 rooms. B&B £18 to £29. No babies. Doors close at 11. Confirm by 6

The entries are compiled from the views of readers who have eaten at the restaurant in the last year, backed up by anonymous inspections and by information supplied and facts verified by the restaurants.

Quo Vadis [10/20]

72 Barker Butts Lane, Coventry CU6 1DY
COVENTRY (0203) 594124 £18

Since 1970, this old-style trattoria in a converted shop has been the best bet for Italian food in Coventry. The extensive menu holds few surprises, but the kitchen delivers decent versions of the classics – spaghetti carbonara, saltimbocca alla romana, bistecca alla pizzaiola. Lobster and sole are at market price, and vegetables are fresh. Pasta dishes are considered a speciality. Good zabaglione or melon stregata in a pool of flaming Strega to finish. Next door is an excellent snack bar serving pasta dishes, omelettes and toasted sandwiches from the restaurant kitchen. Modest, reasonably priced Italian wines, including CELLARMAN'S CHOICE: Montepulciano d'Abruzzo Riserva '82 at £8.95.

CHEF/PROPRIETOR: Carmine Chicarella
OPEN: Mon to Sat, exc Sat L
MEALS: 12 to 2, 7 to 11.30
PRICES: £16 (£18)
CARDS: Access, Diners, Visa
SEATS: 75. Private parties: 80 main room. Vegetarian meals. Children's helpings. Smart dress preferred. Wheelchair access (2 steps). Music. Air-conditioned

CRICKLADE Wiltshire map 2

Whites [15/20]

93 High Street, Cricklade SN6 6DF
SWINDON (0793) 751110 £23–£28

While the London pundits applaud Simon Hopkinson's return to basics, out in this small Wiltshire town Colin and Gwen White continue to develop a cuisine based on fine local produce, its roots deeply embedded in the surrounding countryside. There are very few serious restaurant inspectors who do not rate both the style and execution highly. As a restaurant the twin rooms tootle along, lacking a bit of atmosphere and the sort of trappings that might pick up a clean sweep of gongs through the range of guide-books. But for cooking and for wines it is in the first league. The variety crammed into the small menu is remarkable – a starter with pastry, another of walnut brioche, one butter sauce, one oil, one vegetarian. And there is no leaning back on expensive luxuries for effect – a warm salad of ox-tail with a herb and oil dressing is a good example. Instead, there is investment in the quality of the vehicles of cooking, like Jersey cream for wild mushroom soup or pigeon livers to stuff a pigeon in red wine, and a reliance on the direct effect of intelligent cooking. The style mixes slow cooking, such as 'a miraculous osso buco', with last-minute fish dishes such as roast monkfish with garlic. The themes are French, as in boeuf à la ficelle, for which fillet steak is cooked in a bouillon of marrow bones and vegetables and served with marrow bone, croûtons and the stock vegetables, and modern British, as in fresh gurnard served with an anchovy and orange butter. The pudding repertoire is short and more French – parfait, feuilleté, St Emilion au chocolat, ice-cream and sorbets. The whole tempo is leisured, occasionally slow. The wine list is fairly short, but the choice is extremely good, and mark-ups very reasonable. Not much costs less than £10, however, though house wines, a Sauvignon de Touraine and a Beaujolais, are £7 per bottle or £1.20 per glass. Clarets include a number of not too expensive '70s; Burgundies are from top growers; there are good Italians and interesting Californian, Australian and New Zealand wines. Sweet wines are a trio from Barsac and Sauternes, best value being Château Bastor-Lamontagne Sauternes '83, £13.

CHEF: Colin White PROPRIETORS: Colin and Gwen White
OPEN: Mon to Sat, exc Mon L
MEALS: 12.30 to 2, 7.30 to 9.30
PRICES: £20 (£28), Set L and D from £15 (£23). Licensed, also bring your own: corkage £2
CARDS: Access, Visa
SEATS: 32. Private parties: 20 main room, 20 and 16 private rooms. Vegetarian meals. Children's helpings. No cigars/pipes in dining-room. Wheelchair access

CROYDE Devon map 1

▲ *Whiteleaf* [12/20]

Croyde EX33 1PN
CROYDE (0271) 890266 £14

David Wallington's move from the acclaimed Rhydspence Inn to a guest-house setting has given his cooking a better context and greater authority. Set meals of five stages provide good examples of the understanding of technique, from little pea and radicchio salads with Feta cheese to home-made brown bread. A May meal comprised: scallops, prawns, monkfish, mussels and sole in a saffron sauce; a duck consommé with quenelles made from the livers; trout Wellington with a cream, lemon and coriander sauce; a casserole of duck leg-meat with a sauce of kumquats; a spread of vegetables. A blackberry and apple pizza is a purée of the fruit spread on meringue, covered with clotted cream and flashed under the grill. Cheeses come after the sweets. House French on a well-annotated list is £5.45. CELLARMAN'S CHOICE: Bourgogne Rouge, Pinot Noir '85, £7.40; Arneis Langhe '86, £8.

CHEF: David Wallington PROPRIETORS: David and Florence Wallington
OPEN: all week, D only
MEALS: 7.30 to 8.30
PRICES: Set D £11.50 (£14). Service inc
CARDS: Access, Visa
SEATS: 16. Private parties: 24 main room. Car-park, 10 places. Children's helpings. Smart dress preferred
ACCOMMODATION: 5 rooms, all with bath/shower. B&B £24.50 to £39. Deposit: £25. Baby facilities. Pets welcome. Garden. TV. Phone. Scenic. Doors close at 12. Confirm by 7

Report forms are at the back of the book.

CROYDON Surrey map 3

Dijonnais [11/20]

299 High Street, Croydon CR0 1OL
01-686 5624 £11–£20

A small, unassuming French restaurant though the style is more upmarket than the rough plastered walls and homely checked tablecloths would suggest. The menu is short but there is real choice in the mould of marmite; escargots; filet de boeuf bourguignonne; sauces such as blanquette and basilique. Salads and cheeses are offered as a separate course. Reliable tarts and flans to finish. Twenty wines from £5.75. CELLARMAN'S CHOICE: Côtes du Rhône '85, £11.

CHEF: Lionel Jolivet PROPRIETORS: Mr and Mrs Lionel Jolivet
OPEN: Mon to Sat, exc Mon D and Sat L
MEALS: 12.15 to 2, 7.30 to 9 (9.30 Sat)
PRICES: £14 (£20), Set L from £7 (£11), Set D £13 (£18). Cover 50p
CARDS: Access, Amex, Diners, Visa
SEATS: 28. Private parties: 28 main room. Children welcome. Wheelchair access. Music

Hockneys [10/20]

98 High Street, Croydon CR0 1ND
01-688 2899 £11

Named after the artist whose sense of light, space and colour is reflected in the décor and the menu. Simon Beckett has taken this kitchen into the front line of vegetarian restaurants over the last two years: the International Wine and Food Society (Sunny Hill branch) even held a dinner here. The gazpacho is excellent; so, too, is Stroganoff. An appropriate sense of adventure characterises many dishes: for instance, a potato and parsnip mousseline for the nut and Feta roast, also served with asparagus hollandaise and a salad of strawberry and pineapple. Sweets have a sense of humour. A Kim Philby is a tall glass of fruit salad, yoghurt, strawberry parfait, apricot nectar and cream. Non-alcoholic wines, juices, cocktails, infusions from comfrey to lemon verbena are offered in place of alcohol. Self-service for lunch and in the afternoon; waiter service in the evening.

CHEF: Simon Beckett PROPRIETORS: Rainbow (Croydon) Ltd
OPEN: Tue to Sat
CLOSED: 2 weeks Christmas, 1 week at Easter, 2 weeks Aug
MEALS: noon to 10.30
PRICES: £9 (£11), Snacks from 95p. Unlicensed but bring your own: corkage £1.35
CARDS: Access, Amex, Diners, Visa
SEATS: 80. Private parties: 25 main room. Vegetarian meals. Children's helpings. No smoking. Music

'Mr G's attitude is smug and patronising. In his brochure he says that the hotel is "their home", so we are welcomed "as his guests". I would prefer that it were their business and I were welcomed as a client. On eating in Yorkshire

Willow [10/20]

88 Selsdon Park Road, Croydon CR2 8JT
01-657 4656 and 4667 £17

Previously the Farmhouse restaurant, then a ballet school, then an Italian restaurant, but now, in the way of suburban restaurateuring a Peking/ Szechuan restaurant that has picked up nominations consistently since opening three years ago. Presentation is a key element and there is no compromise on the chilli level. Much seems to be cooked to order. Recommendations run a familiar theme: Imperial hors d'oeuvre; lobster with ginger and spring onion; crispy lamb; chicken with pineapple in an edible woven potato nest with seaweed; peppers stuffed with prawns; special fried rice with bean curd; Szechuan prawns; pancake stuffed with sweet bean paste. No MSG. House French is £4.75, or drink Shaohsing, Chinese rice wine.

CHEF: Dien Tung PROPRIETOR: Michael Man
OPEN: all week
MEALS: 12 to 2.30, 6 to 11
PRICES: £10 (£17). Service 10%
CARDS: Access, Amex, Diners, Visa
SEATS: 95. Private parties: 60 main room; 60 private room. Car-park, 20 places. Vegetarian meals. Children welcome. Music. Air-conditioned

CUCKFIELD West Sussex map 3

▲ *King's Head* [14/20]

South Street, Cuckfield RH17 5VY
HAYWARDS HEATH (0444) 454006 £16–£18

Jeremy Ashpool's franchise on the dining-room of this old village pub by the church continues for at least one more year. Like his mentor, John Kenward (see Kenwards, Lewes), Ashpool's version of modern British cooking is unadorned, forthright, uncompromising, comments which might equally apply to the dining-room. He is fond of wild foods, as in fish and game. There is subtlety in the marinated scallops arranged round a pile of courgettes, or the smoked fish parcels with leek vinaigrette. Other dishes are more robust: pheasant comes with herb dumplings, apple and rhubarb; grilled venison gets a red-wine sauce with shallots. Vegetarian dishes appear in the form of cheese and walnut strudel; sweets bring it all back home with Sussex pond pudding. Thirty wines centre on France and start at £6; CELLARMAN'S CHOICE: Ch. Larroze '85, £8.50.

If, in your opinion, a restaurant is not maintaining the standard of its rating, please inform the Guide *office. Report forms are at the back of the book.*

'Dry white house wine was 85p per glass. I was unwise enough to order a bottle and was charged £5.40 – 90p per glass!' On eating in North Yorkshire

CHEF: Jeremy Ashpool PROPRIETOR: Peter Tolhurst
OPEN: Mon to Fri, exc Mon D
CLOSED: bank hols
MEALS: 12.30 to 2, 7.30 to 10
PRICES: £12 (£16), Set D £12.95 (£18)
CARDS: Access, Visa
SEATS: 33. 3 tables outside. Private parties: 20 main room. Children welcome. Wheelchair access
ACCOMMODATION: 9 rooms, 8 with bath/shower. B&B £30 to £40. Baby facilities. Pets welcome. Garden. Snooker. TV. Confirm by 6

DALLINGTON East Sussex map 3

▲ *Little Byres* [new entry, zero rated]

Christmas Farm, Battle Road, Dallington TN21 9LE
BRIGHTLING (042 482) 230 £14–£29

Christmas Farm is equidistant from Battle and Heathfield. The byres and cow-sheds are now chalets and the two-hundred-year-old barn has been converted into a spacious raftered and beamed dining-room; further expansion is planned. Christopher Davis arrived here via Woods at Bath, which rated 10/20 in the *Guide*, and William's Kitchen at Nailsworth, 12/20. He now cooks almost single-handedly a short menu of four or five dishes at each course. French provincial dishes, such as Provençal vegetable soup with pistou, are mixed with modern British ideas, such as marinated medallions of pork seasoned with Roquefort and walnuts and served with a purée of pears, or lightly smoked fillet of Scotch beef – a Raymond Blanc device – served with a classic madeira sauce and in modern onion confit. It is all plated, and the meal is charged by the cost of the main course. The sense of timing and the ability to bring different tastes together are striking. Take this dish: an escalope of wild salmon, steamed first *à point*, served with a stock of crayfish and lobster shells into which sorrel leaves and an oyster have been chopped. Or this one: a classic caramelised apple tart made with the most buttery, fragile of pastries and served with a tart purée of mango. These are top-drawer dishes and re-affirm all the optimism currently being heaped on the younger generation of chefs. In embryo this is a very fine restaurant. The wine list is predominantly French, with house red and white from Corney and Barrow. CELLARMAN'S CHOICE: the two Australian bottles, Coonawarra Cabernet Sauvignon '84, £10.50, and Pokolbin Chardonnay, Hunter Valley '87, £10.50. More reports, please.

CHEF: Christopher Davis PROPRIETOR: Timothy Westlake
OPEN: all week
MEALS: 12 to 3, 7 to 9.30
PRICES: £20 (£29), Set D £14.50 (£20), Bar meals £6 (£14)
CARDS: Amex, Access, Visa
SEATS: 35. Private parties: 40 main room, 20 private room. Car-park, 18 places. Children's helpings. Wheelchair access (also WC). Music
ACCOMMODATION: 5 double rooms, all with bath/shower. Rooms for disabled. B&B £35. Deposit: 10%. Baby facilities. Pets welcome. Afternoon teas. TV. Phone. Scenic. Confirm 48 hours ahead

DARLINGTON Co Durham map 7

Victor's [12/20]

84 Victoria Road, Darlington DL1 5JW
DARLINGTON (0325) 480818 £9–£18

The Robinsons are well established in this unpretentious, homely restaurant a stone's throw from the station. They have a stated policy of buying fresh and cooking to order whenever possible. Everything is made on the premises, including the petits fours and biscuits for cheese. The menu is eclectic, modern British/French, with a blend of the traditional and plain: melon with white port; salmon with cucumber sauce; salmon with honey and fresh ginger; loin of lamb with coffee-cream gravy. Sauces draw praise. The cheeseboard has a good selection of unpasteurised English cheeses, or try fruit fritto misto. Good coffee. The wine list opens with Côtes du Rhône at £6. CELLARMAN'S CHOICE: Chardonnay, Wyndham Estate Oak Cask '86, £7.95.

CHEFS/PROPRIETORS: Peter and Jayne Robinson
OPEN: Tue to Sat
MEALS: 12 to 2.30, 7 to 10.30
PRICES: Set L £5 (£9), Set D £13.25 (£18)
CARDS: Access, Amex, Diners, Visa
SEATS: 26. Private parties: 26 main room. Vegetarian meals. Children's helpings. Wheelchair access. Music

DARTMOUTH Devon map 1

▲ *Billy Budd's* [10/20]

7 Foss Street, Dartmouth TQ6 9DW
DARTMOUTH (080 43) 4842 £8–£17

The inspiration of Joyce Molyneux attracts yet another entry for this small, inaccessible town, which per head of population must now be the best-served provincial restaurant area in Britain. This is not so much a rival to the other two, but a complement; it knows its place and stays there: pine chairs, marble-topped serving tables, flowers in jugs. The menu shows imagination using local produce, including apples and cider, Devonshire cream, fresh fish and shellfish. There is a good choice: mussels; goujons of plaice; scallop and bacon salad; lentil soup; followed by salmon in filo; ragoût of scallops; fillets of trout with hazelnuts and grapefruit. Sauces tend towards the heavy side. Puddings are 'homely': rhubarb and apple crumble; apple and cider sorbet; and a bread-and-butter pudding that varies in taste each time it is made. Twenty-three wines from house Blanc de Blancs at £5.95, to CELLARMAN'S CHOICE: Graves, Ch. Magneau '83, at £8.85 and Savigny-les-Beaune, La Dominode '82, at £16.30.

Anyone claiming to be from The Good Food Guide *is an impostor. Restaurateurs are advised to contact the office immediately if any fraudulent claims are made.*

CHEF: Keith Belt PROPRIETORS: Gilly White and Keith Belt
OPEN: Tue to Sat, exc Tue D
CLOSED: Feb; Tue in winter
MEALS: 12 to 2, 7.30 to 10
PRICES: L £4 (£8), Set D from £12.25 (£17), Snacks from £1.50
CARD: Visa
SEATS: 35. Private parties: 35 main room. Vegetarian meals. Children's helpings. No children under 7. Smart dress preferred. Wheelchair access. Music
ACCOMMODATION: 2 rooms. B&B £12.50

Bistro 33 [14/20]

33 Lower Street, Dartmouth TQ6 9AN
DARTMOUTH (080 43) 2882 £20–£23

The successful return of Richard Cranfield to the town has seen the bistro expand next door from the converted shop close to the small, privately-owned lower-ferry docks. Cottage tea-room chairs add to the café atmosphere. The set menu is short and seasonal, modern British after Joyce Molyneux, with whom Cranfield trained, and is accurately targeted within the kitchen's reach. At its best it produces cervelas of salmon, sole and prawns, a triumph of taste, textures and skills, spiked with fennel and chervil, lightly browned and served with restraint on a purée of leeks. The style is up to the minute, looking to make impact through combinations – clear chicken soup served with pistachio nut quenelles and home-made pasta or, the Joël Robuchon classic, fillet of lamb baked in a salt crust with rosemary and served with tian. Fruits are used liberally – blackcurrants to sauce duck, a layer of strawberry purée beneath the crème brûlée. Bread is home made; coffee is strong and reviving. Fifty wines form an appropriate list, mostly French, starting at £6.25. CELLARMAN'S CHOICE: Rioja, Vino Real, Gran Reserva '76, at £11.25.

CHEF: Richard Cranfield PROPRIETORS: Richard and Helen Cranfield
OPEN: Tue to Sat, D only
MEALS: 7 to 10
PRICES: Set D £15.75 (£20) to £18.50 (£23). Service inc
SEATS: 30. Private parties: 30 main room. Vegetarian meals. Children's helpings. No cigars/pipes in dining-room. Wheelchair access (also WC)

Carved Angel [17/20]

2 South Embankment, Dartmouth TQ6 9BH
DARTMOUTH (080 43) 2465 £21–£30

On the waterfront, overlooking the river and opposite the passenger ferry that goes to Kingswear, Joyce Molyneux presides over the stoves at her premier, legendary restaurant, backed by a team of eight who share all duties, from cooking to waiting. There is no pretension, just honest cooking developing from Elizabeth David and George Perry-Smith, prompted by supplies from a local network – Dart salmon with samphire and champagne sauce; grilled lobster with tarragon butter in summer; Dartmouth pie of mutton, fruit and spices. The menu of eight dishes at each stage offers genuine choice. It is sensible, pragmatic cooking without affectation and yet there are stunning results, sometimes classical and simple, as in skate with black butter, but also there might be ravioli filled with cream cheese, served with tomato and pesto sauce, or duck with a beetroot sauce, its liver turned into a mousseline, served with a mixed salad. One example of the artistry of the kitchen is that dishes like the roast kid and lambs' sweetbreads somehow maintain a searing hot quality, called in China 'wok hay', literally breath of the wok, when stir-fry pieces come straight out of the wok still sizzling from the heat. At dinner a sorbet, or perhaps a grilled goats' cheese on a brioche, is served after the main course. The combination of flavours in the sweets show that the kitchen is still developing, for instance a hot Grand Marnier soufflé served with an orange and cardamom ice-cream, or fresh cream cheese with rhubarb and rose-petal jam, or a plate of chocolate – marquise, parfait, ice and a ginger roulade. It was a cruel decision for *Michelin* to take away the Angel's star. There has always been a minority who argue that you cannot have a major restaurant without pretensions but the thrust of votes from readers is squarely for a rating between 15 and 17/20. And take this endorsement from a July meal eaten by a senior inspector: 'One constantly wonders how such apparently simple dishes can give the effect of such operatic dimensions. The salmon in pastry consists of a generous chunk of perfectly cooked salmon, its flesh exaggerated by the addition of currants, encrusted in a rough puff pastry oozing with real buttery tastes and accompanied by a light foamy sauce made from butter, cream, onions and an abundance of fresh herbs. The result of the combinations is electrifying. Or take the plate of chocolate puddings, showing four highly individual items ranging from a light spongey roulade to a zebra cake filled with a wonderfully dense but light-weight pot au chocolat filling; together they attest to extraordinary consistency and talent.' The wine list also shows plenty of acumen, offering nearly 200 wines and a good choice of half-bottles (though these include some very elderly clarets, a risky buy, since halves mature much faster than full bottles). A rapid round-up of the world's wines provides a few alternatives away from the traditional French track, but the bulk of the list is a broad range of clarets, some good Burgundies and an interesting selection from the rest of France. For sweet wine drinkers, a dozen sweet Bordeaux includes a number of half-bottles and, by the glass, Blandy's ten-year-old Malmsey, which at £3 is worth the premium over the other by-the-glass ports and madeiras. Six choices of house wine at £8; CELLARMAN'S CHOICE: California Pinot Noir, Clos du Val '82, £15; Givry '84, £13.50; and Ménétou-Salon '86, £11.50.

CHEF: Joyce Molyneux PROPRIETORS: George Perry-Smith, Heather Crosbie, Joyce Molyneux and Meriel Boydon
OPEN: Tue to Sun, exc Sun D
MEALS: 12.30 to 1.45, 7.30 to 9.30
PRICES: L £24 (£30), Set L from £15 (£21), Set D from £24 (£30). Service inc
SEATS: 30. Private parties: 30 main room; 15 private room. Children's helpings

The price quoted in brackets is for an average three-course meal including service, VAT, *coffee and half a bottle of house wine or the equivalent in an ethnic restaurant.*

Devon Round-up

BAR MEALS: *Castle Inn*, Lydford, Okehampton (082 282 242).
AL FRESCO: *Start Bay Inn*, Torcross, Kingsbridge, (0548 580553).
ROOMS: *White Cottage Hotel*, Colyton (0297 52401); *Woodhayes*, Whimple, Nr Exeter (0404 822237).
VEGETARIAN: *Plymouth Arts Centre Café*, Art Centre, Plymouth (0752 660060); *Cranks in Dartington*, Dartington Cider Press Centre, Shinners Bridge (0803 862388); *Herbies Wholefood*, North Street, Exeter (0392 58473); *Café at the Meeting House*, South Street, Exeter (0392 410855).
AUSTRIAN: *Old Vienna*, 6 Lisburne Square, Torquay (0803 25861).
INEXPENSIVE: *Plymouth Catering College*, Kings Road, Devonport (0752 264739).
VIEW: *Artillery Tower*, Durford Street, Plymouth (0752 667276).
ITALIAN: *Hosteria Romana*, 58 Southside Street, The Barbican, Plymouth (0752 667303).

DENT Cumbria map 7

▲ *Stone Close* [9/20]

Main Street, Dent LA10 5QL
DENT (058 75) 231 £10

On the fringe of this most rural of villages, set among some magnificent scenery, is this white-washed seventeenth-century cottage with low ceilings and doors. The old-fashioned range is in keeping. Some of the tables are old Singer treadle-tops. There are few concessions to twentieth-century comforts which would be out of keeping anyway. The Bonsalls stay with a much more genuine version of English catering – an all-day tea-shop, offering also bed and breakfast and an inexpensive evening meal. Everything is home made and Louise Bonsall is a gifted cook. The menu is a modest arrangement of soups, pâtés, pies, stews and baked potatoes. A blackboard offers dishes of the day for variety. Sweets are loaves and cakes. The apple pie is offered in the traditional north-country manner with a slice of Wensleydale cheese. House wine is £5.60 a litre.

CHEF: Louise Bonsall PROPRIETORS: Chris and Louise Bonsall
OPEN: all week (L Sat, Sun only, Nov to Easter)
CLOSED: Jan
MEALS: 10.30 to 5.30, 7
PRICES: L £6, (£10), Set D £6.85 (£10), Snacks from £1.95. Service inc
SEATS: 40. Private parties: 25 main room, 20 private room. Vegetarian meals. Children's helpings. No smoking during meals. Wheelchair access. Music. One sitting at D
ACCOMMODATION: 3 rooms. B&B £10.50 to £19. Deposit: £5. Children welcome. Baby facilities. Pets welcome. Afternoon teas. Scenic

The 1990 Guide *will appear before Christmas 1989. Reports are particularly helpful in the spring. Report forms are at the back of this book, but just write a letter if you prefer. Address to The Good Food Guide,* FREEPOST, *2 Marylebone Road, London NW1 1YN. No stamp is necessary if you post it in the UK.*

DERBY Derbyshire map 5

Water Margin [10/20]

72–74 Burton Road, Derby, DE1 1TG
DERBY (0332) 364754 and 290482 £7–£16

Philip Chan moved from the Water Margin in Leicester (see entry) to open his own restaurant in a new brick building half a mile from the centre of Derby. It is marked by a huge dramatic entrance with red and gold dragon pillars and a vast red and green canopy. Inside it is all chinoiserie, with colourful artwork, ornate panels and an impressively decorative ceiling. At lunch it fills up with Chinese families eating from the handwritten dim-sum menu. Otherwise there's a hundred-strong list of Cantonese, Pekinese and Szechuan dishes, from hot-and-sour soup and sesame prawn toasts to chicken with sweet-pickled ginger and pineapple. Flavours can lack boldness, but this place is good news in a town where most Chinese restaurants cling to their chop sueys. Service is extremely chatty and helpful. House French is £4.95, or drink saké, £2.60, or Great Wall Chinese wine, £8.

CHEF: Tim Ho PROPRIETOR: Philip Chan
OPEN: all week
MEALS: noon to 3, 6.30 to 11.30 (noon to 11.30 Sun)
PRICES: £8 (£16), Set L from £3.50 (£7), Set D from £8 (£12). Service 10%
CARDS: Access, Amex, Diners, Visa
SEATS: 200. Private parties: 120 main room, 45 private room. Car-park, 35 places. Vegetarian meals. Children welcome. Wheelchair access (also WC). Music. Air-conditioned

Derbyshire Round-up

HISTORIC SETTING: *Cavendish*, Baslow, Bakewell (024 68 82311).
BAR MEALS: *Red Lion Inn*, Litton (0298 871458).
FRENCH: *Remy*, 84 Bridge Street, Belper (077 382 2246).
INEXPENSIVE: *Old Original Bakewell Pudding Shop*, The Square, Bakewell (062 981 2193).
ROOMS: *Riverside Hotel*, Fennel Street, Ashford-in-the-Water (062 981 4275).

DORRINGTON Shropshire map 4

Country Friends [13/20]

Dorrington SY5 7JD
DORRINGTON (074 373) 707
5m S of Shrewsbury, on A49 £17–£21

The impressive black and white building is a jumble of accumulated centuries, dating in parts from the 1600s. Inside looks less historic, a rabbit warren of a place, with a real fire in the inglenook in one corner, some good beams, and the occasional painting. There's pink and brown napery, dim lighting and cheap stainless steel cutlery. The feel is of a sophisticated guest-house, and indeed three bedrooms were due to open as the *Guide* went to press. A set menu with a choice of three dishes per course is supplemented by a *carte* with seven choices at each stage. The style is evolved mid-Channel cooking: cream and wine sauces for fish; good pastry work; and some more elaborate dishes such as a herb pancake shaped like a swag bag, filled with a mixture of cooked winter vegetables, and a pool of hollandaise flavoured with tomato purée to the side. Fruits are used to sauce meats, as in guinea-fowl with spiced fruits, and appear in alcohol at the end of the meal, for instance prunes with brandy cream. Good touches such as the rolls, the butter from Applebys' farm nearby, and the coffee impress. Most things now seem to be sauced, which is not necessarily the strength of this sort of cooking, especially when it strays from the seasons. A few simpler dishes would give a better balance. Good-value wines, with a sensible selection under £10. House Fitou is £6.20.

CHEFS/PROPRIETORS: Charles and Pauline Whittaker
OPEN: Tue to Sat
MEALS: 12 to 2, 7 to 9.30
PRICES: £15 (£21), Set L and D £12.50 (£17)
CARDS: Amex, Diners, Visa
SEATS: 40. Private parties: 45 main room. Car-park, 40 places. Children welcome. Wheelchair access

DREWSTEIGNTON Devon map 1

▲ *Hunts Tor House* [11/20]

Drewsteignton, EX6 6QW
DREWSTEIGNTON (0647) 21228 £13

Drewsteignton is a tiny village a stone's throw from Chagford, separated from it by the A382, linked to it by the River Teign. These few square miles have recently provided five *Guide* entries. The village has a Norman church, thatched houses, and a public house called the Drewe Arms which boasts the oldest landlady in the country (in her nineties). Hunts Tor House is extraordinary in that the original building, built around 1640, was extended on all sides, so that the present large square house encloses the original building. At the heart of the house there is a small, low-ceilinged, heavily beamed room – wood everywhere, old wooden floor, great old wooden table, wooden wall benches, built-in wooden cupboards – which is now used as one of the two dining-rooms; plus the kitchens and scullery, where there's a pump that works by hand and draws water from a private well. The building was lived in by the Smith family from 1640 until four years ago, when the last remaining member of the dynasty sold. The house is full of Victorian and Edwardian furniture and fireplace surrounds, and includes a beautiful chiffonière with giant mirror in the lounge. The fireplaces have been restored. The atmosphere in the lounge and larger dining-room is very early 1900s. Dinner – for residents only – starts at 7.30pm and everyone is served simultaneously by owner Chris Harrison while his wife Sue cooks. The four courses offer no choice, and are a modern version of good home cooking with a tendency to the healthy with plenty of fruit, vegetables and fish. Recommended dishes range from chicken with sorrel, wild duck with elderberry wine, red pepper mousse to pink trout with ginger-papillote. Cheeses are English, sweets more classical, such as strawberries Romanoff. Breakfasts comprise 'terrific poached egg, poached haddock, home-made quince jam and marmalade and freshly squeezed orange'. The wine list is recited before dinner according to what is in stock, around a dozen bottles in the £5 to £6.50 region, for drinkers rather than sippers.

CHEF: Sue Harrison PROPRIETORS: Sue and Chris Harrison
OPEN: all week, D only (residents only)
MEALS: 7.30
PRICES: Set D £10 (£13). Service inc
SEATS: 8. Private parties: 12 main room, 8 private room. Vegetarian meals. No children under 14. One sitting
ACCOMMODATION: 4 rooms, all with bath. B&B £16 to £28. No children under 14. Pets welcome

▲ *Old Inn* [10/20]

The Square, Drewsteignton EX6 6QR
DREWSTEIGNTON (0647) 21276 £14

Now a homely restaurant with bedrooms, the Old Inn dates from 1650 and occupies one rambling corner of the picturesque village square. Rose and Vivien Chapman draw in a mixture of holidaymakers and locals. Everything is cooked on the premises, including interesting walnut and milk or herb breads. The menu is recited collectively to all guests in some detail. Local meat and seasonal fish dishes – black bream with lime butter and hake with strawberries and cucumber in white wine – are features, as is the substantial treacle tart. Vegetarians are well looked after with their own menu. Twenty wines, with house French from Georges Duboeuf at £4.90.

CHEF: Rose Chapman PROPRIETORS: V.L. & R. Chapman
OPEN: Tue to Sat D (residents only Sun)
CLOSED: weekdays in Feb
MEALS: 7.30 to 9
PRICES: Set D from £10 (£14)
CARD: Visa
SEATS: 20. Private parties: 20 main room. Vegetarian meals. No cigars/pipes in dining-room
ACCOMMODATION: 5 rooms. B&B £11 to £22. Baby facilities. Pets welcome. Scenic. Doors close at 11.30. Confirm by 5 [GHG]

DULVERTON Somerset map 1

▲ *Ashwick House* [10/20]

Dulverton TA22 9QD
DULVERTON (0398) 23868
signposted from B3223 N of Dulverton £11–£16

The elegant Edwardian house is set in a six-acre estate, with sweeping lawns, specimen trees and two lily ponds. Inside, the Sherwood family have preserved the imposing hall with original William Morris wallpaper. The atmosphere and style can seem rather masculine. Dinner is a four-course menu of home cooking with few fancy touches and an emphasis on good-quality local produce. The style is leek and potato soup, noisettes of lamb with port sauce, home-made coffee pancake. Unpasteurised Cheshire and local goats' cheese appear on the board. The coffee is Costa Rica, the wine list mainly French with a small English contingent and plenty of half-bottles. House wine is £4.75. 'No service charge is added or required.'

CHEF: C.T. Bramble PROPRIETOR: Mrs P.E. Sherwood
OPEN: Tue to Sat D, and Sun L
MEALS: 12.15 to 1.15, 7.15 to 8.30
PRICES: Set Sun L £7.50 (£11), Set D £12 (£16)
SEATS: 30. 3 tables outside. Private parties: 30 main room. Car-park, 30 places. No children under 8. Jacket and tie. No smoking in dining-room
ACCOMMODATION: 6 rooms, all with bath/shower. B&B £39.50 to £61. Deposit: £25. No children under 8. Afternoon teas. Garden. TV. Scenic. Doors close at 11. Confirm by 5 [GHG]

DUNWICH Suffolk map 6

Flora Tea Rooms [9/20]

The Beach, Dunwich IP17 3PU
WESTLETON (072 873) 433 £5

The tea-rooms in a large, converted hut on the beach are well known locally for the quality of their freshly cooked fish and chips. The fish – cod, plaice, skate, sole – comes from the Lowestoft boats. Only fresh is used and there is no pre-frying. Go early. There are bench tables outside for when the weather is good enough. There are also doughnuts, scones, apple pies and cakes, all baked daily.

CHEFS: John Elsley and Daphne Gill PROPRIETORS: Sarah Elsley and Daphne Gill
OPEN: all week
CLOSED: Dec to Mar
MEALS: 11am to 6pm
PRICES: £4 (£5)
SEATS: 70. 10 tables outside. Private parties: 80 main room. Car-park, 700 places. Children's helpings. No-smoking area. Wheelchair access (2 steps; also WC)

DURHAM Co Durham map 7

Undercroft Restaurant [9/20]

The College, Durham Cathedral, Durham DH1 3EQ
091-386 3721 £9

Opposite the Treasury, beside the book shop, inside the cathedral, conceived by the last Dean as a service to visitors, the Undercroft has built up considerable local support. Everything is cooked on the premises: savoury flans, scones, pies. There are fine salads and some traditional puddings – for instance apple and ginger upside-down pudding – as well as meringues and the popular sticky dark chocolate cake. House wine is £4.50.

CHEF: Kevin Dixon PROPRIETORS: Milburns Restaurants Ltd
OPEN: all week, daytime only
MEALS: 9.30 to 5 (2 Sun)
PRICES: £5 (£9). Service inc
SEATS: 80. Vegetarian meals. Children's helpings. No-smoking area. Wheelchair access (also WC). Self-service

Co Durham Round-up

INEXPENSIVE: *Almshouses,* Palace Green, Durham (091-386 1054).
STEAKS: *Stile,* 97 High Street, Willington, Crook (0388 746615).
ITALIAN: *Giovanni & Fabio Pizzeria,* 70 Claypath, Durham (091-386 1643); *Sardis,* North Road, Darlington (0325 461222).
BAR MEALS: *Oak Tree Inn,* Tantobie, Derwentside (0207 235445).
BISTRO WITH ROOMS: *Newbus Arms,* Neasham Road, Neasham, Darlington (0325 721071).
ROOMS: *Hallgarth Manor,* Pittington, Durham (0385 721188).

EASINGTON Cleveland map 6A

▲ *Grinkle Park Hotel* [10/20]

Easington TS13 4UB
GUISBOROUGH (0287) 40515 £13–£23

A long drive lined with rhododendrons leads to this impressive refurbished Victorian stone mansion, set in 35 acres of parkland, for many years the Baronetcy of Grinkle. The kitchen doesn't stray far from traditional English hotel cooking, but the emphasis is on local ingredients, including fresh fish and kippers from Whitby, lamb and game from Grinkle Estate, herbs from the kitchen garden. Smoked trout and avocado mousse, beef bourguignonne and pan-fried plaice with hazelnut butter have all been good. The trolley of home-made desserts groans with creamy confections; coffee comes with home-made fudge. An adequate wine list has a few bottles from Spain, Portugal, Italy and one each from Hungary and California. House French is £5.45; CELLARMAN'S CHOICE: Graves Blanc '85, £7.75; and Rioja, Coto de Imaz, Gran Reserva '78, £9.25.

CHEF: Timothy Backhouse PROPRIETORS: Bass plc
OPEN: all week
MEALS: 12 to 2, 7 to 9.30
PRICES: £18 (£23), Set L from £8.75 (£13), Set D £13.95 (£18), Snacks from £1.25
CARDS: Access, Amex, Diners, Visa
SEATS: 70. Private parties: 50 main room, 32 private room. Car-park, 100 places. Vegetarian meals. Children's helpings (Sun L only). Smart dress preferred. Wheelchair access (also WC)
ACCOMMODATION: 20 rooms, all with bath/shower. B&B £48 to £63. Baby facilities. Pets welcome. Afternoon teas. Garden. Tennis. Fishing. Snooker. TV. Phone. Scenic. Doors close at 11.30. Confirm by 6 [GHG]

Cleveland Round-up

CHINESE: *Peking Villa,* 236 Linthorpe Road, Middlesbrough (0642 222191).
ITALIAN: *Krimo's,* 8 The Front, Seaton Carew, Hartlepool (0429 266120); *Santoro,* 47 High Street, Yarm (0642 781305).

EAST BERGHOLT Essex map 3

Fountain House [10/20]

The Street, East Bergholt CO7 6TB
COLCHESTER (0206) 298232 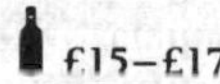 £15–£17

Wendy Anne Sarton cooks in this converted fifteenth-century cottage, offering reasonably priced set menus with a bistro flavour. Avocado with smoked mackerel mousse, baked trout with orange and walnut stuffing and fillet of pork provençale show the style. Sweets are in the same vein: strawberry vacherin, chocolate soufflé, orange salad. The wine list is well balanced and surprisingly inexpensive, with plenty of interesting bottles for under £10, as well as a good selection of medium-priced bottles. The range of Australian and New Zealand wines that opens the list includes many that would be hard to find elsewhere in Britain. The substantial Italian section also offers some fine drinking, from top names such as Quintarelli, Frescobaldi, Poggio, Antinori, Lungarotti and Gaja. French wines are no less impressive, with a selection of affordable clarets, a few Burgundies from excellent estates, good Rhônes, Loires and Alsace. German wines, except for the cheapest, also come from good estates. Choice of sweet wines is limited, but treats could include a bottle of Vouvray Clos Naudin Moelleux '76, £15, or a comparative tasting of half-bottles (£7.50 apiece) of Orange Muscats from California and Australia; or compare perhaps a botrytised Semillon from Australia, £13 per half, with a half of a more familiar botrytised Sémillon Sauternes, Château Filhot '81, £8. House Australian is £6.25. CELLARMAN'S CHOICE: Valpolicella, Monte la Paletta '82, £11; Sauvignon Blanc, Woodstock McLaren Vale '86, £10.50.

CHEF: Wendy Anne Sarton PROPRIETOR: James F. Sarton
OPEN: Tue to Sun, exc Sun D
CLOSED: 2 weeks end Feb
MEALS: 12.30 to 2, 7.30 to 10
PRICES: Set L £9.95 (£15), Set D £11.95 (£17)
CARDS: Access, Visa
SEATS: 32. 3 tables outside. Private parties: 16 main room. Car-park, 12 places. Vegetarian meals. Children's helpings. No cigars/pipes in dining-room. Wheelchair access. Music

EAST BUCKLAND Devon map 1

▲ *Lower Pitt* [10/20]

East Buckland EX32 0TD
FILLEIGH (059 86) 243 £18

The Lyons' converted sixteenth-century farmhouse stands in two acres of grounds on the edge of Exmoor. The atmosphere is warm and homely, and Suzanne Lyons' cooking matches the mood, with the emphasis on robust dishes prepared from local produce. Soups might range from lovage to ox-tail; chicken is casseroled with bacon, mushrooms, leeks and sweetcorn;

fricassee of mixed seafood comes in a tarragon and lemon sauce. Devon produce comes together well in loin of pork from Heal Farm at Kings Nympton, pan-fried with apples, Hancock's cider and mustard sauce. Vegetables are mostly from the garden. Home-made ice-creams are the most popular sweet. Sixty wines are well spread, with a good choice of ten house bottles. CELLARMAN'S CHOICE: Brouilly Ch. des Tours '86, £8.50.

CHEF: Suzanne Lyons PROPRIETORS: Jerome and Suzanne Lyons
OPEN: Tue to Sat, D only
MEALS: 7 to 9
PRICES: £12 (£18)
CARDS: Access, Amex, Visa
SEATS: 28. Private parties: 28 main room. Car-park, 25 places. Children's helpings. Music
ACCOMMODATION: 3 rooms, all with bath/shower. B&B £20 to £30. Deposit: 10%. No children under 11. Garden. Scenic. Doors close at 10.30. Confirm by 6 [GHG]

EAST MOLESEY Surrey map 3

Lantern [11/20]

10 YEARS

20 Bridge Road, East Molesey KT8 9AH
01-979 1531 £15–£27

Lantern's reputation is well earned for good, no-frills French provincial-style menus, one à la carte, two set, with a good representation of fish and seafood – mussels in a cream sauce; fish soup with leek purée; smoked haddock mousse; monkfish and prawns in a tomato sauce; fillet of John Dory and red mullet in a green herb sauce. The vegetables are fresh and well prepared and there is a good sweets trolley. Thirty wines, plus eight half-bottles. House French £6.95.

CHEF: P. Morphew PROPRIETORS: Mr and Mrs Morphew
OPEN: Mon to Sat, exc Mon L and Sat L
CLOSED: Aug
MEALS: 12.15 to 2.15, 7 to 10.30 (11 Sat)
PRICES: £15 (£26), Set L £7.25 (£15) to £17.45 (£26), Set D £15.25 (£24) to £17.85 (£27). Cover 95p. Service 12.5%
CARDS: Access, Amex, Diners, Visa
SEATS: 50. Private parties: 25 main room. Children's helpings. Smart dress preferred. Music

EASTBOURNE East Sussex map 3

Byrons [12/20]

10 YEARS

6 Crown Street, Old Town, Eastbourne BN21 1NX
EASTBOURNE (0323) 20171 £19

Years ago, in its bistro era, the place was all red, but the Scruttons have moved with the times and the dining-room is now elegant by comparison: pale prints, pale walls, pale pink table linen, white octagonal plates. Marian Scrutton remains one of the south coast's most charming hostesses. The menu has also developed. No more mushrooms in garlic butter, but shades of Raymond Blanc in the tartare of marinated fresh salmon, and a quite deliberate and successful step into modern British cooking with British cheeses; sweets such as lemon syllabub, the long-standing and excellent orange Bakewell tart; a greater presence of fruity, pithy sweetness in main courses, such as a warm chicken terrine with herbs and a plain sauce, and a respect for some fine ingredients – fish from the Eastbourne boats, free-range chicken, well-hung Sussex lamb. At its most classic and complex, this might translate into a slightly dry chicken breast stuffed with rough-textured, perfectly fresh crab-meat encased in flaky pastry and served with a professional béarnaise. 'Small scale, straightforward, unpretentious, good value.' Two dozen wines with a good range. House French £5.20, CELLARMAN'S CHOICE: Gigondas, Domaine du Grand Montmirail '84, £11.90, and Muscadet de Sèvre-et-Maine, Château de la Touche, £7.90.

CHEF: Simon Scrutton PROPRIETORS: Simon and Marian Scrutton
OPEN: Mon to Sat, exc Sat L
CLOSED: 1 week at Christmas
MEALS: 12.30 to 1.30, 7.30 to 10.30
PRICES: £11 (£19). Service 10%
CARDS: Amex, Diners, Visa
SEATS: 22. Private parties: 10 main room, 10 private room. Vegetarian meals. Children welcome. No smoking during meals. Music

EDENBRIDGE Kent map 3

Honours Mill [new entry, zero rated]

87 High Street, Edenbridge TN8 5AU
EDENBRIDGE (0732) 866757 £18–£26

The Goodhew brothers run this converted clapperboard mill half an hour's drive from Gatwick, in partnership. Giles is out front, Neville cooks with Martin Radmall and Duncan – the swimmer – is sometimes to be seen. Upstairs, past the running millstream, is an uncluttered dining-room, with pale colour schemes and fresh flowers. The modern French menu reflects Neville's training at Tante Claire and the Waterside Inn – here are wild mushrooms, truffles and foie gras used as a stuffing for galantine of chicken or as a garnish for a salad of duck ham. Fresh fish dishes, which change daily with the market, are a highlight: lobsters are roasted, wild salmon gets a chive and butter sauce, and Dover sole is good too. Other details are impressive, from the tiny canapés and crunchy *nouvelle* vegetables, to the coffee and impeccable petits fours. The wine list is French, with a few English bottles; excellent house wines from Duboeuf are £7.50. CELLARMAN'S CHOICE: St Aubin *premier cru*, Les Dents de Chien '84, £24.75; St Emilion, Ch. Lyonnat '81, £16.85. More reports, please.

CHEFS: Neville Goodhew and Martin Radmall PROPRIETORS: Neville, Duncan and Giles Goodhew
OPEN: Tue to Sun, exc Sun D
CLOSED: 2 weeks after Christmas, 2 weeks summer
MEALS: 12.15 to 2, 7.15 to 10
PRICES: Set L from £14.50 (£18), Set D £21.75 (£26). Service inc
SEATS: 38. Private parties: 20 main room. Children under 12 Sun L only

EGHAM Surrey map 3

La Bonne Franquette [13/20]

5 High Street, Egham TW20 9EA
EGHAM (0784) 39494 £16–£32.50

The ambitions of this modern trend restaurant are plain. Writing to a complaining customer, owner David Turvey declared: 'We would welcome competitors, but there is none.' That may be a moot point, especially when the service is having one of its off nights. There is no doubting the commitment to make this a major restaurant. Paul Smart's menu reads well and has some adventurous ideas: mussels in ginger butter sauce; quail with morels; escalope of salmon with chanterelles. Beef is well hung and vegetables might include artichokes and shallots. At its best the cooking delivers. 'The soufflés were superb... risen to perfection, full of true apple flavour, superb texture outside and inside, light and fluffy but with a nice moist centre, slivers of toasted almonds were scattered on the surface. A chilled glass of Ch. Septy Monbazillac '79 was served with the soufflé and was delicious, full of fruit, not cloying sweetness.' Other desserts are in the style of passion-fruit mousse with a sour cherry sauce, and warm lemon tart with a lemon sorbet and raspberry purée. Mark-ups on the wines are high and there is very little under £10, but quality is on the whole good. Burgundies include some excellent estate wines and there are some good clarets of vintages of the '70s and '80s, plus a couple of '59s. The selection from elsewhere in France is very brief, and from the rest of the world even briefer. House French is £6.50; CELLARMAN'S CHOICE: Hautes Côtes de Beaune, Confréries des Chevaliers du Tastevin, '85, £14.40.

CHEF: David Smart PROPRIETORS: David Turvey and David Smart
OPEN: all week, exc Sat L
CLOSED: bank hols
MEALS: 12 to 2, 7 to 9.30
PRICES: £19 (£27), Set L £12.50 (£16), Set D £20 (£20) to £32.50 (£32.50). Service inc
CARDS: Access, Amex, Diners, Visa
SEATS: 46. 3 tables outside. Private parties: 20 main room, 8 private room. Car-park, 14 places. Children welcome. Smart dress preferred. Wheelchair access. Music

ELLAND West Yorkshire map 5

Berties Bistro [11/20]

10 YEARS

7–10 Town Hall Buildings, Elland HD1 2TA
ELLAND (0422) 71724 £14

The cheery mix of modern green and white décor, Victorian prints and stuffed sofas, next to Elland Job Centre, is well discovered and supported locally. 'Midweek dining is preferred as Saturday especially is too busy.' The cooking seems to be on the up. The scope of dishes is wide, with some unusually colourful combinations: chicken and apricot mousse with a mild curry sauce; warm scallop and langoustine mousse with dill sauce; a vegetarian strudel with celery and Stilton. There is chicken and chips for children. Crudités and dips are set out on each table. Desserts tend to the substantial – ginger and apple steamed pudding, baked Alaska, or Berties Bombe, a cream meringue with sweet sauce. Outside catering is a new service. House wine from £5.75 a litre. CELLARMAN'S CHOICE: Crozes-Hermitage '74, from Jaboulet, £7.45.

CHEF: Michael Swallow PROPRIETOR: Brett Woodward
OPEN: Tue to Sun, D only
MEALS: 7 (6 Sat) to 11 (5 to 10 Sun)
PRICES: £9 (£14)
SEATS: 110. Private parties: 40 private room. Car-park, 60 places. Vegetarian meals. Children's helpings. Smart dress preferred. No-smoking area. Wheelchair access. Music. Air-conditioned

ELY Cambridgeshire map 6

Old Fire Engine House [11/20]

25 St Mary's Street, Ely CB7 4ER
ELY (0353) 662582  £17

Alarm bells have been ringing over the quality of the cooking at this long-established *Guide* entry. As a co-operative venture, it has had a tendency to go up and down in standard. But some reports have been like buckets of cold water on previous years' enthusiasm. As we go to press the position remains hidden behind a lot of smoke, but the foundations laid by Ann Ford and Michael Jarman, who have defended English cooking over two decades in which it was in serious decline elsewhere, are solid. It is not time to give up on them yet, rather perhaps to put the recommendation into a narrower context, to define the strengths more precisely. These are the local game, usually roasted and casseroled; unusual fish, like zander, pike and eel from the Fens; the gatherings from the hedgerows for lovage soup; marsh samphire; asparagus, plus, from wider afield, English cheeses. Real ales would fit this food well, but there is a good, mostly French wine list with low mark-ups. There are some excellent wines but a few dull bottles as well, such as Piat Beaujolais, and Rioja Bilbainas. Choice of sweet wines is limited. Best value is Vouvray Moelleux Le Haut Lieu '76, from Huet, £13, or there's good but young Coteux du Layon, and affordable Sauternes of the late '70s. House French from £5.40. CELLARMAN'S CHOICE: Mâcon-Lugny les Charmes '86, £8.60; Rioja, Vina Alcorta Reserva '81, £6.50; Barossa Valley Shiraz-Cabernet '86, £5.40.

CHEFS/PROPRIETORS: Ann Ford and Michael Jarman
OPEN: all week, exc Sun D
CLOSED: 24 Dec for 2 weeks, and bank hols
MEALS: 12.30 to 2, 7.30 to 9
PRICES: £12 (£17)
SEATS: 36. 8 tables outside. Private parties: 36 main room, 22 private room. Car-park, 8 places. Children's helpings

All inspections are carried out anonymously.

EMSWORTH Hampshire map 2

36 on the Quay [12/20]

47 South Street, Emsworth PO10 7EG
EMSWORTH (0243) 375592 £19–£39

Tim and Vivian Abady have moved from 36 North Street to a converted steak-house down by the quay. Inside, the décor has been transformed with stunning yellow and blue colour schemes and clever lighting; there are views of the harbour from the windows. Each table has a push bell to summon the waitress. Vivian Abady cooks in her own style – elaborately idiosyncratic, technically accomplished. Many of the influences are French, although she leans heavily on British ingredients. Ideas come in twos and threes: harmony of two soups might be carrot and ginger on the outside and a swirl of spinach and nutmeg within; trio of fish – scallops, salmon and sole – is served with lobster mayonnaise; a terrine of English cheeses includes Red Leicester, Stilton and Cheshire. Fillet of oak-smoked beef with truffle sauce and a soufflé of wild mushrooms and truffles is a perfect balance of flavours. Vegetables are individually tailored to each dish. To finish, the chocolate and orange jewel box on a fresh orange coulis surrounded by chocolate sauce, has been memorable. The hefty wine list is very strong on clarets and Burgundies. House Bordeaux £7.45. CELLARMAN'S CHOICE: Graves, Ch. Millet '82, £14.95; Mâcon-Villages, Domaine de la Condémine '85, £13.95.

CHEF: Vivian Abady PROPRIETORS: Tim and Vivian Abady
OPEN: Mon to Sat, exc Mon L and Sat L
CLOSED: 23 Dec to mid-Jan
MEALS: 12.15 to 3, 7.30 to 11
PRICES: £27 (£35), Set L £12.95 (£19) to £18.95 (£25), Set D £20 (£28) to £30 (£39)
CARDS: Access, Amex, Diners, Visa
SEATS: 42. Private parties: 20 main room, 10 private room. Car-park, 7 places. Vegetarian meals. No children under 5. Smart dress preferred. No cigars/pipes in dining-room. Music

EPWORTH Humberside map 5

Epworth Tap [9/20]

9–11 Market Place, Epworth DN9 1EU
EPWORTH (0427) 873333 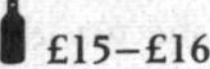 £15–£16

The Tap has arguably the best selection of fine wines of any wine bar in the North of England. There are five choices of Crozes Hermitage, including Jaboulet's top Domaine Thalabert from '82 and '83 at £18.50, and six Hermitages back to '67 (a few frustratingly marked NFS). No fewer than nine Chardonnays from California offset a backbone of good-value vintage claret going back well into the '70s, but with much under £20; and an equally impressive range of Burgundy. Dessert wines include two sweet Vouvrays, one Quarts de Chaume and an Anjou from the Loire, four Sauternes and

Barsacs, a Muscat de Beaumes de Venise, a trio of Malagas and an Orange Muscat from California, plus eight half-bottles. The food is bistro-ish: provençal fish soup, followed by main course casseroles such as beef in red wine or pork with sweetcorn, plus the more usual offerings of chilli con carne and lasagne. Sweets are mainly home made, sticky toffee pudding being one of the local favourites.

CHEF: Helen Wynne PROPRIETORS: Helen and John Wynne
OPEN: Tue to Sat, D only
MEALS: 7.30 to 10 (10.30 Sat)
PRICES: £9 (£15), Set D £10.50 (£16)
CARD: Access
SEATS: 74. Private parties: 50 main room, 24 private room. Vegetarian meals. Children welcome. No-smoking area. Wheelchair access (3 steps). Music

ESHER Surrey map 3

Les Alouettes [12/20]

7 High Street, Claygate, Esher KT10 0JW
ESHER (0372) 64882 £23–£30

After 10 years, the larks are unusually well organised and run. Linen is crisp, glasses gleam and everyone gets on with the business in hand in a pleasant manner. The menu is French, on the long side, but imaginative without being silly. Michel Perraud from the Waterside Inn has moved the menu away from the fruit sauces that used to predominate, into a more French direction of consommés, cassoulets of shellfish and mousselines. Main dish meals of good quality come with reliable stock and wine sauces which betray his training. Trimmings are expansive, from amuse-gueules to petits fours and a choice of coffees. The wines are equally Gallic and carefully chosen.

CHEFS: Thomas Stewart and Michel Perraud PROPRIETOR: Stavros Christou
OPEN: Mon to Sat, exc Sat L
CLOSED: 25 to 31 Dec, 2 weeks Sept
MEALS: 12.15 to 2.15, 7 to 9.30 (10 Fri and Sat)
PRICES: Set L £15 (£23), Set D from £20 (£30). Service 12.5%
SEATS: 75. Private parties: 85 main room. Vegetarian meals. Children's helpings. Smart dress preferred. Wheelchair access (3 steps). Music. Air-conditioned

Good Earth [10/20]

14–18 High Street, Esher
ESHER (0372) 62489 and 66681 £15–£21

This branch of the small chain with other addresses in Chelsea, Mill Hill and Kensington has consistently drawn more reports than all of the other branches together. Prawn dishes, lettuce wraps and Peking duck are all recommended. Most unusual is the exceptionally good vegetarian section, with many dishes containing no animal products. Spring rolls, sweet-and-sour wun-tun and Singapore noodles all come without meat, and there's a good showing of bean curd specialities. House French is £5.50.

CHEF: C.P. Cheng PROPRIETOR: Robert Cheung
OPEN: all week
MEALS: 12 to 2.15, 6 to 11 (10.45 Sun)
PRICES: £12 (£21), Set L and D from £11 (£15). Minimum £9. Service 15%
CARDS: Amex, Access, Carte Blanche, Diners, Visa
SEATS: 90. Private parties: 30 main room. Vegetarian meals. Children welcome. Wheelchair access. Air-conditioned

Read's [12/20]

4 The Parade, Claygate, Esher KT10 0NU
ESHER (0372) 65105 £16–£22

Now in its fourth year, Read's has gone up in the world, adding home-baked breads, petits fours and canapés. The menu runs to five dishes per course and is written in some detail in English. If the elaboration of, say, combining salmon, brill and sole fillets and garnishing them with salmon caviare seems French, the seasoning is definitely English – lime and white port for these fish; mace and pink peppercorns for potted shellfish; pheasant sauced with port and redcurrant and garnished with a miniature cherry flan. From a long list of recommendations: scallop salad with walnut dressing; gravlax; stuffed quail; calf's liver lyonnaise; lamb with tarragon; ravioli of monkfish and lobster; caramel soufflé; crème brûlée. There is also a much-praised English cheeseboard from James of Beckenham, who supply many of the cheeses listed in the feature at the back of the *Guide* under Factors' Choice. On the wine list, Reads has the sensible idea of giving a list of all the bottles in order of price. This counters the often misleading notes and wrongly attributed regions elsewhere (Bergerac and Touraine are a long way from Provence, for instance). Bottles are listed in ascending price order within the regions, too, and few are more than £20 a bottle, with some good *crus bourgeois* clarets, Burgundies and Beaujolais from small growers, and Rhône reds from the likes of Domaine des Entrefaux and Domaine du Grand Tinel. German and Italian selections are perfunctory, but the trio of Spanish wines good. The page of wines from Australia and California is adequate if not exciting. Best choice to accompany dessert is Dürkheimer Feuerberg Gewürztraminer Aulese '83, £12.50. House French £6.50; CELLARMAN'S CHOICE: house champagne, from Alfred Gratten, £19.95.

CHEFS: Stephen Read and Frank DeMengal PROPRIETORS: The Read family
OPEN: Tue to Sat
MEALS: 12 to 2, 7 to 10 (10.30 Sat)
PRICES: £16 (£22), Set L £9.50 (£16)
CARDS: Access, Amex, Diners, Visa
SEATS: 28. Children's helpings (L only). Smart dress preferred. Wheelchair access. Music. Air-conditioned

'We were sitting outside a good café on the Left Bank, having just had lunch, when the waiter came out, bent down, washed his dishcloth in the gutter and cleaned down the tables.' On eating in Paris

ETON Berkshire map 2

Eton Wine Bar [9/20]

82–83 High Street, Eton SL4 6AF
WINDSOR (0753) 854921 and 855182 £15

A new conservatory has been added to this long-standing wine bar owned and run by the Gilbey family. A loyal following of theatre-goers support a short, sensible menu that gets away from the usual clichés, offering, for instance, horseradish pancakes with a beef, mushroom and brown-ale filling. Some wines have actually come down in price on an enterprising list from the family firm; it includes a clutch of half-bottles and a trio of pudding wines. CELLARMAN'S CHOICE: St Véran, Domaine des Dimes '86, £9.15; Côtes du Rhône '83, £6.70.

CHEFS: Caroline Gilbey, Linda Gilbey, the Hon. William Gilbey, Deborah Wicks and Eleanor Berry
PROPRIETORS: The Hon. William Gilbey, Caroline Gilbey, the Hon. Michael Gilbey and Linda Gilbey
OPEN: all week
CLOSED: 3 days at Christmas
MEALS: 12 to 2.30, 6 to 10.30 (11 Fri and Sat, from 7 Sun)
PRICES: £9 (£15)
CARDS: Access, Visa
SEATS: 110. Private parties: 40 private room. Vegetarian meals. Children welcome. Wheelchair access. Music

EVERSHOT Dorset map 2

▲ *Summer Lodge* [12/20]

Evershot DT2 0JR
EVERSHOT (093 583) 424 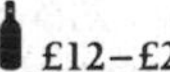 £12–£20

The Lodge, run by the Corbett family aided by a posse of young women, is set in the heart of Hardy country; Tess stopped in the village. Menus are worked to a formula showing the virtues of old-fashioned British cooking, especially baking. The style does not change, but as everywhere else such traditions are frowned upon, they become more precious. A few tables are available to non-residents for three-course dinner if the bedrooms are not all booked. The steak and kidney pie, served in a bowl for two and left on the table, with seconds of gravy brought round, is superb. On other nights main courses centre on classic lamb in a pastry with a soubise sauce; beef Wellington; and baked gammon with Cumberland sauce, either side of which might be melon, tomato and cucumber salad; roulade of smoked haddock; fine Stilton and Dorset knobs; a hot pudding. The strength is in the ingredients – East Coker asparagus; Somerset lamb; wild salmon and so on. Regulars would prefer more choice. It may be wise to check the main dish before booking. Tea can be a glory in itself– a pair of cakes hidden under glass domes; scones; cream; flans – served in the horseshoe lounge reputedly conceived by Hardy himself. Prices on the excellent wine list are reasonable. Clarets are the lengthiest section, with good vintages back to '49 at affordable prices, but some simpler clarets, too. There are good Burgundies and Rhônes, a few good Italians, Californians and even a good selection of English wines from Dorset and surrounding counties. Sweet wines are limited to a few recent vintages of Sauternes and an unusual Muscat de Beaumes de Venise, Domaine de Bernardins, NV, £14.35, or £1.75 per glass. House red, white and rosé, all French, are £5.35; CELLARMAN'S CHOICE: St Emilion, Ch. Franc-Grâce-Dieu, *grand cru* '82, £11.90; Chablis, La Fourchaume, *premier cru* '85, £14.65; Bourgogne Aligoté, Domaine Poithier Rieusset '85, £8.85.

CHEF: Margaret Corbett PROPRIETORS: Nigel and Margaret Corbett
OPEN: all week (L by arrangement only)
CLOSED: 20 Dec to 3 Jan
MEALS: 8
PRICES: Set L £9.50 (£12), Set D £17.50 (£20). Service inc
CARDS: Access, Visa
SEATS: 48. 28 tables outside. Private parties: 28 main room. Car-park, 30 places. Vegetarian meals. No children under 8. Wheelchair access (also WC). One sitting
ACCOMMODATION: 17 rooms, all with bath/shower. Rooms for disabled. B&B £35 to £70. No children under 8. Pets welcome. Afternoon teas. Garden. Swimming-pool. Tennis. Fishing. Golf. Phone. Scenic. Doors close at 12. Confirm by 6 [GHG]

EVESHAM Hereford & Worcester map 2

▲ *Cedar Restaurant, The Evesham Hotel* [10/20]

Cooper's Lane, Evesham WR11 6DA
EVESHAM (0386) 765566 £17

Eclectic is the key word to describe the Jenkinsons' cheerily run restaurant. Ideas and inspiration come from all parts of the globe; plain grills cheek by jowl with more exotic paw-paw with grapefruit and mint; halibut with lime and rosemary butter; guinea-fowl, stuffed with chicken mousse with beetroot and whisky; steamed seafood pudding. The sweets trolley has been replaced by a handwritten menu of home-made puddings, as chatty but informative as the main menu. Good-value buffet lunches. If you have ever wondered about the wines of Algeria, Austria, Brazil, Chile, China, Canada, Japan, Mexico, Turkey, Russia, Rumania, Israel, India or the 'other' wine making states of the USA (Texas, Virginia, Washington, Oregon or Idaho), you will find something here to slake your curiosity. Prices are low enough to encourage experimentation. A good selection of Australian wines includes Rosemount Roxburgh Chardonnay '84, £16.50, and there's an excellent list from New Zealand. Italian wines are also good, but ask for help in identifying them if the photos are out of focus in the quirky wine list – producers' names suddenly disappear in the Italian section. The Spanish selection is far better than usual, and there are plenty of well-chosen Portuguese reds, well under £10. Choice of sweet wines is fairly limited, but unusual. Try a half-bottle of Mondavi's Moscato d'Oro '81, £7.95, a Ruländer Beerenauslese

Eiswein '81, £40, a glass of Moscatel de Setúbal for £1.90, or, a rare find, Picolit from Italy, £19.50, certainly not the 'Yquem of Italy' the list claims it to be, but a tasty and interesting end to the meal. House red from Chile £5.15.

CHEF: Brian Simmonds PROPRIETORS: The Jenkinson family
OPEN: all week
CLOSED: 25 and 26 Dec
MEALS: 12.30 to 2, 7 to 9.30
PRICES: £14 (£17). Service inc
CARDS: Access, Amex, Diners, Visa
SEATS: 55. Private parties: 12 main room; 15 private room. Car-park, 50 places. Vegetarian meals. Children's helpings. Wheelchair access (also WC)
ACCOMMODATION: 34 rooms, all with bath/shower. B&B £42 to £58. Baby facilities. Pets welcome. Afternoon teas. Garden. TV. Phone. Scenic. Doors close at 12. Confirm in writing [GHG]

EYE Suffolk map 6

▲ *Oaksmere* [new entry, zero rated]

Brome, Eye IP23 8AJ
EYE (0379) 870326
at junction of A140 and B1077 £14–£25

The ancestral home enjoys a new form of class division. The bar is well frequented by locals for excellent snacks, while the gracious dining-room is attuned to users of 'our own cricket ground, day yacht charter, helicopter pad and private air-strip (one mile).' The investment in the kitchen pays off in terms of fine ingredients, which benefit both sides, served by the same staff. The restaurant menu has ambitions, witness the 'terrine of venison fillet and sporting birds wrapped in a mousse of their own livers.' But there are good examples of a successful style, as in first-rate fillet of beef in a red wine and shallot sauce and an impeccable tray of petits fours. House French is £5.95. CELLARMAN'S CHOICE: Delegats Hawkes Bay Sauvignon blanc '87, £13.95. More reports, please.

CHEFS: Allison Wells, Rodney Debenham and David Bates PROPRIETORS: Bill and Mike Hasted
OPEN: all week
MEALS: 12 to 2, 7 to 10
PRICES: £18 (£25), Set L £9.50 (£14), Snacks from £1.25. Service 10%
CARDS: Access, Amex, Diners, Visa
SEATS: 80. 12 tables outside. Private parties: 30 main room, 20 and 30 private rooms. Car-park, 50 places. Vegetarian meals. Children's helpings. No cigars in dining-room. Wheelchair access
ACCOMMODATION: 5 rooms, all with bath/shower. B&B £36 to £53. Pets welcome. Garden. TV. Scenic. Doors close at 12

New this year are County Round-ups, mostly, but not always, listed under the county town. To find a County Round-up, check the maps at the back; towns listing a Round-up are underlined.

FARNHAM Surrey map 3

Tirolerhof [10/20]

84 West Street, Farnham GU9 7EN
FARNHAM (0252) 723277 £8–£23

It's rather incongruous to walk in from the Home Counties' sensibilities of genteel Farnham to be surrounded by Austrian Gemütlichkeit, which is as unstinting as the portions. Lots of wood, cheery red Tyrolean tablecloths and the owner in Lederhosen. The décor may be *Sound of Music* but the food tastes authentically Austrian and leans heavily on meaty dishes like schnitzels and goulashes. Everything comes with rösti. Smoked ham with ogen melon is freshly sliced; marinated herring with onions and apple is properly tangy. Good reports of the apple strudel and the Sachertorte. Saturday is accordion night; Wednesday is fondue night. The menu says ladies forfeit a kiss for each piece of bread or meat lost in the pot. A bit daring for Farnham, surely. House Austrian £6.80.

CHEF: Gerhard Krug PROPRIETORS: Helmuth Staffler and Gerhard Krug
OPEN: Mon to Sat, D only
MEALS: 7 to 10.30 (1am Fri and Sat)
PRICES: £15 (£23), Set D £3 (£8) to £20 (£27), Snacks from £2.50. Service 10%
CARDS: Access, Visa
SEATS: 100. Private parties: 60 main room; 60 private room. Vegetarian meals. Children's helpings. Smart dress preferred. Music

FARNLEY TYAS West Yorkshire map 5

Golden Cock [10/20]

Farnley Tyas HD4 6UD
HUDDERSFIELD (0484) 661979 and 663563 £12–£28

Food is the main point of interest in this stone village pub on the edge of the Pennines. Meals in the blue dining-room now centre on set menus, including a five-course dinner. Old-fashioned roasts are outnumbered by more modern French-style dishes, such as sea-bass with tomato, saffron and ginger sauce, or stuffed boned quail with raspberry vinegar sauce. Breads, patisserie and chocolates are home made. The upstairs Charcuterie Restaurant specialises in carvery meats and casseroles, without bookings. Around a hundred wines, including a strong contingent from the Antipodes and California, as well as Spain and Chile. CELLARMAN'S CHOICE: New Zealand Cloudy Bay Chardonnay '86, £19.

CHEF/PROPRIETOR: Peter John Midwood
OPEN: all week, exc Sat L and Sun D
MEALS: 12.15 to 2, 7.15 (6.30 Sat) to 9.45
PRICES: Set L £8.95 (£12), Set D £14.95 (£20) to £22 (£28)
CARDS: Access, Amex, Diners, Visa
SEATS: 125. 11 tables outside. Private parties: 48 main room. Car-park, 75 places. Vegetarian meals. Children's helpings. Wheelchair access (also WC). Music

FARRINGTON GURNEY Avon map 2

▲ *Old Parsonage* [11/20]

10 YEARS

Main Street, Farrington Gurney BS18 5UD
TEMPLE CLOUD (0761) 52211 £15–£20

'I first met Mrs Gofton-Watson when she ran the pub in Stratton-on-Fosse. She had a reputation for serving super lunches and dinners for parents and boys on exeat from Downside. She then moved to the Old Parsonage and became Mrs Gofton-Watson, but everything you say in the *Guide* over the past 15 years has stayed the same. A most reliable restaurant. The last time I went there was eight and a half years ago to celebrate my wife's 60th! We had different food, but the atmosphere, service and both food and wine were excellent.' The cooking is, to quote the same correspondent, no-nonsense and the service impeccable. 'Home-cooking at its best', says another. It is a small-scale operation, taking its impetus from fish and cooking broadly in a mid-Channel manner. Prawns with sherry in cream, pancakes filled with spinach, pipérade, roast pheasant, Dover sole with lemon and parsley sauce and dauphinoise potatoes might all appear on the menu – on Sundays fine roast beef. Sweets can be the most characterful, if rich, course: meringues; gooseberry ice-cream; syrup tart; St Emilion au chocolat. Fifty wines flirt with the major French regions, and also now Australia; they are well chosen and not rapaciously priced. CELLARMAN'S CHOICE: the strangely named white, Rouge Homme Chardonnay '85, from Australia, £11.50.

CHEF: H.M. Gofton-Watson PROPRIETORS: W.E. and H.M. Gofton-Watson
OPEN: all week, exc Mon L and Sun D
CLOSED: 25 to 28 Dec, Good Fri
MEALS: 12.30 to 1.30, 7 to 10
PRICES: £14 (£20), Set Sun L £10 (£15). Service 10%
SEATS: 26. Private parties: 14 main room, 14 private room. Car-park, 100 places. Children's helpings. Wheelchair access (also WC)
ACCOMMODATION: 3 rooms, all with bath/shower. B&B £30 to £50. Baby facilities. Garden

FAVERSHAM Kent map 3

Read's [12/20]

Painters Forstal, Faversham ME13 0EE
FAVERSHAM (0795) 535344 £16–£27

Some say David Pitchford's French restaurant rates alongside the élite, others that the tendency to over-elaboration dulls the kitchen's edge. Much of the impact comes from the complexities – for instance, a fruit terrine, with fine layers of pink and white grapefruit, oranges, pineapple and pomelo in a cider apple jelly, served as a starter. Influences are not always so modern. Rösti potatoes, coq au vin, salmon Véronique sit side by side in a relatively long, nine-dish-per course *carte.* The strength here is in the sauces, from the classic forestière or hollandaise with lobster to the sharp peppercorn sauce served with the fish mixed grill. Desserts include Chocoholics Anonymous

– chocolate truffle cake, chocolate mousse and chocolate marquise, served with caramel ice-cream. The cheeseboard moves away from the French influence; the selection is all British. There is a children's menu at £6. The wine list is interesting rather than great, but knowledgeable lovers of old clarets and Burgundies should be able to pick some fine bottles and a few bargains on the 'odds' list of mature classic wines. Bordeaux and Burgundy are the heavyweight areas, but Louis Latour supplies a great many of the Burgundies on the main list, and Burgundies of the age of most of the wines on the 'odds' list are likely to be well past their peak. A number of off-vintages as well as some very fine wines among the clarets call for careful selection. Some are modestly marked up, some more fulsomely. German wines include a number from excellent producers. The rest of the world is very scantily covered, enlivened by four fine wines from Penfolds in Australia. Choice is not helped by the absence of quite a number of producers' names from the list. House French £6.50. CELLARMAN'S CHOICE: Cabernet Shiraz '84; £13; Ch. de Sales '79, £21.

CHEF: David Pitchford PROPRIETORS: David and Rona Pitchford
OPEN: Mon to Sat
MEALS: 12 to 2, 7 to 10
PRICES: £18 (£27), Set L from £10 (£16)
CARDS: Amex, Diners, Visa
SEATS: 72. 3 tables outside. Private parties: 72 main room. Car-park, 30 places. Children's helpings. Wheelchair access (1 step; also WC). Music

FELSTED Essex map 3

Rumbles Cottage [10/20]

Braintree Road, Felsted CM6 3DJ
GREAT DUNMOW (0371) 820996 £13–£17

Joy Hadley's sense of culinary adventure has seen experimental menus introduced early in the week for regulars to test the new combinations. These are set-price and might offer marbled eggs with sorrel sauce; banana and coconut milk pudding; rhubarb ice-cream, all for about the same price as a normal main course. A hard core of readers are enthusiastic supporters of the snug old dining-room. Recommended dishes show no lack of verve: smoked chicken and sugar-soup; mango mayonnaise for the avocado; but also there is the reliable, more classic strain of chicken with tarragon. House French £6. CELLARMAN'S CHOICE: Chardonnay Réserve '86, from Jaboulet-Vercherre, £11; Rioja, Don Jacobo Reserva '80, £9.75.

CHEF: E. Joy Hadley PROPRIETORS: E. Joy Hadley and M. Donovan
OPEN: Tue to Sat D, and Sun L (Wed to Fri L by arrangement)
CLOSED: 3 weeks Feb, 1 week Aug
MEALS: 12 to 2, 7 to 9
PRICES: £12 (£17), Set L £9 (£14), Set D (Tue to Thur) £8.50 (£13)
CARDS: Access, Visa
SEATS: 46. Private parties: 24 main room; 8, 10 private rooms. Vegetarian meals. Children's helpings. Wheelchair access

FLITWICK Bedfordshire map 3

▲ *Flitwick Manor* [13/20]

Church Road, Flitwick MK45 1AE
FLITWICK (0525) 712242
off A5120, S of Flitwick £19–£38

Somerset Moore's gentrified Georgian manor is now firmly in the mould of English country hotels catering for tourists and conferences, and the kitchen can sometimes be stretched by the influx of visitors. On the day, the kitchen can deliver some excellent dishes: razor-fish and crab bisque; lobster in pastry with cream, brandy and truffle sauce; rosette of salmon and turbot in tomato, chive and basil coulis. Fish dominates – some comes direct from Mr Moore's company in Grimsby – but there are original meat dishes among the ample choice and separate game and vegetarian menus, with dishes ranging from jugged venison with braised red cabbage and apples to spinach and egg noodles in fresh tomato and herb sauce. Reports this year have been rather uneven, but the balance is still tilted in Flitwick's favour. Most quibbles relate to the prices, and the service, which is not what many people would expect from a country-house hotel restaurant. The wine list is a pedigree assortment of classy clarets and Burgundies, and mark-ups can be high. CELLARMAN'S CHOICE: Pouilly Fumé, Les Loges '85 at £15.

CHEFS: Somerset Moore and Geoffrey Welch PROPRIETORS: Somerset and Hélène Moore
OPEN: all week, exc Sun D
MEALS: 12.45 to 2, 7 to 9.30
PRICES: £30 (£38), Set L and D from £13.50 (£19)
CARDS: Access, Amex, Visa
SEATS: 90. 6 tables outside. Private parties: 65 main room, 10 and 20 private rooms. Car-park, 70 places. Vegetarian meals. Children's helpings. No pipes in dining-room. Wheelchair access (also WC)
ACCOMMODATION: 15 rooms, all with bath/shower. Rooms for disabled. B&B £60 to £90. Deposit: £50. Baby facilities. Garden. Tennis. Fishing. Snooker. Air-conditioning. TV. Phone. Scenic [GHG]

FOLKESTONE Kent map 3

India [11/20]

1 Old High Street, Folkestone CT20 1RJ
FOLKESTONE (0303) 59155 £9–£16

In the unpromising setting of a converted shop at the back of town near the cinema and the amusement arcades, Ali Ashraf has created an exceptional Indian restaurant with the atmosphere of a private house plus muzak and incense. The cooking is mainly North Indian with a few Bengali touches and one or two French influences, reflecting Mr Ashraf's background. Tikkas are excellent – sizzling hot and subtly spiced. Also good are prawn bhajias – described as 'beignets', spiced with cumin and coriander. The menu also takes in dhansaks, bhunas and birianis as well as seafood dosas and fish masala. Salade niçoise and poulet provençale are Gallic alternatives. Drink Kingfisher beer or Indian Beena wine.

CHEF/PROPRIETOR: Ali Ashraf
OPEN: all week
MEALS: 12 to 2.30, 6 to 11.30
PRICES: £9 (£16), Set L £3.95 (£9) to £5.50 (£10), Set D £7 (£13) to £10 (£16). Cover 50p. Minimum £5.50. Service 10%
CARDS: Access, Amex, Diners, Visa
SEATS: 52. Private parties: 56 main room. Vegetarian meals. Children's helpings. Wheelchair access. Music

FOWEY Cornwall map 1

Food for Thought [new entry, zero rated]

Town Quay, Fowey PL23 1AT
FOWEY (072 683) 2221 £20–£26

The ancient, slate-walled building is prettily situated right on the harbour, and local fish dominates the Billingsleys' menu. There is great show – lots of sauces, lots of vegetables, lots of garnishes and lots of petits fours – but ingredients are of good quality and timing is spot-on. As a whole, the kitchen has come on noticeably in recent years. Scallops are poached and served with a langoustine sauce flavoured with anise; rosettes of beef fillet are surrounded by a pool of herb-flavoured veal jus and an outer ring of beurre blanc. Lamb en croûte and rendezvous of fish and shellfish have also been good. Sweets veer between sticky-toffee pudding and marquise of two chocolates. Excellent home-baked bread and creamy butter. Around 60 wines (plus 10 half-bottles) are mainly French, with some token representatives from other countries. More reports, please.

CHEF: Martin Billingsley PROPRIETORS: Martin and Caroline Billingsley
OPEN: Mon to Sat, D only
CLOSED: Jan and Feb
MEALS: 7 to 9.30
PRICES: Set D £13.50 (£20) to £18.50 (£26)
CARDS: Access, Visa
SEATS: 38. Private parties: 20 main room. No children under 5. Wheelchair access

Fowey Brasserie [9/20]

1 Lostwithiel Street, Fowey PL23 1BD
FOWEY (072 683) 2649 £17

Fowey is a tourist village full of steep lanes and alleys, with long, narrow buildings. The Brasserie is no exception. There are views of the harbour from the French windows and balcony; the music is from the 1930s and 1940s. The style is cool, laid-back brasserie, with a menu to match. Bacon, mushroom and spinach salad; calf's liver with sage and onion; and sirloin steak with shallot and red wine sauce are backed up by charcuterie, fresh pasta, soups and special sandwiches. Good coffee, basic wines. House Fitou £4.85.

CHEFS: Elaine Elliot, Mark Monk and Arnold Belevics PROPRIETOR: Arnold Belevics
OPEN: Wed to Mon D, plus weekday L in summer
MEALS: 12 to 4, 7 to 10
PRICES: £12 (£17), Snacks from £1.75
CARDS: Access, Amex, Visa
SEATS: 74. 5 tables outside. Vegetarian meals. Children's helpings. Wheelchair access. Music

FRESSINGFIELD Suffolk map 6

Fox and Goose [11/20]

Fressingfield IP21 5PB
FRESSINGFIELD (037 986) 247 £21–£31

For more than two decades the Clarke family has run this early sixteenth-century building as a restaurant with its own rules. Book ahead, have a menu sent on, and order in advance. Adrian Clarke cooks, his wife takes the orders, serves and also bakes the excellent brown bread. Old-style classical specialities dominate the menu, and many dishes are laced with rich, creamy, alcoholic sauces, but are none the worse for that. Noisettes of veal get a cream and lemon sauce, chicken breast comes in a sauce of mushrooms, cream and white wine. Duck is paired with calvados and apples, guinea-fowl with garlic and cognac, and beef Stroganoff is the real thing. Fish and game feature strongly; vegetables are ample and buttered. Good home-made strawberry ice-cream to finish. The extensive wine list has house French at £8. CELLARMAN'S CHOICE: Château Ormes de Pez '82, £19; Chassagne-Montrachet '83, £19.

CHEF: Adrian Clarke PROPRIETORS: Mr and Mrs A.P. Clarke
OPEN: all week, exc Tue, and Sun D (Sept to Mar)
CLOSED: 1 week at Christmas
MEALS: 12 to 1.30, 7 to 9
PRICES: £23 (£31), Set L and D £15 (£21). Licensed, also bring your own: corkage £3
CARDS: Access, Amex, Diners, Visa
SEATS: 24. Private parties: 32 main room. Car-park, 30 places. No children under 10. Jacket and tie. No smoking in dining-room

FROGHALL Staffordshire map 5

Wharf [11/20]

Foxt Road, Froghall ST10 2HJ
IPSTONES (053 871) 486
just off A52, Stoke to Ashbourne £20

The converted warehouse on the canal retains its Staffordshire blue quarry tiles on the floor. A strong vegetarian influence makes for an unusual *carte*, offering such dishes as leek and wine soup, and courgette and watercress soufflé in a wholemeal tart with a rosemary butter sauce. Sauces can lift meals – saffron for a scallop terrine; orange for smoked quail; two – one of redcurrant and one of garlic – for a fillet of beef. The sense of decoration reaches its fulfilment with sweets – walnut Torte, cold lemon soufflé, and chocolate cake draw recommendations. Service is personal. The menu changes every three months and there are occasional gourmet evenings, inclusive of wines, offering six courses for £32. House French at £5.40 opens a short list of 25 well-spread wines mostly under £10.

CHEF: Julia Sargent PROPRIETORS: R. and J. Young and M.L. StClaire
OPEN: Tue to Sat, D only
MEALS: 7.30 to 9.15
PRICES: £16 (£20). Service inc
CARD: Access
SEATS: 40. Private parties: 40 main room. Car-park, 60 places. Vegetarian meals. Children's helpings. Wheelchair access (1 step)

GATWICK West Sussex map 3

▲ *Garden Restaurant, Gatwick Hilton* [10/20]

Gatwick Airport, Gatwick RH6 0LL
CRAWLEY (0293) 518080 £23–£33

Of all the Hiltons in all the world, Gatwick qualifies as one of the best of the airport hotels. The Sunday brunch, when diners can use the hotel pool between 10.30 and 2.30, is a popular local event. Children are charged £1.30 per year old. Early-evening meals before 7.30 are also offered at 20 per cent discount. The group has developed its own particular kind of gastronomy –very picturesque, very widely spread for ingredients, rather showy, with popular lines like prawn cocktails. 'Unusual' is how one inspector puts it. There is a big char-grill on view for the Aberdeen steaks. The pace is more in keeping with the airport timetable than normal time. 'Light years away from the average ghastly food available at most airports.' From the flight side of the airport it is a walkable distance, via the car-park. Wines, alas, are also on an international flight pattern – opening at £10 and rising steeply.
CELLARMAN'S CHOICE: Sancerre, Domaine de Villots '86, £14.30.

CHEF: Patrick John PROPRIETORS: Hilton International
OPEN: all week, exc Sat L
MEALS: 12 to 2.30, 6 to 11
PRICES: £23 (£32), Set L £14.25 (£23), Set D £18.75 (£26) to £25 (£33)
CARDS: Access, Amex, Carte Blanche, Diners, Visa
SEATS: 180. Private parties: 20 main room, 350 private room. Car-park, 90 places. Vegetarian meals. Children's helpings. Smart dress preferred. No-smoking area. Wheelchair access (also WC). Music. Air-conditioned
ACCOMMODATION: 550 rooms, all with bath/shower. Rooms for disabled. Lift. B&B £94.50 to £112. Deposit: one night's stay. Children welcome. Baby facilities. Pets welcome. Afternoon teas. Swimming-pool. Sauna. Air-conditioning. TV. Phone. Confirm by 6

Restaurants are graded on a scale of 1–20. In the category of 10–11 expect to find the best food in the locality. Ratings of 12 and more are given to restaurants we regard as serving the best food in the region.

GILLINGHAM Dorset map 2

▲ *Stock Hill House* [12/20]

Wyke, Gillingham SP8 5NR
GILLINGHAM (074 76) 3626 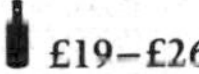 £19–£26

Peter Hauser calls his cooking generous rather than robust, as we said last year, but a couple of regulars advise that they always do a two-hour cross-country beforehand in order to 'deal with the meal'. The house, built around 1830 and reached via a long drive of beeches, the grounds, the chandeliered and moulded décor and the welcome are all in themselves good reason to visit. 'My cooking is French with modern Austrian.' It also reflects the years the Hausers spent in the Channel Islands (where they featured in the *Guide*: Dixcart Hotel, Sark, 1973; Aval du Creux, 1980). There is a rich fusion of different ideas: cream of nettle soup mimosa, jellied pig's trotter with onion vinaigrette, home-cured ox-tongue and chicken liver in brioche with a Cumberland sauce are just three of seven starters on a spring menu. Styles rub up against each other; wiener Schnitzel sits beside fillet of beef poached in consommé. Fish is a strength, as are home-grown vegetables. Recommended dishes have been a fish soup, roast rib with wine gravy, steak beurre maître d'hotel, and of course, Austrian-style sweets such as apple strudel. Service is leisurely, which affords time to admire the Wedgwood and the linen. Most of the wines on the list come from Loire, Rhône and Provence expert Robin Yapp, and the selection from other areas is very brief, although there are good Beaujolais and red and white Burgundies. Of the Yapp offerings, Jean Vatan Sancerres, Gérard Chave's white Hermitage, George Vernay's Condrieu and Robert Jasmin's Côte Rôtie are all superlative. Champagne from Jaquesson and Alsace wines from Schléret are also excellent, as is Domaine de Trévallon from Coteaux des Baux-en-Provence. The only sweet wines offered are Bonnezeaux, Château des Gauliers '59, £36.40, and Muscat de Beaumes-de-Venise, Domaine de Durban, £7.40 per half-bottle, £2.30 per glass. House wine from £6.75.

CHEF: Peter Hauser PROPRIETORS: Peter and Nita Hauser
OPEN: Tue to Sun, exc Sat L and Sun D
MEALS: 12.30 to 1.45, 7.30 to 8.45
PRICES: Set L £14 (£19), Set D £20 (£26)
CARDS: Access, Visa
SEATS: 26. Private parties: 12 main room, 12 private room. Car-park, 25 places. Children's helpings (L only). No children under 7. Jacket and tie. No smoking in dining-room. One sitting
ACCOMMODATION: 7 rooms, all with bath/shower. B&B £50 to £110. No children under 7. Afternoon teas. Garden. TV. Phone. Scenic. Doors close at 12. Confirm by 8 [GHG]

Anyone claiming to be from The Good Food Guide *is an impostor. Restaurateurs are advised to contact the office immediately if any fraudulent claims are made.*

The price quoted in brackets is for an average three-course meal including service, VAT, *coffee and half a bottle of house wine or the equivalent in an ethnic restaurant.*

GLEMSFORD Suffolk map 3

Barretts [13/20]

31 Egremont Street, Glemsford, CO10 7SA
GLEMSFORD (0787) 281573 £13–£21

Restaurants in the Suffolk hinterland divide between the lavish and expensive with the accent on the melon boats, often at £6 plus, and the very personal, bordering on the eccentric. The Barretts are in the second category, the two of them running a tiny restaurant in an out-of-the-way village, with a short menu and a very personal atmosphere. Plainer dishes, for instance smoked salmon, are complemented by more elaborate, extravagantly worked dishes like sole in pastry with chives and artichokes, some of which work better than others. But there have been good mixes of seafood, beautifully poached and served in a stock/cream sauce with some grilled spinach for a contrast of textures; fine sweets too, such as amaretto soufflé with a hot vanilla sauce, and almond meringue. The saucing would be helped by more reduction to define the tastes better. Eighty wines with a good section of half-bottles and much under £10. CELLARMAN'S CHOICE: Côtes du Rhône, Château du Moulas '86, £7.25; Australian Chardonnay Robson '86, £12.25.

CHEF: Nicholas Barrett PROPRIETORS: Nicholas and Diane Barrett
OPEN: Tue to Sat D, and Sun L
CLOSED: 2 weeks in Jan
MEALS: 12 to 2, 7 to 9.30
PRICES: £17 (£21), Set L £9.95 (£13). Service inc
CARDS: Access, Visa
SEATS: 18. Private parties: 12 main room. Car-park, 10 places. Children's helpings (Sun L only). Wheelchair access

GLOUCESTER Gloucestershire map 2

College Green [10/20]

9 College Street, Gloucester GL1 2NE
GLOUCESTER (0452) 20739 £16

The Spencers have been in this fifteenth-century timbered building by the cathedral since 1981. It is on the expensive side of bistro, but the loyalty to fresh produce and local producers is clear. The menu offers a large choice of eight starters, three fish and eight main dishes with an eye for saucing – gooseberry for mackerel; watercress for Severn salmon; madeira and apricot for duck. House claret is £5.75. CELLARMAN'S CHOICE: Côtes du Rhône, Domaine de Saint Cayar '86, £9.

'A great deal of the public has changed its shopping habits and does buy more healthy type foods. One major change is to polyunsaturated oil. Unfortunately this has not happened in the great majority of restaurants. Yet it would be a great benefit.'
On eating in Scotland

CHEF: David Spencer PROPRIETORS: David and Frances Spencer
OPEN: Mon to Sat, exc Mon and Tue D
CLOSED: bank hols
MEALS: 12 to 2, 6.30 to 9.30
PRICES: £13 (£16). Service inc. Licensed, also bring your own: corkage £2
CARDS: Access, Amex, Visa
SEATS: 30. Private parties: 44 main room, 30 private room. Vegetarian meals. Children's helpings. Music

Gloucestershire Round-up

AL FRESCO: *Trout Inn*, St Johns Bridge, Lechlade (0367 52313).
HISTORIC SETTING: *Wesley House*, High Street, Winchcombe (0242 602366); *Lords of the Manor*, Upper Slaughter, Nr. Bourton-on-the-Water (0451 20243); *Greenway*, Shurdington, Cheltenham (0242 862352); *Weylands*, 6 Oak Street, Lechlade (0367 52587).
ROOMS: *Cotswold House*, The Square, Chipping Campden (0386 840330).
ENGLISH: *Malt House*, Broad Campden, Chipping Campden (0386 840295); *Fleece Hotel*, Market Square, Cirencester (0285 68507/8/9).
VEGETARIAN: *Corner Cupboard Dining Room*, Gloucester Street, Winchcombe (0242 602303).
CHINESE: *Tatyin*, 27 Castle Street, Cirencester (0285 3529)

GOLCAR West Yorkshire map 5

Weavers Shed [new owners, zero rated]

Knowl Road, Golcar HD7 4AN
HUDDERSFIELD (0484) 654284 £17–£23

The Savilles have moved on from this eighteenth-century stone cottage but the McGunnigles have the same commitment to fresh produce. The menu is unashamedly English, wholesome and quite subtle. The selection of home-made breads, which include treacle or honey flavour, sets the tone. Good dishes have been leek and potato soup; spinach and Stilton tart; half a roast Gressingham duck with a blackcurrant sauce; sherry trifle. Mrs McGunnigle runs the front of house with modest charm. The wine list has some unusually good bottles such as St. Emilion, Ch. Gros Caillou '79, £13.25, and works hard on the price versus quality equation. More reports, please.

CHEF: Peter McGunnigle PROPRIETORS: Peter and Catherine McGunnigle
OPEN: Tue to Sat, exc Sat L
CLOSED: first 2 weeks Jan, last 2 weeks July, Tue after bank hols
MEALS: 12 to 2, 7 to 9.15
PRICES: L £10 (£17), D £16 (23)
SEATS: 70. Private parties: 40 main room, 30 private room. Car-park, 40 places. Vegetarian meals. Children welcome. Smart dress preferred. Wheelchair access (also WC)

'This was not a successful dish. There was very little edible fish and my friend, who cannot see very well, kept eating the side bits which were full of bones.'
On eating in Hereford & Worcester

GOOSNARGH Lancashire map 5

Solo [10/20]

Goosnargh Lane, Goosnargh PR3 2BD
BROUGHTON (0772) 865206 £14–£20

Family run, set in its own garden, a hundred yards down from the village green, this low-ceilinged, small dining-room has built a loyal local following since the Villas took over in 1984 (previously it was the Willows). The clichés of prawn cocktails are countered by some more adventurous cooking, as in seafood brochette. Fillet Solo is two steaks wrapped in bacon and flamed with brandy. The quality of the meat is high. The Villas are proud also of their sweets trolley. House Italian is £6.60.

CHEF: Raffaele Arrellaro PROPRIETORS: Vincent and Susan Villa
OPEN: all week D, and Wed to Fri and Sun L
MEALS: 12 to 2, 7 to 10
PRICES: £13 (£20), Set Sun L £7.85 (£14)
CARDS: Access, Visa
SEATS: 48. Private parties: 50 main room. Car-park, 40 places. Vegetarian meals. Children's helpings. Smart dress preferred. No smoking in dining-room. Wheelchair access (also WC). Music

GRAMPOUND Cornwall map 1

Eastern Promise [10/20]

1 Moor View, Grampound TR2 4RT
ST AUSTELL (0726) 883033 £17–£26

One of the few creditable Pekingese restaurants in the far South-West of England, in a scenic Cornish village full of English tea-rooms and pubs. The ancient cottage has been transformed with stunning Chinese murals, Chinese fretwork window frames and an aquarium set into the wall. Aromatic crispy duck and sizzling dishes are the centrepieces, backed up by deep-fried seaweed, Szechuan chicken with cashews and stir-fried scallops – complete with corals – with water chestnuts and spring onions. Fried rice is good, too.

CHEF: Liza Tse PROPRIETOR: Philip Tse
OPEN: all week, D only
MEALS: 6 to 11
PRICES: £17 (£26), Set D £12.50 (£17)
CARDS: Access, Amex, Diners, Visa
SEATS: 40. Private parties: 40 main room. Car-park, 8 places. Vegetarian meals. No children under 3. Smart dress preferred. Wheelchair access. Music

If you cannot honour a restaurant booking, always phone to cancel.

Restaurants are checked every year and their entries rewritten. The restaurant scene changes very rapidly. Don't trust an out-of-date Guide.

GRASMERE Cumbria map 7

▲ *Michael's Nook* [13/20]

Grasmere LA22 9RP
GRASMERE (096 65) 496 £27–£37

Many of the gardens of Ambleside are now 100 years old or more, planted at the same time as the houses were built as summer residences for cotton magnates. The Nook – named after Wordsworth's poem – is one of the finer examples, a bowl carved into the fellside within the much greater bowl of the valley. Reg Gifford's taste for antiques maintains the traditions, as do the young crew dressed in flowing shirts. It is an image much liked by visiting Americans, having a certain homeliness and lived-in quality that newer country-house hotels lack. The cooking has a soundness to it – a mix of what might be termed Lakeland and French, offering more of a choice than is normal in the area, with a short *carte*. At one extreme is the robust use of cheese, as in Stilton as croûtons in a white onion soup, or as a sauce for fillet steak. At the other is an inventive touch, for instance a terrine of cold poached salmon, potatoes and artichokes with a tomato coulis. There are good soups, a varied cheeseboard, and modern-inclined sweets, such as gratins of fruit. Rooms are well fitted out in period style. Wines are in keeping. CELLARMAN'S CHOICE: Ch. des Tuileries '78, £6.50.

CHEF: Heinz Nagler PROPRIETOR: R.S.E. Gifford
OPEN: all week
MEALS: 12.30, 7.30 (7 and 9, Sat in summer)
PRICES: Set L £19.50 (£27), Set D £28 (£37)
CARD: Amex
SEATS: 45. Private parties: 35 main room. Car-park, 20 places. Vegetarian meals. Children's helpings (with prior notice). No children under 12. Smart dress preferred. No smoking in dining-room. Wheelchair access. One sitting
ACCOMMODATION: 11 rooms, all with bath/shower. D, B&B £84 to £120. Garden. Swimming-pool. Sauna. Fishing. Golf. TV. Phone. Scenic

▲ *White Moss House* [14/20]

Rydal Water, Grasmere LA22 9SE
GRASMERE (096 65) 295  £24

Rather like a vicarage that has been pressed into service as a hotel, with all the goodwill that that implies. The strict adherence to no-choice menus and dinner at a regimental 7.30 for 8 is not to everyone's taste, but Peter and Susan Dixon carry on her mother Jean Butterworth's fine culinary reputation. There are fine combination soups – mushroom, marsala and marjoram, or celeriac, celery, fennel – and good fish courses; terrines and soufflés are often made with local fish. Puddings might be banana toffee pie or cabinet pudding with fluffy sabayon, and there is a whole menu of English cheeses. Main courses are of splendid quality – memorable Lakeland mallard or roast corn-fed poussin with fennel and ginger – with a shrewdly judged and immaculately cooked array of four or five vegetables, for instance apple and marjoram relish, scalloped potatoes, carrot fingers with chives, green beans stir-fried in walnut oil, and aubergine and three-pepper casserole, shaming all the arbitrary and unimaginative vegetables served nowadays. The Dixons are careful what they release, but White Moss House has a serious wine list at fair prices, particularly and successfully serious in the claret department. Here there are 60 wines ranging from drinkable '85 *petits châteaux* through a splendid clutch of '78s back to seven wines from the unforgettable '61 vintage and three '59 wines. Almost all are good examples, and all are reasonably priced. The Burgundy sections lean more heavily on the merchant houses of Beaune although there are good single estate wines from Vocoret, Dauvissat, Vincent, Bize, de Montilly and Noellat. Alsace wines are good, from the Turckheim Co-operative and Hugel. There are good Loires and a substantial German list, mostly from good vineyards, though producers' names are irritatingly missing. The limited selection from other wine areas offers good Riojas, the stylish Eyrie Pinot Noir from Oregon, some well-chosen wines from Australia and New Zealand, and three English wines. A sweet wine listed on the menu is always available by the glass; there are four German Beerenauslesen, two '76 Hugel Vendanges Tardives (one a Sélection de Grains Nobles) and sweet white Bordeaux wines from Châteaux Coutet, de la Chartreuse and Filhot. House Beaujolais and white Burgundy are £8 and £6 a litre respectively. CELLARMAN'S CHOICE: Riesling, Vendange Tardive '76, from Hugel, at £26, and half-bottles, such as Gigondas '70 at £7 and Ch. Chasse-Spleen '79 at £7.

CHEF: Peter Dixon PROPRIETORS: Susan and Peter Dixon
OPEN: Mon to Sat, D only
CLOSED: mid-Nov to mid-Mar
MEALS: 8
PRICES: Set D £17.95 (£24)
SEATS: 18. Private parties: 18 main room. Car-park, 10 places. No children under 10. Smart dress preferred. No smoking in dining-room. Wheelchair access. Music. One sitting
ACCOMMODATION: 7 rooms, all with bath/shower. Rooms for disabled. Lift. B&B £27. No children under 10. Garden. Fishing. TV. Phone. Scenic. Doors close at 11. Confirm by 4 [GHG]

GRAYSHOT Hampshire map 2

Woods [12/20]

Headley Road, Grayshott GU26 6LB
HINDHEAD (042 873) 5555 £26

Eric and Dana Norrgren preside with friendly professionalism over this converted butcher's-cum-fishmonger's. It is a solid restaurant of quality, where the Norrgrens have achieved a formula that suits them and their customers. The meat hook still hangs in the main room, two other rooms adjoin. The 11-dish menu changes slowly from year to year, never losing favourites, for instance gravlax, and gaining new dishes which seem to be built on previous successes. Lately the tendency is to simplify, as in seafood pancakes. Main dishes are split between fish and meat, all sauced and served with vegetables; choose between fresh salmon in a chive-flavoured sauce or beef fillet in a red wine sauce flavoured with Gorgonzola. Recommended dishes have been: sea-bass en croûte; monkfish with yellow peppers; fillet of beef with a sauce of onions, tomatoes and cream; game soup; quenelles; hot lemon soufflé. The wine list is similarly restrained, from £6.20.

CHEF: Eric Norrgren PROPRIETORS: Eric and Dana Norrgren
OPEN: Tue to Sat, D only
MEALS: 7 to 12
PRICES: £18 (£26)
CARDS: Access, Amex, Diners, Visa
SEATS: 35. Private parties: 12 main room. Children's helpings. Wheelchair access (also WC)

GREAT DUNMOW Essex map 3

Starr [11/20]

Market Place, Great Dunmow CM6 1AX
GREAT DUNMOW (0371) 4321 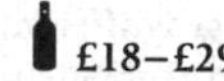 £18–£29

On the approach downhill from the market place, the Starr juts out into the roadway. It is long established as a place to spend money, but as well as attracting a business clientele, it has found its place as a village restaurant, which adds to the atmosphere. The low ceilings, fifteenth-century beams and the fires in the bar lend a lot of character. Menus are on blackboards and there are special fish and vegetarian menus, but in the main, the range stays safely with conservative favourites such as steak with brandy and cream or cream of mushroom soup. Amid the show of sauces ladled out of copper pans, some good kitchen practices shine through – precisely cooked scallops in a pastry case, crunchy vegetables, excellent sultana pudding with proper custard. The set pricing keeps some form of rein on the bill, though service remains a 10 per cent extra. The wine list is encyclopaedic, selective but wide ranging, with good value at all levels and plenty of half-bottles. There's a selection of 'second wines' of some major Bordeaux châteaux (blended from parts of the harvest not quite up to standard of the top wines) and a brief but good selection of other clarets. Good '85 Beaujolais and tempting Burgundies come from both merchants and top single estates such as Leflaive, Grivot and Dujac. There's good but young Alsace, Rhônes from Jaboulet, and a few Australian, Italian and even German wines from serious estates. House French from £7.95.

CHEF: Mark Fisher PROPRIETOR: B. Jones
OPEN: all week, exc Sat L and Sun D
CLOSED: 3 weeks Aug, 2 weeks at Christmas
MEALS: 12 to 1.30, 7 to 10
PRICES: Set L from £12.95 (£18), Set D from £22 (£29). Service 10%. Licensed, but also bring your own: corkage £4
CARDS: Access, Diners, Visa
SEATS: 60. Private parties: 8 main room. Car-park, 15 places. Vegetarian meals. Children's helpings. Wheelchair access (also WC). Music

GREAT MILTON Oxfordshire map 2

▲ *Le Manoir aux Quat' Saisons* [18/20]

Church Road, Great Milton OX9 7PD
GREAT MILTON (08446) 8881/2/3 £30–£62

An oil painting of three fat geese and a turkey dominates the first dining-room and reinforces the strong English accent of this old manor. On a good day in autumn the wild mushroom prospector may have sent up cèpes, girolles, morels and horn of plenty fresh from the New Forest. These find themselves strewn across a plate with some Burgundy snails, tasting sweetly of the garlic in which they were cooked. The combination of tastes, textures and colours is what marks Raymond Blanc's wonderful cooking. The presentation is important but it is the last stage in a process deeply rooted in the earth. The honeymoon of the first years may be over, but Blanc still conducts an ongoing love affair with diners. There is a deep feeling of generosity pervading the house and the cooking. Blanc develops local suppliers and uses different varieties. This makes his cooking a richer, more varied tapestry. In most dishes there is a small olfactory surprise that ignites and changes the perception of the dish midstream. For instance, the old trademark of the terrine of pencil-thin leeks interleaved with an intense, deep-tasting foie gras pâté, a bass drum of flavour, spiked with a little sliver of marinated truffle served with a little diced white-wine jelly and a glass of ten-year-old red Pineau des Charentes providing an even deeper, darker taste than the foie gras. The menu is a joy of increasing stature. The *carte* usually has three bird dishes, three fish, a long list of starters, plus there is the menu of the day or a tasting menu of six courses. Look especially for John Dory with roast scallops and a veal juice flavoured with rosemary; duck, roasted as a half, and sauced with its juices, maize syrup, ginger and lemon, garnished with spring onion and coriander wrapped in strudel pastry; and the little soufflé in its apple with its sabayon and its sorbet. Despite backstage upheavals through 1987 the standards have never dropped below good. The service at its best is as enthusiastic as Blanc himself and his faithful, crucial maître d'hôtel M. Alain Desenclos. Pity the chap who wrote: 'I paid £140 only to be told that Monsieur Blanc was away addressing a chefs' conference.' Such nights are rare enough, but the stresses of running this level of restaurant and being in the constant glare of the spotlight are intense, and M. Blanc would do well to enjoy his glorious manor and secure its long life. Recommendations often glow: 'At every visit there is always one dish that sparkles with life. Last year it was a humble tagliatelle abundant with truffles and wild mushrooms, this year the charlotte of aubergines as an appetiser.' 'Breakfast on day one was bliss: purée of apple, fresh French blackcurrant yoghurt; enormous cups for the delicious coffee that in the drowsiness appeared to transport the whole place across the Channel; fresh croissants with the most delicious home-made jams, particularly the apricot.' The sense of balance and good taste extends to the rest of the house and the increasingly mature gardens. The wine list is expensive, with little solace at the bottom end of the list in terms of half-bottles, but the wines are good. An impressive list of fine claret includes many old vintages and much of the

Burgundy comes from highly respected growers. Loires and Rhônes are also particularly good. Among the sweet wines, Vin de Paille, Domaine de Montbourgeau '83, from the Jura, at £21.50, is an unusual find; there's Vendange Tardive Alsace for between £27.30 and £35; and excellent sweet Loires of the '71 and '76 vintages are relatively inexpensive at between £18.50 and £30.25. A number of *premier cru* Sauternes include mature vintages of Château d'Yquem, and by the half-bottle, there's Essencia, Muscat Fleur d'Orange from Quady in California, at £13.35, and a choice of two Muscats de Beaumes de Venise, £9.20 to £9.95. The invigorating selection of French country wines provides interesting foils to the complexities of the food, but these bottles are priced up with the cheap Burgundy.

CHEF: Raymond Blanc PROPRIETORS: Raymond and Jenny Blanc
OPEN: Tue to Sun, exc Tue L CLOSED: 4 weeks from 22 Dec
MEALS: 12.15 to 2.30, 7.15 to 10.30
PRICES: £48 (£62), Set L from £19.50 (£30), Set D £40 (£51). Service inc
CARDS: Access, Amex, Diners, Visa
SEATS: 70. 4 tables outside. Private parties: 10 main room, 45 private room. Car-park, 45 places. Vegetarian meals. Children's helpings. Smart dress preferred. No smoking. Wheelchair access (also WC)
ACCOMMODATION: 10 rooms, all with bath/shower. B&B to £230. Deposit: £50. No children under 7. Baby facilities. Pets welcome. Afternoon teas. Garden. Swimming-pool. Tennis. TV. Phone. Scenic [GHG]

GREAT YARMOUTH Norfolk map 6

Seafood Restaurant [11/20]

85 North Quay, Great Yarmouth NR30 1JF
GREAT YARMOUTH (0493) 856009 £26

The local seafood restaurant down by the docks gets the very best of the catch from Lowestoft each day, and has tanks for lobsters, crabs and crawfish. Inside, the décor is an incongruous mix of frilly, pink-fringed curtains, high-backed padded seats and classical corniced ceilings, with photographs of the old Yarmouth fishing industry in the bar. Owners and chef are Greek, but the cooking is old-style with a mainly French accent – lemon sole with tarragon sauce, skate with black butter, Dover sole with lobster sauce. Plainly grilled or poached fish with some unadorned vegetables is the best option. Steaks for meat eaters. There are some good white Burgundies on the 140-strong wine list. CELLARMAN'S CHOICE: Chablis *premier cru*, Laroche '85, £16.85.

CHEF: Mathew Chrisostomou PROPRIETORS: Christopher and Miriam Kikis
OPEN: Mon to Sat, exc Sat L
MEALS: 12 to 2, 7 to 10.45
PRICES: £17 (£26)
CARDS: Access, Amex, Diners, Visa
SEATS: 40. Private parties: 40 main room. Children's helpings. Smart dress preferred. Music. Air-conditioning

Reports on shops, cafés and farms are useful, as well as reports on restaurants.

GRIMSTON Norfolk map 6

▲ *Congham Hall* [12/20]

Lynn Road, Grimston PE32 1AH
HILLINGTON (0485) 600250 £14–£35

Between the Rising Sun at Roydon and Grimston, half a mile due west from the B1153, is this small country-house hotel in a mid-eighteenth-century manor. It is grand and humble at the same time – not as personalised as some, nor as anaesthetised as others – and sets the standard for a wide radius. The same thought might extend to the menus, which are all set-price and lunch nearly a third the cost of dinner. On the one hand Robert Harrison, once of Woods at Chesterton, evokes a sort of rustic country cooking effect with the likes of a deep-green broccoli soup, and on the other, an almost Hilton-esque combination of Norfolk duck with mango and red wine sauce. There is no shortage of choice: at night six dishes at each course. And there is serious thinking going on – a French influence here for terrine of duck foie gras with brioche, or home-made noodles for the lamb; an English aspect in pan-fried fillet of veal in a madeira sauce with roasted kidney and sweetbreads with a sweet carrot purée; and some very modern ideas, such as warm apple pastry with rhubarb sorbet. There is always a fish of the day. Herbs are used freely. Service is young and well trained. One hundred wines with at least one or two examples of most styles, grapes. House Côtes du Rhône or Muscadet £7.50. CELLARMAN'S CHOICE: Comtes de Chartogne Blanc '86, from Jaboulet-Vercherre, £13.50.

CHEF: Robert Harrison PROPRIETORS: T.C. and C.K. Forecast
OPEN: all week, exc Sat L
MEALS: 12.30 to 2, 7.30 to 9.30
PRICES: Set L £8.50 (£14) to £9.75 (£15), Set D £25 (£32) to £27.50 (£35). Snacks from £2
CARDS: Access, Amex, Diners, Visa
SEATS: 34. Private parties: 8 main room; 12 private room. Car-park, 50 places. No children under 12. Jacket and tie. No smoking in dining-room. Wheelchair access (also WC)
ACCOMMODATION: 11 rooms, all with bath/shower. B&B £55 to £70. No children under 12. Garden. Swimming-pool. Tennis. TV. Phone. Scenic. Doors close at 11.30. Confirm by 6 [GHG]

GUILDFORD Surrey map 3

▲ *The Manor at Newlands* [11/20]

Newlands Corner, Guildford GU4 8SE
GUILDFORD (0483) 222624
3 miles E of Guildford on A25 £13–£22

This family-run hotel, set in one of the more beautiful parts of Surrey – with splendid walking, the Royal Horticultural Society's gardens at Wisley 10 minutes' drive away and a wealth of historic buildings in the area – is being developed apace. But the dining-room asserts itself as the heart of the operation. David Ostle cooks a set-price, six-dish per course *carte* at night, scaled down at lunch, but neither overly pricey by local comparison. There is a general consensus that the sweets show best his style of quite elaborate cooking and are most consistent – white and dark chocolate mousse, finely sliced fresh figs arranged in a flower shape alongside small scoops of almond ice-cream and a miniature lake of fig purée with cream. From the other courses the simpler dishes tend to be recommended – fillet steak, pigeon salad, sauté calf's liver with a little ginger in the sauce, individual and picturesque terrines, a platter of smoked fish. Wines carry a flat-rate mark-up. The list is good, if not exciting, and prices are very modest – the bin-end list in particular offers plenty of bargains. Wines are mostly French, plus a few German. For sweet wines, choose between a basic Premières Côtes de Bordeaux, £7, a German Trockenbeerenauslese '75, £13, Beerenauslese '76, £16, or Muscat de Beaumes de Venise, Domaine de Coyeux, £11, all for full bottles. House French is £5.90.

CHEF: David Ostle PROPRIETORS: Gillian and Michael Hill
OPEN: all week
CLOSED: 25 Dec D, 31 Dec D
MEALS: 12 to 2, 7 to 9.30 (8.30 Sun)
PRICES: Set L £9.50 (£13), Set D £12.50 (£16) to £18 (£22). Snacks from £1.75. Service inc
CARDS: Access, Amex, Diners, Visa
SEATS: 76. Private parties: 80 main room, 24 and 150 private rooms. Car-park, 100 places. Vegetarian meals. Children's helpings. No cigars/pipes in dining-room. Wheelchair access. Music
ACCOMMODATION: 20 rooms, all with bath/shower. B&B £53 to £75. No children under 7. Afternoon teas. Garden. TV. Phone. Scenic. Doors close at 11.30. Confirm by 6 [GHG]

Rumwong [11/20]

16–18 London Road, Guildford GU1 2AF
GUILDFORD (0483) 36092 £16–£18

Even before the blossoming of Thai restaurants, the Rumwong had a good reputation. There are two rooms, the smaller with cushions on the floor. There is an extensive menu, which gives suggestions on wines to drink with the various courses. At the back there is also a list of inexpensive one-plate meals which is worth exploring. The seemingly enormous range of Thai curries; clear and hot-and-sour soups (including poh-taek with squid, prawn, crabmeat and mushrooms with a lemon-grass and lime leaf flavouring); sweet-and-sour dishes; salads; and of course fried dishes (crabmeat and asparagus; bean sprouts in fish sauce; chicken with chilli) is compounded by the occasional change of a few ingredients: 'same as 20 but with pork'. The heat of the food suggests the not-too-expensive whites will be the best match. House Nicolas £6.60 a litre.

'In summary, all show and no go. They have made the classic error of thinking that fashionable and attractive décor would substitute for properly handled and prepared food.' On eating in Tayside

CHEF: Keow Sae Lao PROPRIETORS: Wanjai and Lumyai Poonum
OPEN: Tue to Sun
CLOSED: 2 to 15 Aug
MEALS: 12 to 2.30, 6 to 10.45 (10.30 Sun)
PRICES: £9 (£16), Set D £12 (£18). Service 10% alc, 12.5% set
CARDS: Access, Visa
SEATS: 100. Private parties: 70 main room, 30 private room. Vegetarian meals. Children's helpings. Smart dress preferred. Wheelchair access. Music. Air-conditioned

Surrey Round-up

INDONESIAN: *Kim's*, 12 Red Lion Street, Richmond (01 948 5777/5779).
CHINESE: *Yen*, 1 Wakefield Road, Richmond (940 6869/5114); *Evergreen*, 102-104 Kew Road, Richmond (01 940 9044); *Ming Garden*, 850 London Road, Thornton Heath (01 684 0991).
ROOMS: *Thatchers*, Epsom Road, East Horsley, (048 65 4291).
ENGLISH: *Ebenezer Cottage*, 36 Walton Street, Walton-on-the-Hill, Tadworth (073 781 3166).
WINE BAR: *Pissarro's*, 1,3&4 Kew Green, Richmond (01 940 3987).
THAI: *Pattaya*, 9 Claremont Road, Surbiton (01 399 2710).
FRENCH: *La Chaumiere*, Gomshall Lane, Shere (048 641 2168); *Le Pelerin*, Hawk's Hill, Leatherhead (0372 3373602).

GUISELEY West Yorkshire map 5

Harry Ramsden's [new owners, zero rated]

White Cross, Guiseley LS20 8L7
GUISELEY (0943) 74641 £8

In 1928, Harry Ramsden borrowed £150 to open a wooden hut as a fish shop next to the local tramway terminus at White Cross. Sixty years on, and now owned by Merryweather, this huge institutional dining-room with chandeliers and stained glass windows, flock wallpaper and waitresses in tight-fitting brown tunics is one of Yorkshire's tourist attractions, serving one and a half million customers each year. Skinned haddock fried in beef dripping is the special here, but it is backed up by less typically northern halibut, plaice and scampi. Most dishes are cooked to order. Unlicensed; most people drink tea. More reports, please.

CHEF: John Carter PROPRIETORS: Merryweather
OPEN: all week
CLOSED: 25 and 26 Dec
MEALS: 11.30am to 11.30pm
PRICES: £6 (£8)
CARDS: Access, Visa
SEATS: 180. 11 tables outside. Car-park, 300 places. Children's helpings. Music. Air-conditioned

Restaurants are graded on a scale of 1–20. In the category of 10–11 expect to find the best food in the locality. Ratings of 12 and more are given to restaurants we regard as serving the best food in the region.

GULWORTHY Devon map 1

▲ *Horn of Plenty* [13/20]

10 YEARS

Gulworthy PL19 8JD
TAVISTOCK (0822) 832528
3m W of Tavistock, off A390 £16–£30

There is an element of relief to eat a meal these days that does not have 'Invention' screaming out loud from the menu. If too many chefs now feel compelled, like singer/song writers, to compose their own music, with varying degrees of success, Sonia Stevenson wisely mixes hers with classic renditions. The dishes on the 1988 retrospective menu celebrating 21 years of the Horn are not exclusive, although the cooking has edged along – scallops are pan-fried in very hot butter and served with a lime and ginger sauce, for example. But the sauces and the 'home country cooking of the highest order' are the thing. A January meal evoked these real strengths: a slightly bland crab soufflé ignited by exquisite hollandaise, with extra sauce arriving in a small jug; the best part of a whole Pentillie pheasant carved on a large platter with slices of fried apple, local black and white puddings, two hunks of roast potato and a jug of five-star juices; to finish, a coeur à la crème with a light, melting texture, the classical heart-shape surrounded by a raspberry and strawberry sauce laced with crème de framboise and a dash of brandy. 'Once again, a memorable evening at the Horn.' Other dishes revived from the early years have been as wide-ranging as chicken poached in white wine and cream, calves' brains sauté in black butter or, from a French country dinner, pot-roast veal with sorrel. Also recommended: avocado mousse with a lemon butter sauce, guinea-fowl pies on a madeira sauce, fruit salad with clotted cream. The house has the feel of pre-Designer Guild era, and the view down the valley from the dining-room balcony can also be had from the bedrooms in a recently converted block at the rear of the house. The new business that has brought may have given the kitchen a fillip. Breakfasts, served on Royal Worcester Evesham china with proper thick slices of toast wrapped in a snowy napkin, have seen home-made fishcakes and honey in the comb. Portions are not small. House French from £5.95; CELLARMAN'S CHOICE: Muscadet de Sèvre-et-Maine, Château de la Jannière '86, £8.60.

CHEFS/PROPRIETORS: S. and P.R.N. Stevenson
OPEN: all week, exc Thu and Fri L
MEALS: 12 to 2, 7 to 9.30
PRICES: £22 (£30), Set L £14.80 (£16)
CARDS: Access, Amex, Visa
SEATS: 60. 6 tables outside. Private parties: 25 main room; 10 private room. Car-park, 30 places. Vegetarian meals. Children's helpings (L only). No children under 10. Wheelchair access (4 steps; also WC)
ACCOMMODATION: 6 rooms. Rooms for disabled. B&B £52 to £68. Pets welcome. Children by prior agreement. Garden. TV. Phone. Scenic [GHG]

Restaurants rating 12 or more serve the best food in the region.

HALIFAX West Yorkshire map 6

▲ *Holdsworth House* [12/20]

Holdsworth, Halifax HX2 9TG
HALIFAX (0422) 240024 £25

Three miles north of Halifax, Holdsworth House is the large hall standing on a rather humble hill. The Grade II listed seventeenth-century yeoman's house of grey local stone, with period furniture and open fires, has been under the present ownership for more than 20 years. The atmosphere is of individual and old-fashioned comfort; inside the restaurant is a wood-panelled cocoon, with silver candlesticks. Eric Claveau cooks an Anglo-French menu of some range, particularly strong on fish and game. There are eight starters, four intermediary courses, another eight main dishes with classical indications – béarnaise for fillet of beef, an envelope of salmon with a scallop mousse served on braised lettuce and a dill sauce. A range of house wines opens at £6.95. CELLARMAN'S CHOICE: Sauvignon/Semillon, Cloudy Bay '87, £16.

CHEF: Eric Claveau PROPRIETORS: The Pearson family
OPEN: all week, exc Sat L and Sun L
CLOSED: Christmas and New Year
MEALS: 12.30 to 1.30, 7.30 to 9.30
PRICES: £18 (£25)
CARDS: Access, Amex, Diners, Visa
SEATS: 45. Private parties: 100 main room, 14,10 and 8 private rooms. Car-park, 40 places. Vegetarian meals. Children's helpings. No pipes in dining-room. Wheelchair access (also WC)
ACCOMMODATION: 40 rooms, all with bath/shower. Rooms for disabled. B&B £48 to £80. Baby facilities. Pets welcome. Afternoon teas. Garden. Snooker. TV. Phone. Scenic. Doors close at 1. Confirm by 6

HAMBLETON Leicestershire map 6

▲ *Hambleton Hall* [14/20]

Hambleton LE15 8TH
OAKHAM (0572) 56991
off A606, 3m SE of Oakham £20–£34

The Hall is a proper, traditional, class-aware provincial seat. The sense of English formality extends to the service, with not a fork out of place; no wine glass is allowed to sink beyond a quarter empty. The six-course set dinner and the changing *carte* with its masses of fish – sea-bass, John Dory, turbot, halibut, lobster and monk were all offered one night – good English meats and also game in winter, have a positively English accent which extends into the cooking. Bramleys, for instance, appear with chestnuts as stuffing for local pheasant and with a sabayon soufflé. Presentation is near-perfect. The saucing, however, has gone awry, being either vapid or over-reduced, often quite blunt, the result being to unbalance dishes in a flavour sense. Inconsistencies have slipped in. Notwithstanding, there is no denying the recommendations for the roast grouse; the pastry case filled with lobster and avocado; toasted rice pudding; the superb cheeses. There are few obstacles to enjoyment. The cellar is one of the finest in the country, though it comes at a price. It majors on fine claret, including old vintages and Burgundy, from both growers and merchants. Excellent Alsace producers include Blanck, Théo Faller and Schlumberger, and there are a few wines from California, Australia, Italy and Germany. Choice of sweet wines is limited to a few Sauternes, mostly of recent vintages, a German Auslese and the occasional sweet Loire, including Vouvray Moelleux, Clos Naudin '76, from Foreau, £23. House wine from £9.

CHEF: Brian Baker PROPRIETORS: Timothy and Stefa Hart
OPEN: all week
MEALS: 12 to 1.45, 7 to 9.30
PRICES: £27 (£34), Set L from £15 (£20), Set D from £30. Service inc
CARDS: Access, Amex, Diners, Visa
SEATS: 60. Private parties: 45 main room, 20 private room. Car-park, 40 places. Vegetarian meals. Children's helpings. Smart dress preferred. Wheelchair access (also WC)
ACCOMMODATION: 15 rooms, all with bath/shower. Rooms for disabled. Lift. B&B £75 to £98.50. Children under 9 by arrangement. Baby facilities. Pets welcome. Garden. Tennis. Fishing. Golf. TV. Phone. Scenic [GHG]

HARROGATE North Yorkshire map 5

Drum and Monkey [11/20]

5 Montpellier Gardens, Harrogate HG1 2TF
HARROGATE (0423) 502650 £19

Downstairs feels like a civilised oyster bar in the City of London, although it gets packed at lunchtime. Upstairs is the cramped dining-room with linen cloths on the tables and fish prints on the walls. The appeal of this long-established restaurant is its no-fuss attitude and the quality of the raw materials, essentially fish – hake, whiting, shellfish and good smoked salmon. Extras can be provincial and old-fashioned – heavy sauces, over-boiled vegetables, butter everywhere. A little less cooking would help quite a few dishes. House wine £4.95. CELLARMAN'S CHOICE: Muscadet, Coupe d'Or, from Louis Métaireau, £9.55.

CHEF: Patrick Laverack PROPRIETOR: William Fuller
OPEN: Mon to Sat
CLOSED: Christmas to New Year
MEALS: 12 to 2.30, 7 to 10.15
PRICES: £13 (£19)
CARDS: Access, Visa
SEATS: 48. Private parties: 8 main room. Children's helpings

Restaurants awarded a rosette have had an entry in every Guide *since 1980. See Restaurants of the decade on page 21.*

▲ *Hodgson's, Russell Hotel* [12/20]

Valley Drive, Harrogate HG2 0JN
HARROGATE (0423) 509866 £15–£21

The dining-room remains the same here – comfortably old-fashioned, somewhat heavy in décor – but the kitchen is beginning to turn away from modern French to include more deliberately British dishes. Chicken and veal ballantine, champagne sorbet and roast whole guinea-fowl with madeira and truffle sauce now sit alongside dishes like medallions of venison with orange and ginger sauce or lamb with wild mushrooms and a red wine sauce with mint and tarragon. The fish dishes – like grouper mousseline or poached fillet of sea-bass with sauce vergé – change every day. Sweets are largely French: chocolate marquise, the Roux brothers' lemon tart, strawberry cocotte with Drambuie. The wine list is good but not outstanding, spanning the world but concentrating on France. A couple of dozen clarets are well chosen, most of them at their peak now, though some look as if they may be past it. Merchants Bouchard Père et Fils feature strongly among the Burgundies, Pascal among the Rhônes. Wines from the rest of the world are generally uninspiring, but the Clos du Val wines from California are a reliable buy, and Montrose and Brown Bros wines from Australia are excellent, as are the Torres wines from Spain, but sadly many producers' names are missing. House French from Duboeuf £6.

CHEF: Richard J. Hodgson PROPRIETORS: Martin and Richard Hodgson
OPEN: Tue to Sat D
MEALS: 7 to 10.30
PRICES: £17 (£21), Set D £11.25 (£15). Minimum £8.95. Service inc
CARDS: Access, Amex, Carte Blanche, Diners, Visa
SEATS: 75. Private parties: 30 main room, 12 private room. Vegetarian meals. No children under 8. Jacket and tie. No cigars/pipes in dining-room
ACCOMMODATION: 34 rooms, all with bath/shower. Lift. B&B £39.95 to £53.50. Baby facilities. Pets welcome. TV. Phone. Scenic. Confirm by 6 [GHG]

HARROW Greater London map 10

Country Club [10/20]

160 College Road, Harrow-on-the-Hill HA1 1BH
01-427 0729 £14

This unassuming Chinese restaurant advertises itself as Peking but Mr Chu is the only Shanghai-born and trained chef working in the London orbit. He will, with notice – up to 24 hours for a banquet – produce authentic Shanghai dishes such as Shanghai dumplings; stir-fried prawns; sand-pot soups; red-cooked mushrooms and bamboo shoots. The difference is seen in the spring rolls stuffed with whole prawns, chopped cabbage and pork or crab with yellow-bean sauce, not the stir-fry with ginger and onion of Cantonese cooking but the crab chopped into whole pieces, richly seasoned with the sauce and the spring onions reduced to a near paste. Stir-fried nian-gao is a pasta made of ground rice eaten during Chinese New Year in

Shanghai. It is stir-fried with pork and bamboo. Mrs Chu serves. They need encouraging to produce such dishes rather than the usual sweet-and-sour but have built a strong following among Chinese, Japanese and Koreans who know the possibilities of the cuisine. Best to book ahead and be explicit.

CHEF/PROPRIETOR: T.H. Chu
OPEN: all week, exc Sat L and Sun L
MEALS: 12 to 2, 6 to 11
PRICES: £10 (£14)
SEATS: 40. Children welcome

HARWICH Essex map 3

▲ *The Pier at Harwich* [10/20]

The Quay, Harwich CO12 3HH
HARWICH (0255) 241212 £12–£26

Fish and chips are served downstairs on polished tables. Upstairs, the restaurant overlooks the harbour and makes the most of its seaside location: local crab salad and native oysters; whole sole and plaice; seafood casserole with herbs, or fish pie with saffron sauce. The wines are ideally suited, a modern, catholic collection from French Colombard, Sauvignon and a quintet of Alsace to first-class whites from Italy to Australia. CELLARMAN'S CHOICE: Alsace Pinot Blanc '86, £7.70.

CHEF: C.E. Oakley PROPRIETOR: G.M.W. Milsom
OPEN: all week
MEALS: 12 to 2, 6 to 9.30
PRICES: £18 (£26), Set L £7.25 (£12) to £10.50 (£15). Service 10%
CARDS: Access, Amex, Diners, Visa
SEATS: 80. Private parties: 85 main room, 50 private room. Car-park, 10 places. Children's helpings. Wheelchair access (2 steps). Music
ACCOMMODATION: 6 rooms, all with bath/shower. B&B £35 to £45. Baby facilities. Afternoon teas. TV. Phone. Scenic

HASLEMERE Surrey map 3

Morels [15/20]

25–27 Lower Street, Haslemere, GU27 2NY
HASLEMERE (0428) 51462 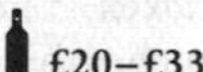 £20–£33

Four years after getting 15/20 in this *Guide*, Jean-Yves Morel was finally discovered last year by the Egon Ronay Guide – restaurant of the year – and *Michelin* – a star. It could not have happened to a more approachable chap, though he will forgive us for saying that he has been consistent over the time – in his faults, such as the bought-in breads, as well as his strengths. The restaurant's amenable Frenchness sets it apart – the waiters, the menu, the drapes, the ivory porcelain steering-wheel plates edged with a confident dash of lapis blue, and the cool spaciousness add up to something not English but with the kind of class that is immediately recognisable. The menu, too, is more interesting than English equivalents and reflects M. Morel's background in charcuterie – andouillette of mussels, confit du canard – but again, not so French as to be uncomfortably foreign. High points have been a pair of limpid home-made ravioli, floating like jellyfish in a pool of creamy smooth cep-flavoured sauce, filled with a duxelles of winter vegetables, basil and ground pine kernels; the immaculate cheeses from Androuët; and petits fours. Other dishes still chase the dragon of perfection but feature refreshing ambitions as in sea-bass steaks with roe and an egg sabayon flavoured with star anise. Wines are almost exclusively French, good to excellent, though sometimes on the expensive side. (The jumbled list offers little help with selection.) Choice is limited for those on a budget, but the house red Torres Coronas, £8, is good, beefy stuff, and Bossard's excellent Muscadet, £9.50, would be better value than the house white.

CHEF: Jean-Yves Morel PROPRIETORS: Jean-Yves and Mary-Anne Morel
OPEN: Tue to Sat, exc Sat L
CLOSED: 3 weeks Feb, 2 weeks end Sept
MEALS: 12.30 to 1.45, 7 to 10
PRICES: £24 (£13), Set L £12.50 (£20), Set D from £15.50 (£24)
CARDS: Access, Amex, Diners, Visa
SEATS: 45. Private parties: 12 main room. Children's helpings. No pipes in dining-room. Wheelchair access (1 step; also WC)

HASTINGLEIGH Kent map 3

▲ *Woodmans Arms Auberge* [12/20]

Hassell Street, Hastingleigh TN25 5JE
ELMSTED (023 375) 250 £21

'We have not served a frozen vegetable for two years,' writes Gerald Campion. Why should anywhere in the *Guide* use frozen vegetables at all, you ask, but alas some, one suspects, still do. If the Campions do not, with their minuscule operation of three bedrooms and only eight seats at dinner –non-residents accepted now only occasionally – then there is proof positive that no-one else need. The former pub is limited, but there is much enthusiasm for it. A three-course set meal offers some fine dishes: superior smoked salmon; roast wild duck; good vegetables; interesting cheeses; 'light, dry meringues', followed by coffee in the sitting-room. 'Tremendous care is taken.' Chicken and other poultry are free-range; the butcher also supplies the Connaught; good varieties of salads, too. No house wine, but CELLARMAN'S CHOICE: Ch. Paveil de Luze '82, £16.50.

CHEF: Susan Campion PROPRIETORS: Susan and Gerald Campion
OPEN: all week, D only
CLOSED: 1 week Apr, 3 weeks from 5 Sept
MEALS: 8
PRICES: Set D £16.50 (£21). Service inc
SEATS: 8. 3 tables outside. Private parties: 8 main room. Car-park, 6 places. No children under 12. No smoking. One sitting
ACCOMMODATION: 3 rooms, all with bath/shower. B&B £38.50 to £50. Deposit: 25%. No children under 16. Garden. TV. Scenic. Doors close at 11.30 [GHG]

HAWKSHEAD Cumbria map 7

▲ *Field Head House* [10/20]

Outgate, Hawkshead LA22 0PY
HAWKSHEAD (096 66) 240 £18

A mile out of Hawkshead, this seventeenth-century country house, once owned by John Harden, artist friend of Wordsworth, has been transformed into a comfortable small hotel. The no-choice menu fits into the Lakeland pattern, offering savoury, soup, some unusual main dishes, such as smoked beef with mustard mayonnaise, farmhouse cheeses and a choice of two sweets – one hot, one cold. Service is personable from Mrs Eeke van Gulik, while husband Bob cooks. Accommodation wins over the kitchen. Fine breakfasts. Plenty of choice on a wine list favouring whites. House wines £5.

CHEF: Bob van Gulik PROPRIETORS: Bob and Eeke van Gulik
OPEN: all week D only, exc Tue
CLOSED: last 2 weeks Jan
MEALS: 7.30
PRICES: Set D £15 (£18). Service inc
CARDS: Diners, Visa
SEATS: 14. 1 table outside. Private parties: 18 main room. Car-park, 15 places. Vegetarian meals (by arrangment). Children welcome (by arrangement). No smoking in dining-room. Wheelchair access (3 steps; also WC). One sitting
ACCOMMODATION: 8 rooms, all with bath/shower. B&B £25 to £50. Deposit: £20. Children welcom (by arrangement). Baby facilities. Pets welcome (by arrangement). Garden. Fishing. Golf. TV. Scenic. Doors close at 12 [GHG]

HAWORTH West Yorkshire map 5

Weavers [10/20]

15 West Lane, Haworth BD22 8DU
HAWORTH (0535) 43822 £13–£16

The converted weavers' cottages offer well-prepared, bistro-style cooking, drawing on the local markets, with the daily menu chalked on a blackboard. Regular dishes include: pear with blue cheese dressing; Yorkshire pudding with gravy; pork loin with Wensleydale cheese and mushroom sauce; little stuffed cabbages with mushrooms, buckwheat and pine kernels, with an onion sauce. The buying of produce is astute. Gressingham ducks, which are getting an increasingly good reputation, are roasted and served with their livers and an apple purée; air-dried Cumberland ham is served with home-made chutney. Desserts are the likes of a fine sticky toffee pudding with toffee sauce, or home-made ice-creams and sorbets. Cheeses are all farmhouse, from the North of England. Two dozen well-spread wines, mostly under £10, from house Burgundy style at £6.50. CELLARMAN'S CHOICE: Fleurie '86, from Loron, £9.50.

It is helpful if restaurants keep the office up to date with any changes.

CHEFS/PROPRIETORS: Colin and Jane Rushworth
OPEN: Tue to Sat D, and Sun L (Oct to Easter)
CLOSED: 3 weeks June/July, 1 week at Christmas
MEALS: 12.30 to 1.30, 7 to 9.30
PRICES: £13 (£19), Set L £7.95 (£14), Set D £9.95 (£16)
CARDS: Access, Amex, Diners, Visa
SEATS: 60. Private parties: 14 main room, 14 private room. Vegetarian meals. Children's helpings. Music. Air-conditioned

HAYDON BRIDGE Northumberland map 7

General Havelock Inn [10/20]

Radcliffe Road, Haydon Bridge NE47 6ER
HAYDON BRIDGE (043 484) 376 £9–£21

An unpretentious atmosphere and good, strong-flavoured cooking characterise the old stone inn overlooking the Tyne. Good soups, fish, baking, roast meats and some indulgent sweets hold up a short, good-value menu. Recommended are the fresh crab salad and the Danish chocolate crumble. Mrs Clyde even gives a hand with the serving. Tetley's beers. Thirty wines, from £5.20.

CHEF: Angela Clyde PROPRIETORS: Ian and Angela Clyde
OPEN: Wed to Sun, exc Sun D
CLOSED: first 2 weeks Jan, second week Mar, last week Aug, first week Sept
MEALS: 12 to 1.30, 7.30 to 9
PRICES: Set L £5 (£9) to £7.90 (£12), Set D £13 (£18) to £16 (£21)
SEATS: 28. 4 tables outside. Private parties: 30 main room. Car-park, 12 places. Vegetarian meals. Children's helpings. Wheelchair access (1 step; also WC)

HELFORD Cornwall map 1

▲ *Riverside* [11/20]

Helford, Helston TR12 6JU
MANACCAN (032 623) 443 £18–£33

A cottagey retreat in the creekside hamlet of Helford, with Susan Darrell trying to maintain the successful format of her predecessor, the great George Perry-Smith. Mixed reports suggest that the kitchen lacks the inspiration of the past but good food is certainly to be had. Hits have been the fresh fish dishes: scallops in saffron cream sauce, turbot with mustard and sherry sauce, monkfish with mussels and tarragon, and an excellent bourride of monk and turbot with aïoli and rouille. Other dishes have been less accurate, less forgiveable since the prices remain high – witness also house French £9.50, and CELLARMAN'S CHOICE: Pavillon Rouge du Ch. Margaux '81, £31.50.

Restaurants are not expected to solicit customers to send in reports. Please let us know if this happens to you.

CHEFS: Susan Darrell, Peter Todd and Sarah Heims PROPRIETOR: Susan Darrell
OPEN: all week D, and L June to Sept
CLOSED: Nov to early Mar
MEALS: 12.30 to 2, 7.30 to 9.30
PRICES: Set L £12.50 (£18), Set D £28 (£33). Service inc
SEATS: 36. Private parties: 20 main room. Vegetarian meals. Children's helpings. No children under 10. Wheelchair access (also WC)
ACCOMMODATION: 7 rooms, all with bath/shower. Rooms for disabled. B&B £75 to £90. Baby facilities. Garden. TV. Scenic

HELSTON Cornwall — map 1

▲ *Nansloe Manor* [10/20]

Meneage Road, Helston TR13 0SB
HELSTON (0326) 574691 — £10–£20

There are manors and manors; Nansloe is just a large homely building, quite away from it all, set in its own grounds, but hardly out of the town centre. Inside is friendly. The bar is full of pipe-smokers and cats and light meals benefit from the same kitchen as the restaurant. Everywhere, especially the dining-room, is full of decorative knick-knacks and fabrics – ne'er a footstep is heard. Fabrics are heavy – thick, bright-red paisley carpet and heavy, generously draped curtains around the many windows and even around the archway. The cooking is direct, upmarket and old-fashioned. Deep-fried Brie with claret jelly vies with scallops with smoked bacon and walnuts. Sweets do not suffer this ambivalence, being straightforward tea-room cheesecakes and trifles. Sometimes the cooking is a bit brutal, as in the fiercest of chilli and tomato sauces to revive some flagging braised turkey breast, which compensates for the lack of seasonality, but it is all done with gusto. The Thomas's were previously at the Mill House Inn, Trebarwith.

CHEF: Martin Jones PROPRIETORS: H.D. and A.M.Q. Thomas
OPEN: all week
MEALS: 12 to 1.30, 7 to 9.30
PRICES: £12 (£20), Set L £5.95 (£10), Snacks from 85p
CARDS: Access, Visa
SEATS: 40. Private parties: 50 main room. Car-park, 40 places. Vegetarian meals. No children under 10. Smart dress preferred. Wheelchair access (3 steps). Music
ACCOMMODATION: 7 rooms, all with bath/shower. B&B £28 to £50. Deposit: £15 per person. No children under 10. Dogs welcome. Garden. TV. Phone. Scenic. Doors close at 12.30. Confirm by 5

HERSTMONCEUX East Sussex — map 3

Sundial [11/20]

Gardner Street, Herstmonceux BN27 4LA
HERSTMONCEUX (0323) 832217 — £20–£31

For over 20 years this restaurant has held its own in its corner of East Sussex, using fresh and local supplies and, especially when cooking simply, producing extremely successful meals. There is now a five-course *menu surprise gourmandise* to add to the choice of the Bertolis' extensive *carte*. Fish, varying with the season and supply, is a feature – Dover sole in butter and lemon, or a bouillabaisse – as is game, such as pheasant breast in calvados and cream boeuf sauce. Though there is a tendency here to over-complicate and recommendations tend to the simpler dishes like plat de boeuf or poached salmon. Sorbets and profiteroles to finish. House French on an extensive but expensive list is £8.25. CELLARMAN'S CHOICE: Gigondas, Domaine de St Gayan '82, from Meffre, £14.75.

CHEF: Giuseppe Bertoli PROPRIETORS: Laurette and Giuseppe Bertoli
OPEN: Tue to Sun, exc Sun D
CLOSED: mid-Aug to Sept, 25 Dec to 20 Jan
MEALS: 12.30 to 2.30, 7.30 to 9.30 (10 Sat)
PRICES: £21 (£31), Set L £12.50 (£20), Set D £17.50 (£26)
CARDS: Access, Amex, Diners, Visa
SEATS: 70. 8 tables outside. Private parties: 50 main room, 22 private room. Car-park, 25 places. Vegetarian meals. Children's helpings. No smoking in dining-room. Wheelchair access (also WC). Music

HETTON North Yorkshire map 5

Angel Inn [12/20]

Hetton BD23 6LT
CRACOE (075 673) 263 £14–£18

The Angel is a fine old Dales pub, with fetching beams, busy as hell, and an atmosphere that buzzes with success. The open fire has been replaced by a handsome black Victorian range. The main part of the building weaves itself around the bar. There is a smaller lounge area to the right as you come in, with Laura Ashley wallpaper and comfy green Dralon seating. Beyond here, through an archway, is the drinks lounge to the restaurant – more green Dralon seats, lighter wallpaper, a few drinks tables. 'The *Guide* has never done proper justice to the Angel Inn. Denis Watkins is a true man of the people, dedicated to serving Real Food of high quality at value-for-money prices. His bar food is exemplary and cannot be bettered. His dedication, support for local suppliers and enthusiasm for fish (which he personally fetches from Manchester market) and for using good quality ingredients, shine out.' Such testimonies are not uncommon. Over the last couple of years the dining-room has risen a good couple of notches both in scope and quality of cooking. It must now be treated as a serious restaurant. The menu is as inventive and ambitious as any. For instance, seafood 'money bags' and a saddle of hare are 'both quite perfect.' The presentation is modern, stylish. The menu is written clearly. Portions are right, neither too small nor too large. As this is Yorkshire, Denis Watkins never stints on the meat. Some tightening on the saucing would lift the rating dramatically. The Provençal fish soup filled with diced vegetables including aubergines, mussels and other fish is a constant delight. Dishes deal in up-to-the-minute contexts – for instance a breast of pigeon carved on to a galette of potato and turnip served with a diced wild mushroom sauce. Fine cheeses are offered individually. The sweets menu shows the true development of the kitchen, mixing traditional summer pudding and sticky toffee with innovations such as an apple and Wensleydale strudel. A much expanded wine list concentrates on value for money, with wide selections of claret and Burgundy, but older vintages are thin on the ground. It is very limited in Rhône and German wines, but good in both red and white Italian. Full marks for an excellent selection of half-bottles. Real ales: Theakston, Old Peculier. CELLARMAN'S CHOICE: Chianti Classico Reserva, Villa Caffagio '79, £7.95.

CHEFS: Denis Watkins and John Topham PROPRIETORS: Denis and Juliet Watkins
OPEN: Mon to Sat D and Sun L
CLOSED: 1 Jan
MEALS: 12.15 to 2, 7 to 9.30
PRICES: Set Sun L £9.50 (£14), Set D £12.95 (£18), Snacks from £1.10
CARD: Access
SEATS: 36. 15 tables outside. Private parties: 40 main room. Car-park, 17 places. Children's helpings (L only). Smart dress preferred. No pipes in dining-room. Wheelchair access (also WC). Music

HINTLESHAM Suffolk map 3

▲ *Hintlesham Hall* [14/20]

Hintlesham IP8 3NS
HINTLESHAM (047 387) 268 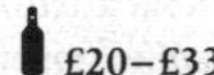 £20–£33

An outstandingly beautiful Elizabethan manor-house with a pale lemon Georgian frontage set in the open cornfields west of Ipswich, on the Hadleigh Road. Ruth and David Watson took over from Robert Carrier in 1984 and have been steadily renovating the hotel to a high standard; it is now one of the most luxurious in England. Outlook, service and atmosphere are unstuffy. Robert Mabey's cooking shows imaginative use of ingredients, on occasion, as in lime with guinea-fowl, very successfully. Good dishes have been a warm salad of langoustines dressed with a white wine and butter sauce and, unusually, fried celeriac; a duo of foie gras and rösti potatoes on a strong truffle sauce; a rich fricassee of langoustines in a curried cream sauce lifted by strips of grilled red pepper. Plainer dishes, for instance grilled sirloin steak or roast Challans duck carved at the table, offset the procession of sauces. Cheeses are well kept and served with raisin bread, but desserts are utterly tempting – the 'chocolate fetishist's fantasy' is a trio of meringue, white chocolate tart and ice-cream studded with bitter chocolate, with the word 'chocolate' written on the plate in chocolate. The wine list has been lovingly prepared. It includes unusual wines as well as classics, with just the right amount of straightforward information to make selection easy. There's an interesting and broad selection of clarets, mostly from top vintages, very fine Burgundies, and a handful of excellent Rhônes, fine Italians, Germans and Australians. Magnums and half-bottles are listed in profusion. House wine is expensive, starting at £9.50, but there are cheaper country wines; CELLARMAN'S CHOICE: Mâcon Solutre '86, £11.50.

An index of restaurants by name appears at the back of the Guide.

CHEF: Robert Mabey PROPRIETORS: Ruth and David Watson
OPEN: all week, exc Sat L
MEALS: 12 to 1.45, 7 to 9.30
PRICES: £26 (£33), Set L £14.95 (£20), Set L £15.50 (£21), Set D £28.50 (£33). Snacks £2.50 (residents only). Service inc
CARDS: Access, Amex, Diners, Visa
SEATS: 65. 6 tables outside. Private parties: 80 main room 16 and 24 private rooms. Car-park, 100 places. Vegetarian meals. No children under 10 at D. Smart dress preferred. No smoking in dining-room. Wheelchair access
ACCOMMODATION: 22 rooms, all with bath/shower. B&B £60 to £130. Deposit: £50 (overseas bookings). Children and pets by arrangement. Garden. Swimming-pool. Tennis. Fishing. Golf. Snooker. TV. Phone. Scenic. Doors close at 12 [GHG]

HINTON CHARTERHOUSE Avon map 2

▲ *Homewood Park* [14/20]

Hinton Charterhouse BA3 6BB
LIMPLEY STOKE (022 122) 3731
off A36, 5m S of Bath 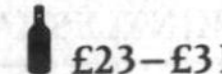 £23–£31

The abbot's house is cut off from its ruined thirteenth-century abbey by the A36, a left turn coming south before the Hinton Charterhouse turn or after, going north. Encircled within the stone wall are paddock, tennis court and gardens. The hotel side has taken an increased incentive. Stephen and Penny Ross matured from pupils to co-partners of Kenneth Bell at Popjoys in Bath to accomplished hoteliers; a new hotel venture, the Queensberry, opened in Bath last May. The house is aptly filled with the perks of the successful country-house hotel business: rag-rolled walls; original etchings; pieces of sculpture; carefully chosen antiques; and a young training staff to keep things ticking over. Like the wine list, the menu is still built on some first-class produce – especially fish later in the week. The necessary accoutrements are all present: two kinds of freshly baked rolls; chocolate truffles with coffee. Ideas bristle: monkfish with sweet and sour leeks; red mullet with rosemary and orange butter; pheasant breast with walnuts and horseradish. Sometimes the interaction of these flavours is more platonic than it might be, but the list of recommended dishes is again a long one: fillet steak with foie gras; venison with figs; brill with a cream sauce tinted with saffron and garnished with samphire. Sweets continue the sauce themes: passion-fruit for tropical fruit bombe; coffee bean for chocolate and crème de cacao mousse; peach purée for hazelnut and carrot cake. There's a good selection of wines from around France, including some mature claret, with a few well-chosen bottles from Spain, Italy, Australia and California. Choice of sweet wines is above average, ranging from good Sauternes to late harvest California to mature Bonnezeaux from the Loire. A pity, though, that not all producers' names are given in the list.

CELLARMAN'S CHOICE *This is a wine recommended by the restaurateur which is usually more expensive than the house wine but is good value and fitting for the kind of food served.*

Bandol '82, £9.30, from Bunan; Coteaux des Baux '84, £9.80, from Domaine de Trévallon; and a surprisingly wide choice of Germans, from the aristocratic heights of Schloss Vollrads on the Rheingau to Escherndörfer Lump in Franconia. The section labelled House Wines should not be overlooked, with old favourites from the Haut Poitou co op, Peter Sichel's pair of red and white new-oak-matured Le Bordeaux Prestige wines, and the soft Jacquesson Blanc de Blancs Champagne, £18.70. An Eiswein (there are three listed) would make an interesting change for dessert, or there is Vouvray Moelleux, Le Mont '76, from Huet, £10.40, and a sprinkling of Sauternes, of which the best is Château Rabaud-Promis '83, at £9.50 per half, in the flush of youth at present.

CHEFS: D.C. Partridge and Justin Partridge PROPRIETORS: D.C. Partridge and M. Partridge
OPEN: Tue to Sat, D only
CLOSED: 2 weeks at Christmas and Easter, 3 weeks July to Aug
MEALS: 7.30 to 9
PRICES: Set D £16.50 (£20). Service inc
SEATS: 50. Private parties: 10 main room. Car-park, 50 places. Children welcome. Wheelchair access (also WC)

HUDDERSFIELD West Yorkshire map 5

Pisces [12/20]

84 Fitzwilliam Street, Huddersfield HD1 5BD
HUDDERSFIELD (0484) 516773 £9–£22

Previously the family business's warehouse, this is now a fish restaurant split on to two levels, with the basement used when busy. The menu is oddly in French with English explanations but the kitchen ethic is admirable: 'Our aim is to keep dishes as simple as possible, adding a minimum of ingredients to complement the fish.' Seafood pistou; scallops sauced with mussels and leeks; salmon on a hexagonal plate with baby vegetables, white butter and orange sauce; and ragout of monkfish have all been fine dishes. Portions are more than generous and time and care are apparent in the cooking. There are a few non-fish dishes, such as roast saddle of hare. Sweets are decorous and accomplished, as are the petits fours. Nearly 40 wines, strongly favouring whites, spread from house wine at £4.95 upwards towards £20. CELLARMAN'S CHOICE: Muscadet-sur-Lie, Château des Gautronnières '86, £6.70.

CHEF: Serge Nollent PROPRIETORS: T. Y. and S. J. Wormald
OPEN: Mon to Sat
MEALS: 12 to 2, 7 to 9.30
PRICES: £16 (£22), Set L £4.95 (£9) to £8.45 (£12), Set D £9.95 (£14). Snacks from 95p
CARDS: Access, Amex, Visa
SEATS: 50. Private parties: 50 main room. Car-park, 10 places. Children welcome. Smart dress preferred. Wheelchair access. Music. Air-conditioned

It is always advisable to book a restaurant in advance.

HUNGERFORD Berkshire map 2

Galloping Crayfish [9/20]

The Courtyard, 24 High Street, Hungerford RG17 0NF
HUNGERFORD (0488) 84008 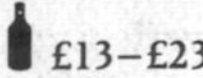 £13–£23

This excellent wine bar benefits from the wines of its parent, The Hungerford Wine Company, and a sensibly limited blackboard menu of food that stays with the market. The style is modern: roast lamb with coriander; John Dory with hazelnuts. The wines are an introductory course – no fewer than 26 offered by the glass, full descriptions, and more than half the list under £10. The name derives from crayfish out of the nearby Kennet which were taken by horse up to court for Henry VIII. House French is £5.50.

CHEFS: Ian Sankey and Tim White PROPRIETOR: Nicholas Davies
OPEN: Tue to Sun, exc Sun D
MEALS: 12 to 2, 7 to 10
PRICES: £13 (£17), Set Sun L £9.95 (£13), Set Sat D £12.95 (£16) to £19.95 (£23), Snacks from £1.95. Service inc
CARDS: Access, Visa
SEATS: 40. 7 tables outside. Private parties: 30 main room, 25 private room. Vegetarian meals. Children's helpings. Wheelchair access (also WC). Music

HUNSTRETE Avon map 2

▲ *Hunstrete House* [new entry, zero rated]

Hunstrete BS18 4NS
COMPTON DANDO (076 18) 578  £27–£39

A welcome return for this elegant lady of the country-house hotel circuit and many congratulations to chef Robert Elsmore (formerly at Buckland Manor) for bringing the kitchen back into the premier division. Roses, wistaria and clematis cover the outside of the house, which has a charmed setting and mature gardens. Inside is a luxurious calm, underlined by floor-length tablecloths and dripping chandeliers, but the Dupays stamp their personality on this too. The Terrace Room looks on to a fountain and courtyard. The menu offers a choice of half a dozen dishes per stage – modern in the sense of a strong emphasis on fish and vegetables, but a surprising lack of the kind of expense-account crutches, like foie gras, that a lesser kitchen would feel obliged to lean on. The style is direct: salad of scallops, salmon and mange-tout with a dressing of basil and garlic croûtons; breast of pigeon and saddle of venison served in a brioche with a madeira cream sauce and vegetables. Trimmings are those of a classy operation: impeccable sorbets; extravagant petits fours; service 'of the best *Good Hotel Guide* type'. As to the wines, whatever induces someone to take the roundabout route of including service but not VAT in the prices we cannot imagine. The list is strongest in traditional areas; Burgundy is wide ranging, and claret goes back beyond

'There were seven waiters, for eleven customers.' On eating in Scotland

the '70s. Jaboulet and Chapoutier Rhônes, and a handful each of Spanish and Italian wines, add interest, as do bin-ends. House French is £7.50. CELLARMAN'S CHOICE: St Aubin *premier cru*, Murgers des Dents du Chien '85, £14.25; Pernand Vergelesses '84, £10.80.

CHEF: Robert Elsmore PROPRIETORS: Thea and John Dupays
OPEN: all week
MEALS: 12.15 to 1.45, 7.30 to 9.15
PRICES: Set L £17.50 (£27), Set D £25 (£35) to £28 (£39). Service inc
CARDS: Access, Amex, Diners, Visa
SEATS: 65. Private parties: 50 main room, 22 private room. Car-park, 40 places. No children under 9. Jacket and tie. No-smoking area. Wheelchair access (1 step)
ACCOMMODATION: 24 rooms, all with bath/shower. Rooms for disabled. B&B £83 to £110. Deposit: £50. Afternoon teas. Garden. Swimming-pool. Tennis. TV. Phone. Scenic [GHG]

ILFORD Essex map 3

Da Umberto [10/20]

361 Ley Street, Ilford 1G1 4AA
01-553 5763 £18–£21

A standard trattoria menu of pasta dishes, risottos and veal or bistecca several ways is supplemented by more interesting choices like mushrooms filled with snails and fish specials – from John Dory and sea-bass to lobster. The sweets trolley includes decent profiteroles. House wine is £5.20 a bottle and the list has some good-value Italian wines for under £10. Summer closing varies, best to check first.

CHEF: Umberto Medaglia PROPRIETORS: Umberto and J.A. Medaglia
OPEN: Mon to Sat, exc Sat L
MEALS: 12 to 2.30, 6.30 to 11.30
PRICES: £13 (£21). Set L or D from £16 (£18). Cover 50p. Service 12%
CARDS: Access, Visa
SEATS: 38. Vegetarian meals. Children's helpings. Wheelchair access (1 step). Music. Air-conditioned

ILKLEY West Yorkshire map 5

Box Tree [14/20]

10 YEARS

29 Church Street, Ilkley LS29 9DR
ILKLEY (0943) 608484 £20–£35

'Who could fail to be charmed – the welcome, the real paintings, the dazzling décor, fine china, the pianist tinkling softly in one corner, the big black statues framing the entrance to the dining-room, the impeccable service?' Eric Kyte, *patron* since November 1986, carries the Malcolm Reed and Colin Long routine on into its 25th year, even if there are one or two critical voices to be heard through the frosted glass windows of the small stone cottages. Meals are, for the most part, professionally executed, like well-rehearsed floor shows. Edward Denny's cooking of a solely French-written *carte* of eight starters, four middle courses, eight main and seven sweets sets the standard for other kitchens in the county, though others are now catching up and mistakes have crept into the repertory. The cooking is absolutely classical in the sense that the sauces take the lead role. It is also rich in cream and deals in ingredients from the international markets. A mousse of guinea-fowl, pale cream in colour, is lifted by its sauce of tomatoes, orange and basil; a fine fish terrine by its lobster sauce; a loin of veal, strangely square-shaped, by a madeira sauce and wild mushrooms, trompettes and chanterelles. A fascination for fruit seasonings preoccupies the main courses – peaches with a roast Bresse pigeon; cherry with duck; lime with trout; gooseberries with monkfish. Roles reverse for the sweets where the fruits take centre stage, most famously with the timbale de fraises Box Tree. The professionalism stands out. Inevitably some of the passion and individuality is lost as the show goes on, and on. The wine list remains as ever, from Yorkshire Fine Wines, with a few Americans to reflect the new patronage, and not cheap.

CHEF: Edward Denny PROPRIETOR: Eric Kyte
OPEN: Tue to Sat D, and Sun L
CLOSED: 25 and 26 Dec, 1 Jan
MEALS: 12.30 to 2, 7.30 to 9.45
PRICES: £26 (£35), Set Sun L £11.95 (£20), Set D £14.95 (£24)
CARDS: Access, Amex, Diners, Visa
SEATS: 50. Private parties: 30 main room; 16 private room. Children welcome. Smart dress preferred. No cigars/pipes in dining-room. Wheelchair access

INKPEN Berkshire map 2

Swan Inn [10/20]

Lower Inkpen, Newbury, RG15 0DX
INKPEN (048 84) 326 £16

The Swan is a long low pub, off the main road in Lower Inkpen. There are three beamed bar areas serving good snacks, with the restaurant at the far end. The menu has some stoic English overtones but more interesting are a number of excellent and properly cooked Singaporean dishes: beef satay; sweet-and-sour prawns; lamb rendang; dill or chicken flavoured rice. Seasoning is bright and genuine. House French £6. Real ales include Flower's, Brakspear and Wethered's.

CHEFS: Lotte Grant and Esther Scothorne PROPRIETORS: Mr and Mrs J Scothorne
OPEN: Tue to Sun exc Sun D
MEALS: 12 to 2, 7 to 10
PRICES: £11 (£16) Snacks from £1.50
CARDS: Access, Visa
SEATS: 38. 7 tables outside. Private parties: 38 main room. Car-park, 40 places. Vegetarian meals. Children's helpings. Smart dress preferred. 2 steps to rest. Wheelchair access (also WC). Music

Restaurants change owners and chefs constantly. It is very useful if you keep the Guide *informed of any changes you find.*

IPSWICH Suffolk map 3

Kwok's Rendezvous [10/20]

23 St Nicholas Street, Ipswich IP1 1TW
IPSWICH (0473) 56833 £11-£31

The rise of the Szechuan in Peking restaurant menus, like some counter-revolution, continues. Here at Thomas Kwok's lanterned and flowered dining-room the 55 dishes seem to be increasingly described with chilli, with hot Szechuan bean sauce, with garlic, with Szechuan peppers. The mainstay is duck done in three ways: Peking (with 24 hours' notice); aromatic; braised, but there is also Szechuan double-cooked pork. Fish is also conspicuous by its small showing beyond prawns, an affirmation of inland cooking. The wine list is of some stature for a Chinese restaurant, with Chablis, Quincy, Sancerre, and Mercurey among others, though their equivalent reds are probably unnecessary. House Jeune Vigne Blanc – from the young vines of Chassagne-Montrachet – is selected by Roger Chapelle, at £6.

CHEF: Thomas Kwok PROPRIETORS: Lucia and Thomas Kwok
OPEN: Mon to Sat
MEALS: 12 to 2, 7 to 10.45
PRICES: £9 (£16), Set L £6 (£11) £20 (£26), Set D £8 (£12) £25 (£31). Minimum £7.50. Service 10%
CARDS: Amex, Diners
SEATS: 50. Private parties: 30 main room. Car-park, 50 places. Vegetarian meals. Children welcome. Smart dress preferred. Wheelchair access (also WC). Music

Mortimer's on the Quay [10/20]

Wherry Quay, Ipswich
IPSWICH (0473) 230225 £18

The glass roof of this converted warehouse gives the clean white dining-room a sense of space. The menu deals in fish out of Grimsby, mostly in classic French sauces, or plain grilled. The range is extensive, from moules marinière to skate in black butter. 'All the fish is cooked to order.' The name comes from the artist whose paintings are on the walls. The parent branch is at Bury St Edmunds (see entry). House wine is £5.75.

CHEF: Kenneth Ambler PROPRIETORS: Kenneth Ambler and Michael Gooding
OPEN: Mon to Sat, exc Sat L
CLOSED: bank hols and day after, 24 Dec to 5 Jan
MEALS: 12 to 2, 7 to 9 (8.30 Mon)
PRICES: £12 (£18)
CARDS: Access, Amex, Diners, Visa
SEATS: 88. Private parties: 8 main room. Children's helpings. Smart dress preferred. No-smoking area. Wheelchair access (1 step)

The Guide *recruits new inspectors from readers who write in regularly. If you would like to apply, write to the Editor with (a) a detailed report on a restaurant where you have eaten and (b) a comparative study of restaurants known to you.*

Singing Chef [11/20]

200 St Helen's Street, Ipswich IP4 2RH
IPSWICH (0473) 55236 £15–£22

Since 1961, Kenneth Toyé has been serving his version of *cuisine grandmère,* matching French regional dishes to good wines. He resolutely avoids the fashionable and the elaborate, preferring the simple style of sea-bass baked with fennel, or duck with orange caramel sauce. From Burgundy there might be a classic pork terrine or chicken braised with white wine and mustard sauce; from Alsace comes lentil soup, onion tart and choucroute; from the Rhône there might be hare or rabbit simmered with wine and salt pork, or a North Sea version of bouillabaisse. Cheeses are French, and sweets are in the style of omelette soufflé, chocolate pots and crêpes with apple purée. Lunch is now by prior arrangement only. The French wine list covers most of the growing areas including some of the lesser regional vineyards, although champagnes are the speciality. CELLARMAN'S CHOICE: Reuilly Vin Gris '86, £10.35; there's also cidre bouché from Normandy.

CHEFS: Kenneth and Jeannine Toyé PROPRIETORS: Cynthia and Kenneth Toyé
OPEN: Tue to Sat D, L by arrangement
MEALS: 7 to 11
PRICES: £14 (£22), Set D £9.50 (£15)
CARDS: Access, Visa
SEATS: 35. 4 tables outside. Private parties: 20 main room, 15 and 20 private rooms. Vegetarian meals. Children's helpings. No-smoking area. Wheelchair access (also WC). Music

Suffolk Round-up

ROOMS: *Marlborough Hotel,* Henley Road, Ipswich, (0473 57677); *Angel Hotel,* Angel Hill, Bury St Edmunds (0284 753926); *Dukes Head,* Coddenham (044 979 330).
INTERNATIONAL: *Countrymen,* Hall Street, Long Melford (0787 79951); *Market Place,* 18 Market Hall, Framlingham (0728 724275).
SETTING: *Pickerel Inn,* Ixworth (0359 30398).
INEXPENSIVE: *Eliza Acton,* Old High Road, Yoxford, Saxmundham (072 877 637); *Wheelwright's,* Well Close Square, Framlingham (0728 724132).
WINE BAR: *Jane's Wine Bar,* 29 High Street, Newmarket (0638 668031).
BAR MEALS: *White Horse,* Easton, Nr Woodbridge (0728 746 456); *Golden Key,* Priory Road, Snape (072 888 510).
ANGLO-FRENCH: *Chimneys,* Hall Street, Long Melford, Sudbury (0787 79806).
FISH: *Aldeburgh Fish & Chip Shop,* 226 High Street, Aldeburgh (072 885 2250).
LATE DINNER: *Regatta,* 171 High Street, Aldeburgh (072 885 2011).

[GHG] *after the details of an entry means that the establishment is also included in* The Good Hotel Guide.

'We feel that, to avoid embarrassment, the restaurant, the waiters, and the customers should all be clear about what is meant by "service charge" and whether or not this is included in the bill.' On eating in London

IXWORTH Suffolk map 6

Theobalds [12/20]

68 High Street, Ixworth IP31 2HJ
PAKENHAM (0359) 31707 £14–£23

Simon Theobald's roots are in the traditions of French cooking, but the menus in his converted corner shop now ring with echoes of the modern British style. Home-made pasta is paired with scallops or mussels and used as a filling for artichoke bottoms and shrimp sauce; ravioli is filled with spinach and ricotta. The fondness for spices and fruit with game looks back five centuries, although the ideas now sound up to the minute: venison liver terrine with orange and cinnamon sauce; Norfolk duckling grilled with cinnamon butter served with tangerine sauce. More recognisably modern, but equally English, are salmon on a bed of leeks and ginger with white port and lime sauce, or pigeon roasted with artichokes. Twice-baked cheese soufflé and fillet steaks are regular features of the seasonal menus. Sweets roam from lemon tart to chocolate truffle cake. Eight house wines lead off a respectable wine list, with plenty of bin-ends and CELLARMAN'S CHOICE: Beaujolais Blanc, Domaine Thibert '85 at £13.80.

CHEF: Simon Theobald PROPRIETORS: Simon and Geraldine Theobald
OPEN: all week, exc Mon L, Sat L, and Sun D
MEALS: 12.15 to 2, 7.30 to 10
PRICES: Set L £8.50 (£14), Set D £14.50 (£20) to £18.50 (£23)
CARDS: Access, Visa
SEATS: 36. 2 tables outside. Private parties: 36 main room. Children's helpings (Sun L only). No children under 8. No-smoking area. Music

JEVINGTON East Sussex map 3

Hungry Monk [11/20]

Jevington BM26 5QF
POLEGATE (032 12) 2178
on B2105, between Polegate and Friston  £21

This is good walking country, and a nine-mile circular stroll taking in Alfriston, the Long Man of Wilmington and Jevington might be worth bearing in mind for after a meal at the Hungry Monk. It is a fixed point in the Sussex restaurant scene and invites comparisons with its neighbour Moonrakers, at Alfriston (see entry). Both verge on the genteel, both are long-standing, both housed in attractive old Sussex flint buildings, both with interiors of the low-ceilinged, heavily beamed, leaded-windowed variety. The Monk is a warren of rooms furnished in olde worlde style. Tables are somewhat cramped and the formula can be regimented, especially on nights when there are two sittings. The menu is a ramble through fashions of restaurant cooking in England over the last 20 years. Late 1960s: terrine of pork and duck with Cumberland sauce; late 1970s: smoked salmon and prawn roulade; late 1980s: warm salad of scallops and ham. The total, though, is more old-fashioned, the above salad arriving with quail eggs and croûtons and radicchio and endive frisée and Webb's and parsley and much dressing. Everything is self-consciously made in-house, from pastry and bread to fudge. Saucing tends to favour fruit coulis rather than sauces. Recommended dishes include pork and duck terrine with bacon and pistachios, smoked salmon roulade, and guinea-fowl with chestnuts. Sweets are the likes of chocolate marquise with coffee sauce and an unsophisticated but good hot date and walnut cake with ice-cream and fudge sauce. On the wine list, clarets are a thoughtful mix of classics with affordable, ready-to-drink lesser wines and there is plenty of enjoyment to be had by picking carefully from the Burgundies. Small selections of Rhônes and Beaujolais are good, and the Rouge Homme wines from Australia and Delegats from New Zealand are excellent value. Seven English wines are a fitting find here in the midst of English vineyard country. The list could be more helpful: what use is a bald 'estate bottled' without naming the estate? And what use, indeed, is an extra price column giving ex-VAT? House claret £6.90, CELLARMAN'S CHOICE: Brouilly, Ch. de la Chaize '85, £10.

CHEF: Kent Austin PROPRIETORS: Nigel and Susan Mackenzie
OPEN: all week D, and Sun L
MEALS: 12.15 to 2.30, 7.15 to 10.30
PRICES: Set Sun L £13.50 (£21), Set D £14 (£21)
SEATS: 36. 2 tables outside. Private parties: 36 main room, 9 and 18 private rooms. Car-park, 17 places. Vegetarian meals. Children's helpings. No children under 3. Smart dress preferred. No cigars in dining-room

KENDAL Cumbria map 7

Moon [10/20]

129 Highgate, Kendal LA9 4EN
KENDAL (0539) 29254 £13

Val Macconnell's converted greengrocer's shop is less cramped than it used to be, now that she has knocked down a wall. Ceiling fans have been installed. The cooking is still an enterprising mix of vegetarian and wholefood, with meat and fish to the fore. Everything is home made and lots of new dishes have been added to the menu – smoked mackerel pâté with gooseberry sauce; beef, ginger and mango casserole; stuffed pepper with cinnamon, apricot and tomato sauce. Other favourites, such as vegetarian goulash and the sticky toffee pudding, are reliably good. The short wine list suits the food admirably, and there are a few interesting bottles, such as CELLARMAN'S CHOICE: Barossa Valley Riesling '86, at £4.50.

CHEFS: Dianne Kinsey, Sharon Moreton and Val Macconnell
PROPRIETOR: Val Macconnell
OPEN: all week, D only
MEALS: 6 to 10 (11 Fri and Sat)
PRICES: £8 (£13)
CARDS: Access, Visa
SEATS: 40. Vegetarian meals. Children's helpings. Music

KENILWORTH Warwickshire map 5

Ana's Bistro [9/20]

121–123 Warwick Road, Kenilworth CV8 1HP
KENILWORTH (0926) 53763 £14

A beamed basement bistro that shares a kitchen with Restaurant Diment upstairs. Décor is simple, with hard chairs and proper napkins. The menu is short and straight – soup, avocado, lasagne, steak – with a handful of daily specials along the lines of sauté chicken in watercress and cream sauce, or beef with tomatoes and butterbeans in red wine. Caribbean trifle and strawberry Pavlova to follow. Queues form at weekends, but it's now possible to book in advance.

CHEF: David Fanshawe PROPRIETORS: Antonio and Jennifer Martin
OPEN: Tue to Sat D
CLOSED: 1 week Easter, 3 weeks Aug
MEALS: 7 to 10.30
PRICES: £8 (£14)
CARDS: Access, Amex, Diners, Visa
SEATS: 34. Private parties: 34 main room. Car-park, 16 places. Vegetarian meals. Children's helpings. Music

Portofino [10/20]

14 Talisman Square, Kenilworth CV8 1JB
KENILWORTH (0926) 57186 £9–£20

A small trattoria conveniently placed in the busy shopping precinct, good, clean and friendly, without pretensions. The cooking is home-style Italian, with an accent towards the south, as in pollo alla pugliese, with pesto sauce, white wine and lemon juice; or the use of chilli to sharpen a tomato sauce for squid. Pasta ranges from ravioli to penne. Endorsements particularly for the spaghetti carbonara; veal escalope with cheese and salad. A carafe of house wine is £6.45.

CHEFS: Vito Ferro and Michele Pomar PROPRIETORS: Michele and Vito Ferro
OPEN: Mon to Sat, exc Mon L
CLOSED: bank hols
MEALS: 12 to 1.30, 6.30 to 10
PRICES: £13 (£20), Set L £5.75 (£9). Service 10% alc, inc Set
CARDS: Access, Amex, Diners, Visa
SEATS: 65. Private parties: 75 main room. Children's helpings (L only). Smart dress preferred. Wheelchair access (also WC). Music. Air-conditioned

'The countryside is no place for pretentiousness; there is quite enough of that in London, Venice, New York and so on. What we need are people who understand that in the country, especially at this time of year, dinner is to be enjoyed, if necessary with your waistcoat off and your napkin tucked in. The place is, after all, overflowing with game and wild fruits from the hedgerows. It is not unreasonable to expect a reflection of this bounty in a local restaurant.' On eating in Suffolk

Restaurant Bosquet [14/20]

97A Warwick Road, Kenilworth CV8 1HP
KENILWORTH (0926) 52463 £20–£26

Where other restaurants might draw attention to themselves by leaping on and off bandwagons, the Ligniers plough a less dramatic furrow. Low-key, consistent excellence marks them out. Ingredients can be indulgent – langoustine and lobster are combined in a mousse with courgette and basil, wrapped in salmon, and served with a tomato and pepper mayonnaise –but richness is generally kept in check, as in a slice of foie gras sandwiched between young leek and artichoke, with a vinaigrette. Simplicity and precision keep the cooking finely balanced between excess and restraint. There is a preference for sweet wines in sauces: Sauternes and raspberry vinegar with calf's liver wrapped in cabbage leaves, or madeira with loin of veal and morel mushrooms. Croustade de Gascogne is a signature pudding among mousses of coffee and chocolate, fruit tarts and mille-feuilles. The wine list offers a good selection of claret and Burgundy, making a determined effort to find decent wines at affordable prices. The list has been expanded slightly, and it is a living list with alternatives having been substituted where lines have obviously run out, as well as vintages updated, often improved. There is a spread from around France, including some less usual wines from the South West, such as two excellent Cahors, Château du Cayrou '83, £9.60, and Triguédina, Cuvée Probus '82, £13.50, plus good examples of Jurançon and Pacherenc du Vic Bilh. Some of the clarets listed are not yet ready to drink, while some look rather old. Quality of the Burgundy is mixed, and many of the producers' names are irritatingly missing. To drink with the pudding, Muscat de Frontignan comes by the glass at £2.30, or there's a Sauternes, a Quarts de Chaume '79, £12 and a Coteaux du Layon '67, from Pierre Chêne, £15. Bookings only at lunch.

CHEF: Bernard Lignier PROPRIETORS: Bernard and Jane Lignier
OPEN: Mon to Sat, exc Sat L
CLOSED: last 3 weeks in July
MEALS: 12 to 2, 7 to 10
PRICES: £19 (£26), Set L and D £13 (£20)
CARDS: Amex, Visa
SEATS: 28. Private parties: 30 main room. Vegetarian meals. Children welcome

KING'S LYNN Norfolk map 6

Riverside Rooms [10/20]

Kings Lynn Arts Centre, 27 King Street, King's Lynn PE30 1HA
KINGS LYNN (0553) 773134 £14

Handy for the arts and theatre complex. The rafters and brick walls give away its provenance as a warehouse. Lunches offer pork fillet medallions in a mustard sauce and cheaper options of lasagne, omelettes or pies. The

The Guide *does not accept free meals.*

evening sees grilled dishes getting sauces for formal dinners. Recommended have been salmon with prawn and cucumber, sirloin steak with green peppers. House Bulgarian £6.50.

CHEF: Dennis Taylor PROPRIETORS: Michael and Sylvia Savage
OPEN: Mon to Sat
MEALS: 12 to 2, 7 to 10
PRICES: £11 (£14). Service inc
CARDS: Access, Visa
SEATS: 65. 24 tables outside. Private parties: 75 main room. Car-park, 10 places. Vegetarian meals. Children's helpings. Music.

KING'S NORTON West Midlands map 5

Lombard Room [new entry, zero rated]

The Patrick Collection, 180 Lifford Lane, King's Norton B30 3NT
021-459 9111
M42 Junction 3, follow signs towards Birmingham on A453 £18–£31

Part of the motoring museum featuring 200 vintage cars in a renovated paper mill, is this grey dining-room with well-spaced tables that has surprised readers with the quality of its cooking. The menu is pitched towards business dining and has more than a whiff of Sloans about it, where chef John Penn worked: terrine of turbot served warm, wrapped in spinach; supreme of chicken boned and stuffed with its own mousse. Fish of the day has included hake, halibut and salmon served on a bed of shredded vegetables with an egg and cream emulsification. Portions are generous. Of sweets, the nut treacle tart has been notable. Wines include a goodly range in claret from £8.50 to £53, Burgundies to £72, but some easier cruising around the Loire and New Zealand. More reports, please.

CHEF: John C. Penn PROPRIETORS: The Patrick Collection Ltd
OPEN: Tue to Sun, exc Sat L and Sun D
MEALS: 12.30 to 2.30, 7.30 to 9.30
PRICES: £23 (£31), Set L £12.75 (£18)
CARDS: Access, Amex, Diners, Visa
SEATS: 40 to 50. Private parties: 50 main room, 40 and 90 private rooms. Car-park, 370 places. Vegetarian meals. Children's helpings. Smart dress preferred. No smoking. Wheelchair access (also WC). Music. Air-conditioned

KINGSBRIDGE Devon map 1

▲ *Queen Anne Restaurant, Buckland-Tout-Saints Hotel* [12/20]

Kingsbridge TQ7 2DS
KINGSBRIDGE (0548) 3055
2m NE of Kingsbridge £20–£25

The estate has a recorded history that goes back to Saxon times. The present house was built in 1690 by Sir John Southcote; it has some generously proportioned rooms, with a view overlooking the rolling South Devon countryside. Since August 1987 it has been part of the Prestige Group. The chef, Alastair Carter, did his training with John Webber at Gidleigh Park, and with George Perry-Smith, and though his style is based on the former, he is now finding his own ways of cooking and style of presentation. The kitchen has its own smoker, makes breads and preserves, and uses local products including salmon, cheeses and eaux-de-vie. The individuality of the cooking shows in mushroom and sage soup; warm salad of home-smoked chicken with mango and avocado; steamed Dart salmon with sorrel hollandaise; rack of English lamb with a madeira sauce, intensely over-reduced to a 'rich man's Bovril'; calf's liver with cassis, simply presented with raspberries and watercress. There is an extensive cheeseboard, and the sweets, though including sorbets and iced lemon soufflé, offers more substantial puddings, such as steamed marmalade sponge. The wine list derives from throughout the world, with a good range of prices, beginning with good house wines at well under £10. Excellent Burgundies are the strong point, but there are also fine clarets, including several mature vintages, excellent Beaujolais, fine estate German wines and short but well-chosen lists from the rest of Europe and the New World. A wide selection of sweet wines includes plenty of sweet '76 Germans, sweet Alsace, top Sauternes of the '83 vintage (too young yet) and late harvest wines from California and Australia. CELLARMAN'S CHOICE: St Emilion, Ch. Vieux Clos '82, £16.20; Châteauneuf-du-Pape, Les Cèdres '83, from Jaboulet, £19.20; and a non-vintage champagne, Canard Duchêne, £22.65.

CHEF: Alastair Carter PROPRIETORS: Mr and Mrs Victor Edward Shephard
OPEN: all week
CLOSED: 2 weeks from 1 Jan
MEALS: 12.30 to 1.15, 7.30 to 9
PRICES: Set L from £14 (£20), Set D from £18.75 (£25)
CARDS: Access, Amex, Carte Blanche, Diners, Visa
SEATS: 26. Private parties: 20 main room, 12 private room. Car-park, 20 places. No children under 9. Smart dress preferred. No smoking. Music. One sitting
ACCOMMODATION: 12 rooms, all with bath/shower. B&B £55 to £75. Deposit: one night's stay. No children under 9. Afternoon teas. Garden. TV. Phone. Scenic. Doors close at 12 [GHG]

KINGSTON UPON THAMES Surrey map 3

Ayudhya [11/20]

14 Kingston Hill, Kingston upon Thames KT2 7NH
01-549 5984 £19

1988 was the Year of the Carpenter for Somjai Feehan's popular Thai restaurant, with teak panelling, newel caps, plus two oil murals changing the face of the dining-room. The menu of around 50 dishes has classic satays, squid salad, and chicken and coconut soup with lemon-grass and laos as well as a few unusual items: curried fish mousse is flavoured with citrus leaves and sweet basil, then topped with coconut cream and steamed in a ramekin (in Thailand they would use banana leaves). Stir-fried pork with ginger has been good, too. There are plans to extend the menu with new dishes, such as roast duck curry and papaya and shrimp salad. Exotic Thai fruits feature regularly. Drink Amarit or Singha Thai beer.

CHEF/PROPRIETOR: Somjai Feehan
OPEN: Tue to Sun
CLOSED: Christmas, 1 Jan, Easter Sun and bank hols
MEALS: 12 to 2.30 (3 Sun), 6.30 to 11 (11.30 Fri and Sat)
PRICES: £11 (£19). Service 12.5
CARDS: Access, Amex, Diners, Visa
SEATS: 84. Private parties: 30 main room, 24 and 20 private rooms. Children welcome. Wheelchair access. Music

KINTBURY Berkshire map 2

▲ *Dundas Arms* [10/20]

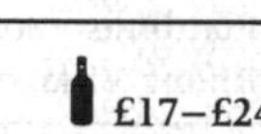

Station Road, Kintbury RG15 0UT
KINTBURY (0488) 58263 £17–£24

This well-used pub by the Kennet and Avon Canal has an elegant, comfortable dining-room offering skilfully prepared dinners. Flavours come straight to the point: a fish soup with fennel that evokes the Mediterranean, gamey quail with a sauce made from good stock. Otherwise the menu takes in broccoli mousse with tomato sauce, roast duckling with lemon sauce, and sea-bass with oysters and scallops. Good-value lunches are served in the boisterous bar. Diners with a limited thirst for wine should not feel done down – four half-bottles of white Burgundies are just as tempting as the red halves, from Bize and Pousse d'Or. Burgundy seems to be a particular passion here, almost all coming from small, quality-conscious domaines, for instance Corsin, Vincent, Durup, Defaix, Raveneau, Dauvissat, Lafon, Gagnard-Delagrange and Leflaive in the whites, and Tollot-Beaut, Mussy, Lejeune, Jean Grivot and Henri Jayer in the reds. Clarets are good, and reasonably priced, and the brief selections from Rhône, Alsace (excellent Faller wines) and Beaujolais are all dependable. Even the German wines (excluding the Niersteiner Gutes Domtal) are good, and the New Zealand Sauvignon Blanc Cloudy Bay, '87 is outstanding. Do not spurn automatically the house wines, which start at £6.90.

CHEF/PROPRIETOR: David A. Dalzell-Piper
OPEN: Tue to Sat
CLOSED: Christmas to New Year
MEALS: 12.30 to 1.30, 7.30 to 9.30
PRICES: Set L £11.50 (£17), Set D £17.50 (£24), Snacks from £1.20
CARDS: Access, Amex, Diners, Visa
SEATS: 36. 10 tables outside. Private parties: 22 main room. Car-park, 40 places. Children's helpings. Smart dress preferred. No cigars/pipes in dining-room. Wheelchair access (2 steps; also WC)
ACCOMMODATION: 5 rooms, all with bath/shower. Rooms for disabled. B&B £40 to £46. Children welcome. TV. Phone. Scenic. Doors close at 11.30. Confirm by 6 [GHG]

All letters to the Guide *are acknowledged.*

KIRKHAM Lancashire map 5

Cromwellian [10/20]

16 Poulton Street, Kirkham PR4 2AD
KIRKHAM (0772) 685680 £13–£18

This two-hundred-year-old building was one of the original Kirkham town-houses, probably owned by a prosperous trader, with the downstairs given over to the goats and chickens. Now, the aroma of warm bread, the chunky cutlery and the fresh flowers give a homely feel to an unfussy French bistro. The style is: a crisp half apple, filled with a herb cheese pâté and tarragon cream; mushrooms with fennel in a creamy herb sauce; a sirloin with tomato and Dijon mustard sauce; pork with raisins and cider. Vegetables have bite. The Fawcetts are not afraid of local dishes; black pudding is popular and a decent cheeseboard features some English examples. Fine Queen of Puddings, too. House French is £5.75; CELLARMAN'S CHOICE: Côtes du Rhône Villages '85, £7.25; Pouilly Fumé '86, £10.50.

CHEF: José Fawcett PROPRIETOR: Peter Fawcett
OPEN: Tue to Sat D, and Sun L
MEALS: 12.30 to 3, 7 to 10.30
PRICES: Set Sun L £7.50 (£13), Set D from £12.50 (£18)
SEATS: 30. Private parties: 17 main room, 12 private room. Vegetarian meals. Children's helpings by arrangement. Wheelchair access. Music

KNUTSFORD Cheshire map 5

▲ *Belle Epoque* [12/20]

10 YEARS

60 King Street, Knutsford WA16 6DT
KNUTSFORD (0565) 3060 and 2661 £25

The restaurant is famous for its extravagant art nouveau décor of mosaic floors, frilled curtains and bronze statues. And it continues to draw a stream of strong recommendations. Yvonne Holt's cooking is modern, French and stylish: quail is boned, stuffed with chicken liver mousseline and wrapped in filo pastry; roast guinea-fowl is served in a sauce of its own juice, lime and Chablis. Fish specials from the market might include grilled tuna with watercress sauce. There are some excellent touches, such as walnut and onion bread served with soup, English cheeses made by a local farmer, home-made petits fours and large cups of coffee. The wine list has a page of champagne and French regional wines to back a strong showing of Bordeaux and Burgundies. House wine £6.95.

'As a customer of your book and the restaurants, the only annoying thing is that even in the first few weeks or months of 1988 the prices were more than quoted.'
On eating in Surrey

CHEF: Yvonne Burke PROPRIETORS: Keith and Nerys Mooney
OPEN: Mon to Sat, D only
CLOSED: first week Jan
MEALS: 7.30 to 10
PRICES: £16 (£25). Service 10%
CARDS: Access, Amex, Diners, Visa
SEATS: 70. Private parties: 60 main room, 20,60 and 80 private rooms. Vegetarian meals. No children under 10. No pipes in dining-room. Music
ACCOMMODATION: 5 rooms, all with bath/shower. B&B £28 to £40. No children under 10. Garden. TV. Scenic. Doors close at 12. Confirm by 2

LACOCK Wiltshire map 2

▲ *At the Sign of the Angel* [10/20]

10 YEARS

Church Street, Lacock SN15 2LA
LACOCK (024 973) 230 £23

Like the Fox Talbot photographic exhibition in the village, At the Sign of the Angel has become a monument to another era. The dining-room is lit by candles and an open fire and the menu reflects an age when a farmhouse would be almost self-sufficient. And indeed the beef – usually a central choice – is from the Levis' own land and cooked traditionally towards the grey. The cooking has become erratic at prices inflated by American visitors in search of something authentic, hence the drop in rating, a pity because there is much to commend in the simple formula and atmosphere. Recommended dishes include creamed carrot soup; kidneys in madeira; roast beef. Half a dozen simple sweets, from meringues with Jersey cream to treacle lick. Stilton or Cheddar to finish, cut from truckles. Sixty wines are strong in Bordeaux and Burgundy; house claret is £8.80.

CHEF: L.M. Levis PROPRIETOR: J.S. Levis
OPEN: all week, exc Sat L and Sun D
CLOSED: 22 Dec to 4 Jan
MEALS: 1 to 1.30, 7.30 to 8
PRICES: Set L and D £16 (£23)
SEATS: 40. Private parties: 20 main room, 20 private room. No children under 8. Smart dress preferred
ACCOMMODATION: 8 rooms, all with bath/shower. B&B £45 to £70. No children under 8. Pets welcome. Garden. Phone. Scenic. Confirm by 5.30 [GHG]

LANGHO Lancashire map 5

▲ *Northcote Manor* [13/20]

Northcote Road, Langho BB6 9BB
BLACKBURN (0254) 40555
7m E of M6 exit 31, on A59 £15–£31

Nigel Haworth's reputation continues to grow at this large, rather nondescript Victorian red-brick house some seven miles east of the M6. The cooking, though, is far from nondescript – firmly modern, and drawing on many influences, the emphasis is on the fresh and the seasonal, with fish and game featuring strongly on the frequently changing menu. Much store is laid on presentation and style, and careful consideration is given to the combination of colours and flavours, with fresh herbs much in evidence: rosemary with quail; tarragon with beef. Arrive in the dullest part of the year, and you are offered a soup of red peppers and leek or a basket of seafood, followed by grilled brill with a lobster butter, or roast guinea-fowl in a gin and juniper sauce. Sweets are on the lines of honey and mango mousse, Queen of Puddings, or there might be a final savoury of quail egg and bacon. Or try the speciality cheese of the month. Sixty wines, with house French £6.50. CELLARMAN'S CHOICE: Torres, Gran Coronas '83, £14.70. Muscat de Beaumes de Venise is £1.80 the glass.

CHEF: Nigel Haworth PROPRIETORS: Craig J. Bancroft and William J. Kelly
OPEN: all week, exc Sat L
MEALS: 12 to 1.30, 7 to 9 (10 Sat)
PRICES: £23 (£31), Set L £9 (£15) to £15 (£24)
CARDS: Access, Amex, Diners, Visa
SEATS: 70. Private parties: 60 main room, 20 private room. Car-park, 50 places. Children's helpings. Smart dress preferred. Music
ACCOMMODATION: 6 rooms, all with bath/shower. B&B £45 to £55. Pets welcome. Afternoon teas. Garden. TV. Phone. Scenic [GHG]

LANGLEY MARSH Somerset — map 2

▲ *Langley House Hotel* [13/20]

Langley Marsh TA4 2UF
WIVELISCOMBE (0984) 23318 — £22–£25

Set among green hills near the small town of Wiveliscombe, Langley House has neat lawns with exuberant flower borders. The house dates from the sixteenth century – seen in the low ceilings and heavy beams – and was extended and altered during the eighteenth century. The walls of the hall are heavily wood-panelled, but the two lounges are bright and pretty in corals and sun yellow. The floral patterns of the curtains are repeated on sofas and chairs. Utter silence is everywhere, outside and in, save for the ticking of the old grandfather clock. Peter and Anne Wilson have countrified themselves in this setting. There is a small dining-room and a no-choice set menu, based on good local ingredients arranged in the modern idiom, but sticking to a tight repertoire. A piquant starter is the fanned dessert pear marinated in walnut oil, tarragon, garlic and coarse mustard seeds, countered with a thick cream cheese and chive savoury on the same plate. Other nights there have been crab tartlets or tomato salad with lemon and basil cream. A second course is a coarse, quenelle-style smoked salmon soufflé. Main dishes are the familiar duck breast with green peppercorns or veal fillet with orange sauce. The walled herb garden provides an array of flavours, often scattered as well across the vegetables. Sweets show the care of pre-preparation as in a five-layered terrine of dark and white chocolate with the central core of a sponge-like meringue into which crushed almonds and hazelnuts have been added. Anne Wilson presides charmingly in a very English way. The wine ist is rooted in Burgundy and claret but blossoms with small examples of nany other regions. House wine is £6.25. CELLARMAN'S CHOICE: Australian Shiraz from Brown Bros, £10.65.

CHEF: Peter Wilson PROPRIETORS: Peter and Anne Wilson
OPEN: all week, D only
MEALS: 7.30 to 9
PRICES: Set D from £16.25 (£22) to £18.75 (£25)
SEATS: 18. Private parties: 35 main room, 18 private room. Car-park, 10 places. Vegetarian meals. Children's helpings. No children under 7. No smoking in dining-room. Wheelchair access (also WC)
ACCOMMODATION: 9 rooms, all with bath/shower. B&B £40 to £69. Deposit: £10. Baby facilities. Pets welcome. Afternoon teas. Garden. TV. Phone. Scenic. Doors close at 12. Confirm by 6 [GHG]

LAVENHAM Suffolk — map 3

▲ *Great House* [10/20]

Market Place, Lavenham CO10 9QZ
LAVENHAM (0787) 247431 — £14–£25

The house dates from the fourteenth century, previously owned by a weaving family and given a Georgian façade; it overlooks the beautiful market-place. As a hotel it rates highly on atmosphere and friendliness, but the dining-room is the main business. The menu is French with nods towards *nouvelle cuisine* and also to the likes of deep-fried mushrooms and pork with Dijon mustard sauce. There are interesting cheeses to go with the 120 mostly French wines, with a big show of champagnes. House Gaillac opens at a stiff £10.50.

CHEF: Regis Crepy PROPRIETOR: John Spice
OPEN: all week
CLOSED: last 3 weeks Jan
MEALS: 12 to 2.30, 7 to 10.30
PRICES: £15 (£25), Set L £6.90 (£14) to £8.75 (£16), Set D £10.75 (£19), Snacks from £2
CARDS: Access, Amex, Carte Blanche, Visa
SEATS: 65. 7 tables outside. Private parties: 50 main room; 30 and 50 private rooms. Vegetarian meals. Children's helpings. No cigars/pipes in dining-room. Music
ACCOMMODATION: 3 rooms, all with bath/shower. B&B £39 to £52. Deposit: £20. Children welcome. Baby facilities. Pets welcome. Afternoon teas. Garden. TV. Phone. Scenic. Doors close at 1. Confirm by noon [GHG]

LEDBURY Hereford & Worcester — map 2

▲ *Hope End* [13/20]

Hope End, Ledbury HR8 1JQ
LEDBURY (0531) 3613
2/3m N of Ledbury, just beyond
Wellington Heath  £25

John and Patricia Hegarty are defenders of two great English traditions: the kitchen and the garden. Their rebuilt eighteenth-century mansion – once the childhood home of Elizabeth Barrett Browning – is anything and everything but average, more of a sanctuary than a retreat. The building nestles in a glacial hollow and all around is the Hegartys' unofficial nature reserve, with wild-flower meadows, rare perry pears and plums planted like some random hillside orchard and, up the hill, the remarkable eighteenth-century walled garden with 60 kinds of vegetable, 50 herbs and 40 varieties of apple. It is sustained by a belief in the rightness of organic methods and by sheer hard work, but this is not the new medievalism. Hi-tech glasshouses, complex irrigation systems and rotavators have their place alongside pottery cloches and the remains of the hollow heated wall for nurturing fruit trees. The same philosophy spills over into the kitchen. This is Dorothy Hartley's *Food in England*, dragged out of the 1950s into the 1980s. The emphasis is on freshness and a blend of traditional and modern British cooking with the details in the rightful place – earthy home-made bread, curds and yoghurts from the goats, preserves and relishes, mighty farmhouse cheeses. The little wholemeal loaves are unsalted, as is the butter. That sets the tone for a daily-changing five-course dinner menu with little choice but immense variety and balance. The style is healthy. To start there might be silky green lovage soup or halibut dumplings with tomato and dill sauce. Main courses are usually meat or game: strips of beef with a sauce of mustard, cider vinegar and winter savoury; pork loin stuffed with pickled quinces; devilled chicken; roast guinea-fowl with Morello cherry relish. Vegetables are loyal to the seasons, and so is the little salad that follows. Then come three farmhouse cheeses – perhaps Martell's Single Gloucester, Colston Bassett Stilton and Welsh Pant-y-Clyn, with a basket of Bath Olivers and apples from the garden. Finally a choice of sweets, from rhubarb and ginger sorbet to curd tart sitting on a pool of intense blackcurrant sauce with an outer ring of thin, pinkish redcurrant sauce. Coffee is taken in the upstairs lounge. Excellent breakfasts take in home-made muesli, yoghurt, free-range eggs and the like. It would be hard to go wrong on the lengthy wine list, which concentrates on France, with a token but interesting presence from the rest of the world. There is an exceptional selection of Burgundies, but also very fine Rhônes, Loires and clarets. Half-bottles are unusually exciting and plentiful. There are a few representatives from the New World and one organic wine. House French is £6.

CHEF: Patricia Hegarty PROPRIETORS: John and Patricia Hegarty
OPEN: Wed to Sun, D only
CLOSED: Dec to Feb
MEALS: 7.30 to 8.30
PRICES: Set D £22 (£25). Service inc
CARDS: Access, Visa
SEATS: 24. Private parties: 6 main room. Car-park, 10 places. No children under 14. Smart dress preferred. No smoking. Wheelchair access (2 steps)
ACCOMMODATION: 9 rooms, all with bath/shower. B&B £63 to £102. Deposit: £30. No children under 14. Garden. Phone. Scenic. Doors close at 11. Confirm by 6 [GHG]

New this year are County Round-ups, mostly, but not always, listed under the county town. To find a County Round-up, check the maps at the back; towns listing a Round-up are underlined.

LEEDS West Yorkshire map 5

Bryan's [9/20]

9 Weetwood Lane, Headingley, Leeds LS16 5LT
LEEDS (0532) 785679 £6

Lacking the razzamatazz of Harry Ramsden's, Bryan's is a more traditional fish and chip shop, a single-storey stone-built block next to a pub, established in 1934, though under Jan Fletcher only since 1984. Fish is delivered daily and fried in dripping. There are few fish shops with parking for 50 cars and a perpetual queue for the take-away, whatever the time of day, this in spite of there being four of five people serving and as many again frying. The dining-room is rather cool and clinical but is air-conditioned, with a head waitress assuring speed and efficiency on the part of the half-dozen red-pinafored, friendly mothers performing the serving duties. Portions are huge and prices low. Sole has been 12 inches from head to tail, the halibut three-quarters of a pound to a pound in weight. The range takes in everything from plaice to hake and lemon sole on the bone. Crisp, dry chips, first-rate mushy peas. Tea is 41p a pot.

CHEFS: David Mitchell, Alan Germaine and Richard Edmundson
PROPRIETOR: Jan Fletcher
OPEN: Mon to Sat
MEALS: 11.30am to 11.30pm
PRICES: £5 (£6), Snacks from 55p. Minimum £2.55
SEATS: 140. Private parties: 100 main room. Car-park, 50 places. Vegetarian meals. Children's helpings. Wheelchair access. Music. Air-conditioned

Grillade [10/20]

Wellington Street, Leeds LS1 4HJ
LEEDS (0532) 459707 and 459952 £11–£18

The brick, whitewashed walled basement is pronounced in its Frenchness. Grills are the main business, from plain steak frites to châteaubriand with a supporting cast of rillettes; prawns in garlic and salad niçoise also feature. The atmosphere bustles. House French is £4.95.

CHEF: Orenzo Padolino PROPRIETORS: Meritlight Ltd
OPEN: Mon to Sat, exc Sat L
CLOSED: Christmas week and bank hols
MEALS: 12 to 2.30, 7.30 to 11
PRICES: £13 (£18), Set L and D £7.95 (£11)
CARDS: Access, Visa
SEATS: 62. Children welcome. No cigars/pipes in dining-room. Air-conditioned

'My basic requirement would be for the provision of interesting, nicely presented sandwiches (preferably wholemeal) followed by freshly baked scones and a selection of fresh cakes. The provision of dainty fresh cream cakes would be asking too much from any establishment calling itself a hotel, except the Ritz or Waldorf in London.'
On eating in Hereford and Worcester

Jumbo Chinese [10/20]

120 Vicar Lane, Leeds LS2 7NL
LEEDS (0532) 458324 £11

The closest rival to the Sang Sang (see entry). The Cantonese menu is more limited and the queues for the basement dining-room are shorter than in the old days. However, the place is still useful for its dim-sum, copious noodle dishes and specialities such as fillet steak with OK sauce and lemon chicken.

CHEFS: Yat Sun Lo and Lin Dai Lai PROPRIETORS: Lin Dai Lai, Tony Kwan and Yat Sun Lo
OPEN: all week
CLOSED: 25 to 27 Dec
MEALS: noon to 11.45pm
PRICES: £6 (£11), Snacks from 95p
CARDS: Access, Amex
SEATS: 120. Private parties: 180 main room. Children welcome. Music. Air-conditioned

Mandalay [10/20]

8 Harrison Street, Leeds LS1 6PA
LEEDS (0532) 446453 and 446340 £10–£18

Recent reports indicate that standards have picked up again at this established, sophisticated tandoori house opposite the stage door of the Grand Theatre. The décor is in the school of post-Raj chic. Ivories tinkle at weekends. The menu has above-average tandoori dishes such as chicken shashlik and sheek kebabs, as well as rich, vividly spiced curries along the lines of jhinga masala, karahi gosht and smooth mild dahl. Most curries are generously sprinkled with fresh coriander, and the nan bread is fresh and light. Service is prompt, attentive and helpful. Drink Grolsch or Kingfisher beer.

CHEFS: Habib Ur-Rehman and Bashir Ahmad PROPRIETORS: P. Breaks, P. Chappelow and W. Prior
OPEN: Mon to Sat, exc Sat L
MEALS: 12 to 2.30, 6 to 11.30
PRICES: £10 (£18), Set L £4.95 (£10). Service 10% (D only)
CARDS: Access, Amex, Diners, Visa
SEATS: 95. Private parties: 30 main room. Car-park, 5 places. Vegetarian meals. Children's helpings. Wheelchair access (1 step; also WC). Music. Air-conditioned

Olive Tree [10/20]

Oaklands, Rodley Lane, Leeds LS13 1NG
LEEDS (0532) 569283 £11–£18

A cut above the average Greek restaurant – clean, efficient, reasonable. The décor and style would not be out of place in a French restaurant. The outstanding feature is the use of prime cuts of meat and fish. Traditional favourites line up alongside some 'international' dishes of the day. Signature dishes – the hummus, tsatsiki, souvlaki – stand out, even when the seasoning is cautious. The Anglo-French restaurateuring touches extend into oak-leaf and radicchio salads. The parent branch at Ilkley has been sold, so effort should now be concentrated here. Predominantly Greek wines, starting with Rotunda at £5.95. CELLARMAN'S CHOICE: Naoussa, £6.95.

CHEFS: George Psarias and Andreas Iacovou PROPRIETORS: George and Vasoulla Psarias
OPEN: all week, exc Sat L
CLOSED: 25 and 26 Dec, 1 Jan
MEALS: 12 to 2, 6.30 to 12
PRICES: £11 (£18), Set L £5.95 (£11), Set D from £9.50 (£15). Service 10%
CARDS: Access, Visa
SEATS: 120. Private parties: 50 main room, 25 and 25 private rooms. Car-park, 25 places. Vegetarian meals. Children's helpings. Wheelchair access (also WC). Music

Sang Sang [11/20]

7 The Headrow, Leeds, LS1 6PN
LEEDS (0532) 468664 £12–£18

The Chinese variations on western songs, like *Scarborough Fair* or *Take My Breath Away*, amaze. Leeds' premier Cantonese restaurant has taken some flak lately. There's a more extensive menu and much wider range of dim-sum than at the nearby Jumbo, which scores for generosity in the quantity of soup, especially mixed meat soup, and in the standard of special chow mein and Peking crunch duck. But for casseroles, roast meats, wok dishes, sizzling dishes and fish and seafood, for instance king prawns with cashews, Sang Sang is more accomplished, though the lack of warming trays for cold plates annoys some. Service is increasingly sketchy. Set meals from £7.50. House French is £4.45.

CHEF: F.C. Cheung PROPRIETORS: Tony Chow, F.C. Cheung, Ng Chuen
OPEN: all week
MEALS: noon to 11.30
PRICES: £10 (£18), Set D from £7.50 (£12). Snacks from £1.05. Service 10% Set
CARDS: Access, Amex, Diners, Visa
SEATS: 120. Private parties: 90 main room; 30 private room. Vegetarian meals. Children welcome. Wheelchair access (1 step). Music. Air-conditioned

LEICESTER Leicestershire map 6

Bobby's [9/20]

154–156 Belgrave Road, Leicester LE4 5AT
LEICESTER (0533) 660106 and 662448 £5–£8

Leicester has one of the largest Asian communities in the country. Many came to England in the early 1970s and settled along the Belgrave Road. Bobby's is the pick of around 20 cafés, restaurants and sweet-centres in the area, and serves some of the best Indian vegetarian food in the city. The Lakhani family use their own recipes, cook fresh each day and offer excellent value for money. Onions and garlic do not appear in any dishes. The real bargains are the thalis, which begin at £3.60 for curries, dhal, rice, chapatis, lassi and poppadums. Also look for the range of snacks, including bhel-pooris, patis (round cakes filled with peas and coconut), dhokla (deep-fried morsels of chickpea flour, yoghurt, coriander, chillies and sesame seeds). Takeaways. Unlicensed, but bring your own, or drink exotic milk shakes or juices.

CHEF: M.B. Lakhani PROPRIETOR: B.A. Lakhani
OPEN: Tue to Sun
MEALS: 11.30am to 10pm (10.30pm Sat)
PRICES: £5 (£8), Set L and D £3.60 (£5) to £4.60 (£6). Cover 40p
CARDS: Access, Amex, Diners, Visa
SEATS: 90. Private parties: 50 main room. Vegetarian meals. Children's helpings. No-smoking area. Music

Lai's [new entry, zero rated]

14–16 King Street, Leicester LE1 6RJ
LEICESTER (0533) 557700 £11–£33

A pink and grey stone building opposite the tall Leicester Council offices has been transformed into an elegant Chinese restaurant. From the outside it hardly looks like a restaurant at all; inside it feels French, with tassled velvet drapes, festooned curtains let down to the floor and arty prints on the pastel walls. The menu is a good second-generation alternative to the old style of the Water Margin (see entry) with bang-bang chicken, Peking crispy lamb, Szechuan garshew prawns laced with chilli, and aubergines in black-bean sauce. There are also a few Cantonese stalwarts, such as stewed beef and Chinese cabbage hot-pot. Impressive seafood dinners have baked lobster as the centrepiece. Polite, well-informed service. A basic wine list has house French at £5.50. More reports, please.

CHEF: John Lau PROPRIETORS: Brian Lai and John Lau
OPEN: all week
MEALS: 12 to 2, 6 to 11
PRICES: £23 (£33), Set L from £6.50 (£11), Set D from £10 (£15). Service 10%
CARDS: Access, Amex, Diners, Visa
SEATS: 160. Private parties: 60 main room, 100, 40 and 60 private rooms. Vegetarian meals. Children welcome. Wheelchair access (3 steps; also WC). Music

Panda [10/20]

215 Fosse Road North, Leicester LE3 5EZ
LEICESTER (0533) 538628 £11–£19

The most unlikely Chinese restaurant in Leicester is out of town, in a red-brick Victorian house next to a second-hand car lot. Knock on the door to gain entrance. Inside, the panda artefacts, garish hand-painted mural of a fisherman and chopsticks are all Chinese; otherwise it feels like a dining-room in a seaside boarding-house. John and Myra Wan offer an old-style menu of Cantonese and Peking dishes with a strong showing of fish and shellfish, and a useful choice of vegetarian specialities, from mushrooms in oyster sauce to spiced bean curd roll. The cooking is robust, ingredients are fresh and flavours full-blooded. Sesame prawn toasts, wun-tun soup, duck dishes, squid in black-bean sauce and barbecued pork have all been above average. House wine £4.90.

CHEF: Benny Wong PROPRIETOR: John Wan
OPEN: all week
MEALS: 12 to 1.30, 6.30 to 11
PRICES: £10 (£19), Set L and D from £7.95 (£11). Service 10%
CARDS: Access, Amex, Diners, Visa
SEATS: 30. Private parties: 40 main room, 20 and 40 private rooms. Vegetarian meals. Children welcome. Smart dress preferred. 3 steps to rest. Wheelchair access. Music

Rise of the Raj [new entry, zero rated]

6 Evington Road, Leicester LE2 1HF
LEICESTER (0533) 553885 £17

Most of Leicester's Indian eating places are either flamboyant old-style curry houses dating back to the 1960s or vegetarian cafés and sweets-centres. This small pink and maroon restaurant out towards the prosperous suburb of Evington has more in common with the new wave in London, and the menu has more than a hint of Lal Qila (see entry) in the non-vegetarian thali and the list of cocktails. The style is mainly North India, taking in tandooris, murgh makhani, jhingri johl and lamb pasanda. Good basmati rice and freshly made breads. Drink lager. More reports, please.

CHEFS: Abdul Bashir and Rouf Ullha PROPRIETOR: Abdul Bashir
OPEN: all week
CLOSED: 25 Dec
MEALS: 12 to 2.30, 6 to 11.30
PRICES: £9 (£17). Minimum £6. Service 10%
CARDS: Access, Amex, Diners, Visa
SEATS: 76. Private parties: 40 main room, 50 private room. Vegetarian meals. Children's helpings (not Fri and Sat). No children under 5. Smart dress preferred. Wheelchair access (1 step). Music

Water Margin [10/20]

76–78 High Street, Leicester LE1 5YP
LEICESTER (0533) 516422 and 24937 £7–£17

Philip Chan's departure to Derby (see entry) caused some disruption in 1987, but this established, busy restaurant close to Leicester's excellent market serves the city well. The strength of the kitchen is in its inexpensive dim-sum, its one-plate meals and Cantonese specialities, although these have a low profile compared to the popular westernised set lunches. Steamed spare ribs with black-bean sauce have been as potent as the best in Soho Chinatown, roast meats are well up to standard and the fried noodles are the best in the city. The brown, functional, box-like dining-room and perfunctory service are in keeping with the old-style image of a Chinese restaurant of the 1950s and 1960s.

CHEF: K.F. Lam PROPRIETOR: Y.W. Lam
OPEN: all week
MEALS: noon to 11.30
PRICES: £9 (£17), Set L £3 (£7), Set D from £8.50 (£13). Service 10%
CARDS: Access, Amex, Diners, Visa
SEATS: 170. Private parties: 100 main room, 100 private room. Vegetarian meals. Children welcome. Wheelchair access. Music

Leicestershire Round-up

CHINESE: *Hong Kong Fountain*, Bedford Square, Loughborough, (0509 216216).
VEGETARIAN: *Dizzi Heights*, 27 Biggin Street, Loughborough (0509 262018).
BAR MEALS: *White Horse*, Empingham, Nr Oakham (078 086 221/521); *Bell Inn*, Main Street, East Langton (085 884 567).
INDIAN: *Curry Fever*, 139 Belgrave Road, Leicester (0533 662941).
TEA GARDEN: *Talkies*, 210 Narborough Road, Leicester (0533 546690); *Talkies* (new branch), 62 Woodgate, Leicester (0533 551859).
ROOMS: *Quorn Grange*, Wood Lane, Quorn (0509 412167).

LEIGHTON BUZZARD Bedfordshire map 3

▲ *Swan Hotel* [10/20]

High Street, Leighton Buzzard LU7 7EA
LEIGHTON BUZZARD (0525) 372148 £14–£24

This impressively refurbished Georgian coaching-inn now functions as civilised town pub and efficiently run Home Counties business hotel. Much of its reputation rests with the elegant dining-room, smartly done out in pink and red with floral drapes and pretty miniature arrangements of seasonal flowers on the tables. Menus also follow the seasons. Artichoke soup, poached Finnan haddock in pastry with chopped-egg sauce, and spotted dick might appear in February alongside more eclectic dishes such as ragout of monkfish with fresh noodles, smoked chicken salad with sesame dressing and supreme of chicken with two sauces – one madeira, the other Boursin cheese. There are steaks and roasts, plus some interesting vegetarian specialities such as bean croquettes with gado-gado sauce. A one-course lunch in the dining-room, with coffee, is around £5. Seventy-five reasonably priced wines.

CHEF: Stephen McNally PROPRIETORS: Eric and Felicity Stephens
OPEN: all week
MEALS: 12 to 2, 7 (7.30 Fri) to 9.30 (10 Fri, 9 Sun)
PRICES: £17 (£24), Set L from £10 (£14), Set D from £15 (£20), Snacks from £1
CARDS: Access, Amex, Diners, Visa
SEATS: 80. 3 tables outside. Private parties: 80 main room, 40 private room. Car-park, 10 places. Vegetarian meals. Children's helpings. Wheelchair access. Air-conditioned
ACCOMMODATION: 38 rooms, all with bath/shower. B&B £49.50 to £60. Baby facilities. Afternoon teas. TV. Phone. Confirm by 1

Bedfordshire Round-up

CHINESE: *Man Ho*, 80 Dunstable Road, Luton (0582 23366).
BAR MEALS: *Knife and Cleaver*, Houghton Conquest (0234 740387); *Cock*, 23 High Street, Broom (0767 314411).
INDIAN: *Akash Tandoori*, Leighton Buzzard (0525 372316).

LEWES East Sussex map 3

Kenwards [14/20]

Pipe Passage, 151A High Street, Lewes BN7 1XV
LEWES (0273) 472343  £22

Is this a restaurant or a political statement? At times, John Kenward's admirable dedication to the principles of simplicity seems to prompt the question: Is this all? And if it is, what are we doing with petits fours and canapés? The attic dining-room epitomises the approach: old ceiling beams and uprights are left exposed. The cooking is modern British at its most raw, but also most deliberate. Restaurant trappings have almost been abandoned. The kitchen is open-plan and the clattering of pots and pans and the coming and going of regulars are part of the ambiance. Ingredients are the prime source of ideas, and the short menu has certain features which recur. Cheeses are always British and will appear in cooked dishes; thus, Wheatland cheese terrine with leeks or flageolet beans and mushrooms with Bonchester. Seafood dishes outnumber meats and both are given bold combinations with herbs and vegetables – for instance, sweetish, pan-fried, very bloody pigeon sliced and arranged in crescents and served with matchstick lengths of red cabbage and celeriac, or, to take another example, superb terrine of lobster with a sorrel sauce. There is technique here too. Take the rabbit and celeriac salad. It is a terrine, the leg of rabbit boned and stuffed, and the slices of fillet interleaved with a julienne of celeriac sharpened by lemon. Sweets are almost exclusively traditional, for instance apricot and walnut tart with cream or hot date pudding with butterscotch sauce or, when they are not, tread very close to the purist borderline. 'The chocolate marquise was good but very similar to a slab of excellent chocolate, though somewhat creamier, and the caramel oranges were, as far as I could tell, just two crossed slices of peeled orange.' Seasonings throughout are bright: orange for leeks and artichokes; ginger and lime for skate and monkfish; whisky for vanilla ice-cream. Especially notable are the Soay lamb with garlic, parsley and malaga, and the mallard with apple and cider. These statements sometimes look a little bald by themselves, so some readers decry the missing sensuality of a richer décor, but in abstract these are important tenets. Waverers should consider the quality of the wine list before dismissing the operation. There is no pretension here. French wines far outweigh the few Italian and Spanish bottles on the very reasonably priced wine list. The French list sticks mostly to the major regions, with claret, which include some interesting lesser properties – something of a speciality – but also good Loires, Rhônes and Burgundies. Sweet wines are a strong point. There's a small range of half-bottles of Sauternes of the early '80s, Château Coutet in five vintages back to '61, some fine mature Loires at irresistible prices (Coteaux du Layon '69, from Baumard, is only £10.90), and a handful of mature, sweet German wines from the excellent 1976 and 1971 vintages. CELLARMAN'S CHOICE: Ch. Cissac '84, £10.70; Mercurey, Clos l'Evêque '84, £13.50, £7.45 per half-bottle.

CHEF: John Kenward PROPRIETORS: John and Caroline Kenward
OPEN: Tue to Sat, D only. L by arrangement
MEALS: 7.30 to 9.30
PRICES: £15 (£22). Service inc
CARDS: Access, Amex, Diners, Visa
SEATS: 25. Private parties: 10 main room. Vegetarian meals. Children welcome

Pattisson's [10/20]

199 High Street, Lewes BN7 2NS
LEWES (0273) 472727 and 473364 £13–£17

The Pattissons' restaurant is in a part of the high street known locally as School Hill. All the action, including morning coffee, now centres on the apricot-walled dining-room below street level. The *carte* lunches are dominated by an excellent cold table, with everything from fresh local mussels to aubergines in yoghurt and garlic. Dinners are unpretentious home-cooked dishes with some well made sauces. Typically, there might be casseroled venison with juniper berries, honey-glazed duck, a fisherman's stew and, sometimes, a vegetarian dish. Start with home-made soups and pâtés, finish with puddings like cream meringue, chocolate mousse or fruit fool. The workaday wine list includes English Breaky Bottom at £7 and house French at £4.50.

CHEFS/PROPRIETORS: Mr and Mrs Pattisson
OPEN: Mon to Sat, exc Mon and Sat D
CLOSED: 10 days at Christmas, bank hol Mons
MEALS: 12 to 2.15, 7.30 to 9.15
PRICES: £9 (£13), Set D £13 (£17), Snacks from £4. Minimum £2
CARD: Visa
SEATS: 24. Vegetarian meals. Children's helpings

LIFTON Devon map 1

▲ *Arundell Arms* [11/20]

Lifton PL16 0AA
LIFTON (0566) 84666
on A30, 3m E of Launceston £16–£27

For more than 26 years, Anne Voss-Bark has run this comfortable country inn for lovers of good fishing, good shooting and good food. The bridge weekends, special events and conferences keep it full through the year. Restaurant menus are geared to the best of the West Country: tournedos of Devon beef with red wine sauce and julienne of vegetables; Tamar salmon cooked with turbot on a bed of celeriac. Grills and roasts are the back-up. Sweets come with clotted cream, and ices and sorbets are made on the premises. House Muscadet is £6.75; CELLARMAN'S CHOICE: Margaux, Ch. des Gondats '81, £10.

Restaurants rating 12 or more serve the best food in the region.

CHEF: Philip Burgess PROPRIETOR: Anne Voss-Bark
OPEN: all week
CLOSED: 4 days at Christmas
MEALS: 12.30 to 2, 7.30 to 9
PRICES: £20 (£27), Set L £11 (£16), Set D £17.50 (£23), Snacks from £3
CARDS: Access, Amex, Diners, Visa
SEATS: 70. Private parties: 80 main room, 30 private room. Car-park, 80 places. Vegetarian meals. Children's helpings. No smoking in dining-room. Smart dress preferred. Wheelchair access (2 steps)
ACCOMMODATION: 29 rooms, all with bath/shower. B&B £40 to £67. Children welcome. Baby facilities. Pets welcome (no cats). Afternoon teas. Garden. Fishing. TV. Phone. Scenic. Doors close at 11.30 [GHG]

LINCOLN Lincolnshire map 6

Harvey's Cathedral Restaurant/Troffs [10/20]

1 Exchequergate, Castle Square, Lincoln LN2 1PZ
LINCOLN (0522) 510333

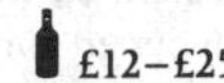
£12–£25

Troffs is part of Harvey's, which has been in the *Guide* for many years, most obviously because of its fine wines, especially Burgundies. This newer brasserie specialises in burgers and vegetarian foods, with prices in line with the quality of the cooking. The main restaurant has become more business-customer oriented. Some items from the original menu have transferred to Troffs, for instance DIY prawn cocktails, steaks and salads. The location hard by the archway to the cathedral brings many tourists. A selection of house wines is available by the glass or on a 'pay-as-you-drink' basis for any portion of a bottle, including an excellent Muscadet, Rossard '87, £8.50, or £1.70 per glass. Burgundies come from good single domaines, and clarets go back to '70. Sweet wines include an excellent Vouvray Moelleux '76, £16.95, a Ste-Croix-du-Mont '83, £10.50, and a good selection by the half-bottle, including Austrian Eiswein, £8.50, and Trockenbeerenauslese, £19.50, Tokay Five Putts, £7.50, and a trio of young Sauternes.

CHEFS: Bob Harvey, Andy Gibson and Linda Wilson PROPRIETORS: Adrianne and Bob Harvey
OPEN: Harvey's Mon to Sat D and Sun L, plus L Mon to Fri in Dec; Troffs all week
CLOSED: Harvey's 1 Jan; Troffs 25 and 26 Dec
MEALS: Harvey's 12 to 2, 7 to 9.30; Troffs 11am to 11pm
PRICES: Harvey's Set L £6.95 (£13) to £8.95 (£15), Set D £13.95 (£21) to £17.50 (£25); Troffs £9 (£12)
CARDS: Access, Visa
SEATS: Harvey's 50; Troffs 60. Private parties: 60 main room, 12 private room. Vegetarian meals. Children's helpings. Music

---

The 1990 Guide *will appear before Christmas 1989. Reports are particularly helpful in the spring. Report forms are at the back of this book, but just write a letter if you prefer. Address to The Good Food Guide,* FREEPOST, *2 Marylebone Road, London NW1 1YN. No stamp is necessary if you post it in the UK.*

Lincolnshire Round-up

LUNCH: *Barkston House*, Barkston, Nr Grantham (0400 50555).
ENGLISH: *Browns Pie Shop*, 33 Steep Hill, Lincoln (0522 27330).
BAR MEALS: *Wig and Mitre*, 29 Steep Hill, Lincoln (0522 35190); *Black Horse Inn*, Grimsthorpe, Nr Bourne (077 832 247).
FISH: *Mr Chips*, 17-21 Aswell Street, Louth (0507 603756); *Mantles*, The Market Place, Horncastle (065 82 6726).
Magpies, 73-75 East Street, Horncastle (065 82 7004).

LIPHOOK Hampshire map 3

▲ *Nippon Kan* [12/20]

Longmoor Road, Liphook GU30 7PE
LIPHOOK (0428) 724555 £16–£33

Deep in the heart of Hampshire, on a golf-course, is this recreation of Japan, supported almost exclusively by Japanese businessmen and their families. Staff are all Japanese, ingredients and pottery are flown in from Tokyo and the totality is by far the most authentic of the Japanese restaurants in the South of England. The menu has far greater range than London restaurants, arranged by cooking method – appetisers; soups; vinegared dishes; steamed dishes; sashimi and so on, each with three or four choices. Set meals run to eleven dishes and there is also a teppanyaki bar, none of which by current standards is overpriced. It is quite possible to eat for £15, for instance on a Nippon-Kan bento, a meal in a black box divided into five sections: grilled salmon; fried, beautifully tender beef; three slices of dark red tuna, two of squid, threads of daikon, perilla leaf and sliced cucumber; vegetables in a chicken stock; plus a rice section. This is served with a clear soup. Other individual dishes, such as the five appetisers, yakitori, sushi matsu, and ice-creams have all been of a level. 'Not haute cuisine, but food to be eaten every day.' To drink there is saké, Suntory beer and plum wine. House French is £6.75.

CHEF: G. Sutton PROPRIETORS: London Kosaido Development Co Ltd
OPEN: Tue to Sun
MEALS: 12 to 2, 7 to 9.30
PRICES: £14 (£20), Set L £10.50 (£16) to £14.50 (£20), Set D £10.50 (£16) to £26.50 (£33)
CARDS: Access, Amex, Diners, Visa
SEATS: 50. Private parties: 80 main room. Car-park, 200 places. Vegetarian meals. Children's helpings. No cigars/pipes in dining-room. Wheelchair access. Music
ACCOMMODATION: 32 rooms, all with bath/shower. B&B £54 to £70. Baby facilities. Afternoon teas. Garden. Swimming-pool. Sauna. Tennis. Golf. Snooker. TV. Phone. Scenic

'Last week I was told by a customer that the young restaurant staff were still letting the food down through careless chatting. The words used were a virtual quote from our entry last year in the Guide. *What was irritating was that I learnt after the dressing down that two of the young waiters were explaining to a work experience student how the espresso coffee machine worked.'* Cornish restaurateur

LISKEARD Cornwall map 1

▲ *Well House* [12/20]

St Keyne, Liskeard PL14 4RN
LISKEARD (0579) 42001 £18–£24

This could be F. Scott Fitzgerald country. The setting is secluded and romantic on the edge of a deep coombe running down towards Looe. The tennis court is perhaps the best situated in the country. Everything is pristine modern design in taste, and yet the place is small enough to have retained a personality behind the gloss. The asymmetrical dining-room is in beige and dusky pinks with soft gold Austrian blinds; the waiters are in grey coat-tails, waitresses in check uniforms. The menu is short, stylish in the fashion of modern country houses, half French and half English, with descriptions longer than Isadora Duncan's scarf: 'steamed leaf parcels of salmon and caviare and sweet pepper in cucumber and Vermouth sauce'. Gravlax is a speciality. Central courses are predictably decorative and brash in their flavour combinations: fillets of red mullet with chive and ginger; champagne sorbet with a hot sabayon sauce. Supply lines of foie gras and pecans now reach this far west. Incidentals charm: home-made chocolates, excellent home-baked walnut and rosemary bread to go with unpasteurised British cheeses, brioches for breakfast. Some dishes have an intensity and power that suggest this coud be a first-division kitchen in the making: witness an essence of parsley served as a soup, with diced foie gras instead of croûtons. Bedrooms are spotless, pastel and filled with fresh flowers. Last year's entry said Nicholas Wainford surprises skilfully – it was meant to say supervises skilfully, which he still does. The wine has a backbone of clarets on an ascending scale, from '83s at £7.95, to '66 at £155. There are champagnes to fit the mood, from Magenta Brut at £16.50. An interesting selection of 20 single malts. House wine is £5.95. CELLARMAN'S CHOICE: Ch. D'Angludet '83, £15.75.

CHEF: David Pope PROPRIETOR: Nicholas Wainford
OPEN: all week, exc Mon
MEALS: 12.30 to 2, 7 to 9
PRICES: Set L £13.50 (£18), Set D £18.50 (£24)
CARDS: Access, Amex, Visa
SEATS: 36. 5 tables outside. Private parties: 40 main room. Car-park, 32 places. Vegetarian meals. Children welcome. Smart dress preferred. Wheelchair access (1 step)
ACCOMMODATION: 7 rooms, all with bath/shower. B&B £38.50 to £52.50. Deposit: £25. Baby facilities. Pets welcome. Afternoon teas. Garden. Swimming-pool. Fishing. Golf. Croquet. TV. Phone. Scenic

LITTLE WALSINGHAM Norfolk map 6

▲ *Old Bakehouse* [10/20]

33 High Street, Little Walsingham NR22 6BZ
WALSINGHAM (032 872) 454 £12–£17

Chris and Helen Padley run this converted village bakery as a restaurant with bedrooms; the £8.25 set dinner is for residents only. The ground-floor dining-room is light and airy, with a pair of huge flour scales hanging from the brick fireplace. The kitchen takes few risks, but handles fresh, and often local, ingredients with care, staying safely with classic, standard recipes. Hot mushrooms and bacon in a brandy and cream sauce, or seafood pancake might precede Barbary duck breast in brandy and orange, fillet of pork with curry and almond sauce, or veal in pastry with red wine gravy. Bread is baked to order in Walsingham itself; vegetables are fresh and abundant; sweets include the unlikely Cointreau and marmalade ice-cream, and home-made puddings. Sixty wines: house French is £5.45. CELLARMAN'S CHOICE: Beaujolais, Domaine de Chatelus de la Roche '87, £8.85 and Bordeaux, Domaine de Justices '85, £8.50.

CHEFS/PROPRIETORS: Christopher and Helen Padley
OPEN: Tue to Sat D and Sun L
CLOSED: 3 weeks Jan; 2 weeks Sept to Oct; Sun to Thur Jan, Feb; Tue and Wed Mar
MEALS: 7 to 9.30, Sun L 12.30 to 2
PRICES: £12 (£17), Set Sun L £7.75 (£12), Set D £8.25 (£12)
CARDS: Access, Visa
SEATS: 36. Private parties: 40 main room. Vegetarian meals. Children's helpings (Sun L only). Smart dress preferred. Wheelchair access (1 step; also WC). Music
ACCOMMODATION: 3 rooms. B&B £13 to £25. Deposit: £5. Pets welcome. Scenic. Confirm by 7

LIVERPOOL Merseyside map 5

Armadillo [11/20]

20–22 Matthew Street, L2 6RE
051-236 4123 **£11–£19**

Martin Cooper has transformed his restaurant, previously an informal hub of city café society, with a fresh coat of paint, upholstered furniture and waitress service. The business sector now comes for lunch, appreciative local clientele in the evenings. The original vegetarian leanings (at the start there were vegan dishes) can still be found in main dishes, such as asparagus mousse in pastry with a green vegetable sauce, and in the wholemeal bread baked in-house daily. Fish dishes, for instance soup, salmon in cream with fresh chives, Goan style with ginger onion and garlic, draw a majority of the praise. Salads are also positive. Sweets have moved away from the cakes of the earlier tea-room into home-made ice-creams, mousses and the like. House wine is £6.40 a litre from a reasonably priced list.

CHEF: John Scotland PROPRIETOR: Martin Cooper
OPEN: all week, exc Sun and Mon D
CLOSED: bank hols
MEALS: 11.45 to 3, 7.30 to 10.30 (plus 5 to 7 Tue to Fri)
PRICES: £13 (£19), Set L £6.95 (£11)
CARD: Access
SEATS: 60. Private parties: 60 main room. Vegetarian meals. Children's helpings on request. Music

If you cannot honour a restaurant booking, always phone to cancel.

Elham [10/20]

95 Renshaw Street, L1 2SP
051-709 1589 £16–£18

A very useful Middle Eastern restaurant, open until the small hours. The long, static menu includes fasha feesha – lamb's liver charcoal grilled – as well as hummus and taramosalata; charcoal-grilled steaks and kebabs; whole sea-bass steamed and served with bulgur wheat and rice. Middle Eastern music and belly-dancing on Friday and Saturday nights. House Italian £6.50 per litre.

CHEF/PROPRIETOR: H.M. Safar
OPEN: all week, D only
MEALS: 7pm to 2.30am (3.30am Fri and Sat)
PRICES: £11 (£18), Set D £10.50 (£16). Service 10%
CARDS: Access, Amex, Diners, Visa
SEATS: 65. Private parties: 70 main room; 20 private room. Vegetarian meals. Children's helpings. Wheelchair access. Music

Far East [12/20]

27–35 Berry Street, L1 9DF
051-709 3141 £6–£15

The best Chinese restaurant in Liverpool is above the best Chinese supermarket in the city. It is one of the big league, competing with the best in Soho and Manchester Chinatown, and is helped by a solid local following. One-plate meals and dim-sum lunches are still excellent value: steamed char siu buns are outstanding and the choice now includes yam cakes and stuffed three delicacies – aubergine, green pepper and bean curd – a speciality confined to Sunday lunch-time when the dining-room is full to bursting with Chinese. The main menu shows its power with around two hundred Cantonese specialities, ranging from rolled fillet of beef stuffed with shreds of celery and carrot to Dover sole with mange tout, and king prawns with chilli and salt. Pai-pa duck is split in half and roasted fiercely skin side up to produce an exceptional dish with most of the fat drained away. The menu also scores with some of its sweets, such as home-made sago pudding with a crust of sugar and cinnamon. Banquets are held on Chinese holidays. House French £4.80, alternatively drink Tiger beer.

CHEF: Kai Wah Chan PROPRIETOR: Tsun Loi Cheung
OPEN: all week
MEALS: noon to 11.30 (11.45 Fri)
PRICES: £9 (£15), Set L from £2.50 (£6), Set D from £3.20 (£7). Snacks from £1.10. Service 10%
CARDS: Access, Amex, Diners, Visa
SEATS: 250. Private parties: 300 main room; 50 private room. Vegetarian meals. Children welcome. Wheelchair access (also WC). Music. Air-conditioned

This symbol is awarded only to restaurants with outstanding wine cellars.

La Grande Bouffe [11/20]

48A Castle Street, L2 7LQ
051-236 3375 £11–£18

There's been a change of ownership at this unprepossessing cellar bistro/restaurant in Liverpool's business quarter. But the chefs are the same and the kitchen continues to deliver some of the best food of its kind in the city. At lunchtime the long narrow room functions as a brasserie with a wide-ranging menu and excellent sandwiches from the take-away counter. Evening meals follow the same eclectic theme, with quails' eggs in a nest of leeks, fillet of beef in filo pastry with red pepper coulis, and duck breast with honey and peppercorns. Good-value wines.

CHEFS: Jean Kassim, Terence Lewis and Ben Kirk PROPRIETOR: Frank Nyland
OPEN: Mon to Sat, exc Mon D and Sat L
MEALS: 12 to 2.30, 6 to 10 (10.30 Sat)
PRICES: £13 (£18), Set L £6.95 (£11), Snacks from 95p. Service 10%. Licensed, also bring your own: corkage £1.50
CARDS: Access, Amex, Visa
SEATS: 90. Private parties: 20 main room. Vegetarian meals. Children's helpings. Music. Air-conditioned

Mayflower [10/20]

48 Duke Street, L1 5AS
051-709 6339 £8–£18

Some say this bright Cantonese restaurant ranks locally second only to the Far East. The standard menu of around 140 dishes centres on classics such as charsiu pork with pickled vegetables, steamed scallops with garlic and spring onion, but also takes in Peking and Szechuan specialities. Hot-pot dishes have been added to the repertoire. Ask for the special Chinese menu that has more esoteric items such as stuffed squid with peppercorn salt or shredded fillet steak with pickled mustard plant, and steamed minced pork cake with salted fish. Jumbo king prawns steamed with garlic and black bean sauce remains a bestseller. The wine list spans the globe with a seemingly enterprising choice, but there is an inscrutable lack of detail. Not so the Chinese beer Tsing Tao. House Hirondelle £7 a litre.

CHEF: H.P. Fu PROPRIETOR: K.H. Sim
OPEN: all week, exc Sat L and Sun L
MEALS: noon (6 Sat and Sun) to 4am
PRICES: £10 (£18), Set L from £3 (£8), Set D £8 (£13) to £12 (£17). Service 10%
CARDS: Access, Amex, Diners, Visa
SEATS: 80. Private parties: 100 main room. Vegetarian meals. Children welcome. Wheelchair access (also WC). Music. Air-conditioned

'Our trip lent credence to the theory that the country's best restaurants are kept solvent by a continuous flow of fellow restaurateurs looking for inspiration, and by an army of Guide *inspectors doing what many regard as an enviable job.'*
Yorkshire restaurateur

Orient [11/20]

54–54A Berry Street, L1 4JQ
051-709 2555 £6–£18

This long-established specialist in Peking, Shanghai and Canton cooking keeps up its tradition of serving good-value lunches, including very good thick Shanghai-style fried noodles, also dum dum noodles, the latter with a spicy peanut sauce and mustard greens. Now refurbished, and open every day, it has introduced an excellent, short dim-sum repertoire. Good service.

CHEFS: C. Wong and Y. Ho PROPRIETORS: Kenneth and Diana Liu
OPEN: all week
MEALS: noon to midnight
PRICES: £10 (£18), Set L £2.95 (£6), Set D from £8.50 (£12). Minimum £2. Service 10%
CARDS: Access, Amex, Visa
SEATS: 210. Private parties: 100 main room, 40, 70 and 100 private rooms. Vegetarian meals. Children's helpings. Wheelchair access. Music. Air-conditioned

Peking Duck [10/20]

471 Smithdown Road, Wavertree, L15 5AE
051-733 0723 £9–£13

All around there is change – a new wine bar has opened next door, the Indian take-away has changed hands, Amigos Cantina down the road has closed – but the Duck stays the same, prices a little higher, the family a little older. It represents the middle class of the Chinese restaurant fraternity, one step up from provincial chop suey houses, but without the pretension of the new second-generation restaurants like, say, Lau's at Rankin Hall in Sefton Park. Food and value come first. Crispy duck is excellent; stir-frying produces fragrant effects on the vegetables. The set meals are inexpensive and even the most basic at £5.20 is a cut above the usual. The rest of the menu has seen good variations on sweet chilli fish and barbecued breast of lamb.

CHEF/PROPRIETOR: Tsang Hong Keung
OPEN: all week, D only
MEALS: 6 to 12
PRICES: £7 (£13), Set D from £5.70 (£9). Service 10%
CARDS: Access, Visa
SEATS: 70. Private parties: 40 main room. Vegetarian meals. Children's helpings. Wheelchair access (1 step). Music

LIVERSEDGE West Yorkshire map 5

▲ *Lillibet's* [new entry, zero rated]

Ashfield, 64 Leeds Road, Liversedge WF15 6HX
HECKMONDWIKE (0924) 404911 £13–£17

The feel is of an old mill-owner's house, rather than a hotel. The Roberts have kept the operation small and at a family level, but also quite smart. The value for money for a four-course dinner is remarkable and has sparked a host of nominations. The menu demonstrates an obvious zeal for fresh produce and some dramatic flavour combinations: cheese and prawn fritters with a cranberry dip; cucumber and mint soup; strawberry water-ice served with melon. Meats are generous: duck is carved from a whole bird and served with a black-cherry sauce; lamb, cooked well beyond pink and cut as thick slices off the rack, is flavoured with rosemary and served with a béarnaise. A traditional vein runs through as well, leading to sticky toffee pudding. Fifty wines include some token New World bottles. House French £6.25; CELLARMAN'S CHOICE: Hawkes Bay Sauvignon '87, £8.25; Givry '83, £9.75. More reports, please.

CHEF: Elizabeth J. Roberts PROPRIETORS: J. Martin Roberts and Elizabeth J. Roberts
OPEN: Mon to Sat D, L by arrangement only (parties of 10 or more)
CLOSED: 1 week between Christmas and New Year, 2 weeks end Aug
MEALS: 7 to 9.30
PRICES: Set L from £8.25 (£13), Set D from £11.95 (£17)
CARDS: Access, Amex, Visa
SEATS: 42. Private parties: 50 main room. Car-park, 23 places. Vegetarian meals. Children's helpings
ACCOMMODATION: 7 rooms, all with bath/shower. B&B £33 to £50. Garden. TV. Phone. Doors close at 12

LONG MELFORD Suffolk — map 3

▲ *Black Lion Hotel* [12/20]

Long Melford CO10 9DN
SUDBURY (0787) 312356 — £13–£17

There is something distinctly French about this country hotel and restaurant with its stripped pine, large sideboard and pleasant, deceptively simple dining-room. Luke and Amelia Brady run the place tightly and have brought in new chef Steven Spooner from the Café Royal. Tomato mousse with a red pepper and tomato coulis and herb salad is attractive and sophisticated; pork fillet gets a well-reduced calvados sauce; good-quality roast beef is served rare. The menu also takes in roast duck leg with armagnac sauce and monkfish with ginger sauce and apples. Sweets and fresh fruit are displayed on the sideboard; French cheeses are kept in good condition. Mr Brady is from the wine trade and the list of around 50 bottles has some moderately priced French regional varieties, as well as a few from the New World. Six pudding wines are offered as half- and quarter-bottles, including Essensia, a California Orange Muscat (£7.50 for the half, £3.70 the quarter).

CHEF: Steven Spooner PROPRIETORS: Luke and Amelia Brady
OPEN: all week
MEALS: 12.15 to 2.30, 7 to 9.30
PRICES: £12 (£17), Set L from £9 (£13), Set D from £11 (£15)
CARDS: Access, Visa
SEATS: 60. Private parties: 50 main room; 35 private room. Car-park, 8 places. Vegetarian meals. Children's helpings. Smart dress preferred. Music
ACCOMMODATION: 10 rooms, all with bath/shower. B&B £26 to £40. Deposit: 10%. Children welcome. Baby facilities. Pets welcome. Garden. TV. Phone. Scenic [GHG]

LOUGHBOROUGH Leicestershire map 5

Angelo's [10/20]

65 Woodgate, Loughborough LE11 2TZ
LOUGHBOROUGH (0509) 266704 £13

Ann and Angelo Marcelli run their useful trattoria in a modern brick building with a bare tiled floor and plain pine tables. The menu is a standard mix of Italian and Continental favourites, from spaghetti vongole and steak pizzaiola to scampi provençal. Specials of the day are worth trying, and there is reasonable zabaglione to finish. Good value for money in an area short on decent eating places. The basic wine list is supplemented by a special selection of one-off wines, not on the printed list. House wine is £4.90.

CHEF: Pramrod Patel PROPRIETORS: Ann and Angelo Marcelli
OPEN: Mon to Sat
MEALS: 12 to 2, 7 to 10 (10.45 Fri and Sat)
PRICES: £9 (£13). Service 10%
SEATS: 50. Private parties: 30 main room. Car-park, 12 places. Vegetarian meals. Children's helpings. Wheelchair access (1 step; also WC). Music

Restaurant Roger Burdell [12/20]

11–12 Sparrow Hill, LE11 1BT
LOUGHBOROUGH (0509) 231813 £12–£25

Roger Burdell has turned the fifteenth-century manor house opposite the church into a restaurant with serious aspirations and gentrified pink and grey décor. There's now a *carte* as well as the elaborate five-course dinner menu, and some dishes are moving into a more traditional vein. Country nettle shoot soup, fillet of salmon with watercress butter sauce, and rack of lamb with mustard and apricots now balance out the lobster and trout sausage with chive sauce and julienne of vegetables, or rolled breast of chicken with wild mushroom mousseline. Well chosen English and French cheeses. The exquisite presentation extends to sweets such as a damson mousse with amaretto, served with a little almond turnover. A hundred wines are dominated by Bordeaux and Burgundies, but CELLARMAN'S CHOICE: Châteauneuf-du-Pape, Domaine du Clos du Roi '78, £22.

CHEF/PROPRIETOR: Roger Burdell
OPEN: Mon to Sat, exc Mon L
MEALS: 12.30 to 2, 7.30 to 9.15
PRICES: £18 (£24), Set L from £5.95 (£12), Set D from £19.50 (£25). Service inc
CARDS: Access, Amex, Visa
SEATS: 60. Private parties: 40 main room, 20 private room. Vegetarian meals. Children welcome. No cigars/pipes in dining room. Wheelchair access

The entries are compiled from the views of readers who have eaten at the restaurant in the last year, backed up by anonymous inspections and by information supplied and facts verified by the restaurants.

LOWER BEEDING West Sussex map 3

▲ *South Lodge* [12/20]

Brighton Road, Lower Beeding RH13 6PS
LOWER BEEDING (040 376) 711 £17–£39

The fine panelled dining-room of this 1883 house looks out across the South Downs and is set in its own fine gardens. James Hayward relies on seasonal and usually local produce, which makes menus less international than other country-house hotels. Specialities include a smoked salmon soufflé with quail eggs and Sussex lamb with truffled potato cake. Fish draws many favourable comments, as do traditional dishes such as liver and bacon, though roast beef has been too rare for some. The pace through the five-course set dinner is leisurely. Wines are from Corney and Barrow and Berry Bros, and start with house claret and Côtes du Rhône at £8.

CHEF: James Hayward PROPRIETORS: Prestige Hotels
OPEN: all week
MEALS: 12.30 to 3, 7.30 to 10.30
PRICES: £28 (£35), Set L £12.50 (£17) to £16.60 (£21), Set D £25 (£29) to £35 (£39), Snacks from £3.50. Service inc
CARDS: Access, Amex, Diners, Visa
SEATS: 34. Private parties: 8 main room, 10, 14, 45 and 50 private rooms. Car-park, 80 places. Vegetarian meals. Children's helpings. Jacket and tie. No cigars/pipes in dining-room. Wheelchair access
ACCOMMODATION: 40 rooms, all with bath/shower. Rooms for disabled. B&B £71 to £92. Children welcome. Dogs welcome. Afternoon teas. Garden. Tennis. Fishing. TV. Phone. Scenic [GHG]

LOWER BRAILES Warwickshire map 2

▲ *Feldon House* [10/20]

Lower Brailes OX15 5HW
BRAILES (060 885) 580 £16–£18

This isn't really a restaurant at all but a private Victorian house for hire. There are two dining-rooms – one tiny, the other an opened-up conservatory. Allan Witherick cooks a no-choice meal of three courses at lunch, four for dinner. It is very English, with good bespoke ingredients and no fancy tricks. Typically there might be game broth or quenelles of whiting before braised wild duck or poached halibut with excellent simple vegetables. Sweets are the likes of banana mousse or apple and almond pudding. Now licensed, with a short, well-chosen list taking in the New World. CELLARMAN'S CHOICE: Quincy, Domaine P. & J. Mardon '86, £8.95.

'Whilst we try to present dishes in an appetising way we stop short of elaboration for its own sake – ultimately it isn't appetising to be presented with picture-book food that looks so contrived one wonders how long the various tit-bits of garnish have been sitting in the fridge!' Gloucestershire restaurateur

CHEF: Allan Witherick PROPRIETORS: Allan and Maggie Witherick
OPEN: all week
MEALS: 12.30 to 2, 7.30 to 9
PRICES: Set L £12.50 (£16), Set D £15 (£18). Service inc
SEATS: 18. Private parties: 6 to 12 main room, 6 private room. Car-park, 9 places. Vegetarian meals. Children's helpings (L only)
ACCOMMODATION: 3 rooms. B&B £15 to £30. Baby facilities. Pets by arrangement. Garden. Scenic. Doors close at 11. Confirm by 4 [GHG]

LOWICK Northumberland map 7

Western House [new entry, zero rated]

Lowick, TD15 2UD
BERWICK-UPON-TWEED (0289) 88259
3m off A1, opposite Holy Island £19

Formerly of Trusthouse Forte, Andrew and Susan Shilton have spent a good deal redecorating and refurnishing this Georgian house at the edge of the village, with its walled and well-kept garden. The menu is four courses, English in style with a no-choice soufflé – flavoured perhaps with fish from Eyemouth – as a second stage. Herbs and vegetables are out of the garden; meat is from local butchers at Longframlington and Coldstream. Good points have been warm bread; onion soup; home-made ravioli; the house pie of beef and pork cooked in Newcastle ale; nut meringues with strawberries. Meals are taken at a leisurely pace and the relatively high price for the area is offset by cut glass and Wedgwood china. Eighteen wines, with house French £6. More reports, please.

CHEF: Andrew Shilton PROPRIETORS: Andrew and Susan Shilton
OPEN: Wed to Sat, D only
MEALS: 7 to 9
PRICES: Set D £16 (£19). Service inc
CARDS: Amex, Visa
SEATS: 17. 4 tables outside. Private parties: 18 main room. Car-park, 8 places. Vegetarian meals by arrangement. Children welcome. No smoking. Wheelchair access (3 steps; also WC). One sitting.

LUTTERWORTH Leicestershire map 5

▲ *Denbigh Arms* [new entry, zero rated]

High Street, Lutterworth, LE17 4AD
LUTTERWORTH (045 55) 3537 £8–£21

The Stephens family – who run the Swan at Leighton Buzzard – have revamped this eighteenth-century High Street coaching-inn into a thriving hotel with a modest beamed dining-room. The kitchen works best with traditional dishes such as hot game pie, roast beef with 'thyme-scented' Yorkshire puddings, spotted dick and rice pudding, but also tries out more modern inventions, from home-made ravioli stuffed with smoked-trout mousse, and chicken with cashews in puff pastry, to Ceylon-tea parfait.

Vegetarians are always offered something enterprising, like bean curd and nut curry with wild rice. Daily-changing fixed-price menus are good value, and ingredients are seasonal. Basic list of around 60 wines starts at £5.95.

CHEF: Derek Anderson PROPRIETORS: Mr and Mrs E.J. Stephens
OPEN: all week
MEALS: 12 to 2, 7 to 9.30 (10 Fri and Sat)
PRICES: £17 (£21), Set L from £4.95 (£8), Set D £14.50 (£17). Snacks from 90p. Service inc
CARDS: Access, Amex, Diners, Visa
SEATS: 70. Private parties: 30 main room, 50 private room. Car-park, 45 places. Vegetarian meals. Children's helpings. Smart dress preferred. No pipes in dining-room. Wheelchair access (1 step; also WC). Music
ACCOMMODATION: 34 rooms, all with bath/shower. Rooms for disabled. B&B £53.50 to £65. Children welcome. Baby facilities. Afternoon teas. TV. Phone. Confirm by 6

LYMINGTON Hampshire map 2

▲ *Provence* [15/20]

The Gordleton Mill, Silver Street, Hordle,
Lymington SO41 6DJ
LYMINGTON (0590) 682 219 £13–£28

First there is the out of the way setting: a lovely converted mill with the River Avon running round one side of the garden. Then there is the cooking. Jean-Pierre Novi is a chef to be reckoned with – French-born, French-trained and with enough potential skill to stay in the first division of British restaurants. His presence is crucial. Standards drop noticeably when he is away. The cooking, with a strong Provençal undercurrent, is impressive when at its best: pigeon with olives and fennel, salt-cod in pastry, roast lamb with garlic, salmon and sole with a parsley butter. The modern style dominates, as in medallion of rabbit with candied lemon, sea-bass with port, celeriac and scallops, or a tresse of salmon and brill with watercress sauce. An old-style dish like carré d'agneau is given new vigour with artichokes and ginger. Feuilletés appear in various guises: with orange and mussels as a starter; with mango mousse for dessert. Meals finish strongly with honey and cocoa ice-cream on sabayon sauce, banana soufflé or a crêpe filled with orange soufflé. There are fine sorbets, too. The dining-room is run by an old guard of professional waiters whose attentiveness makes up for any lack of pace. The French wine list appropriately includes a selection from Provence, starting at £7. CELLARMAN'S CHOICE: two Coteaux d'Aix-en-Provence les Baux wines: Domaine de Trévallon '84, £9.80; and Mas du Gourgonnier '84, £7.50.

Restaurants that we have not been able to assess as fully as we would like are given a zero rating this year. We are particularly keen to have reports on these places.

The price quoted in brackets is for an average three-course meal including service, VAT, coffee and half a bottle of house wine or the equivalent in an ethnic restaurant.

CHEF: Jean-Pierre Novi PROPRIETOR: William F. Stone
OPEN: Tue to Sun, exc Sun D
MEALS: 12.30 to 2, 7.30 to 10
PRICES: Set L £10.50 (£13), Set D £17.50 (£20) and £26 (£28). Service inc
CARDS: Access, Diners, Visa
SEATS: 30. Private parties: 30 main room; 12 and 14 private rooms. No children under 8. Wheelchair access. Music
ACCOMMODATION: 5 rooms, all with bath/shower. B&B £30 to £48.50. No children under 8. Garden. TV. Phone. Scenic. Doors close at 1. Confirm by 6 [GHG]

LYMPSTONE Devon map 1

▲ *River House* [11/20]

The Strand, Lympstone EX8 5EY
EXMOUTH (0395) 265147 £17–£24

Lympstone is a village freeze-framed in time. The River House is in the centre of the village, virtually in the water, with spectacular views across the Exe estuary from the upstairs dining-room. The room is comfortably set with spacious tables. The repertory for lunch and evening focuses on fish from the local boats – sometimes as many as seven different varieties served together in a sauce of wine, mushrooms and cream – with eclectic international additions such as tortilla or moussaka and winter game dishes. There have been recommendations for guinea-fowl casseroled in red wine and salmon hollandaise; the arrays of vegetables accompanying main courses, including gratin of leek and potato cooked in milk flavoured with nutmeg or turnips glazed with brown sugar and butter; and among the desserts almond sponge with black cherries and raspberry ice-cream. The sweets trolley has been replaced ('because of deteriorations') in favour of individual Pavlovas, tarts, bombes and soufflés. Service is hospitable and the greeting positive. House French £5.50; CELLARMAN'S CHOICE: Brown Bros Australian Chardonnay '86, £11.15.

CHEF: Shirley Wilkes PROPRIETORS: Mr and Mrs J.F.M. Wilkes
OPEN: Tues to Sun, exc Sun D
MEALS: 12 to 1.45, 7 to 9.30 (10.30 Sat)
PRICES: Set L and D from £18.75 (£24), cheaper L £11 (£17), fish and vegetarian menu from £13.50. Minimum £6.75
CARDS: Access, Amex, Visa
SEATS: 35. Private parties: 25 main room; 14 private room. Vegetarian meals. Children's helpings. No children under 5. Smart dress preferred. No cigars/pipes in dining-room
ACCOMMODATION: 2 rooms, both with bath/shower. B&B £49 to £58. TV. Scenic

LYTHAM ST ANNE'S Lancashire map 5

▲ *C'est la Vie, Dalmeny Hotel* [10/20]

19–33 South Promenade, Lytham St Anne's FY8 1LX
ST ANNE'S (0253) 712236 £23

The dining-rooms move around the Dalmeny like a game of pass the parcel. There is now an inexpensive carvery, a barbecue and, in the basement, C'est la Vie, which now has a set menu and seems to become ever more French. Good dishes have maintained the reputation locally since Paul Caddy left: duck with the legs crisped, served with a cassis sauce; stuffed quail in filo pastry; fruit terrine. The waiters are rather smarter in their dress than their knowledge but they are prompt with dishes and Keith Davies comes out to talk. House Côtes du Tricastin £5. CELLARMAN'S CHOICE: Vina Real, Gran Reserva '75, £8.60.

CHEFS: Keith Davies and Richard Webb PROPRIETORS: The Webb family
OPEN: Tue to Sat, D only
MEALS: 7 to 9.30
PRICES: Set D £18.50 (£23)
SEATS: 48. Private parties: 48 main room. Car-park, 100 places. Smart dress preferred. Wheelchair access (also WC). Air-conditioned
ACCOMMODATION: 94 rooms, 91 with bath/shower. Rooms for disabled. Lift. B&B £26.75 to £48.75. Deposit: £10. Baby facilities. Afternoon teas. Swimming-pool. Sauna. Fishing. Golf. Snooker. Air-conditioning. TV. Phone. Scenic. Confirm by 6 [GHG]

KFOG [9/20]

54 Wood Street, Lytham St Anne's FY8 1QG
ST ANNE'S (0253) 725161 £20

Su Bloomberg's relaxed but upmarket restaurant is named after the great FM radio station in northern California. The décor is in primary blue and yellow, and the cooking has vivid American overtones, with some eclectic, individual touches. Ribs, burgers and steaks share the stage with spinach salad, jumbo prawns in a teriyaki marinade and roast saddle of English lamb stuffed with leeks and rosemary; there are also vegetarian and low-calorie dishes. Sunday brunch is something of local institution, with smoked salmon and toasted bagels, free-range omelettes, Buck's fizz and the papers to read. Cheaper lunch menu. American beers and French house wines that start at £5.95.

CHEF: Mark Singleton PROPRIETOR: Su Bloomberg
OPEN: Tue to Sun, exc Sun D
MEALS: 12 to 2.30, 7 to 10.30
PRICES: £13 (£20)
CARDS: Access, Visa
SEATS: 42. 4 tables outside. Private parties: 30 main room. Car-park, 50 places. Vegetarian meals. Children's helpings. No cigars in dining-room. Wheelchair access (1 step; also WC). Music

Wade & Fryer's [new entry, zero rated]

74A Clifton Street, Lytham FY8 5EW
LYTHAM (0253) 794258 £21

Over the well-respected fish and game dealer, Lannigan's, which supplies much of the produce, is this small apricot dining-room. It is a two-person operation – Patricia Wade in the kitchen, Steven Fryer front of house; it might have been the other way round, going by the names. The menu changes monthly and offers around half a dozen dishes per course. There is no shortage of imagination or flair: a ginger mayonnaise for avocado balls with a crab purée; potted ham and chicken with rosemary and pickled vegetables; roast duck with caramelised fruits, a calvados sauce and fried apples. Puddings are said to be good, too. First reports and inspection have been unusually positive. House French £5.65. More reports, please.

CHEF: Patricia Wade PROPRIETORS: Patricia Wade and Steven Fryer
OPEN: Tue to Sat, D only
MEALS: 7 to 10.30
PRICES: £15 (£21)
CARDS: Access, Visa
SEATS: 28. Private parties: 30 main room, 30 private room. Children welcome. Music

Lancashire Round-up

GERMAN: *Stocks*, 2 Queens Square, Poulton-le-Fylde (0253 882294).
FISH: *Roberts' Oyster Bar*, 92 Promenade, Blackpool (0253 21226).
BAR MEALS: *Hark to Bounty*, Slaidburn, Nr Clitheroe (020 06 246).
CHINESE: *Jasmine Cottage*, 52 Coronation Street, Blackpool (0253 25303).
ROOMS: *Harrop Fold Hotel*, Harrop Fold, Bolton-by-Bowland, Clitheroe (020 07 600).
FRENCH: *Foxfields*, Whalley Road, Billington, Whalley (025 482 2556).
BISTRO: *Anna's Bistro*, 15 Breck Road, Poulton-le-Fylde 0253 882336).

MALDON Essex map 3

Wheelers [9/20]

13 High Street, Maldon CM9 8TB
MALDON (0621) 53647 £9

One of the best fish and chip restaurants in the area. The atmosphere is more of a tea-shop. Chips are good quality and fish is well fried and crisp. Tartare sauce is home made. Sweets include good-looking charlottes, gateaux, pies and tarts. Muscadet de Sèvre-et-Maine at £5.45.

CHEF: R.H. Wheeler PROPRIETORS: W.H.G. Wheeler, R.H. Wheeler and V.A. Wheeler
OPEN: Tue to Sat
CLOSED: 2 weeks Sept
MEALS: 11.30 to 1.45, 6 to 9.30
PRICES: £5 (£9)
SEATS: 52. Private parties: 52 main room. Children's helpings. Wheelchair access (1 step; also WC)

Files are kept on every restaurant, so reports of poor meals are just as valuable as reports of good meals because they save unnecessary inspections.

'I have crossed vegetarian meals off the menu as they seem to have brought a lot of cranks who want a choice of vegetarian dishes for dinner and then eat bacon and sausage for breakfast.' Scottish restaurateur

MALVERN WELLS Hereford & Worcester map 2

Croque-en-Bouche [16/20]

221 Wells Road, Malvern Wells WR14 4HF
MALVERN (0684) 565612 £27

How is it this little, two-person-run restaurant can earn a rating so high? For the best part of the decade Marion Jones's cooking has been cited by reporters old and new as a yardstick in talking about other restaurants. The Croque-en-Bouche has entered the subconsciousness of restaurant culture, and as such earned its promotion from 15. But if all else in the restaurant firmament is a chaos of stars and crowns and toques, golden spoons and diamond-shaped jellies, the Croque is a good star by which to steer. Robin Jones, ever a stickler for detail, complains of the *Guide* last year calling the menu French. 'Whilst the style has a French influence, the menu is basically English, note also that cheeses are predominantly British now.' He has also sent photographs of the restaurant's splendid kitchen garden edged with railway sleepers. Dinners open with a tureen of soup, left on the table, followed by a choice of three fish, four meats, then a magnificent salad that, rapier-like, cuts through the pace of the meal and readjusts the palate for the sweet. In May, for instance, it was made up of oak-leaf, misticanza, mizuna, endive and red lollo, dressed in walnut oil and coriander leaves. There is a movement and complexity to the cooking, for instance steaks of veal and calf's liver sauté served with a béarnaise and the pan juices, which echo the reassertion of fundamentals being lauded in London. Individual recommendations for: roast pheasant with tarragon, hare in red wine, wild rabbit braised in lemon and coriander, rock lobster marinated in port. Soups, of course, draw much praise, as in vegetable or pea and ham or cauliflower. From the sweets: summer pudding, lime-flavoured creme brûlée with an almond tuile. Some readers have found Robin Jones's absolute insistence on punctuality and rigid approach hard to take but, as a convert explains with more than a little justification, 'at least you do not run the gauntlet of apprentice staff.' And he is as remarkable a waiter as Marion is a cook.

As to the wine cellar, it is one of the greats of the West of England, a foil to the directness and accuracy of the cooking. Though it offers over 400 wines from 18 countries and vintages back to the turn of the century, it is not daunting. This is wine selection made easy: good, brief, trustworthy descriptions annotate every wine; the Jones mean it when they say 'all wines may be assumed to come from good vintages.' Prices encourage experimentation. The low cost of some of the fine, rare mature wines is hard to believe (often way below current auction prices), but there's equally excellent value at the cheaper end. The list of house wines groups 20 well-chosen reds and whites for between £5.20 and £9.60. French wines are the most exciting, the Loire and Rhône vying for interest with Bordeaux and Burgundy; Loires include a list of Vouvrays from various top producers in vintages back to '55, Savennières back to '69, a rare Montlouis Pétillant Sec and red Loires from some of the best growers, back to Chinon Clos d'Olive '64, from Couly-Duteil, at £31. Burgundies and Rhônes are from a good mix of growers and merchants. Clarets start with some affordable petits châteaux and *bourgeois* wines and climb through the growths and back through the vintages at bargain prices as far as 1906 (give notice if you intend to order old wines). There are also interesting bottles, though a more restricted choice, from Italy, Spain, the New World and elsewhere. The choice of sweet wines is spectacular: Sauternes back to '21, fine sweet Loires, a range of Sélection de Grains Nobles wines from Alsace, sweet Californias and a choice of Hungarian Tokay, from Tokay 5 Putts '75, for £7, to the same thing in the '37 vintage at £40. Muscat de St-Jean du Minervois (a delicate Beaumes de Venise taste-alike) comes by the glass at £1.80. As stunning as the wine list is the selection of eaux-de-vie, which include some outstanding cognacs, marcs from unusual areas – Chablis, the Loire and Provence – and grappa from Asti and Valpolicella. CELLARMAN'S CHOICE: Rouge Homme Chardonnay '86, £10.60; Aglianico del Vulture '82, £12.60.

CHEF: Marion Jones PROPRIETORS: Robin and Marion Jones
OPEN: Wed to Sat, D only
CLOSED: Christmas
MEALS: 7.30 to 9.15
PRICES: Set D £22 (£27). Service inc
SEATS: 24. Private parties: 8 private room. Children welcome. No smoking. Wheelchair access

MANACCAN Cornwall map 1

New Inn [9/20]

Manaccan TR12 6HA
MANACCAN (032 623) 323 £6–£13

The pub is a tiny thatched cottage with a steep sloping garden at the back, where children can play. Inside, it is bare brown, with rough stone walls, and planks on the ceiling. The atmosphere is pipe-laden. The menu is no-nonsense home-cooking: decent pâté, proper ham cooked in cider, beef casserole, vegetable curry. There's excellent fresh fish, too. Main courses are accompanied by piles of healthy, well-timed, crisp vegetables. Sweets, such as the famous treacle tart or blackberry and apple crumble, come with a blob of excellent Cornish clotted cream. Devenish beers and eight drinkable wines, starting at £4.50.

CHEF/PROPRIETOR: P.J.F. Cullinan
OPEN: all week, exc Tue D
MEALS: 11.30 to 2, 6.30 to 9.30 (12 to 1.30, 7 to 10 Sun)
PRICES: £9 (£12), Set L £3 (£6) to £8 (£11), Set D £5 (£8) to £10 (£13), Snacks from £1.50. Service inc
SEATS: 30. 12 tables outside. Private parties: 10 main room. Car-park, 10 places. Vegetarian meals. Children's helpings. Wheelchair access

'The entire lounge bar fell silent when I entered. This is not because I bear a striking resemblance to Joan Collins, but because new faces are a rarity at the White Bear.'
On inspecting in the Midlands

MANCHESTER **Greater Manchester** map 5

Blinkers French [11/20]

16 Princess Street, M1 4NB
061-228 2503 £15–£27

This basement dining-room in a Victorian terrace continues as one of the better European restaurants in the area. The plastic flowers have disappeared, otherwise the décor is prints on the rough-plastered walls, with paintings as well as polystyrene tiles on the ceiling. Ian Cheetham's cooking is a busy, ambitious version of modern French, with a good choice of fresh fish and prime cuts of meat. The set dinner menu has been replaced by weekly specials, such as fillets of parrot fish with rosemary butter sauce, or supreme of duckling with coulis of olives and home-made noodles. Mousses are a favourite device: tomatoes stuffed with salmon mousse and mussels; loin of lamb stuffed with chicken mousse, spinach and pine nuts. Sauces are well reduced, vegetables are spot-on, and chocolate sponge with coffee sauce is a fine sweet. Young, clued-up service. The list of 80 mainly French wines has some good vintages at fine prices. CELLARMAN'S CHOICE: Crystal de Pinot Gris '85, at £9.75.

CHEF: Ian Cheetham PROPRIETORS: Lewes and Christine Gerezdi
OPEN: Mon to Sat, exc Sat L
MEALS: 12 to 2.30, 7.15 to 10.30
PRICES: £18 (£27), Set L £8.95 (£15). Service 10%
CARDS: Access, Amex, Diners, Visa
SEATS: 45. Private parties: 70 main room. Vegetarian meals. Children's helpings. Smart dress preferred. Music

Café Istanbul [9/20]

79 Bridge Street, M3 2RH
061-833 9942 £7–£14

Well known as a meeting place for expatriate Turks in the city. It offers good value and gets crowded at lunch-time, when the attraction is the cheap set meal advertised on a blackboard outside. Highlights are the starters and meze; main courses centre on char-grilled meats, kebabs, steaks and salads. Sticky sweets and genuine Turkish coffee to finish. Drink Turkish wine at £6.65 a bottle, or Efes Turkish larger.

CHEF: Hasan Bicer PROPRIETOR: Sacit Onur
OPEN: Mon to Sat
CLOSED: 25 and 26 Dec
MEALS: 12 to 3, 6 to 11.30
PRICES: £9 (£14), Set L £4 (£7)
CARDS: Access, Visa
SEATS: 40. Private parties: 45 main room. Vegetarian meals. Children's helpings. Smart dress preferred. Wheelchair access (also WC). Music

It is always advisable to book a restaurant in advance.

Gaylord [11/20]

Amethyst House, Spring Gardens, M2 1EA
061-832 6037 and 4866 £9–£17

Not far from fashionable King Street is this old-style Indian restaurant with a polite waiter at the door and a setting of beaded curtains and brassware. One view is that it is one of the best of its kind in the city. Tandooris are the backbone of a familiar menu with fish, quail and paneer as well as chicken and lamb. Otherwise there is an extensive choice of vegetable and vegetarian dishes, from spinach with lotus roots to potatoes cooked with cumin seeds. Ornately sculpted fresh mango makes a good finish. Service is smooth and the cutlery sparkles.

CHEF: W. Ram PROPRIETORS: Tandoori Catering Consultants Ltd
OPEN: all week
MEALS: 12 to 3, 6 to 11.30 (11 Sun)
PRICES: £9 (£17), Set L £4.95 (£9), Set D £7.50 (£12) to £9.95 (£15). Cover 25p. Service 12.5%
CARDS: Access, Amex, Diners, Visa
SEATS: 90. Private parties: 90 main room. Vegetarian meals. Children welcome. No-smoking area. Music

The Greenhouse [9/20]

331 Great Western Street, Rusholme, M14 4AN
061-224 0730 £11

A family-run vegetarian restaurant, well thought-of, in a less well-off part of town. Outside the converted corner house are overgrown conifers and window boxes; inside are pot-plants, a tank of goldfish and a splendid conservatory mural. Although the menu contains many standards – samosa, spring rolls, lasagne al forno, cashew and vegetable roast with satay sauce – there is an imaginative use of seasonal ingredients and speciality dishes with a notably unascetic quality – such as oyster mushrooms in a red wine marinade or strudel with mushroom, spinach or cheese fillings. Desserts include seasonal fruit sorbets and an excellent apple strudel with hazelnut ice-cream. Many dishes are vegan. House French £2.75 a half-litre, or drink Rock's elderflower or gooseberry champagne, or house cocktails.

CHEF: Mark Baxter PROPRIETORS: Mark and Rose Baxter
OPEN: all week, exc Sat L
CLOSED: Christmas, 31 Dec and 1 Jan
MEALS: 10am (6pm Sat, 1pm Sun) to 10.20pm
PRICES: £7 (£11), Snacks from 65p
SEATS: 38. Private parties: 38 main room. Vegetarian meals. Children's helpings. No-smoking area. Wheelchair access (also WC). Music. Air-conditioned

The Guide *recruits new inspectors from readers who write in regularly. If you would like to apply, write to the Editor with (a) a detailed report on a restaurant where you have eaten and (b) a comparative study of restaurants known to you.*

Happy Garden [10/20]

743 Wilmslow Road, Didsbury, M20 0DW
061-445 6979 and 8945 £6–£19

A typographical error last year recommended Barclays Bank. Apologies. Ten numbers further up is this Cantonese tea-room in a narrow building. It is a good compromise between the authentic cafés of Chinatown and the westernised suburban venues. Lettuce wraps, lemon and honey chicken, king prawns, duck, beef in black-bean sauce, the combination dim-sum starter of spring roll, spare rib, seaweed, dumpling, prawn toast, crispy wun-tun, all these draw recommendations. Lobster with garlic and butter sauce is a speciality. Mixed vegetables, in a sweet-and- sour sauce, are served inside a pineapple half. House French £5.10.

CHEF: Shun Loy Tang PROPRIETORS: Shun Loy Tang and Yuet Mui Tang
OPEN: all week, exc Sat L and Sun L
MEALS: 12 to 2, 6 to 11.45 (12 Fri and Sat)
PRICES: £11 (£19), Set L £2.50 (£6), Set D from £9.75 (£14), Set Sun D £5.50 (£9). Service 10%
CARDS: Access, Amex, Diners, Visa
SEATS: 50. Private parties: 70 main room. Vegetarian meals. Children welcome. Wheelchair access. Music. Air-conditioned

Hong Kong [10/20]

47 Faulkner Street, M1 4EE
061-236 0565 £14–£16

The one-plate meals and dim-sum are well regarded here. The menu is shorter than the norm but there seem to be many dishes not listed, at least in English, that are available for the asking, for instance grilled eel. The cheap set lunch, which has been £2.80, is a bargain, but all round it can be less expensive than its Chinatown competitors.

CHEF: Chan Ling Kung PROPRIETOR: Dai Lee
OPEN: all week
CLOSED: 25 and 26 Dec
MEALS: noon to midnight
PRICES: £10 (£14), Set L and D from £21 (£31) for 2. Service 10%
CARDS: Access, Amex, Diners, Visa
SEATS: 350. Private parties: 200 main room. Children welcome. Music. Air-conditioned

Hopewell City [11/20]

45–47 Faulkner Street, M1 4EE
061-236 0091 and 0581 £9–£18

The cheerful basement has been given a facelift, but otherwise this quite smart Chinese restaurant continues to deliver fine examples of the Cantonese classics. There are good dim-sum, as well as fine roast meats – including some specialities not found elsewhere in Manchester Chinatown. The full three-hundred-strong menu has some unusual items, such as crispy aromatic duck coated with yam and deep-fried, kin-do ribs with fresh orange, and fried squid with prawn stuffing. Also recommended are seafood and bean-curd soup, Singapore noodles and beef with peppers and black-bean sauce. House Italian £6.50; alternatively drink tea.

CHEF: Kam Hung Yung PROPRIETORS: Tony S.K. Ng and Henry C.Y. Yu
OPEN: all week
MEALS: noon to 11.45
PRICES: £10 (£18), Set L from £2.80 (£8) to £4.50 (£9), Set D from £10 (£15). Service 10%
CARDS: Access, Amex, Diners, Visa
SEATS: 100. 20 tables outside. Private parties: 140 main room. Vegetarian meals. Children welcome. Music. Air-conditioned

Kathmandu Tandoori [10/20]

42–44 Sackville Street, M1 3WE
061-236 4684 £8–£16

One of the most useful Indian restaurants in the heart of Manchester, offering good versions of North Indian curries such as lamb dopiaza and chicken jalfrezi. Tandooris and tikkas are specialities, with everything from kidney to cod; tandoori fish is mackerel. Despite the name, there are few authentic Nepalese dishes on the menu: aloo tama (potatoes with bamboo shoots and spices) is an exception. Set meals – including one for vegetarians – are good value. Drink Grolsch or Kingfisher lager, or house French at £6.90 per litre.

CHEFS: Ram Das and Jay Ram PROPRIETOR: Gopal Mohan Dangol
OPEN: all week
CLOSED: bank hols
MEALS: 12 to 2.30, 6 to 12
PRICES: £9 (£15), Set L £3.75 (£8) to £4.75 (£10), Set D £4.75 (£10) to £10.25 (£16). Snacks from 95p. Service 10%. Licensed, also bring your own: no corkage
CARDS: Access, Amex, Diners, Visa
SEATS: 250. Private parties: 120 main room, 120 private room. Vegetarian meals. Children welcome. Smart dress preferred. Wheelchair access. Music. Air-conditioned

Koreana [10/20]

Kings House, 40 King Street West, M3 2WY
061-832 4330 £8–£17

Britain's northernmost Korean restaurant scores with its city-centre location just off Deansgate, impeccable service and excellent food. Dishes are authentic and cooked to order. Bulgogi - marinated beef cooked at the table on a metal shield – is the centrepiece of a five-course menu, flanked by spicy dumpling soup, bean-flour pancakes with vegetables and a classic starter of four cold vegetables – pickled radish, bean sprouts, cucumber and spinach with sesame seeds, dressed with soy and sesame oil. Main courses of dweji gogi bokum, port slices sauté with garlic and bamboo shoots, and hong-cho, deep-fried fish in a piquant sauce, are well reported, and hot-pot dishes include an ancient Korean court recipe, shinsul-lo, an assortment of meat and vegetables kept hot at table over charcoal (24 hours' notice). Sweet rice-cake is a memorable and unusual sweet. Two-course weekday lunches are good value at £3.50. House wine is £5.50 on a basic list; Korean saké is £2.50 for a quarter-bottle-size jug.

CHEF: Mrs Hyun K. Kim PROPRIETORS: Koreana Restaurant Ltd
OPEN: Mon to Sat, exc Sat L
MEALS: 12 to 2.30, 6.30 to 11.30
PRICES: £10 (£17), Set L from £3.50 (£8), Set D from £7.50 (£12). Service 10%
CARDS: Access, Amex, Diners, Visa
SEATS: 56. Private parties: 60 main room. Vegetarian meals. Children welcome. Smart dress preferred. No smoking. Music

Kosmos Taverna [11/20]

248 Wilmslow Road, M14 6LD
061-225 9106 £11–£14

The crowds and the waiters together create a lively atmosphere at one of the premier Greek restaurants of the North, set among a run of fish and chip shops and takeaways. The murals, candles, and checked cloths are textbook taverna. There is a splendid three-stage meze for £8 a head. Other interesting, well-executed dishes include beef stifado, grilled goats' cheese, Greek sausage, haricot bean and chickpea dishes, the excellent lamb kebabs marinated in yoghurt, and semolina cake. Some game and vegetarian dishes have been brought into the repertoire; the waiters usually advise on the freshness of the fish. Now open all day Sunday. House Valgardello £5.50. CELLARMAN'S CHOICE: Retsina Kourtaki, £5.65.

CHEF: Loulla Astin PROPRIETORS: Stewart and Loulla Astin
OPEN: all week D, and Sun L
CLOSED: 25 and 26 Dec
MEALS: 6.30 to 11.30 (12.30 Fri and Sat, 1 to 11.30 Sun)
PRICES: £10 (£14), Set Sun L £6.50 (£11)
CARDS: Access, Visa
SEATS: 70. Private parties: 40 main room. Vegetarian meals. Children's helpings. Wheelchair access. Music. Air-conditioned

Lime Tree [11/20]

8 Lapwing Lane, West Didsbury, M20 8WS
061-445 1217
2m from M56 exit 10 £12–£17

The cooking has grown in confidence since this popular, inexpensive dining-room opened with its wooden floors and wooden-topped sewing-machine tables. It is a Mancunian version of Mon Plaisir or Le Chef in London. Among the eight starters and eight main courses there are some standards – black pudding with apple, sage and onion sauce; pasta with bacon and salami. The rest changes frequently – mussels in curry sauce; monkfish brochette with a timbale of rice and tomato sauce flavoured with cumin and chilli; calf's liver dijonnaise; roast duck in raspberry and framboise liqueur sauce. Saucing is a bit rough, but not the value, especially at lunch. Of the six sweets, half may be chocolate, for instance a chocolate sponge with butterscotch sauce. Large pots of cafetière coffee are left on the table. Wines start at £5.75. A cheaper branch takes the overflow – Lime Tree Café, 9–11 Wilmslow Road.

CHEFS: Patrick Hannity and Simon Haywood PROPRIETORS: Patrick Hannity and Robert Williams
OPEN: Tue to Sat D, and Sun L
MEALS: 12 to 2, 6.30 to 10.30
PRICES: £12 (£17), Set L £7.50 (£12)
CARDS: Access, Visa
SEATS: 50. 4 tables outside. Private parties: 50 main room. Vegetarian meals. Children's helpings (Sun L only). Wheelchair access. Music

Little Yang Sing [new entry, zero rated]

17 George Street, M1 4HE
061-228 7722 £15–£24

The original premises have been reopened, the layout is similar and the atmosphere relaxed, as it was before the parent restaurant became fashionable. The menu runs to around 180 items, including about a dozen first-rate dim-sum and 20 plate meals of chow mein or roast meats on rice, but the emphasis is on the style of the parent. There are set banquets but the clichés of the sub genre, such as seaweed special, prawns in the shell in special seafood sauce, or tepanyaki-style fillet steak tend to dominate. Consistency and quality are comparable to the Yang Sing, there is a feeling, sometimes experienced at Princess Street too, that flair and development are solidifying into rab a sort of house style. This is conspicuously more westernised than, say, Pearl City or Mr Kuks. The brisket in casserole uses meat that is less fatty and gristly than a Chinese customer might expect. That said, the service is excellent and the cooking is of a level. Good reports of honey and lemon chicken, served with the sauce separate, so the meat does not go soggy, and sea-bass in black-bean sauce. More reports, please.

CHEF: Warren Yeung PROPRIETORS: Warren Yeung and Kui-Keung Yeung
OPEN: all week, D only
MEALS: 5.30 to 11.30
PRICES: £8 (£15), Set D £19 (£24). Service 10%
CARDS: Access, Amex, Visa
SEATS: 80. Vegetarian meals. Children welcome. Music. Air-conditioned

Market Restaurant [11/20]

Edge Street/104 High Street, M4 1HQ
061-834 3743 £17

Opposite the old fruit market – and not to be confused with the newer restaurant of the same name opened at the Smithfields pub on Shudehill. The décor is that of a tea-room, with echoes of the 1940s (some say 1950s), but less claustrophobic than in its first incarnation across the road. The menu's great virtue is its seasonality and taste for new combinations, which

provide an impact, even if the seasoning is muted. Six dishes are offered per course. Recommendations: cheese tartlets; creamed leeks in puff pastry; whole poussin; breast of chicken with honey. Increasingly, the sweets pick up enthusiasm – a pudding club is being formed to meet in the new upstairs function room. Home-made ice-creams, sorbets and a range of old English puddings or favourites from other parts of the world such as Pashka, Nesselrode ice-cream and true roulades, all feature. There is also a range of British cheeses. The safe list of 30 wines is spiced with a few more interesting bottles under the heading 'Miscellany'. House wine is £3 a half-litre.
CELLARMAN'S CHOICE: Jacques Selosse Champagne, NV, £15.95.

CHEF: Lin Scrannage PROPRIETORS: Peter O'Grady, Anne O'Grady and Lin Scrannage
OPEN: Tue to Sat, D only
CLOSED: 1 week in spring, 1 week at Christmas, Aug
MEALS: 5.30 (7 Sat) to 9.30
PRICES: £11 (£17)
CARDS: Access, Amex, Visa
SEATS: 40. Private parties: 40 main room, 25 private room. Vegetarian meals. Children welcome. Music

Mina-Japan [10/20]

63 George Street, M1 4NS
061-228 2598 £17–£21

Outside the concentration of Chinatown, although still in George Street, this Japanese restaurant has been going for three years, but has struggled to build up a regular following. Its exclusion last year through lack of reports was a symptom, but the quality of its food is less in doubt and an inspector endorses a return to the listings. The virtues of Japanese cooking – prime ingredients handled with skill and cooked mostly to order – set out the case for inclusion. Set meals are arranged around the main course of sashimi or paper-thin slices of cold beef. The supporting sushi, soups, yakitori, and fresh fruit to finish all draw praise, and the sauces invigorate the cooking splendidly. The basement's former incarnation as an Italian restaurant is still evident. Wines start around £6, or drink saké.

CHEF: Yasuto Kawano PROPRIETOR: Nori Shibahara
OPEN: Mon to Sat, D only
MEALS: 7 to 11.30 (Sat 1)
PRICES: £13 (£21), Set D from £12 (£17)
CARDS: Access, Amex, Carte Blance, Diners, Visa
SEATS: 50. Private parties: 28 main room. Vegetarian meals. Children's helpings before 10pm. Music. Air-conditioned

Moss Nook [13/20]

Ringway Road, M22 5NA
061-437 4778
on B5166, 1m from Manchester airport, M56 exit 5 £28–£30

Originally a vegetarian restaurant, Moss Nook is currently the most competent exponent of modern French cooking in the city. Virtually on the perimeter of Ringway airport, the converted suburban house, shuttered and festooned at the windows and green with hanging baskets, has a smart, slightly sterile, interior of red plush. The cooking stands up to critical examination over repeated visits. There is an all-inclusive four-course set menu but the *menu surprise* at £24, which offers six 'tasting' courses, puts the diner in the chef's hands and is the more adventurous option. Good examples are seafood tart; roulade of salmon and halibut; warm salad of duck breast on a bed of salad with a nutty vinaigrette. A pink tournedos of fillet steak, topped with breadcrumbs and sage and served on a piquant sweet-and-sour sauce is technically expert and well conceived. Vegetables, for instance deep-fried courgettes and mange-tout have been consistently above average. Skill is evident in the pastry and for dessert an option is a spread of each one garnished with exotic fruits. The wine list is largely French and fairly good, though irratingly many of the producers' names are missing. House white £7.75, red £8.50. CELLARMAN'S CHOICE: Rosemount Chardonnay '87, £15.50; St Véran, Domaine Pacquet '85, £12.50; St Emilion, Ch. Viramon '83, £14.50.

CHEFS: Robert Thornton and Pauline Harrison PROPRIETORS: Pauline and Derek Harrison
OPEN: Tue to Sat, exc Sat L
CLOSED: 24 Dec for 2 weeks
MEALS: 12 to 2, 7 to 9.30 (10 Sat)
PRICES: £26 (£30), Set L and D £24 (£28). Service inc
CARDS: Access, Amex, Diners, Visa
SEATS: 50. 8 tables outside. Private parties: 10 main room. Car-park, 30 places. Vegetarian meals. No children under 12. Smart dress preferred. No cigars/pipes in dining-room. Air-conditioned

Mr Kuk's [12/20]

55A Mosley Street, M2 3HY
061-236 0659 £12–£22

Well patronised by mainland Chinese visiting the city on business, this remains the premier Peking restaurant of Manchester, a few blocks off the main dragway of Cantonese George Street. The cooking brooks no compromise, providing superlative hot-and-sour soup, crispy duck, and crispy deep-fried beef with carrot and ginger. There is an emphasis on noodle dishes for one-plate meals. Set meals are uncommonly interesting. House special banquet (ordered in advance) has three variations of duck – barbecued Peking; deep-fried crispy duck Szechuan style; with eight-jewel stuffing – followed by three of chicken – shredded with garlic Shan-tung style; grilled boneless baby chicken; oil-dripped chicken. The restaurant's parentage is also unusual, being owned jointly by businessman Geoff Cohen and radio announcer Stephen Kuk. Some new watercolours help lift the spartan décor, reminding just how much styles of décor, particularly in this kind of Peking restaurant, have developed in the nine years since it opened. Drink tea or lager.

▲ *This restaurant offers accommodation.*

CHEF: Mr Lau PROPRIETORS: Stephen Kuk and Geoffrey Cohen
OPEN: all week
MEALS: noon to midnight
PRICES: £11 (£18), Set L and D £9 (£12) to £18 (£22). Service 10%
CARDS: Access, Amex, Diners, Visa
SEATS: 95. Private parties: 95 main room. Vegetarian meals. Children's helpings. Music. Air-conditioned

On the Eighth Day [9/20]

109 Oxford Road, All Saints, M1 7DU
061-273 1850 £5

This workers' co-operative vegetarian restaurant produces excellent-value meals. Cooks take turns and the short menu changes from day to day, although the pattern is always one soup, such as minestrone or split pea and mint, one stew, perhaps mung bean curry, and one bake, for instance vegetable and mushroom layer. Good salads and puddings complete the picture. Unlicensed, but drink tea, fruit juice or barley cup.

CHEF/PROPRIETOR: Co-operative
OPEN: Mon to Sat, exc Sat D
MEALS: 10 to 7 (4.30 Sat)
PRICES: £3 (£5). Unlicensed, but bring your own: no corkage
SEATS: 42. Vegetarian meals. Children's helpings. No smoking. Wheelchair access (also WC). Music. Self-service

Pearl City [11/20]

33 George Street, M1 4PH
061-228 7683 £8–£23

There's a sharp contrast between the style of most Manchester Chinese restaurants and their elegant, lavishly appointed counterparts in Birmingham. Pearl City is typical of the brusque café atmosphere that is Manchester's trademark. The décor is minimal, very functional, slightly gaudy, slightly bleak. The view from the first floor dining-room above the re-painted Terrazza restaurant is of warehouses and car parks; orange and green spotlights beam down from the curious greyish ceiling with its plastic, square honeycomb patterns. Service is fast, and on occasion surly. But the food is uncompromising Cantonese at its best, with no punches pulled. Raw materials are impressively good; flavours are subtle and deep. It is in the set lunches and the one-plate meals that it really scores. Three roast meats on rice are served on or off the bone, hot or cold, as a wonderful, huge plateful. There is excellent roast duck, very meaty, soft, rich and strongly flavoured, with a crispy skin. Crispy belly pork is very fatty, with very crunchy crackling; barbecued pork, in thick slices, fragrant and tender, is first rate, with a marvellous contrast of textures and flavours. Chinese greens and rice are spot-on. Or try the Pearl City special chow mein, another brilliant, monumental plateful. Noodles are excellent, a balance of crisp and soft, with fresh squid in whirls, king prawns, fish balls and slices of fishcake, excellent thin slices of liver and lightly cooked fresh pork, various bits of intestines and tripe, a few bits of beef and more Chinese greens, topped with two hunks of barbecued pork.

CHEF: Mr Kan PROPRIETOR: Mr Cheung
OPEN: all week
MEALS: noon to 4am (midnight Sun)
PRICES: £12 (£23), Set L from £2.80 (£8) to £6 (£12), Set D £10 (£16). Service 10%
CARDS: Access, Amex, Diners, Visa
SEATS: 460. Private parties: 150 main room, 250 private room. Vegetarian meals. Children welcome. Music. Air-conditioned

Sanam [9/20]

145–151 Wilmslow Road, Rusholme, M14 5AW
061-224 1008 £4–£9

The Rusholme area of Wilmslow Road is Manchester's little India, full of traders, sweet-centres, cafés and restaurants. Sanam, with its distinctive red canopies, has the edge over most of the local opposition in terms of authentic cooking and value for money. Décor is a garish mix of bright lights, plastic plants and marble-topped tables. The kitchen turns out tandooris, shami kebab and palak gosht as well as brains and quail cooked in a potent chilli sauce. Other details are good, from the home-made lime pickle to the creamy rasmalai. Unlicensed.

CHEF: Abdul Jabbar PROPRIETORS: Abdul Ghafoor Akhtar and sons
OPEN: all week
MEALS: noon to midnight
PRICES: £8 (£9), Set L £3 (£4) to £5 (£6), Set D £4 (£5) to £7 (£8). Minimum £3.20. Snacks from 60p. Service inc. Unlicensed
CARDS: Access, Visa
SEATS: 150. Private parties: 100 main room, 50 private room. Vegetarian meals. Children's helpings. Wheelchair access (also WC). Music. Air-conditioned

Siam Orchid [10/20]

54 Portland Street, M1 4QU
061-236 1388 £7–£17

Manchester's first, and only, Thai restaurant is just round the corner from Chinatown. Above is a Japanese/Korean eating-place; inside there are fresh orchids on the tables, waitresses in costume and pictures of Thai boxers on the green hessian walls. The menu of around 70 dishes spans the full range of accessible Thai specialities – from satays, dim-sum and little fishcakes to chicken soup cooked with coconut milk, lemon-grass and laos. Curries, made with red or green curry-paste, and stir-fried dishes, such as king prawns with chilli and fresh sweet basil leaves, have been praised. Finish with seasonal exotic fruits and drink Thai Singha beer. Good, cheap set lunches.

CHEFS: C. Sirisompan, Doy Parry and P. Prince PROPRIETORS: C. Sirisompan and K. Sirisambhand
OPEN: all week, exc Sun L
MEALS: 11.30 to 2.30, 6.30 to 11.30
PRICES: £9 (£17), Set L £3.50 (£7), Set D from £12 (£16). Snacks from £3.90. Service 10% alc, inc Set D. Licensed, also bring your own: corkage £2
CARDS: Access, Diners, Visa
SEATS: 55. Private parties: 55 main room. Children's helpings. Music. Air-conditioned

That Café [9/20]

1031 Stockport Road, South Levenshulme, M19 2TB
061-432 4672 £14–£17

Joe Quinn's 1930s-look café offers a short, vegetarian-inspired menu with a few concessions to meat eaters. Soups, terrines and pies are the cut of the set menu. Recommended dishes have been cauliflower soup, vegetable and chestnut bake, crab and salmon mousse with mayonnaise, rabbit and herbs in a light pastry case. 'Fresh, home-made, unpretentious.' House wine £7 a litre.

CHEF/PROPRIETOR: Joe Quinn
OPEN: Tue to Sat D, and Sun L
MEALS: 12.30 to 2.30, 7.30 to 11
PRICES: £11 (£17), Set D (Tue, Wed and Thur) £8.95 (£14)
CARDS: Access, Amex, Visa
SEATS: 50. Private parties: 50 main room, 25 private room. Vegetarian meals. Children's helpings. Music

Woodlands [10/20]

33 Shepley Road, Audenshaw, M34 5DJ
061-336 4241 £16–£26

Woodlands' dining-rooms have the doors removed to give the impression of space, and heavy linen, flowers and candles lend a note of distinction. The cooking is modern French in inspiration, a little impersonal. There is a bias towards fish, and towards cream and butter, but also to using fresh and good ingredients and creating an interesting mix of flavours, as with a decorative mint mousse which comes, together with a stout-flavoured sauce, with a pink-roasted and boned loin of lamb. The choice is from eight starters and eight fish main courses, plus half a dozen meat dishes. They range from brill fillet with a crayfish mousse studded with langoustines, in a langoustine sauce, to roast beef, Yorkshire pudding and roast potatoes. There is a certain sense of humour about the sweets: winter fruit tart containing strawberries and raspberries. Excellent petits fours. Forty wines concentrate on Bordeaux, Burgundy and Loire. Good house wine at £5.25; CELLARMAN'S CHOICE: Meursault, Les Narveux '85, £22.50 and St-Véran '86, from Georges Duboeuf, £9.75.

An index of restaurants by name appears at the back of the Guide.

CHEF: William Mark Jackson PROPRIETORS: Mr and Mrs D. Crank
OPEN: Tue to Sat, exc Sat L
CLOSED: first week in Jan, 1 week after Easter, last two weeks Aug
MEALS: 12 to 2, 7 to 9.30 (10 Sat)
PRICES: £20 (£26), Set L £10 (£16), Set D (exc Sat) £12 (£18)
CARDS: Access, Visa
SEATS: 36. Private parties: 22 main room, 14 private room. Car-park, 12 places. Children's helpings. Smart dress preferred. No cigars/pipes in dining-room. Wheelchair access (3 steps). Music. Air-conditioned

Woody and Dutch [11/20]

71 Church Road, Northenden, M22 4WN
061-998 6336 £19

The area around the church evokes the small country village that was Northenden before it became engulfed in suburban sprawl half a century ago. This converted shop is very much in the bistro style – bare boards, mugs and mats, paisley cloths, bentwood chairs and 1950s bric-à-brac –but the proficiency of the cooking puts it somewhat ahead of the competition. Touches such as olives with the drinks are welcome. The menu is small, modern British, with nods in the direction of France and vegetarianism, and changes frequently. Sauces are particularly good, and seasoning, in general, accurate. Portions are generous. Good dishes have been: haricot bean soup; Stilton and port pâté with celery; roast loin of lamb arranged around a superb onion galette and served with a fruity redcurrant and garlic gravy; steak and kidney pie; fresh hake with yoghurt and coriander; salmon en croûte with a dill and cucumber salad. Sweets bear out the English train of thought with sticky toffee pudding with Jersey cream; home-made ice-cream and shortbread; a very sweet rum and fudge sauce for chocolate cake. Twenty-five wines climb steeply into double figures from the good house Bordeaux at £6.50. 'Really very proficient cooking.'

CHEF/PROPRIETOR: Nigel Barnsley
OPEN: Tue to Sat
CLOSED: 2 weeks at Christmas, last 2 weeks July, first 2 weeks Aug
MEALS: 7.30 to 10.30
PRICES: £13 (£19)
CARDS: Amex, Diners, Visa
SEATS: 26. Private parties: 26 main room. Vegetarian meals. Children's helpings. Wheelchair access. Music

Yang Sing [15/20]

10 YEARS

34 Princess Street, M1 4JY
061-236 2200 £11–£15

It is fashionable in some Chinese circles to say that the Yang Sing has sold out and does not fully deserve its high rating. But the English menu does not truly represent the strengths, being a familiar listing of dishes widely available. The specials though have some superb dishes, enough to win over, at last, some critics – a supreme pot casserole; tofu stuffed with black beans and scallop and steamed with soy; salted fish patties. The salt-baked chicken – 'the best I have had outside of Hong Kong' – is marinated in a salt solution and then, with the bird still full of water, baked in the oven, which gives a moist texture and 'exquisite' salt flavour. Some fine dim-sum served here from noon till six and they cost a little over £1 each. Two frying trolleys are wheeled out into the middle of the room with spring rolls, fried crabmeat balls and the excellent Chinese fishcakes. Steamed items are cooked to order in the kitchen. Woo kok, char siu buns and the various cheung-fun are among the most filling items; soup in dumplings, spicy nut dumplings, steamed cockles and winkles and, if you have room left, egg tarts are all excellent. The atmosphere in the week (not Sundays) lacks what the Chinese call 'Go Hing', in the sense of bustling excitement typical of the great dim-sum houses, as might be found in London at New World or Chuen Cheng Ku (see entries). One side of the dining-room is given over to a display of roast ducks, soya chickens, poached chickens, roast pork, crispy pork, marinated offal, roast suckling pig. Cabinets contain Chinese bread and pastries that would put most cake-shops to shame. Here is a proper restaurant, one with a menu of 341 items made up of 32 soups, 15 prawn dishes, 20 chicken, 20 beef, 16 pork, 9 duck, 12 seafood, 13 casserole, 7 barbecue, 15 specials, 28 soup and noodles, 39 rice, 6 congee and 6 extras with barely anything over £5 except prawns and the top-selling fillet steak Cantonese-style. Its main danger is its Europeanisation, but it is a resilient animal and there is an affiliation of Lancashire and the Canton somewhere in the tripe dishes or steamed pork pie with salted egg. The big sellers are the sizzling steaks and the immaculate steamed sea-bass. To an extent, the dining-room is a victim of its own success and there have been instances of bookings not being upheld. But the prices do not pretend anything else.

CHEF: Harry Yeung PROPRIETORS: Yang Sing Restaurant Ltd
OPEN: all week
CLOSED: 25 Dec
MEALS: noon to 11
PRICES: £7 (£11), Set L and D £10 (£15). Service 10%
CARDS: Access, Amex
SEATS: 140. Private parties: 200 private room. Children welcome. Wheelchair access. Music. Air-conditioned

Greater Manchester Round-up

INDIAN: *Deansgate,* 244 Deansgate, Manchester (061-835 1888).
CHINESE: *Wong Chu,* 63–63A Faulkner Street, Manchester (061-236 2346); *Phoenix City,* 10 The Square, Hyde (061-368 4677/7694).
INEXPENSIVE: *Derby Hall,* Market Street, Bury (061-761 7107); *Salford College of Technology,* Frederick Road, Salford (061-736 6541).
FRENCH: *Brasserie St Pierre,* 57–63 Princess Street, Manchester (061-228 0231).
ITALIAN: *Giulio's Terrazza,* 14 Nicholas Street, Manchester (061-236 4033/0250).
VEGETARIAN: *Billies,* 115 Manchester Road, Chorlton (061-881 9338); *Nutcracker,* 43 Oxford Road, Altrincham (061-928 4399).
COFFEE SHOP: *Christian World Centre,* 123 Deansgate, Manchester (061-834 6060).
WHOLEFOOD: *Wild Oats,* 88 Oldham Street, Manchester (061-236 6662).

MELMERBY Cumbria map 7

Village Bakery [11/20]

Melmerby CA10 1HE
LANGWATHBY (076 881) 515 £11

Melmerby is tiny, half way between Penrith and Alston, the highest market-town in England. It supports two eating places, here and the Shepherds Inn. The bakery is in a converted eighteenth-century barn. Wood-fired ovens supply all the cooking for the all-day café opening with croissants, or Loch Fyne kippers; Cumberland sausage with apple sauce at lunch; to old-fashioned afternoon teas. The wholesomeness shines out. Real food is taken to its logical, ecological conclusion – stoneground flours; organic vegetables; fruit wines. The menu changes every week and takes in some substantial and interesting dishes, such as sliced kidneys in a rich brown gravy thickened with Jersey cream and served on a thick slice of toasted wholemeal bread with a side salad of cucumber and lettuce. 'Salads are determinedly green.' But it is the essentially English baking – the Bakery is far closer to being an authentic English eating-house than most restaurants – that stands out. Service is friendly and knowledgeable; dishes are explained and suggestions volunteered. Much of the menu is available to take out. To drink there is home-made lemonade, organic wines and ciders, and Jennings real ale, brewed in Cockermouth.

CHEF: Diane Richter PROPRIETORS: Lis and Andrew Whitley
OPEN: Tue to Sun
CLOSED: Christmas to Easter
MEALS: 8.30 to 5 (L 12 to 2.30)
PRICES: £7 (£11), Set Sun L £7.50 (£11), Snacks from 40p
CARDS: Access, Visa
SEATS: 40. Private parties: 25 main room. Car-park, 8 places. Vegetarian meals. Children's helpings. No smoking in dining-room. Wheelchair access (1 step)

MELTON MOWBRAY Leicestershire map 5

▲ *Stapleford Park* [new entry, zero rated]

nr Melton Mowbray LE14 2EF
WYMONDHAM (057 284) 522 £29

Bob Payton, having made his fortune selling America to London with a chain of theme restaurants including the Chicago Rib Shack, has turned the tables and is now selling a bit of old England to visiting Americans. American Pie meets Melton Mowbray Pie. It's a personal fantasy of a rural retreat: Bob's own country. Previously the stately home of the Earls of Harborough and then Lord Gretton, Payton bought the Grade I listed building in January 1986 for £750,000. Under a business expansion scheme he tried to raise £4 million to finance the conversion. The issue failed. However, later in 1986 a £300,000 grant from the English Tourist Board got the ball rolling again. The house has since been re-plumbed, re-wired, the roof of the oldest section replaced and, in five years' time, it will have 50 bedrooms. It's claimed the tariffs make it the second most expensive country hotel after Cliveden (see Taplow), and a magnificent split-level apartment in the mock-Elizabethan wing at £373.75 a night must rank as one of the costliest in the land. The place reverberates to Payton's ebullient personality – his presence is pervasive. Stapleford is now his home and HQ. The staff call him Bob, and guests are encouraged to do the same. The hotel is set in 500 acres of low, rolling woodland and park not far from Melton Mowbray and bang in the middle of royal hunting country; for centuries a sporting-lodge. It once was nearly bought by Edward, Prince of Wales, but Queen Victoria stopped him because she felt his morals would be corrupted by local hunting society – a nice tale, apocryphal or not, that Payton is not backwards about promoting. As well as turning it into a sybaritic pleasuredome, Payton plans to turn the estate into a national equestrian centre with riding facilities, carriage driving, eventing, polo, etcetera, plus livery stabling for guests' own horses. The house itself is a fascinating mix of periods and styles, saved from Disneyland eclecticism by the beauty of the ivory coloured stone and the gentleness of the lakeside setting.

For all the fancifulness of the hotel, the cooking began as straight from the shoulder British with a few American touches: simple, but soundly executed and relying on the quality of its raw materials for impact. John Johnson joined the team from the Connaught in July with the hope of taking the cooking into a modern American idiom. But for the first months it has been a mix of asparagus, quail eggs in pastry cases, followed by braised ox-tail, roast best end of lamb, crab salad, lobster with mustard and cheese. The signposts are well handled, for instance a plain roast quarter of duck with a little mound of apple sauce and a stir-fry of carrot, mange-tout, beans, peppers, baby corn, mouli, young turnip and broccoli. Sweets, surprisingly, might have moved to the more traditional instead of staying on the international route of crème brûlée and cheesecake, but after big, powerful USA tastes. The dining-room is clotted cream-coloured and dominated by some glorious ornate carvings – 'a grand room but on a mortal scale.' 'On arrival, the welcome was quite theatrical. A young lady dressed in house colours burst through the front door, past two splendid bronzes of horses rampant with riders, and announced our welcome to Stapleford Park in best stateside tradition. Simultaneously, a huge black schnauzer dog – the house mascot, Gunther – amiably ambled up wearing a scarf decorated in the Stars and Stripes. Other dogs are welcome as long as they get along with Gunther and can stand his choice in neckscarves. Depending on how he feels in the morning, it's a toss up between Old Glory, the Rambo one and a classy little silk number from Turnbull and Asser.'

Tea is more British than the British – a large tray with starched linen and white Wedgwood china plus a vase of nearly overblown tulips. Finger sandwiches of cucumber and of ham (good white bread with the crusts off), scones still hot from the oven, strawberry jam and thick cream, leaf tea, lots of hot water, two kinds of cake, chocolate chip cookies and meringues filled with strawberries and cream. Payton has invited a group of interior designers and retailing companies such as Crabtree & Evelyn, Liberty and Wedgwood to create their own 'signature' bedrooms. 'My favourite though were the breakfast room and the ladies' loo. The former used to be the old kitchen and is quite Ruritanian – Gothic arched vaults, antlers on the walls, long tapestry curtains, high-backed brocade chairs and an oak table enclosing a central stone pillar. And on the tables, Peter Rabbit china – personal whimsey or a calculated appeal to the British nursery tendency? Breakfasts feature, among other things, exemplary waffles with maple syrup and cinnamon sugar, pancakes and blueberry muffins. You can also start with Bob's special morning heartstopper (or was it starter?), which was a Bloody Mary *sans* vodka, spiked with lemon juice, Worcester sauce and horseradish. For traditionalists, there was a more conventional choice of the SP special breakfast, curried haddock, fresh fruit salad, croissants and wholemeal toast, along with Crabtree & Evelyn preserves served in the pot.' Wines are from top-class merchants like Reid Wines of Bristol. The house wines are Californian, from Mondavi, at £8.95 and the New World provides an unusual level of interest. More reports, please.

CHEF: John Johnson PROPRIETORS: Bob and Wendy Payton
OPEN: all week
MEALS: 12.30 to 3, 6.30 to 11
PRICES: £20 (£29), Snacks from £3.50
CARDS: Access, Amex, Carte Blanche, Diners, Visa
SEATS: 60. Private parties: 80 main room, 10, 12, 20, 24 and 300 private rooms. Vegetarian meals. Children under 10 by arrangement only. Smart dress preferred. No smoking. Wheelchair access (also WC)
ACCOMMODATION: 30 rooms, all with bath/shower. Lift. B&B £85 to £170. Deposit: £50. No children under 10. Pets welcome. Afternoon teas. Garden. Tennis. Fishing. Golf. TV. Phone. Scenic [GHG]

MIDHURST West Sussex map 3

Maxine's [11/20]

Red Lion Street, Midhurst GU29 9PB
MIDHURST (073 081) 6271 **£13–£20**

In a timber-framed building at one corner of the market square, Robert and Marti de Jager run a small family business which has attracted a loyal following over the last few years. Fresh cod steaks 'delivered and offered as we arrived', in a mustard sauce, and pheasant in an almond and sherry sauce, are examples of what to expect. Dutch apple pie seems to be a favourite dessert. House red and white from Duboeuf £5.

CHEF: Robert de Jager PROPRIETORS: Robert and Marti de Jager
OPEN: all week, exc Mon L, and Tue
MEALS: 12 to 2, 7 to 10
PRICES: £16 (£19), Set L £8.50 (£13), Set D £8.50 (£13) to £16 (£20). Service inc
CARDS: Access, Amex, Diners, Visa
SEATS: 27. Private parties: 30 main room. Vegetarian meals. Children's helpings

The 1990 Guide *will appear before Christmas 1989. Reports are particularly helpful in the spring. Report forms are at the back of this book, but just write a letter if you prefer. Address to The Good Food Guide,* FREEPOST, *2 Marylebone Road, London NW1 1YN. No stamp is necessary if you post it in the UK.*

MILFORD-ON-SEA Hampshire map 2

Rocher's [new entry, zero rated]

69–71 High Street, Milford-on-Sea SO41 0QG
LYMINGTON (0590) 42340 £11–£18

Alain Rocher worked at Chewton Glen at New Milton and Le Select in Poole before setting up with his wife in this tea-shoppy restaurant with a pretty pink dining-room. His cooking is a mixture of classical and modern French, with a few innovative touches: onion soup and entrecôte bordelaise alongside feuilleté of spinach and shallots, or breast of chicken with pink grapefruit. Rocher's home-made red wine vinegar appears in the vinaigrette for a warm salmon salad and in the sauce for roast guinea-fowl. Chocolate mousse with strawberry coulis is the pick of the sweets. Two dozen basic wines, mostly under £10. House wine from Boisset is £4.95 a bottle. There is a plan to close one day a week in winter. More reports, please.

CHEF: Alain Rocher PROPRIETORS: Alain and Rebecca Rocher
OPEN: all week D, and Sun L
MEALS: 12 to 1.45, 7 to 10
PRICES: £12.55 (£18), Set Sun L £6.95 (£11)
CARDS: Access, Visa
SEATS: 30. Private parties: 30 main room. No children under 11 (exc Sun L). Smart dress preferred. No cigars/pipes in dining-room. Wheelchair access. Music

MOLLINGTON Cheshire map 5

▲ *Crabwall Manor* [14/20]

Mollington, CH1 6NE
GREAT MOLLINGTON (0244) 851666 £18–£32

The Manor, complete with clock tower, is quirky in design. Inside is a job lot collection of chintz and chandeliers, luxurious but without the individuality in décor of, say Hintlesham Hall, Stapleford Park, or Hambleton Hall. But the restaurant is an important addition for the North-West. Michael Truelove has brought familiar dishes from the Box Tree at Ilkley, such as the dariole of mushrooms. He is used to working with expensive ingredients: partridge, for instance, is served slightly pink, the breast and leg boned and sliced in a sauce characterised by partridge liver, offset by a pair of tartlets filled with cabbage and livers. But the menu is not a boundless list of expensiveness. Two poussins are poached in light stock with brown and green lentils, the breast meat being unusually flavoursome. The 18-dish *carte* is a fusion of French and English. Technically this is a first-division kitchen not afraid to offer simple things, for instance a little salmon offset with a tomato purée. Nor to deal in more complex flavour relationships such as a ravioli of lobster – 'looking like three David Shilling Ascot hats, circular, crimped, and filled with lobster bound with a salmon mousse flavoured with basil and decorated with a trellis of courgette slivers, dribbled with green olive oil and served on a cream sauce. It sounds excessive but in fact was only so in terms of quantity.' Sweets are plated bavarois and pavés – ritzy sounding, rather over-elaborate and international numbers which are almost overshadowed by the petits fours. Service has not been as confident, quite abashed by the cooking. The wine list is wider ranging in its sources than many, with an unusually interesting choice of Spanish wines, good Germans, Californians, Australians and some minor wines of France, as well as good selections from the classic French areas. Alsace, Loire, Burgundy, Beaujolais are all very good, and clarets go from some good, simple bottles through middle-range wines right up to mature bottles of top-classed growths. A list of alternative champagne-method sparkling wines (Alsace, Germany, Australia) looks interesting, and more affordable than the rather elite champagne list. You have to dig out the sweet wines from among the dry, but an interesting selection includes two simple white Bordeaux (single-château Cadillacs, £10.50), a Monbazillac, a few recent vintages and one '70 Sauternes, some mature Anjou Moulin Touchais and a Coteaux du Layon from the Loire, Vieux Banyuls by the bottle or half, a little sweet German and Muscat de St-Jean du Minervois, £12.75. Plenty of magnums and half-bottles. House French is £7.95. CELLARMAN'S CHOICE: Cuvée de la Commanderie du Bontemps du Médoc et de Graves '82, £12.95; Ch. Reynon, Vieilles Vignes '85, £13.95.

CHEF: Michael Truelove PROPRIETORS: Carl A. Lewis and David M. Brockett
OPEN: all week
MEALS: 12.30 to 2, 7 to 9.30
PRICES: £21 (£32), Set L £12 (£18), Set D £19.50 (£26)
CARDS: Access, Amex, Diners, Visa
SEATS: 120. Private parties: 16 main room, 50 and 100 private rooms. Car-park, 20 places. Children's helpings. No children under 5. Jacket and tie. No-smoking area. Wheelchair access (3 steps; also WC). Air-conditioned
ACCOMMODATION: 32 rooms, all with bath/shower. Room for disabled. B&B £66 to £92. No children under 5. Afternoon teas. Garden. TV. Phone. Scenic. Doors close at 12. Confirm by 6 [GHG]

MORETON-IN-MARSH Gloucestershire map 2

Sheridans [new entry, zero rated]

High Street, Moreton-in-Marsh GL56 0AX
MORETON-IN-MARSH (0608) 50251 £26

Marc Sheridan, formerly at Le Papillon in Greenwich, has taken over this handsome yellow stone restaurant previously under the ownership of Judy Moore and before that Paul Barnard, now at the Plough at Clanfield. The menu has taken on a cosmopolitan air: saffron and champagne sauces; truffle eggs; French cheeses; Dutch calf's liver; Scottish beef; fish via Torbay and Birmingham market. Sauces use much cream and alcohol and come in twos, splitting the plate between them – for example one of Roquefort and another of madeira and walnuts for a roast steak of venison. The mannerisms are of a grand operation – domed service for starters and main courses; a cake-stand with eight petits fours; and opening seven days a week. Extras, for instance mineral water, put the bill up. The wine list is almost exclusively French and almost 80 per cent over £10; in part due to the leaning to Bordeaux and Burgundy. House Cabernet Sauvignon is £6.75. Five bedrooms were due to open late in 1988. More reports, please.

CHEF/PROPRIETOR: Marc Sheridan
OPEN: all week
MEALS: 12 to 2.30, 7 to 10
PRICES: £17 (£26). Cover 90p
CARDS: Access, Amex, Visa
SEATS: 40. Private parties: 10 and 30 private rooms. Vegetarian meals. Children's helpings. No-smoking area. Wheelchair access

MOULTON North Yorkshire — map 7

Black Bull [12/20]

10 YEARS

Moulton DL10 6QJ
BARTON (032 577) 289
1m SE of Scotch Corner, 1m from A1 — £13–£26

At heart the Bull is still a prosperous village pub with settles and whitewashed tables in the bar and a good menu of pub food. There's also a tiled Victorian fish bar done out in mahogany, a plant-filled conservatory and a rabbit warren of private rooms opposite the kitchen. The pride and joy of the place, though, is Hazel – a converted Brighton Belle Pullman dining-car with lace curtains and a mood of old-style civility. The kitchen's reputation rests with its fish – lobsters from the tanks, poached turbot and salmon, grilled Dover sole. There are steaks and roasts too. Much of this harks back to the 1960s, although dishes such as salad of warm chicken livers and scallops keep abreast of the times. Good bread and vegetables are big plusses. CELLARMAN'S CHOICE: Juliénas '87, from Georges Duboeuf, £8.95; Pouilly Fumé, Château de Tracy '87, £9.95.

CHEF: Stuart Birkett PROPRIETORS: Mr G. and Mrs A. Pagendam
OPEN: Mon to Sat, exc Sat L
CLOSED: 24 to 31 Dec
MEALS: 12 to 2, 6.45 to 10.15
PRICES: £20 (£26), Set L £8 (£13), Snacks from £1. Service inc Set L only
CARDS: Access, Amex, Visa
SEATS: 120 to 130. 4 tables outside. Private parties: 30 main room, 8 to 30 private rooms. Car-park, 80 places. Wheelchair access

NAILSWORTH Gloucestershire — map 2

Flynn's [11/20]

3 Fountain Street, Nailsworth GL6 0BL
NAILSWORTH (045 383) 2240 — £15–£22

Reached via some rather unpromising back steps up to the first floor of a modern extension. Inside is a surprising about-face – clean, period, with more than a passing resemblance to the kind of elegance usually found in older buildings. William Beeston, fishmonger – rare enough in these parts –

has now given over the running to chef Garry Flynn, hence the change from William's Kitchen, but the links with the fish-shop and delicatessen remain. The menu, of some length, takes in fish soup; Dover sole spiralled round like a small beehive; scallops, brill and salmon in a champagne and fennel sauce; sea-bass on a bed of pulses. Flynn is Australian and brings a fresh eye to some otherwise familiar combinations. There is some game, pan-fried pigeon breast, and a few meat dishes – beef fillet with red wine or saddle of lamb with rosemary. Sweets are mousses and ice-creams plus the likes of a chocolate cone on a chocolate base with coffee sauce. House French is £5.50; CELLARMAN'S CHOICE: Mâcon-Villages, Domaine de la Condemine '86, £11, and half-bottle, £6; and Rand Hill Chardonnay, Napa Valley '86, £9.

CHEF/PROPRIETOR: Garry Flynn
OPEN: Tue to Sat, D only
MEALS: 7.30 to 10
PRICES: £17 (£22), Set D £12.50 (£17)
CARDS: Access, Visa
SEATS: 40. Children's helpings

NANTWICH Cheshire map 5

▲ *Rookery Hall* [new owners, zero rated]

Worleston, nr Nantwich CW5 6DQ
NANTWICH (0270) 626866
on B5074, off A51 £23–£36

The Hall is a hybrid, the product of a succession of architects, rebuilt in 1867 in the style of a French château. Some rooms in the stable-block overlook the lake; the windows of the grand panelled dining-room have views of the luscious fertile Cheshire pastures. This is the world of classy canapés and champagne cocktails, polished woodwork and crystal glassware. The Marks have sold to Select Country Hotels, who also own Ettington Park, and chef Clive Howe has moved on to the Lygon Arms at Broadway (see entry). Steven Serenczy has been promoted to run the kitchen and cooks a commendable version of modern cuisine with good use of local supplies. The quality does not always match the high prices and some of the finer details are less impressive than before. But there are plenty of good things here: an impeccable warm salad of monkfish, scallops, bacon and pine-nuts with an excellent crossfire of flavours; good reduced sauce with roast Cheshire duck stuffed with apples and prunes; excellent-quality lamb with lentils, red peppers and roasted garlic. English and Irish farmhouse cheeses are served with walnut and raisin bread. The long wine list is dogged by high prices, with house wines opening at £12.50. CELLARMAN'S CHOICE: Côte de Beaune-Villages '82, from Louis Latour, at £17.50. More reports, please.

Restaurants are graded on a scale of 1–20. In the category of 10–11 expect to find the best food in the locality. Ratings of 12 and more are given to restaurants we regard as serving the best food in the region.

CHEF: Steven Serenczy PROPRIETORS: Select Country Hotels Ltd
OPEN: all week
MEALS: 12.15 to 2.15, 7 to 9.30
PRICES: Set L £13.50 (£23), Set D £25 (£36). Minimum £13.50
CARDS: Access, Amex, Diners, Visa
SEATS: 60. Private parties: 40 main room, 20 private room. Car-park, 30 places. No children under 10. Jacket and tie at D, smart dress preferred at L. No smoking in dining-room. Wheelchair access (also WC)
ACCOMMODATION: 11 rooms, all with bath/shower. Rooms for disabled. B&B £62.50 to £100. Deposit: 50%. No children under 10. Afternoon teas. Garden. Tennis. Fishing. TV. Phone. Scenic

NEW MILTON Hampshire map 2

▲ *Marryat Room, Chewton Glen Hotel* [13/20]

Christchurch Road, New Milton BH25 6QS
HIGHCLIFFE (0425) 275341 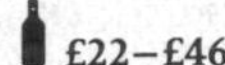 £22–£46

Chewton develops apace – a new bakery, the kitchen brigade up to 19, a new conservatory dining-room reputedly costing £200,000. In its luxury it is coming to look like a southern version of Inverlochy Castle (see entry under Fort William, Scotland). The cooking matches the hotel's international aspirations, being traditional French in the grand style – rich, creamy, fancy, with lots of pastry and some very powerful flavours. Last year's criticisms of over-complexity have to an extent been taken to heart. It remains 'food that you stop and look at – and then eat.' Two outstanding dishes on the summer menu have been the mille-feuille of whole langoustines with spinach and a sauce flavoured with mint and mustard, and the biscuit léger aux framboises. The menu provides a lot of reading, with eight starters, mainly vegetable and seafood; five fish, mostly local, as in turbot in a Noilly Prat sauce with redcurrants; seven meat; eight sweets. Thought and creativity seems to have gone into each one. On a spring menu Dorset veal is casseroled with its sweetbreads and horseradish. By summer the fillet is served with mango and lime. But it is perhaps in the decorative starters and sweets that the kitchen has excelled, for instance the plate of four chocolate sweets. Service is increasingly French in its personnel and more relaxed, which is essential in this overstated atmosphere. The wine list runs to 300 bottles with a predictable emphasis on the expensive, including a dozen Ch. Latour spanning '80 back to '59, but a careful sift through the pages also reveals some good quality wines just under £10, especially in the Rhône.

[GHG] *after the details of an entry means that the establishment is also included in* The Good Hotel Guide.

'Our visit to Glasgow was part of a touring holiday, during which we stayed at hotels listed in the English and Scottish Tourist Boards' guides. These were three-and four-crown listed hotels. In every case the toast at breakfast was made from white, pappy bread. Would it be possible to start a campaign to encourage the serving of wholemeal bread, or at least a proper form of white bread?' On eating in Scotland

CHEF: Pierre Chevillard PROPRIETOR: Martin Skan
OPEN: all week
MEALS: 12.30 to 2, 7.30 to 9.30
PRICES: £35 (£46), Set L £16 (£22), Set D £30 (£38). Service inc
CARDS: Access, Amex, Diners, Visa
SEATS: 120. 6 tables outside. Private parties: 20 main room, 6 and 80 private rooms. Car-park, 100 places. Children's helpings. No children under 7. Jacket and tie. No cigars/pipes in dining-room
ACCOMMODATION: 44 rooms, all with bath/shower. Rooms for disabled. B&B £106 to £116. No children under 7. Afternoon teas. Garden. Swimming-pool. Tennis. Golf. Snooker. TV. Phone. Scenic. Doors close at 12 [GHG]

NEWARK Nottinghamshire — map 5

Gannets [9/20]

35 Castlegate, Newark NE24 1AZ
NEWARK (0636) 702066 — £5–£9

Vegetarian and meat dishes share the bill at Hilary Bower's self-service restaurant by the castle ruins. Daily specials are enterprising: seaweed roulade with sweet pepper filling; meatballs in tomato and celery sauce; spicy rissoles with herby yoghurt sauce. In addition there are pâtés, quiches and colourful, adventurous salads – such as pasta with mange-tout and pepper. House French is £4.50 a litre, otherwise there is Hugh Rock's elderflower wine and locally pressed apple juice.

CHEF/PROPRIETOR: Hilary L. Bower
OPEN: Mon to Sat
CLOSED: 1 week at Christmas
MEALS: 10 to 4.30 (L 11.45 to 2.30)
PRICES: £5 (£8)
SEATS: 38. 4 tables outside. Vegetarian meals. Children's helpings. No smoking between 12 and 2.30. Music. Self-service

NEWCASTLE UPON TYNE Tyne & Wear — map 7

Cafe Procope [9/20]

35 The Side, Quayside, NE1 3JE
091-232 3848 — £11

The quality of the cooking at this incarnation of the famous Paris literary restaurant in the sixth arrondissement, plus some bargain wines and long opening hours, make it an attractive addition to the city's eating places. More of a café than a restaurant in style; jumble-sale décor and an eclectic menu ranging from Afro-Caribbean to traditional British with German specialities and a leaning to vegetarianism. Recommended dishes have been mushroom Stroganoff, marinated lamb casserole, wild mushroom feuilleté, falafel with hummus, chickpea stew, a cheese spätzli. The sweets trolley is rich and gooey, offset by fruit salad – all home-made. Coffee is from

Pumphreys. The 14 wines are all under £6.70 and seem to operate on a flat mark-up of £1.50 a bottle, which is good news. There are also eight imported beers of note, including Orval from Belgium.

CHEFS: Karen Kennedy and Angela Deutschman PROPRIETORS: Karen Kennedy and Nicky Wynne
OPEN: Tue to Sun
MEALS: 9.30am to 10.30pm (5.30 Sun)
PRICES: £7 (£11), Snacks from £1
SEATS: 50. Private parties: 50 main room. Vegetarian meals. Children's helpings. No-smoking area. Wheelchair access (1 step; also WC). Music

Fisherman's Lodge [12/20]

Jesmond Dene, NE7 7BQ
091-281 3281 £17–£33

Set in the park beside a stream, this is generally recognised as the major expensive restaurant in Tyneside and is well supported for special occasions. The emphasis is on fish, but there are good roast meat dishes in wine and stock sauces, too. The repertoire ranges from the plain, as in half a dozen oysters, to ragouts and grills with cream and herb sauces. There are good iced sweets and parfaits. Service is young and professional and the décor benefits from a sunny evening. In an area which often calls itself a culinary desert, it is noticeable that the Lodge is often full, even on a Monday. Wines are well spread out, with much in the £7 to £10 range. CELLARMAN'S CHOICE: Château Les Ormes de Pez '83, £14.50.

CHEF: Simon Tennet PROPRIETORS: Franco and Pamela Cetoloni
OPEN: Mon to Sat, exc Sat L
CLOSED: 25 Dec to 2 Jan
MEALS: 12 to 2, 7 to 11
PRICES: £24 (£33), Set L from £11.50 (£17)
CARDS: Access, Amex, Diners, Visa
SEATS: 70. 3 tables outside. Private parties: 14 main room; 14,40 private rooms. Car-park, 45 places. Children's helpings. No children under 6. Smart dress preferred. Wheelchair access

Great Wall [10/20]

35–39 Bath Lane, NE4 5SP
091-232 0517 and 7616 £8–£20

The décor is smart and comfortable, and the kitchen delivers all-purpose Chinese cooking, including Peking duck, lemon chicken and some elementary vegetarian dishes including imitation sweet-and-sour pork made with cashews, various gluten specialities and lo hon chai (mixed vegetables with Chinese mushrooms and soy). There are also good reports of spare ribs, crispy seaweed and chicken with cashews. In addition to the menu, there's a buffet every weekday evening. Chinese house wine is £7.50 a bottle.

All letters to the Guide *are acknowledged.*

CHEF: Peter Ma PROPRIETOR: Wah Fuk Ma
OPEN: all week
MEALS: 12 to 2, 6 to 11.30 (noon to 11 Sun)
PRICES: £12 (£20), Set L £3.20 (£8), Set D £10 (£15)
CARDS: Access, Amex, Diners, Visa
SEATS: 140. Private parties: 100 main room. Vegetarian meals. Children welcome. Wheelchair access. Music. Air-conditioned

Jade Garden [10/20]

53 Stowell Street, NE1 4YB
091-261 5889 £8–£21

The longest-standing of the old-style Chinese restaurants in the city. The 200-item menu is hard-core Cantonese and some ingredients are only for the brave or the initiated: fish head and stomach, preserved fruit peel, deep-fried conch, pork intestines. Sixty one-plate rice and noodle dishes are huge and good value, highlighting the best roast and barbecued meats in the city. A couple of new dishes – salad duck with mixed fruit, and prawns with milk sauce, crispy noodles, ham and cashew nuts – seem to be designed for a different market. Drinks include a dozen Chinese liqueurs as well as Chinese house wines.

CHEF: Chuen Fai Liu PROPRIETORS: Alex Chung and Chuen Fai Liu
OPEN: all week
MEALS: noon to 11.30 (12 Fri and Sat)
PRICES: £11 (£21), Set L £3 (£8), Set D from £18 (£29) for two
CARDS: Access, Amex, Diners, Visa
SEATS: 120. 20 tables outside. Private parties: 120 main room. Vegetarian meals. Children welcome. Wheelchair access (also WC). Music. Air-conditioned

New Emperor [10/20]

Forth House, Berwick Street, NE1 5EF
091-232 8856 £14–£21

Extensively refurbished, but still one of the most genuine Chinese restaurants in Newcastle. The bizarrely phrased menu, with its 'pure vegetable chilli and sour soup', 'glutament rice parcel' and 'occidentally orientated dishes' is a westernised version of Cantonese. The strength is in the dim-sum, noodles and roast meats. Also look for the daily specials – meat and fish hot-pots, stir-fried dishes with preserved vegetables or mange-tout. On Sunday there is crispy suckling pig. Drink tea, otherwise there is saké or house wine at £6.50 a litre.

CHEF: Mr Yau PROPRIETOR: Peter Wu
OPEN: all week
MEALS: noon to 3.30am
PRICES: £11 (£19), Set D £9 (£14) to £15 (£21). Minimum £4.50
CARDS: Access, Amex, Diners, Visa
SEATS: 200. Private parties: 150 main room, 100 private room. Vegetarian meals. Children's helpings. Wheelchair access. Music

Rupali [10/20]

6 Bigg Market, NE1 1UW
091-232 8629 £15

The décor may be functional, but the food in Abdul Latif's high-profile curry house goes from strength to strength. A long menu is well described and dishes are defined by their regional origins: from the Punjab come tandooris; from South India there is murgh badaami with almond sauce; from Central India and Lucknow are birianis and shami kebab. Vegetarian and vegetable dishes are a strong point: all kinds of dhal from Gujerat, Andhra Pradesh and Kamataka; runner beans with mustard seed from Orissa; aloo dunn from Bengal. There are cheap deals at lunch-time and for early-evening eaters, plus a 'happy night' menu offering a full meal plus a glass of wine for under £6 on Thursdays.

CHEF: Abdul Khalick PROPRIETOR: Abdul Latif
OPEN: all week, exc Sun L
MEALS: 12 to 2.30, 7 to 11.30
PRICES: £9 (£15)
CARDS: Access, Amex, Diners, Visa
SEATS: 54. Private parties: 50 main room. Vegetarian meals. Children's helpings. Smart dress preferred. Music

Sachins [10/20]

Forth Banks, NE1 3SG
091-261 9035 £15–£20

This converted pub now provides some of the best Punjabi cooking in Tyneside, allied to some real ales. Specialities include butter chicken; murgh jalfrezi; hasina kebab. House wine £5.95.

CHEF: Dinesh Rawlley PROPRIETOR: L.G. Cunningham
OPEN: Mon to Sat
CLOSED: Easter and Christmas
MEALS: 12 to 2.15, 6 to 11.15
PRICES: £13 (£20), Set L and D from £11 (£15)
CARDS: Access, Amex, Diners, Visa
SEATS: 98. 3 tables outside. Private parties: 60 main room, 40 private room. Car-park, 6 places. Vegetarian meals. Children welcome. Wheelchair access. Music

Tyne & Wear Round-up

BAR MEALS: *Wooden Doll*, Hudson Street, North Shields (091-257 3747).
ITALIAN: *Mama Mia*, 46 Pudding Chare, Newcastle upon Tyne (091-232 7193); *Amigo's*, 21 Mosley Street, Newcastle upon Tyne (0632 32111).

'I am becoming extremely bored with being presented with selections of miniature desserts. They are so teasingly small that individually they become incoherent. Or sometimes the combinations are so widely fluctuating in flavour and quality they cancel each other out.' On eating in London

NORTH HUISH Devon map 1

▲ *Brookdale House* [13/20]

North Huish TQ10 9NR
GARA BRIDGE (0548 82) 402 and 415 £24

The Trevor-Ropers, formerly at Knight's Farm at Burghfield, have settled into this lovely Gothic house in a wooded dell. Small-holders and local farms provide fruit, vegetables and poultry. British cheeses and salad make a separate third course on a set-price meal. The emphasis has shifted now exclusively to the evening meal, though there are good reports of afternoon tea for residents. There are three choices per course of obviously French-inspired but nonetheless Devon-accented food, unostentatiously assembled so as not to conflict with the cellar. Recommended dishes have been pumpkin soup, chicken and leek feuilleté, lamb with an aubergine charlotte. The Englishness comes out in the sweets, usually a hot, a cold and a freezing, as in chocolate pudding, pears in red wine, sorbets. The selection of 80 wines is exceptional in quality and originality. Good choices from the New World include New Zealand Cloudy Bay Sauvignon '87 at £10.95, Australian Cape Mentelle Cabernet Sauvignon '85, at £14.65, and some excellent Chardonnay and Pinot Noir from Oregon. Some good, familiar wines from Torres in Spain are outshone by the rare, Meursault-like Torres Milmanda Chardonnay '86, £19.95. A select list of Burgundies comes from the best of growers, and clarets are well chosen, from the relatively modest up to a handful of finer châteaux and older vintages. The local Clyston '84 English wine is one of a few offerings under £10. The selection of sweet wines is brief but again original: a German Scheurebe Beerenauslese or Australian Botrytised Semillon might be a tastier bet than under-age ('83) Sauternes. Nothing so common here as a Muscat de Beaumes de Venise; Muscat de Rivesaltes or Muscat de St-Jean du Minervois both come at £2 a glass.

CHEF: Carol Trevor-Roper PROPRIETORS: Charles and Carol Trevor-Roper
OPEN: all week, D only (L residents only, on request)
CLOSED: 23 Dec to 23 Jan
MEALS: 12 to 2, 7.30 to 9
PRICES: Set D £17.50 (£24)
CARDS: Access, Visa
SEATS: 24. Private parties: 8 main room. Car-park, 15 places. No children under 10. No smoking. Wheelchair access
ACCOMMODATION: 8 rooms, all with bath/shower. B&B £45 to £60. No children under 10. Garden. TV. Phone. Scenic. Doors close at 12. Confirm by 7 [GHG]

All details are as accurate as possible at the time of going to press. Please notify the Guide *office of any changes.*

'Let me say it is no easy business getting waiting staff. Wages are good, tips are good but last time I advertised in the local paper for waiting staff, I had no replies at all. We are doing the best we can in a part of the country where waiters and waitresses don't seem to want to work.' West country restaurateur

NORTHLEACH Gloucestershire map 2

▲ *Fossebridge Inn* [11/20]

Fossebridge GL54 3JS
FOSSEBRIDGE (028 572) 721
on A429, 3m from Northleach £22–£30

The inn on the banks of the River Coln dates from Tudor times and the Bridge Bar is the oldest part. Inside, it is higgledy-piggledy. Meals in the first-floor restaurant and the ground-floor bar come from the same kitchen and are along the same lines as at the Roberts' previous pub, the White Bear at Shipston on Stour. Both menus combine usual pub fare with ambitious restaurant dishes: mousse of duck livers with smoked duck breast; mussels in puff pastry with white wine sauce. Copious main courses backed up by plentiful supplies of home-baked rolls are excellent value. Good dishes have included grey mullet with fennel sauce and fillet of local venison. Ploughman's comes with 'British Farmhouse Cheese' and sweets such as bread-and-butter pudding are well made. The cooking also shows a more sophisticated touch: stuffed sea-bass in pastry is a half-inch slice of cut-across flaky pastry enclosing lobster mousse containing chunks of sea-bass, accompanied by small, flaky-skinned potatoes and a mound of French beans. The wine list is very much French based with a sound but uninspired choice of Loire wines and the odd star in the Burgundy selection, Chablis *premier cru* Vaillons '85, from Philippe Testut, £22.50, and Morey-St-Denis Les Sorbets, Domaine Serveau '81, £33.50. Clarets are well chosen and fairly priced – the oldest wine is Ch. de Sales '70, £60. Most Rhône reds are from the reliable Paul Jaboulet-Aîné. Antinori Italians and Bodegas Riojanas Riojas are excellent and the choice of Australian and Californian wines dependable to good. Sweet wines include a Rüdesheimer Berg Rottland Auslese '76 by Deinhard, £25, Sauternes from Château Filhot and Château de la Chartreuse and Southern French Muscat José Sala, £7.50. Otherwise there is Marston's Pedigree on handpump.

CHEF: Bruce Buchan PROPRIETORS: Hugh and Suzanne Roberts, Janis and Andy Rork
OPEN: all week
MEALS: 12.30 to 2, 7.30 to 9.30 (10 Fri and Sat)
PRICES: £22 (£30), Set L and D £16.50 (£22). Snacks from £1.35
CARDS: Access, Amex, Diners, Visa
SEATS: 60. 4 tables outside. Private parties: 24 main room, 24 private room. Car-park, 50 places. Vegetarian meals. Children's helpings by arrangement. Smart dress preferred
ACCOMMODATION: 13 rooms, all with bath/shower. Rooms for disabled. B&B from £45 Deposit: £45. Children are restricted. Baby facilities. Pets welcome. Garden. Fishing. TV. Phone. Scenic. Doors close at 11. Confirm by 4

All inspections are carried out anonymously.

New this year are County Round-ups, mostly, but not always, listed under the county town. To find a County Round-up, check the maps at the back; towns listing a Round-up are underlined.

Old Woolhouse [14/20]

The Square, Northleach GL54 3EE
COTSWOLD (0451) 60366 £29

From the outside, nothing suggests that this old stone house is a restaurant at all. But inside is a classy dining-room with antique chairs and engraved wine glasses on the table. The Astics continue to run the place in their own, personable, kindly way. It is astonishing to find such an idiosyncratic, family-run, utterly French restaurant in the middle of a small Cotswold village, yet it is completely convincing, despite the short, rather limited repertoire. Jacques Astic adds perhaps one dish a year to a set-price dinner menu that takes in fillet of sea-bass nestling against a chunk of lobster on a buttery, boozy lobster sauce; or loin of veal, kidneys and sweetbreads in another powerful sauce, this time with butter and Noilly Prat. Alternatively, there might be turbot in red wine sauce or a rib of beef with mustard sauce. To finish there is always St Marcellin cheese and memorable prune tart with a crisp French pastry case. A pot of strong coffee comes with excellent home-made petits fours. The leather-bound wine list is dominated by pedigree Burgundies and clarets.

CHEF: Jacques Astic PROPRIETORS: Jacques and Jenny Astic
OPEN: Tue to Sat D, L by arrangement
CLOSED: Christmas
MEALS: 8.15 to 10
PRICES: Set L and D £22 (£29). Service inc
SEATS: 18. Children welcome

Wickens [13/20]

Market Place, Northleach GL54 3EJ
COTSWOLD (0451) 60421 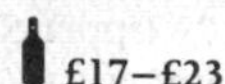 £17–£23

Listed in the *Guide* in the early 1980s as the Country Friends under the Whittakers (now at Dorrington, see entry), the slate-roofed Cotswold stone house in the centre of the village has since gone through three different sets of owners. Since October 1987 it has passed into the steadier hands of Christopher and Joanna Wickens, formerly listed at the Corner Cupboard Dining Room at Winchcombe, 1984 to 1987, and at Food for Thought at Cheltenham from 1976 to 1982. They have their own brand of informality and a fondness for fresh local ingredients, although the cooking seems now to have a lighter touch with less cream and butter than in the Corner Cupboard. The Englishness of their cooking shows in the good soups served with warm granary bread, the vegetables (big leeks, coarsely mashed carrot and celeriac, and potato chunks tossed in yoghurt with cheese all featured in December), and the new generation of farmhouse cheeses – Sharpham, Ashprington goats', Single Gloucester with nettles. Centrepieces have included quail on a bed of shredded vegetables and pheasant with calvados and apples. Other signatures the Wickens have taken with them on their travels include the evolution of a vegetarian cuisine with particularly fine salads, Joanna's excellent puddings, particularly the crème brûlée and the sticky toffee pudding, the home-made chocolate mint squares with the Kenyan cafetière coffee. A new conservatory is being built and is scheduled to open in autumn 1988, which will increase the number of seats (and also bring the toilets indoors). The wine list is small, but with the accent firmly on value. The wine list is very sensibly laid out, providing a selection of between seven and nine wines each at £6.50, £7.75 and £9 per bottle, although around 20 more expensive wines, including mature clarets, Burgundies and Rhônes are displayed in the bar, for more demanding customers. But the three basic selections are imaginatively chosen and extremely good value, ranging from Pinot Blanc d'Alsace and Vin de Pays des Coteaux du Quercy to Killawarra Chardonnay from New South Wales, Romeira Garrafeira from Portugal, Pacherenc du Vic Bilh and Madiran Domaine Bouscasse. There are four English wines on the regular list and six sweeties, including Muscat de Beaumes de Venise, Domaine de Durban, £13.90, Château Doisy-Vedrines '75, £17.80, and Brown Bros Orange Muscat and Flora, £7.75 per half-bottle.

CHEFS/PROPRIETORS: Christopher and Joanna Wickens
OPEN: Tue to Sat D, and Sun L
MEALS: 12.30 to 1.15, 7.15 to 9.15
PRICES: Set L £10.50 (£17), Set D £13.50 (£19) to £16.90 (£23)
CARD: Visa
SEATS: 36. Private parties: 22 main room. Children welcome. No smoking in dining-room. Wheelchair access (4 steps; also WC). Music

NORWICH Norfolk map 6

Brasserie l'Abri [10/20]

79 Upper St Giles, Norwich NR2 1AB
NORWICH (0603) 633522 £19

The setting is the French merchants' quarter of old Norwich, and the owners have continued the Gallic theme. The décor is pure brasserie – bare beechwood floors, uncluttered walls, pot plants – and so is the menu. Spinach and bacon salad, filled crêpes and fish mousse on one side, trio of steamed fish, free-range chicken with wild mushrooms, or venison with port and mango on the other. Vegetables are organic where possible and the cheeseboard is good. House French is £5.50; the list is from Adnams.

CHEFS: Woody Dumas, Michael Richmond and Vanessa Comer
PROPRIETORS: Andy Gibbs and Matthew Rees
OPEN: Mon to Sat, exc Sat L
MEALS: 12.15 to 1.30, 7 to 9.30
PRICES: £15 (£19)
CARDS: Access, Amex, Visa
SEATS: 40. Private parties: 16 main room. Children's helpings. Wheelchair access. Music

If, in your opinion, a restaurant is not maintaining the standard of its rating, please inform the Guide *office. Report forms are at the back of the book.*

Brasted's [10/20]

8–10 St Andrews Hill, Norwich NR2 1AD
NORWICH (0603) 625949 £23

John Brasted's restaurant is in a period house in an historic part of the city, two minutes' walk from the castle and the cathedral. The interior has been designed with flair, with candy-striped Regency drapes, Indian-style lamps and billowing fabrics over the ceiling. After a shaky patch, the cooking seems to be back on course. The menu and presentation veer between *nouvelle* and old-fashioned. Spinach and Stilton crêpes or terrine of chicken, pork and tuna in herb pastry might precede sweetbreads with cream and sherry sauce or noisettes of lamb with honey and rosemary. Fish is a strong point: Cromer crab is potted or served thermidor; steamed fillets of sole are wrapped around salmon mousseline with dill sauce. Vegetables are fresh and well handled. Sweets and petits fours are home made. Useful choice of around 40 wines, including CELLARMAN'S CHOICE: Sancerre, Domaine de St Louis '86, at £11.50.

CHEFS: J. Brasted, P. Morgan and P. Chipperfield PROPRIETOR: J.D. Brasted
OPEN: Mon to Sun, exc Sat L and Sun D
MEALS: 12 to 2, 7 to 10.30
PRICES: £17 (£23)
CARDS: Access, Amex, Diners, Visa
SEATS: 35. Private parties: 14 main room, 8 private room. Vegetarian meals. Children welcome

Green's Seafood [10/20]

82 Upper St Giles Street, Norwich NR3 1AQ
NORWICH (0603) 623733 £24

Fresh fish is the attraction in Dennis Crompton's long, narrow restaurant with its entrance through a courtyard. He buys direct from Lowestoft and visits the local market for Cromer crabs. Dishes work best when they are simple: fresh whitebait; grilled grey mullet. Vegetables follow the same principle. Coffee and petits fours are well reported. House French £5.60.

CHEF/PROPRIETOR: Dennis W. Crompton
OPEN: Tue to Sat, exc Sat L
CLOSED: 2 weeks at Christmas
MEALS: 12.15 to 2.15, 7 to 11
PRICES: £17 (£24)
CARDS: Access, Visa
SEATS: 54. Private parties: 30 main room. No children under 8. Smart dress preferred. No pipes/cigars in dining-room. Music. Air-conditioned

▲ *This restaurant offers accommodation.*

Please keep the Guide *informed of any changes to the restaurants listed. Report forms are at the back of the book.*

Marco's [11/20]

17 Pottergate, Norwich NR2 1DS
NORWICH (0603) 624044 £16–£27

There was a great howl of outrage that Marco's was omitted last year. Why? Why? Why? 'I eat there all the time and it is fine' is the refrain. Maybe so, but the office does not have a crystal ball, nor does the *Guide* have limitless funds to be spent in restaurants that no one can be bothered to write in about. What would these indignant readers say if they went to another city, only to find the *Guide* including restaurants on a nod and a wink? Alas for poor Marco Vessalio, not only were his friends silent, but he was chanced upon by a senior inspector who took him to task for his poor value compared to the cheap pasta places opening around the city, and for some off-hand service. But enough of that, because, plainly enough, customers have endorsed him again and praise the cannelloni, the scampi, the king prawns, the seafood pancakes, the melon enveloped in Parma ham, the fresh fruits and cheeses to finish. House Italian is £7 a litre. CELLARMAN'S CHOICE: Barolo '78, £20; Anglianico del Vulture '82, £16. Italian beer, too.

CHEF/PROPRIETOR: Marco Vessalio
OPEN: Tue to Sat
CLOSED: 20 Aug to 20 Sept
MEALS: 12.30 to 2, 7.30 to 10
PRICES: £20 (£27), Set L £11 (£16). Cover 50p. Minimum £11. Service inc
CARDS: Access, Amex, Carte Blanche, Diners, Visa
SEATS: 40. Private parties: 12 main room, 16 private room. Vegetarian meals. Children's helpings. Wheelchair access. Music

Norfolk Round-up

VIEW: *Blakeney Hotel*, Nr Holt (0263 740797).
VEGETARIAN: *Eat Naturally*, 11 Wensum Street, Norwich (0603 660838).
COFFEE SHOP: *Just John's Delicatique*, 13a White Lion Street, Norwich (0603 21762).
THAI: *Diss Coffee House*, Norfolk House Yard, 5 St Nicholas Street, Diss (0379 651580).
BAR MEALS: *Sir Garnet Wolseley*, 36 Market Place, Norwich (0603 615892).

NOTTINGHAM Nottinghamshire map 5

Les Artistes Gourmands [12/20]

61 Wollaton Road, Beeston, Nottingham NG9 2NG
NOTTINGHAM (0602) 228288 £16–£19

The popularity of this small French restaurant has led to an extension into next door and the taking on of a pâtisserie chef. The cooking is a good slice of provincial France – boned pig's trotters; saucisson de Lyon; snails; steak au poivre – allied to some more modern dishes like fillet of beef with three-peppercorn sauce; salmon with thyme; a fiery, chilli-seasoned consommé with fresh fish. Fish is playing a larger role in the menu generally – pike quenelles, a selection of smoked fish in a velouté sauce, salmon terrine. Cheeses are well kept. Service gets frequent mentions for its charm. The good-value wine list includes seven dessert wines by the glass or half-bottle. House French is £7.80. CELLARMAN'S CHOICE: Jurançon '86, £8.50; Beaumes de Venise, Domaine Les Goubert '83, £12.20.

CHEF: J.L. David PROPRIETOR: Eddy Keon
OPEN: Mon to Sat, exc Mon and Sat L
CLOSED: 1 week Jan, 1 week Aug
MEALS: 12 to 1.30, 7 to 10.30
PRICES: Set L from £11.90 (£16), Set D from £14.20 (£19). Service inc
CARDS: Access, Amex, Diners, Visa
SEATS: 65. Private parties: 35 main room. Vegetarian meals. Children's helpings. No-smoking area. Wheelchair access. Music

Chand [10/20]

26 Mansfield Road, Nottingham, NG1 3GX
NOTTINGHAM (0602) 474103 £9–£15

One of the less anglicised and one of the most consistent Indian restaurants in Nottingham. The menu has well-described Persian, Kashmiri and Punjabi dishes, alongside standard tandooris, bhunas and dhansaks. Baltis also feature and there are good reports of bringal chicken cooked with mint, Kashmiri masala and spring onion, and slow-steamed meat sabji. Drink lassi or one of the imported lagers.

CHEF/PROPRIETOR: M. Ayub
OPEN: all week
CLOSED: 25 Dec
MEALS: 12 to 2.30, 5.30 to 12.30
PRICES: £8, (£15), Set L £3.50 (£9), Set D from £4 (£9) Minimum £6.50
CARDS: Access, Amex, Diners, Visa
SEATS: 75. Private parties: 45 main room, 45 private room. Vegetarian meals. Children's helpings. Wheelchair access. Music. Air-conditioned

Ocean City [11/20]

100–104 Derby Road, Nottingham NG1 5FB
NOTTINGHAM (0602) 475095 £13–£23

Out of the city on the Derby Road, not far from the University, this fine Cantonese restaurant is popular with Chinese students, who come for cheap dim-sum lunches. The full menu moves confidently between old-style Cantonese classics – roast meats, one-plate dishes, hot-pots, and specialities such as steamed eel with crispy pork – and fashionable ideas along the lines of sizzling monkfish with chilli and black-bean sauce, or fillet steak in birds' nest. Young, lively service.

Restaurants awarded a rosette have had an entry in every Guide *since 1980. See Restaurants of the decade on page 21.*

CHEFS: Mr Wong and Mr Wong PROPRIETORS: Dragon Wonder Ltd
OPEN: all week
CLOSED: Christmas
MEALS: noon to midnight (10.30 Sun)
PRICES: £15 (£23), Set L and D £15 (£26) for 2. Minimum £7.50 at D. Service 10%
CARDS: Access, Amex, Diners, Visa
SEATS: 300. Private parties: 200 main room, 80 and 120 private rooms. Vegetarian meals. Children welcome. Smart dress preferred. Wheelchair access (also WC). Music. Air-conditioned

Sagar [10/20]

473 Mansfield Road, Sherwood, Nottingham NG5 2DR
NOTTINGHAM (0602) 622014 £6–£19

Mohammed Khizer sold out his share in Chand (see entry) and is now concentrating his efforts on this restaurant, well out of the city centre in the suburb of Sherwood. The menu is basically old-style curry house, but flavours are authentic and the food is good value (the price of most dishes includes rice, poppadum and chutney). There are good reports of karahi chicken, king prawn pasanda and makhani chicken. Drink lager.

CHEF: Amjaid Habib PROPRIETOR: Mohammed Khizer
OPEN: all week
CLOSED: 25 Dec
MEALS: 12 to 2.30, 5.30 to 12.30
PRICES: Set L £3.50 (£6), Set D £13 (£17) to £15 (£19)
CARDS: Access, Amex, Visa
SEATS: 45. Private parties: 45 main room. Car-park, 6 places. Vegetarian meals. Children's helpings. No pipes in dining-room. Wheelchair access (4 steps). Music. Air-conditioned

Shogun [10/20]

95 Talbot Street, Nottingham NG1 5GN
NOTTINGHAM (0602) 475611 £9–£22

The monolithic old warehouse has been turned into an elegant Japanese restaurant. Lunches and other set meals provide a good introduction to the cuisine. The format is the same, with only the main course changing – hors d'oeuvres, sashimi, grilled fish, rice, soup and dessert. All the main aspects of the cooking are there – sushi, one-pot dishes like shabu-shabu and sukiyaki; tofu; tempura. Kaiseki is served on Tuesday, Wednesday and Thursday evenings – order at least two days ahead. Wines from £5.10. Saké from £3.80.

CHEFS: Keiji Tomiyama and Makoeo Kato PROPRIETORS: Keiji and Sally Tomiyama
OPEN: Mon to Sat, exc Mon L
MEALS: 12 to 1.45, 7 to 11
PRICES: £10 (£18), Set L £4.95 (£9), Set D £10.90 (£16) to £16.30 (£22)
CARDS: Access, Amex, Diners, Visa
SEATS: 53. Private parties: 48 main room. Vegetarian meals. Children welcome. Music

Nottinghamshire Round-up
FRENCH: *Goff's*, 4 Burns Lane, Warsop (0623 844137).
VEGETARIAN: *Ten*, 10 Commerce Street, Lace Market, Nottingham (0602 585211).
ITALIAN: *Lidio's*, 2 Kings Walk, Nottingham (0602 473767).
POLISH: *Starapolska*, King John's Arcade, 13-15 Bridlesmith Gate, Nottingham (0602 502672).

OAKHAM Leicestershire map 5

▲ *Whipper-In* [new entry, zero rated]

Market Place, Oakham LE15 6DT
OAKHAM (0572) 56971 £13–£22

Oakham is fortunate not to be on the main road to anywhere, so it is fairly quiet except on market days on Wednesdays and Saturdays. The shire décor reflects the area and there are certain natural airs and graces to the running of the building, a sister to the Feathers at Woodstock (see entry). The menu is attractive sounding, moderately ambitious and does not go over the top on showiness. There are char-grills for those eschewing the likes of guinea-fowl with honey, leeks, garlic and wild mushrooms. The basics like pastry, hollandaise, soufflé are accomplished. Seventy wines. More reports, please.

CHEF: Paul Cherrington PROPRIETORS: F.S.I. Hotels plc
OPEN: all week
MEALS: 12 to 2, 7.30 to 9.30 (9 Sun)
PRICES: £16 (£22), Set L £8.95 (£13) to £9.50 (£14), Set D £15.95 (£21) to £16.95 (£22), Snacks from £2.25
CARDS: Access, Amex, Diners, Visa
SEATS: 45. 3 tables outside. Private parties: 16 main room, 16 and 45 private rooms. Vegetarian meals. Children's helpings (Sun L only). Smart dress preferred. No pipes in dining-room. Wheelchair access. Music
ACCOMMODATION: 24 rooms, all with bath/shower. B&B £43 to £68. Children welcome. Baby facilities. Pets welcome, by arrangement. Afternoon teas. TV. Phone. Confirm by previous day

OKEHAMPTON Devon map 1

Partners [10/20]

38 Red Lion Yard, Fore Street, Okehampton EX20 1AW
OKEHAMPTON (0837) 4662 £11–£16

The round dining-room gives the impression of a ballroom, but the cut of this venture is less ornate, more that of an eating house than a restaurant offering morning coffee, snacks and teas as well as dinners. The décor is reassuringly like a wine-red tea-room, skilfully run by Jane Masters while David Beazley cooks. The menu is short with four dishes per course and at its best with the simpler dishes that show off the quality of the ingredients which change from day to day. Good tarts and unfancy dishes like grilled lamb cutlets with herb butter, pan-fried lamb with herbs, and precisely timed fish, work well. Saucing can let the more ambitious dishes down. The wine list concentrates under £10 but with 18 of the 28 wines also in half-bottles.

CHEF: David Beazley PROPRIETORS: David Beazley and Jane Masters
OPEN: Tue to Sun, exc Sun D (Mon L in summer)
MEALS: 12 to 2.30, 7 to 9.30
PRICES: Set L £7.50 (£11), Set D £12 (£16), Snacks from £1.15
SEATS: 40. 3 tables outside. Private parties: 45 main room, 45 private room. Vegetarian meals. Children's helpings. No cigars/pipes in dining-room. Wheelchair access (also WC)

ORFORD Suffolk map 3

Butley-Orford Oysterage [9/20]

10 YEARS

Market Hill, Orford IP12 2PQ
ORFORD (0394) 450 277 £12

The Pinney family's black and white-fronted café stands almost in the shadow of Orford's monolithic stone church with its echoes of Benjamin Britten. Not much has changed in 20 years. Like the Aldeburgh Festival, it is still one of Suffolk's landmarks. The enterprise couldn't be simpler, and the place maintains its reputation with excellent oysters grown in Butley Creek and superb smoked fish. Irish salmon is cured using the family's own system, otherwise there are eels, trouts, sprats and bloaters; smoked cod's roe is turned into a thick, pungent taramosalata. Other cooked items can be less memorable. An upstairs bar and dining-room doubles as a picture gallery, and there are take aways from the shop next door. Drink English house wine, a bottle of Muscadet or vinho verde, all around the £5.50 mark (half-bottles offered too).

CHEF: Mrs M. Pinney PROPRIETORS: Mrs M. Pinney, Richard Pinney and William Pinney
OPEN: all week
CLOSED: beg. Jan to mid-Feb
MEALS: 12 to 2.15, 6 to 8.30
PRICES: £10 (£12)
SEATS: 75. Private parties: 25 main room. Car-park, 20 places. Children welcome. Wheelchair access (also WC)

OTTERY ST MARY Devon map 1

Lodge [12/20]

17 Silver Street, Ottery St Mary EX11 1DB
OTTERY ST MARY (040 481) 2356 £25

The Lodge runs on enthusiasm. Diane Shenton is the driving force, working almost single-handed, and the cooking shows her flair for combining ingredients in unexpected ways: smoked mallard is served with a sauce of preserved mushrooms; medallions of veal get a Roquefort sauce. The short menu ranges far and wide, from Normandy pheasant with apples and calvados to American 'blackened' salmon with lime hollandaise, but there's also a strong British undercurrent: mushrooms are topped with bacon and laverbread; pigeon and quail pie is made to an Old English recipe, and vegetables are ample. The substantial list of over 70 wines is well described and arranged by style as well as region. There's a good choice of half-bottles, five house wines from £5.75 a bottle and CELLARMAN'S CHOICE: Brown Bros Chardonnay '86, £11.

CHEF/PROPRIETOR: Diane Shenton
OPEN: Tue to Sun, exc Sun D
MEALS: 12 to 2, 7 to 9.30
PRICES: Set L and D £19.50 (£25)
CARDS: Amex, Diners, Visa
SEATS: 25. Private parties: 28 main room. Vegetarian meals. Children's helpings. Wheelchair access (also WC). Music

OXFORD Oxfordshire map 2

Browns [10/20]

5–9 Woodstock Road, Oxford OX2 6HA
OXFORD (0865) 511995 £15

An institution, on a par with the Bodleian; the extraordinary buzz increases down the years. The potted palms, the hanging plants, the waiters in their long aprons and the waitresses in whatever are all part of the attraction. There is no pretence; the food is casual, but good and fresh, with big helpings of pasta, salads and grills, pies – steak, kidney and Guinness – game and chicken, backed by pub-style specials, such as leg of lamb in Oxford Sauce, salmon cutlet in sorrel sauce, mussels in white wine, vegetables in a green herb sauce, or grilled trout and plaice. There are croissants for late breakfasts and muffins for afternoon tea, when a pianist plays. The no-smoking area has been enlarged. Cocktails (including non-alcoholic versions) and 25 wines; house French is £4.75; CELLARMAN'S CHOICE: house claret from Berry Bros, £6.85.

CHEF: Eamonn Hunter PROPRIETORS: J.L. Mogford and J.P. Mayhew
OPEN: all week
CLOSED: 24 to 28 Dec
MEALS: 11 (12 Sun) to 11.30
PRICES: £10 (£15)
SEATS: 220. 4 tables outside. Vegetarian meals. Children's helpings. Separate smoking area. Wheelchair access (also WC). Music. Air-conditioned

Cherwell Boathouse [11/20]

Bardwell Road, Oxford OX8 1JD
OXFORD (0865) 52746  £15

The drift of quality restaurateuring has been back to the residential areas of the city with the revival of this old fixture, Petit Blanc and also 15 North Parade. The Boathouse is on the banks of the Cherwell, at the end of a narrow lane beside playing fields. Punts can be hired by the hour. The outside setting has the edge on a nondescript inside but the qualities are a long established wine list and a simple short menu with a variety of warm salads, some classical flavour combinations and a healthy vegetarian base. Good pastry and other bakery characterise a reassertion of the kitchen under Abigail Iversen. The breads are superb, as are the British cheeses. Dishes might include fresh lamb, shallot and cream tart; grilled marinated pork spare ribs with onion marmalade; a National Trust-style poundcake with passion-fruit. Bottles over £12 are grouped as fine wines, among which Burgundies in particular are very attractive, from Lafon, Rion, Leflaive and others. Even more impressively, wines under £12 make up a lively and catholic collection, from Chile (Cabernet Sauvignon, '80) to New Zealand (Sauvignon Blanc, Matua Valley '86). There are also some classic clarets that would cost more in a shop. House French £4. CELLARMAN'S CHOICE: Vosne Romanée Les Chaumes '80, £23.50.

CHEF: Abigail Iversen PROPRIETOR: Anthony Verdin
OPEN: all week D, and Sun L
CLOSED: Christmas to New Year
MEALS: 12.30 to 2, 7.30 to 10.30
PRICES: Set L and D £11.50 (£15). Snacks from £1
CARDS: Access, Amex, Diners, Visa
SEATS: 40. 6 tables outside. Private parties: 50 main room. Car-park, 12 places. Vegetarian meals. Children's helpings. Wheelchair access (1 step; also WC). Music

15 North Parade [new owner, zero rated]

15 North Parade, Oxford OX2 6LX
OXFORD (0865) 513773 £16–£26

Georgina Wood has moved into the city from the relative wilds of Woods at Chesterton and brought in Duncan Hewitson from Café Rouge in London. The narrow dining-room has not changed from Michael Yeadon's popular era except that the plants have gone, to be replaced with refined old photographs. The furnishings would not be out of place in a conservatory. The tilt is more upmarket with a short modern menu made up of sensible combinations. The Mediterranean fish soup is a smooth version served with aïoli and Gruyère. Quails are stuffed with apple and served with an onion cream. The style and execution have been taking time to crystallise, hence the zero rating, but a consensus points to the end of the meals for the real quality – chocolate mousses or strawberry tart, and petits fours. Lunch is notably good value. Forty wines with a bottle from just about everywhere; starting with Berry Bros claret or a Sauvignon at £6.50. CELLARMAN'S CHOICE: Ch. Cissac '79, £13.75. More reports, please.

CHEF: Duncan Hewitson PROPRIETOR: Georgina Wood
OPEN: Mon to Sat
MEALS: 12 to 2, 7 to 10.30
PRICES: £19 (£26), Set L £9.75 (£16). Licensed, also bring your own: corkage £6.50
CARDS: Access, Visa
SEATS: 55. Private parties: 50 main room. Vegetarian meals. Children's helpings. Wheelchair access (also WC). Air-conditioned

Munchy Munchy [12/20]

6 Park End Street, Oxford OX1 1HH
OXFORD (0865) 245710 £9

Christmas customers who rang to book were treated to the entire staff singing *We Wish You a Merry Christmas* on the answering machine. 'Fast food of gourmet standard' is one way of describing Ethel Ow's brilliant cooking of Indonesian-inspired dishes. And she really is fast. Order from the blackboard menu of seven or so dishes and almost before you are at the table, so is the food. It is the wealth of the fresh spices, herbs and tropical fruits – a parade of lemon grass, cardamom, clove, mace, garlic, fenugreek, cumin, turmeric, coriander, mango or passion fruit – which characterises dishes. Bowls of rice counteract the heat of sambal, as do fruits and ices at the end of the meal. Before that might be lamb with coriander seeds, marjoram, kumquat and coconut milk; duck in Indonesian soy sauce with cinnamon, star anise, cloves and a chilli dip; shredded chicken and asparagus in seafood sauce with juniper berries and mace. Vegetarians might be offered a stir-fry with spices. The atmosphere is brisk, almost brusque. The café-like décor is pine, offset by fresh flowers and some Indonesian batik pictures. Unlicensed, but bring your own: 40p corkage per person.

CHEF: Ethel Ow PROPRIETORS: Tony and Ethel Ow
OPEN: Tue to Sat
CLOSED: 3 weeks Aug, 3 weeks Dec
MEALS: 12 to 2.10, 5.30 to 9.40
PRICES: £7.50 (£9). Unlicensed, bring your own: corkage 40p
SEATS: 42. Private parties: 7 main room. No children under 6 Fri and Sat D. No cigars/pipes in dining-room

Le Petit Blanc [16/20]

61A Banbury Road, Summertown, Oxford OX2 7DY
OXFORD (0865) 53540 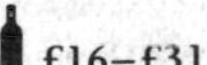 £16–£31

Since the *Guide* first discovered Bruno Loubet cooking almost single-handed in a tiny basement kitchen in Fulham, he has submitted himself to a second apprenticeship, this time with Raymond Blanc. For the last two years he has been charged with the running of Blanc's second restaurant. The powerful Bordelesian sauces that illuminated Gastronome One have been eased into the Blanc manner, but the same canniness and understanding of modern cooking that marked him out early as an exceptional talent run through a *carte* of 21 dishes. Signs of the Manoir (see Great Milton) are obvious –marinated smoked haddock, instead of salmon, as a starter; a cold terrine of pigeon borshch. But there is a distinct difference: no shyness to have roast ribs of beef (albeit slightly smoked), fairly plain lamb on the one hand and on the other some gutsy, earthy bourgeois cooking, perhaps just a ragout of ox-tail with young cabbage. Fish might be brill braised with cream and butter, or sea-bass in an anchovy sauce, on a bed of aubergine with a sweet-pepper purée. All of this is served in the charmed, magical setting of an 18th-century greenhouse, the most romantic dining-room in Britain in summer. Some have said the cooking suffers harshly from comparison to its parent at Great Milton, and being open six days a week, lunch and dinner, puts pressure on standards; but the drift of reports is firmly in the 14 to 16/20 region. Pastry is good, witness a starter with quail eggs and a duxelles of mushroom, the rough-puff pastry just strong enough to hold the filling and brittle enough to be crispy and flaky. Usually there is one dish that is breathtaking, perhaps a suckling pig; a classic fish soup; or a masterpiece of modern cooking: a lemon flavoured crème brûlée, mobile on the plate, its top encrusted like a brandy-snap, beside an almond tuile with a splurge of jasmin tea sorbet in the centre. Time was, when either would have made a dessert on its own. Combined, they bring about a series of contrasts –lemon and jasmin; ice-cream and mousse; the dryness of the tuile and the stickiness of the caramelised top. Blanc's original idea was that this would be a bistro, but it has always aspired to be a restaurant. Even the roast lamb is seasoned with turmeric and served with its own moussaka. The search for quality has pushed the prices up, but it remains more affordable than the Manoir. Service is young, French and friendly. The shortish and fairly expensive wine list (114 bottles) is resolutely French, many of the wines from small and lesser-known domaines. There are enough good names in every section to provide consistently enjoyable drinking, such as Kuentz-Bas Alsace, Duboeuf Beaujolais, Filliatreau Saumur Champigny, Lamblin, Hudelot-Noëllat and Rossignol-Changarnier in Burgundy and Jasmin in Côte Rôtie. Sweet wines include the ever-reliable Château Bastor-Lamontagne '82 at £17.20, or £8.20 per half, the excellent Château Treuil de Nailhac Monbazillac '83 at £10.50, or £2.20 per glass, and a Muscat de Lunel, £10.50 or £2.20 per glass. House Burgundy £7; CELLARMAN'S CHOICE: Givry Blanc '85, £15; Fixin *premier cru*, Clos Napoléon '82, £23.45; Ch. Plagnac '82, £10.50.

CHEF: Bruno Loubet PROPRIETORS: Blanc Restaurants
OPEN: all week, exc Tue
CLOSED: 2 weeks Jan
MEALS: 12.15 to 2.15, 7.15 to 10.30
PRICES: £23 (£31), Set L £12 (£16)
CARDS: Access, Visa
SEATS: 70. 3 tables outside. Private parties: 76 main room. Car-park. Vegetarian meals. Children's helpings. Wheelchair access. Air-conditioned

Wine Gallery [9/20]

11 Wheatsheaf Yard, Oxford OX1 4EE
OXFORD (0865) 250440 £12

An offshoot from the London chain of wine bars spawned by Brinkley's restaurant, set just off Blue Boar Street and up a flight of stairs, with two floors boasting much pine and plant-life. The menu is identical to London. It is a bit like a sentence made up of nothing but prepositions; most of the dishes have a starter feel to them and there are few substantial main courses

[GHG] *after the details of an entry means that the establishment is also included in* The Good Hotel Guide.

except for a group served with chips. The best way is to order everything together, as for a Chinese meal. The ambitious cuisine dishes are more erratic than traditional croquettes, fishcakes or good puddings. Forty multi-national wines staying firmly in the £6 to £13 spectrum. House French is £5.50.

CHEF: Keith Baker PROPRIETOR: John Brinkley
OPEN: all week
MEALS: 12 to 2.30, 7 to 11.30
PRICES: £8 (£12), Snacks from £1.50
CARDS: Access, Visa
SEATS: 60. Private parties: 100 main room. Vegetarian meals. Children welcome. Music. Air-conditioned

Oxfordshire Round-up

BAR MEALS: *Clanfield Tavern,* Clanfield (036 781 223); *Shaven Crown,* Shipton-Under-Wychwood (0993 830330); *Mill House,* Kingham (060 871 8188); *Red Lion,* Steeple Aston (0869 40225).
ITALIAN: *Antico,* 49-51 Market Place, Henley-on-Thames (0491 573060).
INEXPENSIVE: *Barnaby's,* 2 New Street, Henley-on-Thames (0491 572421).
WINES: *Restaurant Elizabeth,* 84 St Aldate's, Oxford (0865 242230).
CHINESE: *Tong San,* 20 The Square, Botley (0865 248230/726414); *Opium Den,* 79 George Street, Oxford (0865 248680).

PADSTOW Cornwall map 1

▲ *Seafood Restaurant* [15/20]

Riverside, Padstow PL28 8BY
PADSTOW (0841) 532485 £20–£32

Rick Stein has developed into one of the most sensitive and creative fish cooks in the country. In the mood of the late 1980s the décor offers a sense of light and space with bright white walls and plenty of daylight. The feel is almost Mediterranean. In June a delicatessen selling charcuterie and cooked dishes opened. Bedrooms overlooking the harbour have been added. All of this has grown from the small upstairs above a night-club in the late 1970s, and the extra rating point is well earned. The place retains an easy-going seaside character with art posters and a loyal following of smart and unsmart; young and old. The menu is a grand sweep of modern thinking on fish cookery, at first seemingly a French derivative with its strident, red-brown soup, its platter of ten shellfish set on ice, and its wary conservatism (no bad thing), as in grilled Dover sole with parsley butter, and char-grilled steak. But hold on, there is more: Eastern spicing in the form of lemon-grass and chilli for grilled prawn brochette; ginger, lime and pink peppercorns for a salmon trout marinade; five-spice powder to season scallops. And most impressive and dangerous of all, the bringing together of different techniques and flavours on the same plate: baked grey mullet with red peppers and aubergine, steamed brill wrapped in spinach and served with a coriander sauce, grilled monkfish with fennel and shallot dressing – all on the same plate, the shallots and peppers creating a fine contrast to the coriander sauce. Ingenuity continues to salmon in filo with a

scoop of tarragon sauce 'ice-cream'. There is an understanding here of flavours and textures that extends to desserts such as fine strawberries in a sweet tart case filled with Chantilly cream and served with a port and black peppercorn sauce, or poached pear sliced onto a nest of puff pastry, served with lime ice-cream. Espresso coffee. 'Happiest meal I've had in a long time.' Not surprisingly, white wines predominate on the list, but only just. The Burgundy lists, both white and red, promise many delights, with wines from Leflaive, Vocoret, Latour-Giraud and Ampeau. There are two dry whites from Bordeaux, Château Reynon '85, £7.95, and the exquisite Domaine de Chevalier '81, £34. The claret and red Rhône sections offer some excellent wines for the cheese course, and the Loire and Alsace are tempting. The German section is well chosen, Italy, California and Australia likewise, and even the two house whites, Sauvignon du Haut-Poitou '86, £6.95, and Bourgogne Aligoté from Cros, £8.50, would flatter a fried flounder. Château d'Yquem '76, £89, tops the list of sweet wines, and there are five other wines from Bordeaux and Monbazillac, as well as Muscat de Beaumes de Venise, Domaine de Durban, £13.50, £7 per half-bottle or £2.25 per glass.
CELLARMAN'S CHOICE: Pouilly Fumé, Domaine des Berthiers '86, £12.95.

CHEF: Richard Stein PROPRIETORS: Richard and Jill Stein
OPEN: Mon to Sat, D only
MEALS: 7.30 to 9.30 (10 Sat)
PRICES: £22 (£32), Set L £13.50 (£20), Set D £16 (£22)
CARDS: Access, Amex, Diners, Visa
SEATS: 75. Private parties: 24 main room. Children's helpings. Air-conditioned
ACCOMMODATION: 10 rooms, 8 with bath/shower. B&B £13.50 to £48. Deposit: £20. Children welcome. Baby facilities. Pets welcome. Fishing. TV. Phone. Scenic. Confirm by 12 [GHG]

PANGBOURNE Berkshire map 2

▲ *Copper Inn* [new owners, zero rated]

Church Road, Pangbourne RG8 7AR
PANGBOURNE (073 57) 2244 £20–£36

From the outside, this looks like an unprepossessing mock-Tudor-style pub and hotel like many others in this prosperous region. Resort Hotels took over Fine Inns plc in May 1988, but as we go to press, reports indicate no hiccups so far. In the restaurant, the mood changes and posh exclusivity hangs heavy in the air. It is all rather solemn and hushed. Stephen Whitney has worked with Anton Mosimann, Paul Gayler at Inigo Jones and Anton Edelmann at the Savoy. His cooking is high modern French with some interpretations of classic regional and bourgeois dishes, backed by high-quality ingredients from Britain and France. It has all the pomp and trimmings of luxury expense-account eating, which means that foie gras from Rungis market is cooked in rendered duck fat, then embellished with lobster, asparagus and truffle flavoured vinaigrette. Sea-bass is roasted in olive oil with tomato and basil sauce and fried squid; crepinettes of sweetbreads are garnished with buttered spinach and more lobster. Gayler's influence shows in the vegetarian dishes, such as chilled bavarois of courgettes with tomato and basil vinaigrette. Vegetables and rare farmhouse cheeses from Patrick Rance deserve better treatment. Sunday lunch is British, with beef from Aberdeen, ducks from Norfolk and suckling pig from Royal Berkshire. The wine list is good, all French apart from a few above-average Germans and local white and rosé from nearby Westbury vineyard. A small selection of top Bordeaux goes back to '69, but there's a range of more affordable clarets. The Burgundy list is liberally sprinkled with wines from Averys and Remoissenet, but the domaine Burgundies are likely to give more pleasure. Among a brief but good selection from the rest of France, a clutch of Coteaux Champenois wines is an unusual find. House French £7.90. CELLARMAN'S CHOICE: Sauvignon de St Bris '86, £9.95, St Nicolas de Bourgueil '83, £8.75.

CHEF: Stephen Whitney PROPRIETORS: Resort Hotels
OPEN: all week
MEALS: 12.30 to 2, 7.30 to 9.30 (10 Fri and Sat, 9 Sun)
PRICES: £25 (£36), Set L £11.95 (£20) to £16.95 (£26), Set D £16.95 (£26) to £23.75 (£33), Snacks from £2.30
CARDS: Access, Amex, Diners, Visa
SEATS: 50. 6 tables outside. Private parties: 12 main room, 10 and 30 private rooms. Car-park, 30 places. Vegetarian meals. Children's helpings. Wheelchair access
ACCOMMODATION: 21 rooms, all with bath/shower. Rooms for disabled. B&B £53.75 to £69. Children welcome. Baby facilities. Afternoon teas. Garden. TV. Phone. Doors close at 12. Confirm by 6

PETWORTH West Sussex map 3

Soanes [new entry, zero rated]

Grove Lane, Petworth GU28 0HY
PETWORTH (0798) 43659
1m S of Petworth £17–£25

Carol and Derek Godsmark have converted this seventeenth-century stone farmhouse into a classy country restaurant with an attractive conservatory complete with a grand piano. Carol is a self-taught cook, drawing her inspiration from Sonia Stevenson, Raymond Blanc, Nico Ladenis. Her ideas are up to the minute: excellent mussel soup with saffron; calf's liver with roasted shallots and beetroot sauce; boned quail in filo pastry stuffed with wild rice. Fashion extends to the array of salad leaves, the walnut oil dressings, wild mushrooms and simple, accurately timed vegetables. To finish there might be a 'soup' of melon with strawberry ice-cream or passion-fruit sorbet. Cheeses come from Androuët in Paris. The short list of about 30 wines is almost exclusively French from good producers. House wines are £7 a bottle. More reports, please.

CHEF: Carol Godsmark PROPRIETORS: Carol and Derek Godsmark
OPEN: Wed to Sat D, and Sun L (other days by arrangement)
MEALS: 12.30 to 1.30, 7 to 10.45
PRICES: £20 (£25), Set D £12 (£17). Service inc. Licensed, also bring your own: corkage £7
CARDS: Access, Amex, Carte Blanche, Diners, Visa
SEATS: 24. Private parties: 28 main room. Car-park, 14 places. Children's helpings (Sun L only). Wheelchair access (2 steps)

PLUMTREE Nottinghamshire

map 5

Perkins Bar Bistro [10/20]

Old Railway Station, Plumtree NG12 5NA
PLUMTREE (060 77) 3695

£15

A friendly, family-run bistro in a country railway station, which is nearly always full. There are outside tables and, from autumn 1988, a conservatory extension on to the platform and a new bar area, which should ease pressure on tables – it's a good idea to book. Tony Perkins' French menu, which he describes as 'old-school classical simplified', favours straightforward presentation and eschews *nouvelle.* Salmon with prawns Dugléré is a speciality; chicken capitolade – with mushrooms, onions and wine – has been recommended. Vegetables have a bite and come with a light Mornay sauce. Desserts, which include trifle and treacle tart as well as more French offerings, are a high point; Mr Perkins has a talent for pastrywork. House French is £4.50.

CHEF: Tony Perkins PROPRIETORS: Tony and Wendy Perkins
OPEN: Tue to Sat
CLOSED: 1 week at Christmas
MEALS: 12 to 2, 7 to 9.45
PRICES: £10 (£15), Snacks from £1.50
CARDS: Access, Amex
SEATS: 72. 6 tables outside. Private parties: 24 main room. Car-park, 60 places. Children welcome. Wheelchair access (1 step). Music

PLYMOUTH Devon

map 1

Chez Nous [14/20]

13 Frankfort Gate, Plymouth PL1 1QA
PLYMOUTH (0752) 266793

£24–£34

The setting is a dreary shopping precinct in Plymouth, but inside, this unpretentious restaurant pays homage to French cuisine. Thick, white-painted louvred shutters cover the window. On the wall hang framed menus from Moulin de Mougins, Chanterelle and Hotel des Frères Troisgros. Jacques Marchal is devoted to food and wine and there are few distractions from the main business of the dining-room. The menu is a daily changing blackboard with fish as a strong suit: scallops with ginger and julienne of vegetables; avocado, crab and lobster salad; John Dory with orange and purée of carrots. Seasonal game features strongly and desserts have included excellent pear bavarois served with a poached pear in Poire William liqueur and hot chocolate sauce. Hot cheese nibbles and olives in garlic oil to start, excellent coffee with petits fours to finish. Wines are almost without exception French, strong in Bordeaux and Burgundy, with more than 25 half-bottles and a page of 'fine and rare' bottles. CELLARMAN'S CHOICE: St Véran, Les Grandes Bruyères '86, £12.50.

CHEF: Jacques Marchal PROPRIETORS: Suzanne and Jacques Marchal
OPEN: Tue to Sat
CLOSED: 3 weeks Feb and Sept, bank hols
MEALS: 12.30 to 2, 7 to 10.30
PRICES: £23 (£34), Set L and D £17 (£24)
CARDS: Access, Amex, Diners, Visa
SEATS: 30. Private parties: 30 main room. Children welcome. Wheelchair access. Music. Air-conditioned

Mister Barretts [10/20]

36 Admiralty Street, Stonehouse, Plymouth PL1 3RU
PLYMOUTH (0752) 221177 £8–£20

Fish and game are the main points of interest in this very red restaurant and bar near the ferry port. Stephen Barrett is an enthusiast, which means a menu that can take in squid with lavender vinegar and hare with chocolate, as well as fish chowder, Quantock veal with apricot gravy, and pheasant with calvados. Bigbury Bay oysters, Tavistock lamb and Hatherleigh beef boost the local contingent, and there are fine West Country cheeses – Beenleigh Blue, Wheatlands, Sheviock ewes', Vashti. Sauces are increasingly made with vegetable stocks and there's a choice of vegetarian dishes. Treacle and walnut tart and Guinness pudding give a flavour of the sweets. A dozen wines are supplemented by the new arrivals' blackboard, which includes CELLARMAN'S CHOICE: Yalumba Semillon Chardonnay '86, £11.50.

CHEF/PROPRIETOR: Stephen Barrett
OPEN: Mon to Sat, exc Sat L
MEALS: 12 to 2.30, 7 to 11
PRICES: £14 (£20), Set L £4.50 (£8) to £7.50 (£11), Set D £7.95 (£12) to £9.95 (£14). Service inc Set only
CARDS: Access, Visa
SEATS: 28. 6 tables outside. Private parties: 32 main room. Vegetarian meals. Children's helpings. Music

POOL IN WHARFEDALE West Yorkshire map 5

▲ *Pool Court* [14/20]

10 YEARS

Pool Bank, Pool in Wharfedale LS21 1EH
ARTHINGTON (0532) 842288/9 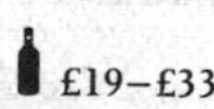 £19–£33

The paupers' menu at £10 makes this otherwise expensive hotel dining-room more accessible. Parsnip soup; veal sweetbreads and kidneys in a light mustard sauce; *à point* vegetables on a side plate; brown-bread ice-cream with strawberries and fresh cream is hardly a poor relation, though the range and breadth of the main *carte* can make it seem that way. Michael and Hanni Gill, now with six bedrooms to their credit, lead a slick, well-disciplined young team with both brio and professionalism. While lesser places might have been content to cruise along at a standard, the Gills have taken on board many new ideas, boldly moving towards modern British cooking. The improvement on three or four years ago is manifest. They do not just ape trends, but are actively contributing to the wider creative purpose. The menu offers a choice of seven starters, three middle courses, nine main dishes and seven sweets. The balance of dishes covers the traditional – calf's liver with miniature Yorkshire puddings; the classic –- hot chicken mousse with wild mushrooms – and the more adventurous – veal sweetbreads pan-fried and served on a potato cake with a carrot-flavoured sauce. It is a far cry from the days when vegetarians were offered omelettes. On a single plate as a main course comes a ragout of mushrooms with saffron rice, a small broccoli and Stilton quiche, and a vegetable kebab with chive hollandaise. Alas for the jelly with the melon though. Service is conducted with calm, unobtrusive efficiency. The solid local following ensures a vibrant atmosphere. Sweets such as a selection of apples dishes make for a fulfilling climax. Rooms are a cut above the usual. 'The powder room is extraordinary – sculpture, paintings, Malvern water and glasses, magazines, etc.. How much time is a woman supposed to spend in there?' The wine list is well chosen, with the accent heavily on France (Burgundy includes some fine estate wines), but some interesting bottles in the section 'from Europe and the New World', including Portugal's best vinho verde, Palacio da Brejoeira, £19.80, and a few good Australians. Out-of-the-ordinary sweet wines might include Australian and Burgundian wines made in the style of Sauternes. Hardly anything comes at under £10 a bottle. House Entre-Deux-Mers and St Véran are £13.95. CELLARMAN'S CHOICE: Tokay Freiberg '83, £17.50; Hautes Côtes de Nuits '85, £22.90.

CHEF: Melvin Jordan PROPRIETORS: Michael and Hanni Gill
OPEN: Tue to Sat, D only, occasionally Mon D
CLOSED: 2 weeks July to Aug; 2 weeks at Christmas
MEALS: 7 to 10
PRICES: £23 (£33), Set D from £10 (£19)
CARDS: Access, Amex, Diners, Visa
SEATS: 65. Private parties: 30 main room. Car-park, 65 places. Vegetarian meals. Children's helpings. Smart dress preferred. No cigars/pipes in dining-room. Wheelchair access. Air-conditioned
ACCOMMODATION: 6 rooms, all with bath/shower. B&B £55 to £75. Garden. Air-conditioning. TV. Phone [GHG]

POOLE Dorset map 2

Le Select [10/20]

129 Parkstone Road, Park Gates, Poole BH15 2PB
PARKSTONE (0202) 740223 £21

On the business card is a signed endorsement from the Beatles, dated March 5, 1963, from l'Oranger in London. Twenty-six years on, Omer Inanir runs a small French restaurant which has picked up a steady number of nominations since it opened in November 1985. Founding chef Alain Rocher has gone to open his own restaurant at Milford-on-Sea (see entry) and his place was taken by Nigel Popperwell last spring, but the style – classically inspired French with modern touches – remains the theme. The dining-room is formal, filled with busts of Verdi and Beethoven and naked women, and the style is reinforced by the Melba toast on the table. But Mr Inanir and his wife, Marie Louise, are extrovert and amicable hosts. The kitchen works with good produce, especially fish – perhaps monk with a sauce of reduced fish stock and white wine with cream and garlic, or monk again as a warm salad to start – and there are changing daily dishes alongside the printed menu. 'Some guests may find our vegetables too lightly cooked in the French style; they can be cooked for longer on request.' Seventy-five wines with something from everywhere, starting at £5.85. CELLARMAN'S CHOICE: St Emilion, Ch. Vieux Fonrazade '83, £11.25.

CHEF: Nigel Popperwell PROPRIETOR: Omer K. Inanir
OPEN: Tue to Sat, D only
CLOSED: 2 weeks Feb and Oct
MEALS: 7 to 10.15
PRICES: £16 (£21). Service 10%
CARDS: Access, Amex, Diners, Visa
SEATS: 28. Private parties: 24 main room. Vegetarian meals. No children under 7. Smart dress preferred. No pipes in dining-room. Wheelchair access (also WC). Music

POUGHILL Cornwall map 1

▲ *Reeds* [11/20]

Poughill EX23 9EL
BUDE (0288) 2841 £20

Two hundred yards down a side road near the church, Margaret Jackson's elegant-looking house stands in five acres of attractive garden. This is a very personal hotel with the dining-room open only to overnight guests. The cooking is exact, to order and makes good use of the fine local fish, be it salmon served cold with mayonnaise or lemon sole on the bone with herbs and tomatoes. There is no choice, but guests are consulted in advance about personal tastes. Recommended dishes have been roast rack of lamb provençal; suprême of chicken with a madeira sauce; snow cheese, a seventeenth-century lemon dessert; strawberry angel pie. 'Breakfasts are grand affairs.' There are as many half-bottles as reds or whites on a short, interesting list, opening at £6 with house French from Duboeuf.

CHEF/PROPRIETOR: Margaret Jackson
OPEN: Fri to Mon, D only
CLOSED: Christmas Day
MEALS: 8
PRICES: Set D £17.50 (£20). Service inc
SEATS: 10. Private parties: 10 main room. Car-park, 10 places. No children under 16. Smart dress preferred. One sitting
ACCOMMODATION: 3 rooms, all with bath/shower. B&B £35 to £60. Deposit: £10. No children under 16. Garden. Scenic. Doors close at 12. Confirm by 1 [GHG]

If, in your opinion, a restaurant is not maintaining the standard of its rating, please inform the Guide *office. Report forms are at the back of the book.*

POWBURN Northumberland map 7

▲ *Breamish House Hotel* [12/20]

Powburn NE66 4LL
POWBURN (066 578) 266 £14–£21

Graham Taylor and Patricia Portus have built a steady local following with their good-value set meals which gets them through the winter months. The Georgian house, previously a hunting-lodge, is set in five acres. Menus run to four courses, centred usually on a roast, with much imaginative use of herbs and vegetables for impact. For instance a soup of wild parsley, mushroom and garlic; or marjoram, parsley, rosemary and garlic with roast loin of pork served with an orange and watercress salad. The baking is done in-house and provides Digestion (*sic*) and water biscuits for a show of English cheeses. Sweets tend to be mousses, parfaits and bavarois. The very reasonably priced wine list is predominantly French. There is good Alsace '85 from Louis Gisselbrecht, Beaujolais from Sarrau and some decent Burgundies, both red and white especially from Luc Sorin. The claret list goes back as far as '79, but is reliable and reasonably priced. Australian wines are from Brown Bros and Bruisyard St Peter Müller-Thurgau from Suffolk should not be overlooked. Three sweet wines are offered: Muscat de Beaumes de Venise, Domaine de Coyeux '84 at £10.95 per bottle, £1.95 per glass. Brown Bros Orange Muscat and Flora '85, £5.95 per half-bottle, and an interesting Romanian sweet wine. House French is £4.25 a carafe.

CHEFS: Patricia Portus and Graham Taylor PROPRIETOR: Graham Taylor
OPEN: all week, D only, and Sun L
CLOSED: Jan
MEALS: 1, 7.30 to 8.30
PRICES: Set L £8.50 (£14), Set D £14.50 (£21)
SEATS: 30. Private parties: 8 main room. Car-park, 30 places. Children's helpings (Sun L only). No children under 12. Smart dress preferred. No smoking in dining-room. Wheelchair access (also WC)
ACCOMMODATION: 10 rooms, all with bath/shower. B&B £35 to £55. Deposit: £20. No children under 12. Pets welcome (by prior arrangement). Garden. TV. Phone. Scenic. Doors close at 12 [GHG]

POWERSTOCK Dorset map 2

▲ *Three Horseshoes* [10/20]

Powerstock DT6 3TF
POWERSTOCK (030 885) 328
4m NE of Bridport £14–£28

Powerstock is virtually a dead end, a tiny village on a steep hill with a church and the pub opposite. The bars are lined with some (very good) paintings by local artists and at the back is a chalet-style dining-room with a fine view down the valley. The kitchen is supplied with excellent fish, from grey mullet and whole sea-bass to Lyme Bay plaice, which is usually pan cooked and lightly sauced; lobster is grilled. There is good bread, a wide choice of starters, local roast lamb for Sunday lunch, cold roast beef and calorific sweets. The prices have risen with the scale of the operation which has lifted it up into the restaurant category, but the food essentially remains excellent pub fare. Palmer's beers.

CHEF: Pat Ferguson PROPRIETORS: Pat and Diana Ferguson
OPEN: all week
MEALS: 12 to 2 (3 Sun), 7 to 11
PRICES: £19 (£24), Set L £7.50 (£14) to £10.50 (£18), Set D £12.50 (£20) to £20 (£28), Snacks from £1.50. Service inc alc
CARDS: Access, Visa
SEATS: 60. 12 tables outside. Private parties: 28 main room, 16 private room. Car-park, 30 places. Vegetarian meals. Children's helpings. Smart dress preferred. Wheelchair access (also WC). Music
ACCOMMODATION: 4 rooms, 2 with bath/shower. B&B £20 to £37.50. Deposit: £10. Children welcome. Pets welcome. Garden. Scenic. Doors close at 12. Confirm by 6.30

PRESTON Lancashire — map 5

Auctioneer [10/20]

B.C.A. Centre, Walton Summit,
Bamber Bridge, Preston PR5 8AA
PRESTON (0772) 324870 — £11–£18

Chef Nigel Brookes has taken over the ownership of this unlikely restaurant situated in a used-car lot opposite the Novotel, just one hundred yards off the M6 at junction 29. The auctioneer theme provides a wacky framework for an enterprising, eclectic menu – Lot 1442 is mushrooms in garlic cream sauce, Lot 0007 roast leg of lamb with cranberry tartlet. The weight of recommendations falls on the popular lines like roast beef and Yorkshire pudding, steaks, chicken breasts and trout. 'Good quality and good value.' Unobtrusive and efficient service. Bar snacks are served at lunch and there is a children's menu. House French £6.50 a litre.

CHEF/PROPRIETOR: Nigel Brookes
OPEN: Sun and Mon L, and Wed to Sat, exc Sat L
MEALS: 12 to 2.30, 7 to 9.30 (10 Fri and Sat)
PRICES: £12 (£18), Set L from £5.45 (£11), Snacks from £1.50
CARDS: Access, Visa
SEATS: 100. Private parties: 100 main room. Car-park, 500 places. Vegetarian meals. Children's helpings. Music. Air-conditioned

PUDSEY West Yorkshire — map 5

Aagrah [10/20]

483 Bradford Road, Pudsey LS28 8ED
BRADFORD (0274) 668818 — £13

This branch of the Aagrah has established itself as quickly as its parent restaurant in Shipley (see entry). It is impossible to miss from the outside: a white miniature palace, Hollywood in style, complete with painted chairs and imitation bells, kitsch but welcoming. Specialities are close to genuine Pakistani home cooking: Balti chicken or prawns, lemon rice, fine rogan josh, chicken zafrani or jalfrezi. Weekly specials are offered too. The oils used are now all polyunsaturated. Finish with fruit marinated in orange juice and herbs. The bill comes with the coffee.

CHEFS: M. Aslam and M. Sabir PROPRIETORS: M. Sabir, Mrs Sabir, M. Aslam, Mrs Aslam, Z. Iqual
OPEN: all week D, and Sun L
MEALS: 6 (noon Sun) to 11.30 (12 Fri and Sat)
PRICES: £8 (£13), Snacks from £1
CARDS: Access, Amex, Diners, Visa
SEATS: 60. Private parties: 65 main room. Car-park, 35 places. Vegetarian meals. Children's helpings. Smart dress preferred. Wheelchair access (also WC). Music

PULBOROUGH West Sussex map 3

Stane Street Hollow [12/20]

10 YEARS

Codmore Hill, Pulborough RH20 1BG
PULBOROUGH (079 82) 2819 £13–£22

The Swiss flag flies outside and René Kaiser is at home in his new improved kitchen. The hallmarks of Stane Street Hollow have been the generous portions and the home-smoked fish and meats which appear in many guises. Leek and potato soup features home-smoked chicken dumplings; horseradish cream accompanies slices of home-smoked salmon. Main courses are hearty: rabbit in white wine with whole garlic cloves and mushrooms; beef fillet with parsley sauce and bacon rolls. Some may find the whole rather rich, in which case the chef offers to cook dishes plainly. For pudding, assiette René offers a plate of four Swiss-style desserts to taste. House French, from the Pyrenees, £8.

CHEF: René Kaiser PROPRIETORS: René and Ann Kaiser
OPEN: Tue to Sat, exc Tue L and Sat L
CLOSED: 3 weeks May and Oct, 24 Dec to 5 Jan
MEALS: 12.30 to 1.15, 7.30 to 9.15
PRICES: £15 (£22), Set L £6 (£13)
SEATS: 35. Private parties: 24 main room, 16 private room. Car-park, 14 places. Children's helpings

RAMSBOTTOM Greater Manchester map 5

Village Restaurant [14/20]

16 Market Place, Ramsbottom BL0 9HT
RAMSBOTTOM (070 682) 5070 £27

Ramsbottom is a town of cobbled streets on the edge of the moors. It may now be part of Greater Manchester, but it still feels like old Lancashire. Chris Johnson's and Ros Hunter's restaurant (which is due to move to number 16 from number 18 late in 1988, leaving 18 as a wine bar) takes its cue from the Englishness of the setting. Their passion is for food and drink and the menu is a vivid celebration of modern British cooking. The six-course extravaganza begins at 8 o'clock and the whole show may last well beyond midnight. Soups, home-made bread, riots of vegetables, farmhouse cheeses and regional specialities – the benchmarks for the cooking – are backed by a loyalty to local producers: vegetables and salads are grown to Soil Association standards by a market gardener in Chorley; naturally reared meat comes from a farm in Market Drayton. Dinner begins with a starter, such as smoked fillet of beef or Loch Fyne gravlax; then comes the soup – cock-a-leekie, Jerusalem artichoke or Stilton, onion and parsley. After this, there is fish, anything from halibut with lime butter to Guyanese fish curry. The main course is served with tracklements: baked air-dried ham from Bar Woodall in Cumbria with minted damson purée; lamb from Scotland with cranberry, rhubarb and ginger compote. Five vegetables are the order of the day. Then comes the unpasteurised English cheese, then the trolley of sweets – redcurrant and raspberry pie, hot apple amber, crème brûlée. Enterprisingly, the wine list is largely arranged by grape variety, offering an interesting assortment of wines made from most of the world's principal grapes. There are mature wines, too, including some unusual finds such as '67 and '71 Alsace Riesling. Mark-ups on the more expensive wines are a flat £10. Another unusual feature is the 'daily selection' of a glass each of three wines (varying from £38 to £50 a bottle) for £8.50. Subsequent glasses are charged at a fifth of the bottle price. Dessert wines, including a German Beerenauslese '71 and Vouvray and Moulin Touchay '64, are also served by the glass.

CHEF: Ros Hunter PROPRIETORS: R.C.P.L. Ltd
OPEN: Wed to Sat, D only
MEALS: 8
PRICES: Set D £19.50 (£27). Minimum £19.50
CARDS: Access, Visa
SEATS: 18. Private parties: 10 main room. No smoking during meals. Music. One sitting

REDLYNCH Wiltshire map 2

▲ *Langley Wood* [11/20]

Hamptworth Road, Redlynch SP5 2PB
ROMSEY (0794) 390348 £14–£20

The Rosens' small country house is set in five acres of woodland at the northern tip of the New Forest. Menus often set the unexpected among more traditional offerings, be it a Brazil-nut crumble with chilli sauce as a starter or chicken breasts poached with cucumber and cream. There are also experiments with fruit, nut and spice combinations. Recommended dishes from a 16-dish *carte* include: mushroom and coriander soup; potato and game soup; Brie en croûte; Stilton and walnut parcel; devilled chicken; roast beef and Yorkshire pudding. Thirty wines cover France and Germany, starting at £4.75. CELLARMAN'S CHOICE: Ch. Tours des Combes '81, £11.50.

CHEF: Sylvia Rosen PROPRIETORS: David and Sylvia Rosen
OPEN: Wed to Sat D, and Sun L
MEALS: 12.45 to 2, 7.30 to 11
PRICES: £14 (£20), Set Sun L £10 (£14)
CARDS: Access, Amex, Diners, Visa
SEATS: 30. Private parties: 65 main room. Car-park, 25 places. Vegetarian meals. Children's helpings. No cigars/pipes in dining-room. Wheelchair access (also WC). Music
ACCOMMODATION: 3 rooms. B&B £13. Children welcome. Baby facilities. Pets welcome. Afternoon teas. Garden. Scenic

RICHMOND North Yorkshire map 7

▲ *Howe Villa* [10/20]

Whitcliffe Mill, Richmond DL10 4TJ
RICHMOND (0748) 850055 £11

'It was too large for our family home but too loved to leave' says Anita Berry about the handsome Georgian mill-owner's house, which has views over the River Swale from the upstairs drawing-room and the dining-room. Her four-course set menus offer a choice at either end and a substantial dish, perhaps a roast with vegetables, in the middle. Start with French onion soup or plaice Dugléré, and after the Linzertorte or home-made ice-cream sample some well-kept local cheeses. Cordon bleu cookery and, at £10 for the set dinner, exceptional value for money. Unlicensed, but an aperitif is included in the price. Bring your own wine: no corkage.

CHEF: Anita Berry PROPRIETORS: Tom and Anita Berry
OPEN: all week, D only
CLOSED: Nov to end Mar
MEALS: 7 to 7.30
PRICES: Set D £10 (£11). Unlicensed, but bring your own: no corkage
SEATS: 10. Private parties: 10 main room. Car-park. Vegetarian meals. Children's helpings by arrangement. No children under 8. No smoking. Music
ACCOMMODATION: 4 rooms, all with bath/shower. D, B&B to £52. Deposit: £10. No children under 8. Garden. TV. Scenic. Doors close at 11.30 [GHG]

RICHMOND Surrey map 3

Lichfield's [13/20]

SURREY NEWCOMER OF THE YEAR GFG '89

13 Lichfield Terrace, Sheen Road,
Richmond TW9 1AS
01-940 5236 £21–£29

Stephen Bull has moved on but his style remains and chef Gerald Haslegrave has proved an able successor. The cut of the pink apricot dining-room has not altered. The menu relies on fine sauces for its character, and there have been exemplary dishes: a fragile mousse of wood-pigeon in a veal stock with crunchy sweet red cabbage and three glazed shallots for contrast; raviolis of crab and sole with lemon butter; baked fresh fig with fig and amaretto ice-cream handsomely presented in a spun-sugar basket. The quality runs through, from the excellent bread, all of which points to a clear attempt to reassert this restaurant among the élite. Home-made chocolates arrive with coffee and there is a trolley of digestifs. Service is professional but slow, which may be due to the perfectionism of the kitchen. The wines – stored in racks at the back of the dining-room – are conspicuously French. Nearly everything on the fairly short list is expensive (only one bottle under £11), but quality is on the whole excellent. Burgundies are especially impressive, from the likes of Simon Bize, Vincent, Michel Juillot, Bonneau du Martray, Roux and Mongeard-Mugneret. Rhônes are less exciting and the claret list is good but not great. There are almost as many half-bottles as full ones. All four sweet wines are available by the glass, but the two sweet Loires from an excellent Coteaux du Layon producer are much too young ('83 and '84), as is Sauternes, Château St Amand '83. The fourth choice is Muscat de Beaumes de Venise, La Vieille Fermé '86, £20 per bottle, £10 per half-bottle, or £4 per glass. House French is £8. CELLARMAN'S CHOICE: Brouilly, Ch. des Tours '87, £15; Pouilly-Vinzelles '83, £18; Margaux, Ch. Siran '81, £24.

CHEF: Gerald Haslegrave PROPRIETORS: Gerald and Stephanie Haslegrave
OPEN: Tue to Sun, exc Sat L and Sun D
MEALS: 12.15 to 2.30, 7.15 to 10.30
PRICES: £23 (£29), Set L £16.50 (£21). Service inc
CARDS: Access, Visa
SEATS: 40. Private parties: 40 main room. Vegetarian meals. Children's helpings. Wheelchair access (1 step). Air-conditioned

RIDGEWAY Derbyshire map 5

Old Vicarage [14/20]

Ridgeway Moor, Ridgeway S12 3XW
SHEFFIELD (0742) 475 814
off A616, on B6054 nearly opposite village church

£20–£33

Last year's county newcomer of the year has justified the faith we had in it and come through to be considered along with the finest restaurants in the North of England. It scores in all departments – décor, setting, service, ingredients, cuisine. It is a solid, handsome stone house built in 1840 and set in large, carefully tended gardens complete with sweeping drive. In May a clematis covers one side of the house with lilac-coloured blooms; and the rhododendrons are out. A kitchen garden dominated by a magnificent 40-year-old espalier pear tree on one wall is full of saladings and herbs; in the summer there is soft fruit. Inside, the claustrophobia of the Laura Ashley prints that bedeck and bedevil nouveau country houses is overcome via a profusion of cottage garden flowers and comfortable Persian rugs. The two dining-rooms rival each other. One is the former drawing-room, framed by two large windows, the other a conservatory, a garden within a garden. 'The kind of studied elegance and formality one finds in French restaurants.' Place settings are just so: white damask; personalised Sheffield cutlery; flowers from the garden; white candles; white Coalport Countryware; large thin glasses. The menu shows flair and imagination. Its roots are in the garden and there is a feeling for both ingredients and the time of year. Fish features strongly. Salads are a course alone and as valid and accomplished as to impress a John Evelyn. Cheeses are unpasteurised and British. Presentation shows consummate care, as does the service from girls in Victorian dresses who wear gloves to carry the hot plates. But what of the dishes? Here is one: in the centre a cascade of opaque scallops set on a rhubarb sauce decorated with the scallop corals garnished with a single spray of forget-me-nots and to one side a crisp brown bulging puff pastry case filled with lightly cooked oysters or a julienne of vegetables. Such up-to-the-minute combination cooking may sound overplayed but the effects can be stunning. There is equally the confidence to leave well alone – as in roast guinea-fowl with sage and apple stuffing; salmon baked with a mousse of lemon sole and served with a chive sauce; fillet of beef with madeira. The list of commendations falls firmly on the main dishes, always the sign of a pedigree kitchen. For a supplement there is a selection of desserts, and their class shows in the details – a fresh hot cherry pancake tied up with a single chive, like a miniature swag-bag, sitting on a hot cherry sauce, or a dark chocolate cake, brittle on top, with a mousse-like filling on dark bitter chocolate sponge, the whole on a strawberry coulis and garnished with the blue speck of a forget-me-not flower. CELLARMAN'S CHOICE: Santenay *premier cru*, Le Passetemps '78, £25.50; Mâcon-Viré '85, from Henri Goyard, £15.50 (both also available as half-bottles).

CHEF: Tessa Bramley PROPRIETORS: Tessa, Andrew and Peter Bramley
OPEN: Tue to Sat D, and Sun L (Tue to Sat L by arrangement)
MEALS: 12.15 to 2.30, 7 to 9.30
PRICES: Set Sun L £11.50 (£20), Set D £15.50 (£25) to £22.50 (£33)
SEATS: 50. Private parties: 30 main room, 30 private room. Car-park, 25 places. Vegetarian meals. No children under 12. Smart dress preferred. No smoking in dining-room

RIPLEY Surrey map 3

Michels' [12/20]

13 High Street, Ripley GU23 6AQ
GUILDFORD (0483) 224777 £17–£31

The dining-room is more graceful than before, with a feeling of spaciousness. Lemon walls, apricot furnishings and modern pictures have replaced the heavy dark beams and rough white paintwork. When Erik Michel is firing on all cylinders, he is really motoring: lightly steamed breast of chicken sitting on a bed of spring vegetables and orange brûlée in a brandysnap basket have been stunning. Dishes are ambitiously constructed, as in a pastry shell lined with spaghetti vegetables flavoured with tarragon, holding a poached egg topped with Beluga caviare and lemon butter sauce. Self-imposed diversions, though, can deflect attention: a quenelle composed of cream and tomato, flavoured with armagnac, adds little to the terrine of layered vegetables, wild salmon and scallop which it accompanies; spring lamb cooked in hay is less impressive than it sounds; lighter saucing would counter some of the oily richness. A taste for the exotic permeates the puddings: hot passion-fruit soufflé, or tropical fruit served with mango and lime sauce and quenelles of banana mousse. Burgundy is the main business of the 70-strong wine list, with bottles from Henri Jayer, Julian Coche Debord and Marcel Vincent (and others whose names are sadly not divulged). Well-chosen claret heads support from around France, and there is Australian Chardonnay as well as a first-class white Rioja, Marqués de Murrieta '83, £10.45. CELLARMAN'S CHOICE: Ch. Millet '82, £16.35.

CHEF: Erik Michel PROPRIETORS: Erik and Karen Michel
OPEN: Tue to Sun, exc Sat L and Sun D
MEALS: 12.30 to 2, 7.30 to 9.15 (7 to 9.45 Sat)
PRICES: £23 (£31), Set L and D from £12.50 (£17)
CARDS: Access, Amex, Diners, Visa
SEATS: 60. Private parties: 60 main room. Children welcome. No-smoking area

RIPON North Yorkshire map 7

▲ *Old Deanery* [10/20]

Minster Road, Ripon HG4 1QS
RIPON (0765) 3518 £18–£21

This fixture and fitting of North Yorkshire eating with its fine site by the cathedral, no booking and a good atmosphere, remains an old-fashioned oasis. The style is Waldorf salad, ham crêpes, poached salmon, steaks. The cooking of fish and vegetables has been less accurate than before, or perhaps such criticisms are just the sign of advancing times and fashions. The lounge is comfortable. The Bleikers celebrate 21 years this year. House French £7; CELLARMAN'S CHOICE: Côtes du Rhône '84, £9.95; Pouilly Blanc Fumé '86, £11.45.

CHEF: Jurg Bleiker PROPRIETORS: Jurg and Jane Bleiker
OPEN: Mon to Sat, exc Sat L
CLOSED: 25 and 26 Dec
MEALS: 12 to 2, 7 to 10
PRICES: £14 (£21), Set L and D £12.95 (£18), L Snacks from £1.25
SEATS: 70. 6 tables outside. Private parties: 30 main room. Car-park, 30 places. Vegetarian meals. Children's helpings. Smart dress preferred. Wheelchair access. Music
ACCOMMODATION: 2 rooms, both with bath/shower. B&B £37.50 to £50. Garden. Scenic. Doors close at 12. Confirm by 10

ROADE Northamptonshire map 3

Roadhouse Restaurant [13/20]

16–18 High Street, Roade NN7 2NW
ROADE (0604) 863372 £15–£20

The Kewleys are working hard to lift their village-centre restaurant sited two miles off junction 15 of the M1. The informal, relaxed mood is matched by some accomplished cooking. The *carte* is sensibly written in English, and inclined to modern British, but with its French ancestry clearly visible. Elegant examples are the warm salmon mousse and mussels with a sauce of red peppers, ginger and cream; duck with port sauce is the pink breast fanned out in slices plus a leg joint cooked separately; calf's liver might be sauté with lambs' sweetbreads and bacon and served with a red wine, port and grenadine sauce. Recommended dishes include gratin of scallops with mushrooms; feuilleté of asparagus with a beurre blanc; salmon with a cream sauce; boned ox-tail with sweetbreads; duck with beetroot and horseradish; fillet of brill in a white wine sauce. Vegetables are staunchly modern British, which is to say generous. Sweets roam farther afield, with cold lemon tart or terrine of peach. Fifty wines start with house red and white from Georges Duboeuf at £6.50. CELLARMAN'S CHOICE: Periquita Fonseca '82, £7.25; Montagny *premier cru* '86, £12.10.

CHEF: Christopher Kewley PROPRIETORS: Christopher and Susan Kewley
OPEN: Mon to Sat, exc Sat L
CLOSED: bank hol Mons
MEALS: 12.30 to 1.45, 7 to 10
PRICES: £14 (£20), Set L £9 (£15). Service 10%
CARDS: Access, Amex, Visa
SEATS: 32. Private parties: 40 main room. Car-park, 15 places. Children's helpings. Smart dress preferred. Wheelchair access

ROBERTSBRIDGE East Sussex map 3

Olivers [new entry, zero rated]

Cripps Corner, Robertsbridge TN32 5RY
STAPLECROSS (058 083) 387
at crossroads of A229 and B2089 £14–£20

The entrance is via the garden at the back, through the small wood-panelled bar. Victorian wall-lamps line the dining-room, Mrs Oliver waits at table, and Mr Oliver's menu is a modern medley that doesn't salute any particular flag. Rabbit and raisin pâté comes with a hazelnut mayonnaise; melon and citrus fruit combine in a terrine with port jelly. There are modern twists – fresh ravioli filled with home-cured beef and pine-nuts – and fish is taken seriously, to the extent of brill stuffed with crab, grilled, with a red wine sauce. Wild boar from Wadhurst Park near Tenterden is served with a stock-based sage sauce with onion. Puddings are pretty, and the 30-strong wine list has a good choice for under £10. House French is £4.95. More reports, please.

CHEF: Gary Oliver PROPRIETORS: Albert and Gary Oliver
OPEN: Wed to Sun
CLOSED: first 3 weeks Jan
MEALS: 12 to 1.45, 7 to 9.45
PRICES: £15 (£20), Set L £8.50 (£14) to £10 (£15), Set D £10 (£15)
CARDS: Access, Visa
SEATS: 36. Private parties: 45 main room, 18 private room. Car-park, 20 places. No children under 5. Wheelchair access (also WC). Music

ROCHDALE **Greater Manchester** map 5

One Eleven [10/20]

111 Yorkshire Street, Rochdale OL16 1YJ
ROCHDALE (0706) 344901 **£14–£16**

Catherine Drewery's neat little restaurant near the centre of town offers set dinners of a home-made, bistro style. A choice of veal escalope with mushrooms, quail with chestnuts, chicken breast with Pernod or poached salmon mayonnaise might follow mushrooms and bacon in a garlic cream sauce, crabmeat gratin and shrimps with orange and brandy sauce. A glass of Muscat de Beaumes de Venise to go with the puddings is £1.75. House French is £6.95 per litre.

CHEF/PROPRIETOR: Catherine Drewery
OPEN: Thur to Sat D; Mon to Wed D and L by arrangement only
MEALS: 7.30 to 9.30
PRICES: Set L from £8.50 (£14), Set D £11.50 (£16)
CARDS: Access, Amex, Diners, Visa
SEATS: 30. Private parties: 30 main room. Smart dress preferred. Music. Air-conditioned

ROCHFORD **Essex** map 3

▲ *Renoufs* [10/20]

1 South Street, Rochford SS4 1BL
SOUTHEND (0702) 544393 **£14–£26**

'Anyone who said in the past we were flamboyant was premature,' comments Derek Renouf, who after 10 years here has embarked on a new working of his menu. The food biz is evident from the awards on every wall. Ideas crystallise on paper as Renouf cocktail, escargot Renouf and salmon Renouf. This is grand-hotel cuisine bound in a restaurant. Pastry can be exemplary, the sweets trolley is five tiers high, and the ducks continue to be a centre of interest, cooked five ways: pressed; with basil and raspberry; with madeira, cherry and cognac; with apple, thyme and raspberry liqueur; or Aylesbury with orange and apricots. The wine list – 'The Renouf Collection' – has house Bordeaux, white and red, at £6.50. CELLARMAN'S CHOICE: Ch. Respide Médéville '83, £14.50.

CHEF/PROPRIETOR: Derek Renouf
OPEN: Tue to Sat, exc Sat L
CLOSED: first 3 weeks Jan, first week July
MEALS: 12.15 to 1.45, 7.15 to 9.45 (10.45 Sat)
PRICES: £18 (£26), Set L and D £9.50 (£14)
CARDS: Access, Amex, Diners, Visa
SEATS: 70. Private parties: 70 main room. Vegetarian meals. Children welcome. Wheelchair access (also WC). Music. Air-conditioned
ACCOMMODATION: 24 rooms, all with bath/shower. Rooms for disabled. B&B £48 to £65. Baby facilities. Pets welcome. Garden. TV. Phone

ROCKLEY Wiltshire map 2

Loaves and Fishes [11/20]

Rockley Chapel, Rockley SN8 1RT
MARLBOROUGH (0672) 53737 £16.50

Being a chapel there is no licence, but nor is there any objection to taking your own wine. Angela Rawson and Nikki Kedge's evocative and unusual restaurant is relatively inexpensive as a result. The set price includes everything. There is a bias to country foods, as in lovage to flavour a cheese mousse, and meats are hormone free. Sauces tend to dominate main dishes, but these are finished in the pan using the juices rather than *nouvelle* long-simmered stock bases – juniper and orange for venison; Dijon mustard, white wine and cream for rib of beef. Sweets follow the theme with strawberry and Cointreau gateau, fruit tarts, and an English accent in hot ginger pudding with ginger cream, or an intriguing black-treacle cream soufflé. Vegetarian and fish dishes are available on request.

CHEF: Angela F. Rawson PROPRIETORS: Angela F. Rawson and Nikki R. Kedge
OPEN: Tue to Sat, D only, and Sun L
MEALS: 12.30 to 1, 7.30 to 8.30
PRICES: Set D £16.50. Service inc. Unlicensed, but bring your own: corkage 5% for parties over 6
SEATS: 28. Private parties: 10 main room. Car-park, 10 places. Vegetarian meals. Children's helpings. Wheelchair access (also WC). Music

ROMSEY Hampshire map 2

Old Manor House [13/20]

21 Palmerston Street, Romsey SO5 8GF
ROMSEY (0794) 517353 £14–£28

The old brick building near the town car-park, with a courtyard, beams and, large open fireplaces, has been here since 1540. Mauro Bregoli has stuck to his own style – '70% French, 20% Italian, 10% other'. In the last year he reports: 'We have put in new table-cloths, carpet, started using silver cloches and silver ice-buckets, introduced a spirit trolley with a selection of armagnacs and cognacs. The excellent selection of cheeses from Philippe Olivier has increased to between 25 and 30 different sorts. We have smartened up the service, without any significant increase in price.' Mr Bregoli is a hunter and shoots the game, including venison, himself. Recommended dishes on a *carte* of seven starters, four fish and five meat dishes, have been: grilled Test trout; confit of duck; John Dory with a raspberry vinegar; tagliatelle with wild mushrooms from the New Forest. Gravlax still appears although Mr Bregoli points out he was serving it long before the fashion began. Sweets are indulgent and there is much praise for trifle; sorbets; bavarois; chocolate cake; fruit salad. Lunch is a bargain at £7.95. The cellar has 600 bottles and is impressive, particularly for its clarets, which range at great length from *petits châteaux* and *crus bourgeois*, some of which look rather elderly, up to several vintages of the '60s and '70s of Châteaux Lafite and Latour. There are also Burgundies in profusion, but these are mostly from merchants, with only a few individual estate wines. The list covers the rest of France, Italy and Spain, with Alsace and Italy the most interesting areas after Bordeaux. House Burgundy £6.50.

CHEF/PROPRIETOR: Mauro Bregoli
OPEN: Tue to Sun, exc Sun D
CLOSED: 24 to 30 Dec, last 3 weeks Aug
MEALS: 12 to 2, 7 to 9.30
PRICES: Set L £7.95 (£14) to £18.50 (£25), Set D £21 (£28)
CARDS: Access, Visa
SEATS: 42. 6 tables outside. Private parties: 12 main room, 24 private room. Car-park, 12 places. Children welcome. Smart dress preferred. No cigars/pipes in dining-room

RUGBY Warwickshire map 5

▲ *Grosvenor Hotel* [new entry, zero rated]

Clifton Road, Rugby CV21 3QQ
RUGBY (0788) 535686 £10–£22

Ambitiously re-vamped as a hotel for conferences, business and weddings. Outside is all canopies and primrose-painted brickwork; inside is full of art deco and antiques. The dimly-lit dining-room is mock-Regency, with pale striped wallpaper, and urns overflowing with greenery. Richard Johnson's cooking is modern and seasonal. A fixed menu always has good-quality steaks, Dover soles and some classic dishes, but interest centres on the monthly changing specialities – sauté of scallops and artichokes with hazelnut oil, pheasant with celeriac purée. Thick slices of fillet of English lamb sit on a bed of shredded Bramley apple and fresh mint, with a sauce of pan-juices laced with cognac. Vegetables are well-timed, plain and simple. Sixty wines offer plenty of decent drinking for around £10. More reports please.

CHEF: Richard Johnson PROPRIETORS: Miss J. Hall and J. Hawes
OPEN: all week, exc Sat L
MEALS: 12 to 2, 7 to 10
PRICES: £16 (£22), Set L £4.95 (£10) to £14.95 (£21), Set D £14.95 (£21)
CARDS: Access, Amex, Diners, Visa
SEATS: 42. Private parties: 40 private room. Car-park, 18 places. Vegetarian meals, on request. Children welcome. Smart dress preferred. No pipes in dining-room. Wheelchair access. Music
ACCOMMODATION: 16 rooms, all with bath/shower. B&B £48 to £58. Children welcome. Baby facilities. Pets welcome. Afternoon teas. Garden. TV. Phone

Reports on shops, cafés and farms are useful, as well as reports on restaurants.

The Guide *does not accept free meals.*

It is helpful if restaurants keep the office up to date with any changes.

RYE East Sussex map 3

Landgate Bistro [13/20]

5–6 Landgate, Rye TN31 7LH
RYE (0797) 222829 £15

The Landgate is an ancient stone gateway that straddles the road. Nick Parkin and Toni Ferguson-Lees were previously at Bistro Down Under just up the hill, whereas this is just down. 'What is exceptional is that it is such a likeable, decent sort of place – modest, unassuming, unpretentious, restrained and very decent value.' Supplies are very local and very good and enhanced by good timing in the kitchen. The menu focuses strongly on fish and game and is evolving steadily, in no great hurry, from French bistro/ provincial into modern British, bringing more fruits, herbs and vegetables into the main stream. Vegetables are charged separately and are generous and imaginative, for instance grated carrot and parsnip with cream, butter and nutmeg, or artichokes with a tarragon hollandaise. The centrepieces –rough stew of four fish, sliced pigeon breasts with a fine red wine sauce, chocolate marquise – shine out. Bit parts like bread, table butter, aïoli, seem to get less attention. Wines match the food: a varied choice of no-nonsense bottles at impressively reasonable prices. All the clarets bar one, and that includes a couple of classed growths as well as a fistful of *cru bourgeois*, are under £15. Bulgaria, Germany, the South of France, and Haut Poitou all contribute very drinkable bottles for around a fiver. Such sensible pricing encourages adventurous drinking, and enhances the pleasure of eating out. House French is £4.50. CELLARMAN'S CHOICE: Vacqueyras '85, £8; Mâcon-Lugny '86, £8.50.

CHEF: Toni Ferguson-Lees PROPRIETORS: Nick Parkin and Toni Ferguson-Lees
OPEN: Tue to Sat, D only
MEALS: 7 to 9.30
PRICES: £10 (£15). Service 10%
CARDS: Access, Amex, Diners, Visa
SEATS: 34. Vegetarian meals. Children's helpings. Music

RYTON-ON-DUNSMORE Warwickshire map 5

Ryton Gardens [9/20]

Ryton-on-Dunsmore, Coventry CV8 3LG
COVENTRY (0203) 303517
5m SE of Coventry, on A45 £6–£9

The modern, open-plan café of the National Centre for Organic Gardening takes all its produce from the 22-acre site and unashamedly aims 'to show that natural food need not be boring'. Inexpensive lunches of quiche or Hungarian pancakes come with spectacular salads. Sweets are traditional British. Scones and herb teas are offered in the afternoon. Wines are organic and there are English country fruit wines. Open for dinner only on special occasions.

PROPRIETORS: The Henry Doubleday Research Association
OPEN: all week, L only
CLOSED: 25 and 26 Dec
MEALS: 12 to 2.30
PRICES: £4 (£9), Set L £2.85 (£6) to £4.05 (£7), Snacks from 95p
CARDS: Access, Visa
SEATS: 30. 7 tables outside. Private parties: 10 main room, 44 private room. Car-park, 80 places. Vegetarian meals. Children's helpings. No smoking. Wheelchair access (also WC). Self-service

SAFFRON WALDEN Essex map 3

Old Hoops [10/20]

15 King Street, Saffron Walden CB10 1HE
SAFFRON WALDEN (0799) 22813 £19

Provides a valuable service in an area where good restaurants have found it hard to flourish. Its virtues are a menu of some interest and prices that do not insist on perfection. The menu is a right old stock-pot of styles, from Hawaiian chicken to calf's liver Girardet. On one hand there is a conservative strain of avocado and cream cheese, on the other classic sauces and garnishes like bigarade, zingara, Talleyrand or just plain mon rêve – a cream, shallot and port sauce for a stuffed chicken breast. The mood is casual, with posters and old metal advertising signs on the dark-green walls. Fifty wines, mostly under £10. House French £5.95. CELLARMAN'S CHOICE: Ch. Lalène '84, at £7.95.

CHEF/PROPRIETOR: Ray Morrison
OPEN: Tue to Sat
CLOSED: 2 weeks in summer
MEALS: 12 to 2.30, 7 to 10.30
PRICES: £11 (£19)
CARDS: Access, Amex, Diners, Visa
SEATS: 40. Private parties: 40 main room. Children's helpings. Music

ST KEVERNE Cornwall map 1

Laden Table [12/20]

2 Commercial Road, St Keverne TR12 6LY
ST KEVERNE (0326) 280090 £20

The surprise is to find a restaurant in St Keverne. The village is small, not near the coast or any other notable tourist attraction, and does not even boast a famous church – all of which may explain why it has taken three years for this reincarnation of Tony Gulliford's Bath restaurant to make the listings. Post Bath, he worked again with George Perry-Smith at the Riverside at Helford – they had worked together at the Hole in the Wall – and that is the style, some of it even pre-dating the David influence of the 1950s, as in gratin of smoked haddock Monte Carlo. There is also the Perry-Smith classic of Tamar salmon in pastry with ginger and currants, but with little saucing and good attention to details. A variation on the salmon has been turbot in pastry with cream, garlic and mint. Recommendations also for the crab tart; fish soup; terrine of guinea-fowl; lamb printanière; 'superbly oily' peperonata; ice-cream. The dining-room is three cottages knocked into one, quite plainly done out. The name Laden Table might be applied to the overdressed tables set well apart. The wine list runs to 40 well-chosen bottles and barely takes a step outside of France. House French is £5.50.

CHEF/PROPRIETOR: Tony Gulliford
OPEN: Tue to Sat, D only; Mon D Jun to Sept
MEALS: 7.30 to 9.30
PRICES: Set D £15 (£20)
SEATS: 30. Private parties: 12 main room. Children welcome. No cigars/pipes in dining-room. Wheelchair access

ST LEONARD'S East Sussex map 3

Röser's [12/20]

64 Eversfield Place, St Leonard's-on-Sea TN37 6DB
HASTINGS (0424) 712218 £27

A slice of Alsace in a row of houses along the Hastings seafront, almost opposite the pier. Strictly speaking, this is St Leonard's. Inside feels more like a restaurant in Germany, with lots of solid dark furniture, brown patterned carpets and deer heads with antlers. Gerald Röser cooks an ambitious, sophisticated menu with a strong showing of local fish: poached salmon and monkfish in tarragon sauce; goujons of turbot with lobster sauce; scallops with Pernod and saffron. Saucing is classy, with plenty of real stock and cream used to good effect. Otherwise the menu spans everything from duck breast in champagne and raisin sauce to noisettes of venison with cinnamon pears or Scotch fillet of beef and grilled Dover sole. To finish, dark chocolate mousse with coffee sauce is the real thing. The 300-strong wine list has a heavy French presence with modest mark-ups, offering a generous choice of Burgundy and a long run of claret. House French, from Mommessin, £5.95. CELLARMAN'S CHOICE: Sancerre, Domaine Saget, £10.95.

CHEF: Gerald Röser PROPRIETORS: Gerald and Jenny Röser
OPEN: Mon to Sat, exc Sat L
MEALS: 12 to 2, 7 to 10
PRICES: £19 (£27). Service 10%
CARDS: Access, Amex, Diners, Visa
SEATS: 50. Private parties: 20 main room, 40 private room. Vegetarian meals. Children welcome. Wheelchair access (2 steps). Music

If you cannot honour a restaurant booking, always phone to cancel.

Restaurants are checked every year and their entries rewritten. The restaurant scene changes very rapidly. Don't trust an out-of-date Guide.

ST MARGARET'S AT CLIFFE Kent map 3

▲ *Wallett's Court* [11/20]

West Cliffe, St Margaret's at Cliffe CT15 6EW
DOVER (0304) 852424 £17–£26

At the Oakley's historic Jacobean house, barns are being converted into luxury suites, the restaurant is being extended, and dinners are now served right through the week to non-residents. An emphasis is placed on robust flavours, the use of local ingredients – game, vegetables and fish – and dishes which echo the period of the house by a vivid use of spices, herbs and fruit, as in duck and port terrine with fresh apricot sauce; salmon with fennel sauce; chicken fillets in lemon and hazelnuts. Fillet of sole on fresh mint and Martini sauce has a more modern ring. To finish there's a selection of desserts like syllabubs, mousses and cakes: again local fruit comes to the fore. The wine list is short and to the point with most bottles around £10.
CELLARMAN'S CHOICE: Ch. Smith Haut Lafite '79 at £19.

CHEF: Chris Oakley PROPRIETORS: Chris and Lea Oakley
OPEN: Mon to Sat, D only; L by arrangement
MEALS: 7 to 9
PRICES: Set weekday D from £12.50 (£17), Set Sat D £20 (£26)
SEATS: 30. Private parties: 30 main room. Car-park, 26 places. Vegetarian meals. Children's helpings
ACCOMMODATION: 12 rooms, all with bath/shower. Rooms for disabled. B&B £26 to £60. Baby facilities. Garden. Snooker. TV. Scenic. Doors close at 12. Confirm by 4 [GHG]

ST MAWES Cornwall map 1

▲ *Rising Sun* [13/20]

CORNISH NEWCOMER OF THE YEAR GFG '89

The Square, St Mawes, Truro TR2 5DJ
ST MAWES (0326) 270233 £16

The re-emergence of this famous old Cornish pub – owned by the Marshall family for 49 years – has been one of the most encouraging signs of the summer of 1988. After a succession of five chefs in 1987, Roger Jones joined the following March and the prospects immediately looked up. Jones trained with Franco Taruschio at the Walnut Tree Inn for six years and it is apparent in the style, sense of exploration in the menu and loyalty to fresh foods and local produce. St Mawes has not traded in its fishing fleet for souvenir stalls and the boats still deliver their catch direct to the kitchen door. The pub is the hub of village life, but a new garden dining-room provides a setting for some fine modern British cooking. The menu changes nightly, offering half a dozen dishes per course, each usually a demonstration of another technique in the cook's armoury: roasting, baking, poaching, sautéing, steaming, pastry making. Fish is the main but not the only glory. Jones has served his apprenticeship well: witness the freshest of tagliatelle on to which is flaked some sea-trout with a sauce of fish stock, cream and nutmeg, the whole then given a smattering of Parmesan; or a shortcrust pastry tart filled with sauté chicken and courgette in a small sauce of chicken stock, madeira and cream;

or – a Taruschio dish – roast quail wrapped in bacon, filled with a handful of sage leaves and sauced with the bird's pan-juices. Vegetables outshine those of his mentor, as in a 'messy, rough, excellent' dauphinois. Bread is baked by Sharon Walker, who has worked here for eight years, and is first class. Sweets are modern: sabayons, plates of fresh fruit, ice-creams, fruit tarts, fruits in alcohol and a rich chocolate slice reminiscent of Taruschio's dolce torinese. Fifty mainly French wines, with House French £5.95. CELLARMAN'S CHOICE: Rully, Domaine de l'Heritage '84, £10.95; Chenin Blanc '85, from Brown Bros, £8.35.

CHEF: Roger Jones PROPRIETORS: R.J. Milan and F.N.B. Atherley
OPEN: all week
MEALS: 12 to 2, 7.30 to 9.30
PRICES: Set D £13 (£16), L Snacks from £1. Service inc
CARDS: Access, Amex, Diners, Visa
SEATS: 46. 12 tables outside (L only). Private parties: 60 main room. Car-park, 6 places. Vegetarian meals. No children under 10. No smoking in dining-room. Wheelchair access (also WC)
ACCOMMODATION: 13 rooms, 9 with bath/shower. B&B £24 to £60. Deposit: £10. No children under 10. Pets welcome. Afternoon teas. TV. Phone. Scenic

ST MICHAEL'S-ON-WYRE Lancashire map 5

Mallards [new entry, zero rated]

Garstang Road, St Michael's-on-Wyre PR3 0TE
ST MICHAEL'S-ON-WYRE (099 58) 661 £11–£21

Formerly a café, but now a distinct step up, taken over by John and Anne Steel who came from Truffles in Manchester (*Guide* listed in 1987). They virtually run it together; he cooks, she serves and they live over the shop. The menu offers seven starters, eight main courses with an array of sauces – horseradish cream for smoked quail; cranberry coulis for breast of pigeon; brown ale for beef fillet – though any dish can be cooked plainly. The central ingredients are of good quality and shine through. Recommended dishes have been: crab soufflé; queen scallops in a rich saffron sauce; loin of venison with Cumberland sauce; and cold, artistic sweets. House French is £5.75. More reports, please.

CHEF: John Steel PROPRIETORS: John and Ann Steel
OPEN: Mon to Sat D, and Sun L
CLOSED: 2 weeks Aug and 1 week Jan
MEALS: 12 to 5.30, 7 to 9.30 (10 Sat)
PRICES: £15 (£21), Set L £7.50 (£11)
CARDS: Access, Visa
SEATS: 24. Private parties: 40 main room. Car-park, 20 places. Children welcome. Wheelchair access. Music

Files are kept on every restaurant, so reports of poor meals are just as valuable as reports of good meals because they save unnecessary inspections.

SALISBURY Wiltshire map 2

Crustaceans [10/20]

2–4 Ivy Street, Salisbury SP1 2AY
SALISBURY (0722) 333948 £25

The all-pervading watery theme of the grey ocean colours inside extends to the blue paintwork outside. There is a long, almost exclusively fish menu that stays, on the whole, with simple and tried and tested dishes which are its main virtue. 'Lemon and Dover sole were beautifully fresh, although plain.' Kebabs of tuna, scallops Mornay and bouillabaisse also draw good reports. There are cold plates of shellfish and lobster according to market price; or of prawns, made up of brown and pink shrimps, prawns, crevettes, tiger prawns and langoustines. Plus there is a char-grill. Saucing and puddings are elementary. Portions are large, but for the price, the trimmings would repay more investment. Eighty French wines do not ease the financial burden. House wine £7.50. CELLARMAN'S CHOICE: Muscadet '85, from Louis Métaireau, at £10.

CHEF: Roy Thwaites PROPRIETORS: Roy and Lois Thwaites
OPEN: Mon to Sat, D only
MEALS: 7 to 10.30
PRICES: £18 (£25). Service 10%
CARDS: Access, Visa
SEATS: 48. Private parties: 12 main room. No children under 8. Music. Air-conditioned

Harper's [9/20]

7–9 Ox Row, The Market Square, Salisbury SP1 1EU
SALISBURY (0722) 333118 £9–£16

For the last six years this small, family-oriented dining-room overlooking the market square has prospered where others have failed. Most of the food is made on the premises. The blackboard menu shifts slowly with the seasons. Good fish is plainly grilled or served, in the case of haddock, with a lemon and caper sauce. To finish, there is usually treacle tart. The value is good, especially at lunch-time. House wine is £5.50 on a surprisingly wide-ranging list. CELLARMAN'S CHOICE: Château Musar '79, from Hochar, £8.50.

CHEFS: Adrian Harper and Julie West PROPRIETORS: Adrian and Ann Harper
OPEN: Mon to Sat
CLOSED: 25 and 26 Dec
MEALS: 12 to 2, 6.30 to 10 (10.30 Sat)
PRICES: £10 (£16), Set L £4.95 (£9), Set D £8.95 (£14)
CARDS: Access, Diners, Visa
SEATS: 60. Private parties: 60 main room. Car-park. Vegetarian meals. Children's helpings. Music. Air-conditioned

Restaurants change owners and chefs constantly. It is very useful if you keep the Guide *informed of any changes you find.*

Wiltshire Round-up

AFTERNOON TEAS: *Corner Stones,* 32 Silver Street, Bradford on Avon (022 16 5673); *Polly Tea Rooms,* High Street, Marlborough (0672 52146).
WINE BAR: *Bentley's,* 7 Kingsbury Street, Marlborough (0672 54776); *Just Brahms,* 68 Castle Street, Salisbury (0722 28402).
ROOMS: *Old School House,* Collingbourne Kingston, Nr Marlborough (026 485 799); *Beechfield House,* Beanacre, Melksham (0225 703700).
VEGETARIAN: *Jenner's,* 45 Market Place, Warminster (0985 213385); *Stones,* High Street, Avebury, Marlborough (06723 514).
BAR MEALS: *Dove Inn,* Corton, Warminster (0985 50378); *Georgian Wine Lodge,* 25 Bridge Street, Bradford upon Avon (022 16 2268).

SCARBOROUGH North Yorkshire map 6A

Lanterna [10/20]

10 YEARS

33 Queen Street, Scarborough YO11 1HQ
SCARBOROUGH (0723) 363616 £19

Old-school Italian and Continental cooking continues to find favour in the Arecco family's long-established trattoria. Steak Diane and pollo coronata –cooked with onions, mushrooms, cream and brandy – are favourites. Otherwise the menu takes in the well-tried mix of minestrone, spaghetti carbonara, bistecca barolo and scampi provençale. Vegetables are freshly cooked. House Italian £6.

CHEF: G. Arecco PROPRIETORS: Mr and Mrs G. Arecco
OPEN: Tue to Sat, D only
MEALS: 7 to 9.30
CLOSED: 3 weeks in summer
PRICES: £13 (£19)
CARD: Visa
SEATS: 36. Private parties: 36 main room. Vegetarian meals. No children under 5. Wheelchair access. Music

▲ *Mark's at Lindhead Cottage* [9/20]

Harewood Dale, Scarborough YO13 0DN
SCARBOROUGH (0723) 870779 £16

A very pretty little country cottage five miles out of Scarborough on the Whitby Road. The Johnstons run the tiny dining-room with good humour offering lunch and teas, plus dinners towards the end of the week. It is pleasant and homely, with wooden cottagey tables and chairs and old-fashioned cutlery. For dinner there's a daily-changing menu of home-cooked dishes – decent potato soup, beef and Guinness pie, casseroled pork with cider, bean and buckwheat bake. Bread and butter pudding and home-made ice-creams to finish. Modest wines. House French £3.95.

Restaurants are not expected to solicit customers to send in reports. Please let us know if this happens to you.

CHEFS/PROPRIETORS: J.M. and P.S. Johnston
OPEN: L Tue to Fri and Sun; D Wed, Fri and Sat
MEALS: 12 to 2, 7.30 to 10
PRICES: £12 (£16), Snacks from 50p
CARD: Visa
SEATS: 18. 8 tables outside. Private parties: 16 main room. Car-park, 15 places. Vegetarian meals. Children's helpings (L and teas only). No children under 14 (D only). Smart dress preferred. Music. Air-conditioned
ACCOMMODATION: 2 rooms. B&B £24 to £32. Deposit: £10 per person. No children under 14. Dogs welcome. Afternoon teas. Garden. TV. Phone. Scenic

SEAVIEW Isle of Wight map 2

▲ *Seaview Hotel* [11/20]

High Street, Seaview PO34 5EX
SEAVIEW (0983) 612711 £13–£19

The epitome of late-Victorian seaside hotels, brought cosily up to date with a little front garden, views of the sea from the lounge and an olive-green dining-room full of clocks. The Haywards support their local fishermen and food producers, gearing their short seasonal menus to supplies. The cooking is no-nonsense, straightforward and sharp, with fish as the highlight. Lobster thermidor is redolent of brandy; sea-bream comes with red pepper sauce; and a parcel of mixed seafood in flaky pastry comes with a creamy crab sauce. Other dishes show up well: poached thigh of chicken is served in a reduction of mushrooms and brandy with spring onions; lamb cutlets come with onion marmalade. Meals can run out of steam by the sweets. About 60 wines include local Adgestone, a few from Australia and plenty of half-bottles. House claret from Corney & Barrow is £5.90. CELLARMAN'S CHOICE: Pokolbin, Hungerford Hill Chardonnay '86, £11.90.

CHEFS: Nicola Hayward and Charles Bartlet PROPRIETORS: Nicola and Nicholas Hayward
OPEN: all week, exc Sun D
MEALS: 12 to 1.45, 7.30 to 9.30
PRICES: £13 (£19), Set L £7.95 (£13), Set D £10.45 (£16), Snacks from £1
CARDS: Access, Visa
SEATS: 30. 10 tables outside. Private parties: 30 main room, 20 private room. Car-park, 12 places. Vegetarian meals. Children's helpings. No children under 3. Smart dress preferred D. No pipes in dining-room. Wheelchair access (also WC)
ACCOMMODATION: 16 rooms, 14 with bath/shower. B&B £27 to £46. Children welcome. Baby facilities. Pets welcome. Afternoon teas. TV. Scenic [GHG]

SHARPTHORNE West Sussex map 3

▲ *Gravetye Manor* [15/20]

10 YEARS

Vowels Lane, Sharpthorne RH19 4LJ
SHARPTHORNE (0342) 810567 £23–£34

'A week after the terrible hurricane-force winds, there was a profound and eerie stillness, giving the area a peculiar kind of desolation. The only sound was the metallic whining of chain-saws. Several trees had been lost and the approach road to the hotel looked as if a drunken giant had rampaged through the woodland, hurling trees around in an uncontrollable rage. Autumn mists and smoke from bonfires hid some of the devastation, but it was heart-breaking to see such destruction in such a beautiful part of England.' By summer it was plain that William Robinson's famous gardens surrounding the Elizabethan manor had retained their beauty despite the losses. The process of regeneration at Gravetye had already begun with the return of the prodigal son, in the form of Leigh, to the kitchens. He instantly injected a fresh force to the old ideas, with no fear of either the inexpensive, like a warm salad of ham hock with lentils, or the expensive, as in a ballotine of foie gras. But the menu has an uncommon grasp of technique – fillet of beef poached in consommé; monkfish roasted with shallots and garlic and served with a rich port sauce. This allows dishes like fillet of red mullet on black noodles to work. A favourite device is to stuff saddle of lamb with a vegetable, perhaps asparagus, then serve it with a light hollandaise, or basil complemented by braised beetroots and an Hermitage sauce. Sweets draw much praise – crème brûlée, pear stuffed with cinnamon ice-cream, sponge pudding with butterscotch sauce. The hotel's attraction is its individuality; it has an air of days gone by without being shabby. The dining-room is oak-panelled and intimate at night. 'I would be proud to take visitors from overseas to show them what a real English country-house hotel should be like.' The wine list is good, though expensive. Apart form a handful of Californian wines, a selection of interesting German estate wines and a little port and madeira, it sticks to the classic areas of France. Magnums are a speciality. Top clarets go back to '49, skipping the bad vintages, and there are some well-chosen *crus bourgeois* and *petit château* wines of recent years. Burgundies and Chablis are from good producers, Rhônes are from merchants including Paul Jaboulet Aîné, with some rare old vintages; and a long list of champagnes goes back, unusually, to '55. Pudding wines take in old and rare bottles of sweet Alsace or Loire, mature sweet Bordeaux (and a few younger unreadies), and Beerenauslesen and Trockenbeerenauslesen from the '71, '75, '76 and '79 vintages from the Mosel, Rhine and even Franconia. House French from Louis Latour and Paul Jaboulet Aîné starts at £11.50; CELLARMAN'S CHOICE: Pouilly Vinzelles, Gobet '85, £21; Hermitage, La Chapelle '84, £34.

CHEF: Leigh Stone-Herbert PROPRIETOR: Peter Herbert
OPEN: all week
CLOSED: 25 Dec D to non-residents
MEALS: 12.30 to 2, 7.30 to 9.30 (10 Sat)
PRICES: £25 (£34), Set L £15 (£23), Set D £19 (£27). Service inc
SEATS: 50. Private parties: 10 main room, 20 private room. Car-park, 30 places. No children under 7. Smart dress preferred. No smoking in dining-room
ACCOMMODATION: 14 rooms, all with bath/shower. B&B £55 to £130. No children under 7. Garden. Fishing. TV. Phone. Scenic. Doors close at 12 [GHG]

Anyone claiming to be from The Good Food Guide *is an impostor. Restaurateurs are advised to contact the office immediately if any fraudulent claims are made.*

SHEFFIELD South Yorkshire map 5

Arcadia [10/20]

560 Langsett Road, Hillsborough, Sheffield S6 2LX
SHEFFIELD (0742) 323382 £15–£20

A converted bank in an unpromising suburb of the city has been turned into a light, functional restaurant not unlike a London dining-room. The wines are kept in the vaults. Despite the name, there's no hint of rustic charm, rather a smart, cosmopolitan air to match a short, eclectic menu that moves from Chinese mushroom and leek lasagne, tagliatelle with asparagus and artichoke hearts, and baked cod marinated in yoghurt and Indian spices to fishcakes with saffron sauce, rack of lamb with goats' cheese sauce, or char-grilled rabbit with tomato and mint. Soup might be spinach and coconut; sweets range from macadamia-nut tart to compote of fresh citrus fruits. Lunch and Sunday brunch offer cheaper eating. Fifty wines from around the world, as well as Chimay beer and cidre bouché. CELLARMAN'S CHOICE: South Australian Semillon, Jacobs Creek '85, at £6.25.

CHEF: Rex Barker PROPRIETORS: Finalbox Ltd
OPEN: Tue to Sat, exc Sat L
MEALS: 12 to 2.30 (3 Sun), 7 to 10
PRICES: £10 (£15), Set D £12.25 (£17) to £15.50 (£20)
CARDS: Access, Amex, Visa
SEATS: 36. Private parties: 12 main room. Children's helpings (Sun L only). Wheelchair access (also WC). Music

Greenhead House [new entry, zero rated]

84 Burncross Road, Chapeltown, Sheffield S30 4SF
SHEFFIELD (0742) 469004 £21–£23

About five miles from the centre of Sheffield is this renovated stone cottage with a well-kept picture-postcard of a garden. The style is smart country living with a few fancy touches in the blue and yellow swagged curtains and the smart Wedgwood crockery. A short handwritten menu has four courses with some imaginative ideas that don't slavishly follow fashions. Queen scallops are cooked in a creamy sauce flavoured with cider vinegar; hot confit of duck is made using the old method of seasoning the bird and roasting it in its own fat before crisping under the grill. A soup precedes main courses such as guinea-fowl with limes, rack of lamb with wild mushrooms or sole and crab timbale decorated with crab legs. Vegetables are good and fresh, bread is baked on the premises and herbs come from the garden. A well-chosen list of around 50 wines centres on France opening at £7.95 for house Côtes du Ventoux. More reports, please.

Please keep the Guide *informed of any changes to the restaurants listed. Report forms are at the back of the book.*

CHEFS: Neil Allen and Christine Roberts PROPRIETORS: Neil and Anne Allen
OPEN: Tue to Sat, D only
CLOSED: last 2 weeks Apr, first 2 weeks Sept and 24 to 31 Dec
MEALS: 7.15 to 9
PRICES: Set D £16.75 (£21) to £18.95 (£23)
CARDS: Amex, Visa
SEATS: 32. Private parties: 32 main room. Car-park, 14 places. Children welcome. Wheelchair access

Nirmal's [11/20]

193 Glossop Road, Sheffield S10 2GW
SHEFFIELD (0742) 724054 £18–£24

Sheffield's best Indian restaurant has been enlarged and refurbished – and the prices have gone up accordingly. It now occupies the corner site, the old red tiles merging in to the red bricks of the extension. New, tall, single-pane arched windows have green frames. A lattice-work wall divides old and new seating. Nirmal Gupta is still one of the few Asian women chefs in the country and apart from the usual menu she cooks a blackboard of daily specialities. Specialities include tomato paneer, made with home-made curd cheese, or king prawns, tandooried or curried with onions in a dopiaza dish. Recommended are the tandoori dishes, the soft, warm nan bread and the potato 'chops'. House white and red is from Paul Masson in California at £5.50; alternatively drink Kingfisher lager, Tiger beer or Grolsch.

CHEF: Nirmal Gupta PROPRIETOR: P.L. Gupta
OPEN: all week, exc Sun L
MEALS: 12 to 2.30, 6 to 12 (1 Fri and Sat)
PRICES: £10 (£18), Set D from £19 (£24). Service 10%
CARDS: Access, Amex, Visa
SEATS: 90. Private parties: 30 main room, 60 private room. Vegetarian meals. Children welcome. Wheelchair access (also WC). Music

SHEPTON MALLET Somerset map 2

Blostin's [11/20]

29 Waterloo Road, Shepton Mallet BA4 5HH
SHEPTON MALLET (0749) 3648 £12–£18

There is an increasingly local feel to Nick Reed's menu at Blostin's. As much produce as possible comes from the immediate area. No longer are salads just from France, but now also from Pilton. Fish is the strength of the set eight-dish menus: terrine of scallops, crabmeat and salmon; brill with crab sauce. The style is English provincial – chutney with galantine of chicken, pigeon and smoked pork; oysters with fillet of beef; treacle tart; syllabub. All good evidence of how high-quality local produce energises and develops a menu that is based on home-made stocks and soups. There are good English cheeses and also English wines, though the Australians and lesser French regions offer better value on a short, interesting list opening at £5.
CELLARMAN'S CHOICE: McWilliam's Cabernet Shiraz '85, £5.95.

CHEF: Nick Reed PROPRIETORS: Nick and Lynne Reed
OPEN: Tue to Sat, D only (L by arrangement)
MEALS: 12 to 2, 7 to 9.30 (Sat 10)
PRICES: £14 (£18), Set L £7.95 (£12), Set D £9.95 (£14) to £10.95 (£15). Service inc
CARDS: Access, Visa
SEATS: 32. Private parties: 30 main room. Vegetarian meals. Children's helpings. Wheelchair access. Music

SHINFIELD Berkshire map 2

L'Ortolan [17/20]

The Old Vicarage, Church Lane, Shinfield RG2 9BY
READING (0734) 883783 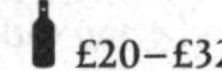 £20–£32

The *Guide* discovered John Burton-Race a few weeks after he had taken on the running of the old Quat' Saisons in Oxford for Raymond Blanc. It was obvious he was a major talent. He was rated 15/20. Then he took the whole operation up the road to Le Petit Blanc and in that conservatory he seemed for a few short months to threaten even Le Manoir. Now he is established in his own restaurant, formerly The Old Vicarage and then Chez Nico, to whom the credit for conceiving and designing the shape of the restaurant must go, though it has an earthier, country feel now. He is a passionate, enthused talent, cooking to a level that demands to be considered along with the élite. Of many endorsements for meals here, there are five that state categorically, 'The best meal I have ever eaten.' Such praise has been reserved in recent years for only one other chef, Burton-Race's mentor, Raymond Blanc. Another testimonial, for the gratin de framboises – 'would someone else have done the raspberry sorbet covered with a spun-sugar cage? When one has gratin de framboises at Georges Blanc at Vonnas, for instance, there are just the raspberries and the sabayon, put under the grill. Very nice, but Burton-Race goes to all that extra and delicious trouble. And who has the three *Michelin* stars?' This lavish praise is offset by a few individual criticisms, such as tough partridge and overcooked pastry, a misconceived pot au feu. His cooking is not immediately in the style of anyone else. To call it fussy or over-cluttered is to misunderstand it. Burton-Race deals in tastes and combinations of tastes. He is perhaps closer to Alain Senderens (see the feature on Lucas Carton, Paris) than anyone else in this country. Consider this sweet: a sandwich of banana parfait, caramel-encrusted bananas and rum mousseline between layers of biscuity pastry, surrounded by lemon-flavoured cream, with a spun-sugar dome. Or a still-life of pan-fried foie gras sitting on a tiny nest of lightly fried celeriac, with slivers of grated apple and a sauce of the cooking juices and cider. Or a rich mille-feuille with crisp, fine pastry, a thick layer of steamed turbot, then a slice of pan-fried salmon and some roe, served with a red wine fumet and a fennel butter sauce garnished with broad beans. The syncopation of textures and flavours is the key. The menu descriptions are necessarily long, but precise. In autumn there are rarities like teal and woodcock. The combinations are seen in this meticulous description of a skate salad: 'the fish is steamed with lemon butter and soy, the cooking juices bound with fruity olive oil spiked with shallots and chives, dressed on a bed of green leaves and garnished with diced tomato.' The sense of seasoning, at a completely different level to most kitchens, has a breast of partridge in a white wine sauce served with a slice of boudin noir, a roasted spiced pear and a choucroûte lined with carrot. Dishes develop in the eating. 'Scallops are grilled and become encircled by a sweet tinged red pepper coulis, a green puddle of watercress and herbs, and a vinegary beurre blanc to counteract the sweetness. The mixture of the different flavours is superb, playing the subtle nuances of sweet and sour against each other.' The exclusively French wine list is expensive in the upper reaches of excellent red and white Burgundies, mostly from individual growers, or the fine clarets. Some people might consider some of the mature vintages of claret to be too old. But the list does offer some very well chosen wines from the Loire, Rhône, Alsace and Beaujolais, and from a few lesser regions, albeit quite highly marked up. The 'regional wines' from the front page offer some interesting drinking for under £16, such as Coteaux des Baux, Domaine de Trévallon '84, £15.95. CELLARMAN'S CHOICE: Chignin-Bergeron '85, £14.10; Cahors, Domaine de la Pineraie, '82, £13.95.

CHEF: John Burton-Race PROPRIETORS: Mr and Mrs Burton-Race
OPEN: Tue to Sun, exc Sun D
CLOSED: last 2 weeks Feb and last 2 weeks Aug
MEALS: 12.45 to 2.15, 7.15 to 10.30
PRICES: Set L £18.50 (£20), Set D £29.50 (£32). Licensed, also bring your own: corkage £5
CARDS: Access, Amex, Visa
SEATS: 70. 10 tables outside. Private parties: 40 main room, 32 private room. Car-park, 15 places. Vegetarian meals. Children's helpings. Wheelchair access (2 steps; also WC)

SHIPLEY West Yorkshire map 5

Aagrah [11/20]

27 Westgate, Shipley BD18 3QX
BRADFORD (0274) 594660 £18

This small Indian restaurant, up a side road, not far from the tax office, won the *Yorkshire Post*'s Restaurant of the Year last year, a salutary warning shot fired across the bows of French and expense-account catering. Compared with the Muslim cafés and sweet-centres in Bradford, it is much more of a restaurant. The confusion of influences that amount to the décor are not found in the menu. 'Genuine home cooking,' says a reader from Karachi. Choice is abundant: four biriani; five bhuna; four pilau; five Qeema; and a good vegetarian section to offset the tandooris, rogan josh and balti chicken. House Italian £8.50.

All letters to the Guide *are acknowledged.*

'Vegetables: I'm getting a bit upset about these. The British used always to overcook. Now we're undercooking!' On eating in Hampshire

CHEFS: M. Sabir, M. Aslam and Zafar Iqbal PROPRIETORS: Mr and Mrs M. Sabir, Mr and Mrs M. Aslam
OPEN: all week, D only
MEALS: 6pm to 12.45am (1.30am Thur, Fri and Sat)
PRICES: £8 (£18), Snacks from 75p
CARDS: Access, Amex, Diners, Visa
SEATS: 50. Private parties: 50 main room. Vegetarian meals. Children's helpings. Smart dress preferred. Wheelchair access. Music

SHIPSTON ON STOUR Warwickshire map 2

▲ *White Bear* [9/20]

High Street, Shipston on Stour CV36 4AJ
SHIPSTON ON STOUR (0608) 61558 £14–£20

The red-brick terraced building in the High Street is still very much the local pub, although its reputation is primarily for food. Linda and Geoff Chapman run the place on behalf of Hugh and Suzanne Roberts (who now concentrate most of their energies on the Fossebridge Inn, see Northleach). Better than average bar food is served in the plain pub lounge, and dishes are eclectic – from veal with white wine and peaches to steak and kidney pie. The little dining-room at the back serves more ambitious, more expensive meals. One bonus is the short, creditable wine list, which has a strong contingent from the New World, including CELLARMAN'S CHOICE: Rosemount Chardonnay '87, £10.80.

CHEF: Geoff Chapman PROPRIETORS: Hugh and Suzanne Roberts
OPEN: all week
MEALS: 12 to 1.45, 7.30 to 9.30
PRICES: £14 (£20), Set Sun L £8.95 (£14), Snacks from £1.75
CARDS: Access, Amex, Diners, Visa
SEATS: 35. 4 tables outside. Private parties: 24 main room. Car-park, 20 places. Vegetarian meals. Children's helpings. Smart dress preferred. Wheelchair access (also WC)
ACCOMMODATION: 10 rooms, all with bath/shower. B&B £27 to £38. Deposit: £20. Children welcome. Baby facilities. Pets welcome. Afternoon teas. TV. Doors close at 11.30. Confirm by 5

SHIPTON GORGE Dorset map 2

▲ *Innsacre Farmhouse Hotel* [11/20]

Shipton Gorge, Bridport DT6 4LJ
BRIDPORT (0308) 56137 £13–£19

'Tired and hungry we stepped out of our car to a smell of wood smoke, poached tomatoes and garlic drifting from the warmly lit farmhouse.' The Smiths have reinforced their kitchen in the last year and stick with a policy of using as much local produce as possible in an evolving menu of five starters and five main courses supplemented by a range of steaks. Typical has been a salad of sweet prawns with mange-tout and asparagus; calf's liver with chives and bacon; a chocolate cup filled with lemon mousse. Bedrooms are small but comfortable. 'No service charge and tipping is discouraged.' Sixty wines from Eldridge Pope at Dorchester, starting with house French at £6.50. CELLARMAN'S CHOICE: Chairman's white Burgundy '86, £10.

CHEFS: Mrs H.M. Smith, Andrew Brine and Stuart Pierrepont
PROPRIETORS: J.H. and H.M. Smith
OPEN: all week
MEALS: 12 to 2, 7.15 to 10.30
PRICES: Set L from £9.25 (£13), Set D from £15.25 (£19), Snacks from £2
CARDS: Access, Amex, Diners, Visa
SEATS: 42. 4 tables outside. Private parties: 60 main room. Car-park, 40 places. Vegetarian meals. Children's helpings. No cigars/pipes in dining-room. Wheelchair access (also WC). Music
ACCOMMODATION: 7 rooms, all with bath/shower. Rooms for disabled (also lift). B&B £25 to £44. Baby facilities. Pets welcome. Afternoon teas. Garden. TV. Scenic [GHG]

SHIPTON-UNDER-WYCHWOOD Oxfordshire — map 2

▲ *Lamb Inn* [10/20]

Shipton-under-Wychwood OX7 6DQ
SHIPTON (0993) 830465 — £12–£17

The Lamb is too much of a restaurant to be called a pub and too much of a pub to be called a restaurant. The buffet at weekends is a sensible compromise. Cooking is good English fare, with generous portions of roast beef or chicken with sage and onions served in the beamed dining-room. First courses might include a choice of fish soup, gravlax, or duck and orange pâté. Vegetarians are always well catered for, say regulars. Nursery-style puddings on the lines of gooseberry and rhubarb crumble. Fifty wines, with house French at £6; alternatively drink Hook Norton Best or Wadworth 6X.

CHEF: George Benham PROPRIETORS: Hugh and Lynne Wainwright
OPEN: Mon to Sat D, and Sun L
MEALS: 12.30 to 1.45, 7.30 to 9.15
PRICES: Set Sun L £7.75 (£12), Set D £12.50 (£17). Snacks from £1.25. Licensed, also bring your own: corkage £3.50
CARDS: Access, Amex, Diners, Visa
SEATS: 26. 9 tables outside. Private parties: 26 main room. Car-park, 30 places. Vegetarian meals. No children under 14. Wheelchair access
ACCOMMODATION: 5 rooms, all with bath/shower. Rooms for disabled. B&B £25 to £40. Deposit: £10. No children under 14. Garden. TV. Scenic. Confirm by 6 [GHG]

SISSINGHURST Kent — map 3

Rankins [new entry, zero rated]

The Street, Sissinghurst TN17 2JH
CRANBROOK (0580) 713964 — £13–£18

The address is indicative of the size of Sissinghurst, known for its Castle gardens and their creator/restorer Vita Sackville-West. Rankins is a superior tea-room of a dining-room in an old Kent building opposite the village stores and post office. It is family-run with Mrs Rankin front of house and Mr Rankin in the kitchen, single-handedly producing a short, well-described menu of light, healthy dishes, using good ingredients, some good modern, stock-based sauces and achieving a balance of flavour combinations. Sunday lunch is roasts but in the evenings there are more creative dishes which suggest a style in the making: ceviche of cod with a rémoulade sauce; noisettes of lamb served with a leek tart and a red wine, madeira and rosemary sauce; brill baked with herbs; Bramley mousse with shortbread and lime syrup. Of the 30 wines, ten are half-bottles and more than half under £10. More reports, please.

CHEF: Hugh Rankin PROPRIETORS: Hugh and Leonora Rankin
OPEN: Wed to Sat D, and Sun L
MEALS: 12.30 to 1.30, 7.30 to 9
PRICES: Set Sun L £10 (£13) to £11 (£14), Set D £13 (£16) to £14.50 (£18). Service inc
CARDS: Access, Visa
SEATS: 30. Private parties: 10 main room, 24 private room. Children's helpings (Sun L only). No children under 8. Smart dress preferred. Music

SKINBURNESS Cumbria map 7

▲ *Skinburness Hotel* [10/20]

Skinburness, Silloth-on-Solway CA5 4QY
SILLOTH (0965) 32332 £12–£17

Skinburness is a hamlet rather than a village and the hotel dwarfs all the other buildings. The view is across the Solway Firth to the Scottish hills. The inside has been attractively done in pastel shades and this new venture provides a useful stopping place in an area that has not been exploited except by golfers at nearby Silloth. The cooking has been competent, within safe hotel parameters, and not overly expensive. The wines are well spread and adequate. House French is £5.95.

CHEF: A.L. Miller PROPRIETORS: Dyke Bros Leisure Ltd
OPEN: all week D, and Sun L
MEALS: 12 to 2 Sun L, 7 to 9.30
PRICES: Set Sun L £7.50 (£12), Set D £12.50 (£17)
CARDS: Access, Amex, Diners, Visa
SEATS: 65. Private parties: 20 main room, 40 and 180 private rooms. Car-park, 80 places. Vegetarian meals. Children's helpings on request. Wheelchair access (2 steps; also WC). Music
ACCOMMODATION: 25 rooms, all with bath/shower. Rooms for disabled. B&B £37 to £65.50. Deposit: £25. Children welcome. Baby facilities. Pets welcome. Afternoon teas. Garden. Sauna. Snooker. TV. Phone. Scenic. Confirm by 6

Report forms are at the back of the book.

Places rating 9 may not be restaurants at all, but still serve good food; expect to find pubs, cafés, small hotels and wine bars.

SLAIDBURN Lancashire map 5

▲ *Parrock Head Farm* [10/20]

Slaidburn BB7 3AH
SLAIDBURN (020 06) 614
1m NW of Slaidburn £16

A country farmhouse hotel and restaurant at the foot of the Bowland Fells. The food is more adventurous than might be expected, with three or four choices at each course; the menu changes nightly. Comice pear and Stilton mousse, scallops in white wine or courgette and marjoram soup might be followed by fillet of pork en croûte or halibut with sorrel. Puddings are syllabubs, shortcakes and home-made ice-creams; the cheeseboard is English. The 40-bottle wine list has a good spread at affordable prices, with bottles from Portugal, Spain, Australia and California as well as France and Italy. House French £5.80 per litre; CELLARMAN'S CHOICE: Rosemount Estates Chardonnay Show Reserve '86, £9.50; Pinot Grigio, Tiefenbrunner '86, £7.50; St Estèphe, Ch. Meyney '80, £10.50; Brown Bros Late Harvest Orange Muscat '85, £5.75.

CHEFS: Vicky Umbers, Stephen Kerfoot and Deborah Wareing
PROPRIETORS: Vicky and Richard Umbers
OPEN: all week, D only
CLOSED: Dec and Jan
MEALS: 6.45 to 8.30
PRICES: £11 (£16)
CARDS: Access, Amex
SEATS: 32. Car-park, 20 places. Vegetarian meals. Children's helpings. No smoking. Wheelchair access
ACCOMMODATION: 9 rooms, all with bath/shower. Rooms for disabled. B&B £19.50 to £39. Pets welcome. Afternoon teas. Garden. Fishing. Golf. TV. Scenic [GHG]

SOLIHULL West Midlands map 5

Liaison [13/20]

761 Old Lode Lane, Solihull BG2 8JE
021-743 3993 £24–£29

Set off the road to Birmingham Airport, in a converted shop in a small shopping-arcade, Liaison is the foremost West Midlands restaurant. Inside, the décor is pale green and modern, giving an impression of efficiency, though the pace is relaxed. Patricia Plunkett cooks modern British, a combination of classic and now, using a balanced but imaginative combination of flavours: sliced lambs' kidneys with ceps and chanterelles or salmon marinated with passion-fruit and grilled with dill. The seasonally changing menu, too, is balanced, with a choice of eight dishes in each course. Main courses range from a paupiette of sole filled with langoustines and asparagus points on cream scented by fresh chervil, through guinea-fowl studded with pistachio nuts in a truffle sauce, to medallions of beef tenderlion roasted in a truffle fumet enriched with Marc de Bourgogne. The cheeseboard has a wide and unusual selection. Service is leisured, but there is great attention to detail, right down to the timing of the removal of the lids from the plates – all at the same moment. Just under a hundred wines, virtually all French, with a good smattering around the £10 mark. House French £7.95; CELLARMAN'S CHOICE: Ch. La Croix de Berny '85, £10.95 and St Véran, Domaine des Vignemonts '85, £13.75.

CHEF: Patricia Plunkett PROPRIETORS: Patricia Plunkett and Ank Van Der Tuin
OPEN: Tue to Sat, D only
CLOSED: 2 weeks at Christmas; Aug
MEALS: 7 to 10
PRICES: £21 (£29), Set Tue D £17.95 (£24)
CARDS: Access, Amex, Diners, Visa
SEATS: 34. Private parties: 40 main room. Car-park, 15 places. Vegetarian meals. Children welcome. No pipes in dining-room. Wheelchair access. Music

SOUTH GODSTONE Surrey map 3

La Bonne Auberge [12/20]

Tilburstow Hill, South Godstone RH9 8JY
SOUTH GODSTONE (0342) 893184 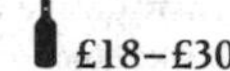 £18–£30

Olivier Nasti has taken over from Jean-Pierre Bonnet and has continued the style of French classical cuisine with *nouvelle* overtones. There are good reports of such dishes as sweetbreads in puff pastry and venison in game sauce. Vegetables are perfectly timed and desserts are light confections such as pear tart or Paris Brest. The wine cellar is a major feature. The user-friendly wine list helps enjoyment in several ways: it includes service in the very reasonable prices; makes short, helpful comments on most of the wines; picks out a few inexpensive bottles worthy of particular attention; and at least explains, and apologises in advance for, any out-of-date information. You feel they understand what they are doing, which is reassuring. The effort to seek out good bottles (apart from a handful of Germans, they are entirely French) takes in southern Burgundy (from around £12), the Rhône, Loires such as Bonnezeaux and Savennières, and some less expensive bottles from Provence. CELLARMAN'S CHOICE: changes bi-monthly but concentrates under £10.

CHEF: Olivier Nasti PROPRIETOR: Antoine L.S. Jalley
OPEN: Tue to Sun, exc Sun D
MEALS: 12 to 2, 7 to 10
PRICES: Set L £14 (£18) to £19 (£23), Set D £20 (£24) to £26 (£30). Minimum £8. Service inc
CARDS: Access, Amex, Visa
SEATS: 48. 4 tables outside. Private parties: 80 main room, 3 private room. Car-park, 70 places. Vegetarian meals. Children's helpings. Smart dress preferred. Wheelchair access. Music

The entries are compiled from the views of readers who have eaten at the restaurant in the last year, backed up by anonymous inspections and by information supplied and facts verified by the restaurants.

SOUTH MOLTON Devon map 1

▲ *Stumbles* [10/20]

131–134 East Street, South Molton EX36 3BU
SOUTH MOLTON (076 95) 4145 £9–£16

Colette Potter and her parents the Neils, who run the Highbullen Hotel at Chittlehamholt, stumbled across this place while looking for new premises, and so it was christened. The wine bar and hotel complex surround a back patio with a fountain, a summer bonus. Full use is made of spices in an eclectic, European menu: the mayonnaise comes pungent with garlic and cayenne, while chilli sauce which accompanies chicken rissoles is a head-blower – good if you like hearty flavours. The pasta is home made on a newly installed machine, and is served, along with pizza and cheaper dishes, in the wine bar. The restaurant menu tends to the more ambitious but is sensibly pegged to a set price. There are good wines with a few '70s vintages and a spread from the New World. House wines open at £6.50. CELLARMAN'S CHOICE: Brown Bros Australian Semillon '86, £10.

CHEF: Colette Potter PROPRIETORS: Mr and Mrs M.J. Potter
OPEN: Mon to Sat
MEALS: 12.30 to 2.30, 7.30 to 10
PRICES: L £9 (£13), Set D from £10 (£16), Set Bar L and D £5 (£9). Service inc L only
CARDS: Access, Amex, Diners, Visa
SEATS: 50. 10 tables outside. Private parties: 50 main room. Car-park, 30 places. Vegetarian meals. Children's helpings. Music
ACCOMMODATION: 7 rooms, all with bath/shower. Rooms for disabled. B&B £25 to £35. Pets welcome. Afternoon teas. Garden. Air-conditioning. TV. Phone

Whitechapel Manor [new entry, zero rated]

South Molton EX36 3EG
SOUTH MOLTON (076 95) 2554 and 3377 £18–£26

Down a couple of very narrow lanes in the heart of North Devon is this rather severe grey fortress of a building with some remarkable features: a magnificent Jacobean carved oak screen running the length of the entrance corridor, carved plaster ceilings and very high, deeply recessed windows. John and Patricia Shapland gave up their dairy herd and guest-house to turn the place into a country hotel and restaurant. They have brought in Thierry Lepretre-Granet to run the kitchen. He was sous-chef at Mallory Court (see Bishops Tachbrook) and the menu reflects his background: it is very sophisticated, technical, with a fondness for fashionable ingredients and excessive decoration. The quality of the meat is outstanding: beef is from a friend who rears Red Devon heifers, the rest from a local butcher or Anne Petch at Heal Farm. Medallions of wild rabbit are stuffed with rabbit mousse and baby vegetables, surrounded by a nest of fresh noodles on a sauce of grain mustard and mint. Other ideas, such as a warm salad of sweetbreads with artichokes and raspberry vinaigrette, have been less convincing. Fish appears in the form of fricassee of Dover sole with oyster mushrooms. The accessories are impeccable: excellent canapés, superb home-baked breads and oat biscuits, good unsalted butter, well-kept English cheeses, including Grant's Somerset Cheddar. Half a dozen desserts range from lime parfait with coconut ice-cream to gratin of cherries with a kirsch sabayon. Sixty wines, almost exclusively French, open with Côtes du Rhône at £6.21. CELLARMAN'S CHOICE: Pinot Noir, Rhinefarm vineyard '83, £72; Mercurey, Ch. de Chaminey '85, £13.53. More reports, please.

CHEF: Thierry Lepretre-Granet PROPRIETORS: John and Patricia Shapland
OPEN: all week
MEALS: 12 to 2, 7 to 9.15
PRICES: Set L from £12.50 (£18), Set D £20 (£26). Snacks from £2
CARDS: Access, Amex, Diners, Visa
SEATS: 20. Private parties: 40 main room, 12 private room. Car-park, 40 places. Children's helpings (L only). No children under 10 (D only). No smoking
ACCOMMODATION: 10 rooms, all with bath/shower. B&B £45 to £67.50. Deposit: 50%. Baby facilities. Pets welcome. Afternoon teas. Garden. TV. Phone. Scenic. Doors close at 12 [GHG]

SOUTHAMPTON Hampshire map 2

Kuti's [10/20]

70 London Road, Southampton SO1 2AJ
SOUTHAMPTON (0703) 221585 and 333473 £9–£18

A sitar player performs twice weekly in this handsome pink and mauve restaurant in the city centre. The menu offers the more unusual as well as the familiar – a bhel puri starter, a vegetarian thali and tandoori fish, for instance. The help-yourself buffet lunch, which offers free seconds and a portion of dessert all for £5.75, is particularly good value. To drink there is chaas, a diluted lassi served salted, sweet or Bombay style spiced with ginger, cumin, coriander and mustard seeds. Kingfisher lager is an alternative.

CHEFS: Abdul Monnan and Anjab Ali PROPRIETOR: Kuti Miah
OPEN: all week
CLOSED: 25 Dec
MEALS: 12 to 2.15, 6 to 11.30
PRICES: £10 (£18), Set L from £5.25 (£9), Set D from £10 (£14). Minimum £4.50. Service 10%
CARDS: Access, Amex, Visa
SEATS: 66. Private parties: 30 main room. Car-park, 10 places. Vegetarian meals. Children welcome. Smart dress preferred. Wheelchair access (also WC). Music. Air-conditioned

Hampshire Round-up

CHINESE: *Kings*, 65 High Street, Odiham (025 671 2559/3811).
VEGETARIAN: *Town House*, Oxford Street, Southampton (0703 220498); *Country Kitchen*, 59a Marmion Road, Southsea (0705 811425).
BAR MEALS: *Hoddington Arms*, Upton Grey (0256 862371); *Swan Hotel*, Swan Street, Kingsclere (0635 298314/297876).
PIZZAS: *Mardi Gras*, 22 Westminster House, Basingstoke (0256 26018).
ROOMS: *Montagu Arms*, Palace Lane, Beaulieu, New Forest (0590 612324).

SOUTHEND-ON-SEA Essex map 3

Alvaro's [10/20]

32–34 St Helens Road, Westcliff-on-Sea, Southend SS0 7LB
SOUTHEND (0702) 335840 £22

The Rodrigues family have built up a solid reputation for good continental cooking in their converted double-fronted terraced house. Steaks, veal cordon bleu, sole and duck are favourites from the long menu. There are also Portuguese dishes, ranging from fish casserole with potatoes, olives and white wine to sauté kidneys in madeira sauce. A revised menu promises a greater choice of authentic Portuguese specialities, to go with the promising list of good-value wines – including CELLARMAN'S CHOICE: Bairrada Reserva '80 at £8.85.

CHEF: José Rodrigues PROPRIETORS: Alvaro, José and Joyce Rodrigues
OPEN: Tue to Sun, exc Sat and Sun L
MEALS: 12 to 2, 7 to 10
PRICES: £14 (£22). Service 10%
CARDS: Access, Visa
SEATS: 60. Vegetarian meals. Children's helpings. Smart dress preferred. Wheelchair access. Music

Slassor's [11/20]

145 Eastern Esplanade, Southend-on-Sea SS1 2YD
SOUTHEND (0702) 614880 £16

The décor doesn't amount to much, but the quality of the cooking in this modest seafront restaurant is well above average. Leslie Slassor buys Dover soles locally and goes to Billingsgate for other fish. The results are wide ranging – from moules marinière and seafood chowder to cat-fish provençale and sole with prawns and Noilly Prat sauce. There are also steaks and meaty dishes such as pigeon breast with blackberry sauce. Bread is home baked and to finish there are meringues and Dutch sweets. Unlicensed, but bring your own wine.

CHEF: Leslie Slassor PROPRIETORS: Margaret and Leslie Slassor
OPEN: Mon to Sat, exc Mon L
MEALS: 12 to 2, 7 to 9.30
PRICES: £12 (£16). Unlicensed, but bring your own: corkage 75p
CARDS: Access, Visa
SEATS: 22. Private parties: 30 main room. Children's helpings. Music

'Would you be interested in applying a little pressure to the numerous restaurants still practising what I call ''creative menu pricing'', the device whereby you make your prices look more reasonable than they actually are by adding such items as service and vegetables and potatoes to the bottom line? The strategy is that most people in the intrigue and distraction of a dinner party don't look into the fine detail of a menu, it's complicated enough making a decision. They scrutinise to find what will tempt them, take a fleeting glance at the prices and get back to the conversation. Doing a rough calculation they figure the food prices.' Manchester restaurateur

SOUTHSEA Hampshire map 2

Bistro Montparnasse [10/20]

103 Palmerston Road, Southsea PO5 3PS
PORTSMOUTH (0705) 816754 £22

The local competition in this part of Southsea is from Indian, Chinese and Greek restaurants. This converted steakhouse serves commendable bistro food in a setting of plants in hanging brass bowls, ceiling spotlights and strawberry-pink colour schemes. Fish shows up well in dishes such as grilled skewer of monkfish with parsley and lime sauce, or salmon in pastry with dill sauce; there is good smoked fish, too. Roast guinea-fowl gets a port sauce, duckling comes with a purée of nectarines. Vegetables are buttery. A version of chocolat St Emilion includes home-made biscuits, and hazelnut meringue is home made too. Fifty modestly prices wines, mostly from France. House French from Duboeuf £5.95.

CHEF: Mark Hull PROPRIETORS: Paul and Claire Rawson
OPEN: Mon to Sat, D only
CLOSED: 1 to 14 Jan
MEALS: 7 to 10 (10.30 Sat)
PRICES: £14 (£22)
CARDS: Access, Amex, Diners, Visa
SEATS: 42. Private parties: 20 main room. Children welcome. Wheelchair access. Music

SOUTHWELL Nottinghamshire map 5

Leos [10/20]

12 King Street, Southwell NG25 0EN
SOUTHWELL (0636) 812119 £25

Ratatouille terrine, a timbale of couscous with raisins, dates and chickpeas, or brandade of smoked fish spell out the mixed influences on Heather Hodgkinson's cooking in this convivial little restaurant. Main courses move from modern-sounding home-salted fish with red and yellow peppers and balsamic vinegar to traditional chicken breast with herb sauce or beef and red wine casserole. The menu changes fortnightly, but you may find chocolate truffle dessert, orange and ginger custard or exotic ice-creams among the sweets. Ninety wines include house Ropiteau at £6.50 and CELLARMAN'S CHOICE: Côtes de Roussillon, Château Moulin Rouge '82, £7.50.

CHEF: Heather Hodgkinson PROPRIETORS: Heather and Tony Hodgkinson
OPEN: Tue to Sat, D only
MEALS: 7 to 10
PRICES: Set D £18.50 (£25)
CARDS: Access, Amex, Diners, Visa
SEATS: 28. Private parties: 28 main room. No children under 5. Smart dress preferred. Music. Air-conditioned

It is always advisable to book a restaurant in advance.

SOUTHWOLD Suffolk map 6

▲ *Crown* [11/20]

90 High Street, Southwold IP18 6DP
SOUTHWOLD (0502) 722275 £13–£19

Once again the postbag for the Crown is fat with endorsements. Here is a justification for the argument that you only have to serve honest, fresh food, reasonable wines in a pleasant atmosphere and you will be a success even in the English countryside. Alas there is sometimes too much justification in terms of customers. The kitchen is overwhelmed. But the prices are not rapacious; this is after all a goodwill and advertising venture on behalf of Adnams. Food is also served in the bar where there is a Cruover machine for serving good wines by the glass. The style is straightforward modern British with imagination and good sense. Fish is usually first class, the soup particularly, though on the thin side on occassion; salads are pungent and generous. There is a leaning towards the bourgeois, as in a good pot au feu, and also to modern British as in a spinach and orange soup or breast of duck with damsons. Service is brisk. Believe the wine list when it bills its first offering, at just £4 for a full bottle, as 'super-plonk'. The Italian section is outstanding. Where else is found a fine Lambrusco, two really good Soaves, and two splendid Valpolicellas (from Tedeschi and Quintarelli)? But there are also two Recioti and one Recioto Amarone della Valpolicella, an interesting selection from Tuscan estates, plus a number of good wines from elsewhere in Italy. France is especially well served in the Rhône, Loire, Burgundy and Bordeaux (clarets go back to '61). Californians include mature Cabernet Sauvignons back to '74, and there are fine Australians. Prices at the lower end of the list are tiny in restaurant terms: no need to stick to 'super-plonk' when there's Tiefenbrunner Lagrein Dunkel for £7.85, Pierre Coste House Claret for £6.05 or Château du Grand Moulas Côtes-du-Rhône '86 for £6.45. In sweet wines, the best value among full bottles is the old Loire, such as Moulin Touchais Anjou '55, £18.50, or Vouvray Moelleux 'Le Mont' '64, from Huet, £17.35; by the half, there are young Sauternes, young German Eiswein, attractive sweet Muscats from Australia and California, or half-bottles of Domaine de Coyeux Beaumes de Venise for £7.70.

CHEF: Tim Reeson PROPRIETORS: Adnams plc
OPEN: all week
MEALS: 12.30 to 2, 7.30 to 9.45
PRICES: £8 (£13), Set L £12 (£17), Set D £14 (£19)
CARDS: Access, Amex, Visa
SEATS: 79. 4 tables outside. Private parties: 20 and 50 private rooms. Car-park, 18 places. Children's helpings
ACCOMMODATION: 12 rooms, all with bath/shower. B&B £24 to £38. Pets welcome. Afternoon teas. Fishing. Golf. TV. Phone. Scenic. Doors close at 11. Confirm by 6 [GHG]

CELLARMAN'S CHOICE *This is a wine recommended by the restaurateur which is usually more expensive than the house wine but is good value and fitting for the kind of food served.*

SPARK BRIDGE Cumbria map 7

▲ *Bridgefield House* [13/20]

Spark Bridge, Ulverston LA12 8DA
LOWICK BRIDGE (022 985) 239
4m N of Ulverston, off A5084 on back road from Spark Bridge to Coniston  £19

Good reports continue to come in about Rosemary Glister's cooking at this Victorian brick hotel. Much of the produce comes from the garden, otherwise from the locality. In Lakeland style there is one sitting of 7.30 punctual for 8. The set menu comprises six courses – starter, with a choice of three; followed by a choice of savoury. Her blending of flavours has style and imagination, and there is an array of unusual fruits and vegetables, for instance turkey breast and lychees with a tarragon cream dressing, or an orange and fennel salad. Vegetables served with the pheasant in red wine sauce include roast sweet potatoes, Jerusalem artichokes in oatmeal, aubergines with turmeric. Sorbets run from elderflower to pomegranate. The centrepieces can be overburdened by the attractive succession of smaller dishes, but sweets such as meringues, syllabub, and cheesecake restore the balance. All the bedrooms have been redecorated and now have bathrooms. Breakfast is traditional and keeps up the standards. The 200-strong wine list offers a vast choice under £10, and very drinkable bottles at little over £5. France provides the bulk of the list, with good wines from Beaujolais (stick to Duboeuf rather than Latour), Alsace (including some very special and expensive bottles) and the Rhône, and a fair spread of clarets. Burgundies, predominantly from Louis Latour and Maufoux, are less tempting. Outside France, some interesting California wines include several from Clos du Bois, and from Spain the single vineyard Rioja Contino (£8.72 for the '81 vintage) is a rare find. It is a shame that all the producers' names are missing from a promising-looking German list. CELLARMAN'S CHOICE: St Emilion, Ch. Clos des Jacobins '78 at £24.10.

CHEF: Rosemary Glister PROPRIETORS: D.K. and Rosemary Glister
OPEN: all week, D only
MEALS: 7.30 to 8
PRICES: Set D £17 (£19)
CARD: Access
SEATS: 20. Private parties: 24 main room. Car-park, 10 places. Vegetarian meals. Children's helpings. Smart dress preferred. No smoking. Wheelchair access (also WC). One sitting
ACCOMMODATION: 5 rooms, all with bath/shower. B&B £25 to £50. Baby facilities. Pets welcome. Garden. Scenic. Confirm by 3 [GHG]

Anyone claiming to be from The Good Food Guide *is an impostor. Restaurateurs are advised to contact the office immediately if any fraudulent claims are made.*

[GHG] *after the details of an entry means that the establishment is also included in* The Good Hotel Guide.

SPARSHOLT Hampshire map 2

▲ *Lainston House* [12/20]

Sparsholt SO21 2LT
WINCHESTER (0962) 63588 £12–£37

The mobile army of *Guide* readers was quick to find this luxury country-house hotel following last year's entry. The backdrop has much going for it: 63 acres of parkland with a twelfth-century chapel, a seventeenth-century half-timbered barn, an eighteenth-century herb garden, a red-brick, William and Mary house covered in climbing roses and wisteria. In the dining-room, the panelling gives way to a pale green garden effect. The menu is of the grand school – printed, classically founded, slick and professional, with good stocks, and some modern influences, although also an inclination to shy away from strong flavours. Rolled roast loin of lamb, stuffed with parsley and rosemary, is served with a courgette, tomato and aubergine bake; more elaborately, boiled quails are filled with prune mousse and served on a bed of Savoy cabbage with a port sauce and game chips. There is much moussing. One fixture of the sweets menu is mousse Lady Chudleigh – chocolate, amaretto and praline mousses in chocolate lace baskets – so called after a previous tenant, reputedly a bigamist (presumably the three mousses allow for an affair on the side). Service is rigid and butler-ish; main courses are revealed from under silver domes. Good points are the inexpensive buffet lunch at £6.10 and an accommodating way with children. The 181 wines open at £8, with some sensible selections written on the menu, but mark-ups on the good clarets seem high. CELLARMAN'S CHOICE: Ch. Millet '82, £22; Ch. Cissac '73, £18; Australian Chardonnay Pokolbin '86, £15.50.

CHEF: Friedrich Litty PROPRIETORS: Pennylain Hotels Ltd
OPEN: all week
MEALS: 12 to 2.30, 7 to 10.30
PRICES: £25 (£37), Set L from £13.20 (£15), Buffet L from £6.50 (£12). Licensed, also bring your own: corkage £8
CARDS: Access, Amex, Carte Blanche, Diners, Visa
SEATS: 129. Private parties: 33 main room, 16 and 80 private rooms. Car-park, 150 places. Vegetarian meals. Children's helpings (Sun L only). Jacket and tie. No cigars/pipes in dining-room. Wheelchair access (also WC)
ACCOMMODATION: 32 rooms, all with bath/shower. Rooms for disabled. B&B £69.50 to £89. Baby facilities. Pets welcome. Afternoon teas. Garden. Tennis. TV. Phone. Scenic

SPILSBY Lincolnshire map 6

Buttercross [9/20]

18 Lower Market, Spilsby PE23 5JT
SPILSBY (0790) 53147 £9–£17

Tim and Janette Boskett make everything from the bread to the yoghurt and ice-cream in their listed Georgian building opposite the Buttercross. The informal, bistro-style suits the character of the town. Lunches and weekend dinners might range from Hong Kong-style pork to potato and onion pancakes with sweet-and-sour sauce, from stew with dumplings to grilled trout with hazelnuts and orange. Soups, sandwiches and home-baked cakes are served through the day to go with a decent range of coffees and teas. Local soft fruits go into the crumbles, tarts and summer pudding. House French £5.25.

CHEF: Tim Boskett PROPRIETORS: Tim and Janette Boskett
OPEN: all week L, exc Tue and Sun; Fri and Sat D
MEALS: 12 to 3, 7.30 to 9.30
PRICES: L £6 (£9), Set D £8.75 (£13) to £12.50 (£17)
SEATS: 36. 2 tables outside. Private parties: 22 main room. Vegetarian meals. Children welcome. No-smoking area during day. Wheelchair access (3 steps). Music

STADDLEBRIDGE North Yorkshire map 7

▲ *McCoy's* [13/20]

The Tontine, Staddlebridge DL6 3JB
EAST HARSLEY (060 982) 671 £19–£34

The McCoys' trademarks, both in the restaurant and the bistro, are their individuality and style. They are their own men, who follow no formulas, no patterns or fashions, save their own. Their food does not suit neat labelling. Upstairs in the restaurant the menu relies on high-quality, even luxury, ingredients. There can be touches of brilliance – foie-gras-stuffed ravioli in a cream sauce; lamb cooked pink with pan juices and served with a tart filled with red-pepper custard; 'Original McCoy crêpes' with a vanilla cream, crumbled amaretti biscuit and Grand Marnier. Downstairs in the bistro, the food is honest and positive, stylish without being pretentious. French influences, or rather attitudes, are obvious, but so are nursery puddings, excellent steaks and avocado with prawns. The ingredients are always first class, the cooking always good and sometimes rises to greater heights. Presentation is thoughtful but plain and unfussy, both up and down. And who else offers a choice of *four* soups? Idiosyncrasies are part of the fabric. The basement décor is in keeping with the name – bare brown tables, dark red tiles, brown Victorian chairs, large mirrors, ferns hanging from the ceiling. Some undoubtedly find it dingy. In one corner is a magnificent stone fireplace, and the main ceiling has some curious eighteenth-century plasterwork. There is a blackboard menu, paper napkins inscribed 'McCoy's', subdued lighting and candles and a little vase of flowers on each table. Music is uncharacteristically loud and post 1960s. Altogether a relaxed, stylish atmosphere which positively buzzes. There is a blow-up print of Georges Duboeuf (there is another at the Black Bull, Moulton) with his vignerons, and another depicting an aged French peasant finishing off his soup with a bottle of Tontine house wine on the table. Upstairs, the dining-room is extraordinary: a raised area off the main lounge has a large mahogany bar, 1940s-style sofas, a log fire, little lamps with tassels and hanging jewels as if they were wearing earrings, and six-foot-diameter Chinese paper parasols fixed upright across the room, so that you do not so much walk to your table as navigate round them. The menu is extensive, with old favourites such as real fish soup, whole lemon sole, spare ribs in piquant sauce, plus daily dishes and occasional new additions. House French from £7.25 a litre.

CHEFS: Tom McCoy (Restaurant), Eugene McCoy (Bistro)
PROPRIETORS: Peter, Thomas and Eugene McCoy
OPEN: all week
MEALS: 12 to 2, 7 to 10 (11.30 Sat)
PRICES: Restaurant £24 (£34), Bistro £13 (£19)
CARDS: Access, Amex, Diners, Visa
SEATS: 70. Private parties: 50 main room. Car-park. Vegetarian meals. Children's helpings. Music
ACCOMMODATION: 6 rooms, all with bath/shower. B&B £55 to £70. Baby facilities. Afternoon teas. Air-conditioning. TV. Phone. Scenic [GHG]

STAFFORD Staffordshire map 5

Curry Kuteer [10/20]

31 Greengate Street, Stafford ST16 2HY
STAFFORD (0785) 53279 £7–£16

Stafford's best curry house is in a black and white, half-timbered building by the bridge over the River Sow. The décor is a hotch-potch of red flock, black ceiling tiles and gold pillars. The menu follows suit, with a standard mix of tandooris and curries. Karahi chicken, meat vindaloo and aloo gobi have been a cut above the usual curry-house average. To finish, there is a pati shapta – a pastry sweetmeat common in the cafes along Belgrave Road in Leicester, but rare in Staffordshire. Service is civilised and polite.

CHEF: Mohammed Rashid PROPRIETOR: Shah A. Quayum
OPEN: all week
MEALS: 12 to 2, 6 to 12
PRICES: £7 (£12), Set L £3.15 (£7), Set D £7 (£11) to £12 (£16)
CARDS: Access, Amex, Diners, Visa
SEATS: 85. Private parties: 50 main room, 60 private room. Car-park, 8 places. Vegetarian meals. Children's helpings. No children under 4. Smart dress preferred. Wheelchair access (2 steps). Music

STAMFORD Lincolnshire map 6

▲ *George* [10/20]

71 St Martin's, Stamford PE9 2LB
STAMFORD (0780) 55171  £23

A portrait of Daniel Lambert, Britain's fattest man (1610 to 1630), is among the prints adorning the foyer. 'Today he seems no advertisement for good cuisine, an early model of a man in an anorak with his face in a fistful of chips and a carrier bag of lager six-packs at his side. But being safely dead he adds to the period charm of the reception.' The George carries on its nine-hundred-year history as a successful coaching house. The garden lounge offers food throughout the day, or else there is a more formal dining-room, panelled in oak with heraldic banners. Accoutrements look like the regimental silver in an unusually well-appointed mess; the ambience is Edwardian rather than medieval. The menu deals in traditional strengths, leaning on excellent roast beef, grilled sole, lobster and salmon, but it is not without its share of more up-to-date combinations – a vegetarian main dish of stir-fried vegetables in a filo pastry case and a soy dressing is first rate. There are barbecues in the courtyard on warm evenings. Prices on the excellent wine list are very reasonable. Burgundies are from top growers such as Henri Lefarge, Jean Durup, Thévenin and Leflaive; a good list of clarets includes many mature vintages and classed growths; and there's a sprinkling of good wines from the rest of France. Brief selections from the rest of the world – Italy, Germany, Australia, California and New Zealand – are also very well chosen. Tuscan Vin Santo, Isole e Olena, £10.95 for a half-bottle, is an interesting if expensive oddity among the sweet wines. More conventionally, Muscat de Beaumes de Venise, Domaine de Coyeux comes by the glass at £1.60; there are good, sweet Vouvrays of the '76 and the fabulous '47 vintages; and sweet Bordeaux at a range of quality and price levels. House Italian red and white £6.95.

CHEF: Chris Pitman PROPRIETORS: Poste Hotels Ltd
OPEN: all week
MEALS: 12.30 to 2.30, 7.30 to 10.30
PRICES: £17 (£23), Snacks from £2.45. Cover 60p. Service inc
CARDS: Access, Amex, Diners, Visa
SEATS: 85. Private parties: 90 main room, 16, 22 and 30 private rooms. Car-park, 150 places. Vegetarian meals. Children's helpings. Jacket and tie. Wheelchair access (also WC)
ACCOMMODATION: 47 rooms, all with bath/shower. B&B £55 to £80. Children welcome. Baby facilities. Pets welcome. Afternoon teas. Garden. TV. Phone. Scenic [GHG]

STANDISH Greater Manchester map 5

▲ *Beeches* [11/20]

School Lane, Standish, WN6 07D
STANDISH (0257) 426432 £11–£23

The correct cooking of fine raw materials is the hallmark of the kitchen at this red-brick Victorian mansion. The *carte* has classical instincts, but has absorbed enough modern thinking not to let the technique overrun the ingredients. The buying is good – Isle of Man scallops, excellent Gressingham ducks served with two tart fruit sauces (lime and blackcurrant), foie gras served as a garnish to fillet of beef. Fish is the main accent and draws recommendations for such varied dishes as moules marinière, langoustine thermidor, scallops with a champagne and saffron sauce. There is a frequently changing *menu surprise* at dinner, a bargain set lunch and good bar meals with home-made ice-cream. Food is served throughout the day on Sundays.

The Guide *does not accept free meals.*

An attached bistro is due to open when the *Guide* is printed. Well supported locally. The wine list of 85 bottles, like the menu, steers a conservative path but is not without its jewels. House hock £5.85. CELLARMAN'S CHOICE: St Emilion, Ch. Larose '83, £20.

CHEF: B. Higginbottom PROPRIETORS: James and Peter Moore
OPEN: all week, exc Sat L
MEALS: 11.45 to 1.45, 6.45 to 9.45 (11.45 to 9.45 Sun)
PRICES: £17 (£23), Set L £6.50 (£11), Set D £19.75 (£23), Snacks from £1.95. Bar meals £7 (£11)
CARDS: Access, Amex, Diners, Visa
SEATS: 60. Private parties: 70 main room. Car-park, 70 places. Children's helpings. Smart dress preferred. Wheelchair access (3 steps). Music
ACCOMMODATION: 11 rooms, all with bath/shower. B&B £32 to £38. Baby facilities. Children welcome. Afternoon teas. Garden. TV. Phone. Scenic. Doors close at 1. Confirm by 5

STANTON HARCOURT Oxfordshire map 2

▲ *Harcourt Arms* [10/20]

Stanton Harcourt OX8 1RJ
OXFORD (0865) 882192 and 881931 £22

The Arms is a picturesque creeper-covered Cotswold pub, with three candlelit dining-rooms, bistro-style wooden tables and chairs, and *Vanity Fair* cartoons by Spy and Ape on the walls. The menu is long and varied, but concentrates on, and is most successful with, fish – mussels in white wine sauce; king prawns as a starter or main course; smoked haddock crumble; seafood pie, with prawns, monkfish and scallops; half a lobster. There are also recommendations for terrines; chicken satay; treacle tart. Steaks and good bar food, in a county increasingly dominated by Indian and Chinese restaurants, are useful. Real ales include Wadworth's 6X, which might give many of the wines a run for their money.

CHEF: Gerard Crowley PROPRIETOR: Peter Polhill
OPEN: all week
MEALS: 12 to 2, 7 to 10
PRICES: £14 (£22)
CARDS: Access, Amex, Diners, Visa
SEATS: 90. 6 tables outside. Private parties: 90 main room. Car-park, 30 places. Children's helpings
ACCOMMODATION: 10 rooms, all with bath/shower. B&B £24.50 to £44.50. No children under 8. Afternoon teas. Fishing. TV. Phone. Scenic. Doors close at 11.30. Confirm by 6

The Guide *is independent, accepts no advertising and survives solely on the number of copies sold.*

STON EASTON Somerset map 2

▲ *Ston Easton Park* [13/20]

Ston Easton BA3 4DF
CHEWTON MENDIP (076 121) 631 £24–£36

Ston Easton is starting to show the kind of solid commitment to building a business that could take it up through the ratings. Head chef Mark Harrington has been developing his style and experience with winter sojourns in other kitchens. Bread is now home made. The selection of British cheeses has been developed and offers many of those featured in the Factors' Choice at the back of the *Guide.* The set-price lunch menu offers exceptional value, with a wide choice of seven or eight starters, and split by a sorbet. The style is a rather rarefied mix of upper-class country-house hotel cooking, relying on high-quality ingredients for impact, for instance fillet of beef with Roquefort butter. Recommended dishes have been: apple and watercress soup; venison in a redcurrant and pear sauce; cinnamon pancakes with orange and Grand Marnier. There is always a vegetarian course. The Smedleys' menus say, 'No service charge included or gratuity expected.' Other improvements to what is already a spectacular Palladian mansion setting are the china, upgraded to Wedgwood, the two Edwardian glasshouses dismantled and rebuilt in every detail by local craftsmen, and 300 new trees for the grounds. The main meat of the wine list is French, although the short Italian, Spanish and New World selections are good and the German section impeccable, from producers such as Deinhard, Reichsgraf von Kesselstatt, von Schörnborn and Bassermann-Jordan. Best is the claret section, from '29, although quite a few of the older vintages, particularly in half-bottle, should be viewed warily. White Burgundies include great names, such as Vocoret, Leroy, Sauzet and Leflaive, though red Burgundies are more reliant on wines from merchants, such as Chanson, Latour, Ponelle and Jaboulet-Vercherre. Rhônes include several Paul Jaboulet Aîné wines, in Loire there is good Sancerre from Bourgeois, and there are Alsace wines from Hugel, Kuentz-Bas and Trimbach. Three German Beerenauslesen would partner desserts, or choose from ten sweet white Bordeaux, ranging from Ch. Bastor-Lamontagne '83, £12 or £6.50 per half, to Ch. d'Yquem '76, £54 per half-bottle. House claret £8. CELLARMAN'S CHOICE: Tignanello '82, £25; Châteauneuf-du-Pape, Domaine du Vieux Télégraphe '84, £18; Fixin '84, £22.

CHEF: Mark Harrington PROPRIETORS: Peter and Christine Smedley
OPEN: all week
MEALS: 12.30 to 2, 7.30 to 9.30 (10 Fri and Sat)
PRICES: Set L £17.50 (£24) to £18.50 (£25), Set D £28.50 (£36)
CARDS: Access, Amex, Diners, Visa
SEATS: 40. 8 tables outside. Private parties: 40 main room, 14 and 22 private rooms. Car-park, 40 places. Vegetarian meals. Children's helpings. No children under 12. Jacket and tie. No cigars/pipes in dining-room. Wheelchair access
ACCOMMODATION: 20 rooms, all with bath/shower. B&B £60 to £95. No children under 12. Pets welcome. Afternoon teas. Garden. Tennis. Snooker. TV. Phone. Scenic. Doors close at 12. Confirm by 6 [GHG]

STONHAM Suffolk — map 3

▲ *Mr Underhill's* [13/20]

Stonham IP14 5DW
STOWMARKET (0449) 711206
on A140, 300 yards S of junction with A1120 — £27

The Bradleys hope to move in 1989, possibly to London, but until then this remains one of the more attractive places to eat out in the area. Christopher Bradley cooks a modern menu which would not be out of place in the city – warm salads; stock-based sauces like madeira for boned rib of veal; good cheeses; marinated fruits like nectarines in Beaujolais; tarte Tatin. The dining-room is small and personal and full of knick-knacks. Wines are taken seriously with recommendations opening at £8.75.

CHEF: Christopher Bradley PROPRIETORS: Christopher and Judy Bradley
OPEN: Tue to Sat, D only
MEALS: 7.30 to 8.45
PRICES: Set D £18.45 (£27). Licensed, also bring your own: corkage £3–£15
CARDS: Access, Amex, Visa
SEATS: 30. Private parties: 30 main room, 16 private room. Car-park, 12 places. Vegetarian meals. Children's helpings, by arrangement. Smoking after meal. Wheelchair access (also WC)
ACCOMMODATION: 1 room, with bath/shower. B&B £40. Garden. Scenic. Confirm by 12

STONY STRATFORD Buckinghamshire — map 2

Stratfords [11/20]

7 St Paul's Court, 118 High Street, Stony Stratford MK1 1LA
MILTON KEYNES (0908) 566577 — £15–£20

This Victorian ex-chapel has the feel of a nunnery or a girls' school from its vaulted ante-room and panelled dining-room. The menu makes much use of local produce, home-baked breads, and home-smoked fish and meat. Soups reflect this domestic quality – tomato and basil or carrot and coriander. Other starters include a pancake with cream cheese, and chicken mousse with Brie in spinach. Imagination shows in some of the main courses – lamb fillet wrapped around basil; deep-fried scallops are in filo pastry; veal is served with a Stilton sauce. Desserts too have some unexpected combinations – cashew-nut and coriander shortbread for example – but there is also a selection of fine home-made ice-cream, with home-made biscuits. The wine list has variety and a laudable selection of half-bottles. House Bergerac and Gewürztraminer at £6.50. CELLARMAN'S CHOICE: Sancerre '86, from André Dezat, £12.25; Fleurie, Domaine des Quatre Vents '86, from Georges Duboeuf, £13.

Restaurants are graded on a scale of 1–20. In the category of 10–11 expect to find the best food in the locality. Ratings of 12 and more are given to restaurants we regard as serving the best food in the region.

CHEFS/PROPRIETORS: Michael Roberts and Linda Membride
OPEN: Mon to Sat, exc Mon and Sat L
CLOSED: first 3 weeks Jan
MEALS: 12 to 2, 7.30 to 9.30 (10 Fri and Sat)
PRICES: Set L £9.50 (£15), Set D from £13.95 (£20)
SEATS: 70. Private parties: 70 main room. Car-park, 20 places. No children under 6. Wheelchair access. Music

STORRINGTON West Sussex map 3

▲ *Manleys* [14/20]

10 YEARS

Manleys Hill, Storrington RH20 4BT
STORRINGTON (090 66) 2331

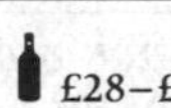

'As a rule, anything that comes in a packet isn't allowed in my kitchen,' explains Karl Löderer, who then goes on, in an advert, to endorse Uncle Ben's rice. A pity customers pay for the skills of this kitchen in its purchasing of the finest ingredients and their interpretation in the cooking. For cooking read: Dover sole soufflé; grilled fillet steak with asparagus tips, a reduction of shallots, red wine and crème de cassis; chocolate parfait. Make no mistake, there is Real Food here – wild salmon; Romney Marsh lamb; fruits and vegetables picked and delivered on the same day – and real seasoning too, as in ginger-flavoured cabbage with a breast of duck; lemon-grass for the salmon, and also a classical, swaggering arrogance of mixing veal with lobster and a Sauternes sauce. 'A consistent and reliable centre of excellence,' is how one regular puts it. Sweets betray a Middle European vein as in Salzburger Nolkerln – for two, lemon and orange flavoured soufflé cooked in honey and flavoured with rum; Kaiser-Schmarrn mit Himbeersaft – light sponge omelette with a purée of raspberries; and the well-named Cage Défendue – a spun-sugar basket filled with sorbets and marinated seasonal fruits. House French £9.80; CELLARMAN'S CHOICE: Ch. Villegeorge, *grand cru exceptionnel* '79, £14.50.

CHEF: Karl Löderer PROPRIETORS: Karl and Margaret Löderer
OPEN: Tue to Sun, exc Sun D
CLOSED: first 2 weeks Jan, last week Aug, first week Sept
MEALS: 12 to 2, 7 to 9.30 (10 Sat)
PRICES: £24 (£38), Set Sun L £17 (£28). Service inc
CARDS: Access, Amex, Diners, Visa
SEATS: 48. Private parties: 36 main room, 22 private room. Car-park. Children's helpings. No children under 7. Smart dress preferred. No cigars/pipes in dining-room. Wheelchair access (also WC)
ACCOMMODATION: 1 double room, with bath/shower. B&B £70. No children. TV. Phone. Scenic

Please keep the Guide *informed of any changes to the restaurants listed. Report forms are at the back of the book.*

STOURPORT-ON-SEVERN Hereford & Worcester map 5

Severn Tandoori [10/20]

11 Bridge Street, Stourport-on-Severn DY13 8UX
STOURPORT (029 93) 3090 £14

A pleasant Indian restaurant with a consistently high level of service and a comfortable, smart interior. The style of food is mainly North Indian, with a fine balancing of spices. Among recommended dishes are: chicken jafrezi; king prawn bhuna; tandoori chicken biriani; lamb tikka masala. House Spanish and French £5.60, or drink lassi or lager.

CHEF: A. Audud PROPRIETORS: S.A. Quayum, M. Miah, A. Audud, Z. Ali and S. M. Meah
OPEN: all week
MEALS: 12 to 2.30, 6 to 11.30
PRICES: £8 (£14). Service 10%
CARDS: Access, Amex, Diners, Visa
SEATS: 70. Private parties: 70 main room, 70 private room. Vegetarian meals. Children's helpings (weekend D only). No children under 4. Wheelchair access (also WC). Music

STRATFORD UPON AVON Warwickshire map 2

▲ *Shepherd's, Stratford House Hotel* [10/20]

Sheep Street, Stratford upon Avon CV37 6EF
STRATFORD UPON AVON (0789) 68233 £19

Shepherd's is an oasis of calm among the gift shops of touristy Sheep Street. During the summer, the south-facing patio is open for eating outside; at other times you look out over the courtyard from the semi-circular conservatory dining-room where the large ceiling fans and greenery give a touch of the tropics. Nigel Lambert's food is English and unpretentious, using good, seasonal ingredients. Daily specialities are shown on a blackboard in addition to the à la carte menu: a typical choice could be between an artichoke mousse with asparagus sauce, vichysoisse or avocado with crab and pink grapefruit; then rack of lamb, roast guinea-fowl with redcurrant and lime sauce or fillet steak with green peppercorn sauce. Crème brûlée comes with oranges and Grand Marnier, and there is a reasonable selection of cheese, which arrives with fruit. After-theatre meals are served on Saturdays, but no bookings are taken. Two dozen wines, with house French from Paul Bocuse at £6.15. CELLARMAN'S CHOICE: New Zealand Marlborough Chardonnay at £7.50.

CHEF: Nigel Lambert PROPRIETORS: Sylvia Adcock and Nigel Lambert
OPEN: all week
MEALS: 12 to 2, 6 to 9.30
PRICES: £14 (£19). Minimum £5
CARDS: Access, Amex, Diners, Visa
SEATS: 40. 3 tables outside. Private parties: 40 main room, 10 private room. Vegetarian meals. Children welcome. Wheelchair access (3 steps)
ACCOMMODATION: 10 rooms, all with bath/shower. B&B £35 to £60. Deposit: £20. No children under 5. Afternoon teas. TV. Phone. Doors close at 12. Confirm by 4

Sir Toby's [9/20]

8 Church Street, Stratford upon Avon CV37 6HB
STRATFORD UPON AVON (0789) 68822 £19

'Of course it is to our national shame' (1988 *Guide*) that there's barely a decent restaurant to be found here, but have you been to Stratford in recent years? In the summer? No restaurateur in his right mind would want to work here. Sir Toby's is not in the absolute town centre, which to their credit they are pleased about; no crowds, parking is not that difficult and the Royal Shakespeare Theatre is separated from Church Street only by Chapel Lane, which is convenient for theatre-goers, as is the fact that Sir Toby's opens at 5.30. The restaurant faces a long line of superb half-timbered buildings but is itself a tiny red-brick façade with a bay window, lace net curtains and hanging flower baskets. The interior makes it clear that originally at least this must have been a very old building: low ceilings, heavily beamed, rooms so tiny they're hardly the size of cupboards. Atmosphere is rather like a combination of healthfood cafe and rather old-fashioned bistro (so is the menu). The food is home-made, and main courses lead off with a vegetarian dish. The ingredients too are noticably good – Gressingham duck, for instance. A full meal works out expensive but lighter meals, pre-theatre, need not be. Elementary wines, starting at £4.50.

CHEF: Joanna Watkins PROPRIETORS: Carl and Joanna Watkins
OPEN: Mon to Sat, D only (L by arrangement)
MEALS: 5.30 to 9.30
PRICES: £13 (£19)
CARDS: Access, Amex, Visa
SEATS: 40. 4 tables outside. Private parties: 34 main room, 20 private room. Vegetarian meals. Children's helpings. Wheelchair access (1 step; also WC). Music. Air-conditioned

Warwickshire Round-up

VEGETARIAN: *Auberge Inn*, Eathorpe Park Hotel, Fosseway, Eathorpe (0926 632245)
FRENCH: *Randolph's*, 19/21 Cotent End, Warwick (0926 491292).
ROOMS: *Ettington Park*, Alderminster, Stratford upon Avon (0789 740740); *Glebe Hotel*, Barford (0926 624218).
BISTRO: *Alastair's Bistro*, 40 Warwick Street, Leamington Spa (0926 225550).
ITALIAN: *Giovanni*, 8 Ely Street, Stratford upon Avon (0789 297999).
ENGLISH: *Bunbury's Eating House*, 3 Greenhill Street, Stratford upon Avon (0789 293563).

STRETTON Leicestershire map 5

▲ *Ram Jam Inn* [9/20]

Great North Road, Stretton LE15 7QX
CASTLE BYTHAM (078 081) 776 £15

Tim Hart of Hambleton Hall now also runs this famous old roadhouse on the left-hand side of the A1, going north, by Shelton Service Station. This is a comprehensive travellers' pit-stop, catering for all appetites, more competently at peak times than others. The open-plan layout is geared to informality and flexibility. Burgers, grills and big BLTs rub shoulders with good home-made soups, *nouvelle* salads, highly spiced Rutland sausages with onions and daily specials such as grilled mackerel with mustard sauce, fish pie, and chicken casseroled with baby onions and black olives. To drink there are well-chosen house wines by the glass, real ales from Ruddles, as well as Murphy's Irish stout and some obscure Belgian beers – from Kriek with cherries to strong monastic Chimay.

CHEF: Paul Towers PROPRIETORS: Hart Hambleton plc
OPEN: all week
MEALS: 11am to 11pm
PRICES: £9 (£15), Snacks from £2
CARDS: Access, Amex, Visa
SEATS: 200. Private parties: 100 main room, 40 private room. Car-park, 60 places. Vegetarian meals. Children's helpings. No cigars/pipes in dining-room. Wheelchair access (also WC)
ACCOMMODATION: 10 rooms, all with bath/shower. B&B £35 to £45. Children welcome. Baby facilities. Pets welcome. Afternoon teas. Garden. TV. Phone. Doors close at 12 [GHG]

STROUD Gloucestershire map 2

Oakes [16/20]

169 Slad Road, Stroud GL5 1RG
STROUD (045 36) 79950
on B4070 ½m from Stroud centre £14–£28

Take the narrow road to Slad rather than the one-way system that is the centre of town. The converted girls' school stands out from the red brick architecture, being of Cotswold stone with unusual mullioned windows. The Oakes family – Christopher in the kitchen, Caroline out front with her parents, all helping and instilling confidence – run a modest house. The dining-room is plainly done in creams, with replaced, but old, varnished floorboards, and plain wooden tables set with straw place-mats. Menus are set meals, each with a choice of two dishes per course, priced differently. They demonstrate such wit and understanding of modern cooking, and the subtlety and accuracy of the saucing is so remarkable, that the high rating is inevitable. Chris Oakes was the original chef to re-establish the Castle at Taunton in the top echelon and now, freed from the constraints of a hotel, he is at liberty to pursue his own thoughts. Fish features strongly: gurnard comes with a root vegetable and cream sauce; a soup of John Dory and oysters is garnished with leek, lentils, shallots and tomato, flavoured with white wine and saffron; baked sea-bass with lime vinaigrette; monkfish braised in red wine, chives and parsley, sauced with its juices; fillet of red mullet served on rösti potatoes with a wine and cream sauce. Some of this reads rather more dynamically than the conservative but precise execution provides – composition is above all impeccable. The mix of French and English is a constant theme. A parfait of chicken livers comes with a lightly toasted brioche and a mound of chutney; entrecôte with burnt onions cooked in red wine. The sauces show the identity of a great French cook – a shade mild but definite and identifiable. Sweets include definitive bread-and-butter pudding, intriguing combinations of ice-creams, such as fig and armagnac, crunched with white chocolate and served with hazelnut biscuits, and a picture book marquise: white plate, pile of chocolate shaved on to a central roundel of chocolate, one-third of the plate covered with a coffee sauce feathered with cream and chocolate. Suppliers are listed on the first page of the menu, some in Aylesbury and Middlesex adding to the locals. 'No service charged and none expected.' Sixty wines, mostly French, range from house white at £5.90. CELLARMAN'S CHOICE: Brouilly, Domaine Martin '87, from Thévenin, £9.

CHEF: Christopher Oakes PROPRIETORS: Christopher and Caroline Oakes, Nowell and Jean Scott
OPEN: Tue to Sun, exc Sun D
MEALS: 12.30 to 2, 7.30 to 10
PRICES: Set L £11.50 (£14) to £25 (£28), Set Sun L £14.50 (£17), Set D £19 (£22) to £25 (£28)
CARDS: Access, Visa
SEATS: 30. Private parties: 30 main room. Car-park, 12 places. Children's helpings, by arrangement. Wheelchair access

STUCKTON Hampshire map 2

The Three Lions [11/20]

Stuckton Road, Stuckton SP6 2HF
FORDINGBRIDGE (0425) 52489
3/4m off A338 at Fordingbridge £8–£23

What was once the village inn has been transformed into a serious restaurant with a bar as an afterthought. Karl-Hermann Wadsack's cooking is rooted in the heart of Europe, with a bias towards his native Germany and his wife's Scandinavian background: gravlax, sweet-cured herrings and home-made bratwurst with Sauerkraut back a menu that takes in roast local duck with Bramley sauce and celeriac and almond stuffing, medallions of New Forest roebuck with marinated apricots and prunes, and fillet of sea-bream with lime and lemon glaze. Lunches, starters and snacks are equally imaginative but unpretentious: sauté calf's brain with black butter and capers, salmon mousse studded with salmon roe. The richness and generosity are tempered with lighter touches and a fondness for steaming. Puddings and the cheeseboard are international, with a wide choice. The long wine list is updated each month and naturally centres on Germany and Alsace. House wines begin at £6.95.

CHEF: Karl-Hermann Wadsack PROPRIETORS: Karl-Hermann and J. Wadsack
OPEN: Tue to Sun, exc Sun D
CLOSED: 24 Dec, 26 to 31 Dec, 1 Jan, 2 weeks Feb, 2 weeks Oct
MEALS: 12.15 to 1.30, 7.15 to 9.15
PRICES: £13 (£23). Light meals from £4 (£8)
SEATS: 55. Private parties: 50 main room. Car-park, 40 places. No children under 14. Wheelchair access. Air-conditioned

STURMINSTER NEWTON Dorset map 2

▲ *Plumber Manor* [11/20]

10 YEARS

Sturminster Newton DT10 2AF
STURMINSTER NEWTON (0258) 72507 £21–£23

Driving out of Sturminster Newton towards Blandford Forum, go over the bridge, right at the T-junction, left opposite the Red Lion signposted to Hazelbury Bryan, and follow on for two miles. The Prideaux-Brune family's country house offers more of a house-party atmosphere than most of today's country-house hotels. Copies of *Country Life* scattered here and there, the family portraits, the sense of space in the dining-room all create an authentic feel. Menus are set-priced and portions anti-*nouvelle.* Recommended dishes: chicken and scallop ragout; châteaubriand with béarnaise; Aylesbury duck with Cointreau and ginger; rack of lamb with Cumberland sauce; chocolate bombe; feuilleté of strawberries. Service is personal. The menu changes nightly but otherwise the style is conservative. Wines are from Averys of Bristol with good choices of claret and Burgundy to counterbalance the better value in the region. House French from £6.50.

CHEFS: Brian Prideaux-Brune, Mrs Baker and Robert Doble
PROPRIETOR: Richard Prideaux-Brune
OPEN: Tue to Sun (Sat Nov to Mar), D only (L for large parties by arrangement)
CLOSED: Feb
MEALS: 7.30 to 9.30
PRICES: Set D £17 (£21) to £19.50 (£23). Service inc
SEATS: 60. Private parties: 40 main room, 12 and 22 private rooms. Car-park, 20 places. Vegetarian meals. No children under 12. Smart dress preferred. No cigars/pipes in dining-room. Wheelchair access
ACCOMMODATION: 12 rooms, all with bath/shower. Rooms for disabled. B&B £45 to £70. No children under 12. Garden. TV. Phone. Scenic [GHG]

SURBITON Surrey map 3

Chez Max [13/20]

85 Maple Road, Surbiton KT6 4AW
01-399 2365 £24–£32

Formerly a chemist's, Chez Max has outlived the other restaurant and wine bar that opened quite suddenly a few years ago in an otherwise residential street – not exactly off the beaten track, but not on it either. Against the odds, the Markarians have maintained a loyal following. The brown and coffee dining-room is intimate and compact. The menu stays with the thinking of *nouvelle cuisine* – offering six to eight choices per course, majoring in standards such as duck breast with raspberry vinegar and making much use of mousses. Crudités with aïoli are set out on each table. Portions are generous. Typical might be breast of guinea-fowl with courgettes stuffed with pine kernels; saddle of venison with calvados sauce. Sauces are properly made, if a little lacking in confidence. Coffee comes with an array of dipped fruits. Sixty wines from £8.50, going up sharply into the £15 to £30 range. CELLARMAN'S CHOICE: Ch. Ségur '83, £11.50.

CHEFS: Max Markarian and Theo Randall PROPRIETORS: Mr and Mrs M. Markarian
OPEN: Tue to Sat, exc Sat L
MEALS: 12.30 to 2, 7.30 to 10.30
PRICES: £19 (£27), Set L £16.50 (£24), Set D £19 (£27) to £24 (£32). Minimum £12.50. Service 12.5%
CARDS: Access, Amex, Diners, Visa
SEATS: 32. Private parties: 32 main room. No children under 7. No pipes in dining-room. Wheelchair access (also WC)

SUTTON Surrey map 3

Partners 23 [14/20]

23 Stonecot Hill, Sutton SM3 9HB
01-644 7743
on A24, near Woodstock pub £19–£27

This totally commendable small operation has settled into a groove. The printed menus at a set price offer five dishes per course and are supplemented by two dishes of the day. Otherwise they change every two months. Stability gives each dish a sense of exactness that is in keeping with French cooking, and there is a long list of compliments: roulade of celeriac and spinach on a red pepper coulis; warm pheasant mousse with muscat raisins; terrine of lobster and sweetbread; duck à l'orange; pavé of beef with mange-tout and celeriac sauce; lamb cutlets with glazed root vegetables; tournedos with morels. The twenty varieties of cheeses are quite excellent and, like the cooking, half French and half English. Sweets include a single plate of miniature versions of the whole selection of bavarois, délice, marquise, gratin. Service is from the owners and personable as a result. Seven house wines at £7.95 include a Pinot Blanc d'Alsace '85, off a largely French list of pedigree bottles. The claret section owes something of its range (which includes Angludet, Meyney and Palmer) to lesser vintages. The Loire is well endowed under £15, and there is a serious selection of half-bottles. House French £7.95. CELLARMAN'S CHOICE: Rully *premier cru* £14.90; Ch. Palmer '77, £23.80; Gewürztraminer '76, £28.

CHEFS: P.T. McEntire, Simon Waterhouse, Rebecca Jones, and Karen MacDonald
PROPRIETORS: Andrew Thomason and Helen McEntire
OPEN: Tue to Sat, exc Sat L
CLOSED: Christmas to New Year, 2 weeks Aug
MEALS: 12.30 to 2, 7.30 to 9.30
PRICES: Set L £13.25 (£19) to £19.25 (£26), Set D £19.95 (£27). Licensed, also bring your own: corkage £7.95
CARDS: Access, Amex, Diners, Visa
SEATS: 34. Private parties: 36 main room. No children under 10. Wheelchair access. Air-conditioned

SWAY Hampshire map 2

▲ *Pine Trees* [10/20]

Mead End Road, Sway SO41 6EE
LYMINGTON (0590) 682288 and 682672 £12–£20

The Davids' mustard-yellow, comfortable, old-fashioned, slightly jaded Victorian house lives in another age. There is no *carte*, just set meals based on the plain, unfashionable treatment of good ingredients, taking in seafood gratin, pan-fried chicken breasts with asparagus, roast beef. Sole meunière is also well reported. To finish, there's an extensive cheeseboard, followed by rich sweets, such as chocolate roulade or orange Boodles fool. Croissants and home-made marmalade for breakfast. Forty wines are virtually all French, with house red and white at £5. CELLARMAN'S CHOICE: Margaux, Ch. Labégorce '81, £12.50.

CHEFS/PROPRIETORS: Mr and Mrs David
OPEN: all week, D only and Sun L
MEALS: 12.45 to 1.15, 8 to 8.45
PRICES: Set Sun L £9 (£12), Set D £17 (£20). Service inc
CARDS: Access, Amex, Diners, Visa
SEATS: 18. Private parties: 24 main room. Car-park, 12 places. Children's helpings. Wheelchair access (also WC)
ACCOMMODATION: 6 rooms, 5 with bath/shower. B&B £24 to £44. No children under 12. Pets welcome, by arrangement. Garden. Scenic. Doors close at 11.30. Confirm by 6

TAPLOW Buckinghamshire map 2

▲ *Cliveden* [14/20]

Taplow SL6 0JF
BURNHAM (062 86) 64246 £35–£39

Cliveden has matured and settled into its own style since being converted into a luxury hotel. John Webber has moved on, probably to open his own restaurant, and Ron Maxfield has been promoted. This is the genuine article in terms of expense – a Grade I listed building, arguably one of the finest in Britain, a wine list with more than 90 vintage clarets, including Ch. Petrus '70 at £280, and a menu that deals in luxuries like asparagus, foie gras, Scotch fillet. A concerted effort to make this a place of excellence is succeeding. Details extend to three kinds of bread baked in house. The menu is sophisticated, ambitious and imaginative; the saucing is subtle but also robust with the typical Webber intense reductions still much in evidence; flavours are distinct and well balanced and portions substantial. Summer examples include a creamed turnip and saffron soup; grilled fillet of red bream with a basil, tomato and olive oil dressing; trimmed noisettes of lamb with wild mushrooms and a red wine sauce. The bread-and-butter pudding made with French bread is a resounding success. Service is composed and assured. There are 500 wines in the cellar, with only the house wine in single figures at £9.

CHEFS: Ron Maxfield and Michael Womersley PROPRIETORS: Blakeney Hotels Ltd
OPEN: all week
MEALS: 12.30 to 2, 7.30 to 9.30
PRICES: £31 (£39), Set L £26.80 (£35)
CARDS: Access, Amex, Diners, Visa
SEATS: 49. Private parties: 100 main room, 50 private room. Car-park, 100 places. Children's helpings. Jacket and tie. Wheelchair access (also WC)
ACCOMMODATION: 25 rooms, all with bath/shower. Rooms for disabled. Lift. B&B £125 to £160. Deposit: £125. Children welcome. Baby facilities. Pets welcome. Garden. Swimming-pool. Sauna. Tennis. Fishing. Snooker. TV. Phone. Scenic

TAUNTON Somerset map 2

▲ *Castle Hotel* [15/20]

Castle Green, Taunton TA1 1NF
TAUNTON (0823) 272671  £38

The mellowed, wisteria-covered Norman castle belies the carpeted luxury hotel within, last year refurbished to the tune of a further £75,000. The first edition of the *Guide* recommended their salmis of grouse as part of the three-course lunch for five shillings. Kit Chapman has carefully steered this town hotel back to the first rank. The last year has seen the kitchen under the talented Gary Rhodes move deliberately back to an English style. A businessman's lunch ('complete within 50 mins') centres on a roast or a traditional dish, perhaps boiled leg of mutton with caper sauce. The *carte* is modern: nut oils used to sauté fillets of John Dory; olive and coriander dressing for red mullet; and also a sophisticated use of fruits – caramelised oranges with the chicken and goose-liver parfait; glazed apples with breast of chicken with toasted almonds and a cider-vinegar sauce; a walnut and strawberry dressing on a warm salad of Dover sole strips garnished with diced tomato. Suppliers are proudly credited on the front of the menu and many are local. Pick carefully from the long wine list, as quality is mixed, though good wines far outweigh the dubious ones. Best areas of the list are the long section of German estate wines, a brief but good selection of Californians and Australians, an immense list of clarets, including old vintages, Paul Jaboulet Rhônes, from north and south, English wines from four local vineyards, and excellent Loires. There are a few interesting wines on the Burgundy list. Some good (and some dull) sherries come by the glass (ignore the poorly informed tasting notes). Choice of sweet wines is not great, especially if you are after a half-bottle. Sweet Germans are expensive. Best buys are the older sweet Loires, for instance Coteaux du Layon, Baumard '69, £14.30 and Moulin Touchais Anjou Blanc '64, £13.60, or Chairman's Rich Old Dessert Wine '76, from Eldridge Pope, £7.65 per half-bottle.
CELLARMAN'S CHOICE: Côte de Nuits, Chambolle-Musigny '78, £26.20, and Pauillac, Ch. Pontet-Canet '82, £15.40.

New this year are County Round-ups, mostly, but not always, listed under the county town. To find a County Round-up, check the maps at the back; towns listing a Round-up are underlined.

CHEF: Gary Rhodes PROPRIETORS: The Chapman family
OPEN: all week
MEALS: 12.30 to 2, 7.30 to 9 (9.30 Fri and Sat)
PRICES: £29 (£38)
CARDS: Access, Amex, Diners, Visa
SEATS: 110. Private parties: 65 main room, 50 and 110 private rooms. Car-park, 40 places. Vegetarian meals. Children's helpings (with prior notice). Smart dress preferred. Wheelchair access (also WC)
ACCOMMODATION: 35 rooms, all with bath/shower. Rooms for disabled. Lift. B&B £52 to £93. Baby facilities. Pets welcome (bedrooms only, by arrangement). Afternoon teas. Garden. TV. Phone. Doors close at 12. Confirm by 6 [GHG]

Somerset Round-up

AFTERNOON TEAS: *Settle*, Cheap Street, Frome (0373 65975).
SETTING: *Old Chapel*, Barton St David (0458 50535); *Lynch Country House Hotel*, Behind Berry, Somerton (0458 72316); *Brottens Lodge*, Doulting (074 988 352).
ROOMS: *No 3*, Magdalene Street, Glastonbury (0458 32129).
NEW: *Richters*, Coxley, Nr Wells (0749 73854).
INEXPENSIVE: *Kingfishers Catch*, Taunton Road, Bishop's Lydeard (0823 432394).
ENGLISH: *Bowlish House*, Wells Road, Shepton Mallet (0749 2022).

TETBURY Gloucestershire map 2

▲ *Calcot Manor* [14/20]

Beverston, Tetbury GL8 8YJ
LEIGHTERTON (066 689) 355 and 227
3m W of Tetbury, on A4135 £19–£37

The fifteenth-century manor with its historic outbuildings is being transformed by the Ball family into a feminine version of country-house elegance, with pale colour schemes and fabrics. The Balls' style is methodical, gracious, but quite personable. Ramon Farthing's menus are classic high modern cooking, more French than British, full of fancy touches and artifice. He can produce first-rate, perfectly reduced sauces – although these don't take kindly to being spooned on to burning hot plates and covered with domes. He cooks fish well and meat too. It is a long menu by country-house hotel standards, with six choices per stage and in each case there is a something with something, with a something sauce. Individually, some dishes are excellent – baked brill with a classy modern sauce of shallots and olive oil; or a smoked loin of veal with cabbage and bacon stuffing and a light artichoke mousse in a dark veal sauce flavoured with truffle essence; Bramley apple tart with calvados and raisin ice-cream and caramelised apple sauce. The wine list does a vertical take-off into double figures, wines from Provence are £15, likewise Beaujolais, though the odd bottles plucked from outside these areas are fractionally cheaper. House wine is an affordable £7. There is an interesting sweet white in Collioure, Domaine de Mas Blanc '83 £18.25. Service is young French and the cheeses are old English.

CHEF: Ramon Farthing PROPRIETORS: Brian and Barbara Ball and family
OPEN: all week, exc Sun D
MEALS: 12.15 to 1.45, 7.30 to 9.30
PRICES: Set L £15 (£19) to £25 (£29), Set D £27.50 (£31) to £33 (£37). Service inc
CARDS: Access, Amex, Diners, Visa
SEATS: 45. 6 tables outside. Private parties: 48 main room, 12 private room. Car-park, 75 places. Vegetarian meals. Children's helpings (L only). Jacket and tie. No smoking in dining-room. Wheelchair access (also WC)
ACCOMMODATION: 14 rooms, all with bath/shower. Rooms for disabled. B&B £45 to £80. No children under 12. Afternoon teas. Garden. Swimming-pool. TV. Phone. Scenic. Doors close at 12. Confirm by 6 [GHG]

THORNBURY Avon map 2

▲ *Thornbury Castle* [13/20]

Castle Street, Thornbury BS12 1HH
THORNBURY (0454) 418511

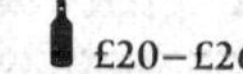

£20–£26

Thornbury's reputation has stayed largely intact since the withdrawal of its founder, Kenneth Bell. The rooms are luxurious, the atmosphere of the old castle is retained and the style of the cooking from Colin Hingston is not much different. One view has it: 'The food is less rich, more varied and better presented.' The French accent is evident in a run of sauces through half a dozen main courses and only gives way to such sweets as treacle tart, hot butterscotch pudding and syllabub. Recommended individual dishes are: calf's liver pâté with pistachio and truffle; smoked salmon; mushrooms à la grecque; medallions of beef with Meaux mustard; Dover sole with a leek mousseline and an onion sauce; salmon, out of the Usk, with a hollandaise sauce; chocolate and rum mousse with Cointreau sauce. Fine English cheeses. Service is well spoken of. You could drink very satisfactorily from the 'Short List' of wines under £12 a bottle, including Hugel Alsace wines, Australian Rosemount Semillon Chardonnay, Montana Sauvignon Blanc from New Zealand and good reds from Burgundy, Beaujolais, Spain, California and the Lebanon. But that would be to dip only a toe into the pleasures of this list, which though expensive is wide-ranging and generally of extremely high quality. In particular, the lists of Alsace, Beaujolais, California, German wines and ports are exceptional, and there are good things to be found in all other sections of the list. Among sweet wines, the list of Sauternes and Barsac goes back to '20, at relatively reasonable prices; there are three wines from California, including Mondavi Moscato d'Oro, £12.85, Essencia Orange Muscat, £16.72 or £8.65 per half, and Firestone Johannisberger Riesling, £23.25; an interesting selection of wines from Hungary and Romania; and three southern French Muscats – an inexpensive Muscat Vin de Liqueur, at £5.85 or £2.50 per glass, and two Muscats de Beaumes de Venise, Domaine de Durban, £14.20, and one inadequately described as 'Cuvée Privée', £21. House red is a Côtes du Rhône at £8.50; house white is from Müller-Thurgau grapes grown in the Castle's own

Restaurants that we have not been able to assess as fully as we would like are given a zero rating this year. We are particularly keen to have reports on these places.

vineyard. CELLARMAN'S CHOICE: Provençal Domaine des Feraud, £7.90; Louis Latour Chardonnay, £9.40; Cabernet Sauvignon Montand, from New Zealand, £8.85.

CHEF: Colin Hingston PROPRIETOR: Maurice Taylor
OPEN: all week
MEALS: 12.15 to 2, 7 to 9.30 (9 Sun)
PRICES: Set L from £14 (£20), Set D from £20.50 (£26). Service inc
CARDS: Access, Amex, Carte Blanche, Diners, Visa
SEATS: 60. Private parties: 25 main room. Car-park, 30 places. Vegetarian meals. No children under 12. Smart dress preferred. No smoking in dining-room. Wheelchair access
ACCOMMODATION: 18 rooms, all with bath/shower. B&B £70 to £85. No children under 12. Garden. Fishing. Golf. TV. Phone. Scenic. Doors close at 12 [GHG]

THORNTON CLEVELEYS Lancashire map 5

▲ *Victorian House* [new entry, zero rated]

Trunnah Road, Thornton Cleveleys FY5 4HF
CLEVELEYS (0253) 860619 £12–£18

Louise and Didier Guérin only took over this established address in July 1988, but first meals have impressed. The menu is extended, with classical use of sauces – tarragon for chicken; basil for monk; sorrel for salmon; gribiche for a skate and shrimp salad. Herbs are used abundantly throughout. 'Our menus will change often to ensure the best of seasonal produce.' The background music ranges from Marche Militaire to Black Bottom. House wines from £6.90; and clarets concentrate on *petits châteaux* '82 to '85. More reports, please.

CHEF: Didier Guérin PROPRIETORS: Louise and Didier Guérin
OPEN: Mon to Sat
CLOSED: last week Jan and first week Feb
MEALS: 12.30 to 2, 7 to 9.30
PRICES: Set L £7.50 (£12), Set D £13.50 (£18). Service inc
CARDS: Access, Amex, Diners, Visa
SEATS: 40. 4 tables outside. Private parties: 40 main room. Car-park, 20 places. Vegetarian meals. No children under 6. Smart dress preferred. Music
ACCOMMODATION: 3 rooms, all with bath/shower. B&B £35 to £50. Deposit: £10. No children under 6. Pets welcome. Garden. TV. Phone. Scenic. Confirm by 6

THORNTON-LE-FYLDE Lancashire map 5

▲ *River House* [11/20]

Skippool Creek, Thornton-le-Fylde FY5 5LF
POULTON-LE-FYLDE (0253) 883497 £29

Craig Brown, writing in *A la Carte*, relates: 'I asked the cheery waitress for a salad rather than vegetables. Mr Scott rushed up to the table and asked me why I didn't want his vegetables. "Of course you don't have to have them, I thought you might not be ordering them because you thought they'd be like over-cooked vegetables in other restaurants. But my vegetables aren't like that. My vegetables are perfect." So I had his vegetables and, of course, they *were* perfect.' The Scotts share the cooking in this small hotel, booked up years ahead for Blackpool conference time but more accessible the rest of the year. The cooking is sensible, product-led, in fact unusually modern in its sense of balance and interplay of flavours, unafraid to experiment with a few novelties like teriyaki. Good dishes have included salmon and turbot in a sauce of vodka and dill; venison with a port sauce; plain grilled fish. You could spend a long time selecting wine from the substantial list, because you would have to ask for supplementary information in order to identify at least three-quarters of the wines on it. Where are the producers' names on the lengthy Burgundy list? But, despite missing information, it is clear from those names that *are* revealed (Masi, Torres, Moss Wood, Cape Mentelle, Eyrie...) that these wines are selected from good producers. Perhaps the wine-buyer should teach the list-writer a thing or two. House claret £9.50. CELLARMAN'S CHOICE: Torres Gran Coronas Black Label '77, £35.65.

CHEFS/PROPRIETORS: Bill and Carole Scott
OPEN: all week, exc Sun L
MEALS: 12 to 2, 7.30 to 9.30
PRICES: £20 (£29)
CARDS: Access, Amex
SEATS: 45. Private parties: 45 main room. Car-park, 20 places. Vegetarian meals. Children's helpings. Wheelchair access. Music
ACCOMMODATION: 4 rooms, 1 with bath/shower. B&B £40 to £60. Baby facilities. Pets welcome. Garden. Fishing. TV. Phone. Scenic. Confirm by 6

TICKHILL South Yorkshire map 5

Forge [10/20]

1 Sunderland Street, Tickhill DN11 9PT
DONCASTER (0302) 744122 £23

A loyal clientele who book tables on a cycle ad infinitum make this probably the most booked-ahead restaurant in England – six months for any day of the week from Tuesday to Saturday. So what makes it so special? It is small, tightly packed, personal, polished, with moderately posh place settings. The set menu offers four starters, a soup or sorbet, four main dishes and a sweets trolley. But it is the sheer Liberace-style, over-the-top presentation that amazes – a flower arrangement in the soup; no fewer than 13, yes 13, different vegetables served on each plate; garnishes a-go-go – with halibut in champagne sauce arrive lemon slices, green grapes, black grapes, a slice of peach, a slice of apple, three chicory leaves, lettuce, cucumber. All of this is done with creditable care and attention. 'The sweets trolley seemed to have everything – Pavlova, fruit salad, crème brûlée, gateaux and I confirm seconds are offered.' Beneath the foliage there are fine dishes, though reaching them through so much generosity dulls the sensibilities, exhausts, and can finally disappoint – but who can argue that it is not all with the best of intentions and not a whole-hearted success? By contrast the wine list is short, to the point of being perfunctory. House French is £5.10.

CHEF: Helen Taylor PROPRIETORS: Helen and Howard Taylor
OPEN: Tue to Sat, D only
MEALS: 7 to 9.30
PRICES: Set D £17.75 (£23)
SEATS: 38. Vegetarian meals. No cigars/pipes in dining-room. Music. Air-conditioned

TIDEFORD Cornwall map 1

Heskyn Mill [11/20]

Tideford PL12 5JS
LANDRAKE (075 538) 481
just off B3249 £19

The converted mill is down a track a short distance outside the village. The Edens put their faith in fresh local produce, and produce some intriguing dishes. Look for the monthly changing menu of specials, which might feature pan-fried scallops with ginger and spring onion, or breast of pheasant stuffed with garlic and cream cheese. Rack of Cornish lamb has been served with mint and kumquats or with cranberries and satsumas. There are daily specials – mainly fish and seafood – as well. Home-made ice-creams are the stars of the sweets. The wine list has some decent drinking from around the world, including Chile, Spain and Australia, whence comes CELLARMAN'S CHOICE: Wyndham Estate oak-matured Chardonnay '86/'87, £9.95.

CHEFS: K. Williams and F.A. Eden PROPRIETORS: F. & S.M.L. Eden
OPEN: Tue to Sat
MEALS: 12 to 1.45, 7 to 10
PRICES: £14 (£19), L Snacks from £2
CARDS: Amex, Visa
SEATS: 60. 6 tables outside. Private parties: 50 main room. Car-park, 25 places. Vegetarian meals. Children's helpings. Music

TISBURY Wiltshire map 2

Garden Room [12/20]

2–3 High Street, Tisbury SP3 6PS
TISBURY (0747) 870907 £15–£22

Set on top of a hill, with a décor that reflects the name. The menu features fish and game in season, and chef Paul Firmin has a fondness for sauces. Tagliatelle with seafood has a Sancerre sauce; terrine of hare with pistachios comes with apple and claret jelly; fillet of beef en croûte is given a hollandaise sauce; salmon en papillote has a saffron and ginger version. A French garden theme returns with the desserts – redcurrant and lemon geranium cream-cheese hearts with a raspberry coulis; tarte des demoiselles Tatin with crème fraîche. Sixty wines open at £7.50 with a page of house wines, including champagne and two Australians.

'A restaurant where the drinks bill is more than the food bill needs to reappraise its wine list.' On eating in Surrey

CHEF: Paul Firmin PROPRIETORS: Paul Firmin and Jonathan Ford
OPEN: Tue to Sat D, and Sun L
MEALS: 12.30 to 2, 7.30 to 10
PRICES: Set Sun L £10.50 (£15), Set D £16.50 (£22)
CARDS: Access, Amex, Visa
SEATS: 36. Private parties: 22 main room, 12 private room. Vegetarian meals. Children's helpings. Wheelchair access (also WC). Music

---

TIVERTON Devon map 1

Hendersons [10/20]

18 Newport Street, Tiverton EX16 6NL
TIVERTON (0884) 254256 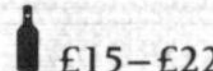 £15–£22

An old fixture of the Devon listings, now owned by the Cookes, who have maintained the personal approach despite a series of chefs, and have built an economic following among, as the lunch menu says, 'busy persons'. The menu is short, most of the cooking concentrates on the main dishes, there are good fish and vegetables, cream and alcohol sauces, sweet sweets, local cheeses, but most of all there is a fine wine list. The merit of grouping wines by style, apart from easing the choice with food, is that it throws up unlikely alternatives. Muscadet and Ménétou-Salon from the Loire, Vernaccia di San Gimignano from central Italy, and Brown Bros Muscat Blanc from Australia all shelter under the dry white umbrella. House red and white from Duboeuf, £5.75. CELLARMAN'S CHOICE: Pouilly Blanc Fumé, Les Bascoins '85, £11.70.

CHEFS: Jean Cooke and Anne-Marie Earls PROPRIETOR: Jean Cooke
OPEN: Tue to Sat
MEALS: 12.15 to 1.45, 7.15 to 9.45
PRICES: £16 (£22), Set L £9.90 (£15) to £13.90 (£20), Set D £13.90 (£20) to £15.90 (£22)
CARDS: Access, Amex, Diners, Visa
SEATS: 44. 2 tables outside. Private parties: 65 main room. Vegetarian meals. Children's helpings. No smoking in dining-room. Wheelchair access (2 steps; also WC). Air-conditioned

---

TONBRIDGE Kent map 3

Office Wine Bar [9/20]

163 High Street, Tonbridge TN9 1BX
TONBRIDGE (0732) 353660 £13

One of the better wine bars in the south-east, offering a fresh, daily-changing menu and some thoughtfully chosen wines. The setting is a beamed sixteenth-century building on two floors – casual downstairs, more formal and carpeted above. Wine bar stalwarts, such as chicken liver pâté and ratatouille, are supplemented by Moroccan lamb with apricots; plaice fillets stuffed with tarragon and almonds; and Catalan broad beans with bacon,

Restaurants are not expected to solicit customers to send in reports. Please let us know if this happens to you.

black pudding and red wine. Sweets are equally wide-ranging. The list of some 60 wines includes six house wines by the glass and a strong showing of decent Burgundies.

CHEFS: Brenda Heritage and Yvonne Blanche PROPRIETOR: J.N. Halfhide
OPEN: Mon to Sat
CLOSED: bank hols
MEALS: 12 to 2, 7 to 9.30
PRICES: £9 (£13), Snacks from £1.20
CARDS: Access, Amex, Diners, Visa
SEATS: 60. Private parties: 35 main room, 20 private room. Vegetarian meals. Children welcome. Wheelchair access (also WC)

TORQUAY Devon map 1

▲ *Mulberry Room* [10/20]

1 Scarborough Road, Torquay TQ2 5UJ
TORQUAY (0803) 213639 £9–£14

Owner, manager, cook and sometime skivvy Lesley Cooper offers excellent-value lunches in her old-fashioned-looking dining-room attached to a small guest-house. Produce is all local and the two main courses change from day to day. It is possible to have three courses or just a light meal. Her style is honey-roast chicken; baked shoulder of lamb with braised vegetables; home-cured ham boiled and served with a parsley sauce; beef and carrot suet pudding. Sunday roasts draw much enthusiasm. Elsewhere the menu offers quiches, soups, salads. Sweets are on display in tea-room fashion, and excellent cakes with clotted cream are supplemented in winter by a hot pudding – perhaps a steamed pudding or a clafoutis. Dinner is on Saturday only. A dozen wines range from house Chardonnay, Vin de Pays d'Oc (also CELLARMAN'S CHOICE:) at £4, to Pouilly Vinzelles at £18.

CHEF/PROPRIETOR: Lesley Cooper
OPEN: Wed to Sun L, and Sat D
MEALS: 12.15 to 2.30, 7.30 to 9
PRICES: £6 (£9), Set L £5 (£7) to £7.50 (£10), Set D £9 (£11) to £11.50 (£14). Snacks from £1.50. Service inc
SEATS: 30. 2 tables outside. Private parties: 40 main room. Vegetarian meals. Children's helpings. Wheelchair access (also WC). Music
ACCOMMODATION: 3 rooms. B&B £9.50 to £12.50. Deposit: 10%. Afternoon teas. TV. Doors close at 9. Confirm by 7

Remy's [12/20]

3 Croft Road, Torquay TQ2 5VN
TORQUAY (0803) 22359 £17

Remy Bopp's converted guest-house is high on Gallic family atmosphere, although the décor is minimal. The decoration is reserved for the ornate cutlery and the careful presentation of the food on the plate. The cooking is genuine French provincial with a proper Gallic respect for materials. The class shows in coarse-textured rabbit and pistachio pâté; salmon on a bed of home-made pasta; straightforward saddle of lamb with tarragon and tomato sauce. Fish comes up from Brixham, and there are also good reports of rillettes of pork, rabbit in mustard sauce and roast guinea-fowl with grape sauce. Unpasteurised French cheeses are from Philippe Olivier. Mr Bopp is from Alsace and it shows in the almond tart with chocolate sauce, also the carrot and almond cake with kirsch. Bread, ice-cream and sorbets are made on the premises; tiny pizzas come with aperitifs, cognac-flavoured truffles with coffee. The wine list naturally has a strong showing of Alsace bottles. House Vin de Pays de l'Aude is £5.50.

CHEF/PROPRIETOR: Remy Bopp
OPEN: Tue to Sat, D only
CLOSED: 2 weeks Aug
MEALS: 7.15 to 9.30
PRICES: Set D £12.85 (£17). Service inc
CARDS: Amex, Visa
SEATS: 40. Private parties: 26 main room, 20 private room. Children's helpings. Smart dress preferred. Music

TREWELLARD Cornwall map 1

Trotters [11/20]

The Barn, Trewellard Hill, Trewellard TR19 7TD
PENZANCE (0736) 787108 and 731072
2m N of St Just £12–£29

The Hubands' converted barn was closed for much of 1988, but reopened as the *Guide* went to press. French-born Jacqueline-Blanche has developed some interesting dishes: crab curaçao has the meat sauté in liqueur and served with a light orange sauce; scampi provençale comes on a bed of spinach with a creamy sauce. Cream predominates without overpowering. Sunday lunches are roasts. Good sweets. Bookings only. There is an essentially French list of two dozen wines, mostly under £10.

CHEF: Jacqueline-Blanche Huband PROPRIETORS: Jacqueline-Blanche and Geoffrey Huband
OPEN: Wed to Sat D, and Sun L
MEALS: 12.30, 7.30
PRICES: £11 (£21), Set L £6.50 (£12), Set D £15 (£23) to £20 (£29)
CARDS: Access, Visa
SEATS: 20. Private parties: 20 main room. Car-park, 10 places. Children welcome. Music. One sitting

TRURO Cornwall map 1

▲ *Alverton Manor* [new entry, zero rated]

Tregolls Road, Truro TR1 1XQ
TRURO (0872) 76633 £27–£29

The manor is a Grade II listed building with brown sandstone walls on a hill outside Truro. It was once a convent, but has been refurbished and transformed by new owners into a luxury hotel, with high-quality fabrics, heavy ruched curtains, and botanical prints. Alan Vickops' cooking is sophisticated and *nouvelle* with lots of expense-account ingredients. Fish and meat are of excellent quality and are perfectly timed. Most dishes involve fragrant delicate sauces that show Vickops' training at the Dorchester. There are some complex, but dazzling ideas: a layered red mullet and puff pastry gateau served on a ginger, chive and raspberry butter sauce; roast rack of English lamb on a truffle-scented sauce with a creamy, cone-shaped timbale of chicken and ratatouille. Warm escalope of grilled salmon gets a passion-fruit dressing; baked marinated duck breast is served with orange and spring onion sauce and poached kumquats. Sweets, such as coffee and walnut ice-cream in a chocolate cup, are also lifted by fine sauces. Other details are in keeping with the serious intentions of the place: home-baked bread, unsalted butter, luscious petits fours. An informative, interesting list of around 50 wines has house wines at £7.75. CELLARMAN'S CHOICE: Côtes de Roussillon, Château de Jau '83, £9.75; Chardonnay, Mount St Helen '86, £16.50. More reports, please.

CHEF: Alan Vickops PROPRIETORS: Mr and Mrs J.J. Costelloe
OPEN: all week
MEALS: 12.15 to 1.45, 7.15 to 9.45
PRICES: £21 (£29), Set D £19.75 (£27)
CARDS: Access, Amex, Diners, Visa
SEATS: 50 to 55. 3 tables outside. Private parties: 35 to 40 main room, 25 and 35 private rooms. Car-park, 70 places. Children's helpings (Sun L only). No children under 12. Jacket and tie (D only). No cigars/pipes in dining-room. Wheelchair access (also WC). Music.
ACCOMMODATION: 15 rooms, all with bath/shower. Rooms for disabled. Lift. B&B £53 to £75. No children under 12. Afternoon teas. Garden. Tennis. Snooker. TV. Phone. Scenic

Le Provencal [10/20]

15 Kenwyn Street, Truro TR1 3BU
TRURO (0872) 72546 £21

The prettiest building in the street has been turned into a tiny restaurant serving peasant Mediterranean food. Inside it is pure Monet – garden paintings on the whitewashed walls, floral prints and fabrics, and vases of flowers everywhere. The cooking is wholesome and unpretentious, taking in bouillabaisse, coq au vin, and fish marinated in olive oil and spices. Lamb is cooked Moroccan style with chickpeas, or with tomato, garlic and herbs. A simpler bistro menu also operates at lunchtime and dinner. A useful list of around 60 wines has house French at £6.25. CELLARMAN'S CHOICE: Gewürztraminer, Rolly Gassmann '86, £13.60.

CHEF: Mike Berriman PROPRIETOR: Chris Jewell
OPEN: all week, exc Sun L
MEALS: 12 to 2, 6.30 to 10.30
PRICES: £15 (£21)
CARDS: Access, Amex, Visa, Diners
SEATS: 30. Private parties: 25 main room. Children's helpings. Wheelchair access (1 step). Music

Cornwall Round-up

BISTRO: *Anthea's,* Newtown in St Martin, (032 623 352).
WINE BAR: *Mounts Bay Vineyard,* Tolver Water, Long Rock, Penzance (0736 60774).
VEGETARIAN: *Woodcote Hotel,* The Saltings, Lelant, St Ives (0736 753147); *Attic Feast,* (Lunch only), Old Bridge Street, Truro (0872 40008).
INEXPENSIVE: *Mr Bistro,* East Quay, Mevagissey (0726 842432/1).
BAR MEALS: *Shipwrights,* Helford (032 623 235).
ROOMS: *Tregony House,* Tregony, Truro (087 253 671); *Port Gaverne Hotel,* Port Gaverne, Nr Port Isaac (0208 880244).
HISTORIC SETTING: *Seafood Bar,* Lower Quay Hill, Falmouth (0326 315129).

TUNBRIDGE WELLS Kent map 3

Cheevers [13/20]

56 High Street, Tunbridge Wells TN1 1XF
TUNBRIDGE WELLS (0892) 45524 £18–£21

The décor is like the food: precise, clear, uncluttered, modern. There is just one large room with tables in three rows and a glass front at one end with Venetian blinds. The menu is short, with six dishes per course, and original, exciting, decidedly modern British. Certain features are consistent: a mousse of seafood; usually a poultry dish using exotic spices; a leek and blue cheese quiche; always a very traditional selection of sweets, such as hot walnut and ginger pudding, and also British cheeses. The kitchen technique is sufficiently sound to follow and play with fashions without coming unstuck. Take this example: an oval-shaped slice of crab mousse encased in a skin of bright green spinach leaves, the oval clearly divided into two lengthways – one half dark meat, the other white, the garnish just a skinned cherry tomato with a herb leaf either side. Other recommended dishes are: pot-roast pheasant; chicken with yoghurt, cardamom and ginger; grilled lamb with tarragon butter. 'The fillet of Scotch beef braised with baby vegetables turned the usual taste experience – strong meat, mild sauce – upside down. It was as if the strength of the beef had moved from meat to sauce. The vegetables punctuated the dark sauce at equal intervals, two turnips; two carrots and stalks; two leeks like blades of grass. Silly, but lovely to look at.' The tarts are especially fine to finish. The wine list is equally interesting and prices are reasonable. Bottles are mostly French, with an odd one from Italy, Spain, England, California and Australia. House French £5.50; CELLARMAN'S CHOICE: Savennières, Clos du Papillon '86, £11.50; Vouvray, Domaine de l'Epinay '86, £10.75; Bourgogne Passetoutgrain '85, £9.95.

CHEF: T.J. Cheevers PROPRIETORS: T.J. Cheevers, M.J. Miles and P.D. Tambini
OPEN: Tue to Sat
MEALS: 12 to 2.30, 7 to 10.30
PRICES: L £12 (£18), Set D £15.95 (£21)
CARDS: Access, Visa
SEATS: 36. Private parties: 36 main room. No cigars/pipes in dining-room. Wheelchair access

Sankeys Seafood at the Gate [10/20]

The Gate, 39 Mount Ephraim, Tunbridge Wells TN4 8AA
TUNBRIDGE WELLS (0892) 511422 £26

The Gate moved here from Hildenborough near Tonbridge. It is part of a small cabal of restaurants that is forming in the orbit of Thackeray's, just up the hill: Furama, a Chinese, is opposite; Pilgrims is a few doors down. Sankeys Seafood at the Gate is in a tall Victorian family residence with heavy gables in the Dutch style. The menu deals exclusively in fish, for the most (and best) part cooked simply – usually grilled or poached. Supplies are far ranging: Scottish salmon; Norfolk mussels; Cornish clams; Newfoundland lobster; Greenland prawns; Guernsey cock crab. Vegetables are equally carefully chosen. Sweets and other more cooked dishes disappoint. The wine list is a prime example of all a short list should be – 30 bottles, mostly under £10. House French is £5.50.

CHEF: Eleuterio Lizzi PROPRIETOR: Guy Sankey
OPEN: Mon to Sat
MEALS: 12 to 2, 7 to 10
PRICES: £22 (£26). Cover £1. Service inc
CARDS: Access, Amex, Visa
SEATS: 60. 6 tables outside. Private parties: 8 main room, 30 private room. Children's helpings, by arrangement. No cigars/pipes in dining-room

Thackeray's House [14/20]

85 London Road, Tunbridge Wells TN1 1EA
TUNBRIDGE WELLS (0892) 511921 £14–£31

William Makepeace Thackeray once lived in this green and white clapboard house, which is now set back off the main road almost next door to the Conservative Club. Bruce Wass produces an exemplary version of sophisticated modern cooking, pulling in all kinds of influences. His favourite dishes show the style and direction of the kitchen: preserved duck and marinated salmon with warm slices of foie gras; fresh tagliarini with mussels; peppered duck breast with bitter orange sauce and raisins; gurnard with fennel, orange and pastis, the sauce made from the bones and guts of the fish. There is a lot of fruit on the menu: quail terrine comes with rabbit rillettes and a pear vinaigrette; calf's liver is served on a bed of buttered Bramley apples. Otherwise, fish is a feature – croustade of mussels; scallop terrine; pike, salmon and spinach mousseline. Sweets span Comice pear roasted with spices on a slice of grilled brioche with ginger ice-cream to sticky toffee pudding; excellent British farmhouse cheeses come from James' of Beckenham. Bruce Wass says that any increase in prices is a reflection of the quality of produce used, which means wild salmon rather than farmed, but farmed rabbit rather than wild; added to this is the 40-mile road trip each week for unpasteurised Jersey milk and cream, and the use of French flour mixed with local Dove's Farm flour to improve the bread – all these details come at a price. Cheaper, more flexible meals are served in the bistro downstairs. House French £7.90. CELLARMAN'S CHOICE: Chardonnay, Étoile '85, from the Jura, £12.75.

CHEFS: Bruce Wass, Gordon Malcolm and Nigel Ramsbottom PROPRIETOR: Bruce Wass
OPEN: Tue to Sat
CLOSED: 1 week at Christmas
MEALS: 12.30 to 2.30, 7 to 10
PRICES: £23 (£31), Set L £9.95 (£14) to £15.75 (£22), Set D £19.85 (£26) to £23.50 (£29). Service inc Set, 10% alc
CARDS: Access, Visa
SEATS: 35. 8 tables outside. Private parties: 16 main room. Children's helpings. No cigars/pipes in dining-room

TWICKENHAM Greater London map 3

Cezanne [13/20]

68 Richmond Road, Twickenham, TW1 3BE
01-892 3526 £14–£19

'The cost of good raw materials seems to be forever rising. Fish seems to be the most inconsistent, price-wise, even good fishmongers resort to freezing to stabilise price and availability.' Tim Jefferson's small restaurant deals comfortably in a fashionable, two-dimensional menu – most main dishes come with something: calf's liver with sage; venison with beetroot; fillet steak with béarnaise. The quality of the cooking is a cut above the unpretentious dining-room, dealing also in quenelles, marquises, fricassee of the above fish with tropical fruit. The wine list is an invigorating read which specialises in under £10 bottles, with half a dozen well-chosen house wines at £5 and £6.50, some '70s claret, albeit a little more expensive, and nine half-bottles. Dessert wines for the tarte Tatin or hot butterscotch and date pudding are Muscat de Beaumes de Venise at a stiff £2.75 a glass or a Graves, Clos St Georges '83, at £2. CELLARMAN'S CHOICE: Savennières, Château de Chamboureau '84, £9.50.

CHEF: Tim Jefferson PROPRIETORS: Tim and Philippa Jefferson
OPEN: Mon to Sat, Exc Sat L
CLOSED: bank hol
MEALS: 12.30 to 2.30, 7 to 10.30 (11 Fri and Sat)
PRICES: £13 (£19), Set L £9.50 (£14)
CARDS: Access, Amex, Visa
SEATS: 38. Private parties: 40 main room. Vegetarian meals. Children's helpings. Wheelchair access. Music

McClements [13/20]

12 The Green, Twickenham TW2 5AA
01-755 0176 £16–£21

Twickenham Green is in the shape of a triangle, its apex perched at the finale of a seemingly never-ending row of drab high-street shops. An old railway bridge marks the entrance to the little piece of suburban tranquillity of terraced houses and antique shops. Next to a furniture restorers called 'Jack the Stripper', the dark green awning of McClements announces itself with equal drama using the subtitle 'Modern French Cuisine'. The decorative elements all have an oriental flavour – there is a black lacquered screen and silk paintings of storks. The room is cramped. John McClements is patriotically British in his selection of prime ingredients, for instance Cornish lobster and Welsh lamb. The French influence is the saucing technique, which is competent and relies on butters and creams. McClements is a serious chef producing very fine starter and main course dishes that compete favourably with the likes of the other modernists. For instance, a central mound of Cornish lobster and its claw sits in a wonderful clear fish fumet; or a three-inch high sandwich of mille-feuille is filled with crab and given a frothy saffron sauce; there is a variation on Robuchon's salt-crust lamb. The menu of 14 or so dishes changes monthly, its virtue but also its drawback (on busy nights). A short wine list has house claret at £7 and CELLARMAN'S CHOICE: Fleurie '85, £11.50 and Chablis, Côtes de Lechet '84, £19.50.

CHEF/PROPRIETOR: John McClements
OPEN: Tue to Sat, exc Sat L
MEALS: noon to 2.30, 7 to 10.30
PRICES: Set L £12 (£16), Set D from £17.50 (£21). Service inc
CARDS: Access, Amex, Diners, Visa
SEATS: 25. Private parties: 25 main room, 15 private room. Car-park, 20 places. Vegetarian meals. Children welcome. Smart dress preferred. No-smoking area. Music

ULLSWATER Cumbria map 7

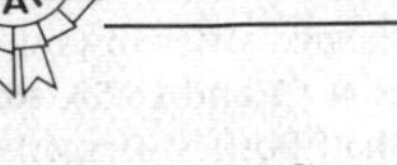

▲ *Sharrow Bay* [15/20]

Howtown Road, Ullswater CA10 2LZ
POOLEY BRIDGE (085 36) 301 and 483
2m from Pooley Bridge on E side of lake,
signposted Howtown and Martindale £19–£34

The story is that when the taxi dropped Francis Coulson off at what was called the Mansion, with his suitcase and pots and pans, he said, 'See you in three days.' That was in 1948. Brian Sack joined three years later. They have created this monument to British catering though four decades of dedication to their respective crafts. By a clear vote of readers, Sharrow, now in its 41st year, is raised a notch to 15/20. 'If we only had one more trip left to a country-house hotel we would go to Sharrow without seriously thinking about anywhere else.' For all its grand airs and graces it has kept up with the times. A new conservatory has been added and Francis Coulson and Brian Sack have scotched rumours of retirement. It is highly principled cooking: baking done twice a day, as much local produce used as possible. In 1955, dinner for 12/6d was ox-tail soup or consommé; spaghetti alla milanese; grilled rump steak, Brussels sprouts, garden peas, sauté and creamed potatoes; fresh fruit salad and cream; cheeses and coffee. Thirty-four years later, the cottages on Ullswater are fussily luxurious and dinners framed in the grand manner. More than 20 starters, the mandatory fish course, the sorbet, then 20 main dishes, and finally as many sweets, to which diners are introduced before the meal. The style spans the decades, essentially classical but with modern British accents – 'roast leg of local spring lamb, cooked in the English style', that is, slowly but surely, on a bed of vegetables, served with croûtons cooked in the lamb juices; mint and onion sauces – and also a recognition of changing styles: ceviche of salmon, for instance, or a warm salad of pigeon. The choice of soups sums it up: 'French peasant vegetable; carrot and orange with basil; French onion; simple beef consommé.' Recommendations have homed in on the mid-meal fish course – Aberdeen sole Vallée d'Auge with calvados sauce and suissesses – but have also named lobster mousse, sauce Nantua; roast pheasant; sea-bass with lobster sauce; saddle of venison; partridge with cabbage, and the sweets: crème caramel with strawberries; pithiviers with ice-cream; apple strudel. The English ethic comes out even more strongly at afternoon tea – on a silver tray in the lounge overlooking the lake – and the superlative breakfasts. In a perverse way it is similar to, almost a forerunner of, the Waterside Inn at Bray. Both are on the water and both cook richly in the grand manner, but alas Sharrow cannot have three *Michelin* stars like the Waterside, because it is English, and ever more so. 'We are tired of all these sauce reductions so prevalent everywhere. We want to emphasise the British style, without continually turning to French cuisine. We use the good old English word gravy and we try to retain the basic flavour of the main ingredient. We feel English hot puddings can be second to none.' The wine list is fair but unexciting, and the absence of some of the producers' names makes selection more difficult. There is plenty of choice under £10 a bottle. Most of the wines are French, Burgundies and even Beaujolais largely from Louis Latour, good Alsace from Hugel, and some good clarets of the '78 vintage, plus a handful of older clarets, including some first growths of the great '66 and '61 vintages. A few of the lesser clarets are too old. Germany is the best represented of the rest of the world. Most tempting among the sweet wines are the '76 vintages of Tokay and Riesling Sélections de Grains Nobles from Hugel, at £35 and £44, and some expensive bottles of '71 and '76 Beeren and Trockenbeerenauslesen from Germany. Muscat de Beaumes de Venise (producer unknown) costs £1.75 per glass. CELLARMAN'S CHOICE: St Estèphe, Ch. Meyney '78, £21.20; Riesling, Réserve Personnelle '83 from Hugel, £17.95.

CHEFS: Francis Coulson, Johnnie Martin, Colin Akrigg, Philip Wilson, Alison Kennedy, Tim Ford, Paul Brodie, Colin Le Voi, Chris Bond and Sally Manchester
PROPRIETORS: Francis Coulson and Brian Sack
OPEN: all week
MEALS: 1 to 1.45, 8 to 8.45
PRICES: Set L £14 (£19) to £20.50 (£25), Set D £29.50 (£34). Service inc
SEATS: 65. Private parties: 10 main room. Car-park, 30 places. Vegetarian meals. No children under 13. Jacket and tie. No smoking. Wheelchair access
ACCOMMODATION: 30 rooms, 26 with bath/shower. Rooms for disabled. D, B&B £65 to £194. No children under 13. Afternoon teas. Garden. TV. Phone. Scenic. Doors close at 12. Confirm by midday [GHG]

An index of restaurants by name appears at the back of the Guide.

ULVERSTON Cumbria map 7

Bay Horse Inn and Bistro [13/20]

Canal Foot, Ulverston LA12 9EL
ULVERSTON (0229) 53972 £17

The prolific John Tovey launches a fourth restaurant to add to his growing Lakeland empire and pile of cookery books. This one is scaled down, a pub with a conservatory dining-room, aiming to build a strong local following by keeping the prices firmly in check. And another fine view they have found, too, on the shore of Morecambe Bay, overlooking sands and fells, though the journey there, past industrial and urban developments, is less than scenic. It is a low-ceilinged beamed pub with horse brasses in abundance, a pool table in the snug and something of the proportions of the Walnut Tree at Llandewi Skirrid (see entry, Wales). The restaurant is in a glass veranda within feet of the sea at high tide. A short *carte* with a minimum charge of £7.50 is the least expensive of Tovey's trio of serious venues. 'We cook whatever is available.' Mention of quiches and soups is to underplay the extent of the cooking. Smoked trout with leek and water-chestnuts arrives in lightly curried choux buns and a cream and Pernod sauce; the local Waberthwaite ham is roasted, served as two thick slices in a glistening demi-glace flavoured with madeira. Also recommended have been smoked duck breast salad with fresh fig and oak-leaf lettuce, and crab escalope in a tomato sauce. Main courses are inclusive of four Tovey vegetables. The platter of cheeses has come with shelled walnuts and hazelnuts and there is always the sticky toffee pudding to finish. Plentiful coffee. The beer is Mitchells. Thirty wines, with Australian house red and white at £7.50 and £8. CELLARMAN'S CHOICE: also Australian, Tisdall Sauvignon Blanc Semillon '86, and Tisdall Cabernet Merlot '86, both £8.95.

CHEF: Robert Lyons PROPRIETORS: Robert Lyons and John Tovey
OPEN: Tue to Sun, exc Sun D
MEALS: 12 to 1.15, 7 to 8.30
PRICES: £12 (£17). Minimum £7.50. Service 10%
CARD: Access
SEATS: 30. 3 tables outside. Private parties: 20 main room. No children under 12. Smart dress preferred. No smoking in dining-room. Wheelchair access (1 step; also WC). Music. Air-conditioned

UNDERBARROW Cumbria map 7

▲ *Tullythwaite House* [new entry, zero rated]

Underbarrow LA8 8BB
CROSWAITE (044 88) 397 £15–£20

This famous Lakeland farmhouse is once again in caring hands. The Greenwoods have picked up the onerous mantle of the legend of Mary Johnson's family – it was the *Guide*'s English restaurant of the year in 1984 when she was 86 – and after a cautious start have lent their own identity to it. There is still an English strain to the four-course menus, and notably the breakfast, but it is coupled to a more international flavour. Hence home-cooked tongue with spiced oranges competes with salmon mousse with a sambal of cucumber among the starters. Some of the liberal combinations of fruits work best at the sweet course, as in Seville orange custard cups or hazelnut lemon meringue gateau. Others dazzle, for instance chicken breasts marinated in lime and served with hollandaise. Other lessons have been learned from the Lakeland school: a minimum choice; good vegetable soups; fine cheeses and much local produce; a generosity that extends to large measures of spirits. Thirty wines are pitched mostly around £6. More reports, please.

CHEF: Janet Greenwood PROPRIETORS: Michael and Janet Greenwood
OPEN: Wed to Sat D, and Sun L
MEALS: 12.30, 7 to 7.30
PRICES: Set L £10.50 (£15), Set D £15.50 (£20)
CARD: Access
SEATS: 16. Private parties: 16 main room. Car-park, 14 places. No children under 12. Smart dress preferred. No smoking in dining-room
ACCOMMODATION: 3 rooms, all with bath/shower. B&B £30 to £45. No children under 12. Garden. TV. Scenic. Doors close at 11. Confirm by 4

UPPINGHAM Leicestershire map 6

▲ *Lake Isle* [12/20]

16 High Street East, Uppingham LE15 9PL
UPPINGHAM (0572) 822951 £12–£18

The Whitfields' converted butcher's shop is a genteel, English middle-class version of a French country restaurant. The value for money is excellent, the wine list exceptional and the cooking anchored firmly to basic principles. 'Like the nicest sort of French holiday meal.' There are few ambitious leaps – the five-course dinner menu is based on the simple handling of good ingredients. Soups are made from proper stock, slices of French-style, home-cured ham are served with a citrus salad, and vegetables come in great mounds. Main courses might be Bresse chicken with Meaux mustard sauce; salmon brochette with coquilles St Jacques, mussels and rice; pork fillet with spinach; outstanding roast lamb with asparagus tips and a béarnaise. The cheeseboard – 'really a cheese occasional table' – is a mixture of French and local and arrives with a glass dish of nuts. Sweets have included good orange crème anglaise. The wine list will delight lovers of variety, or solitary diners, as it has a most impressive line-up of half-bottles. The list also reveals its treasures slowly, starting with a page of house wines, including the excellent English Bruisyard St Peter '86, £7.25, and Masson Light, £5, the only good non-alcoholic wine around. Two pages of half-bottles follow, with wines from all the major French areas, including Bordeaux and Burgundy, and some fine examples, like Savigny-lès-Beaune '84, from Simon Bize, £7, and Crozes-Hermitage, Domaine des Entrefaux '84, £4.65. Even the Muscadet is a domaine-bottled 'sur lie', Château du Cleray '85, £4.15; the '85 Sancerre, £5, is a Clos de la Roche from Jean Vacheron; and the Muscat de Beaumes de Venise '84, £7, is the almondy Domaine de Coyeux. These are succeeded by six pages of adequate to good bottles, and just as you think you've reached the end, a vista of splendid wines from Bordeaux, Burgundy, the Rhône, Alsace, Champagne, Germany and the Douro opens up. There is little that is unrecommendable, and prices are very reasonable. Take particular note of the unusually generous choice of half-bottles of sweet white Bordeaux and Alsace wines. House French £6; CELLARMAN'S CHOICE: Sancerre Rouge, Domaine des Epinières '85, £10.60; Napa Valley Chardonnay '83, £12.75.

CHEFS: David Whitfield and Liam Tinney PROPRIETORS: David and Claire Whitfield
OPEN: all week, exc Mon L and Sun D
MEALS: 12 to 2, 7 to 10
PRICES: Set L from £7.75 (£12), Set D from £13.50 (£18)
CARDS: Access, Amex, Diners, Visa
SEATS: 35. Private parties: 40 main room, 10 private room. Vegetarian meals. Children's helpings. Wheelchair access
ACCOMMODATION: 10 rooms, all with bath/shower. B&B £26 to £38. Pets welcome. TV. Phone. Doors close at 12 [GHG]

WADHURST East Sussex map 3

▲ *Spindlewood Hotel* [10/20]

Wallcrouch, Wadhurst TN5 7JG
TICEHURST (0580) 200430
on B2099, between Wadhurst and Ticehurst £16–£21

Spindlewood had its casualties in the great storm of October 1987; the tennis-court was destroyed. Inside, the oak-panelled library is now used as a smaller dining-room and the bar has been redecorated in the latest of a long history of improvements. Harvey Lee Aram has returned after a spell away to take over the kitchen again. Food is always fresh, fish in particular, as in cod in a white wine and cream sauce. Main courses rely heavily on sauces: grilled breast and boned leg of duck (a staple here) with redcurrant and lime sauces; medallions of venison with juniper berries and a sherry sauce; breast of chicken with a spinach mousse and a cheese sauce. But there is a savoury option to dessert: Welsh rarebit; stuffed mushrooms; Scotch woodcock. Sixty-five wines start with house Mâcon at £5.50.

CHEF: Harvey Lee Aram PROPRIETOR: R.V. Fitzsimmons
OPEN: all week
CLOSED: 4 days at Christmas
MEALS: 12.15 to 1.30, 7.15 to 9 (9.15 Sat, 8.30 Sun)
PRICES: L £13 (£19), Set L from £11.75 (£16), Set D £16.50 (£21)
CARDS: Access, Amex, Diners, Visa
SEATS: 40. Private parties: 50 main room, 18 private room. Car-park, 60 places. Vegetarian meals. Children's helpings. No cigars/pipes in dining-room. Music
ACCOMMODATION: 9 rooms, all with bath/shower. B&B £37 to £60. Deposit: one night's stay. Baby facilities. Garden. TV. Phone. Doors close at 12. Confirm by 6

The Guide *recruits new inspectors from readers who write in regularly. If you would like to apply, write to the Editor with (a) a detailed report on a restaurant where you have eaten and (b) a comparative study of restaurants known to you.*

WALBERSWICK Suffolk map 6

Potter's Wheel [9/20]

Village Green, Walberswick IP18 8TT
SOUTHWOLD (0502) 724468 £12–£14

Shop and gallery also house a vegetarian biased tea-room which makes much use of local produce. Dinners are set three courses. Recommended dishes include gougère with ratatouille and cheese; nut and pea croquettes with blue cheese sauce; lentil and apricot soup; roast venison; lemon syllabub; pear cheesecake. Limited wines and local cider.

CHEF/PROPRIETOR: Lesley Scott
OPEN: all week L, exc Tue; Fri and Sat D
CLOSED: 1 Oct to 1 Apr
MEALS: 12 to 2, 7.30 to 9
PRICES: £7 (£12), Set D £9.50 (£14). Minimum £3.50. Licensed, also bring your own: corkage £1
CARD: Access
SEATS: 26. 5 tables outside. Private parties: 26 main room. Vegetarian meals. Children's helpings (L only). Wheelchair access. Music

WALKINGTON Humberside map 6

▲ *Manor House* [11/20]

Northlands, Walkington HU17 8RT
HULL (0482) 881645 £25

Derek Baugh moved here in November 1987 from Willerby Manor. The transition has been marked by a steep rise in the Gastronomy with a capital G. The brochure and menu are overpoweringly florid – 'a chorus of warm duck' ... 'a harmony of lobster' ... 'knapsacks of prawns'. Beyond the hype there are signs of some good cooking: broccoli and almond soup; deep-fried pancakes filled with prawns in lobster sauce; fillet of lamb stuffed with forest mushrooms. The abundance of effort but lack of sparkle extends to the cheeseboard. The wine list is in keeping, with vintage bottles up to £70. House French £7.50. CELLARMAN'S CHOICE: Châteauneuf-du-Pape, Clos de Pape '83, at £12.50.

CHEFS: Derek Baugh, Lee Baugh and Mark Cook PROPRIETORS: Derek and Lee Baugh
LUNCH: Mon to Sat, D only
MEALS: 7.30 to 9.15
PRICES: Set D £18.50 (£25)
CARDS: Access, Visa
SEATS: 44. Private parties: 26 main room. Car-park, 60 places. Vegetarian meals. No children under 12. Smart dress preferred. Wheelchair access. Music
ACCOMMODATION: 5 rooms, all with bath/shower. B&B £60.50 to £86. No children under 12. Pets by arrangement. Garden. TV. Phone. Scenic. Doors close at 12. Confirm by 8 [GHG]

The Guide *is independent, accepts no advertising and survives solely on the number of copies sold.*

Humberside Round-up

ROOMS: *Grange Park Hotel,* Restaurant l'Eau Vive, Main Street, Willerby, Hull (0482 656488).
FISH: *Cerutti's,* 10 Nelson Street, Hull (0482 28501).
WINE BAR: *Russell's Wine Bar,* 34 High Street, Cleethorpes (0472 690050).

WATERHOUSES Staffordshire map 5

▲ *Old Beams* [12/20]

Waterhouses ST10 3HW
WATERHOUSES (053 86) 254 £17–£27

The renovated, square-set Georgian building on the road from Leek to Ashbourne has a domestic clutter outside and a log fire in the bar. Nigel Wallis cooks an imaginative French menu with some stalwart English touches. Asparagus mousse and terrine of leeks in madeira sauce rub shoulders with veal and kidney pudding with a good suet case, or boiled bacon with pulses. Poached halibut with sorrel sauce has also been first-rate. Other fish might include monk with mustard and orange, and Dover sole with parsley and limes. The details, for instance the home-made bread rolls with the extensive cheeseboard, are those of a serious restaurant. Finish with raspberry and nectarine pie; crème brûlée, good soufflés or home-made ice-cream with fresh pineapple. House white is £8.75, red £9.75; CELLARMAN'S CHOICE: Mâcon-Clessé '85, from Thévenet, £12.65.

CHEF: Nigel J. Wallis PROPRIETORS: Nigel J. and A. Wallis
OPEN: Tue to Sat
MEALS: 12 to 2 (1.45 Sat), 7 to 10
PRICES: £19 (£27), Set L £9.50 (£17)
CARDS: Access, Amex, Diners, Visa
SEATS: 50. 3 tables outside. Car-park, 18 places. Children's helpings (with prior notice). No children under 4. Wheelchair access (also WC). Music
ACCOMMODATION: 2 rooms, both with bath/shower. B&B £42.50 to £58. Garden. Tennis. TV. Scenic. Doors close at 12

WATH-IN-NIDDERDALE North Yorkshire map 7

▲ *Sportsman's Arms* [12/20]

Wath-in-Nidderdale HG3 5PP
HARROGATE (0423) 711306 £13–£22

A lovely old coaching-inn in a leafy, sheltered corner of Nidderdale, set back from the road, over a hump-back bridge, with a willow outside. Inside the building has gone its separate ways and divides into three – bar, old-fashioned lounge and more modern, pink dining-room. The menu shows promise, with real foods and a mix of plainer dishes and more ambitious combinations. Portions are sufficiently generous to fill what must be the largest steering-wheel plates in all of Yorkshire. Typical might be roast duck with passion-fruit sauce, venison with roasted garlic. There is an interesting selection of cheeses and some picturesque sweets, of which the lemon-chiffon torte or sticky toffee pudding draw praise. The wines are uneven in quality, but on the whole fairly priced, with plenty of interest well below £10, from France and around the winemaking world. The extraordinary sweet Mâcon-Clessé Cuvée Spéciale Botrytis '83, from Thévenet, £22.50 is a rare dessert Burgundy; sweet wines are otherwise restricted to three Bordeaux, one very basic Sauternes, the others top wines of '76 and '79. House French £5.95.

CHEF/PROPRIETOR: J.R. Carter
OPEN: all week exc Sun D
MEALS: 12 to 1.45, 7 to 10
PRICES: £18 (£22), Set L and D from £8.50 (£13), Snacks L only from £1.25. Service inc
CARDS: Access, Amex, Diners, Visa
SEATS: 45. 6 tables outside. Private parties: 60 main room. Car-park, 50 places. Vegetarian meals. Children's helpings. Wheelchair access (also WC)
ACCOMMODATION: 6 rooms, 2 with bath/shower. B&B £27 to £40. Baby facilities. Pets welcome. Garden. Fishing. TV. Scenic

WATLINGTON Oxfordshire map 2

▲ *Well House* [10/20]

High Street, Watlington OX9 5PZ
WATLINGTON (049 161) 3333 £17–£20

Patricia and Alan Crawford's well-liked town restaurant is in a converted fifteenth-century merchant's residence. There have been some changes in the kitchen, but the short menus still mix the familiar and the fashionable, from avocado vinaigrette and Scotch fillet steak in red wine sauce to duck breast with oranges and walnuts, scallops in filo pastry, and escalope of salmon with sorrel sauce. Good dishes have included lobster and crab mousse, pork with black pudding, apple and mustard, and apple and cinnamon trifle. House wine is £5.50. CELLARMAN'S CHOICE: Ch. Plagnac '82, £12.20.

CHEFS: Patricia Crawford and Debbie Nunn PROPRIETORS: Patricia and Alan Crawford
OPEN: Tue to Sun, exc Sun D
MEALS: 12.30 to 2.15, 7.30 to 9.30 (10 Sat)
PRICES: £15 (£20), Set L and D £12.30 (£17). Service inc
CARDS: Access, Amex, Diners, Visa
SEATS: 40. Private parties: 50 main room, 10 private room. Car-park, 15 places. Vegetarian meals. Children's helpings (Sun L only). Smart dress preferred. Wheelchair access
ACCOMMODATION: 8 rooms, all with bath/shower. Rooms for disabled. B&B £27.50 to £47.50. Children welcome. Baby facilities. Afternoon teas. TV. Phone. Doors close at 11. Confirm by 6

If you cannot honour a restaurant booking, always phone to cancel.

Restaurants are graded on a scale of 1–20. In the category of 10–11 expect to find the best food in the locality. Ratings of 12 and more are given to restaurants we regard as serving the best food in the region.

WELLS-NEXT-THE-SEA Norfolk map 6

Moorings [11/20]

6 Freeman Street, Wells-Next-The-Sea NR23 1BA
FAKENHAM (0328) 710949 £14–£15

Bernard and Carla Phillips have transformed a run-down caff backing on to the quay into an informal eating place with echoes of a French café. Outside is painted nautical blue. Inside, the small, open-plan restaurant has bare wooden floors, tables close together and the kitchen in full view through the open doorway. The pattern of the floral tablecloths is picked up on the cover of the menus and wine list. Service is by enthusiastic local girls and boys –this is a genuine community restaurant – who also take turns helping in the kitchen, so everyone gets to know the full workings of the place. It is a restaurant that welcomes a wide-ranging eclectic clientele: lords, ladies, farmers, fishermen, dustmen. The menu is dedicated to the full use of local produce, and some dishes show Carla Phillips' American/Russian background. Venison, always served on Sundays with onion marmalade, is from the Queen's butcher at Dersingham. Mike Rhodes at the Cley Smokehouse supplies sweet pickled herrings; fish is from the Wells boats. The British farmhouse cheeses come from Sue Elston's shop in Burnham Market, and a fresh goats' cheese is from a farm in Mattishall. Gravlax is cured on the premises, often with mullet or bass as well as salmon; some items are smoked in a derelict cooker; friends gather wild fungi, berries and samphire. The results might include pigeon with port and cream sauce; meatballs (made with naturally-reared beef) in wild mushroom sauce; devilled clams (the long-necked kind dug up by lugworm diggers); seafood gratin; pâtés and terrines served with pickled marrow and Jewish-style pickled green tomatoes; a layered terrine of bass and sea-trout gravlax-style with dill and brandy. There's always a good choice for vegetarians. Sweets are English or American-inspired tarts, pies and puddings; there are locally made sorbets from Prospero of Wiveton, as well as fresh fruit with fromage blanc. The wine list, which is both interesting and good value, has a choice of about 60. Robust house wines are under £5 a bottle. CELLARMAN'S CHOICE: Muscat d'Alsace '86, £6.55.

CHEFS/PROPRIETORS: Bernard and Carla Phillips
OPEN: Thur D to Tue L
CLOSED: first 3 weeks June, first 2 weeks Dec, 4 days at Christmas
MEALS: 12.30 to 2, 7.30 to 9
PRICES: £10 (£15), Set L £8.70 (£14), Set D £9.95 (£15). Licensed, also bring your own: corkage £2.75
SEATS: 44. Private parties: 44 main room. Vegetarian meals. Children's helpings. Wheelchair access (also WC)

▲ *This restaurant offers accommodation.*

[GHG] *after the details of an entry means that the establishment is also included in* The Good Hotel Guide.

WEOBLEY Hereford & Worcester map 2

▲ *Jule's Café* [9/20]

Portland Street, Weobley HR4 8SB
WEOBLEY (0544) 318206 £6–£14

There are two culinary influences at work in this timbered café/restaurant in the village square. Main courses are often traditional English dishes – a beef, Guinness and smoked oyster pie gives the idea – while starters and lunchtime dishes experiment with Middle Eastern vegetarian cookery. A mung bean and spinach soup is spiked with limes and chilli and served with Greek yoghurt or there might be stuffed vine leaves with fresh lemon mayonnaise. Simpler options, like a baked potato with organic cheese and spicy tomato sauce, are available at lunchtime; there is a selection of cakes and pastries for afternoon teas. House wine only, at £5.50, plus Dunkerton's cider and perry.

CHEF/PROPRIETORS: Julian and Juliet Whitmarsh
OPEN: Tue to Sun
MEALS: 12 to 2, 7.30 to 10.30
PRICES: £10 (£14), Set L from £1.95 (£6), Set D from £8 (£12), Snacks from £1.65
CARDS: Access, Visa
SEATS: 36. Private parties: 30 main room. Vegetarian meals. Children's helpings. Wheelchair access
ACCOMMODATION: 4 rooms. B&B £15 to £25. Children welcome. Pets welcome. Afternoon teas. TV. Scenic. Doors close at 1. Confirm by 6

WEST BEXINGTON Dorset map 2

▲ *Manor Hotel* [10/20]

Beach Road, West Bexington DT2 9DF
BURTON BRADSTOCK (0308) 897616 £13–£19

More of a hostelry than a manor, though the view down on to Chesil Bank is aristocratic. Bar meals in the basement or conservatory compete with more formal set meals in the dining-room; both are trenchant, honest and satisfying. As we go to press there are plans for a grill and pizza bar. The choice is wide, taking in escargots and chicken-liver pâté, but the fish and the generosity of the portions stand out. Cerne Valley trout with prawns and capers, monkfish with garlic and parsley, and West Bay scallops in green peppercorn sauce have all featured, as has warm salad of lambs' kidneys, and a trio of vegetarian pancakes, described by one reporter as 'delicious but gross'. Comfortable, inexpensive rooms. Real beers include Royal Oak, Palmers and Wadworth's 6X. A basic list of 70 wines, starting at £5.25.

Restaurants rating 12 or more serve the best food in the region.

Many of the more expensive restaurants offer bargain lunches for half the price of a meal in the evening. Details are given in the text.

CHEF: Clive Jobson PROPRIETORS: Richard and Jayne Childs
OPEN: all week
MEALS: 12 to 2, 7 to 10 (10.30 Sat)
PRICES: Set L from £8.50 (£13), Set D £13.65 (£19)
CARDS: Access, Amex, Visa
SEATS: 65. 18 tables outside. Private parties: 65 main room, 20 private room. Car-park, 50 places. Vegetarian meals. Children's helpings. Music
ACCOMMODATION: 10 rooms, all with bath/shower. B&B £24.95 to £44. Deposit: £10. Children welcome. Baby facilities. Garden. TV. Scenic. Doors close at 12. Confirm by 6 [GHG]

WEST MERSEA Essex map 3

▲ *Le Champenois, Blackwater Hotel* [11/20]

20–22 Church Street, West Mersea CO5 8QH
COLCHESTER (0206) 383338 £13–£21

'We do not like *nouvelle cuisine* very much,' writes Madame Chapleo. Her small French restaurant is well run and professional. 'We take pride in being able to adjust to people's requests.' The main-line vocabulary is one of onion soup; rack of lamb with herbs; duck with orange; floating islands. Lately, fish has started to appear more: monkfish with a cream and mussel sauce or saffron; brill with a stir-fry of leeks. The wine list is an amalgam of labels, almost exclusively French, cleverly chosen and not overpriced. House red and white are £5.95; CELLARMAN'S CHOICE: the house champagne, £17; Pouilly Fumé '86, £13.95; Bourgogne Clairet, Domaine de la Pousse d'Or '85, £8.80.

CHEF: R. Roudesli PROPRIETOR: M. Chapleo
OPEN: all week, exc Tue L and Sun D
CLOSED: 2 weeks in Jan
MEALS: 12 to 2, 7 to 10
PRICES: £14 (£21), Set L from £7.60 (£13)
CARDS: Access, Amex
SEATS: 46. 3 tables outside. Private parties: 55 main room, 25 private room. Car-park, 20 places. Vegetarian meals. Children's helpings. Smart dress preferred. Wheelchair access (also WC)
ACCOMMODATION: 7 rooms, 4 with bath/shower. B&B £20 to £43. Deposit: £10. Baby facilities. Pets welcome. Afternoon teas. Garden. TV. Scenic. Doors close at 1. Confirm by 9

WESTON-SUPER-MARE Avon map 2

▲ *La Petite Auberge* [10/20]

37 Upper Church Road, Weston-Super-Mare BS23 2DX
WESTON-SUPER-MARE (0934) 22351 £13–£22

From the seafront turn right and go past the pier, and look for the sign that says 'Welcome to Weston-Super-Mare'. The Williams' green-canopied bistro is in a Victorian conservation area, with a wine shop close by. The menu is short and seasonal, with blackboard specials based on market produce. Fish and game are a strong feature; the abundant vegetables are local; eggs are free-range. Guinea-fowl might be cooked with celery and walnuts; salmon fillet gets a chervil sauce; rabbit comes with two mustard cream sauces. Sweets range from Eton Mess (strawberries, brandy, cream and meringue), through coffee mousse with chocolate sauce to bread-and-butter pudding. Sixty wines are grouped by type – light, dry, crisp whites; classic reds –with CELLARMAN'S CHOICE: Vouvray '83, from Gilet, £6.95; and Taltarni Shiraz '82, from Australia, £8.95.

CHEF: Margaret Williams PROPRIETORS: Ian and Margaret Williams
OPEN: Mon to Sat, exc Mon L
CLOSED: 3 weeks a year
MEALS: 12 to 2, 7 to 10.30
PRICES: £16 (£22), Set L from £7.50 (£13)
CARDS: Access, Amex, Visa
SEATS: 32. Private parties: 32 main room. Children's helpings (L only). No children under 7. Music
ACCOMMODATION: 2 rooms. B&B £14 to £28. TV. Doors close at 11

WETHERBY West Yorkshire map 5

L'Escale [12/20]

16 Bank Street, Wetherby LS22 4NQ
WETHERBY (0937) 63613 £13–£25

The converted stone cottages have been a restaurant for the last 20 years and more. The accent is firmly French, albeit with translations. A set-price, four-course, no-choice menu is supplemented by an 18-dish carte. Local game – grouse, partridge, pheasant, hare, woodcock, mallard – is incorporated as seasons allow. Recommended dishes have been broccoli soup; a roll of salmon and sole with a white wine and butter sauce; roast tenderloin complete with crackling; apple tart; Stilton and apple strudel. As befits the atmosphere, the wine list opens with seven champagnes and offers a good range of quality, from the house Rhône at £7.25, onwards. Muscat de Beaumes de Venise is £1.85 a glass. CELLARMAN'S CHOICE: Imperial Gran Reserva '75, £15.25.

CHEF: Paul Bidgood PROPRIETORS: Mr and Mrs Paul Bidgood
OPEN: Tue to Sat D, and Sun L
MEALS: 12 to 2, 7 to 11
PRICES: £18 (£25), Set Sun L £8.50 (£13), Set D £13 (£17). Service inc Set L and D only
CARDS: Access, Amex, Diners, Visa
SEATS: 65. Private parties: 35 main room, 35 private room. Car-park, 7 places. Children's helpings (Sun L only). Smart dress preferred. No pipes in dining- room. Wheelchair access (1 step; also WC). Music. Air-conditioned

Reports on shops, cafés and farms are useful, as well as reports on restaurants.

The price quoted in brackets is for an average three-course meal including service, VAT, coffee and half a bottle of house wine or the equivalent in an ethnic restaurant.

WEYBRIDGE Surrey map 3

Colony [11/20]

3 Balfour Road, Weybridge KT13 8HE
WEYBRIDGE (0932) 842766 £16–£21

The Colony has established itself over and above the local French and Italian competition. It has an edge in terms of value, décor and attentive service. The menu deals confidently with the popular dishes – minced quail wrapped in iceberg lettuce, crispy fried seaweed, smoked shredded chicken in yellow-bean sauce. The centrepieces, steamed sea-bass or Peking duck, are handled with aplomb but put up the bill substantially. Alternatives might be the grilled prawns Peking style, sole in black-bean and chilli sauce, lemon chicken. The deep-fried shredded beef can be very hot and, when the restaurant is not busy, is served in birds' nests. Vegetables are fresh and cooked to order. The range runs out at desserts, which comprise ice-creams, toffeed fruits or red-bean paste pancakes. House French £6.50.

CHEF: Kam Yau Pang PROPRIETOR: Michael Tse
OPEN: all week
MEALS: 12 to 2.30, 6 to 11 (11.30 Fri and Sat)
PRICES: £11 (£21), Set L from £10 (£16), Set D from £12 (£18). Minimum £10. Service 12.5%
CARDS: Access, Amex, Diners, Visa
SEATS: 80. Private parties: 70 main room; 20 private room. Children welcome. Music. Air-conditioned

WHITBY North Yorkshire map 6A

Magpie Cafe [10/20]

14 Pier Road, Whitby YO21 3PU
WHITBY (0947) 602058 £9–£18

'Good Yorkshire cooking using fresh local produce.' All the sweets (more than 30 a day) are home made, down to the jams. Fish comes directly off the boats in the harbour. There is always a choice of at least six varieties of flat fish (grilled, poached or fried to order), plus more expensive crabs, salmon and lobsters. Pots of special teas include Earl Grey. The McKenzies now have a licence; house French is £5.25. They also cater for specialist diets and specialist customers, like children. Panoramic views over the quay, church and 199 steps.

CHEFS: Sheila and Ian McKenzie, and I.M. Robson PROPRIETORS: Sheila and Ian McKenzie
OPEN: all week
CLOSED: end of Oct to week before Easter
MEALS: 11.30 to 6.30
PRICES: £12 (£18), Set L from £5.35 (£9), Snacks from £1.30
SEATS: 100. Private parties: 50 main room. Vegetarian meals. Children's helpings. No-smoking area

Trenchers [9/20]

New Quay Road, Whitby YO21 1DH
WHITBY (0947) 603212 £16

Whitby's fish and chip shops and restaurants are an impressive bunch, largely because they get their fish fresh from the boats. Trencher's is upmarket compared with some of its neighbours, but the quality is high and value for money excellent. As well as exceptional plates of fish and chips there are grills, home-made steak pie, salmon salad and fish casserole. Puddings and sweets may be no match for the Magpie Café (see entry), but this is its nearest rival. Tea by the pot, house wine by the carafe.

CHEFS: Tim Lawrence and Garry Mourtrey PROPRIETOR: Terry Foster
OPEN: all week
CLOSED: Christmas to mid-Mar
MEALS: 11 to 9
PRICES: £10 (£16), Snacks from 50p
SEATS: 150. Private parties: 150 main room. Vegetarian meals. Children's helpings. Wheelchair access. Music

WHITLEY BAY Tyne & Wear map 7

Le Provençale [10/20]

183 Park View, Whitley Bay NE26 3RE
091-251 3567 £9–£21

Beside the butcher's and undertaker's is the small shopfront restaurant. Inside is brown and Regency but the Provençal element is more in inspiration than effect. The long menu is composed of sound, well-liked dishes, often quite rich, mixing classical variations – tournedos five ways: chasseur; au poivre; Rossini; Henri IV and bordelaise – with more provincial ideas, like chicken and asparagus crêpes. A special set-price four-course menu operates on Mondays and Thursdays. Lunches are also inexpensive. Sweets range from French apple tart to rum and raisin ice-cream with meringue, to well-reported classics such as poire Belle Hélène. Service is cheerful, but sometimes slow. Fifty wines from claret at £6.90, all supplied by Abbey Vintners of Morpeth.

CHEF: Michel Guigerro PROPRIETORS: Mr and Mrs M. Guigerro
OPEN: Mon to Sat, exc Mon L and Wed L
CLOSED: 2 weeks in summer
MEALS: 12 to 2, 7.30 to 9.45 (10.15 Sat)
PRICES: £15 (£21), Set L £4 (£9), Set Mon and Thur D £10.95 (£17)
CARDS: Access, Amex, Diners, Visa
SEATS: 26. Private parties: 26 main room. Children's helpings (L only). No children under 7. Music

'It is amazing to find how loyal your readers can be, as first-time customers often order according to the recommendation in the Guide.*'* London restaurateur

WICKHAM Hampshire map 2

▲ *Old House* [12/20]

The Square, Wickham PO17 5JG
WICKHAM (0329) 833049 £24

Since 1970, the Skipwiths have maintained this French restaurant in an early Georgian house and continue to offer good value and consistently high quality. The short menu reads well and keeps pace with the trends without necessarily sounding fashionable. Feuilleté of steamed vegetables with fennel sauce, and roast Barbary duck with a sauce of lime juice and white wine vinegar rub shoulders with fillet of beef bordelaise and pot-roast rabbit with cream and basil sauce. Three chocolate mousses with blackcurrant coulis is a typical sweet. The short list of around 40 French wines matches the food admirably. House French £7.80.

CHEF: Nicholàs Harman PROPRIETORS: Richard and Annie Skipwith
OPEN: Mon to Sat, exc Mon L and Sat L
CLOSED: 1 week at Christmas, 2 weeks at Easter, 2 weeks July to Aug
MEALS: 12 to 1.45, 7 to 9.30
PRICES: £17 (£24). Service inc. Licensed, also bring your own: corkage £3.50
CARDS: Access, Amex, Diners, Visa
SEATS: 35. Private parties: 35 main room, 14 private room. Car-park, 12 places. Children's helpings. No cigars/pipes in dining-room. Wheelchair access (also WC)
ACCOMMODATION: 10 rooms, all with bath/shower. B&B £52 to £75. Children welcome. Baby facilities. Garden. TV. Phone. Scenic. Doors close at 12 [GHG]

WILLERBY Humberside map 6

▲ *Restaurant Lafite, Willerby Manor Hotel* [10/20]

Well Lane, Willerby HU10 6ER
HULL (0482) 652616 £24

Derek Baugh's departure to Walkington (see entry) has resulted in a new name for this restaurant and some extensions to the facilities, as part of a multi-million pound development. The style is relaxed and professional; the food is still carefully prepared. Sauces are good and natural – delicate beurre blanc with scallop mousse; green peppercorn and orange with pan-fried duck breast – and raw materials are fresh. There is a noticeable lack of pretension, and prices are reasonable in this class. Any restaurant that serves Cloudy Bay's Sauvignon Blanc must have its head screwed on. The 70 wines are chosen with an eye to value, and not just from Italy, Iberia, and the New World; there are five clarets under £10. House French from Bocuse is £6.75. CELLARMAN'S CHOICE: St Amour '85, from Bocuse, £11.50.

The 1990 Guide *will appear before Christmas 1989. Reports are particularly helpful in the spring. Report forms are at the back of this book, but just write a letter if you prefer. Address to The Good Food Guide,* FREEPOST, *2 Marylebone Road, London NW1 1YN. No stamp is necessary if you post it in the UK.*

CHEF: Valentine F. Rodriguez PROPRIETORS: Willerby Manor Hotels Ltd and J. Townend & Sons Ltd
OPEN: all week, exc Sat L and Sun D
MEALS: 12.30 to 1.45, 7 to 9.45
PRICES: £17 (£24)
CARDS: Access, Amex, Visa
SEATS: 85. Private parties: 70 main room, 400 private room. Car-park, 250 places. Children's helpings. Smart dress preferred. Music
ACCOMMODATION: 41 rooms, all with bath/shower. B&B £52 to £66.50. Children welcome. Baby facilities. Afternoon teas. Garden. Air-conditioning. TV. Phone. Scenic. Doors close at 1am. Confirm by 6

WILLITON Somerset map 1

▲ *White House Hotel* [14/20]

10 YEARS

Williton TA4 4QW
WILLITON (0984) 32306 £25

After 22 years in residence at this Georgian country house, Dick and Kay Smith are going back to their food roots, while still moving with the times. Their cooking is lighter, with less cream in the sauces, and more vivid tastes, adapting the lessons of *nouvelle* to their first love, Elizabeth David. It is a version of French provincial using the best of local Somerset produce. Classic brandade, pipérade basquaise, bourride and noisettes of lamb with garlic sauce rub shoulders with hake with sorrel sauce, grilled pigeon breast with orange and olives, and English Charter pie. Sweets are in the Gallic style of profiteroles and crème brûlée; cheeses are partisan English – Exmoor goats', Torville, Capricorn, Grant's Hamwood Cheddar. The wine list, not long but very well chosen, is remarkably inexpensive. House wines are served by the glass, quarter, half-litre and bottle, and include some original choices, such as a good Portuguese Garrafeira Tinto '78 from Carvalho, Ribeira & Ferreira, and a Falkensteiner Hofberg QbA '85 from the excellent Friedrich Wilhelm Gymnasium. Dry whites include Sancerre Clos des Perriers '87, from Jean Vatan, at £11, Muscadet sur Lie '87, frum Henri Chéreau, good white Burgundies from Durup, Jaffelin and Guy Roulot. The Schloss Vollrads Trocken Blue-Silver at £11 is an interesting dry wine in a predominantly sweet but unusually good German section. Red Burgundies are even better than white, with wines from Sorin, Labouré-Roi, Jaffelin, Roux, Tollot-Beaut and Louis Trapet. Clarets include good *crus bourgeois* back to '80, some interesting English-bottled wines from older vintages for those who enjoy a gamble, as well as a good range of château-bottled wines and a nice clutch of seven 'second wines', all from good châteaux. There are good northern Rhônes, five Bandols, and brief but good selections from Spain and Italy. Sweet wines include six vintages of Anjou Moulin Touchais, a mature Vouvray and Quarts de Chaume, two Barsacs, Five Putts Tokay, some sweet Alsace and Muscat de Beaumes de Venise at £1.80 per glass. House French £8. CELLARMAN'S CHOICE: Brown Bros Family Reserve Chardonnay '85, £12; Bandol '81, £10.50.

CHEFS/PROPRIETORS: Dick and Kay Smith
OPEN: all week, D only
CLOSED: Nov to mid-May
MEALS: 7 to 8.30
PRICES: Set D £18.50 (£25)
SEATS: 26. Private parties: 20 main room. Car-park, 17 places. Children's helpings. Wheelchair access
ACCOMMODATION: 13 rooms, 11 with bath/shower. Rooms for disabled. B&B £24 to £42. Deposit: £25. Baby facilities. Pets welcome. TV. Doors close at 12. Confirm by 7 [GHG]

WINDERMERE Cumbria map 7

▲ *Miller Howe* [15/20]

10 YEARS

Rayrigg Road, Windermere LA23 1EY
WINDERMERE (096 62) 2536
on A592 between Windermere and Bowness £30

All change and no change. The last year saw John Tovey set up his fourth venture, launch two more cookery books and yet the *grande dame* Miller Howe carries on in the same vein and standard, much appreciated by many over many years. Galton Blackiston steps up to fill the shoes previously worn by Robert Lyons, now at the Bay Horse, Ulverston and before that Tom Peter, now at Uplands, Cartmel (see entries). He has served nine years' apprenticeship with all three men and is an able standard-bearer for the cuisine in its full colours of five-course dinners – starter, soup, fish, meat with seven vegetables, and finally a choice of eight or nine sweets. The sense of *son et lumière* becomes more noticeable, perhaps, as Miller Howe becomes even more widely known and the expectations more stereotyped. The back view of the house, with terrace and a garden down to the lake, is the most photographed, but from the road the aspect is of an Edwardian residence in a suburban street. The antique shop inside offers a third atmosphere of lavish, successful clutter. Some consider the cooking over-fussy and complex, lacking sophistication – 'the word cacophony springs to mind' – and specifically criticise fish dishes as insipid, but it is above all resilient, and rarely loses sight of the biggest truth, that good food is about taste not visuals. Other says that such indivuduality is worth 16/20. It is in vegetable cookery that the style is most advanced and although widely followed, still in the forefront of combinations for soups, and for variety: grated courgette with orange; purée of white turnip. Salads with up to 30 types of vegetation are 'stupendous', for instance. New versions include marinated seafood salad and one of buttered herb eggs and deep-fried leeks with garlic and bacon. The sheer breadth of the palette of ingredients gives meals a sense of variety, even where there is little actual choice. The menu finally relents and offers an array of sweets like chocolate and orange slice with curaçao, or orange syrup sponge pudding with vanilla custard. The Saturday-night double sitting is a crush. Breakfast and afternoon tea demonstrate a determination to maintain standards. The former might take in fresh figs followed by a platter of egg, bacon, Cumberland sausage, mushrooms, tomato, black pudding, kidney, and apple ring, accompanied by home-made rolls, toast and home-made marmalade. 'A good foundation for the day.' Tea is described by another reporter as, 'a delightful combination of crockery, elegant napkins and silver teapot, with a fragrant mixture of teas. Sandwiches, cakes, buttered loaf, scones with cream and jam are all freshly produced.' Residential cookery courses are held in the spring and autumn. Wines start at £8.50 and concentrate on the New World. Menus come with a suggestion for the evening, which is worth following.

CHEF: Galton Blackiston PROPRIETOR: John J. Tovey
OPEN: all week, D only
CLOSED: Dec to Feb
MEALS: 8.30 (7 and 9.30 Sat)
PRICES: Set D £22 (£30). Service 12.5%
CARDS: Access, Amex, Diners, Visa
SEATS: 70. Private parties: 30 main room. Car-park, 40 places. Vegetarian meals. No children under 12. Smart dress preferred. No smoking in dining-room. Wheelchair access. Music. Air-conditioned. One sitting (2 Sat)
ACCOMMODATION: 13 rooms, all with bath/shower. B&B £55 to £110. No children under 12. Pets welcome. Afternoon teas. Garden. Scenic. Doors close at 11. Confirm by 10 [GHG]

Miller Howe Kaff [9/20]

Lakeland Plastics, Station Precinct, Windermere LA23 1BQ
WINDERMERE (096 62) 6571 £8

This little sprig of the Miller Howe tree is actually found in the plastics factory – past the station and straight on. It is open through the day offering Miller Howe-style food at cut prices: soup with wholemeal loaf for £1.40; bobotie; Cumberland sausages. Typical might be diced ham, tongue and chicken in a rich cheese sauce served in a choux pastry puff; duck pâté. Main courses come with salads – 'What a salad, it has something like 22 ingredients.' Sweets are fresh puddings, cakes, shortbread slices. Tables are shared. Good coffee. Wine by the glass at £1.25, red or white.

CHEFS: William Tully and Miller Howe kitchen PROPRIETOR: John J. Tovey
OPEN: Mon to Sat, L only
MEALS: 10 to 4
PRICES: £6 (£8)
SEATS: 28. Private parties: 28 main room. Car-park, 60 places. Vegetarian meals. Children welcome. No smoking in dining-room. Wheelchair access. Self-service

Roger's [13/20]

4 High Street, Windermere LA23 1AF
WINDERMERE (096 62) 4954 £21–£22

There have occasionally been mixed reports about Roger's, especially when the Pergl-Wilsons are away, but the consensus is that Lakeland's premier French restaurant has improved over the last two years. The atmosphere is casual, and the orange-lit, dark dining-room adds to this feeling. The cooking is both imaginative and well presented, and uses as much local produce as possible – salmon, char, deer, hare, quail. From further afield are langoustines, served in a herb pancake, and scallops, made into a mousseline. Fish and game predominate – fallow deer braised with wild mushrooms; Windermere char in a sorrel sauce – but there is also fillet steak with béarnaise sauce, or roast rack of lamb. Desserts can be fairly substantial – Norfolk treacle tart; hazelnut meringue with bananas and apricot cream. Cheeses are British. 'My basic idea is not to have too many contradicting flavours; dishes therefore are usually a combination of three or four flavours served without superfluous garnishes.' The French-dominated list of wines stays mostly under £10 and begins with Jolly Good Claret at £5.80.

CHEF: Roger Pergl-Wilson PROPRIETORS: Roger and Alena Pergl-Wilson
OPEN: Mon to Sat D; Tue to Fri L by arrangement
MEALS: 12.30 to 1.30, 7 to 10
PRICES: £13 (£21), Set D £16.50 (£22)
CARDS: Access, Amex, Diners, Visa
SEATS: 42. Private parties: 28 main room; 18 private room. Children's helpings. Wheelchair access. Music

Cumbria Round-up

VEGETARIAN: *Zeffirelli's*, Compston Road, Ambleside (0966 33845); *Hedgerow*, Lake Road, Bowness-on-Windermere (096 62 5002); *Harvest Vegetarian*, Compston Road, Ambleside (0966 33151); *Rowan Tree*, Grasmere (096 65 528).
GREEK: *Nissi Taverna*, Lake Road, Bowness-on-Windermere (0966 25055).
AFTERNOON TEA: *Grandy Nook Tea Room*, Vicarage Lane, Hawkshead (096 66 404); *St Mary's Lodge*, Cartmel, Grange-over-Sands (044 33151); *Wild Strawberry Tea Room and Gallery*, 52-54 Main Street Keswick (07687 74399).
COFFEE SHOP: *Wythop Mill*, Embleton, Cockermouth (059 681 394).
SETTING AND ROOMS: *Greenriggs Country House*, Underbarrow (044 88 387); *Wateredge Hotel*, Borrans Road, Ambleside (0966 32332).
VIEW AND BAR MEALS : *Drunken Duck Inn*, Barngates, Ambleside (096 66 347).
ROOMS: *Lovelady Shield*, Alston (0498 81203).
BAR MEALS: *Dog and Gun*, Keswick (0596 73463).
ENGLISH: *Water Yeat Country Guest House*, Water Yeat (022 985 306).

WINTERINGHAM Humberside map 6

▲ *Winteringham Fields* [new entry, zero rated]

Winteringham, DN15 9PF
SCUNTHORPE (0724) 733096 £13–£25

Well sited for both North and South Humberside, being just 10 miles from Scunthorpe and 9 from Hull over the Humber Bridge. The Schwabs have spent nearly a year doing up this sixteenth-century farmhouse and done it very well, too. It offers more scope and a better position than their previous place, Beck Farm at Wilberfoss, and also has the prospect of financial security with its bedrooms. The cooking also seems to have come back with renewed confidence. The menu is sensibly short, but deals in some lavish produce which puts it squarely towards the front of modern cooking. Foie gras is served in a fine armagnac sauce sweetened with preserved lemon and melon, a great dish let down only by the enormous, clumsy pieces of toast. But at the same time a humble soup like leek and potato decorated with coriander has been first class. Sauces are classical, so too perhaps the ideas of luxury – a champagne sauce for halibut; strudel of sea-trout and monk with spinach and raisins in a white wine sauce, which reminds of Mr Schwab's hotel background in Switzerland. There is no fear of the spontaneous, as in a summer sweet of raspberries, blackberries with home-made vanilla ice-cream smothered in more champagne. There is a wide choice of cheeses. The wine list has also developed from the early days, still lacks some detail, but has good representation from the major French regions. House French is £6.25. More reports, please.

CHEF: Germain Schwab and Christian Sirurguet PROPRIETORS: Annic and Germain Schwab
OPEN: Mon to Sat, exc Mon and Sat L
CLOSED: 3 weeks from mid-Jan
MEALS: 11.30 to 2.30, 7 to 10
PRICES: £20 (£25), Set L £10 (£13), Set D £19 (£22). Service inc
CARDS: Access, Visa
SEATS: 40. Private parties: 14 main room, 10 private room. Car-park, 16 places. Children welcome. Smart dress preferred. Wheelchair access (1 step; also WC). Music. Air-conditioned.
ACCOMMODATION: 4 rooms, all with bath/shower. B&B £40 to £55. No children under 12. Pets welcome. Afternoon teas. Garden. TV. Phone. Scenic. Doors close at 1. Confirm by 9

WISBECH Cambridgeshire — map 5

▲ *Rose and Crown* [13/20]

Market Place, Wisbech PE13 1DG
WISBECH (0945) 583187 — £17–£23

The age of this market-square hotel is plain from the listing staircase and creaking floorboards. 'London standard' is the unanimous verdict for the smartly decorated first-floor restaurant. Portions have increased in size and there is a sweets trolley, compared to the days John Martin and David Owen were at Tourment d'Amour in Covent Garden. The cut is otherwise very fashionable: black hexagonal plates for the shrimp salad; fine game dishes such as hare, or roast mallard with its juices glazed with brandy; a wide variety of vegetables and also fish. Typical of the cooking might be a chicken mousse inside a puff pastry parcel served with a madeira sauce. Cheeses are French, from Philippe Olivier; sweets are ever richer. 'Surprising and welcome.' Service is polite and the pace of meals leisured. There are good wines on a list arranged simply by price from £7.50 to £65 but with a smattering of half-bottles and a commendable showing from the New World, including the evocatively named Australian, Dead Man's Hill Gewürztraminer '86, £14. For dessert, choose from one of six sweet wines: Ch. Terrefort '83 is £10 on a classical Bordeaux and Burgundy list. Real ales, too.

CHEFS/PROPRIETORS: John Martin and David Owen
OPEN: Mon to Sat
MEALS: 12.30 to 2, 7.30 to 10
PRICES: £16 (£23), Set L and D £12 (£17), Snacks from £2
CARDS: Access, Amex, Diners, Visa
SEATS: 60. Private parties: 14 main room, 20, 60 and 100 private rooms. Car-park, 10 places. Vegetarian meals. Children's helpings. Smart dress preferred. Music
ACCOMMODATION: 21 rooms, 17 with bath/shower. B&B £26 to £34. Children welcome. Pets welcome. Afternoon teas. TV. Phone. Doors close at 12. Confirm by 6 [GHG]

WITHERSLACK Cumbria map 7

▲ *Old Vicarage* [14/20]

Witherslack LA11 6RS
WITHERSLACK (044 852) 381
off A590  £24

On the outskirts of a village that hugs the side of a very wide valley – follow the signs to the church. This has been an increasingly well-supported entry in recent years. Some argue that the rating is high, others low, which may suggest an underlying fluctuation of standards in the formula, but the consensus is strongly in favour. The running is shared by two couples, the Burrington-Browns and the Reeves. They follow the Lakeland style of set menu with no choice, except to finish. A characteristically successful March meal comprised a grainy hazelnut roulade set off by a smooth herb, smoked salmon and cream cheese filling; a concentrated soup of tomato and basil; roast Gressingham duck with Morello cherry sauce, served with roast potatoes, celeriac and watercress purée, glazed carrots with pine nuts, broccoli and courgettes; pancakes with lemon and orange curaçao; local cheeses. The pancakes were out of keeping because usually the choice is between two traditional puddings. The excellent wine list is very strong on France, with a smattering of well-chosen wines from Spain (largely Torres), Italy, Germany, Australia, Chile, California and elsewhere. Tempting estate-bottled Burgundies start with an affordable Bourgogne Rouge Domaine de la Combe '85, from Michel Lafarge, £9.95. Clarets range from basics through some good *crus bourgeois* to mature vintages of a few top wines. There are serious Rhônes and some excellent value in the selection of wines from the South of France. House claret is £8.25; CELLARMAN'S CHOICE: Chardonnay, Venegazzù '86, Loredan Gasperini, £8.25, and St Emilion, Ch. de Belcier '83, £9.55.

CHEFS/PROPRIETORS: Roger and Jill Burrington-Brown, Irene and Stanley Reeve
OPEN: all week, D only
CLOSED: 1 week at Christmas
MEALS: 7.30
PRICES: Set D £17.50 (£24)
CARDS: Access, Amex, Diners, Visa
SEATS: 40. Private parties: 25 main room, 12 private room. Car-park, 18 places. Vegetarian meals. Children's helpings. No smoking. Music. One sitting
ACCOMMODATION: 8 rooms, all with bath/shower. B&B £35 to £54. No children under 10. Pets welcome. Garden. TV. Phone. Scenic. Doors close at 12 [GHG]

WOBURN Bedfordshire map 3

Paris House [14/20]

Woburn MK17 9QP
WOBURN (0525) 290692 £20–£32

The setting is everything at this folly isolated in the grounds of the Abbey and approached via its own stone arched entrance. Leave the M1 at exit 13, follow signs to Woburn village, turn left up the High Street, carry straight on and follow the A4012 out of the village for almost 2 miles. Entrance gates are on the left-hand side. Peter Chandler cooks as if to a Roux brothers' text-book; he stays faithful to the teachings of his mentors. Lunch and dinner are set pieces offering perhaps 11 dishes in total, from coq au vin to cassolette de fruits de mer to impeccable raspberry soufflé. Trademarks are the intense stocks, the extravagant garnishes, the free hand with butter and cream – which can make meals overly rich – and fine pastry work. Individual recommendations extend to baby turnips and a deep meat glaze; pork with a cream sauce flavoured with apricot; guinea-fowl with a brandy and cream sauce. The tartan wallpaper and hunting trophies lend a Christmas feel to the décor. House red and white from Duboeuf £8. CELLARMAN'S CHOICE: Pinot Blanc d'Alsace '86 £12.50; St Aubin, Les Argilliers '85, £19.

CHEF/PROPRIETOR: Peter Chandler
OPEN: Tue to Sun, exc Sun D
CLOSED: Feb
MEALS: 12.30 to 2.30 (12 to 2 Sun), 7 to 10
PRICES: Set L £13.50 (£20) to £19.50 (£26), Set D £19.50 (£26) to £25 (£32)
CARDS: Access, Amex, Diners, Visa
SEATS: 45. 3 tables outside. Private parties: 14 main room, 14 private room. Car park, 20 places. Vegetarian meals. Children welcome. Smart dress preferred

WOODBRIDGE Suffolk map 3

Wine Bar [10/20]

17 Thoroughfare, Woodbridge IP12 1AA
WOODBRIDGE (039 43) 2557 £13

The setting may be modest – a colourfully decorated wine bar above a provisions shop – but Sally O'Gorman's cooking goes from strength to strength. All the more remarkable because she works in the confines of a small domestic kitchen lined with bottles of herbs and pickles. She cooks to order, changes her menu each week and combines modern imaginative ideas with robust peasant dishes; this translates into fresh pasta with smoked halibut and citrus juice, confit of duck leg with quince butter sauce, or rolled loin of lamb stuffed with leeks and shallot accompanied by spiced lentils and mushrooms. There is a strong vegetarian presence: walnut roulade filled with mustard and cream cheese is two contrasting slices – one brown, one white – accompanied by pickled walnuts. Sweets are exotic home-made ice-creams, perhaps orange, cardamom and Cointreau, or fruit tarts. The value for money is exceptional and the wine list has plenty of interesting drinking for well under £10; a Cruover machine provides good wines by the glass. House French £5.

CHEF: Sally O'Gorman PROPRIETORS: Sally O'Gorman and Richard Lane
OPEN: Tue to Sat
CLOSED: 25 and 26 Dec
MEALS: 12 to 2, 7 to 10
PRICES: £9 (£13)
SEATS: 50. Vegetarian meals. No children under 14. Music

WOODSTOCK Oxfordshire map 2

▲ *Feathers Hotel* [10/20]

Market Street, Woodstock OX7 1SX
WOODSTOCK (0993) 812291 £16–£31

In a tourist town of many restaurants, this hotel succeeds with the restrained good taste of its décor and surroundings. The atmosphere is one of polite welcome. The food is 'unfussy *nouvelle*' characterised by fruit and vegetable combinations, but not without a modern tone – an elderflower and apple sorbet in a melon; a fine vegetarian dish of pilau rice with wild mushrooms; good summer pudding. English cheeses. The fifty wines steal some of the thunder with a good range of claret and German wines, madeiras and ports. House Chardonnay £7.95.

CHEF: Sonya Kidney PROPRIETOR: Gordon Campbell-Gray
OPEN: all week
MEALS: 12.30 to 2.15, 7.30 to 9.45
PRICES: £23 (£31), Set L £10.50 (£16) to £12.50 (£18), Set D £18.50 (£25), Snacks from £1.75, L only
CARDS: Access, Amex, Diners, Visa
SEATS: 40. Private parties: 36 main room, 40 private room. Children's helpings. No cigars/pipes in dining-room. Wheelchair access (also Gents WC). Music
ACCOMMODATION: 15 rooms, 13 with bath/shower. B&B £40 to £68. Children welcome. Baby facilities. Dogs welcome. Afternoon teas. Garden. TV. Phone [GHG]

WOOLER Northumberland map 7

▲ *Ryecroft Hotel* [10/20]

Wooler NE71 6AB
WOOLER (0668) 81459 £10–£16

The good value draws uncommon enthusiasm from readers for this small, unpretentious hotel with real ales. The McKechnies keep to a short, conservative, daily menu – four starters, two soups, three main courses –on the lines of avocado with crab; fennel soup; Loch Fyne salmon (in a 'kilt' of sliced courgette); leg of lamb with butter and herbs. The beers are Clark's and Lorimer's and the 20-strong wine list is pegged mostly under £10.

CHEFS: Pat McKechnie and Michael Ord PROPRIETORS: Pat and David McKechnie
OPEN: Wed to Sat D, and Sun L
CLOSED: first 2 weeks Nov, 24 Dec to 1 Jan
MEALS: 12.30 to 1.30, 7 to 8.30
PRICES: Set Sun L £6 (£10), Set D £12 (£16)
CARDS: Access, Visa
SEATS: 50. Private parties: 30 main room; 20 private room. Car-park, 20 places. Vegetarian meals. Children's helpings. No smoking in dining-room
ACCOMMODATION: 11 rooms. B&B £18.50 to £36. Deposit: £5. Children welcome. Baby facilities. Pets welcome. Afternoon teas. Garden. Scenic. Doors close at 12. Confirm by 6 [GHG]

WOOLHOPE Hereford & Worcester map 2

▲ *Butchers Arms* [10/20]

Woolhope HR1 4RF
FOWNHOPE (043 277) 281
off B4224, 7m SE of Hereford £16

An attractive black and white pub half a mile from the centre of Woolhope in the Ledbury direction, overlooking cornfields and a stream. Mary Bailey is in charge of the kitchen and produces meals that rise a notch above good home cooking. Wood-pigeon with chocolate, salmon with rosemary, vegetarian mushroom biriani with dhal, and quail egg salad with celery mayonnaise are the range. Rich, handsome puddings have a chocolatey bias. Twenty wines include two English bottles and house French at £5.35. Alternatively, drink Hook Norton's Old Hooky, Marston's Pedigree, or Weston's Stowford Press cider.

CHEF: Mary Bailey PROPRIETORS: Mary Bailey and Bill Griffiths
OPEN: Wed to Sat D, Bar L and D all week
MEALS: 11.30 to 2.15, 7 to 9 (10 Bar D)
PRICES: £11 (£16), Snacks from £1.55
SEATS: 70 bar, 26 dining-room. 7 tables outside. Private parties: 26 main room. Car-park, 80 places. Vegetarian meals. No children under 14. No cigars/pipes in dining-room. Music
ACCOMMODATION: 3 rooms. B&B £19.50 to £31. TV. Scenic. Doors close at 11.30 [GHG]

WORCESTER Hereford & Worcester map 2

Brown's [12/20]

24 Quay Street, Worcester WR1 2JN
WORCESTER (0905) 26263 £21–£26

This converted corn-mill stands on the bank of the Severn with only the large logo lettering interrupting the original brickwork. Inside is a curious mix of original, rather Spartan surroundings, with whitewashed brick pillars and a modern high-tech mirror on two walls creating an illusion of width, and reinforcing the colours of the still-lifes of flowers and fruit, and the myriad climbing plants. A superb arched window looks over the terrace to the river.

A changing set-price menu offers five dishes at each course. Like the décor, the cooking mixes older techniques, such as chicken quenelles as a main course, with a healthy modern British cosmopolitanism of risotto, smoked fish or panaché of veal fillet, kidney, and sweetbread. Cheeses take in British and European. All is picturesque, as in the three slices of cold rare beef served with an anchovy mayonnaise and a salad of red and green leaves, or a sharp, intense coulis of raspberries to go with its soufflé, or armagnac tart with redcurrants and ground almonds with a neutral crème Chantilly. Many of the vegetables – including some nights as many as 15 different salad ingredients – are locally grown and organic. Also, there is usually a choice of fish dishes of the day. Prices are on the high side but the restaurant's long-standing reputation in the area is a testament to its quality. The 150-strong wine list concentrates on France with token bottles from the New World. House white is £5.95. CELLARMAN'S CHOICE: Fleurie, Domaine de Quatre Vent '86, from Georges Duboeuf, £11.50.

CHEFS: W.R. Tansley and S. Meredith PROPRIETORS: W.R. and P.M. Tansley
OPEN: all week, exc Sat L and Sun D
CLOSED: 1 week at Christmas; bank hols
MEALS: 12.30 to 1.45 (2 Sun), 7.30 to 9.30
PRICES: Set L £15.95 (£21), Set D £20.95 (£26). Service 10%
CARDS: Access, Amex, Diners, Visa
SEATS: 80. Private parties: 80 main room. Vegetarian meals. No children under 10. Wheelchair access (also WC)

Hereford & Worcester Round-up

VEGETARIAN: *Nutters*, Unit 2, Capuchin Yard, Off Church Street, Hereford (0432 277447).
BAR MEALS: *Plough Inn*, Stoke Lacey (088 53 658).
WINE BAR: *Wine Bar*, 24 High Street, Ross-on-Wye (0989 67717); *Applejack Wine Bar*, 44 The Homend, Ledbury (0531 4181).
BRASSERIE: *Fat Tulip*, The Old Wye Bridge, 2 St Martin's Street, Hereford (0432 275808).

WORFIELD Shropshire map 5

▲ *Old Vicarage Hotel* [10/20]

Worfield WV15 5TZ
WORFIELD (074 64) 497 and 498 £15–£24

The converted turn-of-the-century parsonage is up the hill outside the village of Worfield, just off the A442. Peter and Christine Iles have opened up the Edwardian conservatory as a lounge, and added a new private dining-room. Polished antique tables, big wall mirrors and old prints set the style for a menu with English overtones. Terrine of duck comes with damson chutney; lemon sole is poached with lettuce and cucumber sauce; saddle of lamb gets a bacon and parsley stuffing and onion sauce. Other details are in keeping – home-made herb bread, tureens of vegetables left on the table, English cheeses. More than a hundred wines, dominated by the French contingent, including house wines at £7.25.

CHEF: Raymond Williamson PROPRIETORS: Peter and Christine Iles
OPEN: all week D, L by arrangment
CLOSED: 2 weeks at Christmas
MEALS: 12.30 to 2, 7 to 9
PRICES: Set L £10.95 (£15) to £12.95 (£17), Set D £18.50 (£23) to £19.50 (£24), Snacks from £1.95. Service inc
CARDS: Access, Amex, Diners, Visa
SEATS: 40. Private parties: 50 main room, 15 private room. Car-park, 30 places. Vegetarian meals. Children's helpings. No children under 10. No smoking in dining-room. Wheelchair access (1 step; also WC). Music
ACCOMMODATION: 10 rooms, all with bath/shower. B&B £40 to £59.50. Deposit: £40. Baby facilities. Pets welcome. Afternoon teas. Garden. TV. Phone. Scenic. Doors close at 11 [GHG]

Shropshire Round-up

INDIAN: *Old Colonial*, 3 Bridge Street, Low Town, Bridgnorth (074 62 766510).
VEGETARIAN: *Good Life*, Barracks Passage, Wyle Cop, Shrewsbury (0743 50455).
BAR MEALS: *Sun Inn*, Clun (058 84 277/599); *Delanys*, St Julians Craft Centre, St Alkmonds Square, Shrewsbury (0743 60602); *Unicorn (Delanys II)*, Wyle Cop, Shrewsbury (0743 66890).
WINE BAR: *Corn House*, 59a Wyle Cop, Shrewsbury (0743 241991); *Good Companion Wine Bar*, 10 Beatrice Street, Oswestry (0691 655768).
MIDDLE EASTERN VEGETARIAN: *Acorn*, 26 Sandford Avenue, Church Stretton (0694 722495).

WRIGHTINGTON Lancashire map 5

High Moor [12/20]

High Moor Lane, Wrightington WN6 9PS
APPLEY BRIDGE (025 75) 2364 £13–£26

The restaurateuring is writ large in John Nelson's seventeenth-century building in open country. Extravagant italic script adorns the parchment menu and the style of cooking on a *carte* of nine dishes at each course is flamboyant in its combinations, for instance prawn mousse with ginger butter sauce or loin of veal with a mousse of Bramley apples and a sauce of rosemary and Drambuie. Five soups come as a second-course alternative to sorbets and include tomato; mushroom and white onion; potato and leek. These suggest that although the embellishments are modern, the core of the cooking is firmly planted in classical teachings. Meats and sauces are properly executed; pastry is much in evidence. Roasts for Sunday lunch get much support. Sweets vary from the traditional bread-and-butter or trifle to the extraordinary as in chocolate and crème de menthe pagoda. House French is £7.50; CELLARMAN'S CHOICE: Pyrénées Atlantiques '86, £8.95; Vin de Pays des Collines de la Moure '83, £9.50.

If, in your opinion, a restaurant is not maintaining the standard of its rating, please inform the Guide *office. Report forms are at the back of the book.*

CHEF: James Sines PROPRIETOR: John Nelson
OPEN: Tue to Sun, exc Sat L and Sun D
MEALS: 12 to 2, 7 to 10
PRICES: £19 (£26), Set Sun L £7.95 (£13). Service 10%
CARDS: Access, Amex, Diners, Visa
SEATS: 80. Private parties: 52 main room. Car-park, 35 places. Vegetarian meals. Children welcome. Wheelchair access. Music. Air-conditioned. One sitting

WYLAM Northumberland map 7

Laburnum House [new entry, zero rated]

Wylam NE41 8AJ
WYLAM (0661) 852185 £11–£20

In the main street of the village by the Tyne, opposite the Ship Inn. An L-shaped room has been converted into a dining-room with badger and beaver prints on the walls. The long blackboard menu is built on good steaks and expensive prawn cocktails (£6.50). Crudités, Dover sole in a wine sauce, and brown-bread ice-cream draw good reports. The garlic level is high. The investment is mostly in the food. House French is £5, CELLARMAN'S CHOICE: Fitou '86, £6.50. More reports, please.

CHEF: Kenn Elliott PROPRIETORS: Rowan Mahon and Kenn Elliott
OPEN: Tue to Sat, exc Sat L
MEALS: 12 to 1.45, 6.30 to 10
PRICES: £17 (£20), Set L £8 (£11), Set D £9.50 (£12). Service inc
CARDS: Access, Amex, Diners, Visa
SEATS: 40. Private parties: 40 main room. Children's helpings. Wheelchair access (1 step; also WC). Music

YATTENDON Berkshire map 2

▲ *Royal Oak* [14/20]

The Square, Yattendon RG16 0UF
HERMITAGE (0635) 201325  £33

The fusion of three different elements – country-house hotel, pub, serious restaurant – is uncannily successful at Richard and Kate Smith's converted pub in the centre of the village. Each aspect seems to benefit from the other. It is not dissimilar to a Home Counties version, hence slightly posher, of the Walnut Tree Inn at Llandewi Skirrid (see entry, Wales). The menu changes in at least some detail from day to day, according to supplies. The same kitchen caters for the bar as for the attractive dining-room. It deals confidently in a throughput of fine ingredients – scallops are grilled with asparagus tips and served with a lemon sauce; turbot is served with a sauce of oysters and scallops. Soufflés are a signature: spinach with crab sauce; cheese with wild mushroom sauce; Cointreau with raspberry sauce. The menu in the bar runs to more than 30 dishes, not including sweet, and the restaurant menu is barely shorter, mixing luxuries like foie gras, wild rice and morels with humbler black pudding or smoked cod's roe. The wine list is expensive and almost exclusively French, but it offers some excellent bottles, especially in the Burgundy section, which includes wines from some very fine estates as well as wines from Burgundian merchants and some bottled in Britain by Berry Bros. Sweet wines are scarce: try some expensive young Barsac or Sauternes, or a bottle of Alsace Gewürztraminer Sélection de Grains Nobles '76, from Hugel, £50, or one of two Vendange Tardive – £18.50 or £25. Fortunately, at these prices, you may drink half of certain bottles for a supplement of £1.25 on half the bottle price. House St Emilion and Sylvaner £7.50. CELLARMAN'S CHOICE: Montagny *premier cru* '86, £13.50.

CHEF: Richard Smith PROPRIETORS: Richard and Kate Smith
OPEN: all week (bar menu only, Sun D)
MEALS: 12 to 2, 7.30 to 10
PRICES: £22 (£33)
CARDS: Access, Amex, Visa
SEATS: 30. 10 tables outside. Private parties: 30 main room, 8 private room. Car-park, 35 places. Children's helpings. No cigars/pipes in dining-room. Wheelchair access
ACCOMMODATION: 5 rooms, all with bath/shower. B&B £48. Baby facilities. Pets welcome by prior arrangement. Afternoon teas. Garden. TV. Phone. Scenic. Doors close at 12.30 [GHG]

YORK North Yorkshire map 5

▲ *Middlethorpe Hall* [12/20]

Bishopthorpe Road, York YO2 1QP
YORK (0904) 641241 £12–£29

The building dates from 1699, overlooks the racecourse, has a centuries-old yew dominating the lawns, and inside has a mass of mouldings and decorative plasterwork. Kevin Francksen has stepped up to take over the kitchen. The style is set, almost a blueprint of *nouvelle cuisine* – there is a run of sauces through the menu, on to which exotic luxuries are strategically placed. There is a nagging feeling that this hotel may be embarked on a downward slope. Genteel is how one reporter described the flavours last year. And the same point was made again at this year's inspection. The menu slides into the anonymity of international hotel cooking. But that is not to say there is not good food or skill here and also in the Grill Room, but they do not come automatically – the onus is on the customer to seek out the virtues. Sauces are first class: pan-juices flavoured with orange for sweetbreads in pastry; a buttery beurre blanc for turbot; red wine for grilled fillet of beef with mustard and shallots; tomato and garlic with pan-juices for noisettes of lamb. Lunch is conspicuously good value. Presentation matches the best. The wine list is as good as the surroundings (the rooms are highly decorated), with mark-ups on a scale that makes it wise to check you are not looking at the half-bottles by mistake. There is mitigation at least in its encyclopaedic nature – no fewer than 20 dessert wines, ranging from £2.25 for a glass of Muscat de Rivesaltes to £120 for a bottle of Ch. d'Yquem '75. House Merlot and Muscadet open at £8.50. CELLARMAN'S CHOICE: Morton's Hawkes Bay Chardonnay '86, £13.90; Ch. Les Ormes de Pez '80, £17.85.

CHEF: Kevin Francksen PROPRIETORS: Historic House Hotels Ltd
OPEN: all week
MEALS: 12.30 to 1.45, 7.30 to 9.45
PRICES: £19 (£29), Set L £11.90 (£11.90) to £13.90 (£13.90), Set D £20.50 (£25) to £22.90 (£28). Service inc
CARDS: Access, Amex, Diners, Visa
SEATS: 60. Private parties: 40 main room, 14, 20 and 40 private rooms. Car-park, 70 places. Vegetarian meals. No children under 8. Jacket and tie
ACCOMMODATION: 31 rooms, all with bath/shower. Lift. B&B £77.50 to £110. No children under 8. Afternoon teas. Garden. TV. Phone. Scenic [GHG]

Oat Cuisine [11/20]

13A High Ousegate, York YO1 2RZ
YORK (0904) 627929 £11–£15

For much of last winter Oat Cuisine was advertising for a head chef. Quite why is not clear, as during the same period positive reports came in at regular intervals. We have here a mould-breaking vegetarian restaurant. It is not just a matter of permutating three ratatouilles with brown rice, brown pasta or cheese. The menu is imaginative, almost seductive. 'Not wholefood maybe, but wholly interesting.' Almost everything is made on the premises. But it is the cooking that singles the place out: light mousselines, delicate salad dressings, light, crispy filo, short and crumbly pastries, freshly made pizza doughs, pungent spicy cream sauces. Artichoke, wild mushroom and thyme pizza is a revelation. Spring rolls outclass those of many a Chinese restaurant. The same influence is found on a skewer of spiced vegetables with chow mein and a sauce of thickened soy. Other recommendations include: Parmesan and pear tart ('fantastic'); timbale of aubergine; grilled goats' cheese with walnut sauce; spinach soup with cheese scones. Sweets have been superlative: blackberry, apple and elderflower croustade; English marmalade pudding with vanilla cream, especially. The décor is almost clinically white, unpretentious and café-like, and service veers on the slow side at peak times. A handful of wines include house French at £5.50, and two champagnes (with one available as a half-bottle).

CHEFS: Neil David Harley and George Aitken PROPRIETOR: Louisa Farino
OPEN: Mon to Sat
CLOSED: first week Jan
MEALS: 12 to 3, 7 to 10.30
PRICES: £10 (£15), Set L £7.25 (£11), Set D from £10 (£15). Snacks from £1.45. Minimum £2.50. Service 10%
CARDS: Access, Amex, Visa
SEATS: 56. Private parties: 25 main room. Vegetarian meals. Children's helpings. Wheelchair access (1 step). Music

The Guide *does not accept free meals.*

'The organic food has not been sprayed with chemicals and nor have the waitresses, who have well-scrubbed rosy cheeks.' On eating in Cumbria

Yorkshire Round-up

VIEWS: *Knox Manor*, Low Laithe, Summer Bridge (0423 780473).

COFFEE SHOP: *Betty's*, 1 Parliament Street, Harrogate (0423 64659); *Betty's*, 188 High Street, Northallerton (0609 5154); *Bettys*, St Helen's Square, York (0904 659142); *Three Cranes Coffee Shop*, 248 Great North Road, Woodlands, Doncaster (0302 724221); *Betty's*, 32-34 The Grove, Ilkley (0943 609029); *The Coffee Mill*, 25-31 King Street, Huddersfield (0484 25401).

AFTERNOON TEAS: *Mulberry's*, 5 Bridge Street, Pickering (0751 72337); *Taylors in Stonegate*, 46 Stonegate, York (0904 622865); *Stape Inn*, Stape, Pickering (0751 75477); *Bowesgarth*, Caperby, Nr Aysgarth, Wensleydale (096 93 309); *The Tea Cottage*, Bolton Abbey, Skipton (075 671 495).

WINE BAR: *William & Victoria*, 6 Cold Bath Road, Harrogate (0423 506883); *Sous le Nez*, 19-21 Church Street, Ilkley (0945 600566).

BAR MEALS: *Golden Lion Hotel*, Market Place, Leyburn (0969 22161); *Old Hall*, Threshfield, Grassington (0756 75244); *Crown Inn*, 20 Horbury Road, Wakefield (0924 272495).

FISH AND CHIPS: *Silver Street Fish & Chip Shop*, 22 Silver Street, Whitby (0947 603087); *Brett's Fish Restaurant*, 12-14 North Lane, Headingley, Leeds (0532 755228); *Lane End Fish and Chip Shop*, Staithes Lane, Staithes, Nr. Whitby (0947 840093); *Hanover Fisheries*, 14 Hanover Street, Scarborough (0723 362062); *Dilt's*, 2 Princess Square, Scarborough (0723 372863).

INDIAN: *Shabab*, 1 John Street, Harrogate (0423 500250); *Islamabad*, 61-63 Attercliffe Common, Sheffield (0472 445586); *Khanies*, 124 College Road, Rotherham (0709 563144); *Shabab*, 2 Eastgate, Leeds (0532 468988); *Shabab*, 37-39 New Street, Huddersfield (0484 49514); *Shiraz Sweet House*, 113 Oak Lane, Bradford (0274 490 176).

ENGLISH: *Dusty Miller*, Low Laithe, Summer Bridge, Nr Harrogate (0423 780837); *Roberts*, 60 The Grove, Ilkley (0943 607307).

SETTING: *Ryedale Lodge*, Nunnington (043 95 246).

VEGETARIAN: *Bay Tree*, 19 Devonshire Street, Sheffield (0742 759254); *Pulse*, 10 Cross Square, Wakefield (0924 361755).

CHINESE: *China Rose*, 27 Market Place, Bawtry (0302 710461); *Zing Vaa*, 55 The Moor, Sheffield (0742 722432); *Whan Hai*, 20 New Briggate, Leeds (0532 435019).

INEXPENSIVE: *Toffs*, 23 Matilda Street, The Moor, Sheffield (0742 720783); *City Bar* (Lunch only), City Hall, Barker's Pool, Sheffield (0742 734550); *Theatre*, Crucible Theatre, Norfold Street, Sheffield (0742 750724).

ROOMS: *Charnwood Hotel*, 10 Sharrow Lane, Sheffield (0742 589411); *Wood Hall*, Trip Lane, Linton (0937 62033).

INDONESIAN: *Ashtree/Java*, Wharf Street, Sowerby Bridge (0422 831654).

ITALIAN: *Bella Napoli*, 59 Main Street, Gross Hills, Keighley (0535 32224).

INDIAN VEGETARIAN: *Hansa*, North Street, Leeds (0532 444408).

Scotland

ABERDEEN Grampian map 8

Silver Darling [new entry, zero rated]

GRAMPIAN NEWCOMER OF THE YEAR

Pocra Quay, Footdee, Aberdeen AB2 1DQ
ABERDEEN (0224) 576229 £13–£23

It takes a Frenchman, Didier Dejean, to show Scotland what an asset it has in its fish. Right at the harbour mouth in the old granite, castle-shaped customs house, he cooks a barbecue menu built around the daily catch from one of the world's great fishing ports, plus shellfish from the West Coast and, naturally, salmon. 'Our aim is to bring a taste of Southern France to the North-East of Scotland – sun to snow.' Inside, the restaurant is reminiscent of the French provinces – across the counter is a grille with full view into the clean and tiled kitchen, run like a top hotel kitchen. Recommended dishes have been mussels, both marinière and mouclade; fish soup; feuilleté of seafood; barbecued kebabs of mixed fish and shellfish with a nantaise butter; an oval plate with six poached fillets of different fish. There are four meat alternatives; five sweets or cheese, plus two sweets of the day – such as a fine apple tart served flaming with calvados – alongside ice-cream, sliced fruits and a strawberry coulis. Service is French and professional, with charm. The limited wine list starts at £6.75. More reports, please.

CHEF: Didier Dejean PROPRIETORS: Didier Dejean, Norman Faulks and Catherine Duviau
OPEN: Mon to Sat, exc Sat L
MEALS: 12 to 2, 7 to 10
PRICES: £19 (£23), Set L from £9 (£13). Service inc
CARDS: Access, Amex, Visa
SEATS: 35. Private parties: 35 main room. Car-park. Children welcome. Wheelchair access (1 step; also WC). Music

Grampian Round-up
FISH: *Atlantis*, 16 Bon Accord Crescent, Aberdeen (0224 591403).
AMERICAN: *Henry J Bean*, Windmill Brae, Aberdeen (0224 574134).
CHINESE: *Aberdeen Rendezvous*, George Street, Aberdeen (0224 633610).
ROOMS: *Invery House*, Banchory, Royal Deeside (033 02 4782).

The Guide *is independent, accepts no advertising and survives solely on the number of copies sold.*

ABERFOYLE Central map 8

Braeval Old Mill [11/20]

By Aberfoyle FK8 3UY
ABERFOYLE (087 72) 711
on A81, ½m from Aberfoyle £14–£21

The restored grey stone mill on the edge of the Menteith hills looks out over the golf course. The only reminder of its former use is a glimpse of a water-wheel at one end of the dining-room. Nick and Fiona Nairn have established a strong local following in an area not noted for its value for money. She serves, he cooks a menu that embraces both traditional saddle of venison with port and redcurrant sauce, and more modern dishes, such as sea-trout with warm tomato and fresh basil vinaigrette. Enthusiasm can outstrip technique, but the ideas are interesting. Commonplace ingredients are used imaginatively. Small choux pastry buns are filled with different vegetable purées; a filo pastry basket is loaded with mussels briefly poached in white wine, with bacon, onion and mushroom, with a topping of melted Brie. There is baked lemon tart or French cherry pudding to finish, and a largely French wine list with something for most pockets. House French £4.95. CELLARMAN'S CHOICE: Savennières, Clos du Papillon '86, £8.95; Seppelt Chardonnay '86, from Australia, £8.95; Côtes du Rhône, Domaine de la Renjordière '86, £5.95.

CHEF: Nick Nairn PROPRIETORS: Nick and Fiona Nairn
OPEN: Tue to Sun D, and Sun L
CLOSED: 3 weeks Jan to Feb, 1 week May, 1 week Nov
MEALS: 12 to 2, 7 to 9.30
PRICES: £15 (£21), Set Sun L £9.50 (£14)
CARDS: Access, Amex, Visa
SEATS: 34. Private parties: 34 main room. Car-park, 16 places. Children's helpings by arrangement, D only. No children under 10. Smart dress preferred. Wheelchair access (1 step; also WC). Music

Central Round-up
ROOMS: *Broughton's*, Blair Drummond (0786 841897); *Roman Camp Hotel*, off Main Street, East End, Callander (0877 30003).
REAL ALE: *Myrtle Inn*, Stirling Road, Callander (0877 30919).
INEXPENSIVE: *Clifton Coffee House*, Tyndrum (08384 271).

ACHILTIBUIE Highland map 8

▲ *Summer Isles Hotel* [11/20]

10 YEARS

Achiltibuie IV26 2YG
ACHILTIBUIE (085 482) 282  £23

'An hotel is often best judged by its breakfast as this is an area which may easily be disregarded,' writes Geraldine Irvine. In her case this amounts to fresh orange juice; hot cinnamon or wholewheat rolls; porridge with fresh cream; grills; sausages from Inverness; new-laid eggs collected each morning;

kippers; bread and marmalade. The rooms have been upgraded (garish patterns replaced by floral prints), but at heart this remote hotel remains a monument to real food, and the freshness of the ingredients sets it apart. Dinners are five courses without choice and invariably open with a vegetable and herb soup. Second course is usually fish – white and dark meat of crab with lemon mayonnaise, or smoked salmon and dill terrine but always offset by a small salad: broccoli, cauliflower and radicchio with hazelnut oil; courgette and dill with Gruyère; butter bean and mange-tout; tomato, melon and basil; shredded spinach, pear and lardons; cucumber and strawberry; sorrel, lettuce, spinach, basil and endive; watercress and orange. The main dish is a roast meat, cheeses include local ewes' and mature Cheddar with home-baked oatcakes, while the sweets trolley is a parade-ground of Pavlovas, flans, layer-cakes piled high with summer fruits, pies and tarts. Another attraction is the range of vintage clarets, with plenty from the '70s, but there are also some younger Burgundies and a sensible representation from across the rest of the winemaking world. House Burgundy is £5.50. CELLARMAN'S CHOICE: Los Vascos '84, a Cabernet Sauvignon from Chile, £8; Pouilly Fumé, Les Griottes '85, £12.50.

CHEF: Chris Firth-Bernard PROPRIETORS: Mark and Geraldine Irvine
OPEN: all week, D only
CLOSED: mid-Oct to Easter
MEALS: 8
PRICES: Set D £20 (£23). Service inc
SEATS: 28. Private parties: 8 main room. Car-park, 24 places. Vegetarian meals. No children under 8. No smoking in dining-room. One sitting
ACCOMMODATION: 13 rooms, 12 with bath/shower. B&B £30 to £58. Deposit: £30. No children under 8. Pets welcome. Afternoon teas. Fishing. Scenic. Doors close at 10.30. Confirm by 6 [GHG]

ANSTRUTHER Fife map 8

Cellar [13/20]

24 East Green, Anstruther KY10 3AA
ANSTRUTHER (0333) 310378 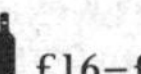 £16–£27

Behind the information kiosk at the end of the harbour. The bare flagstones are laid out with Spanish-style dining chairs and Singer sewing-machine tables. It's an olde-worlde atmosphere but the Jukes' reputation for serving fine fish draws diners from far afield. The catch of local flat fish – halibut, turbot, sole, brill – is usually pan-fried and served with the pan juices thickened with butter and herbs as sauce. Monkfish is roasted with dry cider. Bisques are varied and excellent. And there is cleverness too: a starter of an orange grapefruit terrine with melon and Gewürztraminer ices, or a good haddock stuffed with crab, baked in pastry and served with a shellfish and tomato sauce. To finish there are meringues or ice-cream and hot chocolate sauce. Out of season there is a good value £10.95 menu in the week. The wine list is very good, concentrating on France, with a few good Australian, Californian and New Zealand wines, and New World Chardonnays a special feature. Alsace bottles are particularly good, including wines from Faller and Schlumberger, several '76s (a great year) and several Vendange Tardive wines and a Sélection de Grains Nobles. There's some exciting Burgundy from growers such as Comtes Lafon, Leflaive, Voarick and Vincent, as well as some merchant wines. The claret list is much shorter – some middle-range wines of vintages in the late '70s and early '80s. Dessert wines are sensibly assembled at the end of the list: Australian Brown Bros Late Picked Muscat, £1.95 per glass, a German Beerenauslese '83, an Alsace Sélection de Grains Nobles '86, half-bottles of Jaboulet's Muscat de Beaumes de Venise at £7.95, Australian Sauternes-taste-alike Semillon Noble Late Harvest Botrytis '83, from De Bortoli, £14. House wines from £7.25.

CHEF: Peter Jukes PROPRIETORS: Peter and Vivien Jukes
OPEN: Tue to Sat, exc Sat L
CLOSED: 1 week Christmas and New Year
MEALS: 12.30 to 1.30, 7 to 9.30
PRICES: £10 (£16), Set D £15 (£21) to £21 (£27)
CARDS: Access, Amex, Visa
SEATS: 32. Private parties: 32 main room. Vegetarian meals (by arrangement). Children's helpings (L only). No cigars/pipes in dining-room. Wheelchair access (also WC). Music

APPIN Strathclyde map 8

▲ *Stewart Hotel* [new entry, zero rated]

Glen Duror, Appin, PA38 4BW
APPIN (063 174) 268 £26

A relatively new venture set in five acres overlooking Loch Linnhe and the Morvern Hills. The hotel is family owned and there has been investment in the kitchen. Wayne Smith's menus are visual, with an emphasis on fish and modern presentation, delivered silver service in a Regency-style dining-room. Some combinations are striking: oysters served warm on pastry with a raspberry sauce; lobster with Angostura bitters. Terrines have been exact – quail for instance, with a Cumberland sauce – and soups make use of the seasonal produce, such as marrow. In the autumn there is grouse. The strawberry flambé is prepared at table in a copper pan with sugar, butter and a choice of liqueurs. Cona coffee comes with candied orange peels and commercial mints. Thirty wines. House wine from Provence is £6.80. CELLARMAN'S CHOICE: St Emilion, Ch. Larmande '83, £16. More reports, please.

CHEF: Wayne Smith PROPRIETORS: Dennis and Michael Lacy
OPEN: all week, D only
CLOSED: Nov 6 to end Mar, exc Christmas and 31 Dec
MEALS: 7.30 to 9.30
PRICES: Set D £20 (£26), Snacks from £2.50
CARDS: Access, Amex, Diners, Visa
SEATS: 32. 10 tables outside. Private parties: 50 main room. Car-park, 40 places. Vegetarian meals. Children's helpings on request. No children under 7. Smart dress preferred. No smoking. Wheelchair access (1 step; also WC). Music
ACCOMMODATION: 20 rooms, all with bath/shower. B&B £35 to £60. Deposit: 20%. Children welcome. Baby facilities. Dogs welcome. Afternoon teas. Garden. Sauna. Fishing. Clay-pigeon shooting. TV. Phone. Scenic

ARISAIG Highland map 8

▲ *Arisaig Hotel* [10/20]

Arisaig PH39 4NH
ARISAIG (068 75) 210 and 240 £7–£20

The Stewarts run this large converted coaching-inn with an emphasis on fish: Arisaig king prawns, Mallaig sole and plaice, locally smoked salmon. Deep-frying and grilling are the normal treatments. Sirloin and gammon steaks are simply dealt with, although there are excursions into Scotch fancy, such as beef olives with haggis stuffing or venison with redcurrant gravy. Bedrooms and bathrooms have been refurbished. Some 40 wines, reasonably priced. House Chablis £6.35 per litre carafe; CELLARMAN'S CHOICE: Orlando Cabernet Sauvignon and Chardonnay, £7.25 each.

CHEFS: Janice and Gordon Stewart PROPRIETORS: Mr and Mrs George Stewart and Gordon Stewart
OPEN: all week
CLOSED: Nov and Feb
MEALS: 12.30 to 2, 7.30 to 8.30
PRICES: Set D £15.50 (£20), L and D snacks from £3 (£7)
SEATS: 50. Private parties: 12 main room. Car-park, 60 places. Vegetarian meals. Children's helpings
ACCOMMODATION: 15 rooms, 6 with bath/shower. B&B £23.50 to £45. Baby facilities. Pets welcome. Afternoon teas. Fishing. Phone. Scenic [GHG]

AUCHMITHIE Tayside map 8

But 'n' Ben [12/20]

Auchmithie, by Arbroath DD11 5SQ
ARBROATH (0241) 77223
3m NE of Arbroath, off A92 £6–£17

Perched above the cliffs of Auchmithie, from where the original Arbroath smokie was developed, is this quite admirable unpretentious café-cum-restaurant. For all the pomp and grandeur of more expensive restaurants, at heart the But 'n' Ben has more to say about cooking and Scottish food than any for a long way. Three meals, lunch, high tea and dinner are spread through the day. 'The women are wearing home-made aprons. They bring a table out of the kitchen to put the cakes on for afternoon tea, laying a cloth just like grandmother had.' The cooking is traditional Scottish, with hearty soups and home baking, plainly served high quality meats and fish. Smokies are served hot and buttered; a fry of bacon, egg and sausage uses meat from free-range Kiwie pigs; steaks are Aberdeen Angus. There is often lobster, towering over the other prices at £12.50 – crab is a third of the price. An extension is on the way for an extra 20 covers. Fourteen wines from house claret at £5.50. CELLARMAN'S CHOICE: Mâcon-Lugny, Les Charmes '85, £9.70.

Files are kept on every restaurant, so reports of poor meals are just as valuable as reports of good meals because they save unnecessary inspections.

CHEFS: Margaret and Angus Horn PROPRIETORS: Margaret, Iain and Angus Horn
OPEN: all week, exc Tue and Sun
MEALS: 12 to 2.30, 4 to 6, 7.30 to 9.30
PRICES: L £3 (£6), D £12 (£17)
SEATS: 34. 2 tables outside. Private parties: 34 main room. Car-park, 10 places. Vegetarian meals. Children's helpings. Wheelchair access (also WC)

AUCHTERARDER Tayside map 8

▲ *Auchterarder House* [10/20]

Auchterarder PH3 1DZ
AUCHTERARDER (076 46) 2939 and 3646
on B8062, NE of Auchterarder £18–£43

A modernised Jacobean-style baronial building in red sandstone amid 14 acres. Ingredients can be flashy – lobster for a mousseline, salad of foie gras and truffles – but they underpin a sound Scottish menu of mussel soup, roast grouse, and saddle of venison with sweet-and-sour cranberry sauce. Each dish has a recommended wine – Australian Shiraz with snail casserole, California Chardonnay with poached salmon. The largely French list ranges from minor clarets under £10 to '84 white Burgundy at £60.

CHEF: Paul Brown PROPRIETORS: Mr and Mrs Ian Brown
OPEN: all week
MEALS: times by arrangement
PRICES: Set L £12.50 (£18) to £25 (£32), Set D £15.50 (£21) to £35 (£43)
CARDS: Access, Amex, Carte Blanche, Diners, Visa
SEATS: 25. Private parties: 60 main room. Car-park, 40 places. Vegetarian meals. No children under 12. Jacket and tie. No smoking in dining-room. Wheelchair access
ACCOMMODATION: 11 rooms, all with bath/shower. Rooms for disabled. B&B £70 to £120. Deposit: one night's stay. Afternoon teas. Garden. Fishing. TV. Phone. Scenic

---

AYR Strathclyde map 8

Fouter's Bistro [10/20]

2A Academy Street, Ayr KA7 1XE
AYR (0292) 261391 £18

After 15 years, the Blacks' basement bistro carved out of the old bank vaults is taking on a new lease of life. Fish is from the harbour five minutes' walk from the restaurant and it features strongly on a menu with largely Scottish produce but French and Italian leanings: moules marinière, grilled sea-trout with lemon, Dover sole meunière and home-made pasta with seafood and provençal sauce have all been good. There are home-made pâtés and unusual vegetarian dishes, like devilled mushroom tart, too. Local Ayrshire spring lamb cutlets are pan fried with fresh orange, orange-blossom honey and butter sauce. Sweets include home-made ice-creams. Lunches and weekday suppers are good value. House wines begin at £6.95.

All letters to the Guide *are acknowledged.*

CHEF: Andrew Gilligan PROPRIETORS: Laurie and Fran Black
OPEN: Tue to Sun, exc Sun L
CLOSED: 25 to 27 Dec, 1 to 3 Jan
MEALS: 12 to 2, 6.30 to 10.30 (10 Sun)
PRICES: £13 (£18), Snacks from £2.15
SEATS: 39. Private parties: 39 main room. Vegetarian meals. Children's helpings. No-smoking area. Music. Air-conditioned

BALLATER Grampian map 8

▲ *The Oaks, Craigendarroch Hotel and Country Club* [13/20]

Braemar Road, Ballater AB3 5XA
BALLATER (0338) 55858
1m W of Ballater on A93 £23–£33

A time-share country club halfway between Aberdeen and the Cairngorms might seem an unlikely place to find one of Scotland's top half-dozen restaurants, but Bill Gibb is a home-grown rising star who puts the emphasis firmly on local produce, and who has enough talent and ingenuity to overcome any winter wobbles in his supplies. A classical background, which gives depth to sauces reduced from clarified stocks, is put at the service of a contemporary style that lightens and sharpens with last-minute additions. This creates a tension which lasts throughout a meal: four courses (with two choices) plus a water-ice. A spoon-sized rugby-ball of smooth, farmyardy chicken parfait is paired with apple and celeriac bound together with yoghurty crème fraîche. A trademark is two meats on the same plate, each with its own sauce. A hollow tube of veal is stuffed with an eggy mix of apricot and lightly crushed pistachio, thinly sliced onto a dark sauce of beef stock enriched with curaçao; on the other half of the plate, roast fillet of lamb sits in a sauce of chicken stock with rosemary and tarragon, mounted with butter and crème fraîche. Interest doesn't flag. Chilled beignet soufflé is a sweet poached pear in a light caramel sauce, at the centre of three small, crisply sugared, jamless doughnuts. Lunch is more straightforward with three or four choices at each stage: duck liver parfait salad with Cumberland sauce; lemon sole in filo pastry tart; chocolate bavarois. In the face of all this, the distractions hardly matter: the bar is re-christened a 'study' and lined self-consciously with books; service is squeakily formal; and the wine list, despite some bargains, needs to be better balanced. House French from Justerini & Brooks £7.50, CELLARMAN'S CHOICE: Ch. Giscours '75, £35; Ch. Ruat-Petit-Poujeaux '79, £9.30; Crozes-Hermitage '85, from Jaboulet, £9.75.

Restaurants awarded a rosette have had an entry in every Guide *since 1980. See Restaurants of the decade on page 21.*

CHEF: Bill Gibb PROPRIETORS: Craigendarroch Ltd
OPEN: all week
CLOSED: L 1 Nov to 31 Mar
MEALS: 12.30 to 2, 7.30 to 10
PRICES: £23 (£33), Set L £8.95 (£14), Set D from £12.95 (£18). Minimum at D £22
CARDS: Access, Amex, Diners, Visa
SEATS: 54. Private parties: 12 main room, 120 private room. Car-park, 100 places. No children under 8. Jacket and tie. No smoking. Wheelchair access (also WC)
ACCOMMODATION: 29 rooms, all with bath/shower. Rooms for disabled. Lift. B&B £69 to £80. Baby facilities. Afternoon teas. Garden. Swimming-pool. Sauna. Snooker. Air-conditioning. TV. Phone. Scenic. Confirm by 6 [GHG]

▲ *Green Inn* [11/20]

9 Victoria Road, Ballater AB3 5QQ
BALLATER (0338) 55701 £17

The Hamiltons aim to fill the gap between country-house restaurants and guest-house food. Salmon from the Dee is baked and served with watercress mayonnaise, venison comes with a whisky sauce, and herbs and salad vegetables are from the garden during the summer. Venison is smoked at Rannoch, near Pitlochry. Puddings are traditional, from bread-and-butter or apple and almond, to fruit crumble. Two dozen reasonably priced wines are well chosen and include house French at £5.85 and CELLARMAN'S CHOICE: Brown Bros Cabernet Sauvignon '84, £7.95.

CHEFS: A.C.S. Hamilton and Anne Howden PROPRIETORS: Mr and Mrs A.C.S. Hamilton
OPEN: all week
CLOSED: end Nov to Feb
MEALS: 12.30 to 2, 7 to 9.30
PRICES: £12 (£17), Snacks from £1
SEATS: 30. 2 tables outside. Private parties: 28 main room. Vegetarian meals. Children's helpings. Wheelchair access. Music. Air-conditioned
ACCOMMODATION: 3 rooms, all with bath/shower. B&B £17.50 to £30. Deposit: £10. Children welcome. Baby facilities. Dogs welcome. Afternoon teas. Air-conditioning. TV. Scenic. Doors close at 11.30. Confirm by 5

▲ *Tullich Lodge* [11/20]

Ballater AB3 5SB
BALLATER (0338) 55406
on A 93, 1m E of Ballater £18–£19

The Lodge is the genuine article, filled with genuine antiques, and the kitchen under Neil Bannister is holding firm to its beliefs. The virtues are home-made bread, good soups, old-fashioned casseroles, local fish (the salmon is reputedly smoked in one of the old wardrobes) and fruity puddings. It is firstly a hotel, where 'residents are sacred' – so sacred that if you stay, dinner works out at a mere £8 over the cost of B&B – and over 21 years has grown more characterful and individual. There is no choice, but recommendations extend to the saucing for mussels and sole mousseline; coq au vin; smoked venison with chanterelles; 'old-fashioned' ox-tail; caramelised oranges. Light lunches are served in the bar. The wines are safe and sound, but alas do not go back as far as the current ownership. House claret is £6.50. CELLARMAN'S CHOICE: Ch. Constantin '86, £15.

CHEF: Neil Bannister PROPRIETORS: Hector Macdonald and Neil Bannister
OPEN: all week
CLOSED: mid-Dec to Mar
MEALS: 1, 7.30 to 9
PRICES: Set L £15 (£18), Set D £16 (£19), Snacks from £5. Service inc
CARDS: Access, Amex
SEATS: 26. Private parties: 10 main room. Car-park. Vegetarian meals. Children's helpings (L only). Jacket and tie. No smoking in dining-room. Wheelchair access (also WC)
ACCOMMODATION: 10 rooms, all with bath/shower. B&B £57 to £114. Children welcome. Baby facilities. Pets welcome. Garden. Golf. TV. Phone. Scenic [GHG]

BLAIRGOWRIE Tayside map 8

▲ *Kinloch House Hotel* [13/20]

By Blairgowrie, PH10 6SG
ESSENDY (025 084) 237
3m W of Blairgowrie towards
Dunkeld, on A923 £12–£18

Since this is in cattle country it is not surprising to see fillet steak done four ways. Nor is there anything unusual about salmon, fresh or smoked. But there is more to Kinloch House than these staples of the Scottish repertoire. The smart green dining-room is the setting for a canny, daily-changing blend of traditional and modern, handled with equal flair. Venison is smoked, marinated, and served with a cranberry and apple jelly; a skinless seafood sausage is sliced on to courgettes in a pastry case, and a creamy, buttery, garlicky sauce dribbled over. There is a welcome restraint about the cooking, which avoids exotic distractions and gets the best from its first-rate ingredients: loin of lamb is roasted with herbs and sliced around a timbale of vegetables, with a properly made madeira sauce. Scallops and lobsters come from the Kyle of Lochalsh, smoked eel from down the road; sweets are from the trolley. The strongly French wine list has a good run of claret vintages, but there is some venerable port and a choice from 120 malt whiskies. CELLARMAN'S CHOICE: Haut-Médoc, Ch. Beaumont '82, £10.85.

CHEF: Bill McNicoll PROPRIETORS: David and Sarah Shentall
OPEN: all week
MEALS: 12.30 to 2, 7 to 9.15
PRICES: £8 (£12), Set D £15.50 (£18). Service inc
CARDS: Access, Amex, Diners, Visa
SEATS: 60. Private parties: 30 main room, 25 and 30 private rooms. Car-park, 40 places. No children under 5. Smart dress preferred. No cigars/pipes in dining-room. Wheelchair access (also WC).
ACCOMMODATION: 13 rooms, all with bath/shower. B&B £36.50 to £52. No children under 7. Pets welcome. Garden. Fishing. Phone. Scenic. Doors close at 12. Confirm by 6 [GHG]

CAIRNDOW Strathclyde map 8

Loch Fyne Oyster Bar [9/20]

STRATHCLYDE CAFE OF THE YEAR GFG '89

Clachan Farm, Cairndow PA26 8BH
CAIRNDOW (049 96) 217 and 264 £12

At Easter 1988 Scotland's best-known salmon smokery opened up the whitewashed barn next door, fitted pine benches and tables, and now serves simple fish – from smoked mussels to marinated herrings – on a salad of shredded lettuce with brown bread and butter. In essence it is an indoor picnic spot. The best items are the ones the company produces itself: three, six or twelve Gigas oysters from a mile down the loch, presented on cracked ice; thick-cut slices of smoked salmon. The Scottish Salmon Smokers' Association seal of approval stipulates only fresh Scottish Atlantic salmon as the raw material. House French is £4.90 on a four-bottle list; also soft drinks, tea, half a dozen bottled beers, and a choice of 12-year or 21-year-old whisky.

PROPRIETORS: Loch Fyne Oysters Ltd
OPEN: all week
MEALS: 10 to 9
PRICES: £9 (£12). Service inc
CARDS: Access, Visa
SEATS: 60. 6 tables outside. Private parties: 45 main room. Car-park, 80 places. Vegetarian meals. Children's helpings. Wheelchair access (also WC). Music. Air-conditioned

CANONBIE Dumfries & Galloway map 8

▲ *Riverside Inn* [12/20]

Canonbie DG14 0UX
CANONBIE (054 15) 295 and 512 £13–£20

The river is the Esk, and the turn-of-the-century house feels as if it has been there for ever. Dinners are four courses – one of them cheese – and although the style runs to novelties such as asparagus ice-cream, it is solidly based in more traditional vein. Goose, stuffed with liver, raisins and walnuts, has an apple and calvados sauce; roast rib of beef comes with horseradish hollandaise, mustard pudding and gravy. 'We've found a greater demand for fish over the last year or so', report the proprietors, which they meet with brill and mussels in a saffron sauce, salmon with a watercress hollandaise, and starters of dressed Berwickshire crab or fish soup. Sweets continue the traditional theme with Duke of Cambridge flan and wholemeal crusted Border tart. Sunday dinner is supper in the lounge. The balanced wine list is reasonably marked up. House Mâcon is £5.95; CELLARMAN'S CHOICE: Côtes du Rhône Villages '85, from Jaboulet, £8.85.

If you suspect that a restaurant is using processed food, always ask. It would be a contravention of the Trade Description Act for the restaurant to lie.

OPEN: Mon to Sat, and Sun D
CLOSED: 2 weeks Feb
MEALS: 12 to 2, 7.30 to 8.30
PRICES: L and Sun D £8 (£13), Set D (all week exc Sun) £15.50 (£20)
CARDS: Access, Visa
SEATS: 28. 4 tables outside. Private parties: 28 main room. Car-park, 25 places. Children's helpings. No smoking. Wheelchair access (also WC)
ACCOMMODATION: 6 rooms, all with bath/shower. Rooms for disabled. B&B £36 to £46. Deposit: £15. Garden. TV. Scenic. Doors close at 11. Confirm by 5 [GHG]

Dumfries & Galloway Round-up
AFTERNOON TEA: *Old Bank*, 94 Irish Street, Dumfries (0387 53499).
ROOMS: *Beechwood Country House*, Moffat (0683 20210).
INTERNATIONAL: *Auchen Castle*, Beattock, Moffat (0683 3407).

CRINAN Strathclyde map 8

▲ *Lock 16, Crinan Hotel* [11/20]

Crinan PA31 8SR
CRINAN (054 683) 261 £15–£36

Lock 16 makes the best of the setting: it is up on the third floor of the hotel with views of the Crinan Lock and the Canal. The set dinner menu could not be simpler – a succession of dishes using the fresh local seafood landed daily at Crinan, opening with Loch Craignish mussels or melon with fresh lime and locally smoked salmon or gravlax. Then comes the centrepiece, a huge panful of jumbo prawns Corryvreckan quickly cooked with kiwi, pineapple and papaya. Puddings, like caramel profiteroles or iced hazelnut soufflé, are richer; they are followed by Stilton with oatcakes. Bar meals and a *carte* at lunch-time. Three dozen white wines, including CELLARMAN'S CHOICE: Château Doisy-Daëne '83, at £10.10.

CHEF: Nick Ryan PROPRIETORS: Nick and Frances Ryan
OPEN: Tue to Sun, exc Tue L
CLOSED: end Oct to Easter
MEALS: 12.30 to 2, 8
PRICES: £8 (£15), Set D £27.50 (£36). Licensed, also bring your own: corkage £5
CARDS: Access, Visa
SEATS: 24. Private parties: 24 main room. Car-park, 30 places. Vegetarian meals. Children welcome. Jacket and tie. Wheelchair access (also WC). One sitting at D
ACCOMMODATION: 22 rooms, all with bath/shower. Rooms for disabled. Lift. B&B £37.50 to £64. Deposit: £40. Baby facilities. Pets welcome. Afternoon teas. Garden. Fishing. Phone. Scenic. Doors close at 12. Confirm by 6

CULLIPOOL Strathclyde map 8

Longhouse Buttery [11/20]

Cullipool, Isle of Luing PA34 4TX
LUING (085 24) 209 £12

The last ferry leaves at six, so lunch is served until 5pm, giving ample time to take in the superb views of Scarba, the Garvellachs and Edna White's intriguing etchings. Superb locally-caught fish and shellfish – prawns, wild salmon, lobster – are served simply and honestly on wholemeal bread or with salad. There are also good soups, venison pâté, home-boiled ham, puddings, home-made lemonade and house French at £4.85.

CHEF: Audrey Stone PROPRIETORS: Audrey Stone and Edna Whyte
OPEN: Mon to Sat
CLOSED: Oct to mid-May
MEALS: 11 to 5
PRICES: £9 (£12). Service inc
SEATS: 32. Private parties: 12 main room. Car-park, 10 places. Vegetarian meals. Children's helpings. Wheelchair access (also WC)

CUPAR Fife map 8

Ostlers Close [12/20]

25 Bonnygate, Cupar KY15 4BU
CUPAR (0334) 55574 £19

The Grahams serve in a small, unpretentious dining-room with rustic white plaster walls and kitchen tables, and their style is dictated by local supplies, though bread, petits fours and ice-cream are made in-house. Pittenweem fish stew is infinitely variable, and Gamekeeper's Bag is a pot-roast trio of venison, pigeon and grouse, served with jellies made from brambles, rowans and rosehips that the Grahams pick themselves. Herbs and some salad vegetables come from the garden. Puddings can be rich: sticky toffee with butterscotch sauce; chocolate mousse with champagne sauce. Fifty wines take in Australia. CELLARMAN'S CHOICE: St Amour, Domaine des Billards '85, £9.15. House Burgundy, red and white, is £5.75.

CHEF: James Graham PROPRIETORS: Amanda and James Graham
OPEN: Tue to Sat (and Mon D, bookings only)
MEALS: 12.15 to 2, 7 to 9.30
PRICES: £13 (£19)
CARDS: Access, Visa
SEATS: 30. Private parties: 22 main room. Vegetarian meals. Children's helpings. No children under 6. No smoking during meals. Wheelchair access (also WC)

DRUMNADROCHIT Highland map 8

▲ *Polmaily House Hotel* [12/20]

Drumnadrochit IV3 6XT
DRUMNADROCHIT (045 62) 343 £22

The quiet, country atmosphere is helped by being two miles up Glen Urquhart, well away from the Loch Ness Museum in Drumnadrochit. Flowered fabrics cover deep armchairs in the summery lounge, and antique prints dominate the dining-room. Use of Scottish ingredients, from a chowder of Stornaway mussels to the Parsons' own duck eggs served en cocotte with Dunsyre Blue cheese and cream, is commendable and the result is often like a page from Elizabeth David: pheasant pâté with prunes; roast guinea-fowl with armagnac and juniper berries. The same is true of fish, such as baked turbot with oysters and mussels in a Noilly Prat and cream sauce. Vegetables are a high point; saucing is not. Puddings are on the lines of home-made ice-creams and chocolate roulade; cheeses are Scottish. Service, like an old pencil, needs sharpening. The reasonably priced French-dominated wine list has half as many half-bottles as bottles. House claret £5.95; CELLARMAN'S CHOICE: Chardonnay, Penfold Limited Release '86, £13.70; Gewürztraminer, Bollenberg '85, £12.50; Tignanello '82, £16.20.

CHEF: Alison Parsons PROPRIETORS: Alison and Nick Parsons
OPEN: all week, D only
CLOSED: mid-Oct to end Mar
MEALS: 7.30 to 9.30
PRICES: £17 (£22)
CARDS: Access, Visa
SEATS: 30. Private parties: 12 main room. Car-park, 20 places. Vegetarian meals. Children's helpings. No smoking in dining-room. Wheelchair access. Music
ACCOMMODATION: 9 rooms, 7 with bath/shower. B&B £28 to £62. Deposit: £25. Baby facilities. Garden. Swimming-pool. Tennis. Fishing. Scenic. Doors close at 12. Confirm by 4 [GHG]

DRYBRIDGE Grampian map 8

Old Monastery [10/20]

Drybridge, Buckie AB5 2JB
BUCKIE (0542) 32660 £17–£23

There are impressive views over the Moray Firth from this vantage point a couple of miles along the Deskford road (turn south off the A98 at Buckie). Cane and bamboo chairs in the spacious bar echo the arches of the perpendicular windows, and conversion has left some of the original flowered frieze intact in the dining-room. Homely soups stand out among staple bistro starters of stuffed mushrooms and smoked mackerel pâté. Breast of chicken is coated in oatmeal and served with a mustard sauce; and a large help-yourself cocotte is brought to the table filled with fresh cockles and chunks of salmon in a sauce with leek, dill and parsley, rendering the puddings – meringue with chocolate sauce; iced raspberry soufflé – almost unnecessary. Lunch is a bargain, and the commendable wines are reasonably priced. House French from £7.25. CELLARMAN'S CHOICE: Pouilly Fumé '86, from Dagueneau, £12.55; Côtes du Rhône, Domaine du Vieux Chêne '85, £8.50. Twenty half-bottles.

CHEF: Douglas Gray PROPRIETORS: Douglas and Maureen Gray
OPEN: Tue to Sat
CLOSED: 3 weeks Jan, 2 weeks Nov
MEALS: 12 to 2, 7 to 9.30 (10 Sat)
PRICES: L £11 (£17), D £16 (£23), Snacks from £1.75
CARDS: Access, Amex, Diners, Visa
SEATS: 45. 2 tables outside. Private parties: 45 main room. Car-park, 28 places. Children's helpings. No children under 8. No smoking in dining-room. Wheelchair access

DUNVEGAN Isle of Skye map 8

Three Chimneys [12/20]

Colbost, Dunvegan IV51 9SY
GLENDALE (047 081) 258
on B884, 4m W of Dunvegan £21

Skye is the most touristic of the Hebrides. Promotional leaflets are given out on the ferry and include a map for locating this crofter's cottage on a single-track road by Loch Dunvegan, looking towards the castle in the far distance. Unusually for the Highlands, the Spears have managed to sustain a restaurant without accommodation. Equally unusually, everything is fresh and freshly prepared. Inside are two stone rooms with fireplaces, flowers, hessian mats, polished tables, pottery and candles. The menu makes much use of local ingredients – cheese, wine, fish, oatcakes, puddings, berries – though the French parentage to the cooking is equally apparent. Steaks and crêpes counterbalance more adventurous dishes like a Hebridean ragout of monkfish and prawns in white wine or venison en croûte with a vivid thick red sauce of cranberries. There are plenty of warming, filling puddings for cold evenings. Lunch is a scaled-down version of dinner. More tables for two have been added so there is less sharing of the big tables. House wine, chosen by Paul Bocuse and bottled by Georges Duboeuf, is £6.25. CELLARMAN'S CHOICE: Côtes du Rhône, Parallèle 45 '85, from Jaboulet, £7.25.

CHEF: Shirley Spear PROPRIETORS: Eddie and Shirley Spear
OPEN: all week, exc Sun L
CLOSED: end Oct to Mar
MEALS: 12.30 to 2, 7 to 9
PRICES: £15 (£21). Minimum £9.95 at D
CARDS: Access, Visa
SEATS: 35. 2 tables outside. Private parties: 24 main room. Car-park, 30 places. Vegetarian meals. Children welcome. Music

EDINBURGH Lothian map 8

Alp-Horn [11/20]

167 Rose Street, EH2 4LS
031-225 4787 £12–£19

The Alp-Horn is as reliable as a Swiss watch. It flies the flag with air-dried beef and ham, rösti potatoes, spätzli, and cheese fondue, and definitive dishes include sliced veal zürichoise. Cowbells around the room serve as a reminder that the animal provides a variety of steaks, as well as the cheese that melts on breadcrumbed veal and ham. Muesli gets into the act, in a pear and apple salad, alongside apple strudel, and Swiss wines include Fendant and Neuchâtel. House Mâconnais, red and white, £7.

It is helpful if restaurants keep the office up to date with any changes.

CHEFS: Miggi Meier and Kenneth Dickson PROPRIETOR: Miggi Meier
OPEN: Tue to Sat
CLOSED: 2 weeks at Christmas, 3 weeks June
MEALS: 12 to 2, 6.30 to 10
PRICES: £12 (£19), Set L £6 (£12) to £8 (£14). Service 10%
CARDS: Access, Visa
SEATS: 66. Private parties: 44 main room. Vegetarian meals. Children's helpings (with prior notice). No-smoking area. Wheelchair access. Music. Air-conditioned

Handsel's Restaurant [13/20]

22 Stafford Street, EH3 7BD
031-225 5521 £20–£32

The arrival of Handsel's has generally been much admired. The split between downstairs wine bar with its good-value one-dish meals and the dark green, double-lined drapery of the swish dining-room upstairs is sensible. The cooking in both is imaginative and modern, managing to combine Scottish and international ingredients in an individual fashion that might be called modern British – for instance West Coast crayfish with Mexican asparagus and coral butter sauce. Some of the combinations work splendidly, as in wild and smoked salmon served together with a crayfish butter hollandaise. Other fish, like lemon sole and halibut, have also been combined successfully with smoked fish. Vegetables are *nouvelle* in style. Chocolate sweets draw much enthusiasm and comment, but there are also some novel gratins. Service can be slow. The wine list is another mark of the ambitions here. Clarets go back to '70, there is a good spread across many regions, including California and Australia, and equally in half-bottles. House claret is £7.50. CELLARMAN'S CHOICE: Rully '86, £12.75.

CHEF: Andrew Radford PROPRIETORS: David and Tina Thomson
OPEN: Mon to Sat, exc Sat L
CLOSED: first week Jan
MEALS: 12.30 to 2, 7.30 to 9
PRICES: £12 (£20), Set D £25 (£32)
CARDS: Access, Amex, Diners, Visa
SEATS: 32. Private parties: 40 main room. Vegetarian meals. Children's helpings. Air-conditioned

Helios Fountain [9/20]

7 Grassmarket, EH1 2HY
031-229 7884 £6

Although the staff change, the standards are consistent at this daytime vegetarian café which forms part of a Rudolf Steiner book and craft shop at the foot of Grassmarket. Food is cheap and the options limited, but what there is, is well cooked. The hot choice might be between a quiche or vegetables with a peanut chilli sauce. Salads are colourful and fresh and the vinaigrette tastes of virgin olive oil. Vegetarians argue that the rating might be increased. Unlicensed.

CHEFS: J. Woodhead and J. Innes PROPRIETORS: C. Maclean, J. Bastiaensen and M.L. Bastiaensen
OPEN: Mon to Sat
MEALS: 10 to 6
PRICES: £5 (£6), Snacks from 40p. Service inc
CARDS: Access, Amex, Visa
SEATS: 35. Private parties: 35 main room. Vegetarian meals. Children's helpings. No smoking in dining-room. Wheelchair access. Self-service

Henderson's [9/20]

94 Hanover Street, EH2 1DR
031-225 2131 £9

Salads and sweets are the best buys in this basement, vegetarian, self-service restaurant, and there is plenty of choice. It was founded by Janet Henderson in 1962 as an outlet for her own farm produce, and organically grown local food is still the lynchpin, in dishes as far apart as carrot cake and vegetarian haggis. Scottish, Irish, Spanish, Chinese and Middle Eastern chefs have all contributed something to the repertoire over the years. Queues outside translate into a lively atmosphere once they join the all-day buffet inside, and there is a range of herb teas, juices, and a short wine list. House French £5.25 a litre.

CHEF: Lorreine McCabe PROPRIETORS: The Henderson family
OPEN: Mon to Sat, and Sun during Festival
MEALS: 11.30 to 10.45
PRICES: £5 (£9) Snacks from £1. Service inc
CARDS: Access, Amex, Visa
SEATS: 180. Vegetarian meals. Children's helpings. No-smoking areas. Music. Air-conditioned. Self-service

Indian Cavalry Club [10/20]

3 Atholl Place, EH3 8HP
031-228 3282 £9–£22

Some say that this is the best Indian food in Edinburgh, and it certainly shows up well in the evening. A new club room has been added which reinforces the mood of colonial nostalgia, with lances pinned on the walls of the stylised dining-room and waiters in cavalry uniform. The long menu roams far: Singhalese shrimps stewed in the shell with coconut and green herbs, Burmese steamed cooked pomfret with tomatoes, coriander and bhindis, and Katmandhu chicken, barbecued with cinnamon, lentil and spring onion sauce. Tandooris, lamb vindaloo, chicken tikka massalam and methi gosht are more familiar territory. There's also a good range of vegetarian dishes. To drink there are cocktails, sherbets and juices, as well as lager and house Ropiteau at £5.40 a bottle.

If, in your opinion, a restaurant is not maintaining the standard of its rating, please inform the Guide *office. Report forms are at the back of the book.*

CHEFS: Bilquis Chowdhury and Mohammed Abdullah PROPRIETORS: Shahid and Bilquis Chowdhury
OPEN: all week
MEALS: 11.30 to 2, 5 to 11.30
PRICES: £10 (£18), Set L £4.95 (£9), Set D £8.50 (£13) to £16.50 (£22)
CARDS: Access, Amex, Diners, Visa
SEATS: 63. Private parties: 70 main room, 30 private room. Vegetarian meals. Children's helpings (weekends only). Jacket and tie. No-smoking area. Wheelchair access (2 steps; also WC)

Kalpna [10/20]

2–3 St Patrick Square, EH8 9ES
031-667 9890 £8–£12

This is South Indian vegetarian cooking at its best. Kalpna specialities include kumbh bhajee, a mildly spiced mushroom curry with coconut, onions and tomatoes, and makhani sabzi, vegetables in a sweet-and-sour ginger sauce with nuts; baingan bharta, a dish of crushed, roast aubergines in yoghurt, cashew nuts, onions, garlic and coriander is described as traditional. There are rice pancakes, vegetable tikka, and lentil kachoris to start; set thalis; a choice of parathas; and carrot halva to finish, as well as seero (for vegans) made from wholemeal wheat, brown sugar, ginger, raisins and cashews. The expanding wine list includes Gewürztraminer and organically produced wines. House French £5.25.

CHEF: Ajay Bharatdwaj PROPRIETORS: M.E. Jogee, Mrs Mehta, E. Barton and Ajay Bharatdwaj
OPEN: Mon to Sat
MEALS: 12 to 2, 5.30 to 11
PRICES: £7 (£12), Set L £4 (£8) to £6 (£10), Set D £5.50 (£10) to £7.50 (£12). Service 10%
CARDS: Access, Visa
SEATS: 60. Private parties: 40 main room, 30 private room. Vegetarian meals. Children's helpings. No smoking in dining-room. Wheelchair access. Music

Kelly's [new entry, zero rated]

46 West Richmond Street, EH8 9DZ
031-668 3847 £9–£21

One of the most interesting of the new openings in the city is this former bakery done out over weekends into a raw stone, simple Victorian dining-room filled with flowers in original containers. Sweets and starters on the set menu have been exact: a soufflé of broccoli with a tomato sauce; three chocolate sweets. Some unlikely combinations feature in main dishes, as in monkfish with garlic, whisky and cream, but have worked. There are good wines, too. More reports, please.

Anyone claiming to be from The Good Food Guide *is an impostor. Restaurateurs are advised to contact the office immediately if any fraudulent claims are made.*

CHEFS: Peter Rentenberger and Jackie Kelly PROPRIETOR: Jackie Kelly
OPEN: Tue to Sat, exc Sat L
MEALS: 12 to 2, 6.45 to 9.45
PRICES: Set L £5.50 (£9) to £6.50 (£10), Set D £13.50 (£19) to £15 (£21)
CARDS: Access, Amex, Visa
SEATS: 32. Private parties: 32 main room. Vegetarian meals. Children's helpings. Wheelchair access (1 step; also WC). Music

Loon Fung [11/20]

2 Warriston Place, EH3 5LE
031-556 1781 £8–£16

Last year's *Guide* got its Loons mixed with its Fungs; this is in fact the original branch, not the Grindlay Street one. This one is also the genuine article in terms of the cooking. There are fine fish dishes, such as thick steaks of halibut slightly overpowered by black-bean sauce, good dim-sum through the day and excellent crispy duck with a saffron-coloured runny lemon sauce. 'They say everthing is fresh and freshly cooked and the delays, the smells, and the quality of the food would support that.' Singapore noodles are chilli hot. Check the handwritten menu for the specials. Expect to queue on Saturdays.

OPEN: all week
CLOSED: Christmas Day and Chinese New Year
MEALS: noon (2pm Sat and Sun) to midnight (1am Fri and Sat)
PRICES: £9 (£16), Set L £4 (£8), Set D from £8.50 (£13). Service 10%
CARDS: Access, Amex, Visa
SEATS: 75. Private parties: 45 main room, 45 private room. Vegetarian meals. Children welcome. Music

Martins [12/20]

70 Rose Street North Lane, EH2 3DX
031-225 3106 £12–£24

New chef David Macrae, formerly number two at L'Auberge, has brought with him an emphasis on lighter cooking, and on seafood, especially from British waters. His style takes in grilled mussels in saffron butter and sirloin beef in a wild mushroom sauce. There are leanings towards modern ideas – warm salad with Dover sole and walnut oil; roast monkfish tail with ginger vinaigrette; venison, marinated, roasted and served with bramble vinegar sauce. Desserts from a separate menu include tea sorbet and brown-bread ice-cream, and there is a wide selection of unpasteurised cheeses. The extensive, 80-bottle list takes off with house French at £6.75. CELLARMAN'S CHOICE: Margaux, Ch. Notton '73, £12.95; Pesquera '85, from Alejandro Fernandez, £17.95; Sauvignon de St Bris '83, £8.95.

Restaurants awarded a rosette have had an entry in every Guide *since 1980.* *See Restaurants of the decade on page 21.*

CHEFS: David Macrae, Forbes Stott and Andrew Porteous PROPRIETORS: Martin and Gay Irons
OPEN: Tue to Sat, exc Sat L
CLOSED: 2 weeks from 25 Dec
MEALS: 12 to 2, 7 to 10 (10.30 Fri and Sat)
PRICES: £16 (£24), Set L from £6.75 (£12)
CARDS: Access, Amex, Diners, Visa
SEATS: 28. Private parties: 34 main room, 10 private room. Children's helpings on request. No-smoking area. Wheelchair access (2 steps)

Pierre Victoire [new entry, zero rated]

10 Victoria Street, EH1 2HG
031-225 1721 £8–£13

Pierre Le Vicky moved to the great steep curve of Victoria Street, hence the name, from the Vintners Room. The value Pierre Victoire offers has made it an early success. The former coffee-bar is plainly decorated without frills and without much room to spare. The excellent-value set lunch offers three choices per course; there are twice as many dishes in the evening. Starters and main dishes use local produce without being obsessive and are essentially bistro – for instance good bisques – with a few extravagances, like crayfish sauté with diced bacon or stir-fry of lobster with ginger and lime. Portions are generous and vegetables are inclusive. Sweets seem less good. Fifty wines, with house French at £4.90. More reports, please.

CHEF/PROPRIETOR: Pierre le Vicky
OPEN: all week
MEALS: 11am to 1am
PRICES: £9 (£13), Set L £4.60 (£8). Minimum £3 at L
CARDS: Access, Visa
SEATS: 65. Private parties: 65 main room. Vegetarian meals. Children's helpings. Wheelchair access (1 step). Music

Raffaelli [10/20]

10 Randolph Place, EH3 7TA
031-225 6060 £20

A useful choice for genuine Italian food in the finance-oriented West End of the city. The menu offers classics such as osso buco, escalope zingara and 'sformatino' (spinach cake coated with Mornay sauce); chicken dishes are well reported, too. Cheaper snacks are served in the adjoining wine bar. Good choice of Italian wines including the Gaja range which they import themselves. House Valpolicella and Soave £5.20.

CHEFS: Gerry Duffy and Aldo Scanferla PROPRIETOR: Bruno Peter Raffaelli
OPEN: Mon to Sat, exc Sat L
MEALS: noon to 9.30 (6.30 to 10.30 Sat)
PRICES: £13 (£20). Service 10%
CARDS: Access, Amex, Diners, Visa
SEATS: 65. Private parties: 60 main room, 25 and 60 private rooms. Vegetarian meals. Smart dress preferred. Wheelchair access (1 step)

Shamiana [11/20]

14 Brougham Street, EH3 9JH
031-229 5578 £17

The wall mirrors give the management more eyes than a store detective in this black and white tiled dining-room. After a dozen years this is still one of the best Indian restaurants in the city, with chicken and lamb the centrepieces, served curried, tandoori and Kashmiri. Spicing is gentle for the most part, as in chicken makhni chooza; and Kashmiri chashni tikka comes in a sweet-and-sour sauce. Good vegetables include kofta malai and aloo gobi, and there is phal chaat (fruit in a date and tamarind sauce) and a fiery lime pickle on the side. Carrot halva and kulfi to finish. House French £5.95.

CHEF: K. Mansoori and M.E. Jogee PROPRIETORS: M.E. Jogee and K. Mansoori
OPEN: Mon to Sat, exc Sat L
CLOSED: 25 Dec, 1 Jan
MEALS: 12 to 2, 6 to 11.30
PRICES: £9 (£17). Service 12.5%
CARDS: Access, Amex, Diners, Visa
SEATS: 42. Private parties: 18 main room. Vegetarian meals. Children's helpings. No cigars/pipes in dining-room. Wheelchair access (1 step). Music

Szechuan House [new entry, zero rated]

95 Gilmore Place, EH3 9NU
031-229 4655 £17

Perhaps the only authentic Szechuan restaurant in Scotland, five minutes' walk from the King's Theatre. The décor amounts to a rectangular room, which looks like a hastily converted corner shop, with old-fashioned chairs and a few Chinese lanterns, but the cooking is on target. Choa-Gang Liu trained in Chongging, the capital of Szechuan province, and delivers impressive versions of many dishes. Some are not found elsewhere in Scotland, such as fish-head soup and deep-fried sweet potato. Bang-bang chicken, steamed lamb with chilli and spices, braised prawns with chilli on a bed of crisp root vegetables, deep-fried crispy duck with the necessary accompaniments have all been good. Fish and poultry dominate, and the menu has a vegetarian section. Chinese wine and liqueur available. More reports, please.

CHEF: Chao-Gang Liu PROPRIETORS: Hsueh-Fen Liu and Chao-Gang Liu
OPEN: all week, D only
MEALS: 5.30pm to 2am (3am Fri and Sat)
PRICES: £11 (£17). Service inc
CARDS: Access, Visa
SEATS: 40. Private parties: 24 main room. Vegetarian meals. Children welcome. Music

Restaurants are not expected to solicit customers to send in reports. Please let us know if this happens to you.

Umberto Cantina [10/20]

29 Dublin Street, EH3 6NL
031-556 2231 £12–£20

The restaurant is in a well-maintained basement with rough-hewn stone walls and all the obligatory trappings: jars of olives, strings of onions and garlic, operatic muzak. It feels genuinely Italian. A vast, seven-page menu has some good things if you pick your way through carefully: mussels cooked the Sicilian way with basil, garlic and tomato; squid in batter; pan-fried veal escalopes in mushroom and cream sauce. Pasta is well sauced and there are fresh fish specials ranging from lemon sole to grilled halibut. Zabaglione is a better choice than the sweets trolley. Good espresso and reasonably priced Italian wines, starting with house bottles at £6.25.

CHEF: Enrique Quintens PROPRIETOR: Umberto D'Egostino
OPEN: Mon to Sat, exc Sat L
CLOSED: 25 Dec and 1 Jan
MEALS: 12 to 2, 6 to 11
PRICES: £14 (£20), Set L £7.50 (£12)
CARDS: Access, Amex, Diners, Visa
SEATS: 82. Private parties: 50 main room, 28 private room. Vegetarian meals. Children's helpings. Music

Verandah Tandoori [10/20]

17 Dalry Road, EH11 2BQ
031-337 5828 £11–£14

The pick of a cluster of Indian restaurants close to Haymarket railway station. Inside, the décor is civilised and cool with wickerwork chairs, plain wooden tables and wall hangings. A wide-ranging menu leans towards North Indian and Bangladeshi cooking, with good reports of lamb pasanda, meat dhansak and chicken tikka masala. There's plenty of choice for vegetarians, including pakoras spiked with green chillies, vegetable karai and tarka dahl. Breads are well made and thalis good value. Better than average curry-house wines start at £4.25 for a Yugoslav Gewürztraminer.

CHEFS: Wali T. Uddin and Kaisar Miah PROPRIETORS: Wali T. Uddin, Kaisar Miah, Foysol Choudhury and Nurjahan Uddin
OPEN: all week
MEALS: 12 to 2, 5 to 11.45
PRICES: £8 (£14), Set L and D from £7.55 (£11)
CARDS: Access, Amex, Carte Blanche, Diners, Visa
SEATS: 44. Private parties: 60 main room. Vegetarian meals. Children's helpings (L, and D 5 to 7). Wheelchair access (1 step). Music. Air-conditioned

If you suspect that a restaurant is using processed food, always ask. It would be a contravention of the Trade Description Act for the restaurant to lie.

Waterfront Wine Bar [9/20]

1C Dock Place, Leith EH6 6LU
031-554 7427 £12

Outdoor barbecues by the dockside are a big draw in fine weather; there is also a heated conservatory for when it is not so fine. Inside, the main room now has Victorian-style booths. On a daily changing menu, the simple starters – oysters from Loch Sween, thickly sliced smoked salmon – are particularly successful and a half dozen main courses might include steak and kidney pie, devilled kidneys, or loin of pork with apple and pink peppercorn sauce. A lively list of fifty wines, well under £10, is supplemented by bin-ends, scrumpy and real ale. House French from £5.

CHEFS: Caroline Conway, Helen Ruthven and Melanie Ryland PROPRIETORS: Helen and Ian Ruthven, Sarah Reid and Robin Bowie
OPEN: Mon to Sat
MEALS: 12 to 2.30, 6 to 9.30
PRICES: £8 (£12)
SEATS: 150. 15 tables outside. Private parties: 26 main room, 15 and 40 private rooms. Vegetarian meals. No children under 5. Wheelchair access (1 step). Music

Lothian Round-up

ITALIAN: *Cosmo's*, 58a North Castle Street, Edinburgh (031-226 6743).
WINE BAR: *Whigham's Wine Cellars*, 13 Hope Street, Edinburgh (031-225 8674); *The Vintners Room*, 87 Giles Street, Leith, Edinburgh (031-554 6767).
INDIAN: *Asha Tandoori*, 8 West Maitland Street, Edinburgh (031-229 0997).
VEGETARIAN: *Seeds*, 53 West Nicholson Street, Edinburgh, (031-667 8673).
MEXICAN: *Viva Mexico*, 10 Anchor Close, Cockburn Street, Edinburgh (031-226 5145).
ROOMS: *Greywalls*, Muirfield, Gullane (0620 842144).
CHINESE: *Kweilin*, 19-21 Dundas Street, Edinburgh (031-557 1875).
FISH: *Shore*, Leith, Edinburgh (031-553 5080).

ERISKA Strathclyde map 8

▲ *Isle Of Eriska Hotel* [11/20]

10 YEARS

Eriska PA37 1SD
LEDAIG (063 172) 371
off A828, 12m N of Oban £11–£33

The Buchanan-Smiths' baronial country mansion is more of a retreat than a hotel, set on its own 280-acre island. The remoteness results in a necessary degree of self-sufficiency and an allegiance to local ingredients – eggs, unpasteurised Jersey cream, home-grown vegetables. Roasts, notably Aberdeen Angus beef and gigot of lamb, are carved at the table. They are the centrepieces of six-course dinners and Sunday lunches, flanked by, say, Stilton and grape in filo pastry or cream of celery soup on the one side; desserts from the trolley, Welsh rarebit, and cheeses on the other. Buffet lunches are available during the week. The 150 wines are strong on the big clarets and red Burgundies, to suit the meat. CELLARMAN'S CHOICE: Margaux, Ch. de Candale '82, £12.90.

CHEF: Simon Burns PROPRIETORS: Robin and Sheena Buchanan-Smith
OPEN: all week
CLOSED: Dec to Jan
MEALS: 1 to 1.30, 7.30 to 8.30
PRICES: Set L from £6.33 (£11) to £19.55 (£26), Set D £26.45 (£33)
SEATS: 40. Private parties: 10 main room, 12 private room. Car-park, 50 places. Children's helpings. Jacket and tie. Wheelchair access (also WC)
ACCOMMODATION: 16 rooms, all with bath/shower. Rooms for disabled. D, B&B £115 to £165.50. Deposit: £50. Baby facilities. Pets welcome. Garden. Tennis. Fishing. TV. Phone. Scenic. Confirm by 4 [GHG]

FORT WILLIAM Highland map 8

▲ *Factor's House* [11/20]

Torlundy, Fort William, PH33 6SN
FORT WILLIAM (0397) 5767
3m N of Fort William on A82 £20

Kilted Peter Hobbs and his assistant are cheerful guardians of the Inverlochy gate-house. The impression, from *National Geographic* magazines in the lounge book-case, pictures of sailing ships, and charts in the Wee Room (for Buoys and Gulls), is of a life spent travelling and exploring. The blackboard set menu, by contrast, ventures no further than the style of parcels of smoked trout with prawns, pork fillet with rosemary, and sirloin steak with mushroom sauce, but it changes daily and scores for its straightforwardness. Starters might include fresh pasta with tomato sauce or creamy Cullen skink served in a small tureen, followed by breast of chicken stuffed with a julienne of vegetables, flavoured with tarragon, wrapped in puff pastry, and given a sharp tomato and dill sauce, or poached lemon sole with prawns and mussels. There have been good reports too of venison ragoo. There is cheese to follow, or a clutch of sweets: pineapple soufflé; blood-orange sorbet; Mississippi mud pie. Twenty basic wines do not include half-bottles, but they will open a bottle and charge accordingly. A half-litre pichet of house wine is £4. CELLARMAN'S CHOICE: Ch. Ruat-Petit-Poujeaux '79, £10.30.

CHEF: Steven Doole PROPRIETOR: Peter Hobbs
OPEN: Tue to Sun, D only
CLOSED: mid-Dec to mid-Mar
MEALS: 7.30 to 9.30
PRICES: Set D £15.50 (£20). Service inc
CARDS: Access, Amex, Diners, Visa
SEATS: 24. Private parties: 24 main room. Car-park, 16 places. Vegetarian meals. Children's helpings. No children under 8. Wheelchair access (also WC)
ACCOMMODATION: 7 rooms, all with bath/shower. Rooms for disabled. B&B £40.25 to £63.25. Deposit: £50. No children under 8. Garden. Tennis. Fishing. Golf. TV. Phone. Scenic. Doors close at 12.30. Confirm by 6 [GHG]

▲ *Inverlochy Castle* [14/20]

Fort William PH33 6SN,
FORT WILLIAM (0397) 2177
3m N of Fort William on A82 £24–£43

This is a complete and impressive package, three miles north of Fort William. With a massive baronial front and fine landscaped gardens it looks like everybody's idea of a Scottish castle but, despite the size, is furnished for comfort. The hall-cum-lounge is big enough to lose a grand piano in, antiques are polished till they shine, and silver cockerels strut around a carved wooden dresser in the dining-room. After two years, Graham Newbould is very much into his stride, with a sharply modern menu that avoids flamboyance. Pairings are neat and to the point: warm apple syrup with lightly grilled fresh goats' cheese; galantine of duck with pepper jelly; chive sauce with scallop mousseline in pastry. The deceptively simple three-course lunch (with a choice of four items at each) seems hardly enough to stretch the chef, yet ideas are dealt with fluently: four pasta shells, each filled with lobster and mushroom, set at quarter hours on a basil-infused sauce with tiny scallops in between, sit on thin ribbons of four different vegetables: celery, celeriac, carrot and courgette. Hot-pot of local seafood is served with broccoli sauce. Meals have shape, fine judgement extends throughout, and the net effect is light, and well defined, despite indulgent puddings. 'Do you *really* like chocolate?' asks the waitress. Two tear-shaped cups, one white one dark, make a yin-and-yang pattern on opposite-coloured sauces; both are filled with whisky-infused chocolate mousse. Service could not be more charming. The wines are as classical as Mozart; and at 50 pages, the list is a magnum (as well as a bottle and half-bottle) opus. It is impeccable stuff at no more than standard mark-ups. Top brass from senior vintages, as in Ch. Ducru-Beaucaillou '70, £85, for instance, are supported by a strong cadet force, for example Ch. Beaumont '82, £13, and the bulk are ready for drinking. Ample choice under £15 includes the Loire, Beaujolais, and a mixed dozen from Australia, Spain, Chile and New Zealand.

CHEF: Graham Newbould PROPRIETOR: Grete Hobbs
OPEN: all week
CLOSED: mid-Nov to Mar
MEALS: 12.30 to 1.45, 7.30 to 9
PRICES: Set L £17.50 (£24), Set D £35 (£43)
CARDS: Access, Amex, Visa
SEATS: 40. Private parties: 30 main room. Car-park, 10 places. No children under 10. Jacket and tie. No smoking in dining-room
ACCOMMODATION: 16 rooms, all with bath/shower. B&B £105 to £145. Afternoon teas. Garden. Tennis. Fishing. Golf. Snooker. TV. Phone. Scenic [GHG]

If you cannot honour a restaurant booking, always phone to cancel.

Many of the more expensive restaurants offer bargain lunches for half the price of a meal in the evening. Details are given in the text.

GLASGOW Strathclyde map 8

Buttery [12/20]

652 Argyle Street, G3 8UF
041-221 8188
just off the M8 city-centre cut-off £15–£26

Marooned in an urban development; inside you find a converted pub stuffed with Victoriana. Brian Graham cooks a fancy, refined *nouvelle* menu, high on presentation, with lots of mousses and feuilletés; breast of duck with red wine sauce, apples and raisins is accompanied by an apple gateau; guinea-fowl filled with pistachio mousse is served with a wild mushroom and madeira sauce. There are some simpler ideas, too, such as watercress and orange soup, game and nut terrine with rhubarb chutney, and grilled turbot on lemon and dill butter. Scottish game and fish are a feature. Vegetarian dishes are enterprising; sweets are predictably elaborate – the 'Grand Dessert' is a mini-portion of each one, from cherry sorbet in a chocolate box to hot honey pudding with Drambuie. Around 50 wines, with house French at £6.95. CELLARMAN'S CHOICE: Pouilly Vinzelles '83, £13.70.

CHEF: Brian Graham PROPRIETORS: Alloa Brewery
OPEN: Mon to Sat, exc Sat L
MEALS: 12 to 2.30, 7 to 10
PRICES: £17 (£26), Set L £11.50 (£15). Service 10% alc, inc set
CARDS: Access, Amex, Diners, Visa
SEATS: 50. Private parties: 12 main room, 8 private room. Car-park, 30 places. Children's helpings. Smart dress preferred. Wheelchair access. Music

Café Gandolfi [9/20]

64 Albion Street, G1 1NY
041-552 6813 £12

The décor re-creates the style of Charles Rennie Mackintosh (who designed the Willow Tea Rooms) with individualistic furniture designed by art students. The menu is French-style brasserie, from the croissants to the home-made ice-cream. In between there are salads of goats' cheese, smoked venison and pastrami on rye. Dish of the day might be noisettes of lamb with two pepper sauces. Good cappuccino, half a dozen wines (including two organic varieties) and Duvel beer from Belgium. Relaxed, civilised and very good value.

CHEFS: Margaret Clarence and Andrew Bickerstaff PROPRIETOR: Iain M. Mackenzie
OPEN: Mon to Sat
CLOSED: bank hols
MEALS: 9.30am to 11.30pm
PRICES: £8 (£12), Snacks from £1.10
SEATS: 60. Private parties: 12 main room. Vegetarian meals. Children's helpings. No children after 8pm. Wheelchair access (2 steps). Music

Loon Fung [10/20]

417 Sauchiehall Street, G2 3LG
041-332 1240 and 1477 £8–£25

Probably the best choice for dim-sum in the city. The choice of around 20 includes good steamed prawn balls, chicken and glutinous rice in lotus leaves, and beef dumplings with ginger and spring onion. Otherwise, the hundred-item menu has good Cantonese roast meats and one-plate dishes, as well as a strong showing of seafood. Vegetarian set dinners are a new feature.

CHEF: M. Kan PROPRIETOR: P.W. Cheng
OPEN: all week
MEALS: noon to 11.30
PRICES: £12 (£20), Set L £4 (£8), Set D £12 (£17) to £20 (£25)
CARDS: Access, Amex, Visa, Diners
SEATS: 200. Private parties: 200 main room. Vegetarian meals. Children's helpings. Smart dress preferred. Wheelchair access (1 step; also WC). Music. Air-conditioned

October [13/20]

GLASGOW NEWCOMER OF THE YEAR

128 Drymen Road, Bearsden, G61 3RB
041-942 7272 £16

The changing cultural fortunes of Glasgow and Edinburgh are reflected in their restaurants. Until about four years ago Glasgow lagged behind, but Ferrier Richardson has had a galvanising influence, first at the Buttery and then at Rogano's. He opened October's premises before they could be properly converted, and changes due in the autumn of 1988 may affect the scope of the menu as well as the layout of the dining-room. Richardson says, 'Hopefully, I have now eliminated any pretentious ideas and superfluous ingredients.' Lunch is an array of inexpensive modern snacks. Deep-fried potato skins are served with a sour-cream dressing or curried mango dip; noodles nod to China; pasta plays to Italy with vegetables and pesto. Dishes eschew expensive ingredients and impress with economy and vitality: newly arrived mussels are served in a peppery wine 'consommé'; lamb's liver is cooked pink without distractions. Evening choices might be spinach and cream-cheese mousse with herb toast or mushrooms feuilleté to start, then chicken with Brie and Bayonne ham or teriyaki beef with wasabi and ginger. Puddings keep up the momentum: cinnamon-dusted slices of apple are strewn on a round of puff pastry raised at the edge and given a dollop of honey ice-cream. Alternatives are in the mould of crème brûlée, sorbets, fruit gratin. A concise list of 30 wines, with house red and white £5.95, nonetheless has three champagnes and bottles from Spain, Portugal, Australia and California.

CHEF: Ferrier Richardson PROPRIETORS: Premiere Cuisine Ltd
OPEN: Tue to Sat
MEALS: 12 to 2, 7 to 10
PRICES: £11 (£16). Service inc
CARDS: Access, Visa
SEATS: 45. Private parties: 12 main room. Vegetarian meals. Children welcome. Wheelchair access (also WC). Music

▲ *One Devonshire Gardens* [12/20]

1 Devonshire Gardens, G12 0UX
041-339 2001 £20–£29

The elegant, terraced, mid-Victorian building feels like a townie version of a country house, but Jim Kerr's menus adopt a lighter tone than the one set by the big drapes and sombre pictures. Ginger with a warm salad of scallops, and coriander in vegetable soup, are some of the headier seasonings, although the limited choice may be responsible for safe dishes of chicken with spinach, or rib of beef with Yorkshire pudding. Mousses and parfaits run through from chicken liver to coffee and almond. Lamb is served with tomato and basil or rosemary and redcurrant, and cheeses can include Dunsyre Blue. The exclusively French list makes good use of lesser known (including a brace of organic) wines, and has something for most pockets. House French £9.50. CELLARMAN'S CHOICE: Gewürztraminer, Bollenberg '86, from Cattin, £16.95; Ch. des Moines '83, £14.25.

CHEF/PROPRIETOR: Jim Kerr
OPEN: Mon to Sun, exc Sat L
MEALS: 12.30 to 2, 7 to 10
PRICES: Set L £13.50 (£20), Set D £21.50 (£29). Service 10%
CARDS: Access, Amex, Diners, Visa
SEATS: 56. Private parties: 40 main room, 16 private room. Jacket and tie. Music
ACCOMMODATION: 8 rooms, all with bath/shower. B&B £70 to £95. Children welcome. Baby facilities. Pets by arrangement. TV. Phone. Confirm by noon [GHG]

Peter Jackson at the Colonial [13/20]

25 High Street, G1 1LX
041-552 1923 £10–£29

Of all the chefs working in Scotland, Peter Jackson adopts the most modern stance. His consommé, for instance, is of seafood, and filled with fish dumplings and ravioli. The quality of main dishes underwrites the thought that here the new generation is starting to assert itself. Monkfish is sauced with white wine, avocado and tomato; pheasant, properly hung, is roasted plainly and served with shallots, thyme and chanterelles. The emphasis is towards local produce, but supported by the Paris markets. In the French style the restaurant has been rechristened after the chef. The businessman's lunch is a bargain at £5.25 and the half dozen choices of main course run through the spectrum of techniques – braised lamb's liver; deep-fried chicken; roast pork; shallow-fried bream – and equally of saucing – traditional onions for the liver; mustard for the chicken; apple for pork; brown butter for the bream; tartare for some deep-fried haddock goujons. The main *carte* becomes conspicuously less classical and more French, with a Taste of Modern Scotland set menu and also a *menu surprise.* Sweets can look stunning under superb spun-sugar cages. Coffee is cafetière and served with dipped fruits and truffles. Sensibly, wines are suggested to go with the menus. There are three sweet bottles – Ch. Coutet '79; Tokay Aszu; Veuve Clicquot Riche NV – of which one is offered by the glass at £1.20. House Burgundy £6.45.

CHEF/PROPRIETOR: Peter Jackson
OPEN: Mon to Sat, exc Sat L and Mon D
MEALS: 12 to 2.30, 6 to 10.30
PRICES: £21 (£29), Set L £5.45 (£10) to £9.25 (£14), Set D £16 (£21) to £19.65 (£25)
CARDS: Access, Amex, Diners, Visa
SEATS: 40. Private parties: 40 main room. Vegetarian meals. Children welcome. Wheelchair access

Rogano [11/20]

11 Exchange Place, G1 3AN
041-248 4055 £27

Like sailors hearing the call of the Siren, the Rogano has been seduced by the tune of mass catering. In two respects it is unparalleled in the city – for atmosphere and décor, which is in the same art deco style as the Queen Mary in 1935 and left mainly alone apart from intelligent spotlights over tables; and also for plain unadulterated fish: lemon sole meunière or grilled salmon. But not content with these, the menu has strayed into quasi-cuisine, which the operation is not equipped to handle with any skill or sensitivity – old-fashioned soups; untidy, untrimmed scallops; solid and overly sweet puddings. Alloa Brewery, the current custodian, is not content to leave well alone, more's the pity, as standards are more allied to the prices in the bar upstairs than the restaurant downstairs. Alas, the more so because the waiting staff are exemplary and could not be more concerned that everyone has a good time. The 90 or so wines offer some compensation, being pricey but of good pedigree, especially in Alsace and the Loire. CELLARMAN'S CHOICE: Gewürztraminer, Les Sorcières '85, from Dopff & Irion, £13.95.

CHEF: William Alexander Simpson PROPRIETOR: Alloa Brewery
OPEN: Mon to Sat
MEALS: 12 to 2.30, 7 to 10.30
PRICES: £18 (£27), Snacks from £2.50. Service 10%
CARDS: Access, Amex, Diners, Visa
SEATS: 100. Private parties: 25 main room; 14 private room. Children welcome. Music. Air-conditioned

Ubiquitous Chip [12/20]

12 Ashton Lane, G12 8SJ
041-334 5007 £23

The Chip is consistent in at least one respect: it can be guaranteed to split reporters down the middle. Any amount of congratulatory press cuttings pasted on the walls of the converted warehouse doesn't make up for cooking below par, and one view is that the restaurant is beginning to live off its reputation. The menu is rooted in Scotland, keeps one eye on fashion, and reads well: Oban-landed lemon sole with saffron sauce; tomato and fromage blanc roulade with courgette and mint coulis; dill-marinated, peat-smoked finnan haddie with a quail's egg. It also plays fair by vegetarians, with vegetable and nut parcels in apple and rosemary sauce. Ingredients are fresh, and fish is one of the more reliable recommendations. There is bread pudding or burnt lemon tart to follow. Atmosphere is that of a 1960s café, with stone floor, wooden tables and hanging vines. The excellent wine list, which has a good range under £10, is strong on claret and Burgundy. Mark-ups are gentle – astonishingly so for fine, mature wines. Clarets cover good vintages back to '70, with a few older wines. There's a long list of tempting Burgundies, good Loires, Rhônes largely from Paul Jaboulet Aîné, and vintage Pol Roger at a price you might be happy to pay for house champagne. Apart from Germany, with its big selection of well-chosen estate wines, the choice from the rest of the world is brief but good. Interesting bottles from the New World, some outstanding Spanish wines, unusually good, modern-style wines from Portugal, and even the Valpolicella is superb. You would be unlucky not to find your favourite malt available by the glass.

CHEF: Ronnie Clydesdale PROPRIETORS: R. Clydesdale and I.R. Brydon
OPEN: Mon to Sat
MEALS: 12 to 2.30, 5.30 to 11
PRICES: £16 (£23)
CARDS: Access, Amex, Diners, Visa
SEATS: 100. 12 tables outside. Private parties: 60 main room, 40 private room. Vegetarian meals. Children's helpings. Wheelchair access (also WC)

Strathclyde Round-up

ROOMS: *Isle of Colonsay Hotel,* Colonsay (09512 316); *West Loch Hotel,* Tarbert (08802 283); *Glencloy Farm Guest House,* Brodick, Isle of Arran (0770 2351).
AFTERNOON TEAS: *Willow Tea Rooms,* 217 Sauchiehall Street, Glasgow (041-332 0521).
VIEW: *Rotunda,* Clyde, Expressway, Glasgow (041-204 1238).
SETTING: *Le Campagnard,* Drumcastle Mill Cottage, Dalry (029 483 3544); *Killermount House,* 2022 Maryhill Road, Maryhill Park, Glasgow (041-946 5412).
VEGETARIAN: *Candletree,* 6 The Cross, Prestwick (0292 70047); *Granary,* 82 Howard Steet, Glasgow (041-226 3770); *Third Eye Centre,* 350 Sauchiehall Street (041-332 7521).
PASTA: *PJ's Pastaria,* Maryfield House, Ruthen Lane, Byres Road, Glasgow (041-339 0932).
BAR MEALS: *Manor House Hotel,* Gallanoch Road, Oban (0631 62087). *Bellachroy,* Dervaig, Isle of Mull (068 84 225).
ROOMS: *Dolphinton House Hotel,* Dolphinton (0968 82286).

GULLANE Lothian map 8

La Potinière [15/20]

10 YEARS

Main Street, Gullane, EH31 2AA
GULLANE (0620) 843214 £16–£22

The Browns stick with their proven, unusual formula – lunches only, plus Saturday dinner (booked two years ahead, though it's worth a phone call to see if there have been cancellations) and often as not a variation on a vegetable soup, a fish mousse and chicken main course, followed by Brie and an apple. But that is to slight Hilary Brown's cooking. Everything is understated, almost English in its reserve, but enormous thought has gone in to every aspect, from the pepper mills onwards. The framed claret labels and ends of boxes are all from good bottles. David Brown manages to serve a considerable number of people very well without ever seeming to move very quickly. Often what seems to be so plain and simple in the cooking is nothing of the sort, but a sophisticated interaction of different flavours. Take this main course: chicken breasts with sweet onion compote, the onions very sweet from being caramelised with demerara sugar, sherry vinegar and cassis, the chicken breast coated with a mustard cream sauce seasoned with cider and mustard seeds, served with a moderately garlicky gratin Savoyard and followed by a salad of radicchio, fennel, lettuce and mung beans. Other points that lift dishes are a drop of orange in the red pepper soup; tarragon to sauce a fillet of beef; some basil with the spinach purée, and cream for filo triangles filled with smoked salmon mousse. Apricots have featured with chicken but also as a sweet – an egg yolk and cream infused with lemon rind, mixed with a purée of apricots sealed with brandy and chilled. For all its reputation, the dining-room is a squeeze when sitting or rising. 'The best value of any restaurant in the country.' Lunch ends at about three. The wine list, entirely French, is extraordinarily good value. Pol Roger Rosé '75 costs just £21, the price of a bottle of Moët in most other restaurants. The most extensive sections are a fine list of mature clarets and a long Burgundy list of top names (including many extremely mature vintages of the late '60s and early '70s), but there are also fine Loires, a collection of Chablis *premiers* and *grands crus* from top producers, and tempting Rhônes that include seven different Condrieu wines and seven vintages of Jaboulet's Hermitage La Chapelle. Half-bottles of sweet wines seem to be in short supply, but then full bottles are so inexpensive: a large party could compare Anjou Moulin Touchais '59, £15, with Bonnezeaux, Château des Gauliers of the same year, £21. Or there are affordable Sauternes of the early '70s, sweet Vouvray, sweet Alsace from Hugel, and, by the glass, an uncommon Muscat de Beaumes de Venise, Domaine de St-Saveur '85, £2. House French is £5.75.

CHEF: Hilary Brown PROPRIETORS: David and Hilary Brown
OPEN: all week L, exc Wed and Sat, and Sat D
CLOSED: 1 week June; Oct
MEALS: 1, 8
PRICES: Set L from £11.50 (£16), Set D £17.50 (£22)
SEATS: 32. Private parties: 30 main room. Car-park, 10 places. Children welcome. Smoking after meal only. Wheelchair access. One sitting

HADDINGTON Lothian map 8

▲ *Browns Hotel* [10/20]

1 West Road, Haddington, EH41 3RD
HADDINGTON (062 082) 2254 £14–£23

The Georgian-style house has been spruced up with a redecorated dining-room, paintings by contemporary Scottish artists on the walls of the public rooms and Wedgwood china on the tables. There are echoes of the Auld

Alliance in the fixed-price dinner menus. Typically, soups veer between cock-a-leekie and consommé with quails' eggs. The French influence wins out in the classic sauces – green peppercorn and béarnaise with well-hung châteaubriand; sauce Robert with boeuf en croûte; maltaise with fresh asparagus. There's also some intriguing marinating of pork fillets with madeira, and guinea-fowl with strawberries and tarragon. Forty wines centre on France. CELLARMAN'S CHOICE: Ch. Bibian-Darriet '81, at £9.20.

CHEF: Colin Brown PROPRIETORS: Colin Brown and Alex McCallum
OPEN: Mon to Sat, D only, and Sun L
CLOSED: 2 weeks Oct
MEALS: 1, 7.30 to 9
PRICES: Set Sun L £9.75 (£14) to £16.50 (£22), Set D £16.50 (£21) to £18.50 (£23)
SEATS: 38. Private parties: 38 main room. Car-park, 10 places. Vegetarian meals. Children's helpings. Wheelchair access (also WC)
ACCOMMODATION: 6 rooms, 5 with bath/shower. B&B £37.50 to £49.50. Deposit: £10. Baby facilities. Garden. Golf. TV. Phone. Scenic. Doors close at 12. Confirm by 6

INVERNESS Highland map 8

▲ *Dunain Park* [11/20]

Inverness IV3 6JN
INVERNESS (0463) 230512
on A82, 1m from Inverness £17–£24

The homely end of the country house spectrum: no imposing staircases, but plenty of comfortable chairs and leather settees. Four-course dinners begin with a soup, such as cold fennel and watercress on a warm night, and end with a help-yourself trolley of puddings, from marshmallow with mixed fruit to slabs of a rich, biscuity chocolate cake. In between, the style is roasts, such as boned quail with pistachio nut stuffing, grills from steak to scallops, or beef Wellington. Saucing can be minimal, and there is 'splendid use of herbs and, for us, a pleasing lack of cream-with-everything'. Service moves along smartly. Lunch is the bargain. A heated swimming-pool is a new feature. A pedigree list of wines, on which house French is £5. CELLARMAN'S CHOICE: St Emilion, Ch. Vieux Clos '82, £14.65; Chardonnay, Château Reynella '86, £11.75.

CHEF: Ann Nicoll PROPRIETORS: Ann and Edward Nicoll
OPEN: all week
MEALS: 12 to 2, 7 to 9
PRICES: Set L £12.50 (£17), Set D £19.50 (£24)
CARDS: Access, Amex, Diners, Visa
SEATS: 32. Private parties: 20 main room. Car-park, 30 places. Vegetarian meals. Children's helpings. Smart dress preferred. No smoking in dining-room
ACCOMMODATION: 8 rooms, all with bath/shower. B&B £33 to £90. Deposit: £40. Pets welcome. Afternoon teas. Garden. Swimming-pool. Sauna. TV. Phone. Scenic. Doors close at 12 [GHG]

Restaurants that we have not been able to assess as fully as we would like are given a zero rating this year. We are particularly keen to have reports on these places.

Highland Round-up

ROOMS: *Clifton Hotel*, Viewfield Street, Nairn, (0667 53119); *Glencripesdale House*, Glencripesdale, Loch Sunart (096 785 263); *Ard-na-Coille*, Kingussie Road, Newtonmore, (054 03 214); *Osprey Hotel*, Kingussie (054 02 510); *Glenview Inn*, Culnacnoc, Staffin, Skye (047 062 248); *Harlosh Hotel*, Dunvegan, Skye (047 022 367).

WINE BAR: *Brookes*, 75 Castle Street, Inverness (0463 225662); *Moniack Castle Wine Bar*, Moniack Castle, Kirkhill, nr Inverness (0463 83 336).

INEXPENSIVE: *Ice-cream Parlour and Coffee House*, High Street, Grantown-on-Spey (0479 2001).

IRVINE Strathclyde map 8

▲ *Mirage Restaurant, Hospitality Inn* [new entry, zero rated]

Roseholm, Annick Water, Irvine KA11 4LD
IRVINE (0294) 74272 £15–£26

From the outside, this low, red-brick building looks like a modern factory; inside in the Lagoon Restaurant the style is mock-Tangiers, with a huge lagoon pool surrounded by jungle vegetation. The Mirage is the more formal dining-room. Martin Hollis cooks seriously, pairing top-quality raw materials with concentrated reduced sauces. Notably good have been veal scallops with creamy morel sauce, and beef with a sauce of langoustines. Otherwise the seasonal menus might feature sole, scallop and salmon terrine with a herb centre; mussel and saffron soup; and venison with a tartlet of fresh figs and raspberries. Lambs' kidneys are served on a buttery pillow of puff pastry. Presentation is impressive, particularly on the sweets table. Around 65 wines make up a traditional list, dominated by some good clarets. House French £6.50; CELLARMAN'S CHOICE: Chablis '86, £16.25. More reports, please.

CHEF: Martin Hollis PROPRIETORS: Mount Charlotte Investments plc
OPEN: all week
MEALS: 12.30 to 2.30, 7.30 to 9.30
PRICES: £19 (£26), Set L £9.95 (£15), Set D £16.50 (£22), Snacks from £1.10
CARDS: Access, Amex, Diners, Visa
SEATS: 90. Private parties: 250 private room. Car-park, 200 places. Vegetarian meals. Children's helpings. Wheelchair access (also WC). Music. Air-conditioned
ACCOMMODATION: 127 rooms, all with bath/shower. Rooms for disabled. B&B £22 to £62. Children welcome. Baby facilities. Pets welcome. Afternoon teas. Garden. Swimming-pool. Fishing. Golf. Snooker. Air-conditioning. TV. Phone. Scenic

KELSO Borders map 8

▲ *Sunlaws House* [11/20]

Heiton, Kelso TD5 8JZ
ROXBURGH (0573) 5331
3m outside Kelso on A698 £11–£27

Some of the public rooms in this nineteenth-century house have taken more naturally to conversion than others. The bar is stocked with ancient sporting volumes, the comfortable lounge with up-to-date magazines, while in the dining-room, imitation bamboo chairs give the feel of Copacabana. The menu has exotic touches too, but builds on a sound base of supplies from Border lamb to Tweed salmon, from Loch Fyne oysters to venison and game birds from the estate. It excels in fish; two chunks of turbot spill out of a pastry sandwich, which sits on a butter sauce sharpened with white wine. Main courses are rich: venison is flamed in whisky and served with a mustard and cream sauce; chicken is stuffed with creamed ham and mango and served with a Drambuie sauce. Sweets are from the trolley; cheeses include Orkney and local farmhouse varieties. Service can be disorganised. Wines on the 160-strong, largely French list run from house at £5.95 to CELLARMAN'S CHOICE: Chardonnay, Wyndham's '86, £8.75; Haut-Médoc, Ch. Tour-du-Haut-Moulin '79, £10.75; and Sancerre '86, from H. Brochard, £9.90.

CHEF: Robert Grindle PROPRIETORS: Duke and Duchess of Roxburghe
OPEN: all week
MEALS: 12.30 to 2, 7.30 to 9.30
PRICES: £17 (£27), Set L £9.50 (£11)
CARDS: Access, Amex, Diners, Visa
SEATS: 40. 5 tables outside. Private parties: 45 main room, 20 private room. Car-park, 30 places. Children's helpings. No pipes in dining-room. Wheelchair access (also WC)
ACCOMMODATION: 21 rooms, all with bath/shower. Rooms for disabled. B&B £39 to £59. Baby facilities. Pets welcome. Afternoon teas. Garden. Tennis. Fishing. Golf. TV. Phone. Scenic. Doors close at 11.30. Confirm by 7.30

KENTALLEN Highland map 8

▲ *Ardsheal House* [12/20]

Kentallen PA38 4BX
DUROR (063 174) 227 £10–£29

Loch Linnhe provides more than just views. 'We keep a bag of Colonsay oysters in the loch off our old pier,' writes Mr Bussey, and it is also a source of salmon, prawns (served with samphire and sorrel butter sauce), mussels, and scallops which are turned into a mousse and given saffron sauce and trout roe. The minimal-choice dinners are of five courses: one a salad with Stilton, one a soup, such as yellow pepper with green chillies and crème fraîche. Twice-baked goats' cheese and garlic soufflé, and grilled scallops with two-pepper sauce are both memorable. There are locally picked wild mushrooms in season – morels are served with medallions of sika deer – and the kitchen makes its own preserves, seasoned and herbed vinegars, and bread. Puddings are a high point: rich chocolate cream sandwiched between thin discs of dark chocolate, or hot rhubarb and ginger soufflé. The wine list shows a particularly sharp eye for value, an awareness of the New World, and finds space for interesting bottles such as Pesquera from the Duero in Spain. The range of bottles under £12 is impressive. House French is £6.

An index of restaurants by name appears at the back of the Guide.

CHEF: Colin John Bussey PROPRIETORS: Jane and Robert Taylor
OPEN: all week
CLOSED: 1 Nov to Easter
MEALS: 12.30 to 2, 8.15 to 8.30
PRICES: Set L £6 (£10) to £10.50 (£15), Set D £23 (£29)
SEATS: 34. Private parties: 38 main room. Car-park, 20 places. Children's helpings. Smart dress preferred. No smoking in dining-room. Wheelchair access (also WC). Music
ACCOMMODATION: 13 rooms, all with bath/shower. B&B £27 to £82, D,B&B £50 to £128. Children welcome. Baby facilities. Pets welcome. Afternoon teas. Garden. Tennis. Snooker. Scenic. Doors close at 12. Confirm by 5.30 [GHG]

▲ *Holly Tree Hotel* [10/20]

Kentallen PA38 4BY
DUROR (063 174) 292
A82 3m S of Ballachulish bridge £12–£23

Additions to the fabric blend well with the original art-nouveau-style railway station at the shore of the loch. Views impress. At full tilt, the kitchen runs to ginger hollandàise with Mallaig halibut, and bitter chocolate and barley cakes with pigeon breast, though the simpler dishes – loin of lamb with garlic and rosemary – work as well as any. Sweets take in sticky toffee pudding, plum jam and kummel omelette. There is a fine goats' milk ice-cream. The 120-bottle, largely French wine list is reasonably priced, with house French at £4.95.

CHEF: Alasdair Robertson PROPRIETORS: Alasdair and Jane Robertson
OPEN: all week
CLOSED: mid-Nov to mid-Mar (exc Christmas and New Year)
MEALS: 12.30 to 2, 7.30 to 9.30
PRICES: L £8 (£12), Set Sun L £8.25 (£12), D £18 (£23), Set D £15 (£20). Minimum £7.80
CARDS: Access, Visa
SEATS: 60. Private parties: 16 main room. Car-park, 30 places. Vegetarian meals. Children's helpings. No smoking. Wheelchair access (also WC). Music
ACCOMMODATION: 12 rooms, all with bath/shower. Rooms for disabled. B&B £30 to £52. Deposit: £20. Baby facilities. Pets welcome. Afternoon teas. Garden. Fishing. TV. Phone. Scenic [GHG]

KILCHRENAN Strathclyde map 8

▲ *Taychreggan Hotel* [11/20]

Kilchrenan PA35 1HQ
KILKCHRENAN (086 63) 211 £16–£23

The hotel stands on the shores of Loch Awe – Scotland's largest freshwater loch. The Taylors make good use of local produce – especially seafood – for dishes such as poached scallops with Pastis butter, salmon with dill and lemon sauce, and stuffed fillet of sole with tarragon cream sauce. Otherwise the menu is eclectic, with pan-fried wood-pigeon breast with sweet-and-sour vegetables; Mozzarella-stuffed chicken breast; and roast Barbary duck with orange and grapefruit sauce. Bread, preserves and ice-creams are made on the premises. Salads, sandwiches and sausages in the bar. *Petit château* clarets head the wine list, and there is Meadowsweet dessert wine from Scotland for £5.50. House claret is £6.40. Ch. Vieux-Certan, '78 at £26. CELLARMAN'S CHOICE: Pomerol, Vieux Châteaux C.

CHEFS: Gail Struthers, Joyce MacDougall, Nan MacIntyre and Wendy Avery
PROPRIETORS: John and Tove Taylor
OPEN: all week
MEALS: 12 to 2.15, 7.30 to 9.15
PRICES: Set L £11 (£16), Set D £17 (£23)
CARDS: Access, Amex, Diners, Visa
SEATS: 40. 10 tables outside. Private parties: 16 main room. Car-park, 30 places. Vegetarian meals. Children's helpings. Wheelchair access.
ACCOMMODATION: 16 rooms, 15 with bath/shower. B&B £35 to £70. Children welcome. Baby facilities. Pets welcome. Afternoon teas. Garden. Fishing. Phone. Scenic. Doors close at 12. Confirm by 6 [GHG]

KILFINAN Strathclyde map 8

▲ *Kilfinan Hotel* [10/20]

Kilfinan PA21 2AP
KILFINAN (070 082) 201 £19

The brochure has a pony and trap parked outside this white stone hotel and there's also a picture of a herd of sheep blocking the high street, either of which might account for the sparsity of reports over the last couple of years. But what there is on record is forthright: 'Should be in. It is comfortable and worth the journey for the scenery. All is home made, down to the bread.' Local produce is emphasised on a short, eight-dish menu, spread into four courses by a vegetable soup and dinner-party puddings. A local smokery provides salmon and venison. There is good fish, for example turbot with green peppercorn sauce or feuilleté of seafood with sorrel sauce. Bar meals, teas and business conferences are all accommodated. There is a good sound wine list with some clarets going back to the 1970s and also real ales in Youngers No. 3. CELLARMAN'S CHOICE: Ch. Méaume '83 £8.80.

CHEF: David Kinnear PROPRIETOR: N.K.S. Wills
OPEN: all week
MEALS: 12 to 2, 7.30 to 9.30
PRICES: £14 (£19), Set D £15 (£19). Snacks from £2. Service inc set only
CARDS: Access, Amex, Diners, Visa
SEATS: 24. 2 tables outside. Private parties: 50 main room. Car-park, 20 places. Children's helpings. Smart dress preferred. Wheelchair access (also WC). Music
ACCOMMODATION: 11 rooms, all with bath/shower. B&B £28 to £47. Deposit: 10%. Baby facilities. Pets welcome. Afternoon teas. Garden. Fishing. Golf. TV. Phone. Scenic. Doors close at 1 [GHG]

▲ *This restaurant offers accommodation.*

Many of the more expensive restaurants offer bargain lunches for half the price of a meal in the evening. Details are given in the text.

KILLIECRANKIE Tayside map 8

▲ *Killiecrankie Hotel* [10/20]

Killiecrankie PH16 5LG
PITLOCHRY (0796) 3220 £8–£16

Dinner in this whitewashed former dower-house is a choice of three or four courses. Casseroles, steaks and fish are the mainstays. On the set menu there is a nod towards home produce with Angus fillet and mustard sauce, Ayrshire duckling with bramble sauce, and a Scottish cheeseboard; and there are more local touches like smoked Ayrshire ham, on the bar menu. The wine list has almost as many half-bottles as bottles. House red and white from Justerini & Brooks £3.60. CELLARMAN'S CHOICE: Ch. Cissac '83, £7.50.

CHEF: Paul Booth PROPRIETORS: Mr and Mrs D. Hattersley Smith
OPEN: all week
CLOSED: mid-Oct to late Mar
MEALS: 12.30 to 2, 7 to 9 (bar meals to 10)
PRICES: Bar L £6 (£8), Bar D £8 (£10), Set D from £14 (£16). Service inc
SEATS: 70. Private parties: 20 main room. Car-park, 30 places. Vegetarian meals. Children's helpings (D only). No children under 5 at D. No smoking in dining-room. Wheelchair access (also WC)
ACCOMMODATION: 12 rooms, 10 with bath/shower. Rooms for disabled. B&B £21.15 to £42.30. No children under 1. Baby facilities. Pets welcome. Afternoon teas. Garden. Fishing. Golf. Scenic. Doors close at 12. Confirm by 6 [GHG]

KINBUCK Central map 8

▲ *Cromlix House* [new entry, zero rated]

Kinbuck FK15 9JT
DUNBLANE (0786) 822125 £16–£36

Woodcock, snipe, grouse and blue hare are shot on the 5,000-acre estate. Jacob lambs are bred, too, offering a stronger flavour and a texture closer to beef than normal lamb. Brown trout comes from the loch, wild watercress from the stream. Armed with this support, the kitchen with its six-course menu can offer some fine dishes. The setting is historic: the house has been in the same family for 500 years, and retains some sense of being lived in. The spacious candle-lit dining-room, in a wing of its own, has a pleasant atmosphere which encourages lingering, as long as the tartan-clad waitresses are not overly reverential. The menu is modern, expensive and capable of good ideas, such as a mille-feuille of monkfish and tomato coulis; cèpe consommé with herb quenelles; parfait of wild mushrooms and pheasant; sauté scallops with a fennel and leek compote and a Beaujolais butter; white coffee mousse with toasted hazelnuts and dark chocolate sauce; raspberry and strawberry sorbet. The rating is held back for a year because the pitch of the prices is so steep that one is led to believe this must be the best in Scotland, but as yet the style is developing. 'A seductive place for a second honeymoon – much too fuddy-duddy for a first.' There are some splendid bottles but sadly, considering the six-course structure, little by the glass. Some pretension, too – a page of Krug and another of labels up to

£100 – but the New World is represented and there are house wines under £10. House claret £8.50. CELLARMAN'S CHOICE: Pokolbin Chardonnay, Hungerford Hill '85, £10.65; Château Musar '78, £12.85. More reports, please.

CHEF: Mark Salter PROPRIETOR: The Hon. Ronald Eden
OPEN: all week
CLOSED: 2 weeks Feb
MEALS: 12.30 to 2.30, 7 to 10
PRICES: Set L £10.50 (£16) and £18 (£24), Set D £24 (£30) and £29 (£36). Snacks from £1.50
CARDS: Access, Amex, Diners, Visa
SEATS: 60. Private parties: 30 main room, 24,16, and 12 private rooms. Car-park, 30 places. Vegetarian meals. Children's helpings. No smoking. Wheelchair access (also WC)
ACCOMMODATION: 14 rooms, all with bath/shower. B&B £65 to £100. Deposit: 50%. Baby facilities. Pets welcome. Afternoon teas. Garden. Tennis. Fishing. Golf. TV. Phone. Scenic. Doors close at 12 [GHG]

KINGUSSIE Highland map 8

▲ *Cross* [14/20]

25–27 High Street, Kingussie PH21 1HX
KINGUSSIE (054 02) 762 £19

There are few four-course dinners of this standard for under £20 in Scotland. It is as if the whole enterprise were a hobby, an impression confirmed by the length of time it can take to talk over the menu and link up with the right wines. The glass-fronted converted shop is an unlikely setting for such an obsession; the Hadleys seem oblivious to the second-hand sofas, and to the fact that nothing in the dining-room matches anything else. This is in marked and welcome contrast to the baronial style of eating that plagues much of Scotland. The kitchen is a powerhouse. Simplicity is both keynote, even down to the repertoire, and strength. The salmon for gravlax is wild, fresh, and local, the acme of the genre, served with a tiny blob of dill-flavoured emulsification. Mousseline of scallops is wobbly and delicate, an unfussy, technically assured delight, balanced by a creamy sauce scattered with diced tomato flesh. There is no attempt to dress it up to either sound or look more than it is; the dish itself is everything, which is the essence of good cooking. Mushroom soup is enlivened with dried cèpes, and 'half wild duck' is both half a duck, and half-wild. The Hadleys relate that Queen Victoria, when in the Highlands, so enjoyed a venison dish not cooked by her chef Francatelli, that he determined to outdo his potential rival. The Cross version of venison Francatelli is based on his reply. Fillet of wild, local roe-deer, tender enough not to need much hanging, is seared, sliced, and served on a small plate with a translucent sweet-sharp port and redcurrant sauce. This is Highland cooking at its finest. Cheese comes on a small board covered with a damp cloth: Wellington, Cotherstone, Shropshire Blue, Langres, Gaperon. The heart of the wine list is an extremely good selection of clarets, concentrating on wines from vintages from '81 back as far as '61, although there are a few younger wines as well. Red Burgundy is less exciting but white Burgundy does have some good wines from growers such as Leflaive, William Fèvre and Vincent. Alsace and Loire wines are well selected, though the Rhône seems rather dull. The German section is much longer than is currently fashionable, most wines coming from top-class estates. Spain and Portugal are also well covered, as are some of the New World countries – Australia, California and New Zealand. New Zealand wines include both of the spectacularly good Cloudy Bay whites: Chardonnay and Sauvignon at £13.45 and £11.85. Five pages of half-bottles makes moderate drinkers' choice easy. Sweet wines are one of the greatest strengths of the list, many of them available in half-bottles. They come from all the classic dessert wines areas, including such rarities as Mâcon Clessé, Cuvée Spéciale Botrytis '83, £11.75 per half, and Sauternes Château Gilette '55, £85, as well as good selections from Sauternes, Barsac, the Loire, Germany and the occasional sweet wine from the New World. CELLARMAN'S CHOICE: Sauvignon Blanc, Cloudy Bay '87, £11.85; Rioja Gran Reserva, Domain Domecq '76, £8.85.

CHEF: Ruth Hadley PROPRIETORS: Tony and Ruth Hadley
OPEN: Tue to Sat, D only
CLOSED: 2 weeks May, 3 weeks Dec
MEALS: 6.30 to 9.30
PRICES: Set D from £13.50 (£19)
SEATS: 24. Private parties: 18 main room. Vegetarian meals. No children under 12. No smoking. Wheelchair access
ACCOMMODATION: 3 rooms, all with bath/shower. B&B £14.50 to £25. Deposit: £10. Fishing. Golf

LANGBANK Strathclyde map 8

▲ *Gleddoch House* [new entry, zero rated]

Langbank PA14 6YE
LANGBANK (047 554) 711
1/2m from Langbank on B789 £15–£32

It has taken a couple of years to build up a steady team and get the kind of consistency prices here demand, but opinion is that this has now been achieved. The house, originally that of a Clyde shipping magnate, has a distinct feel of space and luxury; there is a real log fire, gentlemen's-club leather armchairs and settees, a Mackintosh-style carpet of rich red and green in the drinks area and plate glass surrounding the dining-room. In the foreground is the garden complete with rabbits; beyond, a superb view of Dumbarton Rock. Service is excellent. Charles Price uses fresh and local produce, taking care with the quality of ingredients and final presentation. His sauces are to be recommended, but the essence is simplicity. An Easter lunch offered melon with fresh fruit, smoked trout mousse with salmon caviare, roast beef and Yorkshire pudding, loin of lamb with the hotel's own garden herbs and a sherry essence. Serve yourself for sweets and have the choice of a soft cheesecake with guava, madeira cake, profiteroles with dark chocolate sauce and fresh fruit salad – or sample a little of all of them. The cheeseboard is, however, not over-exciting. The wine list includes bottles from Italy, Spain, England, California, Australia, Lebanon and South Africa. House French is £7.50; CELLARMAN'S CHOICE: Cabernet Sauvignon, Napa Valley '78, £16 and, among the Bordeaux, Ch. Cissac '82, £19.

CHEF: Charles Price PROPRIETORS: Gleddoch Hotels Ltd
OPEN: all week, exc Sat L
MEALS: 12.30 to 2, 7.30 to 9.30
PRICES: £27 (£32), Set L from £9.25 (£15), Set D £22 (£28). Service inc
CARDS: Access, Amex, Diners, Visa
SEATS: 80. Private parties: 120 main room, 16, 36 private rooms. Car-park, 100 places. Vegetarian meals. Children's helpings on request. Jacket and tie. Wheelchair access (3 steps; also WC)
ACCOMMODATION: 33 rooms, all with bath/shower. B&B £62.50 to £88. Pets welcome. Afternoon teas. Garden. Swimming-pool. Sauna. Golf. Snooker. TV. Phone. Scenic [GHG]

LINLITHGOW Lothian map 8

Champany Inn [14/20]

Champany Corner, Linlithgow EH49 7LU
PHILPSTOUN (050 683) 4532 and 4388
2m NE of Linlithgow at junction of A904 and A803  £35

'There is no comparable meat I have tasted in Britain, or the US, or anywhere for that matter; and I'm from Texas.' Since the *Guide* discovered this now legendary steak-house in 1983 it has developed and branched out. A sea-water pool has brought lobsters, oysters and crayfish on to the menu (it is one of the few places one could recommend a prawn cocktail). Above all it has acquired that supreme restaurant virtue of consistency, and one or other of the Davidsons is in attendance every night. The menu deals essentially in steaks, salmon, a char-grill and fine wines. Salmon is offered six ways as a starter: grilled; hollandaise; gravlax ('none better'); smoked; marinated; in soup. There are five cuts of steak, all Aberdeen Angus, hung for twenty-eight days: pope's eye; sirloin; the eye from the rib; entrecôte; porterhouse – and another five for lamb from June to October. Spit-roast duckling, poussin and guinea-fowl properly require four hours and are best ordered when booking. Main courses include a choice from eight salads and five dressings. At heart the old-fashioned virtue of choice is a major feature of every aspect, though the choice from the sweets trolley diminishes as the evening progresses. There is a very fine crème brûlée – a shallow, Catalan version – sorbets, soufflés and profiteroles. One cheese only is offered: Colston Basset Stilton. Espresso coffee. The main restaurant borders on the expensive. It is a circular, stone-walled room with hexagonal ceiling; three-branch candelabras on wood tables; cuts of meat and fish are on show; there is a view into the kitchen through a glass window. 'A sociable, non-precious, professional atmosphere with firm suggestions.' The attached chop and ale house is half the price and half as consistent. One view says: 'Why pay more to eat the same steaks?' Another holds that the niggles – no booking, and people come to find it full; the small dining-room – would not earn it a rating in the main *Guide*. A deal has been arranged with Scottish and Newcastle

Breweries for a series of six to eight Champanys to open across Scotland, the first at the old Horseshoe Inn at Eddleston. Burgundy takes pride of place on the wine list (after ten house wines, six of which come from South Africa). Unusually, though, there are nearly five times as many pages devoted to red Burgundies as white, and these include illustrious names such as Domaine de la Romanée-Conti, Hubert de Montille, Domaine de la Pousse d'Or, Domaine Machard de Gramont, Tollot-Beaut, and others too numerous to mention. After this Burgundian cornucopia, the 11 pages of Bordeaux wines come as an anti-climax, although in comparison with most restaurants, the list, back to '45, with several vintages of Châteaux Latour and Lafite, is impressive though not cheap. Other French regions get shorter shrift, but the Italian and German sections are surprisingly good for a list compiled by such a Burgundophile. California and Australia are treated seriously, although not at great length, with wines from Stag's Leap, Mondavi, Beaulieu Vineyards, Penfold, Wynns, Rothbury, and the like. You have to hunt to find the sweet wines: apart from a selection of white Bordeaux sweeties (Château Montalivet, first on the page, is not sweet), there are a couple of Trockenbeerenauslesen from the Rhine, two '76 Vendange Tardive Alsace wines from Trimbach, a Quarts de Chaume, Château de L'Echarderie '78, £25.50, from the Loire, and a Muscat de Rivesaltes, Château de Rey, £18. House wine from £7.50.

CHEFS: David Gibson and Clive Davidson PROPRIETORS: Clive and Anne Davidson
OPEN: Mon to Sat, exc Sat L
CLOSED: 3 weeks at Christmas
MEALS: 12.30 to 2, 7.15 to 10
PRICES: £25 (£35). Minimum £9.50. Service 10%
CARDS: Access, Amex, Diners, Visa
SEATS: 50. 13 tables outside. Private parties: 50 main room. Car-park, 100 places. No children under 8. Smart dress preferred. Wheelchair access

MELROSE Borders map 8

Marmion's Brasserie [10/20]

Buccleuch Street, Melrose TD6 9LB
MELROSE (089 682) 2245 £14

Food in the wood-panelled dining-room is limited outside of mealtimes. Then the style comes into its own with carrot and coriander soup, croque monsieur, or deep-fried monkfish tails doubling as starters or light meals. Falafel, dips, and vegetable lasagne feature among non-meat dishes, and sweets include profiteroles, cranachan and lemon mousse. Service is friendly, and there is decent Beaujolais on the short wine list. House French is £4.95.

CHEF: Seoras Lindsay PROPRIETORS: Ian and Sheila Robson
OPEN: all week
MEALS: 12 to 2, 6.30 to 10
PRICES: £10 (£14), Snacks from £1.10
CARD: Access
SEATS: 60. Private parties: 60 main room. Vegetarian meals. Children's helpings. No pipes in dining-room. Wheelchair access (1 step; also WC). Music. Air-conditioned

NEWTON STEWART Dumfries & Galloway map 8

▲ *Kirroughtree Hotel* [12/20]

Newton Stewart DG8 6AN
NEWTON STEWART (0671) 2141 £18–£29

The modern baroque hotel on the New Galloway road has been under new management since the end of 1987. Ornate chairs in the lounge, a triumphant staircase, and boldly patterned carpets are a suitable *Dallas*-like prelude to the two dining-rooms: red for smokers, and a blue one looking as if Wedgwood had taken to interior design. Lunch is a relatively inexpensive *carte* written in English; dinner comprises the same items translated into French, marked up, and arranged in a four-course format. The style is somewhere mid-Channel. Easily assembled starters such as melon with sorbet, or a salad – of smoked meat, smoked fish, pheasant pâté and a quail's egg – give the kitchen time to concentrate on their meat-plus-sauce formula for main courses: beef with red wine, lamb with mint, red snapper with tomato and basil. A selection of local fish in Noilly Prat sauce runs generously to seven different kinds. Puddings take in crème brûlée and a hot raspberry soufflé, while the wine list has something for everybody. House French £6.25. CELLARMAN'S CHOICE: Moulin à Vent, Domaine de la Rochelle '85, £11.15; Rosemount Cabernet Sauvignon, Show Reserve '85, £13; Ch. Cissac '75, £29.40.

CHEFS: Adi Schmid and Ian Bennett PROPRIETOR: Mr Dilks
OPEN: all week
CLOSED: early Jan to end Feb
MEALS: 12.30 to 1.30, 7 to 9.30
PRICES: L £12 (£18), Set D £23 (£29), Snacks from £1.50
SEATS: 60. 8 tables outside. Private parties: 30 main room, 30 private room. Car-park, 40 places. Vegetarian meals. No children under 10. Jacket and tie. No-smoking area. Wheelchair access (also WC)
ACCOMMODATION: 22 rooms, all with bath/shower. B&B £39 to £78. Deposit: 10%. No children under 10. Pets by arrangement. Afternoon teas. Garden. Tennis. Fishing. Golf. TV. Phone. Scenic

NORTH BERWICK Lothian map 8

Harding's [new entry, zero rated]

2 Station Road, North Berwick EH39 4AU
NORTH BERWICK (0620) 4737 £17

This former hairdresser's down the road from the station has been transformed into an open-plan restaurant with a modern menu and a range of Australian wines. The evening menu on a blackboard offers three dishes per course, but compensates with generous portions and neat presentation. Typical have been spicy marinated herring on a salad of oak-leaf, radicchio, iceberg and cherry tomatoes; fanned avocado dressed with hazelnut oil and served with ham; medallions of beef with a cream and bay sauce. Cheeses are French and British. To finish there has been a filo pastry case filled with peaches on a rum and cream sauce. Ample coffee is served in old-fashioned cups with green borders, with chocolate truffles. The Australian wines run to eight pages compared to two for French – the quality is there, but so is the price, opening at £9.80. More reports, please.

CHEF/PROPRIETOR: Christopher Harding
OPEN: Tue to Sat, exc Tue D
MEALS: 12 to 2, 7.30 to 9
PRICES: Set D £12.50 (£17)
SEATS: 25. Private parties: 30 main room. Car-park, 3 places. Vegetarian meals on request. Children's helpings. Wheelchair access (also WC). Music

OBAN Strathclyde map 8

▲ *Knipoch Hotel* [11/20]

Oban PA34 4QT
KILNINVER (085 26) 251
on A16, 6m S of Oban

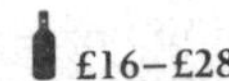
£16–£28

The Georgian building stands just back from the road half way along the shore of Loch Feochan. Local produce, especially fish, dominates the cooking, although the Craigs point out that supplies are not cheap, with competition between the London and European markets pushing up the price of seafood. Also, 'the seas are being cleaned out without any sense of harvesting or management and *all* sizes of crustacean are bought. This will inevitably result in a dearth of lobster, scallops and langoustines in five to ten years. It is not that the Highlands have a low standard of living, it is more that they have a high cost of living.' Even so, the daily-changing menu still delivers: new additions, like hot smoked scallops with lemon mayonnaise, saddle of venison with game mousse, oat biscuit baskets with cinnamon ice-cream and nougat sauce, are often inspired by local produce. Otherwise, five-course dinners can include parsnip soup, duck pâté in pastry with bramble sauce, and medallions of lamb with sorrel sauce. Smoked salmon and gravlax are cured on the premises; sausages and salami are bought in. The wine list is wide ranging in source and price, with about half the bottles coming from France. Clarets go back to '52, and include three from the wonderful '61 vintage. There are good Beaujolais and an impeccable selection of red Burgundies, some of the finest names of the Côte d'Or. White Burgundies are not quite so consistent, but include some excellent wines, and Rhônes are good. The Spanish selection is better than usual, mostly Riojas from CVNE, but with a trio of fine and less usual wines: Cabernet Sauvignon, Marqués de Griñon '82, £12.50, Viña Pesquera '82, £16.60 and Valbuena '82, £21, from the famous Vega Sicilia estate. Italian wines are from excellent to reputable producers. There are a few antipodean wines, and top-class Californians and Germans. Sweet wines range from Muscat de Beaumes de Venise at £2.40 per glass through Brown Bros Orange Muscat and Flora, £6.50 per half-bottle, German Beerenauslesen, Trockenbeeren-auslesen and Eiswein, excellent Vouvray '76 and Hungarian Tokay Five Putts, to the immature glory of Château d'Yquem '83, £67.50 per half-bottle. House wines from £4.80.

CHEFS: Colin and Jenny Craig PROPRIETORS: The Craig family
OPEN: all week
CLOSED: early Jan to mid-Feb
MEALS: 12.30 to 1.30, 7.30 to 9
PRICES: Set L £12.50 (£16), Set D £23 (£28)
CARDS: Access, Amex, Diners, Visa
SEATS: 46. Private parties: 24 main room. Car-park, 40 places. Children's helpings
ACCOMMODATION: 21 rooms, all with bath/shower. B&B £42 to £84. Deposit: £50. Afternoon teas. TV. Phone. Scenic. Doors close at 11. Confirm by 6 [GHG]

PEAT INN Fife map 8

▲ *Peat Inn* [15/20]

10 YEARS

Peat Inn KY15 5LH
PEAT INN (033 484) 206 £17–£31

The unlikely setting seems barely to have changed since the photograph that now fronts the menu was taken by the postman in 1904. The Wilsons defy the logic of restaurateuring but continue to draw people to this crossroads for no other reason than a modern rendition of the Auld Alliance. And now with eight lavish bedroom suites, each named after the furnishing fabric used, and a rosette in the *Michelin*, they are launched into the international stratosphere. But this is no manor – no baronial grandeur, its heritage as an inn is still plain, the six-course tasting menu offering no sorbets. The *carte* has eight starters, six main dishes, eight sweets remarkable for their quality and value. David Wilson has taken a style of cooking about as far as it goes. At heart it is about classical skills being applied to regional foods. For instance, a flan of Arbroath smokies, a pastry-less dish of a hot mousse decorated with a julienne of vegetables, with a warm lemon vinaigrette made with first-class olive oil, set on a bed of cooked cabbage with some toasted pine kernels to create a contrast of smokies and toast. Or, in a tasting meal to avoid too many reduction sauces, a pigeon breast sliced into a julienne set on lentils and sauced with stock thickened with mushroom. Other recommended dishes have been: lobster and crab vinaigrette; monkfish with Barsac; venison with redcurrant and stock sauce; lemon sole with vermouth and dill; caramelised apple pastry with a caramel sauce. 'Surprisingly relaxed for its reputation.' Some have suggested it might be past its peak but inspectors have found no evidence to support this theory. The impressive wine list concentrates on France, with especially goodd sections on Bordeaux and Burgundy, but there are good wines from Australia and California, too, and a few top bottles from Spain and Italy listed alongside the French regions whose styles they most match. Claret in profusion ranges from very good lesser wines and drinkable young vintages of finer châteaux to mature and very mature vintages of the top classed growths. Burgundies and Chablis are also well chosen, mostly from individual estates. A full range from Pol Roger stars in a reasonably priced champagne selection, and briefer selections from elsewhere in France are also good. Choice of sweet wines is fairly limited. By the bottle, apart from a few German Spätlesen (not sweet enough to go with most desserts), there are just a couple of Barsac-Sauternes and three sweet Loires, all from lesser vintages, some of them quite old. Best value look to be two half-bottles of sweet German wines, especially Piesporter Goldtröpfchen Riesling Beerenauslese '76 from the Zentralkellerei in Bernkastel, the Mosel's huge co-operative (£14 per half). 'Bathrooms are marvellous. How they can charge only £82 per double room per night, including breakfast, service and tax, defies imagination. I would recommend you go soon, because as soon as the foreign golfers hear about this gem you will have to book months in advance.'

CHEF: David Wilson PROPRIETORS: David and Patricia Wilson
OPEN: Tue to Sat
CLOSED: 2 weeks Jan, 2 weeks Nov
MEALS: 12.30 to 1, 7 to 9.30
PRICES: £22 (£26), Set L £13.50 (£17), Set D £23 (£26) to £28 (£31). Service inc
CARDS: Access, Amex, Diners, Visa
SEATS: 48. Private parties: 24 main room, 12 private room. Car-park, 24 places. Children's helpings. No smoking during meals. Wheelchair access (also WC)
ACCOMMODATION: 8 rooms, all with bath/shower. Rooms for disabled. B&B £65 to £90. No children under 12. Fishing. Golf. TV. Phone. Scenic. Confirm by 4 [GHG]

PEEBLES Borders map 8

▲ *Cringletie House* [10/20]

10 YEARS

Eddleston, Peebles EH45 8PL
EDDLESTON (072 13) 233
on A703, 2m N of Peebles £14–£22

Floodlit at night, this red-stone, nineteenth-century baronial house looks spectacular approached over a bridge and up a bend in the drive. Inside there is elegance and comfort. Mrs Maguire appears to have regained control of the kitchen to good effect. There is some proper cooking, not the usual hotel clichés – tarts of mustard, Gruyère and tomato; a pâté of smoked cods' roe; excellent stuffed aubergine with walnut, celery, mushroom and onions with wholemeal rolls. Soups are usually vegetable. Main dishes often come with busy sauces – apricots and green peppercorns with pork; or lime and coconut for lamb kebab, plus couscous. Lamb's liver is served simply with a mustard sauce. The sweets trolley offers a good finale, with such temptations as hazelnut gateau and chocolate parfait with Kahlùa. House French from Georges Duboeuf is £6.90 on a basic list. CELLARMAN'S CHOICE: Sancerre, Clos du Chêne Marchand '85, £12; Côte de Brouilly, Ch. Thivin '86, £9.90.

Restaurants change owners and chefs constantly. It is very useful if you keep the Guide *informed of any changes you find.*

The Guide *is independent, accepts no advertising and survives solely on the number of copies sold.*

CHEFS: Aileen Maguire and Sheila McKellar PROPRIETORS: Mr and Mrs Stanley Maguire
OPEN: all week
CLOSED: Jan and Feb
MEALS: 1 to 1.45, 7.30 to 8.30
PRICES: L £8 (£14), Set D £16.50 (£22)
CARDS: Access, Visa
SEATS: 56. Private parties: 30 main room. Car-park, 40 places. Vegetarian meals. Children's helpings. No smoking in dining-room
ACCOMMODATION: 16 rooms, 11 with bath/shower. Lift. B&B £26.50 to £55. Children welcome. Baby facilities. Pets welcome. Afternoon teas. Garden. Tennis. TV. Phone. Scenic. Doors close at 11. Confirm by 5 [GHG]

PERTH Tayside map 8

Timothy's [11/20]

24 St John Street, Perth PH1 5SP
PERTH (0738) 26641 £13

Danish food is the backbone of the Laings' town-centre restaurant, a building dating from 1725. Snitter are predominantly fishy appetisers: sweet herring, pickled mussels, prawns, home-smoked fish pâte or crabmeat wrapped in smoked salmon. Soup is an alternative, from spicy chicken and coconut to beef with orange and walnut. Smørrebrød is the main business – open sandwiches combining ham and curried banana, or roast beef with potato salad and pickle. Fondue bourguignonne (minimum two people) uses Scottish beef, and puddings are traditional British: cabinet pudding, jam roly-poly, strawberry tart. Ice-cold akvavit is £1 a shot. House French £5.45; CELLARMAN'S CHOICE: Torres Viña Esmaralda £6.25.

CHEF: C. Laing PROPRIETORS: C. and A. Laing
OPEN: Tue to Sat
CLOSED: 3 weeks in summer
MEALS: 12 to 2.30, 7 to 10.15
PRICES: £8 (£13). Post-theatre menu. Cover 25p at D. Minimum £5 at D
CARD: Access
SEATS: 54. Private parties: 20 main room. Vegetarian meals. Children's helpings. Wheelchair access. Music. Air-conditioned

Tayside Round-up

ROOMS: *Carriage Room,* Montrose Road, Arbroath, (0241 75755); *Lands of Loyal Hotel,* Loyal Road, Alyth (082 83 3151).
INEXPENSIVE: *Perth Theatre,* High Street, Perth (0738 21031); *Cairn Lodge,* Auchterarder (0764 62431).
COFFEE SHOP: *Penny Black,* 1 High Street, Blairgowrie (0250 5294).

Places rating 9 may not be restaurants at all, but still serve good food; expect to find pubs, cafés, small hotels and wine bars

The price quoted in brackets is for an average three-course meal including service, VAT, *coffee and half a bottle of house wine or the equivalent in an ethnic restaurant.*

PORT APPIN Strathclyde map 8

▲ *Airds Hotel* [15/20]

Port Appin PA38 4DF
APPIN (063 173) 236 £17–£32

The simple whitewashed stone house beside Loch Linnhe, on a tiny road that loops around the peninsula, is more of a guest-house than a hotel. With windows running the length of the dining-room, and facing west, there is no need for excess ornament. The emphasis is firmly on the food. Betty Allen, helped in the kitchen by David Barclay, whom she has trained since he left school, cooks a four-course menu of Scottish provenance. Langoustines are landed in the village, salmon 10 miles away, and scallops and lobster come from Mallaig. Guests assemble in the drawing-room for dinner at eight, and much of it sounds simple: savoury apple with tarragon cream, chicken-liver pâté with toasted brioche, roast rib of Aberdeen Angus beef. But the skill shows through in a mousseline of scallops, hedged round with beurre blanc, and in creamy soups of courgette and rosemary, and pea and mint. There is continuity in the style, and the best dishes survive the passage of time: saddle of venison with rowanberry jelly; roast loin of lamb with onion marmalade. Vegetables are copious and timing is precise: home-grown mange-tout, courgettes and flavoursome waxy new potatoes. Cheeses are Scottish farmhouse, and puddings are in the Franco-British mould: orange and Grand Marnier terrine, chocolate roulade, strawberry Pavlova. Mr Allen rises at 5.45am to bake bread before the kitchen is needed for breakfast. The substantial wine list is strongest on Bordeaux, with some good *crus bourgeois* and well-chosen finer clarets back to '66, and Burgundy, predominantly from merchants, but including also some names of top individual growers, such as Leflaive and Vincent. Champagne has ranges of Bollinger, Krug, Moët and Pol Roger, and there are shorter lists of good wines from elsewhere in France, plus small selections from California, Australia, Spain and, less illustrious than the rest of the list, Italy. Sweet wines are not a strong point, but there are several expensive Sauternes, several Alsace Vendange Tardive from a variety of grapes and including a couple of '76s, and some good sweet Germans, again including some from the exceptional '76 vintage. Only one comes in a half-bottle, and that is an extraordinary rarity: Piesporter Goldtröpfchen Riesling Trockenbeerenauslese '76 from Reichsgraf von Kesselstatt, £40 per half. House French £8.

CHEFS: Betty Allen and David Barclay PROPRIETORS: Eric and Betty Allen
OPEN: all week
MEALS: 12.30 to 1.30, 8 to 8.30
PRICES: Set L from £11 (£17), Set D £25 (£32)
SEATS: 40. Private parties: 40 main room, 8 private room. Car-park, 30 places. Children's helpings. No children under 6. Smart dress preferred. No smoking in dining-room. Wheelchair access
ACCOMMODATION: 14 rooms, all with bath/shower. B&B £50 to £90. Deposit: £50. Children welcome. Pets by arrangement. Afternoon teas. Garden. TV. Phone. Scenic. Doors close at 11.45. Confirm by 4 [GHG]

PORTPATRICK Dumfries & Galloway map 8

▲ *Knockinaam Lodge* [13/20]

Portpatrick DG9 9AD
PORTPATRICK (077 681) 471 £17–£27

The long single-track road that leads to the shore-side lodge makes it secluded even by Scottish standards, but the welcome is a handshake on the doorstep from Corinna Frichot. Despite stags' heads in the small panelled bar, it avoids the excesses of 'tourist baronial' style; a dozen antique flower prints, one for each month, decorate the westward-facing dining-room. Chef Daniel Galmiche wears a modern French heart on his sleeve – turbot is served with lentils, and pig's trotter is stuffed with cèpes and chicken – but the proprietors' background in the Seychelles occasionally injects a dish such as a fillet of sweet, fleshy red snapper in a marigold-coloured sauce gently flavoured with passion-fruit, strewn with tiny shreds of green pepper cooked in sugar. A sense of balance and restraint prevails; the main ingredient dominates each dish, while flavourings are used to sharpen the focus. A warm salad of just-cooked quail on a mound of tagliatelle comes without the usual leafy cliché, in a perfectly judged dressing; the thyme, in a rich sauce for lamb baked in a salt crust, is chopped in at the last minute. Care extends from the ham croissant in the bar to chocolate-dipped tuile in the lounge with coffee, and is supported by a 60-bottle wine list plus an enterprising couple of pages of half-bottles. House claret £7.50; CELLARMAN'S CHOICE: Sancerre '86, £11.80.

CHEF: Daniel Galmiche PROPRIETORS: Marcel and Corinna Frichot
OPEN: all week
CLOSED: Jan to Easter
MEALS: 12 to 1.30, 7.30 to 9
PRICES: £13 (£17) L only, Set D £23 (£27). Service inc
CARDS: Access, Amex, Diners, Visa
SEATS: 28. Private parties: 40 main room. Car-park, 25 places. No children under 12. Jacket and tie. No smoking in dining-room. Wheelchair access (1 step; also WC)
ACCOMMODATION: 10 rooms, all with bath/shower. B&B £55 to £80. Deposit: £100. Baby facilities. Pets welcome. Afternoon teas. Garden. Fishing. TV. Phone. Scenic [GHG]

SCARISTA Isle of Harris map 8

▲ *Scarista House* [11/20]

Scarista, Isle of Harris PA85 3HX
SCARISTA (085 985) 238
on A859, 15m SW of Tarbert £23

Alison Johnson has written the story of her remote hotel in *A House by the Shore*. The Church of Scotland manse looks west towards the Atlantic; inside is a rather Spartan, stone-walled dining-room. The Johnsons' philosophy is to avoid all factory-farmed produce – including fish – and to put their faith in fresh and wild ingredients. Of late they have taken more of a back seat in the operation, to give themselves a breather. Three-course set dinners centre on dishes such as roast rump of venison with rosemary jelly or scallops with mushrooms. Despite the distance from the mainland, meals always feature vegetables in abundance: potatoes in white wine, gratin of fennel and courgettes, turnips in white sauce. The cheeseboard might feature crowdie and home-made 'yoghurt cheese' served with crackers and oatcakes. Help-yourself breakfasts include oatmeal porridge, kippers, black and white puddings, as well as a choice of tea and coffee. Some 70 wines, starting at £3.75 for half a carafe of Corbières red or white. Rosemount Show Reserve Chardonnay '86 is £13.60; claret starts at £7. Eight dessert wines, of which six are in half-bottles.

CHEFS: Alison Johnson, Morag Macleod and Lena Maclennan PROPRIETORS: Andrew and Alison Johnson
OPEN: Mon to Sat, D only
CLOSED: Nov to Mar
MEALS: 8
PRICES: Set D £17 (£23)
SEATS: 20. Private parties: 8 main room. Car-park, 10 places. Vegetarian meals. Children's helpings. No children under 8. No smoking. Wheelchair access. One sitting
ACCOMMODATION: 7 rooms, all with bath/shower. B&B £40 to £56. Deposit: £25. No children under 8. Pets welcome. Garden. Phone. Scenic. Confirm by 6 [GHG]

ST ANDREWS Fife map 8

Grange Inn [11/20]

Grange Road, St Andrews KY16 8LJ
ST ANDREWS (0334) 72670 £11–£20

The Inn is on a hill a mile south of St Andrews, and the panoramic view from the picture window of the dining-room takes in the town, the Tay estuary and the Angus hills beyond. Lunch is as simple as lentil soup, chicken breast with a sauce of stock and cream, and apple pie, and dinner expands to four courses, on the lines of smoked salmon and avocado with yoghurt and wine dressing; noisettes of venison marinated in Alsace wine and juniper berries; duck in a peach and brandy sauce. The cooking has a homely quality, well-founded on good timing and sound ingredients, but moves up a gear for langoustine with wild mushrooms, and pear and ginger ice-cream. There are bar lunches and suppers too. Forty wines start with house French from Duboeuf at £6.50. CELLARMAN'S CHOICE: carafe Fitou '85, £7.50 a litre.

CHEF: George Keith PROPRIETORS: R.H.C.C. Ltd
OPEN: all week, exc Mon
MEALS: 12.30 to 2, 7 to 9.30
PRICES: Set L £6.50 (£11), Set D £15 (£20)
CARDS: Access, Amex, Diners, Visa
SEATS: 34. 4 tables outside. Private parties: 34 main room. Car-park, 20 places. Vegetarian meals. Children's helpings. No smoking in dining-room. Wheelchair access (2 steps)

The Guide *is independent, accepts no advertising and survives solely on the number of copies sold.*

Fife Round-up

VEGETARIAN: *Brambles*, College Street, St Andrews (0334 75380).
ROOMS: *Parkland Hotel & Restaurant*, Kinburn Castle, St Andrews (0334 73620).
BAR MEALS: *Pine woods Hotel*, St Michael's, Leuchar (033 483 385).
COFFEE SHOP: *Riverside Coffee Shop*, 28 Tay Street, Newport-on-Tay (0382 542339).

SCONE Tayside map 8

▲ *Murrayshall Hotel* [12/20]

Scone PH2 7PH
SCONE (0738) 51171 £18–£29

The large 1920s house might have been redecorated by somebody from the Barbara Cartland school of interior design: the bar is overwhelmingly floral, the residents' lounge is awash in blue fabric, the dining-room's watered silk provides a backdrop for Old Master prints. The menu reads like a chapter from one of the books; soups are so 'heart-warming' and salads so 'healthy and refreshing' that there is little left for the food to suggest for itself. That it does is a tribute to Bruce Sangster, who has gathered enough Scottish produce to make an impact: Achiltibuie cheese in the cauliflower soup; breast of Perthshire pigeon, cooked rare, sliced, and served with a sweet and sharp timbale of red cabbage, on a well-reduced juniper sauce. Some dishes can lack flair, and there is a reliance on blackcurrant liqueur, vermouth, madeira, Pernod and the like, for sauces. But puddings are well done; a warm pastry case holding a poached pear is served with a light custard infused with Poire William. The 'cellar book' specialises in young vintages of prestige wines with hefty mark-ups; an '85 Pouilly-Fuissé is £45, for instance, while a Brown Bros Chardonnay of the same year is a quarter of the price. Relative bargains are to be had from the lesser-known sources. House French from Corney and Barrow is £7. CELLARMAN'S CHOICE: Pokolbin Australian Chardonnay '86, £10.75.

CHEF: Bruce Sangster PROPRIETORS: MacOlsen Limited
OPEN: all week
MEALS: 12.30 to 1.45, 7 to 9.30
PRICES: Set L £12.75 (£18), Set D £22.50 (£29)
CARDS: Access, Amex, Diners, Visa
SEATS: 60. Private parties: 20 main room, 70 private room. Car-park. Vegetarian meals. Jacket and tie. No smoking in dining-room. Wheelchair access. Music
ACCOMMODATION: 19 rooms, all with bath/shower. B&B £55 to £80. Deposit: 50%. No children under 12. Pets welcome. Afternoon teas. Garden. Tennis. Golf. TV. Phone. Scenic. Confirm by 6

It is helpful if restaurants keep the office up to date with any changes.

Places rating 9 may not be restaurants at all, but still serve good food; expect to find pubs, cafés, small hotels and wine bars.

SLEAT Isle Of Skye map 8

▲ *Kinloch Lodge* [13/20]

10 YEARS

Isle Ornsay, Sleat IV43 8QY
ISLE ORNSAY (047 13) 214/333
1m off A851 between Broadford and Armadale £26

'Though the food is excellent, you need to stay at the hotel to appreciate its finest qualities. It is a white country lodge situated on its own sea-loch facing the mainland and reached along a half-mile track.' Lady Macdonald's Lodge is now in its fifteenth year among the aristocracy of the northern Scottish country houses. It is less glitzy, the house and rooms less imposing, and the staff more good-humoured than its credentials might suggest. The menus offer three courses with two choices at each stage, and span the many different influences of the last 20 years. At their heart are classic English roasts, local fish with sauces, slow casseroles of game in season and some fine traditional puddings – tea-breads and tarts supplemented with a cordon bleu-style range of meringues and mousses. But in high summer there is more than a touch of the Mediterranean in dishes like aubergine salad or squid with tomatoes and black olives. Soups are often striking combinations, as in leek and chanterelle or tomato, apricot and cumin, while other starters are the decorative terrines and roulades of private dinner parties. Fish is a constant theme. Crab in winter may be a soufflé, a gratin, a tart. Salmon is baked and served with hollandaise. Look also for wolf fish poached and served with a saffron and tomato sauce. Other game dominates the menu according to season. Vegetables are always imaginative, as in spaghetti courgettes with garlic, beetroot baked with cream, pepper ragoût or purée of turnips with cashew nuts. The wine list leans primarily to France, with house claret at £7, and white Bordeaux at £6.50. 'For sheer value and reasonable drinking our house wines are always recommended.'

CHEFS: Lady Macdonald and Peter Macpherson PROPRIETORS: Lord and Lady Macdonald
OPEN: all week, D only
CLOSED: 4 days at Christmas, 11 Jan to 28 Feb
MEALS: 8
PRICES: Set D £22 (£26). Service inc
SEATS: 25. Private parties: 8 main room. Car-park, 25 places. Children's helpings (D only). No children under 10. Wheelchair access (also WC). One sitting
ACCOMMODATION: 10 rooms, 9 with bath/shower. Rooms for disabled. B&B £40 to £80. Deposit: £50. Baby facilities. Pets welcome. Afternoon teas. Garden. Fishing. Scenic. Confirm by 3 [GHG]

All inspections are carried out anonymously.

Restaurants are checked every year and their entries rewritten. The restaurant scene changes very rapidly. Don't trust an out-of-date Guide.

STEWARTON Strathclyde map 8

▲ *Chapeltoun House* [new entry, zero rated]

Stewarton KA3 3ED
STEWARTON (0560) 82696
2m from Stewarton on B769 towards
Irvine £20–£27

'Any restaurant serving pheasant soup with whisky flavouring should not be in the *Guide*,' is one view of this solid, well-built turn-of-the-century re-creation of a manor house, with a lot of dark golden oak panelling, heavy plasterwork ceilings and large light rooms. Colin and Graeme McKenzie have brought the restaurant back to the listings, complete with its fine views over rose gardens to wooded hills, on the strength of some complex set meals. Fillet steak carries a £2.50 supplement. The main business is warm salads of chicken livers with chestnuts and raspberries; parfait of wood-pigeon with a redcurrant and orange compote; filo purses filled with smoked haddock and served on a curried cream sauce; new season's lamb served with a bavarois of scallops and basil. Sweets are more old-fashioned, laid on their own table to help yourself to gateaux, cakes, tarts, exemplary crème caramel and bowls of fruit. Cafetière coffee comes with petits fours. Two hundred wines open with house at £8.50. More reports, please.

CHEF: George McIvor PROPRIETORS: Colin and Graeme McKenzie
OPEN: all week
MEALS: 12 to 2, 7 to 9.15
PRICES: Set L from £14 (£20), Set D £20 (£27), Snacks from £1.70
CARDS: Access, Amex, Visa
SEATS: 55. Private parties: 35 main room, 20 and 55 private rooms. Car-park, 50 places. Vegetarian meals. No children under 12. Smart dress preferred. No smoking in dining-room. Wheelchair access (3 steps; also WC)
ACCOMMODATION: 8 rooms, all with bath/shower. B&B £65 to £90. No children under 12. Pets welcome. Afternoon teas. Garden. Fishing. TV. Phone. Scenic. Doors close at 12. Confirm by 1 [GHG]

TIRORAN Strathclyde map 8

▲ *Tiroran House* [10/20]

Tiroran, Mull PA69 6ES
TIRORAN (068 15) 232 £24

On the south side of the island, beautifully situated overlooking Loch Scridain, is this rambling Victorian house with a conservatory that serves as entrance and dining area. The Blockeys have filled the house with their own taste in furniture, some very fine, some just sentimental. The cooking makes some attempt to get away from the usual. There are interesting soups, such as old English mustard, main dishes such as roast duck or poached trout with a scallop mousseline, surrounded by excellent vegetables (for the duck, roast, sliced, potatoes, cucumber cooked with savory, purée of turnips, baby carrots), then sweet sweets, on the lines of banoffi pie or meringues. Good breakfasts feature fine porridge. House French is £7.

CHEF: Sue Blockey PROPRIETORS: Wing Commander and Mrs Blockey
OPEN: all week, D only (L residents only)
CLOSED: early Oct to mid-May
MEALS: 7
PRICES: Set D £20 (24). Service inc
SEATS: 20. Private parties: 8 main room. Car-park, 20 places. No children under 10. Jacket and tie. No smoking in dining room. One sitting
ACCOMMODATION: 9 rooms, all with bath/shower. B&B £38 to £77. Deposit: £25. No children under 10. Pets welcome. Garden. Fishing. Scenic [GHG]

TURNBERRY Strathclyde map 8

▲ *Turnberry Hotel* [11/20]

Turnberry KA26 9LT
TURNBERRY (0655) 31000 £19–£37

Operations of this scale and reputation present unique problems to guidebooks. They are consistent in the sense that they are always open. More than that, there is usually a genuine effort to set a standard and for any discerning diner prepared to assess the merits in an investigative, forthright fashion there will always be smoked salmon, fine steaks and vintage claret and Burgundy to fall back on. But equally, last year's 13/20 can also prompt the reaction, 'I can't imagine how this got into the *Guide*,' following a lunch in March. There is no overall dropping of standards, rather a hotel of this proportion – dwarfed only by Culzean Castle, five miles up the road – will tend to show itself in fits of good and bad. Like the weather forecast it is rarely all sun or all rain, more often 'changeable'. Alas there is no concession on prices on the *carte* – a £40 bill for one for lunch demands the sternest scrutiny and by that criterion it does not pass. On the other hand, set meals at £12.75 for lunch and £22.50 for dinner offer more reasonable access to the cruise-liner effect of the lemon and white dining-room; it is ironic that the franchise is run by Orient Express, owned by Cunard, on behalf of a Japanese concern, obviously attracted by the golf (see also Nippan Kan, under Liphook in England). The room is vast and sometimes patrolled by nearly as many waiters as there are customers. The real question is, can a dining-room of this pretension and dimension survive in Ayrshire? Even in Paris it might struggle. And what is to be made of a wine list with some horrendous mark-ups, served by a wine waiter who has said to a query about oxidisation, 'Oh, I wouldn't know anything about that.'! What is to be done? Why sell gastronomy if you do not know? Why do it in Ayrshire? Do we take it that three variations of pasta dishes and dishes like roast supreme of guinea-fowl with mousseline of broccoli, turnip and carrot are only there as a sop to restaurant inspectors and the naïve? If so, then this book remains sceptical. Better surely to slash the menu and stay with the restaurant's strengths, which are undoubted in terms of numbers, ambience and presence. House claret opens at £11.25. CELLARMAN'S CHOICE: Ch. Cabannieux '83, £18.

Restaurants are not expected to solicit customers to send in reports. Please let us know if this happens to you.

CHEF: D.S. Cameron PROPRIETORS: Nitto World Company Ltd
OPEN: all week
MEALS: 1 to 2.30, 7.30 to 9.30
PRICES: £29 (£37), Set L £12.75 (£19), Set D £22.50 (£29). Service inc
CARDS: Access, Amex, Diners, Visa
SEATS: 250. Private parties: 150 main room, 20 and 40 private rooms. Car-park, 200 places. Vegetarian meals. Children's helpings. Jacket and tie. Wheelchair access (also WC). Music
ACCOMMODATION: 128 rooms, all with bath/shower. Rooms for disabled. Lift. B&B £65 to £105. Children welcome. Baby facilities. Pets welcome. Afternoon teas. Garden. Swimming-pool. Sauna. Tennis. Fishing. Golf. Snooker. TV. Phone. Scenic

ULLAPOOL Highland map 8

▲ *Altnaharrie Inn* [15/20]

Ullapool IV26 2SS
DUNDONNELL (085 483) 230  £38

Is it really credible that on this tiny peninsula, reached by ferry, a small cottage discovered by the *Guide* in 1983 can offer cooking and wines to 14 people to rival the best in the country? No one who has been says otherwise, though its fame now means that in practice only overnight guests can eat here. The charm is of another era. Reports read like fantasy: 'Fluffy, silky bantams, guinea-fowl, pheasants, ducks and peacocks ran to greet us with retinues of young...', though another reader points out that the 'slippery jetty, DIY carpet laying and matches and candles by the beds... are hazards.' Smoking has been completely banned. Much of Gunn Eriksen's larder is outside her kitchen door. The waters of Loch Broom, visible from the kitchen window, yield superb fresh fish – scallops, sole, monk, lobsters, wolf. The Ullapool boats drop off the catch before going to harbour. Gunn says that to understand how to cook a fish, you need to know what it feeds on. Her rambling wild garden is also a source of inspiration. She is one of the few cooks in Britain to use wild ingredients with authority in soups, salads and sauces; cucumber and hawthorn soup, Brie and nettle soup, bittercress sauce with fish are typical. Ground elder replaces parsley as a garnish. Her style is about contrasts, as in lobster served with two sauces – one hot the other cold; or cooked wolf-fish stuffed with a purée of raw salmon. There is no choice in the four courses before sweets. Some of the complexity is seen in the saucing – leek, juniper and dill for medallions of roe deer flambé in armagnac; or a ravioli made with parsley and filled with oyster mushrooms and grapes for a fillet of port with a sauce of its own juices and Burgundy. Everything, naturally, is home made. Breakfast is exceptional – freshly baked croissants, fresh orange juice, scrambled eggs, venison sausage, marmalades and wholemeal toast. Fred Brown assures us that, contrary to what the *Guide* suggested last year, in fact only one cushion is covered in a Liberty print, the rest of the décor being Eastern rugs and lace. The wine list is good and modestly priced, concentrating on a careful selection of Burgundies and clarets backed up by a few quality Loires, Alsaces and Rhônes, and a handful of good '83 Germans. There's an excellent range of half-bottles. Choice of sweet wines extends to a couple of '80 Sauternes by the bottle, three by the half-bottle, and two German Spätlesen and two Auslesen, though the Germans are not really sweet enough to partner a pudding. CELLARMAN'S CHOICE: Mâcon-Lugny les Genièvres '85, £13.50; Champagne, Cuvée Nicholas '79, £28.50.

CHEF: Gunn Eriksen PROPRIETORS: Fred Brown and Gunn Eriksen
OPEN: all week, D only
CLOSED: late Oct to Easter
MEALS: 7.45
PRICES: Set D £33 (£38). Service inc
SEATS: 14. Private parties: 14 main room. Car-park, 20 places. Vegetarian meals by arrangement. Children's helpings. No children under 10. No smoking. One sitting
ACCOMMODATION: 5 rooms, all with bath/shower. D, B&B £68 to £72. Deposit: £25. No children under 10. Garden. Fishing. Scenic. Confirm by 4 [GHG]

▲ *Ceilidh Place* [9/20]

14 West Argyle Street, Ullapool IV26 2TY
ULLAPOOL (0854) 2103 £5–£18

Jean and Robert Urquhart have converted an old boat shed opposite the loch into a cross between an all-day brasserie/coffee shop and a community entertainment centre. There are no radios or TVs, but live music – including the local butcher playing on the fiddle – theatre and exhibitions. The food is eccentric bistro, with vegetarian leanings extending to meatless haggis. Fish and venison are local; cheese is rennet-free; bread, ices and sorbets are made on the premises. Typically the menu might range from cock-a-leekie soup and beef Stroganoff to sweet pickled herring and avocado and spinach roulade. Teas, espresso coffee and house wine by the glass.

CHEFS: Jane Smart and Alison Napier PROPRIETORS: Jean and Robert Urquhart
OPEN: all week
MEALS: 12.15 to 2.15, 7 to 9.30
PRICES: Set L £3 (£5) to £6 (£8), Set D £12.60 (£15) to £15.60 (£18). Service inc
CARDS: Access, Amex, Diners, Visa
SEATS: 40. 10 tables outside. Private parties: 30 main room. Car-park, 30 places. Vegetarian meals. Children's helpings. No smoking in dining-room. Wheelchair access (also WC). Music. Self-service (L only)
ACCOMMODATION: 15 rooms, 8 with bath/shower. Rooms for disabled. B&B £26 to £48. Children welcome. Baby facilities. Pets welcome. Afternoon teas. Garden. Fishing. Scenic. Doors close at 12.30 [GHG]

▲ *Morefield Motel* [9/20]

Ullapool IV26 2TH
ULLAPOOL (0854) 2161 £22

Supplies of fresh seafood are delivered from the local boats to this modern, low-slung building a mile out of town on the road to Achiltibuie. Roberto Giovannini is cooking more dishes 'au naturelle' – scallops, langoustines, sole, monk, halibut – although there's still a demand for carpetbagger steaks and lobster royale, cooked with scallops and prawn tails in seafood sauce.

It is the quality of the ingredients that stands out, and portions too. The kebabs almost stretch from one table to another in the small, tightly packed room. Cheaper meals are served in the large bar. The short wine list has some inexpensive whites to suit the fish.

CHEF: Roberto Giovannini PROPRIETORS: David Smyrl and David Courtney Marsh
OPEN: all week
MEALS: 12 to 2, 6 to 9.30
PRICES: £19 (£22). Service inc
CARDS: Access, Amex, Visa
SEATS: 106. 6 tables outside. Private parties: 40 main room. Car-park, 35 places. Children's helpings. No-smoking area. Wheelchair access (also WC). Music
ACCOMMODATION: 11 rooms, all with bath/shower. Rooms for disabled. B&B £16.50 to £28. Deposit: 10%. Children welcome. Baby facilities. Pets welcome. Afternoon teas. Scenic. Doors close at 12. Confirm by 6

WALLS Shetland map 8

▲ *Burrastow House* [10/20]

Walls ZE2 9PD
WALLS (059 571) 307
3m W of Walls £17–£24

The Tuckeys arrived in 1982 at this listed house, built in 1759 and warmed by peat fires. The cooking draws heavily on local produce, especially fish. Lamb is also a feature – three-pound legs are boned and stuffed with apricots. There are vegetarian dishes, too. The style, though, is old-fashioned – gratin of scallops; jugged hare. 'Very comfortable.' 'Faultless hosts.' House wine is £4.45.

CHEF: Stella Tuckey PROPRIETORS: Stella and Harry Tuckey
OPEN: all week, D only
CLOSED: Sept to Feb
MEALS: 7 to 9.30
PRICES: Set D £15 (£17) to £22 (£24). Service inc
SEATS: 10. Private parties: 12 main room. Car-park, 8 places. Vegetarian meals. Children's helpings. No smoking in dining-room. Music
ACCOMMODATION: 3 rooms, all with bath/shower. B&B £24.75 to £50. Baby facilities. Pets welcome. Garden. Fishing. Golf. TV. Scenic [GHG]

Islands Round-up
ROOMS: *Creel*, St Margaret's Hope, Orkney (085 683 311); *Kirkwall Hotel*, Kirkwall, Orkney (0856 2232).
HARBOUR VIEW: *Ferry Inn*, John Street, Stromness, Orkney (0856 850280).

Restaurants rating 12 or more serve the best food in the region.

All details are as accurate as possible at the time of going to press. Please notify the Guide *office of any changes.*

WHITEBRIDGE Highland map 8

▲ *Knockie Lodge* [10/20]

Whitebridge IV1 2UP
GORTHLECK (045 63) 276
8m N of Fort Augustus on B862 £21

Dinners are five-course affairs in this two-hundred-year-old shooting-lodge, with no choice before the pudding. Soups – lettuce and mint; courgette and fennel – follow mushroom brioche or stuffed aubergine, and main courses revolve around roasts and bakes: leg of lamb with a stuffing of orange, coriander and pine kernels; salmon with lemon, herbs and sorrel hollandaise. Cheese follows pear and blackcurrant mousse or raspberries and cream. Bar lunches feature soup, quiche, salads, cheese and good sweets. House wine from Loron is £6, or CELLARMAN'S CHOICE: St Amour, Domaine des Billards '85, £10; St Emilion, Ch. Troplong-Mondot '83, £15.50; Pouilly-Vinzelles '84, £10.

CHEF: Chris Freeman PROPRIETORS: Brenda and Ian Milward
OPEN: all week
CLOSED: end Oct to end Apr
MEALS: 12.30 to 1.30, 8
PRICES: Set D £16 (£21), Bar L from £3.50
CARDS: Access, Amex, Visa
SEATS: 22. Private parties: 12 main room. Car-park, 30 places. No children under 10. Smart dress preferred
ACCOMMODATION: 10 rooms, all with bath/shower. D,B&B £55 to £90. Deposit: £50. No children under 10. Pets welcome, by arrangement. Garden. Fishing. Scenic [GHG]

Wales

ABERAERON Dyfed map 4

Hive on the Quay [9/20]

Cadwgan Place, Aberaeron SA46 0BT
ABERAERON (0545) 570445 £14

The converted coal wharf sits between the two harbours of Aberaeron: one half is a whitewashed café/restaurant; the other is a modern conservatory overlooking the water. The Holgate family – famous for their honey – run it as a seasonal family eating place, and their loyalties are to local and organic produce, from fish to cheese and wine. Through the day there's a snack menu of home-baked breads and cakes, honey-flavoured ice-creams, soups and pies. Lunch is a buffet and in high season there are more formal dinners, taking in grilled local mackerel stuffed with cockles, lamb chops with laverbread sauce, ox-tail stew and poached sewin with sorrel sauce. Welsh cawl is served with bread and a hunk of cheese. To drink there's Rock's elderflower wine, Symond's cider and Theakston's bitter, as well as teas, juices and Bulgarian wine at £4.60 a bottle.

CHEF: John Bromley PROPRIETORS: Margaret and Sarah Holgate
CLOSED: end Sept to Spring bank hol
MEALS: 10.30 to 5 (10 to 9.30 July and Aug)
PRICES: £10 (£14) Snacks from £1. Service 10% at D.
SEATS: 55. 2 tables outside. Private parties: 14 main room. Vegetarian meals.Children's helpings. Wheelchair access. Self-service

ABERDOVEY Gwynedd map 4

▲ *Maybank Hotel* [10/20]

Aberdovey LL35 0PT
ABERDOVEY (065 472) 500 £10–£14

The first-floor restaurant overlooks the Dovey estuary from large bay windows. Pine tables and dried flower arrangements create a country farmhouse feel. Robert Hughes runs the front of house while Sally Hughes cooks a bistro-style menu with a sure hand. Avocado mousse is a pale green sandcastle surrounded by prawns, endive and a lemony mayonnaise; a wedge of Stilton and herb savoury tart, cut from a round, is served with a good tomato sauce; sirloin of beef comes rare with Yorkshire pudding and a decent array of vegetables. Sweets are in the vein of bread-and-butter pudding, rhubarb and ginger oatmeal crumble, orange and Cointreau ice-cream, offered with a glass of Muscat de Beaumes de Venise. A new policy is to serve an entirely Welsh cheeseboard. Effort has also gone into the house wines – eight, from £5.75, include champagne – and the list embraces a clutch of bottles from Spain, Australia and California. CELLARMAN'S CHOICE: Côtes du Rhône '84, from E.Guigal, £7.90; Bourgogne Passetoutgrains '84, from Jayer, £8.50; Margaux, Ch. Notton '73, £9.50.

CHEF: Sally Hughes PROPRIETORS: Robert and Sally Hughes
OPEN: all week D, and Sun L
CLOSED: 1 week at Christmas; Nov
MEALS: 12.45 to 1.45, 7 to 9.30
PRICES: Set L £6.75 (£10), Set D £11.50 (£14). Service inc
CARD: Visa
SEATS: 32. Private parties: 32 main room. Children's helpings. No children under 1. Music
ACCOMMODATION: 6 rooms, all with bath/shower. B&B £23.50 to £37. Deposit: £10. Baby facilities. Pets welcome. Fishing. Golf. TV. Scenic. Doors close at 12

Old Coffee Shop [9/20]

13 New Street, Aberdovey,
ABERDOVEY (065 472) 652 £3–£7

This tiny, clean coffee-shop 60 yards from the sea in a former butcher's shop is open only in the daytime and unlicensed. Susan Griffiths cooks while husband Alan deals with the lunchtime queues for fresh tagliatelle with bolognese sauce, egg and cress sandwiches or peaches stuffed with cream cheese and herbs. Locally caught fish and locally farmed meat go to make terrines, pâtés and savoury pies; sweets take in home-made chocolate brandy cake, raspberry and hazelnut meringue cake and a host of other afternoon tea treats. Lunch for two is a bargain £10 or so. Bring your own wine: corkage £1.50.

CHEF: Susan Griffiths PROPRIETORS: Alan and Susan Griffiths
OPEN: Tue to Sun
MEALS: 10 to 5.30 (4.30 in winter; L 12 to 3)
PRICES: £6 (£7), Set L from £2.20 (£3), Snacks from £1. Service inc. Unlicensed but bring your own: corkage £1.50
SEATS: 30. Private parties: 30 main room. Vegetarian meals. Children's helpings. No-smoking area

ABERSOCH Gwynedd map 4

▲ *Porth Tocyn Hotel* [10/20]

10 YEARS

Abersoch LL53 7BU
ABERSOCH (075 881) 2966 £13–£16

The second-longest serving restaurant in the *Guide* – 31 years of continuous listing – seems as solid as Snowdonia, magnificent views of which are to be had from Porth Tocyn's dining-room. The Fletcher-Brewer family, who have been running this hotel/restaurant for even longer, take as their philosophy a spirited sense of fun alongside 'consistency of standards and style combined with an ability to absorb new ideas' in a daily changing menu. Some recent examples of the latter have been the introduction of Welsh cheeses in dishes and on the cheeseboard, and a more imaginative use of fresh herbs, like chervil and coriander. Modern British influences show particularly in the starters – wild mushrooms and bacon cocotte or prawns in a gingery cream sauce – and fish – baked haddock with spicy yoghurt, for example, or poached turbot with lemon coriander butter. Local lamb may come stuffed with rosemary and apricots. There's a good selection of desserts, ranging from the exotic – hazelnut and passion-fruit roulade – to classically British puddings, ice-creams and possets. The cheeseboard is heroically Welsh. House claret is £7 on the 70-bottle list. Muscat de Beaumes de Venise £2.60 the glass.

CHEF: E.L. Fletcher-Brewer PROPRIETORS: The Fletcher-Brewer family
OPEN: all week
MEALS: 12.30 to 2, 7.30 to 9.30
PRICES: Set Sun L £8.50 (£13), Set D from £11.25 (£16). L snacks from £1
CARD: Access
SEATS: 60. 12 tables outside. Private parties: 60 main room. Car-park, 60 places. Children's helpings (with prior notice). No children under 7. Smart dress preferred. Wheelchair access (1 step; also WC)
ACCOMMODATION: 17 rooms, all with bath/shower. Rooms for disabled. B&B £27.25 to £43. Deposit: £40. No children under 7. Baby facilities. Pets welcome. Afternoon teas. Garden. Swimming-pool. Tennis. TV. Phone. Scenic. Doors close at 12 [GHG]

ABERYSTWYTH Dyfed map 4

Gannets [10/20]

7 St James' Square, Aberystwyth SY23 1DU
ABERYSTWYTH (0970) 617164 £12

Near the castle, this is a classic bistro right down to its red and white checked tablecloths. Prices are reasonable for a blackboard menu with plenty of choice along the lines of braised squid, or lamb cawl, followed by local pheasant in red wine, wild duck à l'orange, or various steak and chicken dishes. Fish from Swansea market might include halibut and hake; mussels and skate are from Cardigan Bay; and smoked salmon is from the Teifi smokery in Cardigan itself. In addition, there is always a vegetarian option, such as a pie stuffed with summer vegetables. Ten straightforward sweets to finish – treacle tart, lemon meringue pie, hot toffee pudding. A dozen wines, with house Italian £5.40 a litre.

CHEF: David Mildon PROPRIETORS: David and Dilys Mildon
OPEN: Mon to Sat
MEALS: 12 to 2, 6 to 9.30
PRICES: £9 (£12). Service inc. Licensed, also bring your own: no corkage
CARDS: Access, Visa
SEATS: 40. Private parties: 40 main room. Vegetarian meals. Children's helpings. Wheelchair access. Music

Dyfed Round-up

INEXPENSIVE: *Eifiona's Restaurant and Coffee Rooms*, 31 Lammas Street, Carmarthen (0267 230883); *Patio*, Llangranog (0239 78502); *Hafod Lodge*, Cwmystwyth, nr. Aberystwyth (097 422 247).
ROOMS: *Waungron Farm*, Whitland (disabled facilities) (0994 240682); *Old Rectory*, Llanddowror (0994 230030).
WELSH: *Hen Efail*, Furnace, Talybont (0654 74225); *Penlan Oleu*, Llanychaer (0348 82314).
AFTERNOON TEAS: *Farmhouse*, Glanbryden, Llandeilo (0558 823586).
VEGETARIAN: *Waverley*, 23 Lammas Street, Carmarthen (0267 236521).

BEAUMARIS Gwynedd map 4

▲ *Ye Olde Bulls Head Inn* [12/20]

ANGLESEY RESTAURANT OF THE YEAR

Castle Street, Beaumaris, Anglesey LL58 8AP
BEAUMARIS (0248) 810329 £20

The inn dates from 1472, modernised and rebuilt in 1617. There are still creaking floors at all angles, gurgling Victorian plumbing, low ceilings, and centuries of smoke-stains on the walls. Dickens and Dr Johnson were guests. It is a fine example of the dying breed of old-fashioned country inns, well supported locally. The upstairs dining-room in an attic-like side-wing is filled with Toby jugs, guns and ships' lanterns. Keith Rothwell and David Robertson, previously at the popular basement Seahorse at Port Dinorwic (*Guide* listed 1982 to 1987), have been slowly modernising. The cut of the menu is refreshingly to the point – a sort of British-French mix but based soundly on local produce (fine lamb, fish and seafood especially) supplemented by longer supply lines for vegetables and a few French cheeses to offset the half dozen Welsh versions on offer. The menu rings out to the anthem of home-made gravlax; veal and duck terrine – and local this and that, so much so that Norfolk duck looks quite out of place. The range of different techniques shows the quality and authority of Keith Rothwell's cooking: cassolette of salmon, brill, sole, turbot and prawns in a cream and saffron sauce; stir-fry of vegetables and prawns with ginger and garlic; Welsh beef sirloin served charred outside, pink inside, on a mushroom purée and a classic Bordelaise. Fish tends to be roasted or poached. Sauces favour fruits: cranberries and port for veal; raspberry and blackcurrant for duck; a theme which reasserts itself with the list of puddings. Alcohol is used too: a little brandy to soak the chocolate and chestnut terrine; the fruits steeped in port for a crumble. Bar snacks at lunch. Wines show the same understanding and are well spread, with good examples of most styles. House French is £6.25.

CHEF: Keith Rothwell PROPRIETORS: Rothwell and Robertson Ltd
OPEN: all week
MEALS: 12 to 2.30, 7.30 to 9.30
PRICES: £14 (£20), Snacks from 90p
CARDS: Access, Visa
SEATS: 70. 6 tables outside. Private parties: 70 main room, 40 private room. Car-park, 15 places. Children's helpings. No children under 7 at D (exc residents)
ACCOMMODATION: 15 rooms, 4 with bath/shower. B&B £18 to £29.50. Children welcome. Fishing. Golf. Scenic. Doors close at 1. Confirm by 6

BRECHFA Dyfed map 4

▲ *Ty Mawr* [10/20]

Brechfa SA32 7RA
BRECHFA (026 789) 332
6m from A40 on B4301 £10–£15

A sixteenth-century Big House (Ty Mawr) is more of a large farmhouse converted to a small hotel, run by the Flaherty family, who also operate a bakery. The hotel is filled with lace and pine. Dyfed has a growing reputation as a food centre in Wales particularly for cheese, organic vegetables, local lamb, beef and fish. The menu offers a balanced, interesting choice with the emphasis on good value. Good fish dishes have been haddock smokies; prawns in pastry; herring in sweet pickle. The main courses boast a variety of sauces, with a familiar ring of port, but there are also nut roasts for vegetarians. The range of sweets is wide and has included a butterscotch pudding for the heroic. Unlimited coffee. Twenty wines centre on France. House French is £6.75 a litre.

CHEFS: Alan and Timothy Flaherty PROPRIETORS: The Flaherty family
OPEN: all week, D only, and Sun L
MEALS: 12 to 2, 7 to 9.30
PRICES: Set L from £6.95 (£10), Set D from £11.50 (£15). Service inc
CARDS: Access, Visa
SEATS: 60. Private parties: 30 main room. Car-park, 60 places. Vegetarian meals. Children's helpings. Smart dress preferred. No-smoking area. Wheelchair access. One sitting
ACCOMMODATION: 5 rooms, all with bath/shower. B&B £35 to £45. Deposit 20%. Baby facilities. Pets welcome. Afternoon teas. Fishing. Garden. Scenic. Doors close at 11.30. Confirm by 2

BROAD HAVEN Dyfed map 4

Druidstone Hotel [11/20]

10 YEARS

Broad Haven SA62 3NE
BROAD HAVEN (0437) 781221 £14

The Bells' likeable but rather gaunt stone mansion scores heavily with its views of St Brides Bay and its family hospitality. Dinners in the restaurant move in familiar territory of devilled crab, lamb with herb stuffing and poached salmon with butter cream sauce. Vegetarian dishes provide relief in the form of chickpea rissoles with tomato sauce, and to finish there are alcoholic home-made ice-creams or fruit pies and soufflés. Reliable bar lunches (the dining-room is closed at lunch-time) and suppers come from the same kitchen. A short list of around 20 wines includes house wine from Duboeuf at £5.

Restaurants change owners and chefs constantly. It is very useful if you keep the Guide *informed of any changes you find.*

CHEFS/PROPRIETORS: Rod and Jane Bell
OPEN: all week exc Sun D
CLOSED: Nov, mid-Jan to mid Feb
MEALS: 12.30 to 2.30 (1 to 2 Sun) 7.30 to 10
PRICES: £10 (£14)
CARDS: Amex, Visa
SEATS: 40. 8 tables outside. Private parties: 36 main room, 12 private room.Car-park, 40 places. Children's helpings. Wheelchair access (also WC)
ACCOMMODATION: 8 rooms. Rooms for disabled. B&B £16.50 to £33. Deposit: £10.Baby facilities. Pets welcome. Afternoon teas. Garden. Scenic. Doors close at12

CAERNARFON Gwynedd map 4

Bakestone [11/20]

26 Hole in the Wall Street, Caernarfon LL55 1RF
CAERNARFON (0286) 5846

£16

A modest one-up, one-down bistro, a stone's throw from Caernarfon Castle, down the aptly named Hole in the Wall Street. The building is old and has been stripped back to stone and wooden beams. A combination sort-of-French-and-English menu concentrates on crêpes cooked to order on an electric bakestone. They come nicely folded, generously filled and appetisingly speckled with brown on the outside. But the menu has evolved beyond fundamentals. There have also been: baked sausage with fried quartered apples in a white gratin dish with mustard sauce; sweet cured herring fillets; sea-bass baked in foil with fennel seeds; grilled Dover sole; creamy gratin of potatoes – a dauphinoise made with sour cream and milk; chicken Basquaise – a simple braise with tomatoes, peppers and mushrooms. 'Outside the big names, you could travel the length of England and not find many small-time eating places that lavish so much care on their food.'

CHEF: Yves Monin PROPRIETORS: Guy Cutler and Yves Monin
OPEN: Tue to Sat, exc Thur L
MEALS: 12.30 to 2.30, 6.45 to 8.45
PRICES: £10 (£16). Minimum £3.20 at L, £5 at D
SEATS: 32. 2 tables outside. Private parties: 16 main room. No children under 8. No pipes in dining-room. Music

Gwynedd Round-up
AFTERNOON TEAS: *Farchynys Cottage Garden*, Bontddu, Nr Barmouth (0341 49245); *Blue China Tearooms*, Lon Felin, Criccieth (076 671 3239).
SETTING: *Bryn Gorwel*, Carmel (picturesque chapel) (0286 881120).
CHINESE: *Garden*, 1 High Street, Bangor (0248 362189).
ROOMS: *Portmeirion Hotel*, Portmeirion (0766 770228)

Files are kept on every restaurant, so reports of poor meals are just as valuable as reports of good meals because they save unnecessary inspections.

CARDIFF South Glamorgan map 4

Armless Dragon [10/20]

97 Wyvern Road, Cathays, Cardiff CF2 4BG
CARDIFF (0222) 382357 £18

'I was a reader of the *Guide* before I was a restaurateur and still hold to those principles of freshness, honesty and imagination which I think of as yours.' The Dragon provided a valuable service to the city even before the current wealth of restaurateuring broadened the choice. A small kitchen forces the menu to stay with fresh produce; there is good fish especially, and some eclectic Eastern influences, as well as laverballs filled with mushrooms. Saucing can be vivid, as in almond and tamarind for sauté Welsh lamb. Real ales supplement a functional wine list that opens at £4.90.

CHEFS: Mark Sharples, David Richards and Debbie Coleman
PROPRIETORS: Mark Sharples and David Richards
OPEN: Mon to Sat, exc Sat L
CLOSED: bank hol Mons, Christmas to New Year
MEALS: 12.30 to 2.30, 7.30 to 10.30 (11 Sat)
PRICES: £13 (£18)
CARDS: Access, Amex, Diners, Visa
SEATS: 50. Private parties: 45 main room. Vegetarian meals. Children welcome. Wheelchair access. Music

La Brasserie [9/20]

60 St Mary Street, Cardiff CF1 2AT
CARDIFF (0222) 372164 £15

Well-established French-style wine bar with beams and sawdust and a menu of good steaks, fish and salads. French cheeses and hot garlic bread feature too. There are some decent wines to go with the food; house French is £5.25. Related to Champers, Cardiff and La Braseria, Swansea (see entries).

CHEF: Franco Peligno PROPRIETORS: Keith Brenton and Benigno Martinez
OPEN: Mon to Sat
MEALS: 12 to 2.30, 7 to 12.15
PRICES: £9 (£15)
CARDS: Access, Amex, Diners, Visa
SEATS: 75. Private parties: 6 to 70 main room. Vegetarian meals. Children welcome. Smart dress preferred. Music

Champers [9/20]

61 St Mary Street, Cardiff CF1 1FE
CARDIFF (0222) 373363 £14

The virtue of this bodega-style, Spanish wine bar is its simplicity – a hundred Riojas are matched to eight meats, mostly cooked on the char-grill and including three cuts of steak. Salads are displayed on ice; cheeses, mostly French, are served in fives. A few more ambitious dishes, such as king prawns with a tomato, onion and wine sauce, langoustines with garlic, or stuffed chicken extend the short, practical menu. Gran Reservas start around £10. House Navarra, red and white, £4.45.

CHEF: John Wan PROPRIETORS: Benigno Martinez and Keith Brenton
OPEN: all week, exc Sun L
MEALS: 12 to 2.30, 7 to 12.15
PRICES: £10 (£14). Service inc
CARDS: Access, Amex, Diners, Visa
SEATS: 70. Private parties: 70 main room. Vegetarian meals. Children welcome. Music

Le Cassoulet [new entry, zero rated]

5 Romilly Crescent, Canton, Cardiff CF1 9NP
CARDIFF (0222) 221905 £11–£18

Last in the *Guide* as Grains Diner, a vegetarian and wholefood restaurant, in 1983; it then became the Singapore, which closed in 1987. It re-opened, as Le Cassoulet, in December 1987, keeping the shop-window front, the black-painted woodwork and the half-height red curtains on the brass curtain rod. The door is kept locked; a sign asks you to ring the bell. Step inside this quiet, unpretentious frontage, and you could be in a smartish family restaurant in South-West France. On the floor are white oblong tiles with red and black diamonds; brass oil-lamps with red shades hang from the ceiling; black-gloss radiators provide the heat. The menu offers five starters, five main dishes, and six or seven desserts, concentrating on Toulouse and Carcassonne regional cooking – family-style, not *nouvelle*. The regional menu includes grilled prawns in garlic butter; bouchée à la reine – sweetbreads, mushrooms and chicken in a vol-au-vent case; and of course, cassoulet itself, which has to be tried. The sausages, made to the Toulouse recipe by local butcher John Morgan, the pork steak chunks, the specially-fattened duck's leg are all cooked separately, the duck in its own fat, then combined with haricot beans to make a robust, tasty, filling dish. Follow with tangy lemon tart. Two dozen wines include a good range of vin de pays. CELLARMAN'S CHOICE: Côtes du Frontonnais, Château Clos Mignon, £7.50. More reports, please.

CHEF: Gilbert Viader PROPRIETORS: Gilbert and Claire Viader
OPEN: Tue to Sat, exc Sat L
MEALS: 12 to 2, 7 to 10
PRICES: £13 (£18), Set L £6.95 (£11)
CARDS: Access, Visa
SEATS: 35. Private parties: 35 main room. Children welcome. Wheelchair access. Music

La Chaumière [10/20]

44 Cardiff Road, Llandaff, Cardiff CF5 2DP
CARDIFF (0222) 555319 £11–£21

'The only reliable place to eat after the opera finishes at 10.30pm.' Not easily found – make for the Maltsters pub which has a car-park. The first-floor restaurant is over a betting shop, with old church pews down the side walls offset by neat pink starched cloths and matching pink candles Since Kay Morgan took over the kitchen, rather than just supervising, the cooking has improved in quality, presentation and taste, as a loyal local custom bears witness. The handwritten menu offers a choice of eight dishes at each course. The style is almost classically involved: rolled sea-trout with a wine and basil sauce; spinach set in aspic jelly. The sticky toffee pudding is a one-and-a-half inch wedge with syrup poured over and a swirl of cream. Good sorbets and home-made petits fours. House French is £6.

CHEFS: Kay Morgan and Richard Bowles PROPRIETORS: Cliff and Kay Morgan
OPEN: Tue to Sun, exc Sat L and Sun D
CLOSED: first 2 weeks Jan
MEALS: 12.30 to 2, 7.30 to 10
PRICES: £15 (£21), Set Sun L £6.95 (£11). Service inc set only, 10% alc
CARDS: Access, Amex, Diners
SEATS: 36. Private parties: 44 main room. Car-park, 36 places. Vegetarian meals. Children's helpings

China City [9/20]

207 City Road, Cardiff CF2 3JD
CARDIFF (0222) 462668 £9–£16

The décor is plain and institutional, yet this basic Cantonese eating-house continues to serve some of the best Chinese food in the city. Mr Cheung and his daughters run the place between them. The cooking has its heart in dishes such as stewed fish-head in a pot, although it can also deliver superb wun-tun soup; beef with ginger and spring onions, and spicy aromatic duck with pancakes. Orange segments to finish. Drink tea.

CHEF/PROPRIETOR: Mr Cheung
OPEN: all week
MEALS: noon to 11.45
PRICES: £9 (£16), Set D from £13.50 (£18) for two. Service 10%
CARDS: Access, Amex, Diners, Visa
SEATS: 74. Private parties: 80 main room. Children restricted. Music. Air-conditioned

Everest [11/20]

43–45 Salisbury Road, Cathays, Cardiff CF2 4AB
CARDIFF (0222) 374881 £15

The decor is fairly standard Indian, with lots of varnished wood and velvet upholstery. The cooking is subtle and consistent, occasionally scaling the heights with some exceptional dishes. The sensibly planned menu avoids too many clichés and focuses mostly on North Indian classics, from chicken tikka and boti kebab to lamb pasanda, rogan josh and karahi specialities. There's an Everest special three-course dinner with limited choice. Thalis are particularly good value. A handful of somewhat incongruous cocktails augment the basic wine list; alternatively drink lager.

CHEF: Motiuar Rahman PROPRIETORS: Abdul Kowsor and Abdal Miah
OPEN: all week
CLOSED: 25 and 26 Dec
MEALS: 12 to 2, 6 to 11.30 (12.30 Fri and Sat)
PRICES: £8 (£15). Minimum £5. Service 10%
CARDS: Access, Amex, Diners, Visa
SEATS: 80. Private parties: 80 main room. Vegetarian meals. Children welcome. Jacket and tie. Wheelchair access (also WC). Music

Gibsons [11/20]

8 Romilly Crescent, Canton, Cardiff CF1 9NR
CARDIFF (0222) 41264 £15–£24

The established face of French food in the city. The Canning family manages to maintain a standard while other restaurants come and go. The short menu mixes safe, conservative choices, such as melon with Bayonne ham or roast rack of lamb, with more overtly French bourgeois dishes, such as terrines, pâtés, stuffed chicken breast with Pernod and cream. There is always a fish of the day. Sauces, for instance espagnole, are built around a classic stock-pot. Vegetarians report favourably. Sweets are obviously the centre of much attention and outnumber other dishes: Hungarian chocolate pudding; Just William; angel hair charlotte; coffee meringues with Tia Maria. There are Welsh cheeses. Beaujolais and Loire wines are as well represented on the wine list as more conventional clarets. House Beaujolais £6.80 a litre.

CHEFS: Irene, Andrew and Matthew Canning PROPRIETOR: Irene Canning
OPEN: all week, exc Sun D
MEALS: 12.30 to 2.30, 7.30 to 9.30
PRICES: £16 (£23), Set L £8.75 (£15), Set D £16.80 (£24)
CARDS: Access, Amex, Diners, Visa
SEATS: 38. Private parties: 12 main room. Car-park, 5 places. Vegetarian meals. Children's helpings

Happy Gathering [9/20]

233 Cowbridge Road East, Canton, Cardiff CF1 9AL
CARDIFF (0222) 397531 £10–£20

Dim-sum are served every day until 7pm in this well-supported Cantonese restaurant, with a choice of over 20 items, from steamed lotus buns and deep-fried prawn croquettes to turnip curds. The full menu has sizzling dishes, baked lobster and Peking duck, as well as prawns in paper, lemon chicken and crispy beef with chilli. The unprepossessing exterior hides two dining-rooms that are red, gold and multi-dragoned. Drink tea.

CHEF: Kin Kwun Chan PROPRIETOR: Sui Sang Chan
OPEN: all week
MEALS: noon to 11.45pm
PRICES: £6 (£10), Set D from £15 (£20). Service 10%
CARDS: Access, Amex, Diners, Visa
SEATS: 250. Private parties: 180 main room; 40 private room. Vegetarian meals. Children welcome. Music. Air-conditioned

Indian Ocean [10/20]

290 North Road, Gabalfa, Cardiff CF4 3BN
CARDIFF (0222) 621152 and 621349 £12–£17

The arrival of new-wave India in Cardiff is inspired and funded by London's Red Fort and is already a reputable competitor for the Everest (see entry). Smoked plate-glass from floor to ceiling, pink marble-effect wallpaper and Greek-style marble wall lights, carved arches and round pillars surrounded by green frondy plants create a sumptuous feel. The Indian Ocean offers unusual tandoori meats, for instance quail and duck, both of them moist and spicy. Good choices include peripheral dishes like king prawn sukka, aloo gobi, pilau rice. A good dessert section has home-made ice-creams of coconut or pineapple set in chunks of the appropriate fruit. The kulfi is like an iceberg. There's a separate list of cocktails, or drink Kingfisher beer. Well sited for theatre- and concert-goers or the Arms Park faithful.

CHEF: Abdul Kadir PROPRIETOR: Abdul Muhim
OPEN: all week
CLOSED: Christmas Day
MEALS: 12.15 to 2.30, 6.15 to 11.30
PRICES: £10 (£17), Set L and D £10 (£12). Service inc
CARDS: Access, Amex, Diners, Visa
SEATS: 60. Private parties: 50 main room, 8 private room. Vegetarian meals. Children welcome. Wheelchair access (1 step; also WC). Music. Air-conditioned

Noble House [10/20]

9–10 St David's House, Wood Street, Cardiff, CF1 1ER
CARDIFF (0222) 388430 £15–£20

Of the four most respected Chinese restaurants in Cardiff, the Noble House offers the best service and setting, indeed it is one of the smartest restaurants of any kind in the city. Sited where the Mandarin was, opposite the bus station, the menu is typical of the second-generation Peking restaurant, incorporating more South-East Asian dishes and also ample provision for vegetarians. There have been good versions of popular dishes from aromatic crispy duck to steamed scallops with garlic and sizzling lamb. Also encouragingly good have been the tofu dishes, less so the rice, which is a mark of its westernisation. On the plus side, service has been immaculate – toffee apples and bananas brought out cooking on the hot platter and dunked into cold water at the table to get the contrast of cold crisp batter and hot fruit. Coffee comes with mint creams. Drink tea, or house wine at £5.20.

CHEF: K.M. Chung PROPRIETORS: Charlen Ltd
OPEN: all week
MEALS: 12 to 2.30 (2.45 Sun), 6 to 11.30 (6.30 to 11 Sun)
PRICES: £12 (£20), Set D from £10 (£15). Service 10%
CARDS: Access, Amex, Diners
SEATS: 80. Private parties: 80 main room. Vegetarian meals. Children's helpings (Sun only). Wheelchair access (also WC). Music. Self-service Sun buffet

Riverside [10/20]

44 Tudor Street, Cardiff CF1 8RM
CARDIFF (0222) 372163 £11–£21

For many years now the marker by which Cardiff Chinese restaurants might be judged. Even with the new competition it earns its listing comfortably enough. Age and popularity may be seen in the fading décor of intricate swirls and carvings of many colours. The menu is mainline Cantonese with dim-sum served until eight o'clock. Fish is reliably good. Sundays and early evenings are well patronised by local Chinese families for sui mai, chicken and taro croquettes, spare-ribs in black-bean sauce and stuffed glutinous rice in lotus leaves; egg tarts and water-chestnut jelly for sweet. One-plate rice and noodle dishes are inexpensive. Muscadet, Gewürztraminer and Chablis are alternatives to tea.

CHEF: K.Wong PROPRIETOR: Wendy Chan
OPEN: all week
MEALS: noon to 11.45 (12.15am Fri and Sat, 11pm Sun)
PRICES: £7 (£11), Set L and D £16 (£21). Service 10%
CARDS: Access, Amex, Diners, Visa
SEATS: 140. Private parties: 75 main room, 65 private room. Vegetarian meals. Children welcome. Music. Air-conditioned

Salvatore's [10/20]

14 Romilly Crescent, Canton, Cardiff CF1 9NR
CARDIFF (0222) 372768 £21

A white-stucco-fronted restaurant with bow-windows, iron grilles and orange signs in a partly renovated suburb near Llandaff (find Cowbridge Road East or Llandaff Fields and ask. It is near St Winifrid's Hospital). The restaurant is on two levels and cosy, but with ample space. Daily specials move with the seasons. Choice is from an extensive menu of widely varying dishes, with an emphasis on freshness. Fish is a strong point, always plentiful and cooked to order. The cooking is non-aggressive Italian home style: minestrone, fresh dressed crab, eggs with anchovies, rolled veal escalope filled with Parma ham, garlic and herbs cooked in tomato sauce. Chef Mario Colayera is from Genoa and there is a tendency to recreate Ligurian dishes, so the minestrone contains pesto. Seventy showy wines, from the house Merlot at £6.50. CELLARMAN'S CHOICE: St Estèphe, Ch. Montrose '76, £28.50.

CHEF: Mario Colayera PROPRIETORS: Mario Lo Turco and Mario Colayera
OPEN: Mon to Sat, exc Sat L
CLOSED: 2 weeks in summer
MEALS: 12.30 to 2, 7.30 to 10
PRICES: £15 (£21)
CARDS: Access, Amex, Diners, Visa
SEATS: 50. Private parties: 50 main room. Children's helpings. Wheelchair access. Music

Thai House [10/20]

23 High Street, Cardiff CF1 2BX
CARDIFF (0222) 387404 £18–£20

Mr Ramasut has extended the range of set menus which, for those unskilled in Thai eating, takes away the element of luck. Satay, stuffed chicken's wing and deep-fried crabs' claws are popular choices, but there are plenty of more unusual dishes, for instance spicy duck curry with star fruit, and fried beef with broccoli and oyster sauce. House French £5.25, or drink Thai beer.

CHEF: Nakorn Yimchareong PROPRIETOR: Virul Ramasut
OPEN: Mon to Sat
MEALS: 12 to 2.30, 6.30 to 11
PRICES: £12 (£20), Set D from £12.50 (£18). Minimum £10 at D. Service 10%
CARDS: Amex, Diners, Visa
SEATS: 64. Private parties: 22 main room, 20 private room. Vegetarian meals. Children welcome. Music. Air-conditioned

Trillium [new entry, zero rated]

40 City Rd, Cardiff CF2 3DL
CARDIFF (0222) 463665 £25

Formerly a wine bar, the Trillium has run through a series of proprietors and ethnic approaches before arriving at its present incarnation. It enters the *Guide* this year as a serious, rather formal restaurant which fills the gap left by the sale of Spanghero's, especially for business. There is a gentleman's club air about the high, wood-panelled walls, the book-lined alcoves and the wing armchairs, but the style of the staff softens the formality. Two small dining-rooms operate. A short menu concentrates on caviare, salmon and prawns and the kitchen technique on pastry and some potent, sometimes overly so, sauces. For dishes like fresh scallops in pastry with a rich beurre blanc or, even more complex, fine salmon stuffed with a leek purée and wrapped in filo with a similar sauce, this can work well. House wines at £5.20 balance the list of 130 wines from 15 countries and offset the pages of vintage claret '51 to '71, which are 'subject to valuation'. More evaluations, please.

CHEFS: John McAneney and Richard Buckland PROPRIETOR: Kami Soroush
OPEN: all week L, exc Sat; Tue to Sat D
MEALS: 12 to 2.30, 7 to 10.30
PRICES: £19 (£25)
CARDS: Amex, Diners, Visa
SEATS: 40. Private parties: 60 main room, 20 private room. Smart dress preferred. Wheelchair access. Music

South Glamorgan Round-up

VEGETARIAN: *Sage Wholefood,* Wellfield Court, Wellfield Road, Roath (0222 481223).

WELSH: *Yr Ystafell Gymraeg/The Welsh Room,* 72 -74 Whitchurch Road, Cardiff (0222 42317/ 397660); *Blas Ar Cymru/A Taste of Wales,* 48 Crwys Road, Cardiff (0222 382132).

CILGERRAN Dyfed map 4

Castle Kitchen [10/20]

Cilgerran SA43 2SG
CARDIGAN (0239) 615055 £10

The Moore sisters have added a room to their small cottage restaurant. Watercolours by local artists hang on the walls. The menu is British with traditional pies, and some historical dishes, such as Hindlewake chicken – chicken casserole with lemon and prunes – or Elizabethan pork, a casserole with wine and herbs. There is always a vegetarian choice. Soups are hearty – chicken and vegetable has a thick lentil base – and there is a foreign note in the samosas and hummus among the starters. Desserts are largely traditional, as in fruit salad and banana split, but include apricot and ginger curd tart, and chocolate pot has Cointreau cream. Twenty-five wines, from house French at £4.25 to CELLARMAN'S CHOICE: organically produced Tokay d'Alsace, £6.80.

CHEFS: Barbara, Elizabeth and Beryl Moore PROPRIETORS: Barbara and Elizabeth Moore
OPEN: all week in summer; Thur to Sat D and Sun L in winter
MEALS: 12 to 5, 7.30 to 9.30
PRICES: D £7 (£10), L Snacks from 85p
SEATS: 25. Private parties: 16 main room. Vegetarian meals. Children's helpings (L only). Wheelchair access. Music

COWBRIDGE South Glamorgan map 4

Basil's Brasserie [10/20]

2 Eastgate, Cowbridge CF7 7DG
COWBRIDGE (04463) 3738 £15

Basil's holds to its successful formula of semi-self-service. Order at the bar from a long daily menu, which is exhaustible and shrinks visibly as the evening progresses. A March menu offered duck rillettes, half a Cornish dressed crab, escalopes of halibut and salmon with tarragon butter, stir-fried monkfish with Chinese vegetables, Welsh lamb cutlets grilled over charcoal. About half the 30 or so dishes on the blackboard are fish based. The dessert menu includes standards such as kiwi Pavlova or chocolate roulade. House Bulgarian on a 40-bottle list is £4.60. CELLARMAN'S CHOICE: Berry Bros Good Ordinary Claret, £6.25.

CHEF: Giampiero Fama PROPRIETORS: Giampiero and Virginia Fama
OPEN: Tues to Sat
CLOSED: Christmas; 2 weeks Aug to Sept
MEALS: 12 to 2, 7 to 10
PRICES: £10 (£15), Snacks from £1.75. Minimum £3.95 at Sat D
CARDS: Access, Visa
SEATS: 80. Private parties: 25 main room. Car-park, 10 places. Vegetarian meals. Children's helpings. No pipes in dining-room. Wheelchair access. Air-conditioned

Mulligan's [10/20]

Stalling Down, Cowbridge CF7 7DT
COWBRIDGE (044 63) 2221 £19

Despite the proximity of the Swansea and Cardiff markets, with their reputation for good fish, few restaurants in South Wales specialise. Mulligan's is an exception, a popular roadhouse which presents an unusual combination of robust fish dishes in the traditional British manner – including fish and chips – and scattered Continental classics. Painted white, with dark green shutters, the restaurant boasts a drawbridge across a miniature moat where the lobsters and crabs can be seen. Upstairs there are reserved tables (often booked well in advance), downstairs it is first come first served. The menu, which credits suppliers, is divided according to the style of cooking: deep-fried and battered; sauced; simply cooked; shellfish and crustaceans. Puddings are resolutely British with no concessions: steamed syrup pudding with custard, stewed raspberries with shortbread. The wine list, appropriately, concentrates on whites from France, Italy and Germany, ending with half a dozen champagnes. House red and white £5.50. A Bristol branch opened in the summer of 1988.

CHEF: G. Lilley PROPRIETORS: Mr and Mrs G.A. Villa
OPEN: Mon to Sat
MEALS: 12 to 2.15, 6.30 to 10.30
PRICES: £13 (£19)
CARD: Visa
SEATS: 120. Car-park, 20 places. Children's helpings. Wheelchair access (2 steps). Music

Off the Beeton Track [9/20]

1 Town Hall Square, Cowbridge CF7 7DD
COWBRIDGE (044 63) 3599 £11–£21

In their converted cottage restaurant, overlooking the town hall and clock, the Reardon-Smiths offer a menu based firmly on British and Welsh traditions: game and fish predominate; laver-bread features frequently and names like Widdecombe Fare (sic), a summer starter of warm chicken livers with herbs and salad, or Gladstone hot-pot with lamb chops, carrots, celery, onion and potato put in an appearance. Other influences come from further afield – butterfly prawns in a lime mayonnaise. Desserts are praised: Atholl brose; crème Martinique; and a steamed, strawberry-flavoured Guards' pudding. House French is £4.95.

CHEFS: Rowena Whitbread and Colin Loe
PROPRIETORS: Mr and Mrs John Reardon-Smith
OPEN: Tue to Sun, exc Sun D
MEALS: 12 to 2.30, 7.30 to 10
PRICES: £13 (£18), Set L £6 (£11) to £10 (£15), Set D £7.75 (£13) to £15 (£21). Licensed, also bring your own: no corkage
CARDS: Access, Amex, Visa
SEATS: 36. 3 tables outside. Private parties: 36 main room, 10 private room. Vegetarian meals. Children's helpings (Sun L only). Wheelchair access. Music

CRICKHOWELL Powys map 4

▲ *Bear Hotel* [9/20]

High Street, Crickhowell NP8 1BW
CRICKHOWELL (0873) 810408 £21

There have been some grizzles about the Bear. Standards have wavered badly in the upgrading of rooms and the building of a new kitchen, but a late inspection came down firmly in favour. The building dates from 1432 with an extension built in the late 1900s with stone from the castle. Inside is a Welsh parlour of a bar with dresser and grandfather clock and there is a choice between a small dining-room and a larger function room. The menu takes in some local foods – farmed venison; cheeses; fish – as well as offering a run of steaks, plain dishes and home-baked sweets. On busy days the bar serves 300 meals from home-made soup upwards, backed by real ales: Ruddles, Bass and Webster's Yorkshire. Wines are from Tanners and Gilbeys from £5.40. CELLARMAN'S CHOICE: Ch. Chicane '82, £9.50.

CHEFS: J.L. and Stephen Hindmarsh and Peter Adams PROPRIETOR: J.L. Hindmarsh
OPEN: all week, exc Sun D
MEALS: 12 to 2, 7 to 9
PRICES: £15 (£21), Snacks from £3.50
CARDS: Access, Visa
SEATS: 58. 6 tables outside. Private parties: 70 main room, 30 private room. Car-park, 28 places. Children's helpings. No children under 5. Smart dress preferred. Wheelchair access (also WC). Music
ACCOMMODATION: 25 rooms, all with bath/shower. Rooms for disabled. B&B £29.90 to £38. Baby facilities. Pets welcome. Afternoon teas. Garden. Fishing. TV. Phone. Doors close at 12. Confirm by noon

DINAS MAWDDWY Gwynedd map 4

Old Station Coffee Shop [9/20]

Dinas Mawddwy SY20 9LS
DINAS MAWDDWY (065 04) 338 £6

This is Eileen Minter's fifteenth year, but apart from the Coffee Shop becoming the Old Station Coffee Shop, little has changed. She offers home-made, wholefood snacks in this charming old stone station house with its wooden veranda still intact outside. The self-service choice might be a celery or carrot and tomato soup with wholemeal rolls, pizza with fresh herbs and salad with Eileen's mayonnaise, plus a range of cakes – Bakewell tart, chocolate flapjacks, Welsh cakes. House French £4.

OPEN: all week, L only
CLOSED: mid-Nov to mid-Mar
MEALS: 12 to 5
PRICES: £3 (£6). Service inc
SEATS: 36. 9 tables outside. Private parties: 16 main room. Car-park. Vegetarian meals. Children's helpings. No smoking. Wheelchair access (also WC). Self-service

DOLGELLAU Gwynedd map 4

▲ *Abergwynant Hall* [new entry, zero rated]

Dolgellau LL40 1YF
DOLGELLAU (0341) 422238
on A493, 3m W of DoLgellau £12–£25

A rarity in the Welsh hills, providing good food in a fairly formal setting that doesn't try to ape grandeur. From the sign on the main road from Penmaenpool village go down a big, tree-lined drive that leads to a solid, granite hall, with painted gables and square chimney pots. The house dates from the early 1860s and has been refurbished in Laura Ashley style. It is surrounded by a hundred acres of woodland and lawns, with a natural lake just visible from the conservatory, which forms the main part of the dining-room. There has been a decided effort to acquire first-class fresh ingredients, and the cooking shows imagination and good presentation: warm salad of pigeon breast, with lemon, lavender and hazelnut oil; lemon sole mousse, wrapped in smoked salmon; sirloin steak sauced with tomato and basil; monkfish and scallop kebabs, with herb hollandaise; hot almond tart, cut from a round, with raspberry jam between the pastry and the almond flavoured sponge, served with custard. Welsh specialities include Swansea laverbread, served with cockles and smoked bacon on toast, Anglesey brill, and Welsh cheeses. Sixty wines, plus a comprehensive selection of house bottles from £6.50. Six dessert wines. More reports, please.

CHEF: Mary Saddington PROPRIETORS: Mary and Jonathan Saddington
OPEN: Tue to Sat, D only, and Sun L
MEALS: 12 to 2.30, 7 to 9.30
PRICES: £15 (£22), Set Sun L £7.50 (£12), Set D £12.50 (£18) to £19.50 (£25)
CARDS: Access, Visa
SEATS: 60. Private parties: 30 main room; 30 (45 buffet) private rooms. Car-park. Vegetarian meals. Children's helpings. No smoking in dining-room. Wheelchair access (also WC)
ACCOMMODATION: 3 rooms, all with bath/shower. B&B £35 to £55. Deposit: 20%. Afternoon teas. Garden. Fishing. TV. Scenic. Doors close at 10.30. Confirm by 6

▲ *George III Hotel* [10/20]

Penmaenpool, Dolgellau LL40 1YD
DOLGELLAU (0341) 422525
2m W of Dolgellau on Tywyn road £10–£20

This old, white-stone inn enjoys one of the most magnificent settings in Wales, overlooking the waters of the Mawddach estuary. It has a reputation for consistency that is rare in Welsh hostelries. The cooking is sound and portions are ample with much use of local produce, including vegetables and herbs from the garden. Baked local halibut comes with cream, white wine and tarragon; roast rib of beef is served with mustard and herb butter. Even the clichés are well handled, for instance fresh prawns with home-made marie rose sauce and fresh mango. Vegetables come in tureens; sweets are in the mould of trifle and colourful fresh fruit salad. Book for excellent-value lunches. Rooms are being upgraded. Fifty good-quality wines from the major regions fall mostly in the £6 to £20 spectrum and clarets are strongest but the selection from other regions is wise. CELLARMAN'S CHOICE: Chardonnay, Mezzocorona '86, £8.65; Châteauneuf-du-Pape '84, from Ponnelle, £11.95, and the house wine.

CHEF: David Collett PROPRIETOR: Gail Hall
OPEN: Mon to Sat D and Sun L
CLOSED: Christmas and New Year
MEALS: 12.30 to 2, 7.15 to 8.45
PRICES: £14 (£20), Set L £5.50 (£10), Snacks from 90p. Minimum £4 at D. Service 10%
CARDS: Access, Amex, Carte Blanche, Diners, Visa
SEATS: 46. 15 tables outside. Private parties: 20 main room. Car-park, 100 places. Vegetarian meals. Children's helpings. Smart dress preferred. Wheelchair access (1 step; also WC)
ACCOMMODATION: 13 rooms, 8 with bath/shower. Rooms for disabled. B&B £18 to £46. Deposit: £10. Children welcome. Baby facilities. Pets welcome. Garden. Fishing. TV. Phone. Scenic. Doors close at 11.30. Confirm by 6 [GHG]

ERBISTOCK Clwyd — map 4

Boat Inn [10/20]

Erbistock LL13 0DL
BANGOR-ON-DEE (0978) 780143 — £12–£20

A very old inn where the ferry crossed – pulled by hand – before the bridge was built downstream. The pub and the restaurant are in separate buildings by the churchyard, right on the river, with a good-sized, discreet car-park. The setting in spring is breathtaking yet surprisingly unspoilt by overcrowding. Both bar and dining-rooms have kept the basic simplicity of the old inn. It is run with efficiency, offering a good-value cold table in the bar and a long, ambitious menu built around grills and flambés in the restaurant. Sunday lunch is especially good value. Imaginative vegetarian dishes. Cheeses include local Cheshire; among the range of traditional sweets, baked apple in filo pastry with a whisky sauce is strongly recommended. House French £5.75; CELLARMAN'S CHOICE: Graves, Ch. de Portets '85, £8.60.

CHEF: Martyn Rae PROPRIETOR: John Chamberlain
OPEN: all week
MEALS: 12.15 to 2.15, 7.15 to 9.15
PRICES: £14 (£20), Set L £7.95 (£12), Set D £10.95 (£15), Snacks from £1. Licensed, also bring your own: corkage £4.50
CARDS: Access, Amex, Diners, Visa
SEATS: 70. 8 tables outside. Private parties: 25 main room, 45 private room. Car-park, 60 places. Vegetarian meals. Children's helpings. Smart dress preferred. No pipes in dining-room. Wheelchair access (2 steps)

Reports on shops, cafés and farms are useful, as well as reports on restaurants.

FISHGUARD Dyfed map 4

▲ *Plas Glyn-y-Mel* [new entry, zero rated]

Fishguard SA65 9LY
FISHGUARD (0348) 872296 £12 £19

In Lower Fishguard, set in interesting formal gardens overlooking the Afon Gwaun, with a meadow going down to the river in front and 20 acres of woodland round about. The Georgian mansion has been extensively refurbished with individually designed rooms but, the Moores stress, the dining-room is the heart of the operation. The menu is considerably more imaginative than is normal locally, and offers plenty of choice and a clear use of local materials, especially fish for gratin of mussels, crab bisque and salmon meunière. Sauces tend to the classic – truffle for oven-cooked fillet of beef, green peppercorns for venison – while garnishes are of the tomato rose school. There is a good showing of smoked dishes through the menu. Sweets are charlottes and tarts and there are five local cheeses, such as Llanboidy. Forty-five wines from £6.50. More reports, please.

CHEF: M.J.Moore PROPRIETORS: Mr and Mrs M.J.Moore
OPEN: all week
CLOSED: Feb
MEALS: 12.30 to 2, 7.30 to 9.30
PRICES: Set L from £8 (£12), Set D from £14 (£19). Snacks from £1.75
SEATS: 30. Private parties: 25 main room, 20 to 25 private rooms. Car-park, 25 places. Vegetarian meals. Children's helpings. Wheelchair access (also WC)
ACCOMMODATION: 6 rooms, all with bath/shower. B&B £32 to £56. Deposit: £25. Baby facilities. Pets welcome. Garden. Fishing. Golf. TV. Scenic. Doors close at 12. Confirm by 6

GLANWYDDEN Gwynedd map 4

Queen's Head [10/20]

Glanwydden, LL31 9JP
LLANDUDNO (0492) 46570 £15

The whitewashed shuttered country pub with a large painting of Elizabeth I over the door splits the tiny hamlet into two. Tables squeezed into every available corner of the low-ceilinged, flower-filled bars are testament to the Queen's popularity. Order at the bar. The daily changing menu is good British cooking with the emphasis on local fish, or, when out of season, farmed lobsters; oysters and langoustines come down from Loch Fyne. Of the eight or so choices at each course there might be onion soup with cider; salmon as a salad or with a parsley sauce; kidneys dijonnaise. Sweets are displayed: Pavlova, treacle tart, alcoholic trifle, each for under £1.50. Good coffee. Real ales from Ind Coope, Burton and Tetleys. Fifteen wines, starting at £4.95. 'Worth the drive from the fish and chip joints in Llandudno.'

The Guide *does not accept free meals.*

CHEFS: Robert F.W. Cureton and Bryn Powell PROPRIETOR: Robert F.W. Cureton
OPEN: all week
MEALS: 12 to 2.15, 7 to 11 (6.30 to 9 Sat, 7 to 9 Sun)
PRICES: £10 (£15)
SEATS: 120. 12 tables outside. Private parties: 26 main room. Car-park, 25 places. Vegetarian meals. Music

HARLECH Gwynedd map 4

▲ *Castle Cottage* [10/20]

Pen Llech, Harlech LL46 2YL
HARLECH (0766) 780479 £13

The white terraced cottage is tucked away behind the medieval castle of Edward I and the Castle Hotel. Inside, the beamed, cottagey dining-room sets the tone for a bistro-style menu, equally at home with laverbread and cockles; pancakes stuffed with pork and peppers; crab gratin. Duck is a regular – the breast smoked and served with apple chutney, or grilled as a main course with an unthickened red-wine sauce. Jim Yuill's Scottish background shows in the cranachan and the whisky-laced puddings. Fifty wines offer plenty of decent drinking for around £6, and include a clutch of Italian and Spanish bottles. House French is £4.95; CELLARMAN'S CHOICE: Chardonnay, Vin de Pays des Coteaux de Narbonne '86, £8.75.

CHEF: Jim Yuill PROPRIETORS: Jim and Betty Yuill
OPEN: all week, D only
MEALS: 7 to 9.30
PRICES: Set D from £9.50 (£13)
CARDS: Access, Visa
SEATS: 34. 4 tables outside. Private parties: 40 main room. Vegetarian meals. Children's helpings. No smoking. Wheelchair access. Music
ACCOMMODATION: 6 rooms, 4 with bath/shower. B&B £15 to £32. Deposit: 25%. Baby facilities. Pets welcome. Golf. Scenic [GHG]

▲ *The Cemlyn* [13/20]

High Street, Harlech LL46 2YA
HARLECH (0766) 780425 £15

The Cemlyn, overlooking the sea from the High Street, is named after the first lifeboat in North Wales; inside, however, it is Ken Goody's passion for frogs that gives the key-note to the décor – salt-pots, soap, candlesticks, everywhere but in the menu. The kitchen goes back to the sea for its inspiration, using local crab, lobster and fish. An August menu offers monkfish and smoked salmon terrine; smoked fish plate; local wild salmon, grilled and served with sherry cream sauce; sewin, grilled, with hollandaise sauce. Later in the year Conway mussels appear, in a light curry sauce; and, from inland, wild mallard, served with orange butter sauce and gratin dauphinois. Sweets take in Pavlova meringue, pecan pie, hot apple charlotte, chocolate marquise. On the cheeseboard, Welsh versions, including goats', are supplemented by imports from Philippe Olivier of Boulogne. The petits fours with the coffee are home made. The wine list is largely under £10, with house French £6, and ten half-bottles include an Australian Orange Muscat at £6.90.

CHEF/PROPRIETOR: Ken Goody
OPEN: all week, D only
CLOSED: Jan to Easter
MEALS: 7 to 9.30
PRICES: Set D from £9.95 (£15)
CARDS: Amex, Diners
SEATS: 36. 3 tables outside. Private parties: 40 main room, 10 private room. Vegetarian meals. Children's helpings. Wheelchair access (also WC)
ACCOMMODATION: 2 rooms, 1 with bath/shower. B&B £10.50 to £30. No children under 10. Golf. TV. Scenic. Doors close at 12. Confirm by 6

HAVERFORDWEST Dyfed — map 4

Jemima's [10/20]

Nash Grove, Freystrop, Haverfordwest, SA62 4HB
HAVERFORDWEST (0437) 891109
S of Haverfordwest, on the Burton road — £16

This unassuming, rough-cast roadside dwelling, somewhat more attractive inside than out, is on Puddleduck Hill, hence the name. Everything is cooked on the premises and there is an honesty about the cooking that is welcome. A rough-textured duck and Seville orange terrine makes good use of home-grown herbs; kidneys come in an exemplary madeira sauce. The menu offers half a dozen courses at each stage, fish often with citrus sauces –orange for plaice; lime for Dover sole. Alternatives might be venison with cranberries and port, and lamb with green ginger and coconut. To finish, ices and tarts. Thirty wines, with house French from Georges Duboeuf at £5.50.

CHEF: Ann Owston PROPRIETORS: Ann Owston and Wendy Connelly
OPEN: Tue to Sat, D only
MEALS: 7 to 9
PRICES: £11 (£16)
CARD: Access
SEATS: 20. Private parties: 26 main room. Car-park, 10 places. Children welcome. No smoking in dining-room
ACCOMMODATION: 2 rooms, 1 with bath/shower. B&B £15 to £30. Afternoon teas. Scenic. Doors close at 12. Confirm by 5

HAY-ON-WYE Powys — map 4

Lion's Corner House [10/20]

6 Market Street, Hay-on-Wye HR3 5AF
HAY-ON-WYE (0497) 820175 — £16

The inside of Colin Thomson's restaurant facing the open market hall is fitting for this secondhand-bookshop town; the décor verges on junk shop. Colin Thomson seems inordinately fond of hats: top hats, a policewoman's hat and a helmet are grouped above the mantelpiece, and the furniture continues the theme; altogether, attic bistro. Mr Thomson calls his food 'wholesome, solid... none of these pretty pictures on plates.' The short menu has daily dishes and a lot of interesting sweets: summer pudding, pashka, orange and coffee bombe, steamed jam sponge and custard. Main courses include something for everybody: home-made beefburgers; vegetable and nut roast; braised chicken in a mushroom and fennel sauce. Value for money at lunch-time is excellent. The evening menu is more ambitious – spicy shark steaks; quail in an almond and cucumber cream sauce; poached trout with a mussel and Pernod sauce – but the accent is still informal. Fifty wines include bottles from California, Australia, New Zealand, Chile, Hungary, Spain, Italy and England. House French is £4.50; CELLARMAN'S CHOICE: Châteauneuf-du-Pape, Domaine du Vieux Télégraphe, £11.65.

CHEF: Colin Thomson, Bernice Brown and Alun Williams PROPRIETOR: Colin Thomson
OPEN: Mon to Sat
CLOSED: Mon and Tue Nov to Mar, exc at Christmas and half-term
MEALS: 11 to 2.30, 7 to 9.30 (10 Sat)
PRICES: £12 (£16), Snacks from £1. Licensed, also bring your own, corkage £1
SEATS: 60. Vegetarian meals. Children's helpings. Wheelchair access. Music

LALESTON Mid Glamorgan map 4

Great House [10/20]

High Street, Laleston CF32 0HP
BRIDGEND (0656) 57644 £16–£21

A beautiful Grade II listed building, lavishly restored, with a very high, half-timbered ceiling. An open fireplace at one end faces a tapestry at the other. The menu is in keeping with the grand setting, Continental in inspiration though making use of local produce: spaghetti carbonara rubs shoulders with smoked chicken terrine, parcels of filo filled with French cheese on a grape coulis, chicken suprême with a pineapple and ginger sauce and grilled lemon sole. Sweets from the trolley tend to be rich and generous in portion; Wales is well represented on the cheeseboard. Lunchtime snacks in the coffee-shop are good value for beef and onion pie, salads, meat loaf. House French £5.20.

CHEFS: Barry Bingham, Steven Mudd, and Norma Bond PROPRIETORS: Steven and Norma Bond
OPEN: Mon to Sat, exc Sat L
MEALS: 12 to 2, 6.30 to 9.30 (9.45 Sat)
PRICES: £15 (£21), Set D £10.95 (£16), L snacks from 95p
CARDS: Access, Diners, Visa
SEATS: 120. 3 tables outside. Private parties: 80 main room; 40 private room. Car-park, 30 places. Vegetarian meals. Children's helpings. Wheelchair access (2 steps; also WC). Music

All details are as accurate as possible at the time of going to press. Please notify the Guide *office of any changes.*

LLANBERIS Gwynedd map 4

Y Bistro [12/20]

43–45 High Street, Llanberis LL55 4EU
LLANBERIS (0286) 871278 **£12–£19**

Set in the former slate-mining area – not active since the end of the 1960s – on the edge of Snowdonia National Park, Nerys Roberts' small restaurant has a loyal and supportive custom, and is not overly geared to the tourist business. The result is that the somewhat discreet building with large windows works like a well-oiled machine. Meals are charged by a set price, but usually offer half a dozen market-led dishes per stage. The many recommendations give a flavour: home-smoked and cured salmon with dill; a mussel gratin; consommé; clam chowder; roast rack of lamb with an almond cream sauce; breast of pigeon with a port sauce. Sweets tend to the calorific, as in a heavy sponge gateau served with a fruit ice-cream and garnish of peaches and strawberries, or to the traditional, in Bakewell tart. House French on a substantial list is £5.25.

CHEF: Nerys Roberts PROPRIETORS: Danny and Nerys Roberts
OPEN: Mon to Sat
CLOSED: L Sept to Whitsun
MEALS: 12 to 2, 7 to 9.30
PRICES: Set L £8 (£12), Set D £14.50 (£19). Licensed, also bring your own: corkage £2
CARDS: Access, Visa
SEATS: 48. Private parties: 36 main room, 20 private room. Vegetarian meals. Children welcome. Smart dress preferred. Wheelchair access (2 steps; also WC). Music. Air-conditioned

LLANDDERFEL Gwynedd map 4

▲ *Palé Hall* [11/20]

Llandderfel LL23 7PS
LLANDDERFEL (067 83) 285 **£14–£28**

The setting is a fabulous Gothic mansion built in the great age of the railways and flanked by acres of hills and woodland. It is remote, but the Duffin family take care, obtaining the very best ingredients from near and far. Beef is slaughtered locally, fish is from the North Wales coast, while rare fruit, vegetables and cheeses come from further afield. This translates into a flamboyant menu taking in deep-fried goats' cheese on an exotic fruit sauce, or salmon and monk cooked with pear and ginger. Loin of lamb is paired with blackcurrants; calf's liver gets a white wine and grape sauce; pork comes with calvados and apples. Sticky toffee pudding with Palé Hall ice-cream is still the pick of the sweets. The wine list runs to about 150 bottles from most wine-producing countries, and includes Lebanese Château Musar. House French is £7.50. CELLARMAN'S CHOICE: Australian Chardonnay, Lindeman Bin 45 '87, £12.75, and California Merlot, Sonoma Clos Dubois, £12.75.

CHEF: Anthony Allcott PROPRIETORS: The Duffin family
OPEN: all week
MEALS: 12 to 2, 7 to 9.30
PRICES: £21 (£28), Set L £10 (£14), Set D £17.50 (£22) to £19.50 (£24), Snacks from £1.95. Service inc. Licensed, also bring your own: corkage £4
CARDS: Access, Amex, Diners, Visa
SEATS: 50. Private parties: 50 main room, 24 and 45 private rooms. Car-park, 150 places. Vegetarian meals. Children's helpings. Jacket and tie. No smoking in dining-room. Wheelchair access (also WC)
ACCOMMODATION: 17 rooms, all with bath/shower. Rooms for disabled. Lift. B&B £57 to £90. Deposit: £20. Baby facilities. Afternoon teas. Garden. Swimming- pool. Sauna. Fishing. TV. Phone. Scenic. Doors close at 12.30 [GHG]

LLANDEWI SKIRRID Gwent map 4

Walnut Tree Inn [15/20]

10 YEARS

Llandewi Skirrid NP7 8AW
ABERGAVENNY (0873) 2797
on B4521, 2m NE of Abergavenny  £31

The great thing is that the Walnut Tree has been in the same hands and given the same style since the early 1960s. To call it a pub is to do it an injustice, to call it a country restaurant is inappropriate – no starched cloths, frilly drapes and hushed tones here. The bar and side room (no booking, which can result in a long wait) draw crowds to eat on small, round pub tables. The restaurant is run with a magnificent, deceptively casual skill. The menu is long and varied – in a lesser establishment that might mean bad news. The food is classic, skilfully handled and plainly presented, a wonderful combination of real Welsh and real Italian. Typical are trenette con pesto; excellent gravlax; wild salmon with samphire; rack of lamb with garlic; stewed ox-tail; fillet of brill with a Meaux mustard sauce; rose petal ice-cream; summer pudding; raspberry bavarois. 'On a summer's day it is possible to sit outside and startle the carriage trade with a plateau de fruits de mer, the like of which is rarely seen this side of the Channel.' With hindsight, Taruschio's contribution to modern restaurateuring seems to grow in importance; notable are his support of Vin Sullivan at Abergavenny from the early days, and his dedication to finding good supplies elsewhere. Taruschio was among the first to take the Gressingham duck and to encourage its development. And he has stuck unwaveringly to his principles, when others have been seduced into the spiral of higher décor ambitions and higher prices. The wine list is excellent, with a fine list of clarets including many good old vintages, reasonably priced. But the expertise of Bill Baker from Reid Wines has also helped provide a shorter but tempting selection from Burgundy, Rhône, Loire and Alsace. An unusually interesting list of Italian wines includes quite a few bottles imported by the restaurant, and a smattering of good wines from other parts of the world. House Italian is £7.50.

'You do need to point out that offal is to be lightly cooked.' On eating in Brighton

CHEF: Franco Taruschio PROPRIETORS: Franco and Ann Taruschio
OPEN: Mon to Sat, exc Mon L
CLOSED: 2 weeks Feb
MEALS: 12 to 2.30, 7.15 to 10
PRICES: £24 (£31)
SEATS: 80. 5 tables outside. Private parties: 30 main room. Car-park, 60 places. Vegetarian meals. Children's helpings. Wheelchair access (also WC). Air-conditioned

LLANDRILLO Clwyd map 4

▲ *Tyddyn Llan* [10/20]

Llandrillo LL21 0ST
LLANDRILLO (049 084) 264
on B4401 at end of village; turn off A5 at Corwen £15

A relaxed, eighteenth-century country-house hotel off the A5 at Corwen, within reach of shooting, walking, and fishing on the River Dee, directly behind. The dining-room is in an extension. Bridget Kindred's menu is eclectic, following the seasons. Grilled trout with hot onion and raisin chutney might sit alongside Moroccan lamb with garlic and cumin. Anglesey eggs – baked with leeks, cream and cheese – is a popular starter, while soups of fish, and of carrot, orange and coriander have been praised, likewise roast beef and salmon. Fish, particularly, comes with vivid sauces – orange for brill; mustard with roach. Vegetables might include glazed parsnips and buttered courgettes with basil. To finish, sweets mix meringues with a taste for tradition, as in apple porter cake and bread-and-butter pudding with Grand Marnier. Coffee and mints are taken in the hotel sitting-room. Some readers have called the service slow; others find it unfussy. Seventy wines embrace Spain, Australia and California, with CELLARMAN'S CHOICE: Gran Colegiata Tinto de Crianza Toro, £6.75. Music and entertainment evenings are on the increase.

CHEF: Bridget Kindred PROPRIETORS: Peter and Bridget Kindred
OPEN: all week, exc Mon L
CLOSED: Mon and Tue Nov to Mar (exc residents)
MEALS: 12.30 to 2, 7 to 9.30
PRICES: Set D from £11 (£15)
CARDS: Access, Visa
SEATS: 35. Private parties: 45 main room. Car-park, 15 places. Vegetarian meals. Children's helpings. Smart dress preferred. Wheelchair access. Music
ACCOMMODATION: 9 rooms, all with bath/shower. B&B £29 to £49. Deposit: 10%. Baby facilities. Pets by arrangement. Afternoon teas. Garden. Fishing. Phone. Scenic. Doors close at 12. Confirm by 6 [GHG]

The Guide *is independent, accepts no advertising and survives solely on the number of copies sold.*

Please keep the Guide *informed ~~of~~ any changes to the restaurants listed. Report forms are at the back of the book.*

LLANDUDNO Gwynedd map 4

▲ *Bodysgallen Hall* [13/20]

Deganwy, Llandudno LL30 1RS
DEGANWY (0492) 84466
from A55 join new A470 and follow
Llandudno signposts; hotel 1m on R £13–£33

The Hall represents the high profile of Welsh catering and through a series of talented young chefs – among them Peter Jackson, now at the Colonial at Glasgow and David Harding, now nearby in Craigside Manor – has kept a standard. The cooking has roots, although in the light modern style. The Hall is in, but not of, the Victorian seaside resort of Llandudno, and stands on a hill, surrounded by woods, to the south of the town. The hall's several wings were built over a period of six centuries but maintain a surprising homogeneity. From an unkind angle it looks like a Victorian mental institution, but its warm-coloured stone, truly magnificent gardens and lavish internal panelling soon dispel that picture. The dining-room is in a Victorian wing and comes into its own at night when the orange drapes are drawn across the windows and the chandeliers lit. Dinner is a set price £19.75 with surcharges for some dishes. It's modern cooking, descended from *nouvelle*, but with plenty of local produce as well as offloads from the van-run to Paris of goose liver, green olives, exotic fruits. Baking provides two breads and brioches. Loin of lamb is roasted, carved into rounds and arranged in a circle around a mound of sweet onion marmalade with a good strong reduction poured around. Chicken breast is stuffed with crabmeat and sauced with its pan juices, orange, tomato and a little cream, white poached salmon is given a julienne of vegetables and a white wine sauce. Sweets – served before the fine Welsh farmhouse cheese – have a more luxurious air: champagne sorbet in a brandy-snap, surrounded by sliced fruits and a blackcurrant coulis; mille-feuille of pineapple; blackcurrant parfait with a cassis sauce. Interesting home-produced petits fours with coffee. The wine list is good, mostly French and rather expensive, both at the 'cheap' end (little but *vin de table* is under £10) and for the finer wines. Bordeaux and Burgundy are the weightiest areas. There are some pricey petits châteaux, *crus bourgeois*, some of them past their peak, and some top châteaux from good vintages. Burgundies come largely from merchants. A dozen Italian wines are largely well chosen, and offer some of the best value in the lower price range. A handful of Californian, Australian, New Zealand and Spanish wines are also good, and five English and Welsh wines include Croffta '84. House red and white are £7.90; CELLARMAN'S CHOICE: Rioja, Carta d'Oro '85, £11.50, and Bourgogne Chardonnay, £12.

'The menu given to my wife had no prices. Mine had. I thought such chauvinism was dead.' On eating in Lancashire

County Round-ups list additional restaurants useful in their area. To find a Round-up, see the maps at the back: towns listing round-ups are underlined. *See also page 15.*

CHEF: Martin James PROPRIETORS: Historic House Hotels
OPEN: all week
MEALS: 12.30 to 2, 7.30 to 9.45
PRICES: Set L £8.25 (£13) to £10.25 (£15), Set D £19.75 (£26) to £26 (£33), Snacks from £2. Service 10%
CARDS: Access, Amex, Diners, Visa
SEATS: 62. Private parties: 48 main room. Car-park, 50 places. No children under 8. Jacket and tie. No cigars/pipes in dining-room. Wheelchair access. Music
ACCOMMODATION: 28 rooms, all with bath/shower. Rooms for disabled. B&B £67 to £93. No children under 8. Pets welcome. Afternoon teas. Garden. Tennis. TV. Phone. Scenic. Confirm by 5 [GHG]

Craigside Manor [13/20]

Colwyn Road, Little Orme, Llandudno LL30 3AL
LLANDUDNO (0492) 45943 £12–£24

The gastronomic star of Gwynedd is in the ascendant. David Harding, formerly head chef at the nearby Bodysgallen Hall, has taken on this former convent and offers a neat dovetailing – not as expensive or as formal as the Hall, with the emphasis strongly on good-value but nonetheless first-rate fresh produce. The usually packed bar, done out in terracotta and khaki, looks as if it has been given a big brewery facelift – bamboo chairs, red 'leather' chesterfields, gas log fire – and the dining-room itself might double as a set for *Dallas*. There is an accomplished young team front of house. The *carte* offers seven starters and a dozen main dishes, modern cooking with French ancestry and an international feel. The printed menu suggests a certain rootlessness or anonymous, duty-free cooking, but this is not borne out by the technical excellence of the individual dishes – a tart of crab, tomato and laverbread or a beurre blanc for instance or a subtle butter, honey and ginger sauce for poached salmon. Surf and turf is listed as a speciality. The quality of the meat from Evans in Market Street has been a feature. Charcoal biscuits are served with the brilliant cheeses, either unpasteurised British or from Philippe Olivier in Boulogne. Caramel ice-cream in a crisp brandy snap basket mirrors the dining-room décor. Eighty wines, biased towards France, from £6. CELLARMAN'S CHOICE: Zeltinger Himmelreich Riesling Spätlese '85, £10.50.

CHEF: David Harding PROPRIETOR: Mr D. Ward
OPEN: all week, exc Sun D
MEALS: 12 to 2, 7.30 to 9.45 (10 Sat)
PRICES: £18 (£24), Set L from £7.50 (£12)
CARDS: Access, Amex, Diners, Visa
SEATS: 60. Private parties: 20 main room, 120 private room. Car-park, 120 places. Vegetarian meals. Children's helpings. Smart dress preferred. Wheelchair access (3 steps; also WC). Music

Files are kept on every restaurant, so reports of poor meals are just as valuable as reports of good meals because they save unnecessary inspections.

▲ *St Tudno Hotel* [10/20]

North Parade, Llandudno LL30 2LP
LLANDUDNO (0492) 74411 £21

The real-life Alice in Wonderland stayed here in 1861, says a plaque at the front entrance. Well, that makes a change from Queen Victoria. The St Tudno's great virtue is its position on the promenade, with views over the beach, pier and ornamental gardens. The modern dining-room of this upmarket hotel has a conservatory feel, busy with plants and a light-green, wicker-effect wallpaper. Menus can be quite elaborate: chicken and crab feuilletés are garnished with mock caviare, and a creamy tarragon sauce, while breast of duck comes with a fig coulis. Simpler options, for instance salmon steaks in a butter and cream sauce, have been praised. Desserts are often fruity and alcoholic – the fruit salad employs a local Welsh liqueur, Can-y-delyn – while the cheeseboard offers a good selection of organic Welsh cheeses. House French from CELLARMAN'S CHOICE: Château Musar '79, £11.

CHEFS: John Gabbatt and PROPRIETORS: Martin and Janette Bland
OPEN: all week
CLOSED: Christmas and New Year
MEALS: 12.30 to 1.45, 6.45 to 9.30 (8.30 Sun)
PRICES: Set D £15.50 (£21)
CARDS: Access, Visa
SEATS: 60. Private parties: 45 main room. Car-park, 4 places. Vegetarian meals. Children's helpings. No children under 5. Smart dress preferred. No smoking. Wheelchair access. Air-conditioned.
ACCOMMODATION: 21 rooms, all with bath/shower. B&B £45 to £56. Deposit: £25. Baby facilities. Afternoon teas. Swimming-pool. TV. Phone. Scenic. Doors closeat 12 [GHG]

LLANDYBIE Dyfed map 4

Cobblers [12/20]

3 Church Street, Llandybie, SA18 3HZ
LLANDYBIE (0269) 850540 £5–£17

By the church on the main road. Much of the custom is local at this old corner shop, with its stripped pine and Laura Ashley interior, its large collection of 'antique' and junk household equipment and china and strident pale blue, almost rimless plates. The monthly-changing menu is written partly in Welsh and features local produce – roulade of laverbread and tomato-flavoured cream cheese; salmon in herb crust, or in tartlets with lovage; Welsh lamb in a variety of ways, including with an elderflower sauce; sewin in a cheese sauce; salmon en croûte. An elderflower champagne jelly is served with fresh fruit, and there are Welsh organic farmhouse cheeses. Thirty wines, among them Welsh Monnow '86, £8, and house Bulgarian, £4.25.

All details are as accurate as possible at the time of going to press. Please notify the Guide *office of any changes.*

CHEF: Margaret Rees PROPRIETORS: Hywel and Margaret Rees
OPEN: Tue to Sat, and bank hol Mons
MEALS: 12 to 1.30, 7 to 9.30
PRICES: Set L £2.50 (£5) to £5.50 (£8), Set D £12.50 (£15) to £14.50 (£17)
CARDS: Access, Visa
SEATS: 70. Private parties: 50 main room; 20 private room. Vegetarian meals. Children's helpings. Wheelchair access (also WC). Music

LLANGOLLEN Clwyd map 4

Caesar's [11/20]

Deeside Lane, Llangollen LL20 8PN
LLANGOLLEN (0978) 860133 £17

Since 1981, Caesar's has set the standard for restaurants in the area, which can mean it gets overbooked at peak times. The dining-room is by the Dee and the bar is filled with the hand-me-down furniture from the former Wrexham court-room. The menu cuts a sensible dash, using good wines for sauces and making some interesting combinations. Stilton is used to sauce hot eggs with braised lettuce or as a stuffing with apple and hazelnut for sirloin of pork. Half a dozen choices for starter and main course are split by a fish course (£2.75 supplement), soup or sorbet. Specials are the mussel soup and the steak au poivre. Fifty wines from house Rhône at £5.25. CELLARMAN'S CHOICE: Saumur, Jehans de Soubrans, méthode champenoise, £8.25.

CHEFS: R.J. Hendey, J. Robbins, and S. Plevin PROPRIETORS: G. Hughes, B.P. Hughes and R.J. Hendey
OPEN: all week, D only
MEALS: 6.30 to 9.30
PRICES: Set D £13.95 (£17). Service inc
CARDS: Access, Visa
SEATS: 28. Private parties: 28 main room. Vegetarian meals. Children's helpings. Wheelchair access. Music

▲ *Gales* [9/20]

18 Bridge Street, Llangollen LL70 8PF
LLANGOLLEN (0978) 860089 £10

Set in the middle of the town, this reliable wine bar is furnished with oak panels and church pews. The blackboard menu takes 12 quiches, salads, smoked fish, garlic mushrooms, mousses and a couple of hot dishes – chicken Alsace, Red Sea lamb casserole. Good cheeses and cheesecakes. The wine list is unexceptional, except perhaps in its low prices – there is plenty of choice well below £10. House French is £4.60.

'It was the longest hotel table d'hôte menu I've seen since I was in the middle of Ireland in 1965.' On eating in Cumbria

CHEFS: Gillie Gale, John Gosling and Maggie Gosling PROPRIETORS: Richard and Gillie Gale
OPEN: all week, exc Sun D
CLOSED: Sun and Mon Sept to May
MEALS: 12 to 2, 6 to 10.15
PRICES: £6 (£10)
SEATS: 70. Private parties: 12 main room, 8 private room. Children's helpings. Wheelchair access. Music
ACCOMMODATION: 8 rooms, all with bath/shower. B&B £23 to £34.50. Deposit: £10. Baby facilities. Pets welcome. TV. Phone. Scenic. Confirm by 7 [GHG]

Clwyd Round-up

ROOMS: *Llwyn Onn Hall Hotel*, Cefn Road, Wrexham (0978 261225); *Llyndir Hall*, Rossett (0244 571648).
WINE BAR: *Churtons*, Chester Road, Rossett (0244 570163).

LLANRWST Gwynedd map 4

▲ *Meadowsweet Hotel* [12/20]

10 YEARS

Station Road, Llanrwst LL26 0DS
LLANRWST (0492) 640732 £23–£29

Although its reputation as a country-house hotel, its fine wines and the Belle Epoque posters suggest the Evans' civilised place to stay is dealing in variations of *nouvelle* and *haute cuisine*, in fact the kitchen is more relaxed and stays with upper-class country cooking, albeit strongly French. It is a stone house, painted white, on the outskirts of Llanrwst with views over the River Conwy and the valley. The restaurant is spacious and modern with cool beige walls and wicker furniture. Raw materials are good – plump scallops, maize-fed chicken and good cheeses. Recommended choices have been: monkfish medallions poached in apple and cream sauce; lamb braised in white wine, olives and garlic; fillet steak with red wine; hare with port and orange; lamb with orange and ginger. Sauces tend to lean heavily on cream or garlic. The cheeses come in a basket and some of the hard Welsh ewes' versions outshine the French specimens. Good sweets have included chocolate marquise, lemon syllabub, raspberry parfait and walnut cheesecake. The wine list is immense and well-annotated, though with some terrible spellings. It offers a great many delicious wines. France is the strongest area, but there are also good Germans (though many of the producers' names are absent from the list), well-chosen Italians, a better than usual selection from Spain, a fairly extensive and interesting collection of Australians, and a scattering from elsewhere. France offers excellent Alsace, good Rhônes from north and south, including an unusual array of whites and five vintages of Condrieu. Burgundies, Chablis and Beaujolais are all from good producers and an interesting list of clarets from the simple to classed growths in good vintages back to '53 is backed up by a tempting collection of 'second wines'. Some enjoyable 'French country wines' offer value in the £7 to £8 range. House French is £6.75; CELLARMAN'S CHOICE: Chardonnay, Mildara, Church Hill '86, £10.50; and any of the Bordeaux châteaux second wines.

CHEF: John Evans PROPRIETORS: John and Joy Evans
OPEN: all week, D only
MEALS: 6.30 to 9.30
PRICES: £21 (£29), Set D £15.75 (£23)
CARDS: Access, Amex, Visa
SEATS: 36. Private parties: 50 main room. Car-park, 10 places. Vegetarian meals. Children's helpings. Smart dress preferred. No smoking. Wheelchair access. Music
ACCOMMODATION: 10 rooms, all with bath/shower. B&B £28 to £38. Deposit: £5 per person, per night. Baby facilities. Pets welcome. TV. Phone. Scenic. Doors close at 12. Confirm by 6.30 [GHG]

LLANWRTYD WELLS Powys map 4

▲ *Llwynderw Hotel* [11/20]

Abergwesyn, Llanwrtyd Wells LD5 4TW
LLANWRTYD WELLS (059 13) 238 £22–£25

One attraction is the sheer remoteness of this Georgian mansion surrounded by wild moorland and approached by unimproved roads. Michael Yates offers a set dinner menu with little choice, which translates into a simple but subtle mix of traditional English and classical French. Stuffed crêpes or pâté might precede iced cucumber soup or vichysoisse. The centrepiece is usually a roast – Welsh lamb, fillet of beef, duck with apple sauce. A salad comes before the sweets, which are sorbets, soufflés and fruit pies. You have to take a lot of the wine list on trust – or ask to see the bottles. In the Burgundy and Rhône sections, few producers are listed, and who made the wine makes a great difference to what's in the bottle. There are some good clarets, although putting these in a more coherent order would be helpful. Riojas are from the ever-reliable La Rioja Alta. Prices start at £7.50.

CHEF: Valentino Bayona PROPRIETOR: Michael Yates
OPEN: all week D, L by arrangement
CLOSED: Jan and Feb
MEALS: 8
PRICES: Set D from £18 (£22) to £21 (£25). Service inc
SEATS: 24. Private parties: 24 to 26 main room, 8 private room. Car-park, 12 places. Vegetarian meals. No children under 10. One sitting
ACCOMMODATION: 12 rooms, all with bath/shower. D, B&B £65 to £130. No children under 10. Pets welcome. Afternoon teas. Garden. Fishing. Golf. Scenic. Doors close at 11.30

MACHYNLLETH Powys map 4

▲ *Ynyshir Hall* [new entry, zero rated]

Eglwysfach, Machynlleth SY20 8TA
GLANDYFI (065 474) 209 £16

Just by the Ynyshir bird reserve on the River Dovey, this sixteenth-century manor-house stands in 12 acres of woodland and garden. It has undergone several changes of ownership; the present owners have been here for nearly two years and are much in evidence. The dining-room, discreetly decorated with cream-striped wallpaper and well-spaced dark polished wood tables, overlooks the driveway and woodland. The menu moves from day to day and uses local produce wherever possible: Welsh lamb, salmon and trout from the River Dovey, vegetables – including watercress – from the garden, local smoked halibut and goats' cheese. Notably good has been salmon served in a pale yellow, light white wine and dill sauce. Thoughtfulness extends to vegetables, as in potatoes sliced and baked with onions, cream and garlic. Thirty-four wines, from house French at £3.90. More reports, please.

CHEF: David Dressler PROPRIETORS: Jane and Richard Allison
OPEN: all week
CLOSED: Dec to Feb
MEALS: 12 to 1, 6.30 to 8
PRICES: Set L and D £13 (£16). Service inc
CARDS: Access, Amex, Diners, Visa
SEATS: 24. Private parties: 30 main room. Car-park, 15 places. Children's helpings on request. No smoking in dining-room
ACCOMMODATION: 9 rooms, all with bath/shower. B&B £27 to £48. Baby facilities. Pets welcome. Garden. TV. Phone. Scenic. Doors close at 11.30

MATHRY Dyfed map 4

Ann FitzGerald's Farmhouse Kitchen [12/20]

Mawbs Fawr, Mathry SA62 5JB
CROESGOCH (034 83) 347 £10–£14

As befits a working bakery, the ovens are used as much as possible. Salmon is baked on the plate and served with a chive sauce. The greeting on entry is a display of home-baked breads and pies. The FitzGeralds resist the temptation of a licence ('we'd end up as a pub') and keep their loyalty to the food. A stop-press column on the menu allows for late deliveries of sea-bass – served as a fillet covered with a crust of crabmeat, breadcrumbs and pine kernels, with a sauce of white wine, shallots, fish fumet and butter – and lobster. The food also is of the home persuasion and cream and alcohol are in abundance. Starters such as farmhouse pâté, with an onion, red wine and grenadine chutney, curried crab pancake, or bream fillet en croûte, and main courses like roast or casseroled grouse in red wine with spiced red cabbage, venison steak with poivrade sauce, give the range. Wherever possible the FitzGeralds use local produce. The desserts lean towards fruit, with or without alcohol – strawberries Escoffier, pineapple marquise, pear meringue soufflé, or pistachio ice-cream with lime syrup. Coffee to follow is limitless. Booking is essential. The Sunday lunch beef is blue at 1pm, rare at 1.30 and well-done from 2. Bring your own wine; no corkage.

CHEFS: Lionel and Ann FitzGerald PROPRIETOR: Ann FitzGerald
OPEN: all week
CLOSED: L Christmas to Easter
MEALS: 12 to 3, 6.30 to 10
PRICES: £14 (£16), Set L £9 (£10), Set D £12 (£13). Unlicensed, but bring your own: no corkage
SEATS: 30. 4 tables outside. Private parties: 40 main room. Car-park, 40 places. Vegetarian meals. Children's helpings. No children under 9. Wheelchair access. Music

NEWPORT Dyfed map 4

▲ *Cnapan* [10/20]

East Street, Newport SA42 0WF
NEWPORT (0239) 820575 £16

The Lloyds and the Coopers run this pale pink Georgian house as their home; the mood is relaxed, welcoming, free and easy. Lunches have a wholefood bias – robust soups, savoury flans, salads and wholemeal puddings. Dinners range far and wide, although the emphasis is on fresh fish, local produce and old-fashioned recipes. Sewin comes with laverbread and cucumber sauce; chicken breasts are baked with honey and ginger; pork Stroganoff is garnished with grilled grapefruit. Afternoon teas have a Welsh flavour. Around 30 wines, including house French from Duboeuf at £4.50 and CELLARMAN'S CHOICE: Sancerre Rouge, Domaine Les Romains '84 at £7.95.

CHEFS: Eluned Lloyd and Judi Cooper PROPRIETORS: Eluned and John Lloyd, Judi and Michael Cooper
OPEN: all week, exc Tue
MEALS: 12.30 to 2.30, 7.30 to 9
PRICES: £11 (£16)
CARDS: Access, Visa
SEATS: 34. 4 tables outside. Private parties: 36 main room. Car-park, 6 places. Vegetarian meals. Children's helpings. No smoking in dining-room. Wheelchair access (also WC)
ACCOMMODATION: 5 rooms, all with bath/shower. B&B £19.50 to £29. Deposit: 10%. Baby facilities. Afternoon teas. TV. Scenic. Doors close at 12. Confirm by 5 [GHG]

PONTYPRIDD Mid Glamorgan map 4

John & Maria's [9/20]

1–3 Broadway, Pontypridd, CF37 1BA
PONTYPRIDD (0443) 402977 £7–£19

This bright, well-heated, and functional café has always had a local reputation as a good steak, fish and chip shop, a useful place to go on market day. Posters of Italy, an endorsement by Tony Benn, and a photograph of the entire Pontypridd Rugby Club provide the décor. The menu is wide with the emphasis on Italian dishes, which are the best choices. Portions are large, coming automatically with fat chips and vegetables. The minestrone is home made; there is good pasta, halibut in white wine with cauliflower cheese and peas, or steak and kidney pie. 'Far superior to any other Rhondda café.' House Italian £3 per carafe.

CHEF: Mrs Orsi PROPRIETORS: The Orsi Family
OPEN: Mon to Sat
CLOSED: bank hols, 25 and 26 Dec
MEALS: 11.30 to 3, 5.30 to 10
PRICES: £14 (£19), Set L £4.50 (£7)
CARDS: Access, Visa
SEATS: 120. Private parties: 35 main room, 30 private room. Vegetarian meals. Children's helpings. Music

PWLLHELI Gwynedd map 4

▲ *Plas Bodegroes* [13/20]

GWYNEDD NEWCOMER OF THE YEAR

Pwllheli LL53 5TH
PWLLHELI (0758) 612363 and 612510
1m W of Pwllheli on A497 £11–£21

The improved quality of the cooking in North Wales in the last year is symbolised by this very remote country house with cooking of a calibre that would not be out of place in London. Pwllheli is known for its beautiful wide beaches; Criccieth is the upmarket sailing town nearby. Plas Bodegroes (BODE-ER-GROYS; the place of the rosehips) is a Georgian house with a slate roof, perfect and simple, set in ancient beech woods and lawns, a small estate. Chris Chown looked for four years before finding the right house. The menu is written in English, inspired by the flavour of real food. It is ingredients-led. The remoteness has been turned to advantage, the restaurant making use of the local produce to wonderful effect. A variety of sauces and cooking techniques run through the menu – a small crumbling pastry tart filled with wild mushrooms; a plait of salmon and turbot; guinea-fowl stuffed with lemon and celeriac; spring lamb served with its kidney sliced and arranged in a crown with an appropriately strong jus. There is fine local fish – lobsters (£2 million-worth go to France), bass, black bream, sewin (best in late June). Some of the combinations stand out as being right up to date: an elderflower sauce for summer puddings, or Cointreau-steeped oranges to garnish a chocolate mousse. The menu is arranged as five courses, with three or four dishes for each, priced either per course or for all five. Fine modern dishes have been thin slices of smoked salmon wrapped around crab mousse with a salad dressed with pineapple vinaigrette; a terrine of sole and lobster laced with bacon fat garnished with cherry tomatoes and served with a yoghurt sauce; tenderloin of pork with an apricot and orange sauce. Service like the food is efficient, relaxed and confident. Accommodation is excellent value. Wines carry a flat-rate £2 mark-up irrespective of quality, which makes the pedigree wines more attractive. A quintet of sweet wines and ports opens with Muscat de Beaumes de Venise at £1.75 a glass; there are some fine Alsace wines, and some claret in the £20 plus range, as well as the solitary Welsh Monnow Valley '87 made with Muller-Thurgau and Madelaine-Angevine grapes. House Pinot Blanc or Tricastin £6. CELLARMAN'S CHOICE: Santenay, Les Passetemps '82, from Lequin, £12.75.

CHEF: Christopher Chown PROPRIETORS: Christopher Chown and Gunna a Trodni
OPEN: all week D (residents only Tue), and Sun L
CLOSED: 3 Jan to 13 Feb
MEALS: 12.30 to 1.30, 7 to 9
PRICES: £13 (£20), Set L £7.50 (£11), Set D £16.50 (£21). Minimum £12 at D
CARDS: Access, Visa
SEATS: 63. 5 tables outside. Private parties: 60 main room, 18 private room. Car-park, 25 places. Children's helpings. No smoking in dining-room. Wheelchair access (1 step; also WC). Music
ACCOMMODATION: 7 rooms, all with bath/shower. B&B £23 to £36. Deposit: 10%. Baby facilities. Pets welcome. Garden. TV. Phone. Scenic. Confirm by 6 [GHG]

REYNOLDSTON West Glamorgan map 4

▲ *Fairyhill* [11/20]

Reynoldston, Gower SA3 1BS
GOWER (0792) 390139
M4 junction 47 to Gorseinon, then B4295 to Fairyhill £13–£20

The Fraynes' personable hotel out on the peninsula has set the standard for the county in recent years. The old adage that 'le patron mange ici' holds true. A spread of fine sweets displayed on a central table in the dining-room sets the tone for a menu alert to the possibilities both of local produce – rightly famous Gower cockles are offered in the bar as well as in a pâté with laverbread – and lately of more international influences, such as foie gras marinated in port and brandy served with a Muscat jelly and hot toast. Recommendations especially for melon; warm pigeon breast salad in walnut oil; baked goat's cheese salad; roast duck; vegetarian red bean rissole. Bedrooms are comfortable. The bar offers Buckley Best Bitter and the wine list, arranged by type, which accentuates the best-value wines, is increasingly interesting. Bulgarian Cabernet Sauvignon and Chardonnay open at £4.50.

CHEF: Kate Cole PROPRIETORS: John and Midge Frayne
OPEN: all week D, and Sun L
CLOSED: Sun D Sept to Easter
MEALS: 12 to 1.45, 7 to 9.30
PRICES: £15 (£20), Set Sun L £8.95 (£13)
CARDS: Access, Visa
SEATS: 60. Private parties: 40 main room, 20 private room. Car-park, 60 places. Vegetarian meals, by arrangement. Children's helpings (L only). Smart dress preferred. Wheelchair access (also WC). Music
ACCOMMODATION: 12 rooms, all with bath/shower. B&B £39 to £55. Pets welcome. Garden. Sauna. Fishing. TV. Phone. Scenic. Confirm by 2 [GHG]

RHAYADER Powys map 4

▲ *Workhouse* [10/20]

South Road, Rhayader LD6 5BL
RHAYADER (0597) 810111 and 810735 £11–£17

The Workhouse is part of Brynafon Country House, an up-market self-catering and B&B complex near the River Wye. Theresa Ledford uses local produce like Wye salmon and Welsh goats' cheese but her menus emerge as cosmopolitan, taking in chicken satay with peanut sauce, falafels, stir-fry vegetables with ginger, chicken in calvados and cream, as well as roast beef Sunday lunch. Fresh pasta dishes often appear. She also cooks simpler meals along the lines of steak pie, pizza and lasagne, which can be eaten in the Conservatory Bar. House Fitou and Verdicchio at £5.50; CELLARMAN'S CHOICE: Gewürztraminer, Hugel, Réserve Personnelle '83, £14; Hermitage de la Sizeranne '82, from Chapoutier, £18.50.

CHEF: Theresa Ledford PROPRIETORS: Alison and André Gallagher
OPEN: Wed to Sat, D only, and Sun L
CLOSED: Christmas to early Jan
MEALS: 12.30 to 2, 7 to 10
PRICES: £12 (£17), Set Sun L £6.95 (£11)
SEATS: 28. 5 tables outside. Private parties: 35 main room, 20 private room. Car-park, 20 places. Vegetarian meals. Children's helpings (Sun L only). No children under 6. Wheelchair access (also WC). Music
ACCOMMODATION: 26 rooms, 8 with bath/shower. Rooms for disabled. B&B £18 to £30. Deposit: 33%. Children welcome. Baby facilities. Pets welcome. Garden. Swimming-pool. TV. Scenic

Powys Round-up

AFTERNOON TEAS: *Carole's Cake Shop and Tea Rooms*, South Street, Rhayader (0597 811060).
VEGETARIAN: *Granary*, Broad Street, Hay-on-Wye (0497 820790).
ROOMS: *Castle Hotel*, Main Street, Trecastle, Sennybridge (0874 82354).
AL FRESCO: *Radnor Arms*, Llowes (049 74 460).
INEXPENSIVE: *Coffee Bean*, The Old School, Gaufron, Rhayader (0597 811007).
SETTING: *Felin Crewi*, Penegoes, Machynlleth (0654 3113).

SWANSEA West Glamorgan map 4

Annie's [10/20]

56 St Helen's Road, Swansea SA1 4BE
SWANSEA (0792) 55603 £6–£17

The proper evolution of the British restaurant is from a café or a pub base into a wider operation. Ann Gwilym's café and restaurant has over the last five years begun to emerge from the chrysalis of the solid principles of a committed team and a small seasonal menu. The style is French, being both bourgeois in, perhaps, a coq au Riesling or salmon croquettes and quite adventurous in, for instance, steamed Seychelles fish filled with mousse and served with fennel and lemon grass. The tone of sweets is sorbets and summer puddings. Forty wines reinforce the Frenchness, gathered in from all the major producing regions, but emphasising the less expensive. House wine £5.20; CELLARMAN'S CHOICE: Sauvignon du Haut-Poitou £6.20.

CHEFS: Ann Gwilym and Stephane Rivier PROPRIETOR: Ann Gwilym
OPEN: Tue to Sat, exc Sat L; plus Mon D in summer
MEALS: 12 to 2, 7 to 10.30
PRICES: £13 (£17), Set L from £2.80 (£6), Set D £9.50 (£14), Snacks from £2.80. Service 10% at D
CARDS: Access, Visa
SEATS: 56. Private parties: 34 main room, 22 and 34 private rooms. Vegetarian meals. Children's helpings. Music

If you suspect that a restaurant is using processed food, always ask. It would be a contravention of the Trade Description Act for the restaurant to lie.

La Braseria [9/20]

28 Wind Street, Swansea SA1 1D2
SWANSEA (0792) 469683 £17

Opened by the owner of the Brasserie in Cardiff (see entry) and run along the same lines. The wine bar décor is all light oak beams, sawdust floors, wine barrels and huge blackboards listing hundreds of wines on offer. Good-quality steaks, ribs and fish – some baked in rock salt – plus serve-yourself salads. House wines – German, Spanish and French – open at £4.45.

PROPRIETORS: Iceimp Ltd
OPEN: all week
MEALS: 12 to 2.30, 7 to 12
PRICES: £11 (£17).
CARDS: Access, Amex, Diners, Visa
SEATS: 200. Private parties: 100 private room. Children welcome. Wheelchair access (also WC). Music. Self-service

Green Dragon Bistro [10/20]

Green Dragon Lane, Swansea SA1 1DG
SWANSEA (0792) 41437 £15

At night, this cavernous warehouse is used for traditional Welsh evenings, but at lunch it becomes a French-style café run by Kate Taylor. The emphasis is on fresh, simply prepared dishes and naturally, just a stone's throw from the splendid stalls of Swansea market, that means fish. There is a sizeable choice, considering the bistro is only a part-time operation. Sewin is served cold with mayonnaise as a starter or warm with sorrel and butter as a main course. Other good examples are a thick seafood soup with aïoli, properly made tartare sauce for marinated mackerel, and a gratin of excellent Gower cockles with wine, lemon and breadcrumbs. The kitchen's first priority is taste, so even dishes that are not strictly correct, for instance a cassoulet with just pork and smoked sausage, work well. Vegetables are plain. There is a patriotic choice of cheeses, which might include Shropshire Blue and Pencarreg, though sweets are demonstrably French in the vein of petit pots au chocolat and fine crème brûlée. 'No frills, no complexities, no disasters, no complaints.' The list of wines is not as basic as it might seem. House Rhône £3.45 a half-litre. CELLARMAN'S CHOICE: Ch. Carcos '84, £6.75.

CHEF/PROPRIETOR: Kate Taylor
OPEN: Mon to Sat, L only
MEALS: 12 to 3
PRICES: £10 (£15)
CARDS: Access, Amex, Diners, Visa
SEATS: 50. Private parties: 100 main room. Vegetarian meals. Children's helpings. Wheelchair access (1 step; also WC). Music

West Glamorgan Round-up

INDIAN: *Red Fort*, 81 St Helens Road, Swansea (0792 48509).
WINE BAR: *P.A.'s*, 95 Newton Road, Mumbles, Swansea (0792 367723).
INEXPENSIVE: *Schooner*, 4 Prospect Place, Swansea (0792 49321).

TALSARNAU Gwynedd map 4

▲ *Hotel Maes-y-Neuadd* [10/20]

Talsarnau LL47 6YA
HARLECH (0766) 780200
off B4573, 1m S of Talsarnau £12–£20

The name means Mansion in the Meadow – a beautiful grey stone building looking across the estuary to the mountains. The inside is filled with old and modern paintings, the décor leaning to the modern, with a dining-room of creams and fawns and tables set with cream cloths overlaid with cream lace cloths. The Horsfalls and Slatters have built the hotel side up into one of the most accomplished in Wales. The menu takes a wide sweep with nine dishes per course. Bread is home baked. New chef Trevor Pharoah has brought some complex ideas, some of which work well – a salad of scallops in filo pastry with peppers, and a turban of sole and salmon – to sit beside more traditional roast lamb with honey. Fine sweets have included an array of fruit sorbets; passion-fruit mousse; Pavlova. Good Welsh cheeses. Eighty wines, mostly in double figures, but starting at £6.10. CELLARMAN'S CHOICE: Mercurey, Chanteflutes '84, from Chandesais, £13.45.

CHEFS: Olive Horsfall and Trevor Pharoah PROPRIETORS: Michael and June Slatter, Malcolm and Olive Horsfall
OPEN: all week, D; L Easter to Oct, other times by arrangement
CLOSED: 2 Jan to 2 Feb
MEALS: 12.15 to 1.45, 7.30 to 9
PRICES: Set L £8.95 (£12) to £10.50 (£14), Set D £16.50 (£20). Service inc
CARDS: Access, Visa
SEATS: 40. Private parties: 60 main room, 1 private room. Car-park, 50 places. Vegetarian meals. Children's helpings. No children under 7. Wheelchair access
ACCOMMODATION: 15 rooms, all with bath/shower. Rooms for disabled. B&B £30 to 60. Deposit: £20. No children under 7. Pets by arrangement. Afternoon teas. Garden. TV. Phone. Scenic. Doors close at 11. Confirm by 6 [GHG]

TALYLLYN Gwynedd map 4

▲ *Minffordd Hotel* [10/20]

Tallyllyn LL36 9AJ
CORRIS (065 473) 665
at junction of A487 and B4405 £14

'One feels an instant return to Mrs Thatcher's Victorian values in this beautifully kept old coaching-inn at the base of the Cader Idris mountain.' The Pickles family have a loyal clientele who appreciate the short, unfancy menu and the comfortable, rather gentlemanly feel. There is little imagination, but good soups, such as Welsh onion or cream of carrot, fine sauce for chicken supreme. Good baking for the nursery sweets lifts the menu in what is a homely dining-room. 'A hotel for *Daily Telegraph* readers.' House wine is £5; CELLARMAN'S CHOICE: Gran Vina Sol Penedés, Torres '85, £7.50 and Puligny-Montrachet '83, £17.55.

CHEF: Jonathan Pickles PROPRIETORS: Bernard and Jessica Pickles
OPEN: Tue to Sat, D only
CLOSED: Jan and Feb
MEALS: 7.30 to 8.30
PRICES: Set D £11.50 (£14). Service inc
CARDS: Access, Diners, Visa
SEATS: 28. Private parties: 28 main room. Car-park, 12 places. Vegetarian meals. Children's helpings (D only). No children under 3. Smart dress preferred. No smoking. Wheelchair access
ACCOMMODATION: 7 rooms, all with bath/shower. B&B £25.50. Deposit: 10%. No children under 3. Garden. Phone. Scenic. Doors close at 11. Confirm by 6

THREE COCKS Powys map 4

▲ *Three Cocks Hotel* [11/20]

Three Cocks LD3 0SL
GLASBURY (049 74) 215
on A438, between Brecon and Hay-on-Wye £18–£21

This stone-built roadside inn with cobbled forecourt provides a definite French accent in the hills. The menu reads attractively, with unusual ingredients, such as excellent smoked Ardennes ham and wild boar served in a cream sauce, side by side with local produce. Good dishes have been the carrot and parsnip soup; warm goats' cheese in puff pastry; lardons and bacon salad; poached salmon in vinaigrette; chocolate mousse. Forty wines make up a good basic list, from the house French at £4.60; CELLARMAN'S CHOICE: Sauvignon de St Bois '86, £11, and Haut Médoc, Ch. Liversan '81, £15.

CHEF: M. E. Winstone PROPRIETORS: Mr and Mrs M. E. Winstone
OPEN: all week, exc Tue
CLOSED: Dec and Jan
MEALS: 12 to 1.30, 7 to 9
PRICES: £17 (£21), Set L and D £16 (£18), Snacks from £1.25. Service inc
CARDS: Access, Visa
SEATS: 35. Private parties: 35 main room. Car-park, 30 places. Children welcome. Smart dress preferred. Music
ACCOMMODATION: 7 rooms, all with bath/shower. B&B £25 to £46. Baby facilities. Pets welcome. Garden. Scenic. Doors close at 12. Confirm by 5

TREFRIW Gwynedd map 4

Chandler's [10/20]

Trefriw LL27 0JH
LLANRWST (0492) 640991 £18

Three ex-catering students have transformed this old ship-chandler's into a good-value restaurant with a polished slate floor and old school desks for tables – complete with ink wells and pencil holders. A short, bistro-style menu is based largely on local produce and there are some good touches: sauté of chicken livers and grapes in sherry; hot goats' cheese salad with sage dressing; quails with pine nuts and raisins on a bed of raw sorrel leaves. Roast rack of Welsh lamb is served with Shrewsbury sauce. Fish and vegetarian specialities change daily. Home-made sorbets and unusual ice-creams to finish. Around 20 reasonably priced wines, including house French at £5.30 a bottle.

CHEF: Adam Rattenbury PROPRIETORS: Adam and Penny Rattenbury and Tim Kirton
OPEN: Tue to Sat, and Sun L
CLOSED: Tue to Sat L Oct to end May
MEALS: 12 to 2, 7 to 10
PRICES: £13 (£18)
CARDS: Access, Visa
SEATS: 36. 5 tables outside. Private parties: 36 main room. Car-park, 10 places. Vegetarian meals. Children's helpings. No smoking. Music

TRELLECH Gwent map 4

Village Green [new entry, zero rated]

Trellech NP6 4PA
MONMOUTH (0600) 860119 £14–£22

The village is noted for its prehistoric stones (Trellech means 'three stones') and its medieval healing well. Bob and Jane Evans, who used to run the Bridge Inn at Llangwm, have transformed a derelict, run-down pub into a restaurant with bare stone walls and paintings for sale. Colin Sparks, from Le Beaujolais, Cheltenham, cooks a short modern menu using fish from Cornwall and meat from Monmouth. Typically there might be warm salad of quail and mange-tout; brochette of seafood on a bed of courgettes with vermouth and coriander sauce; and John Dory with ginger and chive butter sauce. Best end of lamb is boned cutlets, with the bone on the side of the plate, accompanied by baby vegetables and a thyme-flavoured tomato concasse, with a reduced, unthickened lamb stock. To finish, the chocolate marquise can compete with the best. Unpretentious, sensible list of 30 wines, including house at £5.95 a bottle, £3.50 a half-bottle. CELLARMAN'S CHOICE: Australian Chardonnay '86, £9.95; Georges Duboeuf Morgon '86, £14.50. Bedrooms are planned, to be open by the spring of 1989. More reports, please.

CHEF: Colin Sparks PROPRIETORS: Bob and Jane Evans
OPEN: Tue to Sat
MEALS: 12 to 2, 7 to 9.45
PRICES: £17 (£21), Set L £9.50 (£14), Set D £17.50 (£22). L Snacks from £2.50. Service inc. Licensed, also bring your own: corkage £2
SEATS: 50. Private parties: 12 main room, 16 private room. Car-park, 14 places. Children's helpings. No children under 6. Smart dress preferred. No pipes in dining-room. Wheelchair access (1 step; also WC)

'When I said my roll was stale, the sweet American waiter admitted they all were, but helped me choose the least stale one.' On eating in London

WOLF'S CASTLE Dyfed map 4

▲ *Stone Hall* [new entry, zero rated]

Welsh Hook, Wolf's Castle SA26 5NS
LETTERSTON (0348) 840212
W of A40 between Letterston and Wolf's Castle £15–£17

'The cuisine is unashamedly French with the exception that a selection of vegetables is served with the main course.' With a salade composée of toasted goats' cheese, bacon and frisée, come ten or so bottles of fruit and herb oils and vinegars. This Frenchness is cocooned in a six-hundred-year-old, secluded manor with three-foot-thick oak beams, inglenook and flagged floors, surrounded by ten acres of mature grounds filled with rhododendrons and azaleas. The menu of nine starters, four fish, six meats and six sweets is text-book regional France: confit of duck; duck breast Vallée d'Auge; steak tartare; spinach soufflé. Sea-trout, sea-bass and scallops come from local inshore boats. Strips of home-cured salmon served as a lattice on a bed of frisée is excellent. To finish there has been fine tarte Tatin. Service is from Alan Watson while his wife Martine controls the kitchen. The set meal of the day is a bargain at £10.50 for four courses. Forty wines spread across France from house Gamay and Sauvignon at £6.55 to CELLARMAN'S CHOICE: St Estèphe, Ch. Lavillotte '79, 15.35. More reports, please.

CHEFS: Martine Watson and Barry O'Dare PROPRIETORS: Alan and Martine Watson
OPEN: Tue to Sun, D only
MEALS: 7.30 to 9.30
PRICES: £11 (£17), Set D from £9.50 (£15)
CARDS: Access, Amex, Visa
SEATS: 34. Private parties: 45 main room, 30 private room. Car-park, 50 places. Vegetarian meals. Children's helpings
ACCOMMODATION: 5 rooms, all with bath/shower. B&B £24 to £38. Deposit: £20. Baby facilities. Afternoon teas. Garden. TV. Scenic

▲ *Wolfscastle Country Hotel* [11/20]

Wolf's Castle SA62 5LZ
TREFFGARNE (043 787) 225 £18

The Stirlings have established their hotel over eleven years, with local support via their tennis and squash courts. The kitchen produces a *carte* of eight dishes for each stage, with cheaper bar meals available. 'A cross between nouvelle and honest home-cooked food.' Local fish from Fishguard might be sewin baked with lemon and herbs, or monk with a cream and vermouth sauce. Steaks and lamb are grilled and offered with béarnaise. A new addition is a six-course tasting menu. Meals finish with a sweets trolley that features iced soufflés and sticky toffee pudding. Fifty wines are drawn from across Europe, with most of the interest in the minor clarets. House wine £5.80. CELLARMAN'S CHOICE: Pauillac, Ch. Haut Batailley '76, £19.50.

'I don't think they are awfully interested in their supplies – or can't one buy good fish in Brighton?' On inspecting in Brighton

CHEFS: Michael Lewis and Alex George PROPRIETOR: Andrew Maxwell Stirling
OPEN: all week, D only, and Sun L
MEALS: 12 to 2, 7 to 9.30
PRICES: £13 (£18). Snacks from £1.50
CARDS: Amex, Access, Visa
SEATS: 60. 6 tables outside. Private parties: 50 main room, 120 private room. Car-park, 60 places. Vegetarian meals. Children's helpings. Smart dress preferred. Music. Air-conditioned
ACCOMMODATION: 15 rooms, all with bath. B&B £25 to £40. Baby facilities. Pets welcome. Air-conditioning. TV. Phone. Scenic. Doors close at 12. Confirm by 6

Isle of Man

BALLASALLA Isle of Man map 4

La Rosette [11/20]

Main Road, Ballasalla
BALLASALLA (0624) 822940 £19–£23

The Rosette is of the old school with a long menu written in French which includes 'Filet Beefburger Vari'. There is a cover charge and certain other tendencies indicate, perhaps, a 'business executive off the plane' touch –Ronaldoway is only a mile away – at lunch. But Rosa Phillips is a flexible and charming hostess who can bring most people face to face with what they want. Local fish underpins the menu, served plainly grilled or with classic sauces. The Manx queenies are 'tossed in garlic butter and served with a side salad.' There is range of steaks and sorbets, but also some creative desserts, like caramelised apple pudding with ice-cream. Twenty-five wines from £5.95 are a well-picked tour of the major French regions. CELLARMAN'S CHOICE: St Emilion, *grand cru*, Clos des Menuts '83, £15.

CHEF: Robert Phillips PROPRIETORS: Robert and Rosa Phillips
OPEN: Mon to Sat, exc Mon L
MEALS: 12 to 2.30, 7 to 10.30
PRICES: L £12 (£19), D £15 (£23). Cover 25p L, 60p D
SEATS: 47. Private parties: 24 main room, 8 and 15 private rooms. Children's helpings. Music

ONCHAN Isle of Man map 4

Boncompte's [10/20]

King Edward Road, Onchan
DOUGLAS (0624) 75626 £14–£27

Fine views over Douglas Bay, elegant décor and good-value business lunches are the main attractions in this highly popular restaurant. The lounge is boarding-house Dralon; the dining-room feels more like Regency. Dinners are classically international – consommé, beef Wellington, sole fillets wrapped round smoked salmon, osso buco. There is a good Chianti Ruffino for quaffing, otherwise try CELLARMAN'S CHOICE: Chardonnay, Coteaux Champenois, £13.50.

CHEF: Jaime Boncompte PROPRIETORS: Jaime and Jill Boncompte
OPEN: Mon to Sat, exc Sat L
MEALS: 12.30 to 2, 7.30 to 10
PRICES: £19 (£27), Set L £8.50 (£14)
CARDS: Access, Diners, Visa
SEATS: 90. Private parties: 90 main room. Car-park, 10 places. Vegetarian meals. Children's helpings. Smart dress preferred. Wheelchair access (also WC). Music

Isle of Man Round-up

ENGLISH: *Silverburn Lodge,* Ballasalla (0624 822343); *Shore Hotel,* Port St Mary (0624 832269).
ITALIAN: *Little Italy,* Mannin Hotel, Broadway, Douglas (0624 75335).
SETTING: *Ravensdale Castle,* Ballaugh Glen, Ballaugh (062 489 7330).
FISH: *Harbour Bistro,* 5 East Street, Ramsey (0624 814182).
AFTERNOON TEAS: *Gophers,* 2 West Quay, Ramsey (0624 815562).
INEXPENSIVE: *Chablis Cellar,* 21 Bank Street, Castletown (0624 823527).

Northern Ireland

BALLYNAHINCH Co Down map 9

Woodlands [10/20]

29 Spa Road, Ballynahinch BT24 8PT
BALLYNAHINCH (0238) 562650 £20

Alison Sandford cooks while David Sandford greets guests at the front door and serves drinks in the sitting-room. This eighteenth-century country house, rurally situated half a mile off the Spa road, overlooks rolling County Down countryside as well as having its own lovely and extensive gardens. Inside, the pale green walls and curtains, antique tables and sideboard give an elegant feel to the dining-room. The menu, although not adventurous, makes use of high-quality ingredients. Good starters have been melon with mint sorbet and curried parsnip soup. Main courses are fairly traditional: roast chicken, fillet steak or veal with a red pepper sauce, Connemara salmon or local pheasant with spiced oranges. Desserts come with a free glass of sweet wine, if desired, and coffee with good home-made fudge and truffles. House French is £5.70.

CHEF: Alison Sandford PROPRIETORS: Alison and David Sandford
OPEN: Thur to Sat, D only. Private parties (min 12) Mon to Wed
MEALS: 7.30 to 9.45
PRICES: Set D £14.95 (£20)
CARDS: Access, Diners, Visa
SEATS: 45. Private parties. 45 main room, 14 private room. Car-park, 20 places. Children's helpings. No cigars/pipes in dining-room

BELFAST Co Antrim map 9

Belle Epoque [10/20]

103 Great Victoria Street, Belfast BT2 7AG
BELFAST (0232) 223244 £18

Statuettes and clever use of mirrors, plus a roving accordion-player help to evoke the Belle Epoque in the popular restaurant on Belfast's Golden Mile. The food is classically French – duck liver or trout with orange sauce for starters; to follow, steak, fillet or *au poivre.* Sauces are cream-based and can be over heavy but sweets are made to order, tartlets and sorbets both good. House French is £3.95.

CHEFS: Alan Rousse and Chris Fitzgerald PROPRIETOR: J. Delbart
OPEN: Mon to Sat, D only
MEALS: 6pm to 12.30am (11.30pm Sat)
PRICES: £12 (£18)
CARDS: Access, Diners, Visa
SEATS: 80. Private parties: 40 main room. Vegetarian meals. Children welcome. Music

Strand [9/20]

12 Stranmillis Road, Belfast BT9 5AA
BELFAST (0232) 682266 £12

A busy bistro, with university students mingling with media types. Plenty of popular choices on the cosmopolitan wine-bar menu, from fresh pasta with vegetables to roulades of chicken breasts and Stilton, smoked salmon rolls or chicken provencale. Cheapish, cheerful and casual. House French is £4.25.

CHEFS: M. Paine, M. McAuley, Stephen Galway and Marie Hickey PROPRIETOR: Anne Turkington
OPEN: Mon to Sat
MEALS: noon to 11pm
PRICES: £8 (£12)
CARDS: Access, Amex, Diners, Visa
SEATS: 80. Vegetarian meals. Children welcome. Music. Air-conditioned

BELLANALECK Co Fermanagh map 9

Sheelin [10/20]

Bellanaleck
FLORENCECOURT (036 582) 232
4m from Enniskillen £8–£19

The Cathcart family run this thatched cottage as a restaurant and bakery, the latter known throughout the province. The restaurant is noted for its Saturday night gourmet meal – five courses at £15 is relatively good value in the area. The hors d'oeuvre, crêpe and sorbet are set, with a choice of five main courses, including duckling with apricots; salmon hollandaise; pork loin with cream and muchroom sauce. Seven sweets follow, all linked by cream. Lunches and afternoon teas too. House French is £4.50.

CHEFS: The Cathcart Family PROPRIETOR: Arthur Cathcart
OPEN: Mon to Sat L, and Fri and Sat D; plus Sun and Tue to Thur D June to Aug
MEALS: 12.30 to 2.30, 7 to 9.30
PRICES: £11 (£15), Set L £5 (£8), Set D £10 (£13) to £15 (£19), Snacks from £1.20. Service 10%
CARDS: Access, Amex, Visa
SEATS: 30. Private parties: 30 main room. Car-park. Vegetarian meals. Children's helpings. Smart dress preferred

Reports on shops, cafés and farms are useful, as well as reports on restaurants.

COLERAINE Co Derry map 9

▲ *Macduff's* [10/20]

112 Killeague Road, Blackhill, Coleraine BT51 4HH
AGHADOWEY (026 585) 433
4m N of Garvagh £18

The Erwins have recaptured the grace of this Georgian country guest-house and restaurant built by the Bishop of Derry: the cellars have been turned into a lounge and restaurant with red velvet upholstery, chintz curtains and military prints on the walls. The setting, too, is lovely – mature grounds planted with shrubs, set in rural farmland. Using the 'natural resources of Ulster', the menu is largely, simple international fare, with a country-house emphasis: chilled melon with fresh fruit to start, then a suprême of chicken, grilled salmon with caper sauce or roast quail with a light wine sauce to follow. Tandoori chicken might be on offer one day, a dish with German inspiration the next. The fresh vegetables are home grown and the desserts – fruits, sorbets and ice-creams predominating – echo the light touch elsewhere. House French is £5.20.

CHEF: Alan Wade PROPRIETORS: Joseph and Margaret Erwin
OPEN: Tue to Sat, D. only
MEALS: 7 to 9.30
PRICES: £11 (£18)
SEATS: 34. Private parties: 34 main room, 15 private room. Car-park, 20 places. Vegetarian meals. No children under 10
ACCOMMODATION: 6 rooms, 5 with bath/shower. B&B £25 to £40. No children under 10. Afternoon teas. Garden. Swimming-pool. Fishing. Golf. Phone. Scenic. Doors close at 1. Confirm by 6

HILLSBOROUGH Co Down map 9

Hillside Bar [10/20]

21 Main Street, Hillsborough BT26 6AE
HILLSBOROUGH (0846) 683475 £7–£18

Best known for its good-value pub lunches, but the small restaurant upstairs is also interesting if you pick carefully through the menu. 'An Irish version of French cooking,' is how one correspondent described her pork in cider and cream sauce. Whiting in noisette butter is presented with puff-pastry crescents. Excellent home-made sorbet before the main course, well cooked vegetables and good coffee. Attentive service which tries hard to please. House French £5.

CHEFS: Noel Doran and John McAvoy PROPRIETORS: Harlequin (Hillsborough) Ltd
OPEN: all week
MEALS: 12 to 3 (12.30 to 2 Sun), 7 to 9.30
PRICES: £13 (£18), Bar L £4 (£7)
CARDS: Access, Amex, Diners, Visa
SEATS: 46. 4 tables outside. Private parties: 30 main room. Vegetarian meals. No children under 18

HOLYWOOD Co. Down map 9

Iona [11/20]

Holywood BT18 9BU
HOLYWOOD (023 17) 5655 £17–£21

On the first floor above an Iona shop selling bric à brac and herbal stuffs, and run by Dutch-born Bartjan Brade. The blue and white décor is fresh and clean and the guitarist plays 'easy listening'. Cooking is well-executed *nouvelle cuisine*. Start with oysters in raspberry vinaigrette or sweetbreads with Chinese mushrooms. A selection of meats is presented with three sauces meeting in the middle of the plate. Baby corn, baby leeks in cream, and cabbage in soya sauce make a carefully chosen trio of vegetables. Puddings are well reported. No licence, no corkage, no ice-buckets, so take pre-chilled wine.

CHEF/PROPRIETOR: Bartjan Brade
OPEN: Tue to Sat
MEALS: 12 to 2, 6.30 to 10.30
PRICES: £14 (£17), Set D £16.95 (£18) to £19.95 (£21). Service inc. Unlicensed, but bring your own: no corkage
SEATS: 28. Private parties: 32 main room. Vegetarian meals. Children's helpings on request. No cigars/pipes in dining-room. Music

KILLINCHY Co Down map 9

Nick's [11/20]

18 Kilmood Church Road, Killinchy BT23 6SB
KILLINCHY (0238) 541472 £18

The black and white exterior of the old court matches that of the church hall next door. The pine panelled room is dominated by the balcony on which the judge's seat would have been. Dark green Sanderson wallpaper and green linen hanging lamps complete the renovation. The menu shows flair and sophistication and some dishes arrive dressed with flower heads and herbs. Nick Price cooks fish particularly well, marrying brill and home-smoked trout in a beurre blanc or, in another recipe, serving the brill with a trout mousseline, mussels and prawns. Other good dishes have included a cucumber and garlic cheesecake. Interesting vegetables, for instance celeriac Mornay or fennel in garlic sauce. Minimum of formality in atmosphere and service. House French is £5.

CHEFS: Nick Price and Jenny McCrea PROPRIETORS: Nick and Kathy Price
OPEN: Tue to Sat, D only
CLOSED: 2 weeks Sept to Oct, one week mid-Mar
MEALS: 7.30 to 10
PRICES: £12 (£18)
CARDS: Access, Diners, Visa
SEATS: 45. 3 tables outside. Private parties: 30 main room. Vegetarian meals (by arrangements). Car-park, 60 places. Children's helpings. Music

PORTRUSH Co Antrim map 9

Ramore [11/20]

The Harbour, Portrush BT56 8DQ
PORTRUSH (0265) 824313 £20

Enjoying the reputation of being one of Northern Ireland's best restaurants, Ramore is in an unprepossessing modern building overlooking the harbour. The lounge area, with black leather and chrome furniture and a richly coloured abstract stained window, acts as the thoroughfare for both restaurant and the revamped wine bar underneath. The restaurant follows the *nouvelle* glossy magazine ethos of large plates with pools of sauce under petite, carefully fashioned, flavourful dishes. Duck breast is wrapped in filo pastry and served on an orange and chervil sauce; chicken breast is stuffed with snails and served with a garlic cream sauce. For dessert, George McAlpin's speciality is a hot lemon or chocolate soufflé. The wine bar serves bistro food less expensively: moussaka and charcoal grilled pork fillet are typical of recommendations. House French is £5.50.

CHEF: George McAlpin PROPRIETORS: John and Joy Caithness, George McAlpin
OPEN: Tue to Sat, D only
CLOSED: last 2 weeks Jan
MEALS: 7 to 10
PRICES: £13 (£20), Snacks in wine bar from £1.90
SEATS: 55. Private parties: 60 main room. Car-park, 8 places. Children welcome. Music

SAINTFIELD Co Down map 9

Barn [10/20]

120 Monlough Road, Saintfield BT24 7EU
SAINTFIELD (0238) 510396 £14–£20

Robbie and Jane Wright knocked two barns together to create this cosy restaurant deep in the countryside. Sit around an open turf fire for pre-dinner drinks in the lounge before moving next door to the dining-room. Favourites such as cheese stuffed tomatoes in a mild mustard sauce and lamb with a rosemary and lemon sauce are the staples. Choice lies with the excellent daily fish dishes – sea-trout with a gooseberry and lemon sauce; salmon en croûte with a creamy watercress sauce. Hearty cooking and generous platefuls are the tenor. The sweets trolley is equally straightforward – a rich walnut fudge cake and meringues with cream are examples. 'The coffee pot came round *five* times,' accompanied by home-made fudge. House French and Spanish £5.95.

Restaurants are graded on a scale of 1–20. In the category of 10–11 expect to find the best food in the locality. Ratings of 12 and more are given to restaurants we regard as serving the best food in the region.

CHEF: Robbie Wright PROPRIETORS: Robbie and Jane Wright
OPEN: Tue to Sat, exc Sat L
CLOSED: 2 weeks Jan to Feb
MEALS: 12.30 to 2.30, 7.30 to 10
PRICES: Set L £9.50 (£14), Set D £14.95 (£20)
CARDS: Access, Amex, Diners, Visa
SEATS: 40. Private parties: 40 main room. Car-park, 12 places. Children welcome. Jacket and tie. Wheelchair access (1 step). Music. Air-conditioned

Channel Islands

ST SAVIOUR Jersey map 1

▲ *Longueville Manor* [14/20]

St Saviour
JERSEY (0534) 25501 £16–£38

Strange that one of the great hopes of modern British cooking should find himself not only on an island where the cooking is generally 20 years behind the times, but also in an aristocratic setting which depicts an era of 1930s cocktails. Barry Forster was Michael Quinn's star pupil, first at the Ritz and then at Ettington Park. Here he runs a *carte* of six starters, followed by a trio of sorbets including cucumber, then six main dishes; alternatively an eight-course tasting menu; or, at lunch, a short, good-value set meal. Forster points to the warm strudel of foie gras with wild mushrooms and his roast duck breast with a prune and armagnac glaze as typical of his work. Seasoning is vivid, as in red onion and orange pepper for salmon, but not at the expense of conventional modes. But what about this for an April lunch: crab and langoustine bisque; roast duck breast salad with honey and the first Jersey Royals; hot rhubarb crumble. Somehow the marriage of modern instincts and the conservative hotel dining arena produces an effective and direct cuisine. Recommended dishes: vegetable consommé with ravioli; baked turbot in pastry with spinach and oysters; iced Grand Marnier soufflé. Service is helpful without snobbery. There is also a vegetarian menu: asparagus, mange-tout and French bean vinaigrette; truffled tartlet of quail eggs and wild mushrooms; cornet of spring vegetables scented with coriander and ginger; sweet or unpasteurised farmhouse cheese. Curiously, on a wine list that is almost entirely French, the non-French wines are more reliable than the French, with top-class Australian, Spanish, Italian and German bottles. The selection of claret is good if expensive. Burgundy is better in red than white and Rhône and Loire average and not cheap. A limited selection of sweet wines includes Châteaux Coutet, Clos Haut Peyraguey and d'Yquem, a German Beerenauslese and Jaboulet's Muscat de Beaumes de Venise '85, at £16, or £2.25 per glass. House French is £4.75; CELLARMAN'S CHOICE: St Estèphe, Ch. Beau-Site '82, £16.75.

Many of the more expensive restaurants offer bargain lunches for half the price of a meal in the evening. Details are given in the text.

CHEF: Barry Forster PROPRIETORS: The Lewis family and the Dufty family
OPEN: all week
MEALS: 12.30 to 2, 7.30 to 9.30
PRICES: £23 (£29), Set L from £8.50 (£16), Set D £17.50 (£22) and £32 (£38), Snacks from £1.80. Service 10%
CARDS: Access, Amex, Carte Blanche, Diners, Visa
SEATS: 65. 8 tables outside. Private parties: 75 main room, 16 private room. Car-park, 30 places. Vegetarian meals. Children welcome. Smart dress preferred. Wheelchair access (also WC). Air-conditioned
ACCOMMODATION: 34 rooms, all with bath/shower. Rooms for disabled. Lift. B&B £58 to £124. Deposit: £45 per person. No children under 7. Pets welcome. Afternoon teas. Garden. Swimming-pool. TV. Phone. Scenic

Channel Islands Round-up

INEXPENSIVE: *Guernsey College*, Route des Coutanchez, St Peter Port, Guernsey (0481 23026).
STEAKS: *Steak & Stilton*, The Quay, St Peter Port, Guernsey (0481 23080)
REMOTE: *Pembroke Hotel and Restaurant*, Pembroke Bay, Vale, Guernsey (0481 47573).
FISH: *Nautique*, Quay Steps, St Peter Port, Guernsey (0481 21714); *Old Court House*, St Aubin, Jersey (0534 46433).
AL FRESCO: *Apple Cottage*, Rozel Bay, Jersey (0534 61002).
SETTING: *Victor Hugo*, Saint Pierre Park Hotel, St Peter Port, Guernsey (0481 28282); *La Sablonnerie*, Sark (048183 2061); *Old Government House*, St Peter Port, Guernsey (0481 24921).
ITALIAN: *La Capannina*, 65 - 67 Halkett Place, St Helier, Jersey (0534 34602); *Da Nello*, 46 Pollet Street, St Peter Port, Guernsey (0481 21552); *Piazza*, Under the Arch, Trinity Square, St Peter Port, Guernsey (0481 25085);
VIEW: *Idlerocks Hotel*, Jerbourg Point, St Martin's, Guernsey (0481 37711); *La Fregate Hotel*, Les Cotils, St Peter Port, Guernsey (0481 24624).

International

French Channel ports

by Patricia Fenn

The Channel port restaurants have an enviable stability compared to equivalents in Britain – the picture has not developed much over the last couple of years.

East of Calais *La Meunerie* at **Téteghem** (tel 28 26 01 80) is indisputably one of the best tables in the north of France, making use of the good vegetables and fish in the area. **Calais** itself offers nothing new and nothing exciting. **Boulogne** is still the major restaurant port with *La Matelote* (80 bvd Ste-Beuve, tel 21 30 17 97), *La Liégeoise* (10 rue A.-Monsigny, tel 21 31 61 15) and *Hostellerie de la Rivière* at **Pont-de-Briques** (17 rue Gare, tel 21 32 22 81) all above average. Nearby, the *Relais de la Brocante* at **Wimille** (2 rue de Ledinghem, tel 21 83 19 31), and at **Montreuil** the *Château dé Montreuil* (chaussée Capucins, tel 21 81 53 04) and *Auberge la Grenouillère* (La Madeleine-sous-Montreuil, tel 21 06 07 22) are even better. None has strong regional alliances. **Dieppe** is disappointing. It provokes a feeling that somewhere there should be talent lurking, but if so I have yet to find it. Newcomer *La Mélie* (2 Grande-Rue du Pollet, tel 35 84 21 19) failed to live up to the expectations of its pedigree. **Le Havre** is dismal.

Ouistreham, predictably, has not been slow to cash in on its new importance as a ferry destination and in restaurant terms has gone downhill. But in nearby **Caen** there is a young, admirable chef, Michel Bruneau of *La Bourride* (15 rue Vaugneux, tel 31 93 50 76), who has flair and talent, makes good use of Norman ingredients, and would rate a strong 16/20 plus.

St Mâlo starts off with the advantage of being easily the most attractive port, backed by a colourful history, with the rocky coast and the pasturelands of the bay of Mont St Michel contributing prime ingredients. In the town itself, *La Duchesse Anne* (5 place Guy la Chambre, tel 99 40 85 33) continues to plod her stately time-honoured way, but has nothing new to say. On the other side of the peninsula, however, just 14 kilometres away, lies the little oyster port of **Cancale**, and here is the restaurant that above all others fires the imagination – *Restaurant de Bricourt* (1 rue Duguesclin, tel 99 89 64 76). Chef/patron Olivier de Roëllinger abandoned his first career as a chemical engineer to become a cook. With scientific thoroughness he served his apprenticeship to three exalted chefs, researched the recipes of his region, discovered which varieties of vegetables and herbs grown in his potager would yield best crops for his purposes, and experimented diligently with different cooking methods. His cooking, he says, 'doit refleter l'air, l'esprit de cette région, liée à la fois à la terre, et à la mer, et très richée par son passé.'

From the countryside, he takes the salt-marsh lamb. The quality and flavour of this unique animal is allowed to come through in simple roast gigôts and carrées, flavoured with rosemary and served with baby vegetables from his garden. His ducks are reared 'en semi-liberté' and cooked according to an old recipe of his mother's, with prunes, cubes of smoked ham and drops of honey to crisp the skin concealing the dark fondant-like meat of the mature bird. He sharpens and perfumes casseroled pigeon breasts with vinegar flavoured with elderflower and serves the legs as a separate course in a bouillon enriched with foie gras. A cheap, humble main ingredient is given luxurious treatment, while a superb lobster might be presented with the simplicity born of absolute conviction – sauté with just 'une pointe' of parsley for intensity.

The sea, as one would expect in the area from which the best restaurants in France draw their supplies, features strongly on a short, daily-changing menu. Cancale has long been famous for its oysters – Louis XIV would eat no other. The rocks on which the little town is built shelter fine lobsters, abundant mussels cluster to every submarine surface and the Cancalais fishing fleet brings back shoals of glistening bass, brill, turbot, red mullet, sole.

But it is not only these bastions of cuisine which de Roëllinger exploits. He has investigated and continues to learn 'les petits secrets' of the old fisherwomen down in the port as how to treat the less aristocratic fish. One of the most successful springtime dishes is his Cotriade Cancalaise, a composition of several little fishes of the bay with small sweet oysters (which you can still buy from the stalls along the quayside for under a £1 the thirteen), and served with sprays of wild fennel picked from the cliff-tops.

De Roëllinger is deeply conscious of his roots and passionate about his heritage. *De Bricourt* is the house in which he was born, son of the doctor. It is typical of many pleasing small eighteenth-century mansions known as Malouinières. The fortunes of St Mâlo were founded on swashbuckling voyages on which members of the Compagnie des Indes and a variety of *corsaires* (a word that doesn't have the derogatory implications as 'pirates'), set out to collect precious spices and discover uncharted parts of the world. When they returned, they enriched their descendants not only by building these elegant houses but by introducing exotic spices to the local cooking. This tradition has never died out and de Roëllinger did not need current culinary fashions to persuade him to experiment with coriander, cumin, cardamon, ginger, peppers and green mangoes in what he describes as a cuisine of adventure, offering a palette of almost infinite variations.

With steamed fillets of sole he serves a sauce both powerful and subtle, 'aux épices de la Compagnie des Indes'. He varies his simple lobster with an outrageous additions to its juices of a dose of Tafia, an old soldier's rum; he calls his sparklingly fresh and light fish soup, based on langoustines and clams and flavoured with green mango, mint and coriander, 'le petit bouillon aux saveurs de Siam'.

Desserts continue to exemplify his mixed affiliations; nothing Breton about a tartelette aux bananes flavoured with ginger, but the next item on the list is 'Reinette d'Armorique' (an apple rarely found outside Brittany) 'au four grannysmith' (sic), 'doré a la crème d'amandes,' and a dish of local pears is presented in 'craquelins de Cancale' – a sweet biscuit pastry, traditionally eaten on the days of the Pardons.

All the rules of the usual successful ambitious restaurateur have been broken. Bricourt is still very much a home, with only five tables apiece in each of its two antique-furnished salons. At least another three could be squeezed in each if cost-effectiveness were the prime concern. New recognition is wont to push up prices unduly, but here the cheapest menu, 90f mid-week (£8.50) must be the bargain of the year. The very finding of the place, not down in the port with all the action, all the tourists, but hidden shyly in a lane behind the town square, is not easy. Six bedrooms were opened in 1988, in a former fisherman's house nearby, overlooking the Bay of Mont St Michel.

Paris: *Lucas Carton*

by Drew Smith

Restaurant cooking for the best part of this century has had a two-dimensional approach, offering a focal point offset by something else. It is static in the sense that each mouthful is approximately the same as the one before it. In recent years there have been signs of third and fourth dimensions appearing. Critics say this is not proper cooking at all, just a series of pretty tastes, one piled on top of the other. At its least effective it provokes the I-had-to-go-and-have-another-meal-afterwards reaction. But that is just poor cooking – poor because it falls down on one of the chef's key areas of activity, balance.

Starting to take shape is a change of role for the chef, from soloist to conductor. The basic skills are taken as read. Creating a rhythm of different flavours on the plate becomes the objective.

An arch proponent of this approach is Alain Senderens, formerly of *L'Archestrate*, now of *Lucas Carton*, diagonally opposite from *Fauchon* on the Place de la Madeleine, Paris. This is now one of the major restaurants in Europe. Enter through two pairs of electric sliding doors and you are in an old Parisian brasserie of mahogany and mirrors – the wood of the drawers worn smooth through years of use – and met by a line of men in black suits and bow ties, blue for seniority. (Upstairs is more modern, with smaller rooms for business entertaining.) The dining-room is split into two and tables are arranged around the walls and partitions, giving staff the use of the central floor to present the dishes.

The clientele – in leopard skins, leather, kimono, obi, pin-stripe, grey flannel – reflect the prices – £100 a head is common; it is hard to eat for less than £70. The atmosphere is deeply Parisian. The tempo is that of a brasserie; there is no overwhelming sense of cossetting or luxury.

Uncomfortably big menus arrive in profusion, bound up in each other in an outsize folder a foot wide and eighteen inches tall and etched in 3D in pale green and blue of lilies which are also in abundance in the room. There are menus for business lunches, the most accessible financially around £35; menus to celebrate the truffle season; menus with wines. Most are permutations of the basic *carte* of eight starters, five fish, eight meats, two cheeses, including one for tasting, allied to chosen wines, and ten sweets, which are ordered along with everything else, plus there may be a few dishes of the day – scallops perhaps either with anise or in a filo purse with a cèpes sauce.

Senderens' cooking challenges. It appeals as much to the mind as the palate. There is an invitation to move from one side of a dish to another. For example, a ravioli is filled with a bay scallop and a single sliver of courgette skin and sauced lightly with thyme flowers. On the far side of the plate the courgettes have been sliced into spaghettini, blanched and cooked very simply in butter to reinforce the courgette taste and create a contrast between the smooth pasta and shredded vegetable, the sweetness of scallop and the slight bitterness of courgette. Description gives this a pretension it does not deserve.

The Italian influence is found again with red mullet, using Calabrian ingredients – three fillets are poached and strewn with a few slices of olive and caper and garnished with a tapénade, a croûton and a little head of celery. Each component plays a crucial part in altering the harmony of the tastes. Or, again, a veal sweetbread is roasted, slightly caramelised on the outside for contrast, placed in the middle of the plate and completely encircled by deep-fried herbs and crisps. Underneath the sweetbreads sits a marmalade of onions. Again there are three components – deep-fried, crisp herbs (mostly parsley and chervil), silky meat and sweet, texturous onions.

The point is made most dramatically with the sweets. The last course has always been the Achilles heel of modern cooking – sorbets, fruits and an occasional tart or mousse have been the frontiers. Senderens' sweets are dramatic. 'Tarte aux zestes d'oranges confits au Grand Marnier et sorbet au chocolat amer' is breathtaking: the tart itself is thin and not much wider in diameter than the label on an LP. It is smeared with a marmalade and a Grand Marnier cream, and topped with curls of caramelised oranges. To offset this, both visually and in terms of tastes, are two ovals of bitter chocolate ice-cream, rather than sorbet, and a garnish of orange segments, each crossed with a sliver of peel.

On the same principle but completely different is an apple tart, this one a fraction thicker and wider, and encircled by a garnish of apple sabayon, dried apple and deep-fried curls of apple dusted with sugar and the whole ignited by a few sprigs of fresh mint.

How has Senderens achieved the range of skills to produce these effects? The pastry section draws heavily on different disciplines – filo here, wun-tun there. Surprising herbs and other seasonings are used to give the dishes energy – mint with the apple tart above, vanilla with lobster or, an old dish from his days at *l'Archestrate*, horseradish with grilled smoked salmon.

His canvas extends almost naturally to the wines. Menus for six match bottles and dishes: langoustines with a Chablis; roast turbot with a Condrieu; foie gras, served whole, roasted, with a salad of potatoes and artichokes, with Ch. Filhot '81; duck, in the Roman style with spices and honey, with a glass of the sweet Banyuls.

At the back of the menu is a complete list, developed by Jacques Puisais, of wine recommendations to go with cheese, which concludes that white wines and eaux-de-vie are the most compatible. Some examples: Camembert, vin Jaune from the Jura; fresh goats', Vouvray or champagne; Livarot, calvados; Munster, Gewürztraminer; Stilton, port. For Roquefort there are no fewer than five suggestions – Jurançon, vin jaune, Ch. Filhot, Banyuls and port.

Senderens is defining the limits of cooking for the nineties.

Lucas Carton, 9 place de la Madeleine, Paris 8 (tel 45 65 22 90).

Lyon: *Paul Bocuse*

by David Ashen

The restaurant itself is vulgar but the food superb. We had a fixed menu. When I refused the frogs' legs soup they replaced it with the best foie gras that I have every eaten.

Interestingly there were two fish courses: 'rouget barbet de roche en écailles de pommes de terre' followed by 'viennoise de dorade au Pouilly-Fuissé', the first to me being the highlight of the meal. The mullet had been filleted and scaled. They had then created 'scale' from thin discs of potato, and the whole had been grilled from the potato side only. The finished result was similar to pommes Anna on the top but very moist fish beneath.

Paul Bocuse, 69660 Collonges-au-Mont-d'Or, Lyons (tel 78 22 01 40).

Nice: *Chantecler*

by Paul Manias and Sophie Butler

Sitting half way along the Promenade des Anglais like an enormous ice-cream sundae topped with its strawberry dome, the *Negresco* attracts compliments. The *Chantecler* on the ground floor with entrances both through the hotel and from the street has a grand if brassy face. Approach with reverence. 19½ and four red toques in *Gault Millau*, three stars *Michelin*. The feeling of privilege initiated by the frontage is heightened by the immaculate bow-tie-and-tails waiters, the silver place settings and the careful pink and white flower arrangements. Being half an hour late for a reservation appears no problem. We are ushered to a table for four but set for two. A silver candle lantern adds to the already generous lighting and a bowl of pink rose buds brightens up the expanse of white linen and silver ware.

Looking around the main half of this double room the décor seems a surprising mish-mash, designed to impress but arranged with a heavy hand. Chintz wall coverings are seemingly so valuable that the owners have seen fit to protect them with perspex panels. Fussy crystal and brass chandeliers are in abundance and large heavy antique chairs covered in burgundy upholstery create a gaudy sense of elegance. A tapestry of an enormous urn of flowers is mimicked by a large vase of gladiolus, while on the opposite wall an assortment of paintings of cockerels signal the restaurant's motif. All this to the mindless piano of Richard Clayderman tapes.

The service is swift and well rehearsed. Waiters appear from the wings, each with their part to play. One rules the bread, carefully arranged on a large, circular wicker tray. Another bears the wine list with page after page of rare and expensive wines, and bows with overplayed appreciation at economical choices. Provençal whites open around £12 but it is a steep climb to the vintage clarets at £100. Another waiter acts as our narrator, explaining each course as it appears and courteously demanding assurance of our constant satisfaction. Meanwhile the minor parts rush on and off the scene bearing food.

Four set menus from 360f to 500f (£34 to £47) open the proceedings, each of four courses; one Niçoise-inspired; one fish; one shellfish; one prestige, using foie gras and truffles. The *carte* reads more internationally, the more so as the last two pages are an English translation of what goes before. There is the odd hint of Jacques Maximin's individuality – three ravioli dishes – one with foie gras and turnips; another a *pot au feu* with beetroot; another with lobster and tomato.

What appears on the plate is a fresh approach. Take the Niçoise menu. The gourmet salad is the traditional Niçoise dish but transformed: sprigs of lettuce are tied at the stem; a tiny pastry tart of anchovy; a crusty roll – of minute proportions – is filled with egg, cucumber and tomato, a perfect mushroom is ruptured and heaped with a vegetable purée, a central slice of terrine, a thimble of smooth pâté: each a little island of taste.

The cutlery is reset for the next act. Mouthfuls of sea-bass alternate with cubes of lightly fried potato served in a strong wine and garlic sauce. Anchovy provides a link with the previous course and a subtle interest to the flavour.

The wine waiter fills glasses, others remove the empty plates and cutlery is once more reset. Next arrives a plate of lamb, divided into quarters, each served in an entirely different way: a chop, boned, with a kidney nestling inside; zucchine stuffed with herbs and chopped meat; another quarter with a moussaka influence; the last, fillet in lightly fried potato. A rich meat gravy blends the quarters together.

A vast cheese tray appears from the wings and portions of local goats' cheese, eaten with a knife and fork, marks the transition from savoury to sweet.

The dessert is an ice-cream rich in candied fruits and syrupy brandy sauce. Coffee is a course in itself. Three choices of sugar and a dish of macaroons, candied fruits, chocolates, truffles and wafers.

The fish menu delineates precisely between techniques. A salmon mousse wrapped in spinach, small fillets of turbot rest on a bed of endive, lettuce and raddichio with tiny mussells hidden in the green and red leaves. The turbot is draped with truffles and finely chopped peppers with a sprinkling of caviare. It is accompanied by two slices of a creamy herb pâté.

The next course arrives safely encased in silver covers. Slices of sole lie in a generous bowl of a light, broth-like sauce, with ravioli adding a slightly stronger flavour. By the time the main course arrives, concepts of fish have taken on new meaning. Layers of sea-bass separated by layers of creamy herbs and vegetable crust are delivered in a wine sauce that catalyses the taste.

Nothing is rushed, nothing too much trouble. Take a passing interest in the label of your wine and the waiter returns with it inserted into a folder. The prices are astronomic, the décor undeserving, but the cooking rises above it.

Chantecler, 37 Promenade des Anglais (tel 93 88 39 51).

Bruges

by Aileen Hall

Despite the splendid medieval Flemish architecture, the dark gleaming canals, and the excellent English spoken by almost everyone you meet, it's easy to fancy yourself in France. The number of first-rate restaurants comes as a surprise after coachloads of tourists, a rash of shops hawking lace or chocolates, and the many cheap eateries promising pancakes, pizzas or croque-monsieur in four languages.

Three places visited are resolutely French, with much in common and intriguing differences. Husband-and-wife teams were in charge of all three, the décor was carefully matched to the cooking style – from austere to florid – and the same expensive ingredients dominated the menus: salmon, asparagus, goose liver, lobster, caviare, truffles . . . The wine lists would have shamed many top restaurants in France: sonorous *grand cru* Bordeaux and Burgundies, intelligently chosen Alsace and New World wines.

Least impressive was *Die Snippe*, a handsome eighteenth-century building, given a smart boudoir treatment. Murals compete with 'polychrome gold-leather wall-cover' (their brochure) but are defeated by spectacularly flamboyant chandeliers and candelabra. It almost goes without saying that Vivaldi's Four Seasons was on tape.

All the restaurants offered generous nibbles before and after the actual meal. Here it was a small helping of new matjes herring and green beans, dressed with superb olive oil, and a heap of brown shrimps to pick at. The *menu gastronomique* at 1950BF (£30) includes many dishes of the *carte*: 'le petit gateau d'écrevisses et sauce au fenouil', a talented mix of crisp filo pastry, creamy crayfish filling, and slightly curry-flavoured buttery fennel sauce; an escalope of fresh, *à point* salmon, topped by an unannounced and unexpected – but effective – slice of fried goose liver with a thinnish artichoke-flecked sauce; 'le baby-lobster braisé au riz sauvage', sweet lobster flavour but carelessly cooked, so that some chunks were tough, with two sauces, one dull white, one rich pink, an aura of curry spices again. 'Le cochon de lait et sa garniture d'été' was a drab, clumsily carved beast, his garniture even more inept. Spirits rose with the next course, a delicate puff of pastry containing warm, tangy goats' cheese, the honey sauce pointed by a drop of vinegar and some nuts. 'Poires caramelisées et framboises au glace de pistache' delivered the *coup de grace*: not only the warm pears, sliced strawberries and rather artificial tasting ice-cream, but also a brandysnap case and a garnish of gargantuan redcurrants. The final bill was 6075BF (£93) for a rather ill-balanced meal (too much fish, pastry, curry) and fairly *dégagé* service from the white-aproned wine waiters; it seemed worth it, but only just. *Die Snippe* smacks of successful complacency.

Guy Teerlinck, owner of *Vasquez*, is another restaurateur who has moved to central Bruges from the suburbs, although in his case there were several intervening years in the United States. With only two tables occupied on a late spring Thursday evening, he is far from complacent and obviously not yet enjoying the success he deserves. The house is fifteenth-century, with Gothic ceilings, elaborate fireplaces, and expensive good taste in the dove grey and apricot furnishings. Tables are large and solid, china and sauce-spoons tastefully understated, the flowers charming, and there is even a tiny garden for summer aperitifs.

There are two set menus (*menu dégustation*, 2100BF, £32), as well as a list of traditional dishes and another 'creative' one, with such dishes as home-made foie gras with sweet-and-sour onion marmalade (875BF, £13). *'Menu Isabella'* (1680BF, £26), contained several of the dishes listed on the other menus. The amuse-gueules included smoked salmon pinwheels, doll-sized quiches and herbed pastry pillows. The elaborate breads – sesame, poppyseed, nut and raisin – were addictive, and offered half a dozen times.

The first course was a lobster bavarois with asparagus, tomato vinaigrette and celery: a vigorously flavoured mousse (Tabasco? even Worcester sauce?) was topped with a thick disc of perfect lobster flesh and served with a firmly flavoured vinaigrette flecked with spring onion and celery; a very definite dish, overwhelming the tiny white asparagus spear garnish.

On to salmon, two thick, perfectly cooked slices, sandwiching sliced French beans (the most generously served vegetable of the weekend) in a skilful lemon butter sauce with a frivolous garnish of tasteless winkles.

The main course was tenderloin of lamb steamed in hay, presented in a huge black iron cocotte so that one could admire the clean hay and savoury aromas. It was very pink, very tender, very springlike, tasting delicately of rosemary and – presumably – subtly of hay. The *nouvelle*-pretty vegetables included outsize peas: where do the Belgians find such mammoth 'spring' vegetables?

Dessert was something of an aberration in the pattern of near-perfection: a rather hard disc of pastry looking as spotty as a chapati, a highly perfumed and oversweet sorbet, rhubarb purée and strawberries.

We drank the house Champagne and Framboise Royale as aperitifs, and an Alsace – chosen because if you wish to stick at only one bottle, Alsace matches fish, shellfish, meat and rich sauces supremely well. This one was Vogelsgarten Gewürztraminer '83 from Sigolsheim, a rich counterpoint to the menu. Iced water appeared in an elegant decanter; coffee, as elsewhere, was excellent (and – as elsewhere – cost 300BF (£5) for two, including pretty fruit tartlets, chocolate-coated peel, and so on). The final bill was 5260BF (£80).

Further afield, along cobbled streets and over hump-backed bridges is *De Karmeliet*, a converted monastery owned by Geert Van Hecke and his wife. No sighting of the chef here and no parading of waiters – the proprietress deals with the six ground-floor tables and two young waiters with the six above.

Décor is simple but not artless: flag floors, plain walls, heavy beams, good pictures, glossy white linen and enchanting flowers. Van Hecke has been here five years, time enough to develop his very individual style, owing something to Alain Chapel and the other top chefs he has worked with, even more to his own fervent individuality.

Knowing nothing of the generosity of his portions and extras, we opted for the seven-course *'Brugge die scone'* (Bruges the beautiful) menu at 2000BF (£31). The amuse-gueules were attention-getting: two very fresh oysters, a gamey terrine of rabbit and prune, and crevettes in a jelly under thinned crème fraîche, the whole tasting electrifyingily fishy and spicy. The bread was rough and homely.

Grilled noisette of Scotch salmon was nicely undercooked, wrapped in *jambon cru*, served with a light buttery sauce and al dente white asparagus (this time with some flavour). On to a mouthful in both senses: 'mille-feuille de pommes de terre, grenouilles et dès de foie d'oie aux mousserons des prés, morilles fraîche et à la fleur de ciboulette'. Thin oval slices of unevenly browned potato were sandwiched with a richly interesting filling of the frogs' legs, liver and fungi, sitting in a sticky, clear, slightly sweet sauce, and garnished with individual bells from chive flowers. An original dish, which tasted much more coherent than it reads.

'Homard bleu pané de céléri vert, rôti aux spaghetti de légumes, sa croquette au beurre à la coriandre' was the best-tasting lobster of the trip, flanked by strands of red pepper, courgette and carrot, wild and 'ordinary' rice, and a golf-ball croquette from which flowed a beurre blanc pointed with tomato dice and fresh coriander. Almost OTT but not quite.

'Suprême de pigeonneau et ris de veau en laitues braisées aux petits pois, jeunes carottes confites et gratin de navets' was a pretty round slice revealing the pale soft sweetbread and pinkly tender pigeon, wrapped in lettuce and served with another immaculately clear and sticky sauce and careful vegetables, including the gratin of young turnips which tasted as gentle as potatoes.

French cheeses from Olivier in Boulogne, very much *à point*, served with toasted sultana-and-nut bread, and then the excess – two sweets where one would have seemed *de trop*: the almond tuile with its superb green melon sorbet and strawberries hardly needing the dun rhubarb sauce; and the slightly scorched pâte feuilleté with delicate pistachio ice-cream and apricot sauce – both adequate rather than brilliant. The petits fours were, of course, generous and imaginative, the coffee good.

We drank the house cocktail – sparkling Saumur and grapefruit juice, very nice too; a Trimbach Gewürztraminer Réserve '83, and – with too much food and too much time on our hands – a half-bottle of Ch. Patache d'Aux '83 (500BF, £80), a charming petit château wine. As at *Vasquez*, water came iced in a decanter. The bill was 6370BF (£97), the most we spent, but we ate more, drank more, and had our minds engaged as well as our palates, with the extraordinary originality of this man.

Here are three very good restaurants offering different versions of haute cuisine, generously enough to keep the local burghers content, but each pursuing some sort of individual goal within the French context. To find them within a few streets of each other in Belgium's tourist trap is extraordinary.

Die Snippe, 53 Nieuwe Gentweg (tel 050 33 70 70).
Vasquez, 38 Zilverstraat (tel 050 34 08 45).
De Karmeliet, 1 Jerusalemstraat (tel 050 33 82 59).

Brussels
by GFG reader

'Brian Macy writes in the *Good Food Guide 1988* that the city lacks dynamism. Well, we must disagree. The food in Brussels is outstanding at most levels in quality of ingredients, cooking and service – you get an international selection from world-wide professionals. We recommend especially *La Trente Rue de la Paille,* 30 rue de la Paille, Brussels, tel 2 5120715.'

Milan: *Gualtiero Marchesi*
by Frances Roxburgh

Amateurs, in the true sense, of Italian cooking cannot fail to be intrigued by the accolade of three *Michelin* rosettes, the only such award in Italy, to a Milanese restaurant. The terribly dull situation, however, outside the heart of this most chic of cities, and the entrance, which is more like an office reception than a restaurant, are not encouraging.

The subterranean dining-room is beige and rather hushed. Other guests are tourists or older men with pale girls. The only splashes of colour are on the menus, echoed in the specially designed plates and later in the food itself. A waiter automatically explains, in reverential tones (just slightly more reverence for the food than the guests) that the 'insalata di carne cruda alla rucola, tartufi di norcia' is a 'raw meat salad with . . . ' and that 'involtini di spinaci e branzino, salsa ai grani di senape' is 'raw sea-bass rolled round spinach'. This is rather patronising to an Italian.

The raw meat salad is pretty, the other an intriguing combination of textures and colours, showing Marchesi's affinity with Japanese cuisine; simplicity, freshness, prime ingredients. The sushi flavours are slightly offset by daubs of mustard. Over the amuse-gueules – exquisite terrines of Sanpietro in a tennis-ball sized pool of watercress sauce – we fell to analysing the décor. Each table has its own sculpture; here a Vasarely, there a Tadini, over there a Pomodoro or a Man Ray. Branching aluminium lamps are elegant but reminiscent of carnivorous plants. All this sobriety concentrates the mind (but, oh for the gilt and mirrored glory of Del Cambio in

Turin!). A gratin of prawns, with little orange and green diamonds of peperonis and zucchini is served in a pool of light curry sauce, a slight skin on the surface.

The famous *raviolo aperto*, a perverse Marchesi creation, owes more to the Orient than to Italy. His glorious saffron risotto, a celebrated Milanese dish, comes correctly prepared with an intoxicating stock, but graced with a square of pure gold leaf. Zinc or iron supplements are all very well, but gold?

The well-worn joke in Milan is that if you go to Marchesi, you should eat first. This is not quite fair; dishes are certainly tantalisingly light but well-balanced, unlike the traditional top-heavy Italian meal where from antipasto and pasta the decline, qualitively and quantitively, sets in. Waiters circulate eternally offering more bread. Why, at this price, is the bread not better? Italian waiters are the best in the world. Here, however, they lack the customary brio and seem ponderous and even lugubrious. The weight of responsibility of serving in this awesome place seems too much for them. Damask napkins are discreetly replaced if you leave the table, which seems to prove they are professionals, if not naturals.

Now it is time for the rosy fillets of red mullet ranged in ranks and 'impanati al profumo di tartufi di norcia' ('black truffle flavour') and for tender lamb cutlets with a neat stack – or *timballo* – of aubergine discs and a hint of lemon-grass. All worlds away from the solitary bistecca, the scaloppine or grilled liver with sage of the average trattoria.

An elegant cheese basket has a French bias, an improvement on the usual selection of Gorgonzola or Bel Paese. Desserts are a rare delight with Italian additions to a repertoire with its roots in a French training (chez Frères Troisgros, Roanne). Pine nuts are added to an exquisite chocolate fondant with candied orange strips; the inevitable three-chocolate bavarese comes with gianduia and almond biscuits; there are pistachio ices, freshest fruit immaculately presented, and fragile miniature *pasticcerie*. Bravo.

But what of the family atmosphere, the allegria of that provincial trattoria? What of the pungent ragus on plates of pasta? Of luscious opaque green olive oil and jugs of Chianti. (Here an average bottle of Chianti is L50,000, £22.) What of enjoyment and joy? This place is Lugano at lunchtime and it deadens the undoubted flair of the maestro as surely as his latest venture into superior frozen foods sends shivers down the spine.

Gualtiero Marchesi, 9 via Bonvesin de la Riva, Milan 20129 (tel 741246).

Venice
by Edith Rudinger

Venice is famous for a thousand and one reasons, but good food is not one of them. This is not because there are too few eating places – on the contrary, you will find in Venice establishments of all categories. In theory, in Italy there is a kind of hierarchy: starting from the top, ristorante, trattoria, locanda, pizzeria, fiaschetteria (which serves bits of food and snacks but mainly wine), and osteria. There are seven pages of restaurants listed in the 'yellow pages' of the Venice telephone directory: trattoria, five columns; ristorante, nine columns; pizzeria two and a half columns; locanda three-quarters of a column – so the ristoranti have it.

But in Venice these names are used quite indiscriminately. One of the best places to eat, and also among the priciest, calls itself a 'locanda' – the *Locanda Cipriani* on the island of Torcello. The same owners (Cipriani is their family name and that of the most expensive hotel in Venice, which has indifferent food) run the famous *Harry's Bar* (not to be recommended for value for money, but possessing snob appeal, especially to Americans), and a new restaurant called *Harry's Dolci* on the Giudecca overlooking the canal. The Cipriani in Torcello is so expensive and so far away that a free water-taxi will take clients there, leaving from the Riva degli Schiavoni near the Hotel Danielli at 12.30pm and returning from Torcello at 3.45pm.

You can also go to Torcello on the No. 12 water-bus every hour at five minutes to the hour from the Fondamente Nuove stop. The No. 12 passes other islands on the way: first Murano (no gastronomic stopover), then Mazzorbo where just a few steps away from the water-bus stop is very good small restaurant, used more by locals than foreign visitors, called *Ala Maddalena*. This offers good value for money, but has no written menu, so it helps to know Italian when the dishes of the day are being rattled off by the waitress or the signora herself.

The No. 12 water-bus also stops at Burano, recognised as the gastronomic island in the Venetian lagoon: even the well-known guide-book *Venice for Pleasure* by Links recommends *Da Romano* there. Also mentioned in the Links book is what is apocryphally 'Bernard Levin's favourite place', the *Ristorante ala Vecia Cavana*, which is in Rio Terra Dei Franceschi and is expensive, with a fixed-price basic menu at around 30,000 lire (£13), plus wine and cover charge.

Considerably cheaper, not very far from there (at Canareggio 4888, the *Vecia Cavana* is at 4625), in the Salizada del Spechieri quite near the beautiful church of S. Maria Assunta (called the 'Gesuiti') is the *Trattoria dall'Aurelia*, a typical Venetian place with certainly no airs and graces, where gondoliers and boatmen from the nearby Fondamente Nuove come and eat dishes such as *sepie* (cuttle fish) *alla Veneziana con polenta* (8,500 lire (£3.50). Polenta is the staple side-dish of the Veneto, made of maize, and worth trying at least once while you are in Venice. This place announces itself as providing *cuccina casalinga* – home cooking, claimed by many eating places in Venice with far less reason. It is shut on Wednesdays.

Another place where local people eat, but tourists are made very welcome unless the restaurant has been taken over by a large family party, perhaps a wedding, is the *Trattoria da Remigio* (3416 Castello in the Salizada dei Greci). It is medium-expensive and shut on Tuesdays.

The expensive restaurants that are listed in guide-books and described in articles about Venice, which, it seems, copy from each other – but should not necessarily therefore be ignored – include the *Antico Martini*, which is very expensive, very good, and close to the Fenice Opera House. Under the same management as the *Antico Martini* is a wine bar with a sensible selection of good wines and reasonable snacks, open when everything else is shut, called *Vino-Vino*. While on the subject of wine, do not try Chianti, nor be fooled into remembering that Soave comes from the Veneto. Almost any wine from the 'Colli Orientali de Friuli' is a good, medium-priced local wine. A poor man's local champagne of low alcohol content is prosecco.

At the *Vino-Vino* it is possible to eat just one dish. Another place where this can be done, also just beside the Fenice, is a good all-purpose restaurant called *Al Theatro* (shut on Mondays). It is one of the dwindling number of places where a pizza is made in a real pizza oven, not an electric contraption.

A one-dish meal with a view of the famous equestrian Colleoni statue is also offered at the *Caffee al Cavallo* outside the church of SS Giovani e Paolo. For 9,000 lire (£4) you can get lasagne alla bolognese with a beer or Coca-Cola or wine, or inded, a pizza with beer or Coca-Cola or wine or cappuccino. The view, there, is definitely better than the food.

A few restaurants have gardens – for instance the *Trattoria da Ignazio* (S. Polo 2749, near the Frari church, water-bus stop S. Toma). They serve local foods, good but highly spiced, for example spaghetti alle vongole (clams) with fresh herbs and lots of garlic, or triglie (very small red mullet) or zuppa di cozze (mussels) which can be eaten as a starter or as a main dish, cooked, again, with much garlic. It is shut on Saturdays. Another restaurant for outdoor sitting used to be the *Trattoria Malamocca* (4650 Castello, shut on

Thursdays), well-known, reliable, expensive – but in spring 1988 there were extensive building works going on in the cortile outside, pre-empting the outdoor dining which is part of its charm.
The *Corte Sconta* in Calle del Pestrin (3885 Castello) is among the best and most expensive restaurants in Venice where the locals stand around the bar drinking wine and giving the place a rustic appearance. Those who sit and eat are not the local rustics but mainly visiting French, who appreciate the good food (mainly seafood) and are willing to pay the very high prices and to put up with paper napkins and bare-board tables. This restaurant is shut on both Sunday and Monday.

Much less expensive and good value for money is the *Taverna San Pantalon* (near the church of that name, at 3757 Dorsoduro), concentrating on fish dishes; the old established *Montin* (1147 Dorsoduro) with its lovely garden; the *Alla Madonna* (San Poalo 594, near the Rialto, shut on Wednesdays), which is listed in most guide-books and by now perhaps overrated.

Practically everyone who goes to Venice has some bad eating-out experiences and will make sure never to go to that one (or two, or many) particular restaurants again. But most visitors discover 'their' restaurant and swear by it and will recommend it to you or me. New to my list of recommendations is *Da Raffaele* (2347 S. Marco), where you sit at the edge of a romantic canal and the view and the food are wonderful, so wonderful – according to some friends who 'discovered' it recently. But they were in Venice on their honeymoon.

A note about those numbers: you can find any address or any house in Venice if you know the district – S. Marco or Castello or Dorsoduro or Canaleggio or S. Polo and so on – and its number. All the houses are numbered consecutively and you just use this numbering as an Ariadne's thread to lead you to your destination.

Leningrad: *Metropol*

by Susie Robinson

At three o'clock on a wet Monday afternoon in Leningrad the impossibly long shiny black Ministry Volga – looking as if it has come straight out of a spy-movie – arrives at the arched entrance to the city's oldest eating establishment. The *Metropol* first opened its doors in 1866. When the original owner, Nemchinsky, went bankrupt a group of chefs and waiters clubbed together to buy it with such success that in 1904 they were building yet another dining-hall. Pre-revolutionary co-operative enterprise perhaps, but not in the eyes of Messrs Trotsky and Lenin who doomed it to post-Revolutionary life as a workers' canteen. Times changed, even before *glasnost,* and today the *Metropol* has official Soviet status equal to the Order of the Michelin rosette.

The imposing entrance sports the ubiquitous cloakroom since it is considered non-U to be seen in a coat indoors. The warren of dining rooms of all shapes and sizes on the upper two floors have a jaded air but refurbishment is in train and the largest marble pillared Georgian-style dining hall is about to be restored from floor to crystal chandeliered ceiling.

There is nothing jaded about executive chef Babikov (the Russian term is 'director of production'), a distinguished-looking and charming young 60-year-old Tartar. He has worked in the same kitchen for 45 years. The walls of his tiny office-cum-dining-room are festooned with certificates of excellence. The real boss is deputy director of production, Madame Antoninia Feodorovna, splendidly rotund and much given to apologising for the spotless kitchens. The term 'brigade' was never more aptly used than here, for only military precision could operate a kitchen of 200 chefs producing 3,500 meals a day – daily turnover is 15,000 roubles.

The cold kitchen, *chalodni serch,* has six cold rooms, two low-temperature counters and a staff of six plus two students. Large, old-fashioned fridges are crammed with fresh fish, including a pair of massive yellow-fleshed sturgeons from the Caspian.

There are newly stuffed *soudark,* whole pike perch in aspic (gefilte fish like Grandma never did make) but no carp since, as Madame explains 'these sleep under the ice till autumn'. Cheek by jowl on the counters lie delicately decorated and mouth-wateringly tasty savoury and sweet mousses of this and creams of that with little pots of *zalivnoya,* a meat julienne once again in its own jelly. These are to grace the table of a wedding party.

At another counter a student learns to fillet *ivaci,* a maroon-toned herring naturally sweeter than gaffelbitter despite its salting. At the next, Reitziana (22 years' service) weighs portions of caviare. Considering its value this may not surprise, but what does is the Russian concept of portion control. Chefs may look with disdain on the idea of measuring quantities – prefering the mystique of 'a little of this and a pinch of that' – but here, every single item of food from bread to Beluga is weighed. All is priced and sold by weight.

Only bread is bought in at the *Metropol,* so the pastry kitchen thrives on producing rack after rack of savoury puff pastry whimsies prepared to accompany the lunchtime bouillon or chicken consommé.

At the hot counters a central island holds the ever-changing dozen or so soups and sauces, each in a square stainless steel container designed by chef Babikov to eliminate staff steam burns. *Salyanka* is a soup of tomato and onion paste with olives, pickled cucumber and sausage, a hefty, spicy meal, well suited to the weather outdoors.

Meat is delivered by the carcase and butchered and portioned by weight, as in any classic kitchen the bones go directly to the stockpots. This is the only area where men in toques outnumber the women chefs who wear large fluffy muslin turban arrangements on their heads. Chickens are plump and yellow. The chefs are astonished that anyone would want to add garlic to the butter of chicken Kiev so destroying the flavour of the meat. One assumes they should know.

The tour of the kitchens complete, we are now about to tackle the seven dining-rooms, some still echoing to the mirth of left-over lunch-goers. Can one cancel the afternoon even here? It is, after all, gone 5pm.

In spite of the heat the waiter is dressed in formal black jacket. *Zakushkaya* arrives, a selection of hors d'oeuvres – including canapés of jellied meats and fishes, fresh sliced cucumber (with a taste to remind me of a childhood spent in the Clyde Valley when such things used to ripen naturally in the sun); the *smetanya* makes the pasteurised soured cream of the British supermarket a poor substitute. To drink there is mineral water, always with a metallic flavour for some reason, and smooth, full-bodied white wine from Georgia. The glass is crystal.

Chicken soup is a clear, fat-free consommé and on the side piping hot *piroshka* and *risolik.* These are not the effete ravioli-sized pastry numbers favoured by chefs of the modern British school. The *piroshka* are palm-sized puff pastry turnovers, baked golden brown, their insides revealing a combination of savoury minced meats and onion. The *risolik* are smaller, rounded mouthfuls, containing the same mixture but, in this case, deep-fried in olive oil and in taste like crispy wun-tun. One alternates a bite with a spoonful of soup – the effect is ambrosial.

Unlike the British, the chefs make no market visits. Instead, deliveries arrive throughout the year in accordance with Chef Babikov's Individual Enterprise Plan, a service available only to those with the status of a top restaurant. The implication is that skill in ordering is as important as cooking ability. It is said that the shortages or lack of choice in lesser establishments is primarily the result of bad forward planning rather than a lack of actual produce.

The pièce de résistance arrives: a small triangular dry-spirit stove – another Babikov design – with a covered dish atop. The flame is lit and the cover removed. This is *xarchoi* – an ethnic dish of Russia which uses the escalope cut of veal and mushrooms in a *smetanya* sauce garnished with baby potatoes, slivers of tender carrot and a pinch of chopped fresh flat parsley to balance the colours. Only a fork is needed.

To finish, dome-shaped choux buns oozing fresh cream arrive with the espresso coffee.

So there is no food in Russia?

So you cannot obtain an edible meal?

So everything is off and you have to wait an hour to be served?

It does not have to be so. The food at the *Metropol* is produced with love as well as technique. It is also available to all, not just foreigners and bureaucrats and black marketeers.

Russian restaurants rarely have a bar: instead, much in the French manner, one goes directly to the table. It is expected that the diner will want to order the *zakushskayas* when booking. Thus, on arrival, these will be waiting on the table and the drinks are set out at the same time.

Lunch is the main meal of the day and may continue into the early evening. Different places, different customs. Here soup is for lunch-time and never served after 7pm. And if you don't want the exuberant dance band with the meal you only have to book a private room. Pizza Hut may be coming to Moscow and the Pepsi-Cola plant already arrived, but fast food is not a Russian concept.

Having visited five markets and more than fifteen restaurants in nine days, I can say that there is Real Food in Russia. The raw produce has flavour and there *are* establishments which give it the care and attention it deserves. Service can be good or bad. A great deal has to do with the diners' expectations, which all to often turn out to be jaded preconceptions.

Metropol Restaurant, Leningrad, Sadovaja Ul, 221–2 (tel 225 66 73).

Bangkok

by Ken Jacobs

Bangkok is a sprawling city of noise, continuous traffic jams and car fumes. Traditional shimmering Buddhist temples sit alongside very much twentieth-century buildings. Much of this huge city is like any other but there are intensely colourful flashes of the nineteenth century in the side streets and canals.

It is an assault on all the senses. Riding through the crowded city streets, views of gleaming modern hotels and department stores are interspersed with bizarre sights: a line of open lorries each carrying an elephant; a *tuk-tuk* (noisy open three-wheeled taxi) laden with a single rider and ten large sacks of chillies; a cramped shop in Chinatown selling what look like turn of the century sewing machines; a shop selling only replicas of the famous gold Buddha in *all* sizes; or the sight of an entire family driving out for dinner balanced precariously on one moped.

It is also a city that eats 24 hours a day. Virtually every street has food stalls which materialise out of nowhere at different moments of the day or night. Portions of both dry and soup noodles at about 25p seem to be continually consumed by hungry and miraculously thin Thais. Markets sell an abundance of fresh and dried produce of every kind. The lower level of a hotel car-park inexplicably contains cages of live chickens and men barbecuing dozens of them over wood fires.

A walk down a narrow side street introduces curiously mixed smells of inefficient sewers and rich meat broths. If the wok/wind trajectory is right one may be overcome by the sensation of searing chilli fumes shooting up one nostril and bringing a fit of coughing, running nose and streaming eyes. The intensity with which life is lived is partly reflected in the colourful variety of street food stalls which are in stark contrast to both the unappetising smells and relative greyness of what might be called street food in Britain.

Another face of Thai cuisine is presented at Bangkok's many 'proper' restaurants. Among these the city boasts *Tum Nak Thai* (131 Ratchadapisek Road), in the *Guinness Book of Records* as the world's largest restaurant. This mammoth operation consists of numerous authentically constructed, connecting open-air Thai pagodas surrounded by water like a series of floating islands, each pagoda itself the size of a normal restaurant. Despite such gimmickry as waiters on roller skates, the food is of a good standard, considering up to 3,000 people are being fed. The service is also surprisingly labour intensive, with two rows of specially garbed young ladies whose only job is to bow in greeting to entering customers.

The top floor of the *Mah Boonkrong Centre* (Phyathai Road) is a good place to start sampling the diversity of Thai food at the bewildering number and variety of booths. Here one may taste the many Thai dishes that tend to lean heavily on ingredients such as lime, lemon-grass, coconut, coriander root, fish sauce, deep-fried garlic and a great variety of curry pastes made from fresh and dry ingredients and usually including lots of ground chillies. A similar initiation might be undergone at the branch of the *D'Jit Pochana* at 1082 Paholyothin, which serves a bargain Thai buffet lunch as well as a respectable and extensive *carte*.

The prestigious *Bussaracum Restaurant* (35 Soi Pipat 2) provides 'Royal-style' Thai food, a refined type of cuisine lacking the burning heat of many common Thai dishes. Here *cho muang*, flower-shaped dumplings with natural violet colouring, are a delicious, superior dim-sum. *Gai tom kah*, a silky textured chicken and coconut soup flavoured with a subtle root similar to ginger, is also impressive. The *gaeng panang* is a very coconuty yet subtle and extremely mild curry by ordinary Thai standards. Those ordinary standards would not allow even the fiercest Indian vindaloo into the starting blocks of the heat stakes.

On a raised platform a striking girl with dark, darting eyes sits all evening among gold cushions and a golden deer playing a Thai instrument like a zither. Despite the indelible memory of this young lady, the handsome bronze cutlery, the authentic and sometimes excellent food, the atmosphere does not quite ring true. The wooden beams, orange tasselled lamp-shades and slightly grubby menus are more Regent's Park than Rama I. The clientele appear to be almost exclusively Thais taking Westerners out for a 'special' evening. On their own, Thais prefer a more robust style of food.

Probably the most memorable eating experiences are of food consumed in the street, in markets or scruffy open restaurants with chipped vinyl-top tables. On Soi Chula 60, just off Phaya Thai Road near Chulalongkorn University, is a series of colourful Chinese and Thai street stalls. There are hanging Chinese roast ducks glistening with their sweet lacquer, noodle stalls, occasionally whole suckling pigs cooking over charcoal – but the speciality here is seafood. A fish scooped out of a tank drops at my daughter's feet and a waiter chases the writhing creature around the pavement with a large stick. My daughter is unimpressed by this demonstration of the freshness of local produce. Live giant crayfish pathetically try to crawl out of the wire press which holds them over the charcoal grill, their little feelers scrambling hopelessly above the searing orange coals. Across the street from all this activity, running alongside an iron fence, there is a narrow pavement containing a row of tables filled with people eating seafood.

Initially it is not clear where the food comes from, but it transpires this is where the largest restaurant on the street, *Somboon Pochana*, serves. Smart waiters do everything – pour drinks, clear tables, park cars, take orders and bring the food. Many cars, including gleaming Mercedes, continually pull into the narrow street. The Thais are remarkably lacking in snobbery when it comes to food. At the *Somboon*, succulent crab in reddish curried cream sauce is a speciality. There is fish done many ways, including Thai sweet-and-sour style using tamarind for the sourness. Charcoal grilled prawns and those pitiable but delicious crayfish are served with chilli dips.

Pork satay is a generous stack of bamboo skewers containing flavourful meat interspersed with pork fat. It is served with a superior peanut sauce and some cucumber slices in vinegar. Lacking fluency in the Thai language (in which one word can mean up to eight different things depending on the tonal nuance), pointing is the best way of securing the dishes you want. By this tactic, we dine also on delicate asparagus, the thickness of a pencil, combined with Chinese spinach in a simple mixture of stock and soy sauce. A request for a second portion of this seems imperative.

With bottled water and soft drinks, prawns, crayfish, vegetables, satay, rice and curried crab come to 436 baht (under £10). Tipping is not necessary in Thailand despite what must be some of the best service in the world. The quality of that service remains similarly high, whether from the finest hotel or the humblest street stall. This may include the possibility of ordering something different from a stall far up the road from where you are eating. The waiter will obtain whatever you want and pay the stall owner.

Sitting in the darkness of the warm night air, the table piled high with broken crustacean shells, we watch the steam billowing out of bubbling woks, the orange glow of the charcoal burners and the constant ebb and flow of the yellow-jacketed waiters crossing the street. It is a long way from the stewed burgers and dehydrated onions of Piccadilly Circus.

Tokyo
by Brian Macy

The land of the rising sun is more akin to a gigantic amusement arcade taken straight out of *Blade Runner*. There is a distinctive clear blue Northern light which elevates the drab monotone grey of the city and its spidery horizon of overhead cables and tangled telephone lines. At night the garish neon lights spring into action, becoming an elaborate freeshow of animated reds, greens, yellows and blues. The mood of Tokyo is frenzied, fuelled not by brashness but structured in a highly disciplined fashion. Youth is dressed in uniforms of black, with sharp short angular haircuts swathed in diagonally cut caps and black suits, like miniature mannequins. They parade to highly visible cafés like *Cafe Bongo*, whose interior is made out of fragments of twisted metal and the façade is framed by the wing of a jumbo jet. Those with fashionable accessories eat at *Sushi Bar Sai* where wines are served in a Californian setting. Prissy sushi dishes are presented with élan. Some stroll through a mini Kaiseki banquet at *Nadaman* in the basement of the Imperial Hotel, where each of the eleven courses is an artistic expression.

Glimpses of the more old-fashioned Japan can be found in cafés and restaurants of longer standing. Two are in the Central district, which is somehow eschewed by the style – oriented young. *Edogin* is an old haunt next to the Tsukiji fish market. This is no fashionable minuscule sushi bar. *Edogin* has a rough, asphalt-like floor on which the chefs and waiters trudge around in wellington boots. The atmosphere is café-like, full of noise and bustle. Seating is either benches at tables or stools by the bar.

The immense selection of raw fish stretches among the long glass counter, behind which half a dozen chefs prepare the cuts. Behind them stands a charcoal grill for the eels and a bubbling stock-pot that fills the room with the aromas of fish stock, vegetables and tofu. The quality of raw fish in Japan is typically first class, but in *Edogin* the freshness is spectacular. Belly of tuna has the texture of a soft ice-cream, its flavour subtle and excited by some green horseradish. White fish include sea-bream, yellow-tail and a delicate flounder with a springy bounce to the flesh. *Uni* is sea urchin wrapped in seaweed, the orange coral appearing almost like whipped cream in texture, tasting slightly livery, with smells of the sea. To finish, the chef presents a bowl of sumptuous fish broth, light and quite restrained, topped with greens and spring onions. The take-away section wraps all the different *sushi* in florid green boxes and makes a mockery of office lunches back at home.

The Japanese usually rely on cold or raw fish as their daily sustenance. Where foods are hot in quickly prepared ways like *sukiyaki, shabu shabu* or *tempura*, they have a touristy air to them. Even the most celebrated restaurants like *Hassan*, in the ultra smart district of Roppongi, which features sukiyaki, tends to have a business-executive-entertaining-foreign-counterparts feel.

Tenichi means Sky Gardens or Heaven. It occupies three floors of a modern corner block at the bottom of Ginza, the commercial district. The bowing of the team of matronly waitresses is deep and formal. Seating is either on mats, stools or tables according to the degree of formal dining requested. Apart from satisfying some of the more expense-account-oriented dining, *Tenichi* specialises in tempura and its reputation is unsurpassed. The basement restaurant sports a square room with a sunken corner and a counter which becomes a bar when one sits on the tatami floor. The lacquerware is a lovely mars black with a rich orange red tinge, and the chinaware gleams in a vivid blue glaze. An old, seasoned chef presides aided by a young assistant. The chef will adjust the batter mixture and judge the cooking while the assistant chops and slices.

The ten customers are presented with a menu based on three grades of tempura menus, ranging from £30 to £50. The price reflects variety, not quality. The meal is set at a leisurely pace as the chef cooks every item to order and only when the previous course has been finished does he cook the next pair of items. Pickles and gingery appetisers start the proceedings, followed by a variety of fish and vegetables presented in pairs. The parade of items includes baby courgettes, small onion, green pepper, lotus root, a lettuce with a cauliflower texture, cuttlefish, scallops and conger eel. Each are dipped in a frothy light batter constantly being adjusted by the addition of egg, flour and water and sizzled in a wok full of prime sesame oil. There is not even a hint of grease. The batter is fragile and ultra crisp in a refined way, and ordinary vegetables like courgette take on an exaggerated sweetness and firmness which is a revelation. Prawns are outstanding, their bodies firm, again slightly sweet and very soft. Their legs are broken off, battered and fried to become minuscule crispy, nettle-like appetisers. This is food at its most simple and unadorned.

Edogin, 4-5-1 Tsukiji, Chuo-ku, Tokyo (tel 543 4406).
Tempura Tenichi, Namiki-dori, 6-6-5 Ginza, Chuo-ku, Tokyo (tel 571 1949).

Manila: *Seafood Market Restaurant*

by Brian Macy

The sunset over Manila Bay is breathtaking. Framed by a row of palm trees stretching out the whole length of the semi-circular bay, the glowing orange sun seems eternally transfixed, hovering just beyond the silhouettes of the palms. In contrast to this natural tranquility, the history of Manila used to be dominated by the ferocious Spanish colonists who introduced sophistication, Catholicism and culture; the Americans after the Second World War took everything away and substituted instead Coca-Cola, jeeps and the way of the fast buck.

It is no wonder that the native raw ingredients of rice, sugar, coconut and fish take second place to the US influence. Big Macs and Shakey's Pizzas are plentiful in supply, but to find an old-style Spanish tapas bar serving authentic paella, squid or tapas is still difficult. The notable exception is a minute café in the Makati Commercial Centre which serves Churoz and Chocolate, the batter twisted and fried to order, piping hot and crisp accompanied by a small, sticky, hot cup of sweet chocolate. Alternatively, the prolific Chinese restaurants, catering for a large community which demand the use of fresh local produce, are the reliable answer to good food. Otherwise eating out in Manila is subject to novelty and anything based on European.

Into this scene has stepped an idea imported from the street markets of Bangkok and Singapore. The *Seafood Market Restaurant* is a hybrid of real-life supermarket and showpiece kitchen. The frontage of the restaurant, lit by vulgar neons in red, yellow and green, of an enormous lobster, is a 50-foot long glass front. Three rows of a dozen chefs whisk, chop, batter, deep fry, stir fry, boil and bake behind the glass in a frenzy of animated gestures and motions. Hand movements are small and circular, sometimes mechanical, sometimes impulsive, but constant. There are glints from the large choppers, bellows of steam bursting uncontrollably from vast aluminium stock-pots. Woks like inverted turtle-shells are swayed to and fro when all of a sudden there will be a burst of flame as the fire jumps up to seal the juices. The fluorescent lights overhead are ultraviolet, which makes the whites of the chefs glow amid a radiant purple shimmer. It is a little like the restaurant windows of Chinatown compacted into one, and fully orchestrated to one baton.

The interior is no more than the local megastore, but customers are ushered by an army of girls in pink and served by an army of boy waiters in green. The girls hand over a wire basket for the trek through the aisle looking at the produce. A table some 60 feet long has been covered in ice and two dozen varieties of fish, their eyes deep black and glistening. Small chalky white native fishes abound, but the luxurious rich flesh of the black lapu lapu can be found swimming live in aquariums sunk into the wall. Lobsters gargle with their long tentacles poking out, crawling around in a glorious cream and tourquoise armour. Prawns, alive and kicking, jump, splash and splutter in a shallow pool. There are about 80 common crabs tied neatly in a corner, next to a shelf sporting three rock crabs, gigantic and fearsome in vivid orange and green.

The vegetable table spreads a further 60 feet: baby asparagus, which is a pencil-thin version, grassy in taste, ginger and cabbages, plump yellow mangoes from Luzon where they are sweetest, baby bananas with their green taste, and orange papayas larger than watermelons. The ever-smiling girls at the till weigh each item as at any ordinary check-out system before the army of green men take over to serve.

The dining-area is as impersonal as a launderette. The hall is massive yet boxy, the lights above are pinkish plain fluorescents, artificially accentuating the fresh reds and greens of the food. Ordering is based on cooking techniques shown on a card. To steam, sauté, grill or fry costs between 75p and £2 per dish. Despite the visible dexterity of the kitchen, the freshness of the ingredients, the simplicity of the cooking techniques, the results lack excitement. Most notable is the careless timing of dishes which depend on retaining the searing heat of the wok. When allowed to stand, the food quickly becomes staid and heavy. Lobster and crabs require very accurate saucing which is both rich and spicy to accent the meat. Black-bean or spring onion and ginger sauces are gooey and nondescript. The vegetables, stir-fried with a splattering of oyster sauce, are better, due to the addition of three cloves of garlic. Although the cooking does the ingredients little justice, it is in the novelty of the supermarker-diner idea and the theatrics of the kitchen that the restaurant succeeds.

Seafood Market Restaurant, 7829 Market Avenue, Makati, Metro Manila (tel 8154237).

Indonesia

by Sri Owen

Friends on their way to Indonesia sometimes ask for advice about food and restaurants. I tell them that the country is changing so fast that what was good advice a year ago may be misleading today.

Broadly speaking, the visitor can eat in the street, in a local restaurant, or upmarket. Street food at its best is excellent, very cheap and very accessible. It is not always the best thing for the new arrival, but once you have become acclimatised and learnt a few words of the language you can do well. The old 'car-park' eating places, which used to be set up in the evening in any available open space in the city centre, have now been put on a regular basis and are well worth going to: *Sarinah Jaya*, in Jalan Thamrin, is a good one in the middle of **Jakarta**.

A street-food vendor has to be good, because there is so much competition; perhaps for the same reason, he is usually a specialist. So too is the average *warung* proprietor. A *warung* is a more or less permanent stall, with a roof to keep off the sun and some of the rain, a small table and cooking area and a bench for customers. The food is inevitably simple: look for *soto* (varieties of stew, with plenty of meat and vegetables), *bakmie* (noodles) and of course *satay*.

A few successful *warung* owners are setting up *warung* chains, specialising in the food that made them locally famous. An example is *Soto Ma'aruf*, which uses offal, for instance ox-liver, lungs and tripe, kept simmering in a rich soup of coconut milk and spices in a big cauldron so it has no chance to pick up any bugs. The *Soto Ma'aruf* near the Taman Marzuki arts complex is a good site because it is near a great many offices whose staff live too far away to go home for lunch. Six can eat for less than £10 in all. Apart from *soto*, there is boiled rice ad lib, *krupuk udang* (big prawn crackers, which really do taste of prawns), raw vegetables with *sambal* (very hot chilli relish) and *asinan*, a sour-tasting mixed raw salad. As I did not suffer my usual MSG-induced headache, I concluded that they didn't use the stuff. MSG is well known in Indonesia because Chinese cooks use it, as do the Japanese and Koreans who are now establishing themselves in the restaurant trade. It is usually known locally as *vetsin* or *ajinomoto*.

The small neighbourhood restaurant may be the next step up the ladder. Traditionally, its owner is often not a local a man at all, but either Chinese (there are many Chinese restaurants in even the smallest towns, and some very good ones in downtown Jakarta, in the Glodok area) or an immigrant from another city or island famous for its cooking. Almost everywhere, for example, you will find a

Rumah Makan Padang. *Rumah makan* simply means 'eating house', and *Padang* is the capital of West Sumatra, where the cuisine is particularly savoury and chilli-hot. These places are patronised mainly by travellers and therefore depend more for their trade on location than the cook's good name. There is a tendency for them, too, to develop into restaurant chains.

Another, newish type of restaurant, for which there is very little precedent, is aimed at a distinctly middle-class clientele, especially in Jakarta, where there is a sizeable expatriate business community, and in Yogyakarta and Bali where there are plenty of tourists. A new suburb of Jakarta, Jalan Raya Kali Malang, has a fish restaurant called *Pondok Ikan*. Jakarta being one of the fastest-growing cities anywhere, these suburbs are very distant from the centre and best reached by taxi. Fish in the tropics obviously has to be absolutely fresh, and most such restaurants have a tank on the premises, from which customers take their pick. Here, the tank is an artificial stream around the restaurant area: within this are eight or ten little Balinese-type cottages for parties and small groups. You can eat western style, or the old way, with your fingers. The cooking is excellent.

A somewhat grander place is the *Handayani* restaurant (Jalan Matraman Raya 45), which claims to serve East Javanese food. *Handayani* is a chain of four restaurants: two in Jakarta, one in **Bandung**, one in **Surabaya**. In this one, the walls are hung with good Jepara woodcarving, the furniture is modern and comfortable, everything is spotless, the room is air-conditioned. Air-conditioning keeps the flies out and keeps you cool while you eat; the only practical alternative is to have hot *sambal* on the table, which the flies don't like and which cools you by making you sweat a lot. *Handayani* is fully licensed and the wine list quite impressive, even several champagnes. One does not go to Indonesia for the sake of the drink. There are some decent local beers, but imported alcohol is very expensive. Freshly pressed fruit juices, tea and coffee are all excellent. Indonesians have said that the *Handayani* food is bland and the *sambal* not hot enough, but dishes are very well cooked and presented piping hot, despite the Indonesian tradition that food is cooked in the morning and left on the table all day. Seven can eat for under £40 with service.

Avoid the tourist trap of *rijsttafel*, which merely gives you far more than you can eat of a bewildering number of dishes, many of them indistinguishable, most of them cooked hours or even days previously. No one these days will think you impolite if you refuse this monstrosity (which many hotels and restaurants still try to foist on the unwary); ask instead for just one or two dishes, preferably those that are specialities of the house or of the region.

In Padang restaurants that I mentioned earlier, the custom is to put all the available dishes stone cold in front of you; you pay only for what you eat, and if you want to have your food heated up the proprietor is very willing to do this for you. The food you don't eat reappears for the next customer. At the restaurant in the *Natrabu* head office in Jakarta, however (National Travel Bureau, Jalan Haji Agus Salim 29a), the food appears to be freshly cooked and is good and hot – *pedas* is the word. Since many foreigners come here, the food will only be chilli-hot if you ask for it that way.

The Javanese have a way of frying chicken that knocks Colonel Saunders into a Confederate cocked hat; they compete successfully with the numerous Kentucky Fried Chicken franchisees. One of the best is *Ayam Goreng Nyonya Suharti* (Mrs Suharti's Fried Chicken, Jalan Adisucipto 208), conveniently next door to the biggest tourist hotel in **Yogyakarta**, the Ambarukmo Palace. The chicken is delicately spiced and fried very crisp, served with sweetish *sambal* and crudités, and best eaten with your fingers. Try *air kelapa* (coconut water) to start and ice-cream to finish. Six can eat here, with all the trimmings, for Rp30,000 (£12). It must be said that prices change all the time, always in one direction, and the exchange rate of the Rupiah is never predictable.

One more place is *Warung Murni* (Campuhan, **Ubud**), a charming little restaurant built around 1980 from traditional materials in the hills near **Ubud, Bali**. It has an idyllic site, at the head of a wooded gorge and next to the bridge that carries the road by which every visitor passes to this famous artists' village. The story is that Murni herself saw the potential of the site and opened the warung, but only really got going when an American admirer gave her an electric blender. With this she started to produce, in quantity, the fruit juices, syrups and shakes that made her famous.

Some say the one good thing that Australian mass tourism has done for Bali is to make sure you can find a passable seafood restaurant in most streets in **Denpasar**. Passable, perhaps, but when you think of what *could* be done with such magnificently fresh ingredients, you can only feel regret.

That leaves the hotels. Jakarta is a city of skyscrapers and luxury hotels, and the tourist can follow a well-blazed trail around the country without ever sleeping rough. Bali is especially well kitted out, with the *Bali Beach* (**Sanur**), whose manager, Anak Agung Gde Rai, is a member of an ancient Balinese princely family, and the *Bali Oberoi* (Legian Beach, **Jalan Kayu Aya**), run by a young Indian, Kamal Kaul. Both have Swiss executive chefs and European menus. At the *Beringin Restaurant* in the Bali Beach Hotel you get the best of traditional Indonesian cooking, acknowledged as such by the discriminating groups of Dutch tourists who frequent it. Prices are very high by Indonesian standards but reasonable by those of Europe.

At the *Oberoi*, I think I shall longest remember breakfast – Balinese coffee and fresh croissants (both superb) taken on an open terrace looking out across the sea towards distant mountains and islands. For lunch, I'd as soon eat noodles and soup at the side of a Denpasar street, which would probably cost me a twentieth of what I paid for the coffee and croissants.

New York: *Lutèce*

by Ken Jacobs

For more than 25 years *Lutèce*'s discreet French townhouse restaurant on 50th Street between 2nd and 3rd Avenue has been a landmark on the New York gastronomic scene. For much of that time Alsatian André Soltner's cuisine has been regarded almost universally by critics as the best, or equal with the best, in the city and probably the country.

There is scant evidence of such a powerful reputation when arriving through the unobtrusive, below-ground entrance leading to the tiny bar with its mix of Paris street signs, posh diplomas and a Rotary club-like Mobil travel award. Drinks are offered when the table is not ready. At 7.45 people are already pushing towards the narrow exit to leave for the theatre. As the coat stand is often jostled against our little bar table, I am several times almost suffocated inside a large mink coat.

The friendly, balding barman insists we take some matches but chides us to remember never to play with them. My New York companion tips him what seems a shocking but apparently expected amount just to finally show us to our table upstairs.

The upstairs dining-room is sedate. There is a chandelier, a large tapestry and several classical-style oil-paintings, including a number of still lifes. The atmosphere is relatively informal, however, with white plates, simple glassware and scurrying waiters. We are ignored for some minutes. Then a waiter gruffly asks who is the host in order to know who to give the menu with prices. Many, mostly traditional-sounding dishes are listed in a difficult-to-read pyramid shape. Typical are roast chicken with herbs, foie gras, blinis with caviare, duck with seasonal fruit sauce, scallops meridionale, fish soup with crab, game.

The main wine list is almost solely an epic catalogue of fine clarets and Burgundies, with often a whole page devoted to one Château. There are classed growths going back to 1890 and a 1961 Ch. Latour for an even $1000 (£558). If you don't want to dig that deeply into your pocket, there is a reasonable list of house wines, the disadvantage of which is the lack of any years or shippers, making selection an act bordering on blind faith.

Service is brusque. Very brusque. The last of the early diners have left by about 8.15, but the pace does not flag. Having heard *Lutèce*'s strength is turning out wonderful new creations every day, we ask if the celebrated *menu dégustation* is available, which we expect to be a combination of *Lutèce* classics and recent inventons. It is not listed anywhere on our menu.

'Of course we have it – two fish, sorbet, two desserts. Do you want it?' demands our waiter at rapid staccato pace without taking a breath. After a brief discussion, the whole table (this menu is served only to a whole party) does opt for the tasting menu. 'Veal, lamb or venison?' he wants to know, his pace of speech now akin to that of a New York hot-dog vendor asking if we want relish, mustard or sauerkraut. After minimal descriptions we select veal when told it is prepared with seasonal vegetables, not knowing why we are being asked to select a course on a supposedly set menu.

Seemingly instantaneously, three small plates are slammed on to the table. With little chance to study the menu, scant description of the daily specials, and having not yet been asked for our wine selection, we are suddenly eating, apparently the first course of our tasting menu. It is a meaty terrine containing chunks of veal in jelly with a good old-fashioned sharp sauce containing shallots and chopped egg. A good start, though surprisingly simple. It is garnished with grated carrot. I mention this since it is the most noteworthy garnish of the evening. There are few frills with the food here. One exception is a large masted ship made of croûtons of bread which keeps sailing across the room to accompany certain dishes.

We finally make our wine selection – two quite reasonable half-bottles, a Pouilly-Fuissé and a Ch. Greysac, which the waiter thought 'might be a 1981' (it was).

The simple goodness and modest presentation of the terrine is much as one would expect at an honest provincial restaurant in France. One wonders if perhaps *Lutéce* is just about honest French country cooking but has been hyped by the food press into something more.

The next course is harder to explain away. This is a cream of unintense tomato soup with some roughly chopped pieces of spring onion thrown into it. It is difficult to add much more, except to state it is better but not that much better than a product sold in small metal containers in the supermarket.

This is followed by a cereal-bowl containing two ravioli stuffed with a mousse of 'codfish' (presumably salt cod). The pasta is delicate but the stuffing lacks any extra dimension and tastes like a bland smoked fish mousse. The surrounding beurre blanc-like sauce is much too lemony, even with the slightly salty filling.

The second fish dish is a thin slice of salmon cooked on the serving plate (and ahered to it), topped with a brown and white grilled blanket of foamy mustardy cream sauce. There is more sauce than fish and the salmon is only just able to peek out from under the blanket. The escalope has dried at the edges and is not that inspiring in the middle.

Our boneless veal chops are presented straight from the oven along with the vegetable mixture which, it transpires, goes beside the veal rather than being integral to its preparation. The veal comes with what appear to be shitake mushrooms and simple thin pan-juices de-glazed with wine. The meat is very slightly pink and extremely tender but without a delicate veal flavour. The vegetables are decent but do not taste of being just cooked before serving. Not at all a bad dish but unremarkable. A side salad contains only chicory and slightly soggy green lettuce with a tart dressing.

By this time it is clear that the tasting menu is literally that – a taste of most of the dishes of the day. It is not the hoped-for mythical harmonious combination of balanced dishes to show off the chef's compositional ability and range. The thought does occur that this is a little like getting rid of leftovers, but surely this cannot be so at $75 (£43) per head without tax or service. Another let-down at this price is knowing that the ingredients going into our meal are not really out of the ordinary. Most could have been bought at any supermarket, even if not necessarily of the same quality.

The sorbet course is less analogous to the embrace of a delicate palate cleanser and more akin to a blind-side attack by a 300-pound blitzing American football linebacker on an unsuspecting quarterback. It is an oversweet, under-intense lemon confection which tastes commercial and contains some large ice crystals. There are a few raisins soaked in liqueur thrown into the bottom of the glass.

Sweet number one is some nicely stewed kumquats in syrup served around some slightly tough puff pastry filled with a mundane crème pâtissière. Sweet number two is a quite decent slab of praline parfait with little sweet veins of pure praline running through it. The parfait is served very cold and is garnished with a very sweet blob of whipped cream. Almond cookies and other petit four biscuits are good quality, as are candied fruits. Decaffeinated coffee tastes sour.

We overhear another table asking for a special dessert, perhaps a soufflé. 'I'm sorry, but the kitchen is closed now, sir,' the waiter says at around 10.15. I quickly suppress the thought that over on 6th Avenue the kitchen at Burger King is open 24 hours and a meal is available there for less than we tipped the bartender. But it is nice to know that this adjacent group, dining liberally on caviare and Tattinger champagne, is not receiving treatment superior to ours.

The chef spends some time with a table of regulars and then comes around to ask if we enjoyed our meal. We make a sort of cowardly noncommittal grunt. Though I have heard of favoured New Yorkers having meals here which include tastes of wonderful dishes not on the menu and better service, our evening was a disappointment. The bill came to $335 (£187) for three with two modest half-bottles of wine and service.

Lutèce, 249 East 50th Street, New York (tel 212 752 2225).

Philadelphia: *Susanna Foo's Chinese Cuisine*

by Yan-Kit So

Philadelphia, PA, home of the Liberty Bell and the Philadelphia Orchestra, has in the 1980s acquired a reputation of a very different nature, as a town of restaurants. *Susanna Foo's Chinese Cuisine* in smart centre-city Walnut Street, opened in the autumn of 1987, adds scope to this new gastronomic citadel.

On the old premises of the solid steak restaurant, *Arthur, Susanna Foo* has modern décor with a Chinese accent. The main dining-room, with seating capacity for a hundred, has round, white tableclothed tables each encircled by six comfortable armchairs upholstered in burgundy mock leather; there are similar banquettes along the walls to go with rectangular tables. The eye-catching feature is the pair of glittering curvy screens, glassily silver, panelled with one-inch, ribbon-like vertical strips; one is on the far end of the room, the other on one side of the wall. The overhead track lights suspended from rectangular brass bars are, however, incongruent with the attractive blue and white chrysanthemum-patterned china on the table. Knives and forks rather than chopsticks complement these round dinner plates. Rice bowls are conspicuously absent.

This sets the tone of Foo's version of Chinese cuisine: a synthesis of traditional Peking/Szechuan and modern American French/Italian, presented more as sophisticated home-cooking than Chinese restaurant fare. Born in China but brought up in Taiwan, Foo, having taught herself the art of Chinese cookery, took in 1980 eight weeks' intensive training at the Culinary Institute of America in New York and in 1985 went to France to further her knowledge of French cookery. She has had experience as a chef, doing her stint in *Hunan* in Chestnut Street, her husband's family concern. Now that she and her husband have set up their own restaurant, she hopes to live out her ambition to be a chef/proprietor.

To this end, she designs the menu, instructs the chefs, then lets them loose in the kitchen while she and her husband, E-Hsin, look after the guests up front. 'I do not want Chinese cooks already set in their bad habits,' she says, 'so I recruit Cambodian cooks and train them myself.'

One of the most taxing skills of a wok-chef is the ability to make the perfect last-minute sauce to a stir-fried dish. If the sauce is too thick, the dish will be laced with an unsightly, gluey mess: if it's too watery, the wok-fragrance, essential to any stir-fry, will be dissipated. Foo prides herself on having found the solution whereby her cooks will always have to hand ready-made sauces of the right consistency and quality. The technique is a combination of Chinese and French. First, she simmers a stock wtih pork and veal bones or poultry carcasses, browned and seasoned with onion and ginger, then adds cornflour to the stock and slowly reduces it for a couple of hours until it thickens to the desired consistency, creamy but not gluey. With these sauces – meat, seafood and vegetarian – always accessible to them, her chefs will have no cause to sneak into the dishes mono-sodium glutamate, which she forbids in the kitchen.

Clear-cut, if at times arbitrary, in her likes and dislikes of certain Chinese ingredients, she does not use Cantonese oyster sauce and, surprisingly, loathes the cross-regional sesame oil, but she is keen on South-East Asian lemon-grass and Mexican ancho-chilli. Her menus, a shorter one for lunch and a more elaborate one for dinner (which is about 30 per cent more expensive for the main courses), are select and imaginative but printed only in English. The starters, classified under *dim-sum*, comprise four kinds of dumplings, spring rolls, spare-ribs, lamb satays, stuffed peppers and paper-wrapped prawns. Five noodle dishes follow, the majority pan-fried, then only two soups, wun-tun and hot-and-sour. Next comes a salad section which could well be found in a French restaurant menu: smoked duck with radicchio and Belgian endive; charcoal-grilled quail and watercress with sesame vinaigrette.

The entrées, some 25 dishes on the dinner menu but only 15 on the luncheon, show Foo boldly stepping out of the traditional Chinese line to evolve her own style of food. Thus, lemon-grass sauce is used on grilled chicken breast, sweetbreads are szechuanised with spicy Kung Pao sauce, filet mignon is given an orange, rosemary and garlic sauce, Norwegian salmon is grilled then seasoned with the Cantonese black-bean sauce, and prawns and pear are paired off in a curry.

The six desserts – a large number for a Chinese restaurant – are Western, although some have an Eastern twist to them. Two chocolate mousses and a chocolate ice-cream account for half while the other half calls for ginger and coconut.

We had two meals at *Susanna Foo*, both at lunch-time. I have nothing but praise for Foo's starters, but main courses are less consistent. Dumplings are her forté, reflecting her origins in Northern China, where folks huddle together to roll out thin and smooth pasta skins, wrap them round chopped stuffing then boil, steam or sauté them. Veal dumplings in spicy ancho-chilli sauce, stuffed with velvetly minced veal instead of the traditional pork and finished with a spicy Mexican chilli sauce in lieu of the vinegar and soy dip, are worthy innovations. Pan-fried dumplings with pork and herb filling are more in line with Shanghai dumplings, sauté on one side and steamed on the other. Steamed crabmeat sui-mei are perfumed with ginger; spring rolls, filled mostly with vegetable and a mere suggestion of pork as seasoning, are crisp to the bite, bursting with flavour.

The two noodle dishes we ate reflect Foo's home-cooking style. Seafood pan-fried noodles, wheat noodles tossed with pieces of succulent scallop and prawn, is *laomein* at its most delicious. Singapore noodles with wild mushrooms (Chinese black mushrooms) and curry sauce, moist with a light curry sauce rather than dry-fried, is a hybrid of the Singapore and Fukien/Taiwan brand, with successful results.

Among the seven entrées sampled over two lunches, four are winners, elegant in presentation, well-balanced in taste and flavour and thoroughly thought-through in ingredient ensemble. Hu-Nan shrimps, as expected, has a spicy sauce; the prawns themselves, attractively centred on the plate, are surrounded by asparagus tips relieved with chopped red pepper. In lamb with Chinese eggplant in black-bean sauce, slivers of tender lamb are stir-fried with wedges of aubergine and finished with a spicy black-bean sauce. For my palate, the aubergine could have been cooked just a little longer, to melt in the mouth, but Foo apparently intends the aubergine to have a bite left to it, and so it's a matter of personal taste. Another aubergine dish, Chinese eggplant in spicy garlic sauce, cooked with onion, did melt in my mouth and I couldn't have enough of it. Stewed fresh and wood mushrooms with broccoli has a home-like quality to it.

Of the remaining three dishes, two were rather disappointing and one passable, but could be better. Even though as spicily flavourful as it should be, the chicken in the Kung Pao chicken with roasted peanuts was overcooked, hence dry rather than juicy. The batter in Mandarin scallops with lemon and almond was too thick and heavy, and what was worse, not deep-fried thoroughly; even its picturesque appearance with spinach could not save the day. More or less the same fault applied to Peking pork loin with caramelised sweet-and-sour sauce; the pork pieces dredged through clumps of flour then deep-fried were very dry and chewy. Significantly, these three dishes were ordered during our second visit, a late lunch after 1.30pm, and Susanna Foo was temporarily absent from the restaurant. She came back in time to shake her head with displeasure at the sight of the scallops and pork. Can she never slacken her control over her chefs?

For dessert, we had on both days ginger cream with fresh seasonal fruit and found it light and refreshing, made more interesting by the crystallised ginger bits buried at the bottom of the glass. Foo's fortune cookies, ritually served at the end of the meal in any Chinese restaurant in the States, are unusual with their delicious chocolate bottoms.

Lunch for three, on both occasions, was at a reasonable price, certainly by London standards: between US$65 and $75 (£36–£42) – 15 per cent service included. We drank only tea and no alcohol.

Susanna Foo's Chinese Cuisine, 1512 Walnut Street, Philadelphia, PA 19102 (tel (215) 545 2666).

West Coast Chinatowns

by Jenny Lo

The biggest cultural influence on America in the twenty-first century may prove to be the Hispanic and Far Eastern immigrant groups – the former by sheer weight of numbers, the latter by a score of statistical measures: the nation's largest proportion of graduates, highest family income, lowest unemployment rate.

In San Francisco the Asian/Chinese presence is 1:3 and in Los Angeles 1:5. Their share of the cities' proportion is rising, augmented by the Hong Kong and Taiwan exodus. San Francisco Chinatown is a combination of a settled community and a tourist site of Disneyland-style garish Chinese arches and telephone boxes. It is also seemingly a treasure-trove of food. The hilly avenues, tiny back streets, Chinese hotels and old folks' homes and local Cantonese dialects are much the same as in Kowloon. London's Soho, with its smaller area and flat terrain without the smell of the ocean may have equally high-quality fresh fruit and vegetables, but loses out on the range available throughout the year, especially the fish, seafood, fresh mushrooms and pickled vegetables.

While I have enjoyed sensational western dinners in San Francisco – at *Chez Panisse* and *10 Campton Place,* I have never had a memorable Chinese meal in the city, nothing to compare what is available in Hong Kong, Toronto or London. Perhaps a settled community loses touch with homeland tastes; perhaps restaurants modify their recipes for native Americans. On the whole I found most dishes slightly bland. More recent arrivals have set up food stores and restaurants in the Richmond district and though I have only had Vietnamese (*Garden House,* 133 Clement Street; dinner for three with beer $40) and Thai meals there, it may be that more authentic first-generation food can be had.

Out of Chinatown, *Harbour Village* (4 Embarcedero Centre) has the décor, atmosphere and cooking to echo the new style of Hong Kong/Cantonese cooking. The restaurant has branches in LA and Hong Kong and specialises in seafood and dim-sum. Other than the usual range of dim-sum – *har gow, siu mai, fan guo* – it offers more unusual dumplings in sharkfin and birds' nest as well as a range of freshly made noodles. Service is comparable to that in a five-star hotel (meal for three, $40).

A visit to LA a couple of years ago had proved disappointing – three indifferent meals, with enormous portions, tasteless stock and watery sauces, in restaurants mostly run by Vietnamese or Chinese. This time I was taken to the new Chinatown – Monterey Park, next to the Chicano territory of East LA – with a population of 60,000,

50 per cent Asian, mostly Chinese but a sprinkling of Japanese and Filipinos, 15 per cent middle-class Latinos and the rest the original working-class white community. The presence of the Chinese newcomers is augmented each day by many others who come in to shop, bank and entertain friends. City Council election candidates run on ethnic issues such as the right to have bilingual street names and shop signs.

Monterey Park is a Brent Cross in a Singapore, exuding the aura of an international boom town. A dozen Chinese-run banks, three Chinese-language newspapers with world-wide circulations, 60 restaurants and several Chinese nightclubs are based in eight square miles. Instead of there being just food shops and restaurants grafted on to a city, the entire district appears to cater for the majority Chinese community. The signs on the shops are in Chinese. There are firearm stores, real estate offices, shopping malls, investment centres, banks, computing agencies, cinemas, churches and even counselling and therapy centres. Add on the sight of Chinese families washing their cars or going into the huge supermarkets, plus the intense sun, and it feels more like Kuala Lumpur than Chinatown California.

Here *Hong Kong Supermarket* (127 N. Garfield) is on the scale of a French hypermarket. Other than the vast array of provisions, fresh fruit, vegetables and types of tofu, there are breads and pastries (black sesame rice cake, ang koo) from various regions, such as Fujian, that I had not set eyes on outside South East Asia. The meat counter offers a range of different cuts of cooked, fresh meat and poultry, while the fish market had tropical and Pacific varieties such as garoupa, fresh water and sea-crabs, even terrapin swimming in their tanks for $4.99 a pound.

On Sundays the *NBC Seafood Restaurant* (404 S. Atlantic) sees queues of hundreds of Chinese families (I saw only three Caucasians) all loudly speaking Cantonese, Vietnamese and Mandarin. The décor is a mix of early '70s British provincial business-hotel ballroom and large West End cinema. As we sat down, we were offered a choice of eight teas. A parade of trolleys surrounded the table, bringing the usual dim-sum, and though the fillings were up to standard, their dough (especially the *cheung fun*) was powdery. But the range was wider and took advantage of Californian produce to replicate south Chinese fare – conch in chilli, vinegar and garlic, suckling pig and jelly-fish were sublime and not the usual rubbery texture as encountered in London. To finish, almond jelly pudding and red bean pudding (meal for four, $40, £22).

Republic of Ireland

by Pat MacAllister

Ireland has an abundance of good earth, unpolluted air and a mild climate. She also has a network of rivers and lakes, and is surrounded by sea: thus, you have a green and pleasant land of fat cattle dining on the best grass in Europe, of well-fed sheep, increasing herds of deer, free-range hens, blackberries and mushrooms wild and free in the fields, vegetables bursting out of the ground, soft fruit for jam, flowers for the honey bee, and fish, fish, fish.

But to find the restaurant which does justice to fine Irish produce while offering good value may well be a treasure hunt. Ireland is still finding itself.

Legends refer to the kingly salmon, the griddle bread baked over the open fire, the mead made from honey, and the good, strong tea. Tea is something of a speciality in Ireland, and in the hey-day of the tea merchants the Irish were very fussy about their tea, and only the best leaves would do. In the middle part of this century, eating out meant conservative meals in hotel dining-rooms with meat and two veg. or a salad plate. Over the past twenty years, there has been a giant step forward, and a sprouting of restaurants of all kinds in almost all places.

This has included many mediocre establishments who think that a menu in French is the main essential. There have been good and not-so-good ethnic restaurants, the ubiquitous and reliable fast-food chains, promising pub grub, and some restaurants which are very good indeed. The tourist board's *Dining Out* book acts merely as an (incomplete) index and price indicator. The humble but frequently excellent Bed and Breakfast houses offer value, a homely welcome and usually such a good breakfast that a traveller may skip lunch.

If you do want lunch, you may do very well in a pub on brown bread and smoked salmon, a good Irish draught Guinness (remember the rolling fields of barley?), often good soup, and hopefully a fresh sandwich. Some of the pubs will provide much more elaborate meals, but if your nose shouts a warning as you open the door, back off and try the local shop for good bread and cheese. Irish brown bread has bewitched many a visitor, who will remember it as a 'special', rather in the same way as Irish whiskey, Irish coffee and Irish liqueurs – all part of Ireland's answer to *vin de pays*.

Milk, cream and butter are very good, and Irish farmhouse cheeses are now superb, and range over 30 to 40 varieties extending out over the country from the peninsula in west Cork where they first emerged in recent years in all their tasty excellence. Add to this regional specialities, like the ham and bacon of County Tipperary, the lamb in Wicklow and Connemara, and the beef of the midlands. Glory in the fish and seafood of Kerry and Donegal, and the mussels and strawberries of Wexford. In Cork you might come on not only their black puddings, but the unimaginable deliciousness of smoked beef, venison and pork. Your salmon must be 'wild Irish salmon' and not 'Irish wild salmon'. And potatoes – where but in Ireland would you hear a chef and a customer discuss the merits of a potato vis-à-vis the variety, the area and the very field of origin?

Increasing attention is paid in Ireland to the merits of organically grown produce. There is also a limited but growing interest in the wild harvest. In late spring and early summer, the enthusiast can find the young nettles which can go into soup and cheese, or the shore can offer such gifts as seaweeds like dulse and carageen. In high summer on the hillsides or over the bogs, there are crops for the picking, of the distinctive little blue fraughans (or bilberries). 'Fraughan Sunday' is the last one in July. Later in summer, in the right conditions, field mushrooms are delicious beyond words. In September all over the country the briars droop with the weight of the wild blackberries. Bright red crab apples twinkle from a tree in the ditch and hazelnuts are plentiful on the by-roads of Co. Clare and Galway. October is the time for sloe picking in the fields and lanes. Irish sloe gin is now on the market and a treat not to be missed.

The restaurant scene is still in a state of change. In places you will find haute cuisine at its best, and even in unsophisticated surroundings you could have the luck to be offered a menu which would include: fresh crab, poached spring salmon, a sole toppling over the ends of the dish, freshly picked raspberries or strawberries or crumbly apple and blackberry pie.

If you are south of the capital in the Dublin suburb of **Blackrock**, make straight for Colin O'Daly's *Park Restaurant* in the Main Street (tel 01 886177). The *Park* epitomises all that is best in high quality Irish restaurants. It has cool, green restful and dignified décor, sparkling linen, glass and white porcelain, extremely skilled cooking and elaborate presentation of the best of materials. It also offers very kind, caring service. Here you can find treasures like the unusual bacon and cabbage soup, a hot mousseline of vegetables, marinated raw fillets of best Irish beef, or John Dory with sorrel and mustard grain sauce. There is a changing menu, and such desserts as a stunning pear mousse which comes in a delicate chocolate case, accompanied by its other half of the poached pear, garnished with tiny slices of plum with a puddle of patterned plum juice sauce, all topped with a little mint sprig and a dusting of icing sugar.

Down South, there is a more humble gem at the *Crawford Gallery Café* beside the Opera House in **Cork City** (Emmet Place, tel 021 274415). This is the offspring of the famous *Ballymaloe* restaurant and cookery school, and here in the centre city you will find lunches, teas, snacks and for some of the week, dinner. There is home-made soup, fish 'landed last night on the pier' with superb butter sauces, or good Irish beef cooked in stout, or Clonmel bacon chop with whiskey sauce. All the home-bakes are on display, like brown bread and puds, for very reasonable cost in the unusual surroundings of a picture gallery. Friendly service is lightening fast.

In wild and beautiful County Donegal, the hunt could lead by a detour to **Rossnowlagh**. Straight off the shore is the agreeable *Sand House Hotel* (tel 072 517774). You will find a friendly Irish welcome, beaming staff and very good Irish meal. Inside that plain exterior is a colourful décor and a promptly served meal with starters such as crab and cucumber mousse, fish chowder, Donegal ham or grilled trout and all the homely old-fashioned puddings you can remember. They don't just smile – they laugh!

Travelling hopefully: the view from the dining-car

by David Dale

The best omelette was on a train in Spain. Somehow, in the cramped kitchen attached to the dining car of the *Catalan–Talgo Express*, about an hour out of Barcelona, the chef managed to produce the perfect ham and cheese omelette: slightly crunchy on the outside, rich and moist on the inside. And not just *one* perfect omelette. All 20 people in the dining-car were commenting, in different languages. The rest of the meal maintained the standard – fresh grilled trout, veal with a red-pepper sauce, and a light apple tart. A half-bottle of Rioja set it off perfectly.

Experiences like that have made me a dining-car freak. In every country I visit, I try to catch trains at lunch or dinner time. I study rail timetables obsessively, looking for the crossed knife and fork symbol which tells me that I'll be able to do better than sandwiches.

The worst dining-car meal I ever had was in Yugoslavia, on a train going from Venice to Athens. The set lunch consisted of cold spaghetti with vinegar sauce, chopped cabbage with vinegar sauce, a thin slice of what may have been meat in globular gravy, and stale sponge. Dinner (what else is there to do on a train going through

Yugoslavia at night?) offered the same menu, with one exception – the cold spaghetti had scrambled egg over it.

The joy of the dining-car is not only a matter of what's in your mouth. It depends on a whole range of sensations. You sit before a crisp white tablecloth (or, in the case of Yugoslav dining-cars, a stained grey tablecloth); you listen to the clink of spoons in saucers; you handle the heavy silverware (engraved with the symbol of the railway company, or, in French and Italian trains, with the symbol of the Compagnie Internationale des Wagon Lits); you watch plate-balancing acts performed by waiters in brightly coloured uniforms (blue on British Rail, orange on the trains in Spain, red on the Italian expresses, yellow on the Rio Grande Zephyr through the Rockies, green on the Southern Aurora from Melbourne to Sydney). And through the window the panorama changes endlessly. What stationary restaurant could offer this floorshow?

Breakfast on the Crescent Limited, travelling from New Orleans to New York, was taken just after sunrise, as we moved on to one of the world's longest bridges – 18 miles across Lake Pontchartrain, Louisiana. The bridge is low and narrow, so it's as if the train is gliding through the water. I looked out the window and met the eyes of an old man in a rowboat. He held up a small fish. I held up a forkful of pancake with maple syrup. We both smiled.

Each nation has its own dining-car habits. Italians are formal. In the dining-car of the Rapido from Milan to Bologna at 12.30pm, I'm unwrapping my breadsticks, watching the olive groves roll past, and trying to make sense of the epic menu, when a waiter in a white coat walks down the aisle, uttering this incantation: '*Gassata o non gassata, gassata o non gassata.*' Once you've made the choice between carbonated or flat mineral water, another waiter parades past, intoning 'Bianco o rosso, bianco o rosso'.

The ritual does not include actually ordering from the menu, which is apparently just a theatrical prop. Five set courses, carried on silver salvers by waiters in red coats, follow each other with due solemnity – prosciutto with figs, a tube-shaped pasta with tomato and bacon sauce, chicken with mushrooms, a slice of cake and a choice from a basket of fresh fruit, eaten with a knife and fork. And finally, tiny cups containing the world's strongest coffee, guaranteed to keep you awake for days.

Americans, in my experience, like their dining-cars to be full of conversation. As soon as they hear an unfamiliar accent ordering food, the questions start, followed by an account of their own life stories. By the time the dessert arrives, you're onto the second divorce. It distracts attention from the meal. Amtrak, the US Government agency which runs all intercity passenger trains (carrying 20 million people a year), has the bizarre notion that train travel should be as much like plane travel as possible. So the food is served in pink polyester trays rather than on plates. During a journey on the Lakeshore Limited between New York and Chicago, I was offered a choice of sirloin steak, boiled scrod (apparently a fish) or a 'regional special' of chicken Kiev. Amtrak has not forgotten the great dining-car tradition, started last century on the Orient Express, of having a single flower in a slender metal vase on every table. A label is attached to each stem which says 'Formosa Silk Flower. Made in Taiwan'. The flower is welded into the base. British Rail does it better, at least at breakfast.

Malaysian dining-cars are mysterious. During the six-hour journey on a crowded train from Fort Butterworth to Kuala Lumpur, a friend and I spent an hour in the dining-car and never saw another passenger. We ordered a spicy noodle dish from a blackboard menu and watched it being fried up in a wok by a wizened ancient. It cost about a pound. As we ate it, in a booth with a laminated tabletop, the ancient and his assistant stood at the kitchen door staring at us. What had we done wrong? Why was no-one else eating? I will probably never know.

For the French, the important thing is panache. The dining-car experience is like a night at the opera. I boarded the Trans-Europe Express one morning in Amsterdam, heading for Paris, and, as is my custom, strolled through the train to get my first glimpse of the dining-car and think of the pleasures to come. I found nothing but carriages full of people. I returned to my seat in the front carriage in evil mood.

At Brussels, they sprang the surprise. The locomotive separated from the train, and after 10 minutes I saw from way down the track another carriage backing towards us. With a crash it connected, and from it burst a horde of waiters who deftly erected tablecloths from hidden recesses next to our seats. The carriage was filled with flapping white tablecloths like a flock of angels landing, as the waiters tried to outdo each other in speed and flourish. Unknown to me, I had been travelling in the dining-car all the time. Those who did not want to eat were shooed out of their seats. We were in the hands of the Compagnie Internationale des Wagon Lits, the catering company which is all that's left of the organisation that started the Orient Express last century. And with a whole extra carriage to work in, they have space to cook lavish meals and even to store some vintage wines.

Home thoughts

The search for flavour

by Tom Jaine

A discussion of English cooking often seems to be a conspiracy of optimism. This *Guide*, after all, lists some thousand places where you may find a reasonable table as you plan a cross-island foray. Who needs more than a thousand? But have you paced your journey to synchronise meals with triangles or squares on the maps in the back? No mean feat if you manage it. Suppose, then, a cartographic miracle. Turn to the entries themselves: *closed Tue; open D only; No children under 7; No children under 12; steps to restaurant; no credit cards; no cheques over £50; no smoking; must book; jacket and tie essential.* The list becomes more fantastic; irritation mounts; the book is thrown across the room; lunch ends up as a Happy Eater, tea as a Pizzaland and supper as a Little Chef – so much for your gastronomic tour.

No, in England you have to travel to eat, not eat to travel. First find restaurants that suit, second pick a destination. If necessary, move mother-in-law, country house, sales conference.

Restrictions on entry remain an aggravating characteristic of British catering. They are part and parcel of the continuing disjunction between eating out and everyday life. *Tante Claire*, as French (thus self-proclaimedly Republican) as you can get, refuses people without jacket and tie; *Simply Nico* and Jacques Astic of the *Old Woolhouse* in Northleach will not accept bookings from someone on their own; many of the swish country houses turn away couples with children in tow. If that is not bad enough, some 50 per cent of the country entries in the 1988 *Guide* (with the honourable exception of Chinese, Indian, Thai and Pakistani restaurants) don't even offer a comprehensive restaurant service, either closing for more than half the day or week, or not giving a choice on their menus. Along with these self-imposed limitations, I would include the one-choice meal. *Chez Panisse* in California was praised last year for its courage in serving such a menu – evidently the writer had never been to England, where many (even good) cooks cop out of the true challenge of running a restaurant, which is to please people and offer a service, not indulge in self-expression at the customer's expense. The fact that more than 80 per cent of diners at the Dorchester's *Terrace* restaurant used to opt for Anton Mosimann's no-choice *menu surprise* when he was cooking there, did not, as he was the first to appreciate, release him from the responsibility of offering a full menu as well.

The dual effect of geographical rarity and strange, self-imposed limitations is to remove eating out from the realm of diurnal practicality to that of special event. The rest of the time you just suffer. Cooks and restaurateurs often defend their practices by claiming that Britain has no habit of restaurant use. True, but it is they who encourage this lack – by supine acceptance of what may be the effect rather than cause of their own inactivity. Despite our conspiracy of optimism, the general run of eating is still diabolical. There will be as many horrific meals served in 1989 as ever there were in 1960. The short-cuts beloved of low-grade catering are just as prevalent, even if their outward dress may offer a spurious quality.

Take two classic instances: motorway services and supermarket bakeries. The motorists' havens have been revamped – responding to collective outrage. But the food is not better. The improvement lies almost entirely in externals. The individual filter coffee, encouraging at first sight, is invariably stale and tasteless. So, too, at the supermarket bakery. The bread looks great, smells great and tastes dreadful.

Parallels from the world of restaurants are manifold. Even medium-priced restaurants adopt the attitude that eating out is only for special events, for dressing up, for some sort of gesture of social solidarity. By doing so they abandon the high ground of public service to the pub and the ethnic cook. The latter may be our life-raft, but the former is still fraught with trouble. Glowing exceptions, such as the *Walnut Tree* at Llandewi Skirrid, the *Crown* at Southwold or the *Dundas Arms* at Kintbury should not disguise the fact that most pubs, even those with fair reputations, fail to offer normal civilised eating positions or service, and perpetrate a host of short-cuts that would not be allowed in most self-respecting restaurants, all in the name of cost. 'It's only a pub, dear.' So we justify a trifle of tinned fruit and custard powder? Served that in Europe, you would think the sky had fallen in.

By contrast to almost any other European country, the traditional basis of British cooking is difficult to pin down, especially in terms of flavour. This lack of starting point lends alarming significance to the role of fashion and external influence. And it makes generalisation even more suspect. The cycle of fashion is longer than might be thought from a reading of the Sunday colour-supplements. Take wine for example. Dining in a fancy Brussels hotel one night, we heard the only other customers, themselves British, saying '*Red* Sancerre! What a surprise – how nice – we *must* try it again.' That was fully 15 years after Gerald Asher and Robin Yapp had shown us its charms. Similarly, Muscat de Beaumes de Venise (or de Frontignan – which many, misguidedly I think, hold to be better, or more novel) can still be encountered as the *dernier cri* of metropolitan sophistication. The simple deduction is that *nouvelle cuisine* has not yet rolled through every kitchen and may miss some altogether.

Every entry in the *Guide*, therefore, constitutes an arrow to a kitchen where the tide-mark of fashion has left its ring. When there are lines from more than one ebb and flow, each leaving a distinct ripple across the menu, assessment can be difficult. It is easy to meet a mousse or mould that figured, pictorially and schematically, in *A la Carte*, yet is executed according to flour and gelatine precepts of irrefragable tenacity, as imbibed from a course for mass-catering. So, in the lower reaches, our restaurants appear to offer the flotsam and jetsam of long discounted favourites – somewhere, I bet, there is even one still serving moussaka, just as quiche and cheesecake have slipped down the ladder of culinary ambition, and as surely as the juxtaposition of soft fruit and game and the current pre-occupation with hot gratins for dessert will figure in the repertoire of corner bistros of the year 2000.

Viewed as a department of French cookery, the opinion is that English chefs are discarding *nouvelle cuisine* in favour of more traditional recipes of regional integrity. The ludicrous point of fact that the territory is generally some small *département* in south-eastern France does not often occur. (Equally ludicrous is that the most serious reappraisal of English food has been undertaken by a Swiss, Anton Mosimann.) A more precise description of the tendency might be that we are no longer reading Michel Guérard but have turned back to Elizabeth David. But movement there is, no doubt of that. It is best expressed in terms of the search for flavour.

During the 1970s (and even more recently in some nooks and corners) the hunt was on for outrageous combinations. The hope was that out of contiguity on the plate there would arise new fusions of tastes – novel flavours. Most of these – lamb and raspberries was my favourite horror – were misbegotten. Some did us the service of validly extending our palate range.

Manipulation of materials apart, the flavour types of much recent cooking can be seen in the sauces. One is in direct descent from classic cuisine: the reduction combining pan juices and some sort of *fond*. Many latter-day French cooks have given up using a long-cooked and reduced *glace* as a constituent of their sauces. They, and many diners, have found that it dominates too readily. Nonetheless, the Bovril tones of the reduction permeate a high proportion of British meat sauces. So strong are they that many of their variations – madeira, brandy, or pepper, for instance – become imperceptible. Here, chef has gone overboard on classical training, developing a one-pot sauce that is *espagnole* by another name and technique and no more exciting. He can even buy his reductions in a tin or sachet; I have eaten one that started life as a stock cube and, I would swear, had nothing else added to it – that was something else again.

Also classic in origin, but given a new lease of life with the revolution of the 1970s, are apparently light cream and butter sauces or egg-based sabayons flavoured by the components of the dish itself or given point by means of herbs or some vegetable infusion. If the chef is skilled, these are masterpieces of subtlety and allusion; John Burton Race's leek sabayon with oysters is a case in point. If not, their flavour does not rise above the richness of their ingredients. A meal containing two such sauces may floor you without memorable pleasure.

The particular difficulty of these sauces is monotony, which is also true of the third great strand of flavour, sweet-and-sour, on the up and up since the first marmalade of onions and guinea-fowl with lime. In close, nefarious alliance is the sweet/savoury, where means other than vinegar or citrus, such as a strong wine reduction, have been used to temper your surprise at meeting soft fruit with chicken. It might be objected that both sweet-and-sour and sweet/savoury are among the few traditional English tastes – redcurrant jelly and mint sauce *inter alia* – so who are we to protest? Nevertheless, the new wave sweet-and-sour/savoury strikes me as one of the greatest solecisms of recent cooking, following only the combination of strawberries or raspberries with chocolate, and blue cheese with meat.

For all that, it's damnably attractive – what did *you* eat on your first visit to a Chinese restaurant? – though it ruins red wine and has to be carefully managed to be anything other than crude. Sweet-and-sour, at its crudest too much vinegar or lemon juice, does answer one crying need: simple, identifiable and lusty flavour. Herein lies its charm to a harassed chef. Though monotonous, it has a different quality of boredom to meat reductions, nor is it understated, as are too many of the egg/butter/cream sauces. Its popularity stems from a desire for what the Middle Ages termed 'high taste'; closely related in turn to the success of ethnic restaurants.

A lot of people have decided to chase 'high taste' down other paths than the simple sweet-and-sour; their search perhaps marks that which is most attractive about current metropolitan cooking. It was never certain, in the hey-day of *nouvelle cuisine*, that what was described on the menu would turn up on your plate. Quite apart from the connotations of the name given to the dish being turned upside down – a soup would turn up at the pudding stage; a stew would be deconstructed into component, unrecognisable, parts – the flavour elements identified in the description would be scarcely perceptible.

Twin causes existed for this. First, the chef was so excited about the appearance and image of the dish, he forgot to wonder what it tasted like. Second, he had a failure of gustatory nerve and technique. Yes, technique abounded – no-one would deny a tremendous surge in skills in the best kitchens – but it was harnessed to the wrong ends. Technique is necessary to a light mousse or an emulsion without thickeners, but it should also be bent towards securing the absolute penetration of flavours through the unyielding surface of undilute protein and bland vehicles of egg, cream or butter. Technique needs to be allied to a desire to take risks and, hush now, to spend money. Just compare a dish with truffles in one, nerveless, place, and somewhere like Sean Hill's *Gidleigh Park* or *Tante Claire* in Chelsea.

So what paths are being followed? Two very different poles have been taken as signposts. The first is the whole business of ethnic cuisine – worked out to a higher point in England than anywhere else in Europe. The second is the more robust cooking of the French bourgeoisie and European peasantry lovingly described by a generation of cooking writers and elaborated by an army of Italian, Spanish, French and Belgian cooks.

The point of Indian, Chinese and Thai success has not been lost. To begin with, here are restaurants that are used every day, without pretension. Next, they deal in unfamiliar, yet strong, flavours. They have shown that a dish may at once be vigorously seasoned, yet not crude. A cuisine of flavour, not of protein and richness. Small wonder that home cooks have turned wholesale to the lessons of Madhur Jaffrey or Ken Hom as a means of enlivening the monotony of English cooking. The lesson has continued in the restaurant world with the apparent popularity of the new-wave American places. Cajun cooking is nothing if not full of raunchy tastes (even if the mediation of some of its practitioners has caused its enervation).

European traditional cooking has contributed a degree of directness, as well as a willingness to explore parts of animals or of the vegetable kingdom hitherto closed to the exponents of *haute cuisine*. Everyone is cooking lentils; *fromage de tête* has a new lease of life; sausages are number one. The quality of this style is that it has pushed to one side the vapidity and over-complication of much recent cooking. In restaurants that have espoused it, there is a greater chance that the taste stated on the menu will turn up on the plate – with a vengeance.

The two most publicised exponents of this style in the capital are Simon Hopkinson at *Bibendum* and Alastair Little in Soho. In the provinces, however, there is a whole school that has reached the same ends without passing these turnings. People such as Hilary Brown at *La Potinière*, Anna Smith at *Danescombe Valley*, Marion Jones at *Croque-en-Bouche* or Joyce Molyneux at the *Carved Angel* (every one a woman, be it noted) succeed without ever leaving the starting blocks: their hallmark is directness, and a close reading of the value of French bourgeois cooking.

An encouraging sign of the way things may progress in Britain may be described in how we assess the skill of a chef. I would say that what used, a long time since, to mark a male chef from a female cook was his attitude to crisis management. From an impoverished larder, he could spirit a simulacrum of a dish from a vast à la carte menu that spanned a hundred variations on sole or steak. In twenty seconds he could have *consommé à la florentine* bubbling on the hob – substituting beef for chicken stock and parsley for chervil. What did it matter if it was correct or not? The customer had a plate. A lady cook, however, would take things literally. Not for her to cook the joint on Saturday, carve it on Sunday and reheat it in the gravy. No, there she would be on Sunday at six in the morning, getting ready to roast, suffering a thousand *crises de nerfs* as she carved to order. (Some) chefs killed cooking.

Then that changed. There was the fight-back of the amateur as we emerged from post-war drab. Directness and taste (as well as tastefulness) seemed all-conquering – only to fall again to the assault of the professionals. The spirit of modernity that swept through French kitchens in the early 1970s was entirely professional-led. Whole sectors of cooking had to be relearnt, redefined. The amateur was left standing. Some, Nico Ladenis for example, went into retreat, only to emerge more expert than the experts – *how* many times does he tamis that sauce? Others bowed to the inevitable and watched as the mousses, the clever tricks with tomato skins and radishes, the simple yet different reductions and glazes and the manipulation of technology through the freezer and microwave enabled dishes of unparalleled sophistication to leave the hotplate unsullied, of course, by interference from the waiter. And to what end? Very little, I fear, because taste was left out of the reckoning. Now that it is returning, the amateur may have his day again.

Meals depend on memory to make them absolutely successful. Cooking is an evanescent art, living only in the mind once consumption is done. Hence the importance of ambience and hence, much more so, the importance of flavour. Without the hook of flavour on which to hang your memories, the meal will die by next week. All that labour will be for nought. The English cry out for flavour, sometimes in the crudest and most distressing forms: pickled onions, all that boring smoked stuff that litters menus incapable of producing flavour by other means, HP sauce. The art of the chef is to satisfy it without resort to blockbusting sweet-and-sour, without burning our heads off with chilli or garlic, but with subtlety and taste.

The plight of the northern restaurateur

Restaurateurs' beefs about customers, suppliers, cooks, indeed the whole world, are legion and legendary. Peter Bramley *puts the case for a more understanding customer, remarks he prefaces with the comment, 'We find the more sensitive and appreciative customers have found us from the* Guide. *These people are a pleasure to serve and are usually objective enough to compare us on a national scale. Often, with no direct point of comparison in the immediate area, locals condemn us for being ''different''.'*

We believe we have evolved and progressed further in style since our very early days. We see ourselves moving more towards 'granny' cooking and the use of plain, simple ingredients where warranted, alongside more sybaritic luxuries, and towards using simpler methods of cooking as well as processes requiring more technical expertise. Having spoken to other people in sympathy with us, it seems more restaurateurs are finding this a natural spin-off from Modern British Cooking. With a wider audience now to understand the concept, it is thankfully no longer necessary to impress people by the one-upmanship of exotic ingredients or the alarmingly rapid upward spiral of ever more complex dishes. (Perhaps the Modern British style will lead to 'affluent peasant cooking'. Stockbrokers will commute to their palatial artisans' cottages and eat designer rustic casseroles of finest roe deer fillet with white truffles.)

Any problems we encountered in the city centre have amplified themselves threefold since our move to the country. At least in those small, unimpressive premises we were feeding a small band of discerning followers interested in the food alone (since we had very little else to offer). The few people not in tune with our thinking stood out of the crowd, and many of the silly scenarios we experienced there have gone down in our annals. Now, with more seats to fill, and a grander disposition, we see a much wider variety of local people. We had not realised the size of the problem! (If Nico Ladenis had chosen his vicarage here instead of Shinfield . . . .) Trying to keep a restaurant running smoothly does have its lighter moments, of course.

We placed a main course of plainly cooked lamb fillet before a lady. 'Oh dear, its been messed about with,' she said, 'I can't eat anything fancy.' At a loss to understand the fanciness of lamb in a plain meat gravy, or the way in which plain steamed vegetables had been messed about, we offered her anything else she cared to choose. She then proclaimed all our meats too fancy and said she wanted 'some good plain fish – nothing funny on it.' She chose wild salmon infused with dill topped with a mousseline of sole, the whole thing baked and served on a sorrel and cream sauce.

Fanciness, it seems, is a common failing in our gravies – witness the man who complained his hare saddle had been completely ruined by 'that fancy foreign type sauce poured all over it.' A strange comment you might think from the land of gravy and Yorkshire pudding. Perhaps a Yorkshireman can no longer tell a gravy if it hits him in the face. . . . Fanciness, however, is not confined to such over-elaborated abominations as gravy, it even stretches into the realms of that eternally reprehensible substance, water. We used to serve complementary still Ashbourne water until one man forcibly thrust the bottle away and said indignantly, 'I don't want no fancy watta!'

If the forbidden fruit of Adam was the apple, then the forbidden food of Northerners has to be the scallop. 'What were those little white decorations on the salmon?' The waiter stared blankly, searching for an explanation. 'They were soft and wet, I didn't eat them – look there they are.'

'Ah, those are scallops, madam.'

'Well, yes I know, but scallops of what?'

Four weeks later, different lady.

'What are these like little squashy things?'

'They are scallops, madam.'

'What?' she said, then in a confidential aside to her spouse, ''E says they're scallops.' The husband suppressed a snigger of mocking for me, poor fool that I am. The lady turned back to me and said, 'What, potato scallops?' (This is a local chip-shop delicacy of which you may be unaware.)

Asparagus causes similar turmoil. One evening we served a light intermediate course of asparagus with tarragon cream. One party of six people ate the bottom half inch of every stalk, leaving the rest entirely intact. As it was placed before them one lady enthused, 'Oh good, them artichokes is my favourite.'

As well as the 'ignorance is bliss' brigade we also suffer from the professional self-appointed expert. A professional confectioner asked us, 'What is *fondant*?' A man claiming to be a *pâtissier* said he knew why our Pavlova was so good. He confidentially pronounced, 'The secret is to use *Swiss* lard – most people use the wrong kind.'

And then there is the amateur, who usually picks the easier option of pontificating on wine. 'Well, you find me a good white – I mean, there aren't any, are there?' The enormity of that statement gives me bad dreams even now. A man watched us pour his tasting measure of Morgon. He gazed disconsolately for many a stunned moment until he turned his eyes plaintively upward to meet mine and proclaimed, 'It's red.' Another man pointed out our error in listing St Emilion among the clarets, because he had driven 'right through Bordeaux on holiday and not seen any signposts for it.'

A lady with a party drinking Bollinger R.D. '75 through the meal, asked for a tonic water. 'Certainly madam' (with that conciliatory tone used for drivers who've had enough wine). I'm afraid we gaped when she poured the 'Sch – you know what' into Madame Lily's best. 'That's better', she said, 'it just wasn't fizzy enough.'

However, the outright winner, with a special award for 'brevity in stating the plight of the Northern restaurateur' must be the lady who, faced with an array of our own baked biscuits of several varieties, plus walnut bread, nut loaf etcetera, to accompany her cheese, pouted sadly and asked, 'Don't you have any *proper* cream crackers?'

The Last Frontiersman

by Victor Sassie

He stands alone at the front of the house. It is High Noon and his darkest hour. Like that other old-timer, Gary Cooper, he faces forward, his look cool, composed and resolute. But there is a turmoil of nagging thoughts going around the back of his head.

Have the hired hands below stairs finished their card games and worked out the last of the cross-trebles? (Since dishwashing machines came in all sculleries have become gambling-dens.) Have the three hours of clearing and cleaning, fetching and filling, rushing and running, pushing and pulling, Hoovering, manoeuvering, mixing, fixing, arranging, locating, counting, checking and near-collapsing, resulted in a state of grace? Did Harry clean the mirrors? They look streaky. Is there fresh soap in the Ladies? And what's the Pledge spray doing on Table 3 where there should be a flower vase? Switch 'em pronto.

But it is now 12.30 pm. Perish these thoughts and smilingly greet the eager, early customers.

Such were the daily traumas of the front-of-the-house resident restaurateur, the owner-driver so to speak. I use the past tense deliberately because his day has long gone. As has the era of the original front-of-house-men – the maître d's, major-domos, the known-by-name personalities whose skills were as much, if not more profitably employed creating style and ambiance out front chatting to the customers, than ruling the roost in the kitchens. This was, of course, before terms like customer relations, PRO, or marketing men were ever heard outside advertising agencies. Such men were usually to be found in the restaurants attached to grand hotels; usually, too, they were waiters who had worked their way up through the 'waiting' grades. (The great chefs wouldn't dream of socialising with the customers.) Just one or two of them became owner-occupier restaurateurs. Undoubtedly, the greatest of these was Mario Gallati, who started his *Caprice* with the financial backing and faithful support of the superstars of the London stage he had served as head waiter at the *Ivy*.

But one by one, or sometimes in batches, the great and the good eating houses owned and run by the personally appearing proprietor were taken over or merged into catering chains. Now their trainees are taught about portion control – a little thing some of my old customers with less than Hungarian-sized appetites have said they wished I had learned – how to count napkins by computer and 'conversational procedures' – how to chat up a customer and keep him or her happy. But that's a trick of the trade that cannot be learned at catering college. Mario Gallati once prophesied that the great change in catering, away from the individual touch to the mass-produced, would eventually result in self-service cafeterias where the food was cooked by robots. But robots cannot replace the one-man show when the one man has to do three things at the same time.

It is because we are creatures of habit that we are so much victims of change. There we were, ensconced in our favourite little eating place, discovered by ourselves without the aid of guide-books, until the post-war catering explosion culminated with the dropping of the *nouvelle cuisine* bomb.

The French kitchen has made a great contribution to the English table but *nouvelle cuisine* has done a great disservice to restaurants. It has enabled unscrupulous entrepreneurs to blind us with science, and make fortunes by ensuring we leave their tables with empty stomachs and thick heads. But what is worse and more damaging, it has eliminated those service skills which elevated the status of the waiter far above his demeaning classification of domestic servant, which is how the Board of Trade classified both cooks and waiters in answer to a request from the Chefs & Cooks Circle, given to their representative E. H. Laffineur in 1970 and to my knowledge never modified.

Instead of the skilled waiter's dexterity at table, that is, using a wild duck press, ability to dissect a chicken or duck, carve a fore-rib of beef, bone out a grey mullet or peel an orange, and all these skills performed in front of the customer, we get plate service. Lukewarm food unhygienically assembled by hand on to lukewarm plates, then bandied about from hand to hand before being plonked down before the guest, is an intimidation both for the customer (made to feel that is all he or she is worth) and the service worker (made to feel like a hash slinger).

The fast-changing catering trade brings to mind refugee words on the run from catering vocabulary. Although most catering workers know their meaning, they nevertheless look askance at anyone using words like pantry, larder, still room, cellar, dispense, dining-room, napkin, condiments, cruet, side-board, service plate, salver, port tongs, bill of fare. They are rarely heard today because who needs a pantry just to keep bread and make a few butter pats, or a larder to keep a few convenience foods, or a cellar when the best-selling house wine ('Red or white, sir?') is delivered and sold daily with a 300 per cent mark-up? No need for a dispense either, when the wine can be kept conveniently at hand in airless cupboards under the bar and dispensed by anyone handy.

Equally, who needs a service plate to serve accompaniments when the untrained service worker can carry a veg. dish or sauce-boat in his or her hand just as safely, so long as his or her thumb is inside the lip. Presenting bills on a silver salver quite rightly has no place in a democracy, while port tongs went out with the last of the '27 vintage.

The rapid change in catering is probably due to the vast growth in the leisure industry. We are bulging at the sides with restaurants, cafés, wine bars, hotels, boarding-houses, and fast food shelters. They spring up in remote places, and not only do most succeed, but some win gastronomic awards. Are we so affluent that we can support and encourage these up-market establishments selling food at £5 per ounce, or so poor that we cannot afford the raw materials for home cooking? Is it because we are so hungry that we consume hydrolysed, processed, grey vegetable matter – the cheapest prepared junk food available?

There is abundant evidence that the massive change in catering has been successful and profitable for investors. A student from a catering college wrote seeking my help on his exam project, entitled 'How to be a Successful Restaurateur'. My dilemma was which of two choices to advise, either to aim for fame, poverty and ill health, or go for obscurity, security and much wealth. Among many things I quoted to him was what the great Karoly Gundel said to me in 1938: 'The secret of success is originality and mystery.' When I asked him how to reconcile the two he said, 'Retain the primitive values'. Upon asking for further enlightenment he said, 'Just think, millions of Russians live off cabbage soup, salt herrings, raw onions, pickled cucumbers and black potato bread, these are all original items peculiar to the Russian diet.' The mystery is, considering the climate, how do they survive, and the answer is, apart from the nutrition, the combined flavours of these foods converge on the doorstep of luxury, an extension of this primitive repertoire would be strange and unwelcome to the Russian palate.

As I pointed out to the student, to succeed he must learn the pain and frustration of long hours and hard work. He needs to seek qualification, classification, and certification. He can attend courses either at his place of work or at a catering college and must aim to qualify in restaurant operations, culinary knowledge, room service and wine service, hygiene, first aid and fire drill: these courses can all be taken through the auspices of the Hotel and Catering Training Board. A short secretarial course on business letters, typing and telephone conversational procedures is very useful. All these courses offer certificates which should be framed and hung in a discreet place where they are not obtrusive but can be seen. This is to promote professionalism and boost confidence. Restaurant classification will not come from a Government Department of Tourism as in other countries, since actors, lawyers, noblemen and dustmen and anybody else are free to open a restaurant without qualifying and without authority, so it follows they cannot be classified, but are free to poison people simply by not knowing the effect of different temperatures on food. However, classification will come from the food quides, trade associations, food writers, and trade magazines.

To be successful, a restaurant needs the atmosphere that only the proprietor can create. His personality will reflect in the room whether it be gloomy or joyful. No large, company-owned restaurant under management can ever hope to create the necessary atmosphere, since the manager is preoccupied with implementing company policy and is forever striving to improve or at least maintain his wicked profit-margin target.

A proprietor must himself be up front, ready to welcome his guests by name, to dispense good cheer, to give with a good heart. He must also assess what kind of food certain clients need to make their day. He should know the regional and national differences of palate expectation and their food habits. For instance, never give a Spaniard shepherds pie, nor a Lancastrian capsicums in any form. Celts prefer boiled foods but no herbs or spices. Anglo-Saxons prefer roasts. You can safely serve mutton to a Welshman, pork to an Irishman, beef to a Scotsman and poultry or beef to an Englishman, but if you want to make an enemy of a Hungarian serve him a meat and potato pie with boiled cabbage.

When I opened the *Budapest* in Greek Street in 1948 – three course lunch of soup, goulash and pudding, 1/6d – I was frontman, back-man, upstairs (the kitchen) and downstairs man. My functions would have fitted that old saying 'head-cook and bottlewasher'. However, the word 'bottle' brings blushes to my cheek. There is a legend that persists to this day, and I have to admit its truth because there were two eye-witnesses to the sorry incident. The *Budapest* of old was a 'caff' with a take-away counter trade as well as table service. My wife Elizabeth, who is Hungarian, helped out there. A couple of youths came in with two empty Coca-Cola bottles on which they had paid a deposit and wanted to reclaim their money and put it towards the purchase of two more bottles. Neither Elizabeth's English nor her grasp of mathematics was very strong. She called for help to get this complicated transaction sorted out. I solved it by giving the lads their deposit back in exchange for the empty bottles, saying, 'Now go outside and come back in and just buy a couple of Cokes in the ordinary way'.

From the beginning the *Budapest* became a water-hole for Labour MPs and a smattering of Trades Union officials. This came about largely through *The Good Food Guide* when it was edited by Raymond Postgate with help from Margaret Cole and Margaret Costa (the *Budapest* was an early entry). He wrote for Reynolds News and brought along another contributor, Tom Driberg. Reynolds News was financed by the Co-op and involved with USDAW. And from that nucleus the circle widened to take in their friends among the fellow-travellers of the time.

When in the early 1950s I acquired the Yugoslav restaurant three doors along the road called *Joseph's*, we all moved up-market together, and *Joseph's* was re-opened as the *Gay Hussar*. (Incidentally, I chose that name when gay meant merry and bright and there had been a nightclub in the thirties called the *Gay Adventure* and I knew and admired the owner, a great Soho character called Mrs Lottie Thiebault.)

Over the forty years, from the *Budapest*, through the *Gay Hussar* until my retirement, I think I can claim to have had a family business. Not family run (heaven forbid), nor family inherited – but family customered, yea even unto the third, and in one case fourth, generation. My first customer, so he claims, at the old *Budapest* was Ben Perrick from Foyles who came almost daily. He brought his then seven-year-old daughter Penny for coffee and a bun one Saturday morning. *Her* two children, now aged 23 and 25, join her and their grandparents at the *Gay Hussar* on all their respective birthdays, anniversaries and other celebrations. With the Perricks, we have welcomed an extended family, embracing brother, cousins and in-laws (three sets) from all over – New York, Vancouver, San

Diego, Phoenix – and they bring their children. When Penny helped organise a surprise party for my seventieth birthday – she arranged for all the regulars to make bookings weeks in advance – four extra Perrick connections had to be fitted in. Their oldest friends in New York happened to arrive in London that day with their grandchildren. I get very involved with family relationships and this can be awkward when my customers change wives or husbands or quarrel with their kinsfolk. When the split is amiable, there is no embarrassment about exes seeing each other; when it is otherwise, it has to be decided among the ex-partners who gets custody of the regular table reservation at Victor's.

I never thought of calling my restaurant *Victor's*. There was an old-established and very good restaurant in Soho called *Chez Victor*, which specialised in French cuisine. As it happened, the 'French' Victor turned out to be Czechoslovakian. Joseph, whose Yugoslav restaurant became the Hungarian-styled *Gay Hussar*, was born in the Austro-Hungarian Empire.

But I must surely be the only Hungarian restaurateur who comes from Barrow-in-Furness?

The rise and rise of industrial bread

by Jill Norman

'You can travel fifty thousand miles in America without once tasting a piece of good bread' wrote Henry Miller in 1947. At that time a comparable statement about Britain would not have been true.

Wartime legislation had laid down that the milling of white flour was no longer permitted; the minimum extraction rate for flour was increased from the usual 72 per cent for white flour to 85 per cent in order to use more of the grain for human consumption, which meant that less wheat needed to be imported. No white flour was produced until the milling industry was decontrolled in 1953. Bread factories were not yet of any importance; bread was made by the traditional long fermentation method, and up and down the country there were good bakers.

Unhappily, since then Henry Miller's predicament has come to be familiar here, due largely to the advent of the industrial loaf, produced according to strict commercial principles.

Until the 1870s all flour in Britain was stone ground, but then steel roller mills were introduced and were soon installed at all the large mills. Roller mills are able to grind a greater range of wheats and grind them more finely than millstones. They separate the parts of the grain, extracting the wheatgerm and the bran, so that the resulting flour is whiter and less variable. The bran and other 'offal' is sold as animal feed; the flour is graded, processed, 'enriched' with assorted chemicals, calcium (chalk), and nutrients (including B vitamins, present in the outer layers of the wheat but lost in the roller milling process).

In 1962 the Flour Milling and Baking Research Association invented the Chorleywood Bread Process, a high-speed mixing process which can use less high-protein hard wheat, more water and yeast to flour, requires added 'improving agents' and eliminates the need for slow maturing of the dough. It makes possible the use of a proportion of home-grown soft wheats which are lower in protein and normally more difficult to make into bread than hard wheats imported from Canada and America. By 1986/7 some 75 per cent of wheat used for bread was British, and the Chorleywood Process was responsible for 75 per cent of all the bread sold in Britain.

In order to be able to use higher proportions of the cheaper soft flour the industry adds wheat glutens produced from wheat starch to it. In my view this produces pulpy, flavourless bread that turns gluey when chewed and sticks between the teeth. It is light for its size, with less protein, less flour and more water, yet unrivalled in the world, we are told, for 'cheapness, nutritional value and keeping quality,' (submission to the Monopolies Commission on Bread and Flour, 1977).

What the millers and bakers who made the submission failed to say is that the British white loaf may be cheap but its nutritional value when compared with wholemeal bread is unimpressive and its boasted keeping quality requires additives which are not used in the rest of Europe.

More than 40 additives are permitted for our flour, bread or both, according to the 1984 Bread and Flour Regulations. The list includes 1 bleaching agent, 9 improving agents, 5 anti-oxidants, 4 preservatives, 8 emulsifiers, 2 stabilisers and caramel for colouring. A selection of these may be used in just about any bread, except for bleach and a few improvers which are prohibited in wholemeal.

National Food Survey figures showed a significant move to wholemeal bread from 1981 to 1986, the year in which the consumption of wholemeal overtook that of brown bread. In 1987 sales dropped back somewhat when soft-grain white hit the supermarket shelves. These loaves, marketed with names like Mighty White and Champion, have grains of wheat, rye and maize in them (as well as a range of the usual additives) and claim to contain up to 30 per cent more fibre than ordinary white bread. They took 10 per cent of the wrapped bread market in less than a year. Since the majority of the population prefers white bread (two thirds of the ten million loaves we consume each day are white), it seems likely that some of those who had shifted to wholemeal for nutritional reasons turned to soft grain because it too offers fibre but at a lower price.

The total consumption of bread has been declining steadily over the last 20 years. The 1987 Ministry of Agriculture, Fisheries and Food figure for bread consumption at home is 30.66 oz per head per week, with an estimated 4 to 5 oz more eaten out, and according to the 1988 annual report of the Federation of Bakers (whose members produce 70 per cent of our bread) demand has now stabilised. The report also confirms a return to white bread: 'The rapid rise of wholemeal has halted, at least temporarily, while other premium breads continue to increase. The standard white loaf is still regarded by customers as the best-value convenience food, but they are also willing to pay more for quality and taste.'

'Paying more for quality and taste' needs looking at.

These days chain stores, High Street bakers, in-store bakeries and most supermarket shelves offer a great array of different loaf shapes. Almost all the traditional British shapes are there – except, usually, the cottage loaf which is notoriously difficult to make. We are certainly asked to pay more for the shape we choose – 43p for an 800g sliced white compared with 63p for a bloomer in my local supermarket – but what about quality and taste? Having tried a range of breads from different outlets I found texture varied somewhat but the taste did not: factory bread, whether white, brown or wholemeal and regardless of presentation, remains tasteless, dull and uninteresting.

Fancy breads, or what the industry likes to think of as 'quality' lines, come at fancy prices too: anything from 60p to more than £1 for a 400g loaf. They may have more texture – usually in the form of added grains, nuts, seeds or herbs – but the dough itself is seldom a great improvement on the rest of the factory stuff.

I assume this has to do with where bakers buy their flour. In 1987 the National Association of British and Irish Millers (NABIM) had 48 members operating 89 mills. Ten members were small, stoneground millers and the top three produced over three-quarters of our flour. Two of these three are Rank Hovis McDougall (whose possible acquisition by Goodman Fielder Wattie Ltd. has been referred to the Monopolies Commission) and Associated British Foods, who between them own about 80 per cent of the bread factories and also supply flour to other bakers.

and 1215 in France. NABIM may boast that milling in the UK has rationalised itself into a compact, highly efficient (and highly profitable) industry – but that is precisely also the reason why our bread is so dismal. The industry is in the grip of a few millers who bought up bakeries 30 years ago, so apart from buying from a small, independent baker who in turn buys flour from a small, independent miller there is little chance of getting anything but bread made with whatever flour the big millers choose to produce.

It takes another industrial giant to have any effect on an entrenched industry like milling.

In 1986, Asda moved to own-label bread and put pressure on its suppliers to use unbleached flour and to stop adding preservatives. The millers and bakers responded, and much of our bread is now labelled accordingly.

When you travel in Germany or Scandinavia, breads vary from region to region, still made with a range of grains, and they have an individual taste, good crumb and pleasing texture. In Italy and France there is some bad bread, too, but at least it is a cause of complaint and good bread is never hard to find. No wonder the company Délices de France imports 38 tons of bread per week to supply baguettes, brioches, croissants and the like to hotels, restaurants and shops in London.

Few restaurants bake their own bread, and many otherwise excellent chefs seem surprisingly ignorant on the subject, perhaps because here it is not eaten throughout a meal as it is in much of Europe. So, many otherwise good restaurants offer dreadful bread – fake baguettes and chunks of that dark brown stuff that owes its colour to caramel and has nothing to do with the German dark rye bread it is presumably imitating.

If you want to bake your own bread, go to a small local miller for your flour if you can; they are unlikely to use any additives. If you buy your flour from a grocer or supermarket, it is worth looking at the small print on the bag. Strong white and brown bread flour produced by the big millers contain additives, so do some supermarket own brands (Sainsburys' notably does not). Jordans state on their bags that the flour contains no additives, colourings or preservatives; other flours which are less clearly labelled but good are Howards Irish stone-ground (hard to find but worth looking for), Prewitts and Doves Farm. The 1981 Nutritional Aspects of Bread and Flour report recommended that all one hundred per cent wholemeal flour sold in retail shops should be free of additives and that is still the case, but remember that brown does not mean wholemeal.

About 30 per cent of UK bread sales are from small bakers and the growing number of in-store bakeries. Many of the latter buy their dough, frozen, from the big plant bakers, so they may offer a kind of freshness, but not much more. Equally many small bakers produce indifferent bread, still buying their flour from the same dominant sources and tipping in the 'improvers', even if preservatives are left out. Some shops have good wholemeal but there are still a lot of those dense little bricks of unsliceable bread produced by earnest healthfood bakers who have not mastered their craft. The best bread often seems to come from the small ethnic bakers, usually Italian or Cypriot – but make sure you actually buy the baker's own wares, as breads like pitta and daktyla have been taken up by the big guns as 'variety breads'.

How do you know what you are buying? If your bread is wrapped, the label must state what the bread is made from, but not, unfortunately, what the flour itself consists of; the millers are still effectively immune to consumer inspection. It is accepted that labelling an unwrapped loaf was impractical but that the shops should display a list of ingredients of the breads they sell. I have yet to see one.

Cheese

by Drew Smith

The revival in farmhouse cheesemaking has attracted much interest. The sheer quality of many of these cheeses has astounded restaurateurs and readers alike. But for all the publicity, these cheeses remain a very small, specialist part of the industry that has re-established itself despite, rather than with the assistance of, the Milk Marketing Board.

A visit to the major cheese competition stands at the Bath and West Show at Shepton Mallet in June 1988 was instant proof that the cheese industry as a whole is heading in a different direction to that of farmhouse cheesemaking. Far and away the largest number of entries came from large creameries. These cheeses were square, not traditionally round, the result of heavy pressing in factory moulds. Nearly all the large creameries pasteurise the milk to standardise the product. Indeed some cheesemakers have been encouraged to pasteurise their milks in order to sell through supermarkets. This is anathema to the farmhouse cheesemaker who seeks to exploit the differences in the milks from cows that might have grazed on different pastures. Mass-produced cheeses are meant for wide consumption. Used in cooking or as meat substitutes they have a role, but they are not equal to the high-quality cheese eaten on its own at the end of a meal. This part of the market has been largely abandoned. And it is this area the independents have begun to penetrate, initially via restaurants, with critical success.

But how good are these cheeses? Is it just the cachet of being rare and rather eccentric that has given them a reputation? How do they compare with the pasteurised creamery cheeses commonly found in supermarkets? The *Guide* set up a panel of cheese experts to nominate those cheeses – both farmhouse and creamery – they regarded as achieving the most consistent high quality. The panel was chosen to include those people who were most likely to have had first-hand experience of a wide variety of cheeses over the last few years. Most of the eleven were cheese factors, but also included were representatives of Dairy Crest and two independent experts. The results are presented in two lists. The first list is of those cheeses that a majority of the jury agreed ought to be on any list of the best of British cheeses. The details on production and maturing were supplied by the cheesemakers. Their assessment of when milk is at its best for cheesemaking can vary according to elements such as the type of pasture and kind of animal, and will depend on the local climate. It will also depend on the desired identity for the cheese. For instance, Park Farm Exmoor produced using summer milk has a different texture to that produced using creamier winter milk. Sometimes two sets of dates are given by the producers for maturity: the point at which cheese is sold to factors, and the length of time the farm matures a cheese for direct sale to customers.

The second list is of cheeses that received a number of nominations, but not a clear majority.

Two significant facts emerge from the results. The first is the very high percentage of cheeses made with unpasteurised milks that have come through – 21 out of 26. Secondly, the very poor showing of Dairy Crest cheeses – only one cheese in the premier list. Not all the cheeses listed are widely available, though many of the restaurants listed in the *Guide* do offer at least one or two. By their nature, they are not produced for nationwide distribution.

Cow's milk cheese

Bonchester

Easter Weens Bonchester Cheese
Bonchester Bridge, Nr Hawick, Roxburghshire TD9 8JQ

CHEESEMAKERS: John Curtis and Marjory Young

Jersey cows, grazing on the pastures of the River Rule, provide all of the milk, which is best in the summer. Each week, up to 210kg are made in 10oz and 3½oz sizes. It is matured until soft, and left until almost runny for a mature taste. Shops want a shelf life of about four weeks at 4°C. The process is a variation on the Camembert method, made daily from March until December. The key features are: the area is exceptionally good for livestock production; Jersey milk is very rich in solids; cheese milk is not stored, except the evening milk which is chilled and kept overnight; the hygiene quality is very high. Bonchester is best when it has softened and gone a deep cream colour almost to the middle. This happens in a fridge (at 4°C) in about four or five weeks, or in a room (at 15°C) in about three or four days, or variations between the two. It has a stronger flavour than Brie or Camembert and is delicious spread on fresh bread or with Scottish oatcakes. John Curtis started in 1980 with two Jersey cows and has slowly improved the quality and therefore the quantity of production since then. In 1987, he transferred to a new dairy and employed Marjory Young as full-time cheesemaker and relief milker. They will have 12 cows in 1988 and hope to work up to a maximum of 18.

Caerphilly

Caws Cenarth Caerphilly

Fferm Glyneithinog, Pontseli, Boncath SA37 0LH

CHEESEMAKER: Mrs Adams

Pedigree Friesian and Holstein cows, grazing on meadow pasture, provide 25% of the milk used. A maximum of 800lb is produced each week in 1lb, 2lb, 6lb and 10lb wheels. It is normally matured for one month, or for three months for a mature taste. The cheese has a fresh, clean flavour, with a creamy aftertaste. The unique flavour is due to storing it for a month before sending it to the supplier, and to the exclusive use of their own cows' milk. Mrs Adams had been making cheese for family and friends for 15 years before the milk quota was introduced in April 1984. She then decided to try and make it into a money-making operation and subsequently won £5,000 for the best food-related idea in a competition sponsored by Barclays Bank.

Walnut Tree Farm Caerphilly

Heath House, Wedmore, Somerset BS28 4UJ

CHEESEMAKER: C. Duckett

Friesian cows grazing on meadow and Somerset Levels moorland provide all of the milk. Up to 2,000lb is made up each week in 3lb, 4lb and 9lb sizes. It is normally matured for 10 days, 30 days for a mature taste and seven days by the farm. The Caerphilly is made in the traditional way using vegetarian rennet. The curd is cut with a hand knife 45 minutes after renneting, then scalded to 93°F. After approximately 45 minutes hand stirring, the whey is drawn off. The curd is cut several times with a hand-held knife, finishing with approximately one-inch cubes. Salt is then mixed in and the curd is placed in moulds. Here it is lightly pressed for half an hour then turned and salted before being pressed again until the next day. The cheese is then placed in a brine bath for 24 hours. It has a mild and creamy flavour with a slightly acidic background, slightly moist with an open texture but not crumbly. Flavour develops for up to two months. Caerphilly has been made on this farm for three generations, originally relying on sales to South Wales. The renewed interest in traditional farmhouse cheese has opened up markets all over the country with much of the production (doubled over the last three years) going to London.

Cheddar

Dairy Crest Cheddar

Sturminster Newton Creamery, Station Road, Sturminster Newton, Dorset DT10 1BD

CHEESEMAKERS: Dairy Crest Foods

The pasteurised milk is collected from different farms. Cheeses are produced in 6kg, 20kg and 27kg sizes. The cheese is matured according to customer specification, which can be up to 10 months. Cheddar takes its name from the famous gorge close to the

Mendip Hills and was first recorded as being made in Somerset in the early sixteenth century. Elizabeth I ate Cheddar at banquets. In this country two out of every three pounds of cheese bought are Cheddar. Mild Cheddar has a mellow flavour and is about three to five months old. 'Cheddar should always have a close texture with no signs of oiliness or excessive dryness. It should be wrapped in cling-film or put in a closed container to prevent picking up the odours of other food.'

Hamwood Farm Unpasteurised Traditional Farmhouse Cheddar

Trull, Taunton, Somerset TA3 7NX

CHEESEMAKERS: H. and E. J. Grant

Friesian cows grazing on meadow and long-term leys provide all of the milk except during August. It is at its best from December to April. Up to 2 1/2 tonnes are made each week in 56lb cylinders. It is matured for nine to twelve months. The cheese is stored on wooden shelves for nine months at 52°F. 'It should be firm and nutty and free of mould penetration.' Mr Grant's father was a cheesemaker who went into farming. He moved to the present farm 36 years ago and has expanded gradually since.

Keen's (or Moorhayes) Cheddar

Moorhayes Farm, Verrington Lane, Wincanton, Somerset BA9 8JR

CHEESEMAKER: Jack Parsons

Friesian cows provide all of the milk, which is at its best in May and June. Up to 64 cheeses of 26kg are produced each week, also in 7lb sizes. It is normally matured for eight months, or twelve months for a mature taste, although they also have older cheese available. The cheese is made in the traditional way from natural milk with no colouring or additives. It is drained on wooden racks between cheese muslin, pressed in cylindrical moulds for three days and then cloth bound and matured. The cheese is well matured and ripened with a full, nutty flavour. It is close-textured, creamy and a natural yellow, with a fine rind. 'Cheese has always been made on Moorhayes Farm and fits into the natural farming cycle of cows, milk, cheese and whey, pigs, manure, soil, grass and cows again.'

Manor Farm Cheddar

North Cadbury, Nr Yeovil, Somerset BA22 7DW

CHEESEMAKERS: J. A. & E. Montgomery Ltd

Milk is provided by a Friesian herd, a selected breeding for high-protein milk of consistent quality. The cheese is made only from their own farm milk. The herd grazes mostly on old meadow pasture and parkland but there is some high-quality sown grass for hay and silage for winter feed. The high-yielding cows in early lactation receive a balanced ration of special cake including minerals and vitamins. Cheese is made every day. It is neither pasteurised nor heat-treated before cheesemaking. The starter used is constantly renewed. The rennet is usually of animal origin. In the process of making the cheese, the milk is gently heated to a precise temperature and when the whey is separated from the curd it is still hot. Approximately 1 3/4lb of salt to 100 gallons of milk will make 100lb of cheese. The fat in the milk varies from 3.8 per cent to 4.2 per cent. The cheese is pressed starting at 20lb per sq inch increasing to 80lb on the third day in the press. When necessary, a weighted quantity of pure dried skimmed-milk powder is included to bring the protein and fat content of the milk into proper balance. Up to 3,500lb is made each week, in 50–55lb cylindricals) and some 8–9lb truckles. The cheese is normally 9–12 months old when sold at maturity, with the oldest having the strongest flavour. During the evening's milking the milk passes by stainless steel piping from the milking parlour through a pre-cooled water-plate-type cooler in the dairy to the cheese vat in the making room. At the morning's milking the milk enters the vat uncooled and, mixed with the overnight milk, is immediately gently heated to 87°F for the prepared starter to be added and later the rennet. The milk is gently agitated by a paddle to prevent the curds settling too quickly to the bottom of the 500-gallon vat. The process is the traditional one for West Country Cheddar. The 'cheddaring' is done on the cooler tray until the moisture content is reduced, and the required solidity of the curd attained by constant hand stacking and restacking of the increasingly resilient slabs of folded curd. When the acidity reaches the required figure the curd is milled with a peg-type mill and the salt added, soon to be filled into the metal moulds ready for the initial pressing to complete the first day's work. The next day the cheeses are bumped out of the moulds to be 'bathed'. This is the process of dipping the cheese into hot water for a minute to form the 'rind' that will prevent mould penetration. They are then rubbed with lard to keep the skins in good condition under the banding of cheese cloth, which keeps the cheese in shape throughout storage until maturity. It is then returned to the moulds for pressing at increased pressure from the self-adjusting compressed air rams for a further day. 'Cheese is made as it has been for more than a century, the only changes have been in the use of electricity to power the paddle in the vat, the peg mill and the press, all formerly done by hand. It has been done on this farm for more than half a century.'

Quicke's Traditional Extra Mature Cheddar

Home Farm, Newton St Cyres, Exeter EX5 5BT

CHEESEMAKER: Barry Rowe

Friesian and Holstein cows provide all the milk, which is judged to be at its best in October when the weather is not too hot but the cows are still eating grass. The milk is pasteurised. 600lb is made up each week in 56lb sizes. It is matured for 15–18 months.

Tyn Grug Farmhouse Cheddar

Goetre Isaf Farm, Goetre Isaf, Bettws Bledrws, Lampeter, Dyfed SA48 8NP

CHEESEMAKERS: Dougal and Alexandra Campbell

A mixed herd of Friesians, Ayrshires and Channel Islands cows provide the milk, which is at its best from May to July. Up to 5cwt is made up each week in 6lb, 18lb and 36lb sizes. It is normally matured for three to four weeks, or six to eight weeks for a mature taste. The cheese is a slightly different type of unpasteurised farmhouse Cheddar, with a higher than average fat content. It is best at six to eight weeks, producing full flavour rather than high acidity. Cheeses are not bandaged, but rinded naturally, then scrubbed clean before use. Dougal and Alexandra Campbell came into farmhouse cheesemaking in West Wales in 1977, after learning the craft in Switzerland from an old-fashioned cheesemaker. They started with a smallholding and have recently moved to a 120-acre dairy farm to be able to farm organically as well as increase production over the next few years.

Cheshire

Appleby's Hawkstone Cheshire

Hawkstone Abbey Farm, Broadhay, Lower Heath, Prees, Whitchurch, Shropshire

CHEESEMAKER: Mrs Appleby

Friesian cows provide half of the total milk output. Up to 4,500lb is made each week in $2^{3}/_{4}$lb, 17lb and 50lb sizes. It is normally matured for five to six weeks, or twelve weeks for a mature taste, and from twelve weeks to a year at the farm. The milk from the Appleby herd arrives in the cheese dairy fresh from the cows. After the starter culture is added, the process of milk into junket into curd into cheese moves along slowly, being watched and tested by the cheesemaker. When it reaches its final stages the whey is drawn off and salt added to the curd. The cheese is then put into the moulds and taken into the press room. Here is goes into the original screw presses where it remains under pressure for two days. On the third day it is cloth bound and put on the shelf to mature. After five weeks, when each day it is tested for quality, some is selected for customers, and some remains on the shelf to mature for up to twelve months. Cheshire cheese in recent years has been bought at a very young age, possibly only two to three weeks old. A good Cheshire has a lovely mellow flavour at five to six weeks. It should be moist, but not wet with excess whey trapped in its wrapping. The texture should be slightly crumbly, but not so it falls into pieces as you take it out of its pack. After six weeks, if kept in storage in its cloth-bound state, Cheshire will continue to mature and develop more taste. A good flavour is reached at twelve weeks but for a stronger cheese keep for up to a year. The Applebys are a traditional cheesemaking family. Cheese has been made at Hawkstone Abbey Farm for over 40 years. The cheese is still hand-made in the same way. The cheese is marketed by the family, ensuring the cheese reaches the customer in the best possible condition. Selection for different customers' markets takes place depending on maturity required.

Hinton Bank Farm Blue Cheshire

Whitchurch, Shropshire SY13 4HB

CHEESEMAKERS: Hutchinson Smith & Son

Originally Shorthorn cows provided all the milk but they are joined now by Holstein and Friesian herds. Cheeses are produced in 8kg and 2kg sizes. Most customers prefer them to be matured for six to eight weeks; this is done on the farm. Blue Cheshire is an open-textured Cheshire. It will remain a Cheshire until pricked with stainless steel needles. Once the air is allowed to penetrate the matured skin, the mould begins to grow. It is best eaten at six to ten weeks but this depends on individual taste. It should be marbled in appearance. Geoffrey Hutchinson (no relation) sought out Cheshire that was blueing 'naturally' and made a business of it. He died in the early 1960s. The Milk Marketing Board asked Hutchinson Smith to try to make Blue Cheshire intentionally, which had never been done. After about two years they had a basic formula and after 10 years they were supplying Sainsbury's. They are to date the only commercial makers of Blue Cheshire.

Cornish Yarg

Lynher Valley Dairy Cornish Yarg

Netherton Farm, Upton Cross, Liskeard, Cornwall PL14 5BD

CHEESEMAKER: Katharine Piggot

Friesian and Holstein cows provide all the milk, which is judged to be at its best in high summer, because of the calving pattern and quality of pasture. Up to 400lb is made up each week, in 2lb and 7lb sizes. It is normally matured for four weeks, up to six weeks for a mature taste and two weeks at the farm. Each morning, as milking is concluded, milk is drawn directly from the dairy to the cheese room, pasteurised and gently stirred in the vats with starter culture at blood heat. Vegetarian rennet is added later, after which the curd is cut and whey drained. After further hand cutting and turning, the curd is placed in cloth-lined moulds and pressed overnight before immersion in brine baths. Cheeses are then coated with nettle leaves and removed to the maturing room for daily turning as they ripen. The pattern of mould growth on the nettle leaves gives this cheese its obvious identity. As it ripens, a creamy layer develops underneath, while the centre of the cheese retains its moist, crumbly and fresh tasting characteristics. It should reach its peak of flavour before the nettle leaves begin to discolour, but it is often preferred younger. With increasing economic pressures on them as dairy farmers, culminating in the quota regime imposed by the EEC, Lynher Dairy began pasteurising milk for bottling in 1981, and added the cheese venture 2½ years later. It is a family dairy farm, with two neighbouring herds on the Duchy of Cornwall estate.

Double Gloucester

Appleby's Double Gloucester

Hawkstone Abbey Farm, Broadhay, Lower Heath, Prees, Whitchurch, Shropshire

CHEESEMAKER: Mrs Appleby

Friesian cows provide all the milk for the cheese. 730lb is made up each week, in 4lb, 15lb and 30lb sizes. It is normally matured for three months, six months for a mature taste and a minimum of six to eight months at the farm. The cheese is made in the traditional way, by hand. The cheeses are cloth-bound and put on the shelf for maturing. Here they are turned and rubbed regularly to help the maturing process. This cloth-binding helps the cheese to breathe and go on maturing and developing a good flavour for several months.

Exmoor

Park Farm Exmoor

Park Farm, Umberleigh, North Devon EX37 9DD

CHEESEMAKERS: P. J. and H. Charnley

Jersey cows, grazing on meadow, hillside, wild flowers and watermeadow (untreated for 15 years) provide all the milk. The richer winter milk allows this cheese to mature properly. Up to 300lb is made up each week in 4lb wheels. It is matured for a minimum of four weeks at the farm, and eight weeks for a mature taste. Exmoor came about by the Charnleys' use of old recipes and equipment, trying to see what the original method of the cheesemakers might have been, since they must have been working with animals that had lower milk yields and possibly higher butter fats than modern animals. They have tried to respect traditional recipes, but say they interpret them. The cheese is made strictly within English traditions but is softer and richer than usual modern cheeses. Every attempt is made to preserve the cream within the cheese so that the end result is a 'quiet, melting character'. The skin should be opaque, clean and dusty white. When the cheese is at its best is very much a matter of personal taste.

Lancashire

Lancashire Farmhouse Cheese

Lower Barker Farm, Inglewhite, Preston, Lancashire PR3 2LJ

CHEESEMAKER: Mrs J. M. Butler

Friesian cows grazing on meadow provide all the milk. Up to 4 tonnes is made up each week in 3lb, 20lb and 40lb sizes. It is normally matured for two months, six months for a mature taste and three months at the farm. A natural starter is added to ripen the clean whole milk. Then rennet is added to set the milk and produce curds and whey. Whey is extracted as acidity develops and curd is pressed to form cylindrical cheese. All cheeses are individually bandaged and waxed or greased to form rind. Lancashire Farmhouse cheese should be of a pale creamy colour and buttery with a crumbly texture. It is best eaten when matured for approximately two months. Mrs Butler started cheesemaking in October 1969, making 100 gallons per day. She has increased to 1,100 gallons per day at present. New equipment is currently being installed to further increase production in order to supply the demand.

Llanboidy

Llanboidy Farm Cheese

Cilawen Uchaf Farm, Login, Whitland, Dyfed SA34 0TJ

CHEESEMAKERS: Chris Avieyard and Sue Jones

Red Polls provide all the milk, at its best from July to November when the cows graze spring and summer pastures. A quantity of 10lb wheels are made up each week. They mature normally for eight weeks, up to eleven months for a mature taste, and up to eight weeks at the farm. Llanboidy Farm Cheese is an old-style Welsh farmhouse cheese. It is hand made, pressed and matured in the traditional way. Red Poll cows were selected not for the quantity of milk they produce but for the quality. The cows graze traditional pastures and the fields are fertilised organically.

Llangloffan

Llangloffan Farmhouse Cheese

Llangloffan Farm, Llangloffan, Castle Morris, Haverfordwest, Dyfed SA62 5ET

CHEESEMAKER: Leon Downey

A pedigree Jersey herd grazing on permanent meadow (Soil Association Symbol of Organic Quality) provides all of the milk: it is not pasteurised or heat treated. The cheese is only made from April to December when the cows are on grass. Up to 7cwt is made each week in 4lb, 9lb, 20lb and 30lb cheeses. It is normally matured for six weeks, three months for a mature taste. Llangloffan is made from evening and morning milk. A starter bacteria is added to the unpasteurised milk and rennetting takes place about 1¼ hours later. The curd is cut with vertical and horizontal curd knives. This is followed by hand stirring the curds and whey, and at the same time the curd is textured by breaking by hand and eventually milled. 'We feel very strongly that real farmhouse cheese can only be made on the farm. The cheesemaker needs to have experience of the cows, their eating habits, a thorough knowledge and control of hygiene conditions in the cowshed as well as the cheesemaking room. If this is carried out immaculately, problems in cheesemaking are greatly reduced.' As soon as the cheeses are removed from the presses to the cheese store they are turned and hand rubbed every day for the following six weeks. Thereafter, they are turned once a day. The cheese develops a natural rind. The nearest comparable cheese would be the old-fashioned creamy Cheshire, not quite as dry and being of a tighter texture. The more mature cheese develops quite a characteristic tang. Occasionally Llangloffan cheeses will develop a natural blueing. When the Downeys first arrived in West Wales 11 years ago, cheesemaking was non-existent. They started in a very small way, 'one cow, a book and a bucket'. They soon realised that there was a very rewarding opportunity in front of them and over the following years developed Llangloffan as a tourist attraction incorporating the farm and cheesemaking. They are now milking 18 cows and making cheese in a model dairy. They sell 80 per cent of the cheese from their own shop and supply around 35 specialist cheese shops dotted about Great Britain.

Stilton

Colston Bassett and District Dairy Stilton

Colston Bassett, Nottingham NG12 3FN

CHEESEMAKER: E. T. Wagstaff

Milk is provided by a farmers' co-operative of five farms from Friesian cows grazing on meadow pasture. Its quality is highest in the summer when grass is at its best. Up to 6½ tonnes of cheese is made up each week in 7½kg and 2½kg sizes. It is

matured normally for 10 weeks, or 12 weeks for a more mature taste. The cheeses are produced from unpasteurised milk delivered to the dairy by farmers who run the co-operative. It is heated to 85°F in vats and a starter culture is added and coagulated with rennet. The cheese is cut 70 minutes after clotting and the whey and curds are allowed to separate for 2$^1/_2$ hours. The curds are ladled into shallow trays called curd coolers.The following morning the curds are milled, salted and mixed before being placed in the mould. The cheese is turned every day for five days after which the mould is removed, smoothed with a knife and replaced in the mould for one more day, with a muslin cheese cloth around it. Cheeses are kept in a cool store for three weeks and pierced by machine at five to six weeks. It is ready for sale four weeks after piercing. Blue mould-ripened cheese is also ripened by the action of enzymes and bacteria creating blue veins in creamy white curd. The flavour of a ripe Stilton should not leave an after-taste in the mouth when swallowed. It is at its peak when cheese sticks to the knife when being served. It should not be crumbly. The cheese factory was built by farmers in 1912. Stilton cheeses previously were produced in the local farmhouses during the summer months. Stiltons have been made throughout the year since the early 1930s. The majority of the produce is marketed to hotels, restaurants and higher class retail outlets.

Sussex Farmhouse

Castle Hill Sussex Farmhouse

Rotherfield, Crowborough, Sussex TN6 3RR

CHEESEMAKER: David Doble

Friesian cows provide 80 per cent of the milk which is at its best during spring and summer when grass quality is optimum. Up to 900lb is made up each week in 8–10lb wheels and 4$^1/_4$lb truckles. It is matured for seven weeks normally and four months for a mature taste. The farm matures it for seven to eight weeks. A starter culture is added followed by vegetarian rennet. It is then scalded, pitched, textured, milled, salted, put into moulds and pressed. It is a full fat hard cheese from their own herd milk which is unpasteurised. It has a smooth firm texture with a clean sharp lingering flavour. It ripens naturally in controlled temperature and humidity. At its peak at eight weeks. David Doble came into the cheese business as result of quotas and effluent problems. The business has developed steadily over two years, from 50 gallons twice a week to 160 gallons five days a week.

Goat's milk cheese

Appleby's Hawkstone Goat

Hawkstone Abbey Farm
Broadhay, Lower Heath, Prees, Whitchurch, Shropshire

CHEESEMAKER: Mrs Appleby

Goats of all varieties provide the milk which is good all year round. Each week, 150lb is made up in 7lb and 10lb sizes. The cheese is normally matured for one month, two months for a mature taste. It is traditional hand-made cloth-bound cheese, naturally matured on the shelf at the farm for up to three months. It is pressed hard, with a mild flavour when eaten young developing in maturity to a mellow tasty cheese.

Harbourne Blue

Lower Sharpham Barton Harbourne Blue
Ashprington, Totnes, Devon TQ9 7DX

CHEESEMAKER: Robin Congdon

Various breeds of goat provide the milk. They graze on meadow pasture where no artificial fertilisers are used. Up to 30 6lb cheeses are made up each week. It is normally matured from four to six months at the farm. The starter, blue-mould culture and rennet are added to warm milk. The curd is cut and stirred for about two hours and then ladled into moulds. It is turned over two days, salted over four days, spiked to allow blue mould to develop and the cheese is matured until blue veins are well developed and the taste is right. Harbourne Blue is a blue-moulded, full-fat cheese weighing 6lb. There is naturally some seasonal variation but it's not particularly marked. The taste is not usually especially strong.

Mendip

Sleight Farm Mendip
Timsbury, Bath, Avon BA3 1HN

CHEESEMAKER: M. Holbrook

The milk is judged to be at its best in spring and autumn since the higher fat and solid content of milk produces a better textured cheese. The cheeses are made in 4–5lb sizes. It is normally matured for two months and six months for a mature taste. The milk is heated to 85°F and starter is added, followed by rennet after a ripening period. Batches of between 50 and 150 gallons are usually processed. When the curd has been cut (after an interval of approximately 1½ hours) a proportion of whey is drawn off, then hot water is added to cook the curd. When the curd is ready, and the temperature is 95°F, the curd is taken directly from the whey and put into basket-shaped moulds. Here the cheeses are turned frequently during the first

24 hours. After about two days, the cheeses are put in brine for 24 hours and then they are oiled. Although not pressed, Mendip has a firm but creamy texture with a unique nutty (but not acid) flavour. The oiled rind has a golden appearance during the summer months.

Ewe's milk cheese

Barac

Windyknowe Farm Barac
Annan, Dumfriesshire DG12 5LN

CHEESEMAKER: Carol Neilson

British Friesland sheep provide 95 per cent of the milk which is best in autumn when the weeds and blackberries in the pasture enhance the flavour. Up to 220lb is made each week in 3lb and 1¼lb sizes. It is matured normally for three months, five months for a mature taste and it is sold as mature at the farm. The milk is warmed, ripened, rennetted. After 40–45 minutes the curd is cut, warmed with gentle stirring, settled, drained, allowed to coagulate, salted, put into hoops and pressed. Pressure is increased gradually to 40lb. It is taken out of presses, air-dried, waxed lightly and put to mature. It is turned daily for two weeks then weekly to maturation. The cheese ripens slowly, developing an almost malty taste. Spring and early summer cheeses are clean, acidic, fresh tasting, even at one year, compared to autumn cheeses, which are fuller, rounder and develop for up to two years. Variation is due to the balance of grasses in pasture with the season. The business started in 1980 as the third sheep's milk cheese producer in the UK. There is gradual expansion as the market becomes more aware of the availability of UK specialist cheeses.

Beenleigh Blue

Lower Sharpham Barton Beenleigh Blue
Ashprington, Totnes, Devon TQ9 7DX

CHEESEMAKER: Robin Congdon

Friesland x Dorset and Friesland sheep provide the milk which is at its best in June when there is the greatest variety of herbage in the pasture. Up to 80 6lb cheeses are made each week. The cheese is matured for five to eight months at the farm. Starter, blue mould and rennet are added to the warm milk. The curd is cut and stirred for 1½ hours and then scooped into moulds where they drain with frequent turning for two days. The surface is salted over four days, then spiked to allow air through. Beenleigh Blue is a full-fat blue ewe's milk cheese. Its character changes considerably over the making period (mid-April to August) dependent on many things – pasture, temperature, staged ewes' lactation etc. At the beginning of the season (September), the cheese has a clean white background, is slightly crumbly and has a fairly mild taste. As the ripening progresses the flavour intensifies and becomes more 'sleepy' until in March the cheese is decidedly strong, of an ivory hue and a creamier texture. It is often at its best around Christmas. Not an easy cheese to handle, it must be kept refrigerated once mature. The cooler it's kept, the longer it will keep. The business started with a smallholding and 30 ewes in 1976. The milk was processed into yoghurt and yoghurt cheese (Labna). Beenleigh Blue developed in 1980 when sheep were moved to a larger holding. In 1983, they moved to the above farm of 120 acres, with sheep numbers up to 200 where they also developed Harbourne Blue, a similar cheese made from goats' milk.They have their own cheese shop in Totnes now and sell a range of British farm-made cheeses, yoghurts and ice-cream.

Lanark Blue

Ogscastle Lanark Blue

Carnwath, Lanarkshire ML11 8NE

CHEESEMAKER: H. J. Errington

Dorset x Friesland and Greyface x Friesland sheep grazing on hillside pasture (with abundant wild white clover) provide the milk. Midsummer grass is best for flavour (without the fat/protein ratio upset which is associated with spring/early summer grass). Up to 390kg is made each week in 2½–3kg cheeses. It is normally matured for three months. The process is very similar to the Roquefort recipe. The milk is warmed and starter and penicillin mould suspension added. At the correct acidity the rennet is added. When the coagulum (curd) is at the correct degree of firmness, the curd is cut with a sharp knife into 1-inch cubes. The whey is drained, the curd is filled into moulds (no pressing), and the cheese is brined twice, then dry salted and pierced. It spends three months in the curing room at 8–10°C and 95 per cent humidity where it is turned daily. The cheese is semi-hard with no rind and wrapped in foil. When ripe, it is slightly creamy, the curd is white and there is an even (but not dense) blue mould throughout the cheese. There is an excellent clean aftertaste and sometimes a slightly nutty flavour. These hill farmers became worried about the viability of their sheep farming about five years ago. At the same time, they believed there was a gap in the market for a Roquefort type cheese with less 'bite'. They started with 40 ewes, now have 500 milking, and employ seven staff full-time. Their cheesemaker has 20 years' experience.

Redesdale Ewe

Redesdale Sheep Dairy

Soppitt Farm, Otterburn, Newcastle upon Tyne NE19 1AF

CHEESEMAKER: Mr Robertson

Friesland ewes, grazing on meadow, provide all the milk which is at its best in mid-summer since the milk tends to get heavier later on in the year. Up to 80kg is made up each week in ½kg and 2–2½kg round wheels. The cheese is sweet and white with a clean rind. It has a slightly Emmenthally taste. Mr Robertson started the business out of curiosity. He also makes three kinds of cows' cheese although he no longer makes Blue Wensleydale. He has many visitors to the farm.

Also well-thought-of . . .

Cow's milk cheese

Botton

Botton Village Creamery
Danby, North Yorkshire

Cheddar

Horlicks
Ilminster, Somerset

W. H. Longman & Sons
(Farmhouse Cheesemakers) Ltd
North Leaze Farm, North Cadbury,
Yeovil, Somerset BA22 7BD

Newton Farm
West Pennard, Glastonbury,
Somerset

Cotherstone

Teesdale Supply Stores
The Post Office, Main Street,
Cotherstone, Barnard Castle,
Co Durham DL12 9PG

Devon Garland

Park Farm
Umberleigh, North Devon
EX37 9DD

Double Gloucester

J. C. Quick & Partners
Woodley, Newton St Cyres, Exeter
EX5 5BT

Gospel Green

Gospel Green Cottage
Gospel Green, W Sussex
GH27 3BH

Creamery Lancashire

Milk Marketing Board Creamery
Inglewhite Road, Longridge,
Lancashire

Lancashire

Dew Lay Products
Green Lane West, Cabus, Garstang,
Lancashire PR3 1NJ

Singleton's Dairy
Mill Farm, Preston Road, Longridge,
Lancashire PR3 3AN

Leicester

Mollington Farmhouse
Cheese Co Ltd
Grange Farm, Great Mollington,
Chester CH1 6NP

Pantyllyn

Pantyllyn
Blaenycoed, Carmarthen, Dyfed
SA33 6HB

Sage Derby

Mollington Farmhouse
Cheese Co Ltd
Grange Farm, Great Mollington,
Chester CH1 6NP

Shropshire Blue

Colston Bassett and District Dairy
Colston Bassett, Nottingham
NG12 3FN

Single Gloucester

Laurel Farm
Dymock, Gloucestershire GL18 2DP

Somerset Brie

Lubborn Cheese Ltd
North Street, Crewkerne, Somerset
TA18 7AS

Stilton

Dairy Crest
Hartington Creamery, Hartington, Buxton, Derbyshire

Express Dairies (Tuxford & Tebbitt)
Thorpe End, Melton Mowbray, Leicestershire

Long Clawson Dairy Ltd
Long Clawson, Melton Mowbray, Leicestershire, LE14 4PJ

Teifi Cheese

Glynhynod
Ffostrasol, Llandysul, Dyfed SA44 5JY

Wensleydale

Wensleydale Creameries
Gayle Lane, Hawes, North Yorkshire

Goat's milk cheese

Capricorn English Goats Cheese

North Street, Crewkerne, Somerset TA18 7AS

Ribblesdale

Ashes Farm
Horton-in-Ribblesdale, Settle, North Yorks BD24 0JB

Ewe's milk cheese

Acorn

Little Acorn Products
Mesem Fach Farm, Bethania, Nr Llanon, Dyfed SY23 5NL

Spenwood

Village Maid
22 The Square, Spencers Wood, Reading RG7 1BS

Jurors

James Aldridge, member, Guilde de Fromage
Stephen Bull, Culinary Institute, ex-chef/proprietor of Lichfield's, Richmond
Sue Cloke, former General Manager of Paxton & Whitfield Ltd
Henrietta Green, Editor of *British Food Finds* and *RAC Food Routes*
Juliet Harbutt, Jeroboams, London, member, Guilde de Fromage Prud'homme
Randolph Hodgson, Neal's Yard Dairy, London
Jim Ormiston, Chief Technical Officer of Creamery Proprietors' Association Grading Service
Ken Raine, Consultant to National Dairy Council
Hugh Rance, Wells Stores, Streatley
Eurwen Richards, Quality Assurance Manager, Dairy Crest Foods

Wines

Sweet things

Muscat de Beaumes de Venise has led the fashion for sweet white wines to accompany desserts on many restaurant wine lists. Former Which? Wine Guide *editor* Kathryn McWhirter *offers some other suggestions*

'Spot the sweet wine' is an irritating game restaurateurs seem to have cooked up to enliven our last moments in their company. So often, on the finest or the simplest of wine lists, the sweet wines are buried amongst the dry whites, sometimes with no indication that they are sweet at all. Wine buffs might sniff out the Cadillac or the Australian Flora, but to most of the world they might just as well be large American limousines, margarine – or dry white wines. How much easier to be presented with a separate list of sweet wines, or at least sweet extracts from the list on a final page.

Why sweet?

The fine sweet wines of the world are sweet for three main reasons: botrytis, concentration and fortification, and which route they took very much affects their flavour. *Botrytis cinerea* (a mixture of Greek and Latin meaning 'ashen bunch of grapes') or 'noble rot' is an evil-looking grey-brown mould that attacks ripe grapes in certain climatic conditions, concentrating sugars, acids and other components of the grape, while bringing about chemical changes that make the juice and resulting wine unctuous, honeyed and pungently delicious.

The necessary mist and autumn warmth come together in very few parts of the world. The famous regions producing botrytised wines are Sauternes, Barsac and a few other parts of the Bordeaux region, the Layon and Aubance valleys and Vouvray in the Loire, Germany, Austria and Tokay in Hungary, but Alsace produces a little, and Australia and California now turn out a few, sometimes even spraying botrytis cultures on to the grapes if nature fails to do its stuff. In exceptional years, 'noble rot' can even strike in other places. Even Chardonnay grapes in Burgundy grew 'noble rot' in the extraordinarily hot and humid 1983 vintage (Chardonnay skins are usually too thick for the mould to get a hold) and a few restaurant wine lists currently offer the fascinating rarity, Mâcon-Clessé Cuvée Spéciale Botrytis '83 from the cellars of Jean Thévenet.

Even regions such as Sauternes, renowned for botrytised wines, can't make them every year. Some years are too hot and dry, some not hot enough, and sometimes it seems wise to pick before the mould appears, pre-empting bad weather. But in hot years, fine Sauternes or German wine can still be made by the drying effect of sun on grapes that are left late in the season on the vines. The flavours may still be intense and concentrated, but they will lack the extra pungent dimension of the 'rotten' years.

A new process, 'cryoextraction', used in some châteaux in Sauternes, helps the concentration along by freezing the grapes and then pressing out only the sweetest part of the juice. Vin de Paille in the Jura and Vin Santo in Italy are made from grapes that have been cut and then dried outside in the sun, or in an airy attic on straw mats, or have had their stems twisted on the vine to encourage them to turn to raisins.

Sweet fortified wines, generally made from the super-sweet, super-grapey Muscat, are ultra-sweet because alcohol is added to stun the yeasts part way through fermentation, before all the grape sugar has been turned to alcohol.

Sweet selection

Alsace

Most Alsace wines can be reliably assumed to be dry, but some producers, in hot years, make a fairly sweet Vendange Tardive (Late Harvest). Confusingly, some Vendanges Tardives are bone dry, and the label may give no clue as to whether the wine is sweet or dry. The really sweet wines of Alsace, concentrated by botrytis, are called Sélection de Grains Nobles, an official category only since 1983, though Hugel were making their own version long before that. Sweet Vendange Tardive wines, usually flowery-fragrant and fairly alcoholic, are only sufficiently sweet to accompany fruit, but Sélections de Grains Nobles can cope with intensely sweet dishes. Alsace's best ripeners are the soft, spicy Gewürztraminer, meaty-spicy Pinot Gris (Tokay d'Alsace) and sharp, flowery Riesling, and these are the producers of sweet wines. Rieslings, with their high acidity, make the best partners for most fruits. The years to go for are super-ripe '83s and rich, very mature '76s.

Loire

Loire wines often offer the best value at the sweet end of restaurant wine lists – even fine, old vintages back as far as the '40s and '50s can be remarkably cheap. All the sweet wines of the Loire are made from the Chenin Blanc grape, which can make stunning, honeyed yet piercingly fresh sweet wines, overlaid in the best years by the pungent aromas of botrytis. The *moelleux* (sweet) wines are the ones to look for – several of the Loire's sweet wine-making areas make medium or dry wines in lesser years, or with less ripe grapes. Perhaps most commonly found in restaurants is Vouvray, from Touraine, with high acidity and often a clove-like spiciness superimposed on the honeyed flavour of the Chenin and the pungency of botrytis. Vouvrays need sharp food – containing lemon juice or acid fruits – to partner their high acidity. Montlouis is much rarer, similar to Vouvray but from just across the river. The finest sweet Loires are from Anjou, and more particularly from the Coteaux du Layon, which is also renowned for its botrytis. Within this area, Bonnezeaux and Quarts de Chaume are especially luscious and complex. Layons tend to be less tart than Vouvrays, but they still have piercingly fresh acidity along with honeyed, appley and botrytised flavours, becoming much more intensely honeyed as they age. They are also good partners for fruit puddings and desserts, though they are *really* sweet only in the best years. In a nearby valley, Coteaux de l'Aubance makes wine in a similar style, much less rich, cheaper still, but a rare find on a British restaurant list. A much more common bargain is Anjou Moelleux from Moulin Touchais, whose cellar of old vintages was sold to the British trade for give-away prices a few years ago. These are botrytised wines grown outside botrytis's usual Loire haunts, delicious, mature and usually excellent value. Best years for sweet Loires are '76, '69, '64, '61 and the wonderful '59; '78, '75 and '67 were good light vintages.

Bordeaux

Bordeaux has a number of lesser sweet wine appellations – light-bodied Cadillac, Cérons and Graves Supérieures (of which some is dry), and sweeter, richer Loupiac and Ste-Croix-du-Mont – as well as the famous pair, Sauternes and Barsac. Monbazillac, in Bergerac, south-east of Bordeaux, produces sweet wines in a similiar style, often with a slightly resiny flavour. The lesser appellations are generally less sweet than most Sauternes, and they rarely have much if any botrytis flavour, since the prices they fetch are so low that it's not worth their producers' leaving the grapes on the vines to rot (these areas are in any case less prone to botrytis). The main grape is the same, however, the rich-flavoured Sémillon, helped generally by a little Sauvignon and perhaps some Muscadelle. Bordeaux sweet whites are rounder, richer and less acidic than those from the Loire, but in 'nobly rotten' years, the botrytis ensures that they have fresh acidity, too, as well as a spicy-musky, nutty, honeyed flavour. Even Sauternes and Barsac vary enormously in quality and concentration, hardly surprising when prices range from very low for basic, generic Sauternes, blended by merchants, to extremely expensive for top châteaux, culminating in Yquem. Sweet Bordeaux is a wonderful match for peaches, and a good Sauternes or Barsac is perfect with crème brûlée. The Sauternais drink it with foie gras, and the traditional match with Roquefort works well, but it's excellent also with smoked cheeses, and good with Cheddar. Only the better Sauternes and Barsacs will mature for more than a few years. The cheaper ones, like all the lesser appellations listed above, are best drunk within their first six years or sooner. Best of the cheaper Bordeaux for drinking now are '83 and '86. In the better wines, look for luscious '76, '75, '71, '70, superb '69s with loads of botrytis flavour, and glorious '67s.

Germany

German wines are categorised according to sweetness, and only the sweetest, Beerenauslesen and Trockenbeerenauslesen, are sweet enough to partner most puddings and desserts. The Riesling grape produces these top wines only in the finest years, when botrytis strikes in profusion, but some of the earlier-ripening, less fine grape varieties, such as Bacchus or Ortega, can reach this level of sweetness in lesser years. Auslesen, next step down from Beerenauslese, can match raspberies for sweetness and acidity. Surprisingly, German Riesling Auslese is delicious with hare, and traditionally drunk with hare on the Mosel. The acidity of German wines and especially Mosel wines and Rieslings is high, so they go especially well with acidic fruits. '83 Auslesen are starting to be drinkable now, but the sweeter wines are too young. For Beerenauslese and Trockenbeerenauslese, go for the big, super-sweet, richly botrytis-flavoured '76s and elegant, mature '71s.

Austria

Following the glycol scandal, Austrian wines are an even rarer find than before on a British wine list. Yet sweet wines are a speciality of the Rust-Neusiedlersee area of Austria, where lakeside conditions are so perfect for the growth of botrytis that it appears every year. Austria uses the same sweetness categories as Germany, inserting an extra one, Ausbruch, between Beerenauslese and Trockenbeerenauslese. But Austria, being warmer, demands higher standards of ripeness than Germany, so that wine with the same category name will generally be sweeter and possibly higher in alcohol than the German equivalent. They are generally made with less interesting grapes than the German Riesling, such as Wälschriesling, Bouviertraube or Gewürztraminer, and this, along with the warmer climate, gives them much gentler acidity, so that they go better with less acid fruits. Austrian wines develop quickly, so go for recent vintages.

California

The Rhine Riesling (sometimes alias Johannisberg Riesling or White Riesling) is used for full, Late Harvest botrytised wines in California –botrytis has even been cultivated there artificially. These wines lack the enlivening acidity of German sweet versions and can be cloying, but some are good, though they are not very long lasting.

Australia

'Botrytised Semillon' is Australia's answer to Sauternes. It has the botrytis and concentration of good Sauternes, without the complexity of the top châteaux – but is far better value than most middling to lesser Sauternes. Australia also makes Late Harvest Riesling, in a similar style to the California ones. Not very long lasting.

Muscats

Commonest of sweet wines from this grapey-flavoured grape on restaurant lists is fortified Muscat de Beaumes de Venise, from the village of that name in the Rhône valley. France produces other similar Muscats: the delicate Muscat de St Jean du Minervois and the coarser Muscat de Rivesaltes. In a similar style, slightly coarser than Muscat de Beaumes de Venise, there's Moscatel de Setúbal from Portugal, and a rich, complex Moscato Passito di Pantelleria from a little island way off the coast of Sicily. These fortified Muscats are some of the only wines that go well with chocolate. They are also a good match for almond desserts. Australia makes wonderfully rich, dark, sometimes even treacly Liqueur Muscats, with orangy, raisiny, honeyed perfume, extremely sweet and suitable only with the sweetest of desserts, or to drink afterwards, instead of port. Unfortified Muscats, still and sparkling, can be delicious, delicate wines. One example, Asti Spumante, has somehow developed a down-market image, but try it again – it's delightfully delicate and grapey-spicy and, despite its sweetness, is one of the world's least fattening wines, because it's extremely low in calorie-rich alcohol. Asti is a wonderful accompaniment for Christmas pudding, a perfect match for the spiciness, with fizz and acidity to cut through the fatty stodge. Clairette de Die Tradition is similar, but more alcoholic. There's an equally delicious but still, sweet Moscato Naturale d'Asti. Both California and Australia make lovely, fairly delicate, unfortified sweet Muscats, such as Mondavi's Moscato d'Oro or Brown Bros Orange Muscat and Flora. These are all wines for drinking young.

What to drink in 1989

by Roger Voss, editor of *Which? Wine Guide*

*Double-starred (**) wines are especially good for drinking this year, though single-starred (*) bottles are good if ** wines are either too expensive or not available at all. Countries are listed alphabetically, wine-growing regions alphabetically within their countries. Vintages that are unlikely to appear on restaurant lists are not included.*

Argentina

Drink **whites** as young as possible – the **1988** vintage would be ideal. Argentina being in the southern hemisphere, grapes are picked in February and March. Any whites older than **1986** will be past it. **Reds** of older vintages occasionally surface: any up to ten years old should still be enjoyable.

Australia

WHITES
Drink the ***1986** vintage of Rhine Riesling – Chardonnay and **Sémillon are better after three or four years; ***1985s** and ***1984s** are both enjoyable now – so are **1983s** if the wines are of top quality.

REDS
****1983** and ***1984** are good now, as are some **1985s**. Drink Merlot younger than Cabernet Sauvignon or Shiraz, and drink Shiraz/Cabernet blends at the same age as pure Cabernet.

Austria

Drink ***1987**, **1986** and **1984** dry whites, and start on some sweet whites from **1983**. The sweet whites of ***1982** are good now. Drink reds from **1985** and **1986**.

Bulgaria

WHITES
1987 wines are very drinkable at the moment, especially Sauvignon and Riesling. **1986** Chardonnay is the best vintage.

REDS
1985, ***1983** and ***1981** are the best vintages at the moment for Cabernet Sauvignon. Drink Merlot or wines made from Bulgarian grape varieties – or the blended wines – within two or three years. Most Bulgarian reds are ready to drink once they are released by the producers.

Chile

Drink most **whites** as young as possible, although Chardonnay will keep for four years. Most **reds** are better after three or four years. Older vintages of Cabernet Sauvignon can be excellent, ageing with considerable grace and elegance.

England and Wales

Drink wines from the **1986**, ***1985** and ***1984** vintages now. Most other wines are past it, except for occasional wines from **1983**.

France

Alsace

1987 Only Pinot Blanc or blends should be drunk yet.
1986 This was a middle-weight vintage, but there are some good Muscats and Rieslings. Pinot Blanc, Gewürztraminer and *Muscat can be drunk now – but leave other wines, especially the Vendange Tardive wines.
****1985** Wines of this vintage will last well – but most can be drunk now. Riesling and Tokay Pinot Gris are the ones most likely to be immature.
1984 Good sound wines, but with few excitements. In some cases these wines go better with food than the greater vintages of **1985** and **1983**. All are drinkable at the moment.
****1983** A very fine year, and Riesling, Tokay Pinot Gris and Gewürztraminer are fine for drinking now, although they will keep. A few Vendanges Tardives are ready to drink. Most wines from this vintage will last a good while yet.
1982 Riesling and Tokay Pinot Gris are still attractive. The few Vendanges Tardives are ready for drinking.
1979 Occasional Rieslings are still attractively mature. Vendanges Tardives and top Réserves are good to drink now.
1978 A few of the best Rieslings and Gewürztraminer are good to drink. The rest are past it.
1976 **Vendanges Tardives and the occasional Gewürztraminer are still superb.

Beaujolais

1987 A typical Beaujolais Nouveau year, which produced quite light wines. The *cru* wines are ready for drinking, and most Beaujolais and Beaujolais Villages are very much at their best.
1986 A year that is coming into its own after poor Beaujolais Nouveau. The only wines to drink now are the *cru* (Chiroubles, Fleurie, Moulin-à-Vent, Brouilly, Côtes de Brouilly, St-Amour, Morgon, Chénas, Juliénas).
1985 A superb year. *Villages wines are still worth drinking, and the ***cru* wines are still superb.
1984 Forget it.
1983 Only a few *cru* wines from top producers are worth drinking.
Older vintages still worth trying are **1981** and **1978** for *cru* wines only.

Bergerac

Drink dry whites and rosés as young as possible. Drink **1986** and ***1985** standard Bergerac reds, and ****1983**, **1982** and **1978** of Côtes de Bergerac and Pécharmant. Drink **1985**, **1983**, ***1982**, and ***1978** sweet white Monbazillac.

Bordeaux

Red Bordeaux (claret) ranges from very simple, inexpensive wines for drinking young to some of the world's finest wines, which need keeping for many years. Clarets (most are labelled Ch. something) called Bordeaux or Bordeaux Supérieur, or those simply called house claret, fit into the first category. Look for **1986**, ****1985**, **1984** and ***1983**.
For more expensive wines labelled Cru Bourgeois, Graves, St Emilion Grand Cru, Montagne St Emilion, St Georges-St Emilion, Fronsac or Lalande de Pomerol:
***1985** Good, ripe wines which on the

whole need more time. But some wines from St Emilion, the surrounding villages and Pomerol are drinkable now, as are some Graves wines.

1984 Light wines, with quite a lot of acidity. The best wines for drinking now will be labelled Cru Bourgeois rather than St Emilion (or villages with St Emilion in the name) or Lalande de Pomerol.

***1983** St Emilion, Fronsac and Lalande de Pomerol will be ready now. The *cru bourgeois* and Graves should be kept.

****1982** Some are developing well. Others need time, especially the *cru bourgeois*.

***1981** Classic wines in the *cru bourgeois*, if a little tannic and austere. All are worth drinking.

1980 A few *cru bourgeois* are still good, others are fading.

****1979** All the *cru bourgeois* are good, as are Fronsac and St Emilion *grand cru*.

****1978** A very fine year, and many of the wines are still very drinkable. Wines from villages around St Emilion may be fading.

Earlier vintages: **1976**, **1975** (if chosen with care – many are too old), **1970**. Avoid most others.

For classed growths (including St Emilion *grand cru* Classé and Pomerol):

1984 Some lesser classed growths from the Médoc are ready to drink. There are only a few St Emilion and Pomerol – and they can be drunk as well.

***1983** A few wines from this vintage are ready to drink – especially St Emilion and Pomerol.

***1981** St Emilion and Pomerol wines are beginning to be attractive, as are the lesser classed growths. Big names need some time yet.

1980 Some wines are drying out, but they are all good value so worth trying.

***1979** A vintage that is good, firm and fruity and should last a little longer.

****1978** St Emilion and Pomerol are very good now. Others are just beginning to lose their toughness.

1977 Occasional top wines are good value. Avoid others.

1976 Very ripe wines, some of which have faded. Seek advice.

***1975** Pomerol is enjoyable, as are top St Emilion. Médoc and Graves classed growths still haven't opened out and show no signs of doing so.

1974 Avoid.

1973 Only top classed growths.

1972 Avoid.

1971 St Emilion and Pomerol are better than Médoc or Graves.

****1970** Superb wines, but the top classed growths are still too young. Try everything else.

Good vintages from the 1960s are ***1966** and ****1961**; from the 1950s, ****1959**, ****1955** and ****1953**. On older vintages, except ****1949**, ****1947** or ****1945**, ask advice.

DRY WHITES

Drink most young (**1986**), unless the wine is expensive and comes from a fine red wine château (Haut-Brion, Margaux, Domaine de Chevalier, for example), when older vintages – back to **1970** and even earlier – will be good. See list of red vintages for the best years.

SWEET WHITES

Young sweet whites are not ready to drink.

***1985** There will be good wines from the top estates, but they aren't ready yet. Try Premières Côtes de Bordeaux, St-Croix du Mont now, leave Sauternes and Barsac.

1984 Light wines that will never amount to much.

****1983** Marvellous wines. You could drink some now, but they will get much better.

1981 Not much honeyed sweetness, but the wines are elegant enough.

***1980** Light but very good value, with plenty of honeyed fruit. Drink now in preference to 1983.

1979 They're softening out and

losing their clean dryness and acidity. Drink now.

*1976 The best Sauternes and Barsac are still good. Others are past their best.

**1975 Wines that are at their best now. Hang on to the very top estates.

*1971 One-dimensional wines which need drinking now.

**1970 A big, fat year, and the wines are tasting very good.

Earlier vintages: *1969, **1967, *1955, **1945. On anything older, ask advice (except **1937).

Burgundy

Vintage information for Burgundy can only be approximate. The quality of the producer is almost more important than the year – always ask advice when ordering.

REDS

1986 Some of the lesser wines are already good to drink – but don't touch *grand cru* and *premier cru* from famous villages.

**1985 A fine vintage of great quality which is developing well. Most wines – except top *premier cru* – are worth drinking now.

1984 Most wines are getting a little tired. Choose with care.

*1983 Choose carefully, because some wines aren't developing well. Others, though, are very good indeed.

1982 Drink with great care. Many are past it, others never made it.

1981 Avoid.

*1980 Good value. It all depends on the grower. The Côte de Nuits made the best wines.

1979 Best avoided.

**1978 The best wines are just coming out of their shells, the others are becoming deliciously mature, while others are past it. Nothing is cheap, though.

In earlier vintages look for **1971**, **1970**, **1969**, **1961**. Côte de Nuits wines mature better than Côte de Beaune or Côte Chalonnaise.

WHITES

1987 Soft wines. Wines from Chablis and Mâcon are already worth drinking, but others should be kept.

**1986 Good wines that should age well. Again, Mâcon and Chablis are best to drink now.

*1985 Not quite as good as reds, but still very attractive. Most areas are ready to drink – although the wines will last. Chablis is softening and losing its bite.

1984 Quite acid wines. Choose carefully. Côte de Beaune is best.

*1983 One of the best recent vintages, and the prices reflect this. But quality does vary even in this year. Chablis is too soft, and tiring now.

1982 Drink up now.

1981 Avoid.

*1979 A few top wines are still very good.

*1978 The wines, though great, are softening dangerously. Only a few will last, so drink the rest now. Treat older vintages with caution.

Buzet, Frontonnais,

Gaillac (reds)

Look for **1986**, *1985, **1983** or older vintages of top wines (**1982**, *1978).

Cahors

1985 Lighter, fruitier wines are good now. The tougher wines are still just that.

**1983 The big wines are good now, although they will last.

*1982 Most wines are very good and this is the year to drink for all but the top wines.

**1978 The best year to drink now for the top wines.

Champagne (vintage)

Vintage Champagne and *de luxe cuvées* (Dom Perignon and the like) need some time to mature in bottle. Most non-vintage wines are intended to be ready to drink once they reach the restaurant, but it's worth asking which brands are the most mature. Green, young Champagne, is a great disappointment.

*1983 A few houses have already released this vintage, but it is too young.

**1982 This is a good time to drink this vintage, although the very best wines will last a long time yet.

*1981 A few producers are making this vintage, which is delicious now.

**1979 This is the vintage to drink now for the true mature champagne taste. A pity there are so few bottles left.

*1978 Another good vintage, if drier and less rich than 1979.

*1975 A few top *cuvées* are still delicious.

Loire

DRY WHITES AND ROSÉS

Drink the youngest vintage. Anybody selling Muscadet older than **1986** should be out of business, while ***1987** is the best at the moment. Vouvray, Sancerre and Pouilly Fumé of **1986** or **1985** will still be drinkable. Savennières needs between five and eight years before being ready to drink.

SWEET WHITES

1985 This was a superb vintage, but it would be a shame to drink anything but the most ordinary *Coteaux du Layon.

1984 Avoid.

***1983** The first vintage which should be touched. Even so, the best wines from Quarts de Chaume or Bonnezeaux are still young.

1982 Drink now.

****1978** These wines are just coming into their own – and superb they are.

****1976** Excellent wines with great concentration and richness.

***1975** Will be better than 1976 – but not just yet.

Older vintages: **1969, 1964, 1961, **1959.**

REDS

Many Loire reds, especially Sancerre and Gamay-based reds, need to be drunk young. Saumur-Champigny, Bourgueil and Chinon age better.

1986 Drink the lighter wines from this year with pleasure. Try them chilled.

***1985** St-Nicholas-de-Bourgueil, Saumur-Champigny and red Sancerre are the wines to drink this year. Keep Chinon and Bourgueil.

1984 Avoid.

****1983** Excellent year all round. Chinon and Bourgueil will keep, though.

1982 Drink up.

***1981** Good for the top producers of Chinon and Bourgueil.

1980 Avoid.

Older vintages: ***1978** for Chinon and Bourgueil.

Rhône

WHITES

Recent vintages that should be enjoyable are: **1987, 1986, *1985, 1983,** and **1978.** Older vintages should be approached with caution.

REDS

Northern Rhône – Crozes-Hermitage, Hermitage, Côte Rôtie, St Joseph, Cornas:

1985 A very good year, but it's a definite case of infanticide to touch most of them yet. Crozes-Hermitage should be ready, though.

1984 Lightweight wines, which are maturing quite fast. St Joseph is right to drink now, Crozes wines are beginning to fade a little.

1983 Excellent, top-quality wines. Try **Crozes, **St Joseph, but keep everything else for years.

***1982** Soft wines, ready for drinking, although Hermitage is still immature.

1981 Avoid.

***1980** At its peak, and very good value.

1979 Drink most wines now.

****1978** A truly great year, and many wines, especially Hermitage and Cornas, are not ready. Others are superb. Older vintages: **1976, 1971, 1969** for Cornas, Côte Rôtie, and Hermitage. Most others will have faded.

Southern Rhône – Côtes du Rhône, Côtes du Rhône-Villages, Lirac, Gigondas, Châteauneuf-du-Pape. Other wines – Côtes du Ventoux, Côtes du Lubéron, Coteaux du Tricastin – should be drunk as they come on to the wine list:

1986 While *Côtes du Rhône is good to drink now, the better Côtes du Rhône-Villages need between two and three years, and Châteauneuf needs for ever.

****1985** A great year. Côtes du Rhône and Villages are now good. Gigondas and Châteauneuf should be kept.

1984 Drink now.

***1983** Another good year. Gigondas and Lirac are just maturing, best Châteauneuf can be kept. Côtes du Rhône-Villages is mature. Avoid Côtes du Rhône.

1982 Avoid.

1981 Some big Châteauneuf, which is only just starting to mature. Not much else though.

***1980** Drink Châteauneuf, Gigondas and Lirac. Avoid others.

****1978** Gigondas and Châteauneuf superb. Most others are fading.

Germany

1987 A vintage that won't last. Only the best wines made from Riesling in the best vineyards have real quality, the rest need to be drunk during 1989.

***1986** Ordinary QbA wines are to be drunk now. Better wines can be kept. Beerenauslese wines were made in Rheinpfalz, but they need keeping.

***1985** A good all-round vintage, to be drunk now. Rheingau wines are particularly good.

1984 Avoid.

***1983** The top Rieslings are still superb, with Mosel-Saar-Ruwer faring best. Most other wines have tired.

1982 Drink up

***1981** A vintage that has matured well, and now looks very good.

****1976** Still superb. Try anything you can find (apart from Liebfraumilch). Older vintages: ***1975, **1971.** Many of the sweet wines age seemingly for ever.

Italy

WHITES

Drink young vintages – **1987, 1986.** Avoid anything older, unless it's a Chardonnay.

REDS

Most Italian reds need to be two or three years old before being drunk.

1986 This has turned out to be a middle-weight vintage. Best wines are Barberas or Dolcettos from Piedmont or *normale* Chianti.

Chianti

(These vintage notes also apply to Brunello di Montalcino and Vino Nobile di Montepulciano – but these wines need much longer to mature than Chianti.)

1986 A good year, with some good standard wines quite ready to drink.

****1985** The best wines are slowly coming into their own. Less expensive wines are very good. Very good value all round.

1984 Avoid.

***1983** Riservas are showing well. Ordinary Chianti (*normale*) is rather too mature.

****1982** This is a year for the super *vino da tavola* made by Chianti producers as their top wines. Also for Chianti Riserva.

Older vintages: **1978, *1975** for Riservas only.

Barolo and Barbaresco

Avoid anything younger than 1983.
1983 An average vintage which produced some light wines which are ready to drink now. Better quality wines need some time yet – keep until 1990.
***1982** Good, ripe wines, which can be drunk now, but really should be kept.
1981 Dull wines.
1980 Lightweight Barolo and Barbaresco – approach with caution.
****1978** One of the great vintages. Only light wines are good now.
Older vintages: ****1974, *1971, 1970.**

Lebanon

Best vintages of Château Musar at the moment are **1982, 1980, *1979, *1978** and ****1972.**

New Zealand

Anything before **1986** in whites and **1984** in reds is likely to be tiring. Drink **1986** or **1987** – or even **1988** (except Chardonnay) – whites. Drink **1986, 1985, 1984** reds.

Portugal

Table wines

WHITES
Drink vinho verde as fresh as possible. The wine doesn't have a vintage, but should certainly be no older than from the **1987** harvest.

REDS
Some Portuguese reds age remarkably well.
Bairrada: **1983, 1982, 1980, 1978.**
Dão: Similar vintages – but also **1974, 1971.**
Other wines (such as Garrafeira or branded wines): **1982, 1981, 1980, 1978, 1974.**

Port

All late-bottled vintage, late bottled, vintage-character and tawny ports are ready for drinking as soon as they reach the restaurant list.
Vintage and single quinta ports (single quinta – single vineyard wines – mature faster than true vintage ports). Don't touch **1977, 1980, 1982, 1983** or **1985** ports. A few **1980s** will be approaching maturity during the year.
1978 Some single quinta wines are ready to drink. Not a vintage year.
1975 A year to drink up. Good value, though.
****1970** This is the year to drink now, although some of the top wines still taste young.
1968/67 Some single quinta wines are worth drinking. Not official port vintage years.
***1966** Good-value ports, considering their age, and worth drinking now.
****1963** One of the best post-war vintages. Drink now, but they will keep for ever.
***1960** On very good, ripe form.
****1955** Maturing well.
Older vintages: **1950, *1947, **1945, *1935, **1927.**

Spain

WHITES
Most Spanish whites need to be drunk young. Buy **1986** vintages. Exceptions are some Torres wines (Gran Viña Sol) and white Rioja from Marqués de Murrieta (Ygay), Lopéz de Heredia (Tondonia) and CVNE (Monopole).

Rioja (reds)

1986 Some wines made *sin crianza* (without wood ageing) can be drunk, but nothing else.
***1985** Good wines here, but only *sin crianza* wines are ready.
1984 Drink up.

1983 An average year for ordinary Crianza Rioja. Some Reservas are just maturing.

****1982** We are about to see some top quality Reservas, although most should be kept.

****1981** Try the Reservas as well as ordinary Rioja.

***1980** Reasonable vintage. Look for the Reservas only, and most can be drunk now.

****1978** Reservas and Gran Reservas are very good. Approach ordinary Riojas with care.

***1975** and ***1973** Gran Reservas only.

Ribera del Duero

The Rioja vintage notes apply. Vega Sicilia needs years and years, but other wines need between eight and ten years.

United States

California

WHITES

Drink wines from **1987** (Sauvignon or Fumé Blanc, Riesling only), **1986** (all whites, including Chardonnay), **1985** (**Chardonnay are at their best), ***1984** and **1981** (Chardonnay only).

REDS

1985 The youngest reds to try. Keep the **Cabernet Sauvignon, but drink Zinfandel or Pinot Noir.

1984 A good year for Cabernets, avoid other reds.

1983 Drink now.

1982 Drink Cabernet Sauvignon. Other reds are fading.

1980 **Cabernet Sauvignon and some *Pinot Noir only.

General lists

The *Guide's* longest-serving restaurants

Connaught Hotel, W1	36 years
Gay Hussar, W1	32 years
Porth Tocyn Hotel, Abersoch, Gwynedd	32 years
Gravetye Manor, Sharpthorne, West Sussex	28 years
Sharrow Bay, Ullswater, Cumbria	28 years
Blooms, EC1	26 years
Dundas Arms, Kintbury, Berkshire	26 years
Box Tree, Ilkley, West Yorkshire	24 years
French Partridge, Horton, Northamptonshire	24 years
Walnut Tree Inn, Llandewi Skirrid, Gwent	24 years
Butley-Orford Oysterage, Orford, Suffolk	22 years
Splinters, Christchurch, Dorset	22 years
Chez Moi, W11	20 years
Cleeve House, Bishops Cleeve, Gloucestershire	20 years
Horn of Plenty, Gulworthy, Devon	20 years
Pool Court, Pool in Wharfedale, West Yorkshire	20 years
Rothay Manor, Ambleside, Cumbria	20 years
Sundial, Herstmonceux, East Sussex	20 years
At the Sign of the Angel, Lacock, Wiltshire	18 years
Chueng Cheng Ku, W1	18 years
Le Gavroche, W1	18 years
Summer Isles Hotel, Achiltibuie, Highland	18 years
Timothy's, Perth, Tayside	18 years

Restaurants with the most positive reports

London

1 Gay Hussar, W1
2 RSJ, SE1
3 Leith's, W11
4 Harvey's, SW17
5 Simply Nico, SW1
6 Turner's, SW3
7 Bibendum, SW3
8 Bahn Thai, W1
9 Le Mazarin, Sw1
10 Kensington Place

England

1 Manoir Aux Quat' Saisons, Great Milton
2 Atkin's, The Old Plow (now sold)
3 Crown, Southwold
4 L'Ortolan, Shinfield
5 Oakes, Stroud
6 Al San Vincenzo, Cheam
7 Funnywayt'mekalivin, Berwick-upon-Tweed
8 Yang Sing, Manchester
9 Petti Blanc, Oxford
10 Old Vicarage, Ridgeway, Sheffield

Scotland

1 Handsel's Restaurant, Edinburgh
2 Peat Inn, Peat Inn
3 Murrayshall Hotel, Scone
4 Champany Inn, Linlithgow
5 Martins, Edinburgh
6 Altnaharrie Inn, Ullapool
7 La Potinière, Gullane
8 Arisaig Hotel, Arisaig
9 Airds Hotel, Port Appin
10 Riverside Inn, Canonbie

Wales

1 Walnut Tree Inn, Llandewi Skirrid

2 Cemlyn, Harlech
3 Fairyhill, Reynoldston
4 Meadowsweet Hotel, Llanrwst
5 Plas Bodegroes, Pwllheli
6 Ye Olde Bulls Head Inn, Beaumaris
7 Castle Cottage, Harlech
8 Ty Mawr, Brechfa
9 Tyddyn Llan, Llandrillo
10 Bakestone, Caernarfon

Exceptional wine cellars

These restaurants, marked with a bottle symbol in the text, have outstanding wine cellars.

London

La Bastide, W1
Bibendum, SW3
Boulestin, WC2
Cavaliers, SW8
Clarke's, W8
Cork & Bottle, WC2
Corney & Barrow, EC2
Le Gavroche, W1
La Giralda, Pinner
Inigo Jones, WC2
Leith's, W11
Magno's, WC2
Mijanou
RSJ, SE1
Savoy Grill, WC2
Sutherlands, W1
Tante Claire
Tate Gallery, SW1
Turners
Waltons, SW3

England

Bell, Aston Clinton
La Bonne Auberge, South Godstone
Bridgefield House, Spark Bridge
Buckland-Tout-Saints Hotel, Kingsbridge
Carved Angel, Dartmouth
Castle Hotel, Taunton
Cedar Restaurant, Evesham
Chedington Court, Chedington
Copper Inn, Pangbourne
Country Club, Harrow
Crabwall Manor, Mollington
Crown, Southwold
Croque-en-Bouche, Malvern Wells
Dundas Arms, Kintbury
Epworth Tap, Epworth
Fossebridge Inn, Northleach
Fountain House, East Bergholt
French Partridge, Horton
Galloping Crayfish, Hungerford
George, Stamford
Gidleigh Park, Chagford
Grafton Manor, Bromsgrove
Hambleton Hall, Hambleton
Harvey's, Bristol
Harvey's Cathedral Restaurant, Lincoln
Hendersons, Tiverton
Hintlesham Hall, Hintlesham
Homewood Park, Hinton Charterhouse
Hope End, Ledbury
Hungry Monk, Jevington
Hunstrete House, Hunstrete
35 Kenwards, Lewes
Lake Isle, Uppingham
Landgate Bistro, Rye
Lichfield's, Richmond
Lygon Arms, Broadway
Mallory Court, Bishops Tachbrook
Manley's, Storrington
Manoir aux Quat' Saisons, Great Milton
Marryat Room, Chewton Glen Hotel, New Milton
Michels, Ripley
Moonrakers, Alfriston
Morels, Haslemere
Old Manor House, Romsey
Old Rectory, Campsea Ash
Old Vicarage, Ridgeway
Old Vicarage, Witherslack
L'Ortolan, Shinfield
Partners 23, Sutton
Petit Blanc, Oxford
Pool Court, Pool in Wharfedale
Porthole Eating House, Bowness on Windermere
Le Poussin, Brockenhurst
Priory Hotel, Bath
Restaurant Bosquet, Kenilworth
Rothay Manor, Ambleside
Royal Oak, Yattendon
Seafood Restaurant, Padstow
Sharrow Bay, Ullswater
Sir Charles Napier Inn, Chinnor
Splinters, Christchurch
Starr, Great Dunmow
Stock Hill House, Gillingham
Ston Easton Park, Ston Easton
Summer Lodge, Evershot
Teignworthy Hotel, Chagford
Thornbury Castle, Thornbury
White Horse Inn, Chilgrove
White House Hotel, Williton
White Moss House, Grasmere
Whites, Cricklade
Wickens, Northleach

Scotland

Airds Hotel, Port Appin
Altnaharrie Inn, Ullapool
Cellar, Anstruther
Champany Inn, Linlithgow
Cross, Kingussie
Inverlochy Castle, Fort William
Knipoch Hotel, Oban
Peat Inn, Peat Inn
Potinière, Gullane
Summer Isles Hotel, Achiltibuie

Wales

Bodysgallen Hall, Llandudno
Meadowsweet Hotel, Llanrwst
Walnut Tree Inn, Llandewi Skirrid

London restaurants open after midnight

These restaurants take last orders after midnight.

The Bengal Lancer, NW5 (Fri, Sat only)
Good Food, WC2
Hard Rock Café, W1
Langan's Brasserie, W1 (Sat only)
Maroush I, W2
Maroush II, SW3
Mayflower, W1
Melati, W1 (Fri, Sat only)
Yung's

London restaurants by cuisine

AFRO-CARIBBEAN

Bambaya, N8
Blue Nile, W9
Red Sea, NW6

CHINESE

China, China, W1
Chuen Cheng Ku, W1
Dragon's Nest, W1
Forum Court, SE25
Fung Shing, Wc2
Good Food, WC2
Good Friends, E14
Ho-Ho, E18
Hung Toa, W2
Jade Garden, W1
Mandarin Kitchen, W2
Mayflower, W1
Ming, W1
New World, W1
Poons, WC2
Si Chuen, W1
Wing Ki, Edgware
Wong Kei, W1
Yung's, W1
Zen, NW3
Zen, W1
Zen, SW3

FISH & CHIPS

Faulkner's, E8
Leek's Fish Bar, SW11
Seafood Fish Restaurant, SW1
Seashell, NW1
Upper Street Fish Shop, N1

GREEK

Daphne, NW1
Lemonia, NW1
Nontas, NW1
White Tower, W1
Kalamaras, W2
Beotys, WC2

HUNGARIAN

Gay Hussar, W1

INDIAN TANDOORI

Bayleaf Tandoori, N6
Bengal Lancer, NW5
Bombay Bicycle Club, SW12
Bombay Brasserie, SW7
Brilliant, Southall
Fleet Tandoori, NW3
Ganpath, WC1
Great Nepalese, NW1
Jamdani, W1
Kanishka, W1
Lal Qila, W1
Last Days of the Empire, W1
Malabar, W8
Ragam, W1
Rajdoot, W6
Shapla Tandoori Restaurant, SW9
Suruchi, N1

INDIAN VEGETARIAN

Mandeer, W1
Rani, N3
Sabras, NW10
Spices, N16
Sree Krishna, SW17

INDONESIAN

Mandalay, SE10
Melati, W1
Singapore Garden Restaurant, NW6

JAPANESE

Ginnan, EC4
Ikeda, W1
Ikkyu, W1
Miyama, EC4
Miyama, W1
Nanten Yakitori Bar, W1
Ninjin, W1
One Two Three, W1
Ryoma, W1
Suntory, SW1
Wakaba, NW3

ITALIAN

Baita Da Piero, E4
L'Incontro, SW1
Il Passetto, WC2
Orso, WC2
Pollo, W1
River Café, W6
San martino, SW3
Santini, SW1
La Seppia, W1

JEWISH

Bloom's, E1
Grahame's Seafare, W1

KOREAN

Korean House, W1

MIDDLE EASTERN

Al Hamra, W1
Efes Kebab House, W1
Elgin, W9
Maroush I, W2
Maroush II, SW3
Phoenicia, W8
Topkapi, W1

POLISH

Brewer Street Buttery, W1
Lowiczancka, W6
Zamoyski's, NW3

PORTUGUESE

Ports, SW3

SPANISH

Guernica, W1
Rebato's, SW8
La Rueda, SW4

SWEDISH

Anna's Place, N1
Garbo's, W1

THAI

Bahn Thai, W1
Blue Elephant, SW6
Chiang Mai, W1
Oh Boy, SW17
Pearl of Siam, E1
Royal Thai Orchids, SW15
Tuk Tuk, N1

VIETNAMESE

Saigon, W1

VEGETARIAN

Cherry Orchard, E2
Dining Room, SE1

Afternoon teas

These hotels serve afternoon teas to non-residents.

London

Augerge de Provence, SW1
Blakes Hotel, SW7
Britannia Intercontinental Hotel, W1
Capital Hotel, SW3
Connaught, W1
Dukes Hotel, SW1
Halcyon Hotel, W11
Ninety Park Lane, W1
Nontas, NW1
Oak Room, W1
Savoy Grill, WC2
Le Souffle, W1

England

Alverton Manor, Truro
Arundell Arms, Lifton
Ashwick House, Dulverton
Beeches, Standish
Bell, Aston Clinton
Bilbrough Manor, Bilbrough
Breamish House, Powburn
Brockencote Hall, Chaddesley Corbett
Buckland-Tout-Saints Hotel, Kingsbridge
Calcot Manor, Tetbury
Castle Hotel, Taunton
Cedar Restaurant, Evesham
C'est la Vie, Lytham St Anne's
Champenois, West Mersea
Charingworth Manor, Chipping Campden
Chester Grosvenor, Chester
Cleeveway House, Bishops Cleeve
Copper Inn, Pangbourne
Corse Lawn House, Corse Lawn
Courtyard, Broughton
Crabwall Manor, Mollington
Crown, Southwold
Denbigh Arms, Lutterworth
Farlam Hall, Brampton (Cumbria)
Feathers Hotel, Woodstock
Gatwick Hilton, Gatwick
George, Stamford
Gidleigh Park, Chagford
Great House, Lavenham
Grinkle Park Hotel, Easington
Grosvenor Hotel, Rugby
Harcourt Arms, Stanton Harcourt
Holdsworth House, Halifax
Homewood Park, Hinton Charterhouse
Hunstrete House, Hunstrete
Innsacre Farmhouse Hotel, Shipton Gorge
Jule's Café, Weobley
Kirkstone Foot Country House Hotel, Ambleside
Lainston House, Sparsholt
Langley House Hotel, Langley Marsh
Langley Wood, Redlynch
Little Byres, Dallington
Lygon Arms, Broadway
Mallory Court, Bishops Tachbrook
Le Manoir aux Quat' Saisons, Great Milton
The Manor at Newlands, Guildford
Mark's at Lindhead Cottage, Scarborough
Marryat Room, New Milton
McCoy's Bistro, Staddlebridge
Middlethorpe Hall, York
Miller Howe, Windermere
Morton's House Hotel, Corfe Castle
Mulberry Room, Torquay
Northcote Manor, Langho
Old Thorns, Liphook
Old Vicarage Hotel, Worfield
Park End, Caldbeck
Parrock Head Farm, Slaidburn
Pier at Harwich, Harwich
Pine Trees, Sway
Plough, Clanfield (Oxon)
Priory Hotel, Bath
Ram Jam, Stretton
Restaurant Lafite, Willerby
Rising Sun, Saint Mawes
Sheridans, Moreton in Marsh
Rose and Crown, Wisbech
Rothay Manor, Ambleside
Royal Oak, Yattendon
Ryecroft Hotel, Wooler
Seaview Hotel, Seaview
Sharrow Bay, Ullswater
Shepherd's, Stratford upon Avon
Sheridans, Moreton in Marsh
Skinburness Hotel, Skinburness

South Lodge, Lower Beeding
Stapleford Park, Melton Mowbray
Stock Hill House, Gillingham
Ston Easton Park, Ston Easton
Stone Close, Dent
Stumbles, South Molton
Summer Lodge, Evershot
Swan Hotel, Leighton Buzzard
Teignworthy Hotel, Chagford
Well House, Liskeard
Well House, Watlington
Whipper-in, Oakham
White Bear, Shipston on Stour
Whitechapel Manor, South Molton
Winteringham Fields, Winteringham

Scotland

Airds Hotel, Port Appin
Ardsheal House, Kentallen
Arisaig Hotel, Arisaig
Auchterarder House, Auchterarder
Ceilidh Place, Ullapool
Chapeltoun House, Stewarton
Craigendarroch, Ballater
Crinan Hotel, Crinan
Cringletie House, Peebles
Cromlix House, Kinbuck
Dunain Park, Inverness
Gleddoch House, Langbank
Green Inn, Ballater
Holly Tree, Kentallen
Hospitality Inn, Irvine
Inverlochy Castle, Fort William
Kilfinan Hotel, Kilfinan
Killiecrankie Hotel, Killiecrankie
Kinloch Lodge, Sleat
Kirroughtree Hotel, Newton Stewart
Knipoch Hotel, Oban
Knockinaam Lodge, Portpatrick
Morefield Motel, Ullapool
Murrayshall Hotel, Scone
Stewart Hotel, Appin
Summer Isles Hotel, Achiltibuie
Sunlaws House, Kelso
Taychreggan Hotel, Kilchrenan
Turnberry Hotel, Turnberry

Wales

Abergwynant Hall, Dolgellau
Bear Hotel, Crickhowell
Bodysgallen Hall, Llandudno
Cnapan, Newport (Dyfed)
Druidstone Hotel, Broad Haven
Jemima's, Haverfordwest
Llwynderw Hotel, Llanwrtyd Wells
Maes-y-Neuadd, Talsarnau
Pale Hall, Llandderfel
Porth Tocyn Hotel, Abersoch
St Tudno Hotel, Llandudno
Stone Hall, Wolf's Castle
Tyddyn Llan, Llandrillo
Ty Mawr, Brechfa

Cover charge blacklist

These restaurants still have a separate cover charge, which is added as an extra to the bill. Check the entry for details.

London

Al Hamra, W1
Andrew Edmunds, W1
l'Arlequin, SW8
Bahn Thai, W1
La Baita da Piero, E4
Bambaya, N8
Beau-Rivage, NW6
Bengal Lancer, NW5
Beotys, WC2
Blue Elephant, SW6
Bombay Bicycle Club, SW12
Le Caprice, SW1
Le Chef, W2
La Dordogne, W4
Efes Kebab House, W1
Elgin, W9
Faulkner's, E8
Fifty One Fifty One, SW3
Garbo's, W1
Gay Hussar, W1
Grahame's Seafare, W1
Green's, SW1
Ikeda, W1
L'Incontro, SW1
Inigo Jones, WC2
Julius's, N1
Kalamaras, W2
Langan's Bistro, W1
Langan's Brasserie, W1
Lou Pescadou, SW7
Ma Cuisine, SW3
Magno's, WC2
Malabar, W8
Manzi's, WC2
La Mascotte, NW2
Miyama, W1
Miyama, EC4
Monsieur Frog, N1
Neal Street Restaurant, WC2
One Two Three, W1
Il Passetto, WC2
Phoenicia, W8
Le Quai St Pierre, W8
St Quentin, SW3
San Martino, SW3
Santini, SW1
Si Chuen, W1
Soho Brasserie, W1
Suntory, SW1
Le Suquet, SW3
White Tower, W1
Wiltons, SW1
Zazou, W1
Zen, SW3
Zen, W1

England

Bobby's, Leicester
Chilka, Brighton
Da Umberto, Ilford
Di Jonnais, Croydon
Gaylord, Manchester
George, Stamford
India, Folkestone
Lantern, East Molesey
Marco's, Norwich
Plaka, Birmingham
Rajdoot, Birmingham
Rajdoot, Bristol
Sankey's Seafood, Tunbridge Wells
Shao Tao, Cambridge
Splinters, Christchurch
Tuo e Mio, Canterbury

Scotland

Timothys, Perth

The Good Food Club 1988

Many thanks to all the following people who contributed, in one way or another, to this year's *Guide* . . .

Mr & Mrs R. W. Abbott
Peter Abbott
John Abel
James Abelson
Dr A. H. Abrahams
Dr S. Abrahams
Mr A. D. Abrams
Professor R. M. Acheson
J. D. Ackland
Martin R. Adams
Dr J. C. S. Adams
Robert Adams
J. K. Adams
Professor J. N. Adams
Dr & Mrs A. Adamson
Karen Addison
Ian Addison
Ms N. Aduba
Marcus Agius
The Marchioness of Ailesbury
Mrs M. Ainley
Dr J. B. Ainscough
John R. Aird
Mr D. O. Aisher
D. L. Albert
Mr and Mrs R. Aldred
Minda and Stanley Alexander
Ms E. Alexander
Tania Alexander
Dr & Mrs A. A. Alibhai
Mrs S. Allan
S. R. & A. J. Allan
Mr E. M. Allen
W. J. Allen
Anthony Allen
Stuart Allen
Genesta Allen-Butler
Mrs J. Allom
D. R. Allum
Sir Anthony Alment
Mr M. Amphlett
R. E. Anderson
I. Anderson
D. D. Anderson
Robert Anderson
Sue Anderson
David Anderson
A. J. Anderson
Chris Anderson
Stephanie Andre
S. C. Andrews
Mr and Mrs P. Andrews
Michael Andrews
Lee Andrews
L. Andrews
Iain F. Andrews
Gwen & Peter Andrews
Mr P. Andry
Mr R. M. Angell
R. M. Anger
Mrs P. M. Ansell
Timoney Anthony
M. J. Anwyl-Davies
Michael and Betty Appleby
Mrs A. Appleby
P. Appleby
T. Appleton
Mr D. Archer
Dr & Mrs M. I. Archer
Dr J. R. Archibald
Mandy Arkless
Mr B. J. Armstrong
Mrs K. Armstrong
Miss D. Armstrong
Mr D. Armstrong
Mr & Mrs Michel Arnaud
G. J. Arnold
Mrs M. E. Arnold
C. S. Arnold
Mr J. Arnold
Mrs S. Arrowsmith
Mr D. A. Ash
Joe Ashton MP
H. W. Ashton
Mr & Mrs P. M. Ashwell
Judy Askey & Coralie Clark
Hazel Astley
Mrs E. A. Aston
Dr P. Aston
J. C. Astro
B. D. Atkin
T. W. Atkinson
Mr G. Atkinson
Michael Atkinson
Mr W. Atkinson
W. S. Atkinson
Philip Attenborough
Richard Attoe & Amal Khoony
N. & R. Audley
Nick Austin
Kathie Austin
N. C. Avery
Cyril Aydon
Mrs N. A. Aylmer
Mr V. Bach
Dr M. C. Bachard
Susan Badman
C. Bagshawe
Lieutenant Colonel A. R. Bailey
Mary D. Bailey
Jane & Martin Bailey
C. T. Bailhache
N. D. Bain
Mrs E. Bain
Mr P. Baines FCIS
Mr A. Bakall
Judith Baker
Ms D. L. Baker
Dr A. S. Baker
Mr J. E. Baker
Paul & Margaret Baker
Valerie Baker
Gary Baker
Mary Baker
Mr A. J. V. Baker
F. A. K. Baker
A. E. Baker
Howard Baker
R. B. H. Baker
J. Baker
Caroline A. Baker
Mrs G. Bakes
Joan Baldwin
Richard Bales
Richard Balkwill
John Ball
Mr D. Ball
William Ballmann
Joseph A. Balsano Jr
Mrs C. M. Banks
P. Bann
T. Bannister
Dorian Bannister
A. J. Barber
Archie Barclay
D. L. Barends
K. & B. Barker
John A. Barker
Anthony Barker
Dr J. A. Barley
P. J. Barlow
Mr and Mrs Barna Wayne Peak
Mr A. S. Barnes
Erica Barnett
Mr M. J. N. Barnett
Mrs J. Barnfather
Peter Barnsley
Penny Barr
Geoff Barratt

Mrs S. E. Barratt
Ms J. M. Barratt
D. H. Barrett
Caroline Barrett
P. A. Barrett
J. L. Barrons
K. E. Barrott
Mrs B. J. Barry
C. R. Bartholomew
G. P. Bartholomew
C. M. J. Barton
P. Bartram
Shakib Basma
Christine Bassadone
Georgina L. Bassett
Mrs G. M. Bastausy
Mrs M. A. Batchelor
Mr M. J. Batchelor
Mr D. R. Bates
Mrs M. Bates
Valerie Bateson
Albert A. Bath
David Batten
John R. Batty
Mr D. N. Baty
Valerie Bauer
Patricia Bawcombe
A. P. Baxter
R. A. Bayliss
Lt Col Sir John and Lady Baynes
Philip Bearman
Wilfred Beckerman
Rev. & Mrs John Beech
J. & S. M. Beech
Peter Begbey
E. C. M Begg
Mr A. Beken
Dr J. & Mrs M. R. Belchem
Mrs J. Belfield
Mr J. H. Bell
C. H. R. Bell
Mr A. A. Bell
Mr L. Bell
Michael H. Bell
Mr R. Bellars
Mrs A. Bellerby
F. Bellingham
Marshall L. Bellow
Mr M. J. Benenson
Michael and Kathryn Benenson
Frank Benjamin
R. S. O. Bennett
Gillian Bennett
Barbara Bennett
Mr J. Bennett
Lee and Dale Bennett
M. E. Bennett
Lincoln A. Bennett
Gordon F. Bennett
D. R. Benson
Edna F. Benson
Marjorie Bentham
Peter Bentley
Anne Benton
William and Ellen Bentsen
Mr and Mrs H. I. Berkeley
Gabriele Berneck
Harrold Berrston
Anita Berry
Edward A. M. Berry
P. E. Berry
Wg Cdr & Mrs I. G. Best
Mr W. J. Best
Val Bethel
Mr G Betts
D. M. Bidgood
Fred and Vera Biel
Vincent Bifulco
Dr & Mrs J. Biggs
Ms S. J. Billington
Mr I. Binder
Ms V. Bingham
Mr & Mrs J. McBinney
John Binnie
Dr G. G. Birch
Mr K. R. Birch
Mrs J Bird
David Bird
Mr & Mrs B. A. Birmingham
Mr P. M. Bisby
Mr and Mrs J. Bishopp
John Black
Mr M. Black
Mrs. J. Blackbird
J. C. Blackburn
Paul Blackburn
Miss D. Blackburn
Mr R. Blackburn
Mr & Mrs B. J. Blackburn
Joan A Blackmore
V. B. Blackstone
Mr P. A. Blake
Timothy Blake
Henry T. Blakeston
Caroline and Alan Blandford
Mrs J. A Blanks
Mr R. Blatch
Mr & Mrs J. M. Blinco
Lionel Bloch
Ruth Bloom
George & Michelle Bloore
Mr R. K. Blumenau
Dr S. M. Blunden
Mrs B. Boarder
Rev John F. Boardman
S. Bobasch
K. W. Bogle
C. F. David Boit
Mr A. W. Bone
D. Bonham
R. Boniface
Mr L. Bonner
E. Bonner-Maurice
Maurice Bonnor
N. Bookbinder
Dr C. Booth
Philip Booth
G. P. Booth
Mr P. J. Bordiss
Martin & Elaine Borish
W. M. A. J. Borkowski
Mrs A. A. Bough
Mr T. B. Bouton
Rev M. A. Bourdeaux
Mr J. S. Bourne
R. Bourne
Chris Boutell
Ann & Roger Bowden
Lance Bowden
Mr A. S. Bowell
Mr A. J. Bowen
Patricia Bowen
Bruce Bower
Mary Bowers
Isobel Bowler
Arabella Boxer
Tony Boyd
Stephen Boyd
Mrs P. Boylan
R. Boyse
Dave Brabants
Heather Brace
Roy J. Bradbrook
Mrs C. A. Bradburn
Kristin Bradbury
Mrs C. Braddick
The Earl of Bradford
P. G. Bradley
Mrs A. Bradshaw
P. Bradshaw
Joan Brady and Dexter Masters
J. P. Brady
B. P. Brahams
T. M. Brain
Rodney Braithwaite
D. J. Brame
Mrs R. Brand
Mr and Mrs D. C. Brand
Mrs M. E. Brannan
Dr A. M. Braverman
Coral Bray
Nicholas Bray
N. P. Bray
W. T. Brennan
Simon Brenner
Ron Brenton
John Brett
Mrs S. H. Brewer
Paul K. Brewin
Juilietta Brian
C. E. Bridge
John S. Bridge
Mrs C. Bridgewater
D. Brief
C. A. Briere-Edney
J. B. Brierley
Mr T. G. Brierly
H. M. M. Brierly
Major & Mrs C. F. Briggs
Mr & Mrs D. J. Brine
Mr K. H. Brining
Richard Britton
Mr R. C. Broad
Maurice Plain Broady
Kim R. J. Brogan
Mrs C. A. Brogden
Roy Y. Bromell
Keith R. Brook
Mr & Mrs M. C. Brooke
Mrs H. Brooke
Dr Clare Brooke
Mr Brooke
Ian A. Brooker
Douglas Brooks
Claire Brooks Matthew
Mr & Mrs V. Brooman
K. B. Brotchie
Norman Brown
H. M. & A. E. M. Brown
Dr P. Brown
Mr A. Brown
Thomas Brown
Sheila Brown
Dr Carole Brown

Dr & Mrs D. G. Brown
Anita Brown
D. Brown
Dr W. N. Brown
Robert H. Brown
Graham Brown
James M. Brown
Mr D. G. Brown
Alan Brown
Peter and Ann Brown
Michael Brown
Dr C. S. Brown
R. M. Brown
Dr Brownlow
S. Brownrigg
Robin A. Brumwell
W. H. Bruton
Peter Bryan
R. K. Bryan
Ian Bryant
John Bryant
F. M. Buchan
Mrs A. L. Buchanan
R. W. Buckle
Mr H. Buckle
Marcus Buckley
Mr M. I. Buckley
W. K. Buckley
Mrs F. A. Buckley
G. H. Budgen
Jane Budgen
Tina R. Bull
Ian and Angela Bull
W. J. Bull
Adam Bunting
J. A. Burckhardt
Roy Burden
Carolyn Burge
James P. C. Burgess
A. J. Burgess
B. M. Burgess
Susan Burke
Miss A. Burnand
Tracey Burnett
Air Commodore P. Burnett
Mrs E. B. Burns
Mrs N. C. Burns
Mrs L. Burns
June Burrough
Dianne M. Burton
Clive Burton
Barry Burtt
Helen Busby
Harry Bush
A. Bushell
Mrs K. B. Bushen
Hugh Butcher
Mr M. Butler
John Butler
George Butler
Jane Butler
John Butler
Roy Butler
F. G. Butler
D. Butterfield
Decan Butterly
Noel Buxton
Peter Bye
R. Byer
Dr W. F. Bynum
Paul E. Byrne
Azeema Caffoor
Professor Robert Cahn
Rob and Vivien Caird
Brian T. Cairns
Susan Callard
D. M. Callow
Montague Calman FRSA
J. R. Calrow
D. G. Calvert
Ian Cameron
Mrs R. Cameron
A. H. Campbell
J. D. Campbell
Mr & Mrs T. Campbell
Mr & Mrs James Campbell-Smith
Susan & Gerald Campion
Michael Camps
Eric Campus
James Cane
Irene Canning
Angela Cannon
Nigel Cant
A. D. Cantwell
C. P. Cardiff
Mary Carewe
Dr J. J. Carless
S. P. Carline
Mr J. C. Carlyle
Mary Carmichael
Sir Andrew Carnwath
John Carolan
Janifer Caroline
John Caros
Jeremy Carpenter
Peter Carpenter
Mr M. D. Carr
Dr Paul Carr
Patricia Carr
Anne Carr
Lt Cdr G. Carr
Mrs V. Carroll
Mr P. J. Carroll
Diana Carson
Penelope Carter
Mr M. Carter
Simon Carter
Ms P. J. Carter
Philip Carter
Simon Carter
Vicky Carter
Mr J. R. Carter FCA
Mr P. E. Carter
Ms S. Cartlioye
Mrs J. A. Cartwright
Dr Neville Cartwright
Geoffrey W. Case
Mr J. C. Castle
Victoria Castledine
R. E. Catlow
Leslie Caul
Judy Cave
Mr & Mrs T. T. Cawdron
Simon Cawkwell
John Cawston
Angela Cerfontyne
George C. Cernoch
A. A. Chadeyron
J. Chaldecott
C. J. Chalmers
Mrs L. E. Chambers
Michael and Rosemary Chambers
J. M. Chandler
R. D. Chaplin
Helen Chapman
D. E. Chapman
Alison Chapman
M. Chapman
W. M. Chapman
E. B. H. Chappell
Mr S. Charles
Barry Charles
Mary Charnley
Peter Bliss Chatsworth
Mrs E. Chatten
Mrs G. A. Cheadle
Guy Cheeseman
Mrs E. M. Cheetham
Mr & Mrs S. Cheetham
Mrs J. E. Chenevix-Trench
Richard J. Cherry
W. J. Chesneau
Maureen Chilvers
C. E. D. Chilvers
H. A. Chistie
Judith Chivers
Jonathan Choat
Alumana Choudhury
Mr J. D. Choudhury
Mr K. Choudhwry
Irene Christie
George W. Christie
P. Chui
C. Church
Valerie Church
Mr and Mrs Churchin
A. V. Chute
Dr P. J. Ciclitira
Mrs A. Cuifd
Norman Civval
Miss M. E. Clamp
K. Clancy
Deborah Clark
Mrs P. M. Clark
Stewart Clark
Margaret Clark
Mr D. H. Clark
Stephen and June Clark
Susan Clark
J. R. Clarke
Paul J. Clarke
Mr D. Clarke,
Maggie Clarke
D. A. and P. F. Clarke
David Clarke
Ms D. Clarke
Imelda Clarke
Derek Clarkson
Mrs S. Clay
John J. Clayton
R. T. Clayton-Jolly
Mrs A. J. B. Cleave
Elizabeth Clegg
Terence Clegg
Alan M. Clegg
Mr W. H. Cleghorn
Cathryn Clements
Mr G. Clements
Kenneth Cleveland
Ms P. Cliffe
Mr H. Cliffe
Val Clifton
Mr P. J. Clymer
Mr R. C. Coates
J. R. Coates
Ms S. P. Coates
Adam Cochrane
Mr & Mrs D. B. Cockburn
Dr Michael Cockcroft
Mr R. J. Cockerill
C. H. Cockrem
David Cocks
Dr & Mrs Coe

M. D. & S. D. Coe
Ian Coghill
W. F. Coghill
Muriel Cohen
Stephen and Charlotte Cohen
Mr & Mrs Harold Cohen
Mr & Mrs S. Cohen
Dr J. R. Coke
Colbatch Clark
Dr Frances Cole
John and Moira Cole
Michael Cole
Rt Revd Peter Coleman
Mr J. Coleman
R. Coleman-Wood
Frances Coleridge
Philip Collcutt
Mrs M. Collett
Mr C. Colley
Prof. Leslie Collier
Peter Collins
Mr I. D. B. Collins
Patricia Collins
Mr & Mrs Robert Collins
S. D. Collinson
Mr H. Collinson
Mr N. Colombe
Sara E. C. Colville
R. T. Combe
Michael P. Comiskey
Mr & Mrs A J Comyn
Sean Connolly
Ian Conolly
Mr C. A. Constantine
Tim Cook
J. Cook
Christopher W. B. Cook
Godfrey J. Cook, FRICS
J. P. F. Cooke
Mrs J. Cookson
Barbara Cookson
Elaine Coomber
Mr L. G. Coombs
G. V. Coombs
Montague Thompson Coon
Mrs A. M. Cooper
Peter John Cooper
Mr C. J. Cooper
S. N. Cooper
Marianne Cooper
Diana Cooper
P. J. Cooper
A. J. Cooper
Liz Cooper
Mr & Mrs Cooper
Mrs S. Cooper
Mr M. Cooper-Bland
Mrs K. Coralles
Val Corbett
B. H. Corbett
Mr J. Corbluth
Susan Corby
Roderick C. Cordara
H. J. C. Cornish
Mr S. Corrin
Mrs B. Corsan
Antoinette Cosgrove
H. F. & E. Cosser
Mr A. L. Cotcher
C. J. Cotesworth
Mr D. G. Cotterill
Simon Cottle
M. Cotton
Mrs A. J. V. Cotton MBE
Gerard Coulaud
B. R. Couzens
Mr A. Coverdale
Stephen Coverly
A. Cowan
Stuart Cowan
Christopher and Jean Cowan
Mr & Mrs H. L. Cowdy
Mrs M. Cowdy
Mr & Mrs T. E. Cowell
Julia Cowell
Dr K. J. Cowen
Mr & Mrs S. J. Cowherd
Mr. C. J. Cowlin
Mrs H. I. Cowling
Peter and Elizabeth Cowsill
Mrs S. M. Cox
Andrew Cox
Stuart C. Cox
Mr & Mrs K. Cox
Prof. A. P. M. Coxon
Mrs D. Coy
David Croft
L. J. P. J. Craig
John S. Craig
Alison Craig-Wood
W. and I. Crammond
R. D. Cramond
Peter Crane
Philip Cranmer
Mr J. D. Cranston
R. G. A. Craven
Dr K. W. E. Craven
Neil Crawford
Richard Creed
Miss E. A. Cresswell
Mr M. G. Cripps
Mrs P. Critchley
Julian Critchley
Gloria M. Crocker
G. S. Crockett
Mrs P. A. Croft
Mr T. E. Crompton
Mrs J. H. Crook
Helen Crookston
Mr D. Croser
Maurice and Anne Crosier
Rodney Cross
W. Crossland
Gilda Crosthwaite
Paul Crowley
John Crowley
T. Crowther QC
Mrs Cubitt
Mr J. F. Cudahy
Mr M. F. Cullis
John Culshaw
Frank Cummins
B. J. Cummins
Mr & Mrs E. Cummins
Ms J. A. Cummins
M. C. Cumpsty
Mrs E. C. Cundall
Miss J. Cunliffe
Lynne Cunningham
Dr James Stevens Curl
R. A. J. Curtis
R. V. Curtis
Sir John Curtis
Margaret Curtis
Peter Curtis
Richard A. Curtis
Mike Cushman
R. Cussons
Dr John Cuthbert
J. A. Cuthbertson OBE
Geoff Cutting
Peter Cutts
Mr K. C. Cutts
Mrs W. D'Arcy
C. A. Daeley
Colin Daff
Dennis Pehrson Dalberg
Mr F. W. Daley
Dr V. M. Dalley
Mrs M. Dallisson
Joseph Daly
T. D. Dampney
Gerry A. Danby
Dr V. J. Daniel
Peter Danny
Mrs P. Danvers
Mr Dar
Janet Dartnall
D. J. Daruvala
Daniel Darwood
B. H. Davenport
Mr & Mrs J. Davey
Dr T. J. David
Mr & Mrs Robert David
P. J. Davidson
John Davidson
J. Davies
J. B. Davies
Dr Gareth Davies
Anne Davies
Mr & Mrs Davies
Mrs D. H. Davies
Edward Davies
Sydney G. C. Davies
Mr G. Davies
Jonathan M. Davies
Meinir Davies
F. A. Davies
Mari Davies
Mr. T. A. Davies
Miss E. A. Davies
Huw Davies
Dr R. J. & Mrs K. B. Davies
Malcolm Davies
John Davies
Stephen Davies
Mrs D. M. Davies
Ben Davies
Dr W. H. E. Davies
C. V. Davies
E. Davis
Michael Davis
Mr B. A. Davis
Mr D. Davis
Mr E. C. Davis
Mr W. Davis
Miss J. Davis
C. Davison
Dr G. Davison
Dr & Mrs R. P. R. Dawber
Iris M. Dawes
Ursula Daws
Janet Dawson
Mr & Mrs C. L. Dawson
Edward Day
Timon Day
Jonathon Day

Cindy Day
John Day
Mr & Mrs E. R. Day
Mr & Mrs John Day
J. M. A. de Burgos
F. C. de Paula
Mr & Mrs J. I. de Villiers
Mr & Mrs K. D. Deacon
John Deacon
Mrs B. A. Deacon
Mr & Mrs Alan Dean
D. A. Deans
Dr G. de Lisle Dear
Rosalind Dearly
Mr & Mrs B. Deasy
N. C. Dee
Michael Deeny
Conrad Dehn
Len Deighton
D. B. Delany
Lee Van Delden
Ann Delenne
Emily Delso
Margaret E. Denning
Steve Dennis
B. J. Dennis-Browne
John F. Derbyshire
Ken & Janet Derham
Anne Derrett-Smith
Muriel Derry
Mr G. Desler
Mr R. J. Dew
I. C. Dewey
V. H. & B. Dewey
Charles Dewhurst
Mrs S. B. Diamond
Alexander L. Dick
Rt Hon. Geoffrey Dickens MP
Dr D. O. Dickie
Keith H. Dickinson
I. Dickson
G. C. Dickson
Mr & Mrs Peter Diggory
S. A. Din
Mr S. Dingle
Timothy Diplock
E. A. Dirkson
Hugh Diver
Mr & Mrs C. P. Diver
John Dixon
Mrs B. E. Dixon
Richard A. Dixon
A. Dobson
Anthony Docherty
P. M. R. Dodd
Mrs A. Dodsworth
Mr and Mrs R. A. Dolbear
Mr W. P. Donald
Alexander Donaldson
L. M. Donaldson
James Donaldson
J. G. Donlan
A. Donnelly
A. H. Doran
H. Doran
James & Mary Douglas
C. T. Dourish
Mr D. Dowen
B. Dowling
T. J. & C. Downees
Sidney Downs
Colin Dowse
K. Draper
B. J. Drew
Mrs C. M. Drew
Garth Drinkwater
Jeff Driver
Mr D. Drummond
Roger P. T. Duckworth
G. S. B. G. Dudley
Ms J. A. Duffin
Albert Duffy
A. C. Duffy
Francis Duffy
J. S. Dugdale
A. Dukes
Mr & Mrs Dummett
The Rev. James Duncan
Mrs G. Dundas
Mrs M. Dunford
J. K. Dunkerley
P. J. Dunkin
Robert Dunkley
A. J. Dunlop
David and Eileen Dunn
Mr & Mrs A. Dunn
Anne Dunn
D. J. C. Dunstone
Ian Durant
Francis Durham
Denis Durno
Mrs S. F. Durrell-Walsh
Norman R. Dutsson
Mr & Mrs N. Dutson
Mr F. Dvorak
Paul Dwyer
D. J. J. Dyer
A. M. Dyer
Mr L. Dyer
Dr & Mrs Dykes
Mr R. D. Eager
Mr & Mrs Eagle
Linda Eales
Peter Earl
Denis J. Earl
M. J. Earl
Mrs D. Earnshaw
D. M. Easton
Dr Lindsay Easton
Jill Eastwood
Dr W. R. Easy
Mr J. Eaton
Mr & Mrs R. W. Eaton
Anna Eban
Mr R. C. Eburne
Mr C. H. Eckert
Brian A. Eckhardt
F. G. Lacey Edelweiss
Dr S. Eden
John Edington
R. J. Edwards
Joan Lipkin-Edwards
A. W. Edwards
Mr R. Edwards
Mrs S. Edwards
Mr J. M. Edwards
A. R. Edwards
K. H. Edwards
Ms L. Edwards
P. G. Edwards
Mrs M. G. Eeuweng
M. Egar
Richard Ehrlich
Mr E. Eisehandler
Richard Elber
Myra and Ray Elderfield
Mr T. M. Eldrid
J. Elledge
Iain Elliot
Mark Elliott
Mr I. R. Elliott
K. Elliott
Mr L. C. Elliott
Mrs Ellis
Mr R. Ellis
Ms C. M. Ellis
Mr & Mrs John Ellis
Peter W. Ellis
Alan A. Ellis
D. R. Ellis
Miss S. Elsbury
Major J. G. D. Elvin
Michael Emmerson
Michael & Anita Emmott
Jonathan Engler
J. English
F. E. English
Mrs English
Robert Entwistle
Ronald Epstein
Mrs J. Erswell
Mr W. D. Ervine
R. A. Evans
Jeremy Evans
M. J. Evans
R. G. Evans
Mr P. Evans
Mr & Mrs Evans
Lord Evans of Claughton
W. D. Evans
T. L. Evans
George W. Evans
D. I. K. Evans
Angela and Ray Evans
Mrs Evans
Deborah Evelyn
Mr & Mrs M. Everett
Barry E. Eves
H. D. L. Evett
Thomas G. Exley
Mr E. G. Eyre
I. Fair
Mr & Mrs Peter Fairley
P. A. Fairley
Mr R. B. Fairweather
Helen C. Falk
Mr F. Fallows
Timothy Fancourt
Dr John K. Fanning
Mrs C. E. Farmer
Rosalind Farnese
Sarah Farquharson
Anne Farr
Mr R. A. Farrand
Mrs G. Farrell
Lynne Farrell
Nicholas Farries
Ann Farrow
E. R. C. Farwiek
Jean-Claude Faucher
Matthew Fawcett
David Fearnley
Mrs O. R. M. Featherstone
M. Federighi
Kristine Fedewa
Catherine Feeny

Mrs Hilary Feingold
David G. Felce
F. Feller
Mr K. L. Fenner
Mrs C. Fenton
Mr & Mrs Ferdinando
G. Fergus
Andrew Ferguson
Dr W. M. Ferguson
Mrs S. Ferguson
Michael R. Ferguson
Mrs S. Fergy
Mrs J. Ferrett
Jon Ferrier
Mr B. A. Ferris
Steve Few
Mr H. Few
Sheila Fewtrell
Ms B. Fidler
Mrs C. A. Field
Dr M. J. Neal
Dennis C. Fill
Mr & Mrs J. Finkel
Mrs D. G. Finlay
Mary Finn
Mr M. Firth
Alan Firth
M. V. C. Firth
Mr & Mrs M. Firth
John Fisenberg
Rita Fish
Michael Fishberg
V. A. Fisher
Julie Fisher
Chris Fisher
Anthony Fitzgerald
P. D. Fitzgerald
A. J. Flanagan
T. C. Flanagan
James and Mary Flannery
Dr Michael D. Flannery
J. G. Fleming
Victoria Fletcher
Mr P. A. L. Fletcher
Miss N. Fletcher
Mr M. Flinn
R. A. Flint
Susan Russell Flint
Miss S. M. Flynn
Mrs Flynn
Christopher Fogg
Mr & Mrs J Forbes
K. W. Forbes
Mr J. S. Ford
Stafford Ford
Walter Ford
Grahame Y. Ford
Mr J. W. Ford
Brian Ford
Christopher Forman
Peter G. Forrest
Christina Forster
Marie Forsyth
Gordon Fortune
Richard Foster
Tracie Foster
A. S. Fotheringham
A. Fotheringham
Maria Fountain
Mr R. A. Fowler
John Fowles
Basil V. Fox
Mrs C. Foy
Dr B. Foyle
P. G. Fradgley
Derek and Marilyn Frampton
Jean France-Hayhurst
P. N. Francis
Dr A. Frank
Sir Douglas Frank QC
Pamela Frankel
Mr R. Frankenburg
Mr R. Frankland
Mr & Mrs W. Frankland
Liz Fraser
F. Fraser
Mrs G. M. Fraser
Jane Fraser
R. H. Fraval
Mrs W. A. Fray
John Freebairn
Elizabeth and Norman Freegard
Ann and George Freeman
R. Freeman
Prof. H. L. Freeman
Robert Freidus
Sy Friedman
Ms A. L. Friedman
C. E. Frost
E. G. Frost
Mr G. Froyd
Jonathan Fry
Dr Anthony Fry
M. C. Furey
John Gagg
Mr & Mrs C. M. Gallacher
Mr & Mrs O. Gallagher
Mr & Mrs T. Gamble
R. Gamblin
Dr P. Ganeri
Jean and Peter Garbutt
Mary Gardin
Miss S. Gardiner
Mrs F. Gardiner
Dr J. Gardner
Mr C. Gardner
Dr N. Gardner
Mark R. Garner
Amanda Garrett
G. N. Garside
John S. Gartside
Dr R. E. Garwood
Mrs M. Gascoigne
Eunice and Tony Gaskell
Mr J. M. Gasson
Dr Gillian Gau
Mr J. Gaunt
Dr M. R. & Mrs J. I. Gavin
Donald Mervyn Gay
Mrs V. M. Gaymer
W. Geddes
M. Gedney
Ann M. Geen
Lee Gek-Ling
Mr B. Gell
Paul Gelling
S. T. Genders
C. Gentinetta
Mr R. C. George
E. J. George
K. George
Mr R. Gerrard
Mrs J. Gerrard
Gillian Gerry
Alex Gibb
Mr & Mrs Austin Gibbons
Mr & Mrs S. Gibbons
Ms J. B. Gibbons
M. Gibbons
Tony Gibbs
Angela Gibson
Roy Gibson
Richard J. Gibson
Cynthia Gifford
Kenneth Gilbert
Susan Gilbert
Mr W. Gilbertson
R. Gilchrist
Mary Giles
Neil M. Gill
Mr & Mrs G. Gill
Malcolm Gillett
John Gillett
Judy Gilligan
Basil Gillinson
Jennifer Gillman
Peter M. Gillmore
John & Sue Gilmour
James Gilroy
Dr Alan Gilston
Sandra Giorgetti
Barbara Girt
Mr W. J. Glare
Margaret Glassey
Bruce Glassick
Joan Gledsdale
P. J. Gleeson
B. M. Glover
R. J. N. Glover
Mr H. Glover
Mrs P. M. Glover
A. J. Goater
Jennifer K. Goatley
Mr & Mrs J. F. Goble
Peter Godbe
G. S. Goddard
Mrs J. Godfrey
Mr & Mrs Godfrey
N. & P. A. Godley
Jeremy Godwin
M. I. Goh
Joy and Raymond Goldman
D. C. Goldrei
A. Goldsmith
Michael Goldwater
J. P. J. Gomer
Tom Gondris
M. Gonzalez
M. F. Good
J. M. Goodall
Mr A. R. Goodden
Mr & Mrs R. A. J. Goode
Mrs T. A. Goodger
C. Goodhand
William Goodhart
H. M. Goodman
Sharon Goodman
Mrs B. Goodman
Mrs M. K. Goodman
B. J. Goodman
Mrs P. Goodson
Mrs J. Goodwin
Ken Goody
Ronald Goodyer
Howard Gordon
R. C. J. Gordon
Miss R. Gordan
John Gorman
S. J. Gorton
Dr J. R. Gosden
Roger Goss
David M. Goss
Miss Gough and Mr Jones
Dr R. Goulding

Mr R. J. Goundry
D. W. Gower
Mrs J. C. Goymour
Catherine Grace
Ms M. F. Grace
Mrs B. L. Graham
Mr J. W. R. Graham
M. and L. Graham
J. C. Graham
Mrs G. Graham
Mr C. S. Grainger
F. W. P. Gramlick
Mr & Mrs John Granger
Mr S. Grant
Denise M. Grant
Mrs S. Grant
Ruth Grant
Ms M. Grasar
Mr B. S. Graves
Ms Paula Gray
Mrs J. E. Gray
Peter Gray
Oscar Gray
Mr C. V. Greasley
Mr A. J. Green
Mr & Mrs Kenneth Green
Ms J. M. Green
Mrs M. Green
Ignatius Green
Judy Green
Dr P. J. Green
John Green
N. Green
J. C. Green
Pauline Greenhalgh
Mrs G. Greening
Susan Greening
Mrs D. P. Greensil
Mr & Mrs Greenslade
M. N. W. Greenwood
Mr & Mrs K. Greenwood
Mr A. Greenwood
Mr J. Greenwood
Fiona Greeson
Dr P. R. Gregory
Irene Gregory
Mr & Mrs P. V. Gregory
Dr P. R. Gregory
Dr D. R. Grey
A. K. Grice
A. R. Griews
P. W. Griffiths
Alan Griffiths
W. T. G. Griffiths
Michael Grigsby
Mr R. F. B. Grimble
Shirley Grimwood
Don Grisbrook
Mr & Mrs Grose-Hodge
A. Grossman
Elizabeth Grove
R. Grover
J. Groves-Hill
Daniel Gruffydd Jones
A. D. Grumley-Grennan
J. R. Grundy
Anthony Gubbins
Mr & Mrs R. K. Guelff
Mr M. G. Guest
Mrs S. D. Guilfoyle
Mr & Mrs C. R. Gull
Mrs E. M. Gulyas
Jackie Gunn
Rosalind Gunning
Mrs S. Gunter
C. A. Gurney
Edward L. L. Gush
Mr A. Guthrie
Patrick Gwen
Mrs J. Gyde
S. C. Hacker
Bridget Hackshaw
Karen Haddad
Mr W. F. Haggerty
Alan Haigh
Mary Haigh
Martin Hainey
Mr & Mrs H. R. Hale
Mr C. Haley
M. S. Haley
Mr D. W. Hall
I. Hall
J. Hall
Dr & Mrs Hall
David Hall
Hazel Hall
Miss J. F. Hall
Mr & Mrs G. J. Hall
Colin Hall
Mrs J. M. Hall
Mr P. K. Hall
Lyn Hall
Mr & Mrs W. Hall
Diana Hall
Mr J. H. Hallam
W. J. Hallett
John Hallion
Mrs G. Hallsworth
Hilary Halpin
Tom Halsall
R. Hamilton
D. S. Dagmar
John G. Hamlin
Mr Andrew Hammett
Carol Hammond
P. G. M. Hancock
Mr A. R. Hancock
E. J. Hand
Jane Handcock
Mr & Mrs Handley
Lorraine M. Handley
Jenny Hanksford
Peter Hannaford
Robert Hannay
Mr D. E. Hanson
O. J. Hanson and L. D. Hall
Maurice Hanssen
Arthur J. Hanvey
Mrs M. G. Hardingham
Dr Michael Hardman Lea
A. T. Hardwick
Jean Hardwicke
C. M. Hardy
Mrs A. Hardy
Joan Hare
Mrs P. Hargrave
Mrs D. A. Harlow
Mr & Mrs A. Harmer
J. E. Harmsworth
Corinne Jane Harper
Tim Harper
D. & E. Harries
Martyn Harris
Chris Harris
Robert Harris
Raymond Harris
Alan Harris
Jerry Harris
Mr & Mrs Harris
Mrs D. Harris
Mr R. Harris
Clifford Harris
Mrs C. Harris
Dr P. R. Harris,
Malcolm Harris
Mrs G. M. Harrison
Annette Harrison
Vanessa Harrison
Mr & Mrs P. T. Harrison
Dr and Mrs T. A. Harrison
D. C. Harrison
Mrs Harrison
D. T. Harrison-Sleap
Dr R. Harrod
F. Harrop
John Harrop
John Harry
Mr & Mrs P. Hart
Mr and Mrs D. J. Hart
G. B. Hart
Christine Hart
C. T. Hart
M. G. and V. A. Hart
P. J. Hartley
Anne Hartley
J. D. Hartley
D. B. M. Hartman
Donald Hartog
Dr Peter Harvey
David Harvey
Mr P. Harvey
C. I. Harvey
E. T. Harvey
Miss M. Harvey
R. Harvey
J. Harvey Hallam
Mr J. K. Hassell
Janice Hassett
Mrs C. Hastings
P. E. Hattersley
Hedley Haward OBE, JP
C. D. Hawer
Charles Hawes
Mrs P. D. Hawker
Canon P. C. Hawker
Ms M. O. S. Hawkins
Mr R. G. P. Hawkins
Mrs P. Hawkins
Mr P. B. Hawley
R. Haynes
R. B. Haynes
Mr Hayward
A. R. M. Holsey
Mr & Mrs C. Hazzard
Rev. Bruno Healy
J. W. S. Hearle
Tony Heath
A. V. Heath
David Heath
Mr G. Howard Heaton
Rev. N. C. Heavisides
Mr & Mrs Heber-Percy
Jenny Hedges
Sandra Hedges
Mrs R. E. Heginbotham
Dr Marc E. Heine
Mrs J. C. Heisler,

R. A. Hellawell
Betty Heller
C. J. Hemming
Michele Henderson
Dr W. A. Henderson
Dr A. F. Henderson
A. L. Henderson
Daphne Henderson
Paul Henderson
Mrs Jean Henderson
Andrew S. Hendrie
Bill Hendry
Mr D. Heney
Anne Hennell
Mrs L. G. Henry
B. A. Henry
Niell Hanson
Mr & Mrs Herber-Percy
Roy Herbert
A. James Herbert
Craig Herron
Rita Hetherington
Mr A. J. Hetherington
Mr & Mrs B. Hewins
S. Hewitson
Mr A. J. Hewitt
John Hewkin
Jack R. Heyden
Mr N. Heyworth
E. V. Hibbert
Mr & Mrs R. Hibbett
Mrs M. A. Hickman
John Hicks
Mr & Mrs J. Hicks
Mr M. Hicks
P. F. Higgins
Mr J. R. Higgins
Dorothy Highland
Ashley Hildebrandt
Mr B. I. Hill
Neville D. Hill
Mr H. A. W. Hill
Wendy Hillary
Wendy Hillary
Mr L. C. Hillier
J. R. Hillman
Mr & Mrs D. W. Hills
A. P. G. Hilton
B. J. Hind
Mrs J. Hind
Miss C. E. Hind
Ronald and Maureen Hinde
Stephen Hindle
Dr B. P. Hindle
Andrew and Frances Hindle
Stanley Hindle
David Hindley
P. J. H. Hindley
Mr E. Hinds
Jennifer Hinton
Mrs S. J. Hipwell
G. S. Hislop
Michael Hjort
Elizabeth Hjort
Mr T. T. Ho
Ophelia Ho
Mrs Olive Hoad
P. A. Hoare
Jeremy Hoare
Valerie C. Hobson
Brian W. G. Hodds
Mr W. G. Hodges
Mr J. E. and Ms M. G. Hodgkin
Frank and Daphne Hodgson
Catherine M. Hodson
Edmund Hoe
Jonathan Hoffman
Dr & Mrs K. Hofheinz
Patricia Hogben
Michael Hoggett
David Holbrook
Miss S. Holden
A. C. Holden
Derrick Holden
Mr M. P. Holden
Dr & Mrs H. M. Holding
Kevin Holland-King
J. B. Hollingsworth
A. G. W. Holloway
M. Holloway
R. W. Holmes
Mrs J. T. Holmes
Dr R. L. Holmes
L. Holt-Kentwell
Bance F. Hom
F. J. Homer
S. Homer
Brian Honan
Peter Hood
D. & V. Hooley
N. Hooper
Mr N. S. Hooper
L. Hopcraft
Mrs B. M. Hopewell
Miss J. L. Hopkins
R. C. Hopton
B. L. H. Horn
Simon Hornby
J. A. Horne
Chris Horner
Robert Horner
Mr P. R. Hornsby
Rita Horridge
Pauline A. Horrigan
W. Horsfield
G. & A. Horsfield
Simon Hosein
T. W. Hoskins
Kieran M. Hosty
Mr & Mrs J. Hough
Barry Houghton
D. R. Houston
V. A. Howard & R. F. Rogerson
Michael Howard
B. R. Howard
Mr & Mrs Derek Howard
Keith Howell-Jones
John I. Howells
Mr T. H. Howells
Mrs G. Howey
R. Howgego
Dianne Howlett
W. T. Howorth
Mr J. W. Howsam
E. W. Hoy
Mr N. T. E. Hoyle
Robert Hubble
Joan and Peter Hudson
E. V. Hudson
A. M. Hudson
Paul S. Hudson
Janice Hughes
Mr J. Hughes
Raymond Hughes
Mr R. C. Hughes
Miss R. Hughes
Mr M. Hughes-Chamberlain
James Hugonin
Joy Hulbert
Mr & Mrs K. Hulbert
B. P. Hull
G. E. J. Hunt
P. Hunt
T. V. Hunt
Dr James M. Hunter
C. M. Hunter
D. R. Hunter
Dr D. N. Hunter
Hugh C. Hunter
Tracy Huntleigh-Smith
Mr C. J. Hurd
Mr & Mrs Peter Hurford
Winifred B. Hurley
Sue Hurt
Mr M. Hurwitt
Ian Huskisson
Ahmed Hussan
G. R. Hutcheson
V. Hutchinson
Janet Hutchinson
Andrew Hutchinson
W. A. Hutton
Mrs S. A. Hutty
N. J. Huxley
Ms M. Hyde
Mr T. J. Hypher
Mr & Mrs B. Igra
Mrs V. A. Iles
Dr N. R. Ineson
A. D. Ingham
Sally Ingham
Mr P. Inglesant
Fred Inglis
Mrs A. Ingram
Brian Ingram
Micheal Innes
Jane Isaac
A. M. Isaacs
Mr & Mrs Philip Ison
J. Izod
Mr & Mrs Jack
H. R. S. Jack-School
Jill Jackson
Ms S. P. Jackson
Sheila Jackson
Nicholas Jackson
Calvin Jackson
Mr R. J. Jackson
C. Jackson
Mrs L. M. Jackson
H. C. Jackson
Jack L. Jacobs
A. A. Jacobs
Tom Jaine
Mrs F. James
Mr N. James
Mr P. & Mrs C. James
Mrs P. James
Mr D. James
Mrs L. James
Mabel C. James
Mr M. D. Janson
Moira Jarrett
Antony Jay
Prof. Barrie Jay
P. & J. Jeans
Mrs P. M. Jefferis
The Rev. K. C. Jeffery
Mr P. A. Jeffery
A. H. Jeffery

W. Jeffery
Paul Jeffreys Powell
Mr D. L. Jelley
Rowan Jenkins
A. B. Jenkins
Frances Jenkins
Clive Jenkinson
B. H. Jenkinson
Martin Jennings
Mary Jennings
Christopher and Jane Jennings
J. C. Jennings
S. W. Jennings
J. M. Jennings
Dr & Mrs P. F. Jessen
Mrs P. M. Jeyes
Deborah Jeynes
Mr C. A. Joannides
Brian Jobson
Dave A. D. John
Martyn John
C. Johnson
N. J. Johnson
Chris Johnson
Mrs J. K. Johnson
S. Johnson
Michelle Berriedale Johnson
Mr R. H. Johnson
Mr T. E. Johnson
Janet A. Johnson
Maureen Johnson
Iris Johnson
Dr I. H. D. Johnston
Mrs Johnston
Andrea Jolly
Dr D. Jones
J. K. Jones
Mr K. Jones
Mr K. D. Jones
K. H. Jones
Dr R. W. Jones
B. W. Jones
Mr & Mrs J. Jones
Mr & Mrs W. Morris Jones
Pauline Jones
G. T. Jones
Pamela Jones and Gerry Northam
James Cellan Jones
Tessa Jones
Mr T. E. Jones
Dr J. B. Jones
T. L. Jones
Mr & Mrs G. Jones
S. E. Jones
Mr W. C. M. Jones
Ian Jones
Miss P. A. Jones
Canon Ronald Jones
Mr N. F. Jones
D. Jones
I. R. Jones
C. G Jones
Angela and Graham Jones
Peter Jones
S. R. Jones
S. H. Chiswell Jones
Tracey Jones
Mr B. Jordan
Mr C. J. F. Jordan
P. Jordan
James Joseph
A. Josephs
W. R. R. Joy
Mrs M. A. Joyce
M. R. Judd
R. E. Judges
I. R. Judson MB,B. Chir. ,MRCP
Richard J. Jutty
Eric Kahn
J. Kamper
Alexandra Karan
Margo Kasdan
Peter Katin
R. Hagon & Mike Kaufman
Mrs B. M. Kay
Mr T. M. Kay
J. M. Kaye
D. L. Kaye
Terry Keane
Jane Kearley
R. E. Keen
Sheila Keene
Mrs K. Kelly
Kathleen Kelly
Mr & Mrs J. B. Kelsall
Robert Kelso
H. S. Kemp
Mr G. Kemp
Joan Kennedy
Joan Kennett
Miss D. J. Kent
Mrs D. Kent
Ms A. Kent
Jill Kent
W. J. Kent
Mr R. Kerby
Dr A. M. Kerr
Robert Kershaw
E. Kester
R. A. Kettle
Mr B. Kettlewell
C. G. Kew
M. R. Khan
Sally Kibble
D. I. Kidman
L. G. Kieran
Alan Kilburn
J. H. Kilby
Sir Robert and Lady Kilpatrick
Mr & Mrs Kimbel
The Earl of Kimberley
Rev. A. B. King
I. W. King
Mr H. F. King
Captain R. E. H. King RM
Alan King
Charles Kingsley-Evans
Dr B. W. Kington
Ann Kinnerson
Mr R. Kinnon
Mr & Mrs W. A. Kinsman
Ms D. Kirby
Mrs C. Kirk
Jean Kirk
Terence Kirwan
John Kleeman
A. B. Knapp
Robin Knapp
J. C. Knappe
Mr J. C. Knight
A. B. Knight
D. A. Knight
J. O. Knight
Richard Knight
G. J. Knight-Adams
Peter Knipe
J. Knott
Peter Knowles
Dr J. Knowles & Mr N. Harris
Mrs A. K. Knox
Mrs L. Skjodt Knudsen
H. K. Kohler
Mr M. Krag
Dr K. Krcmar
Marianne & Lionel Kreeger
Mr P. D. Kudelka
Hubert Kueh
Robert Kuehn
Dr D. W. Kyle
Yvonne Lahaise
Mr I. Laidlaw-Dickson
Dr Gavin Laird
M. Laird
Mrs C. Lake
Francesco Lama
Mr A. J. Lambert
Dr J. G. Lambert
Jeanette Lammey
Norman Lanaro
Mr J. Lancaster
Jack Lang
Alistair Lang
Mr J. Langford
Tony and Christine Langrick
A. T. Langton
C. B. Lanyon
Susan Larg
R. W. Larkin
Jeffrey Latham
Mrs Laughton
Anne Laurence
Mr L. Lavender
Mrs J. E. M. Lavers
Erif Lawler
E. Lawn
R. Lawrence
J. and M. Lawrence
John H. Lawrence
Mr Lawson
Michelle Lawson
Vivien Lawson
M. A. Lawson Smith
Ferrers Le Mesurier
A. S. Lea
Clyde Lea
David Lea-Wilson
Dr S. Leach
J. D. Leach
Dr A. D. Leading
Dr W. E. Leathem
Mr J. Leavens
Jane Lee
Mrs M. Lee
P. Lee
Micheal H. Lee
Mr & Mrs D. Lee
P. T. Lee
Mrs C. A. Lee
Martin Lee-Warner
James Leek
A. & J. Leeming
Mrs R. M. Lees
M. B. Leggett
Mrs S. Lehrer
Mrs J. Leigh
Cdr D. R. Leighton,RN
Mr J. A. Lemkin CBE
P. L. Leonard
Hugh Leonard
Mrs Leslie
Mr & Mrs M. R. R. Leslie
S. Lester
David James Lester
Grace Leung

Brian Levene
Ms J. H. Leventhal
I. E. Levey
Dr & Mrs J. Levi
J. R. Levick
Judy Levine
Jane Levine
Mr B. P. Levitt
Mrs C. Levy
Felix Levy
Mr & Mrs Lewin
Mr & Mrs T. J. Lewin
Heather Lewis
Miss Mary Lewis
Mrs C. Y. Lewis
Mr & Mrs E. Lewis
Mr D. J. B. Lewis
Clive R. Lewis
Mrs C. Lewis
Tony Lewis
Mr & Mrs Lieberman
Mr E. Lightman
Mr C. D. R. Lightowler
David J. Lilly
Ms L. Lim
Mrs A. Lincoln
Frank Lincoln
Mr R. J. & Mr A. Lincoln
Helene Lind
Katherine Lindap
Zena Linfield
Mr M. M. Lindley
Donald C. Lindon
Angus Lindsay
Lady Lindsey
Mr & Mrs K. Line
J. H. Ling
D. R. and A. J. Linnell
P. A. Lintott
David Lipton
Chris Liptrot
Ann Liss
Sherrell Litchfield
Claire F. Little
Mr S. C. Littlechild
R. Littlewood
Dr Roland Littlewood
M. Llewellyn
Mrs J. D. Lloyd
Lorna Lloyd
Mr T. P. Lloyd
Brian and Pat Lloyd
Ellyn LLwyd
N. Loasby
Andrew Lobbenberg
Sue Lockwood
Elvira Lord
Cliff Lodge
Mr M. C. Lodge
David Lodge
Gloria Loeur
Victoria Logue
Lord Londonderry
Mr M. Longman
Charles R. Longsworth
Miss R. D. Longworth
R. C. Loombe
Matheos T. Los
Prof. & Mrs R. Loudon
A. Loudoun
Raymond Love
Mr & Mrs Lovell
R. F. Lovelock
Gareth Lovett Jones
P. A. & J. B. Lowater
I. Lowe
Corinne Lowe
P. Lowman
Gary Lowrey
Graham John Lucas
Maureen Lucas
J. R. Lucas
F. G. Luff
Mrs D. J. Lund
Dr John Lunn
M. Lunnon
Ralph Lunzer
D. F. Lyle
G. Lynch-Watson
J. R. Lyons
Suzanne Lyons
P. Macaulay
Lady Claire Macdonald
Dr B. E. W. Mace
Dr D. MacEoin
Mrs B. E. Macfarlane
Lindy Macfarlane
R. B. MacGeachy
Mr & Mrs MacInnes
Mr M. Macintosh
G. Macintyre
Miss K. Mack
Miss. T. Mackay
Alistair J. Mackechnie
Shirley A. Mackenzie
Ennyd Mackenzie
L. T. Fraser Mackenzie
Helen Mackie
D. Mackle
Ruth Mackler
Mrs P. Maclaurin
Dr N. Maclean
Lesley Maclean
Mr & Mrs G. Maclean
D. Maclean
Barbara Maclean
E. W. F. MacLeish
A. MacLennan
Dr I. R. Macleod
Mr J. MacManus
Iain A, MacMillan
A. M. Magnaghten
Patrick MacNamee
Mr C. D. Macqueen
James Macrae
Mr M. Madden
W. A. Maddison MBE
G. F. & J. Maddocks
Mr G. Maddocks
Mr & Mrs K. L. Maddocks
Mrs H. M. Magen
R. P. Magennis
Geoff Magnay
Prof. I. A. Magnus
Mr & Mrs G. Mainwaring
R. J. Maisey
Mrs J. W. Makinson
Dr P. Mallinson
Mrs C. F. Malone
S. R. Mamdani
Stuart Manger
Ms D. Manley
C. A. Mann
Phillip Mannion
Stephen Mannion
Graham Mansbridge
K. Mansfield
Mark R. Manson
Jonathan Marchbank
G. Marconi
Kerry Marcus
Henry Marcuzzi
H. W. Marden Ranger
Jonathan P. Margolis
R. W. Marjoram
Darryl Marks
Mr R. Marleyn
Mrs J. Marquand
M. L. Marriott
Melvin Marriott
Rosemary Marsh
Warren Marsh
Mrs P. M. Marsh
Adrian Marsh & Ms M. Stoker
R. O. Marshall
R. F. D. Marshall
Tony and Valerie Marshall
Mr T. Marshall
S. Marshall
Dr Alan Marsland
Mrs A. Martin
P. Martin
A. H. Martin
Mrs M. P. Martin
Mrs J. Martin
Belinda Martin
Emilia Marty
Mr R. Marven
Ms O. Marx
Daniel Maskell
Mrs A. Mason
Ruth Mason
Avril Mason
Peter Mason
Ms M. Masten
Mr & Mrs Mathias
Dr Anne Matter
Mrs C. Matthews
John Matthews
C. Matthews
Roland Matthews & Angela Wells
D. Maury
Michael Maxwell
Mr A. P. May
Kenneth and Suzanne May
J. May
Ruth Maynard
Mrs Y. Mazzocent
Jean McConnell
Andrew McAlpine
D. McAndrew
R. B. G. McCall
A. J. McCall
James McCann
B. Scott McCarthy
Dr & Mrs J. W. McClenehan
Mrs A. McClurkin
David McConaughy
K. McConaughy
K. I. McCrea
M. C. McCrindle
Miss M. McCuire
Cynthia McDowall
Prof. T. J. McElwain
Mr & Mrs J. V. McEntee

M. J. McErlain
Sue McEvoy
Dr Shirley R. McEwan
Mrs E. M. McEwen
Marion McFarlane
Fiona McFarlane
Prof. & Mrs I. D. McFarlane
Mr C. J. McFeeters
Mr & Nrs N. J. McGalagly
Mr D. McGavin
Mrs P. McGee
Colin and Lilian McGhee
Robin McGhee
Simon Mitchell
Mr & Mrs D. A. McGreavy
Mr D. S. McGuire
G. P. McHugh
Sheila McIlwrick
Charles McKee
Jackie McKenna
Nancy McKenzie
J. McEown
J. A. McKinnell
Declan W. McLoughlin
Dr J. Fraser McLuskey
Mrs C. McMahon
Susan McManus
Mr & Mrs F. McMaster
Neil McMillan
Ian R. McNeilage
Ronald S. McNeill CBE
Moira McNichol
K. McNicholls
Mr S. McNulty
Mrs F. McQuade
Anne McQuade
Gordon McSweeney
Jonathan Meades
Jeremy Meadow
Prof. S. R. Meadow
Sally Meadows
Rick Mee
Iona Meek
Mr & Mrs Meek
Louis Meeks
Michael Meldrum
Mr D. Mellor
Ms S. Melling
C. I Mellor
Dr D. Melzack
Miss E. J. Menzies
Dr & Mrs A. P. Mercer
Mr N. J. Merryweather
A. Mertens
David Messum
Philip Metcalfe
A. W. Metherell
Mr C. J. Methley
E. F. P. Metters
Moynur Miah
Mr & Mrs Michaelson
Danielle Michalitsianos
Katrina Michel
C. A. & J. Michelmore
John M. G. Michelsen
Patricia Michelson
Robert Middle
Jenny Middlemass
Elizabeth Middlemiss
R. C. Middlesford
Robin Middleton
Mr N. D. Middleton
Glyn Middleton
Mr J. R. Miele
Paul Miles
Mr & Mrs P. H. Miles
Mr & Mrs A. P. Miles
Mr & Mrs A. T. Miller
Gordon Miller
Paul Miller
Pamela Miller
Mrs C. Miller
Mr G. S. Miller
T. W. Miller-Jones
Mr & Mrs Millington
Mr & Mrs L. Mills
Mr A. D. Mills
Mr H. G. Millward
Mr D. V. Milne
Mr & Mrs Milne
F. J. Milward
I. W. Mitchell
Ruth Mitchell
Mrs J. C. Mitchell
Ross Mitchell
Barrett R. Mitchell
Sandra Mitchell
Mrs T. M. Mitchell-Fox
Mr & Mrs H. Mlynarski
Philip Moger
Mrs J. Mole
Mr J. W Moles
Dr A. Moliver
Michael Moliver and Dorothy Jordan
Ragnar Mollan and Elin Anderson
Ralph Molland
Mr A. Momen
Ronald Monjack
Miss K. R. Monk
Janet Monk
Robin Monks
J. Montagnon
A. P. Montblat
Mrs E. Moody
W. Mooney
Eric Moonman
B. Moorcroft
Simon Moore
Caroline M. Moore
Alun Brooks Moore
Mr & Mrs W. E. Moore
Mr R. H. Moore
Timothy Moore
R. K. Moore
Michael W. Moore
Mr R. G. A. Moore
Nigel K. Moore
Jane Moore
Joan M. Morbey
Alan and Greta Mordue
S. A. Morel
M. H. Morgan
Hazel Morgan
Mr R. F. Morgan
Mrs M. Morgan
Mrs T. Morgan
Michael Morgan
Dr D. R. Morgan
F. Moriarty
D. P. Morland
Ms G. Morley
P. A. Morley
Mr F. Morrell
Michael Morrice
A. L. Morrich
Mr R. Morris
Isobel Morris
Renee Morris
Carolyn Morris
D. Morris
A. C. Morrison
Deborah Morrissey
Ralph Morrow
David Mort
Marisa Morteo
Sir Claus Mose
Mrs J. Moss
Mr & Mrs A. Moss
Ann Moss
Christopher Moss
Mr R. W. Mottram
John Motum
N. J. Mould
Mrs E. Mouttoo
K. B. Mowle
Mr & Mrs W. A. Moxon
Stewart Muir
M. S. Mullay
Miss S. Mullins & M. Tungey
Mrs S. C. Mulvey
Mr & Mrs G. L. Munday
Anthony Mundy
Mr P. Munnoch
Miss E. A. Munro
Mr. A. H. Munro
Mr & Mrs D. Munt
rah Murdoch
Miss G. Murfin and Miss M. Sanderson
Paul Murphy
Braham Murray
Mrs M. L. Murray Smith
A. Murray Smith
Mr R. Musel
Dr M. Myszor
Sue Naden
Nicholas and Madeleine Nadin
Arthur Nardone
Mr F. Nash
Harold J. Nash
T. H. Nash
Ann Nash
P. J. L. Nash
Rob and Jenny Nathan
M. H. Neeves
Gideon Nellen
Dr & Mrs Harry Neubauer
Julia Neuberger
Sylvia Neumann
Dr Richard Neville
Peter Gold New
Dr J. M. Newbery
Dr Peter Newbould
M. C. Newbury
David Newell
Philip Newfield
Mr T. Newman
Mrs G. Newman
Deborah Newman
Mrs V. L. Newport-Butcher
Mr A. Newsham
Sandra Newton
Mr & Mrs C. S. Newton

Jeffrey Ng
Peter Nicholls
Mr & Mrs G. Nicholls
Tom Nicholls
M. L. Nicholson
M. C. Nicholson
Mr & Mrs P. Nicklin
Mr I. H. Nicol
Mr & Mrs M. C. D. Niemyski
Ms A. Nightingale
Dr Angela Ning
Rev. Ronnie Noakes
Mrs D. A. Noble
Roger Noble
Mr L. W. Norcott
Shirley Norris
Michael Norris
S. North
Lt Col. R. P. Norton
John Julius Norwich
Mr C. L. Notton
Richard Nowell
Frank Nuthall
David Nutt
M. Nutter
Mrs A. O'Brien
Dr C. G. O'Bryan-Tear
J. B. O'Connor
Teresa O'Connor
Mr L. J. O'Hara
Mrs O'Keefe
Rory and Agatha O'Moore
W. B. O'Neill
Mr G. M. O'Reilly
Jacqueline Oag
M. D. Oakley
Mr & Mrs K. A. Oates
Charles Oatwig-Thain
John Oddey
Dr R. Odedra
Mrs L. V. Offord
Mr P. A. Ogden
R. A. L. Ogston
E. Oldfield
David Olier
A. J. Oliver
Rt Hon. S. Oppenheim-Barnes
H. S. R. Orde
Mrs E. Orme
Ewan and Karen Ormiston
Miss L. Orriss
Mrs A. Orton
Mr & Mrs R. E. Osborne
Mrs S. E. Osborne
Mrs M. E. Oswald
Mr T. Ottaway
Mr A. Otter
E. J. Owen
Keith Owen
Mr & Mrs J. A. Owen
Mr & Mrs G. R. Owen
James and Sheila Owens
Mrs A. Owston
Ann Owston
Huseyin Ozer
P. Stafford
Bruce Packham
Mrs A. M. Padgett
J. D. Page FRICS
A. M. Page
Sue and Geoff Page
Dr & Mrs A. Page
Mr. Meilir Page
R. Pagett and S. Butler
Jonathan P. R. Palfrey
Dr A. C. Palmer
Mr & Mrs J. Palmer
Ms J. Palmer
Mrs J. C. Palmer
Kathryn Palmer
Andrew and Laurella Parffrey
Miss G S Parker
Daney Parker
Jean Parker and Eric Winter
Mr J. S. Parker
Mr R. Parker-Jervis
Mr Chris Parkin
Mr A. C. Parkinson
Ross Parland
Mrs A. Parnum
Mrs F. Parr
Andrew Parrish
E. M. Parrish
Michael B. Parrish
John W. R. Parrott
R. E. Parry
Dr Heather Parry
J. Parsons
Mr C. J. Parsons
Dr Christopher Parsons
A. D. Parsons
Mrs K. Parsons
S. Parsons
Christopher Parsons
Michael Paster
Mr & Mrs R. A. Pasterfield
Mr & Mrs K. Patel
Paul and Gill Pateman
Mrs D. S. Paterson-Fox
Carolyn Patey
Mr R. Patmore
G. M. Patrick
Mrs J. A. Patterson
Mrs M. G. Patterson
Dr R. A. Patterson
Dr R. A. Pattison
Miss C. Payne
Mr & Mrs R. W. Payne
R. E. J. Payne
A. and R. Peace
Robert A. Peacock
J. F. Pearce
Rosalind Pearcy
Michael S. J. Pearson
M. J. Pearson
John Pearson
Mrs I. Peasley
Mrs A. M. Peile
M. A. Pelham
Mr H. F. Pennington
Mr John Penny
D. M. Penny
Mr N. E. Penty
Mr D. Peppercorn and Ms S. Sutcliffe
C. M. Perkins
Mrs L. R. Perkins
Roy Perrott
Tim Perry
K. Perry
Ann Peters
Robert W. Petersen
Mr R. C. Petherick
Miss I. A. Petrie
Linda Pettit
G. W. Petty
Mr & Mrs Neal Peyre
Toni Pfeiffer
Mr J. K. Phelps
Maureen Philbin
Mrs C. M. Philip
Morvan Jezu Philippe
Mr B. J. E. Phillips
Mr & Mrs S. Phillips
Mr R. L. Phillips
I. D. Phillips
Berre and Peter Phillips
Ms C. Phillips
P. J. R. Phillips
A. Phillips
Mrs M. Phillips
Sally Phillips
Alicia Gregg Phillips
Dr & Mrs R. M. Phillips
Judith Phillips
Mrs I. L. Phillipson
P. E. Pickering
Mr G. H. and Ms B. J. Pickles
Mr & Mrs J. R. Pickup
A. M. Pickup
D. R. Piedot
Dr Gerald G. Pierce
June Pierce
Mr D. B. E. Pike
Major G. L. S. Pike
Malcolm Pim
Clare Pinder
Dr & Mrs N. J. Pinfield
Mrs B. M. Pinfold
Veronica Pinney
Nancy Pistrang
Michael Pitel
R. N. Pittman
Mr H. Plaskow
Ian Pleeth
Mrs L. J. Plumb
Nicola M. J. Y. Plummer
A. Pointon
Naomi Pokroy
R. G. Poland
K. Pollit
D. G. Poole
D. J. Poole
Steve Poole
Mrs D. V. J. Pope
Maggie Poppa
David Porter
E. D. Potkins
David Potter
Charles Potter MBE
Dr J. M. Potter
P. J. D. Pottinger
Ms B. Pound
Naomi Powell
M. Powell
B. R. Powell
Miss J. Powell
Y. Powell-Caley
Mrs V. J. Power
Ms A. Power-Smith
Mr & Mrs Prager

Mr & Mrs G. Pragnell
David Prais
Jean S. Pratley
Mr F. C. Pratt
Andrew Pratt
Mr S. R. G. Pratt
M. J. Prendergast
John Prentice
Mr K. W. Prescot
Alan Prescott
Simon Preston
Dr D. A. Preston
M. Preston
M. C. Price
Pamela Vandyke Price
Mrs E. Prideaux
Gerald Price
J. P. Priestley
Mr & Mrs C. B. Pringle
Peter J. Prior
J. F. Pritchard
Melanie Prole
Mr A. Prosser
Marie Prutton
Alan Prytherch
Col. Donald Pudney
W. L. Pugh
Shirley and Michael Pugh
N. G. and B. H. Pullan
Dr Oscar Puls
Andrew Pumphrey
Susan M. Punch
E. Punchard
Howard Pursey
Dr M. Purshouse
The Old Rectory
Mrs J. Puxley
Mr & Mrs R. Pycroft
Mr E. Pyke
Michael Quine
Paul Quinlan
Stanley P. Quinn
Michael Quinn
Angela and Ivor Quinn
Dr Frank Rackow
Ian and Daniele Radcliffe
N. A. Rae
Dr Stewart Rae
Ian Ragg
S. Raggett
Rita Rahman
Manoj Raichura
Alvin Rakoff
Philip Rallison
Mr D. S. Rampton
Mr A. Rampton
S. R. Ramsden
Col. G. K. Ramsey MBE
Selina Rand
Dr & Mrs D. G. S. Randall
Rosemary Randall
Nicholas Randall-Smith
Sarah J. Randell
Derek G. Randles
M. E. Rankin
Mr T. A. Rankin
Dr A. M. Rankin
J. Ranpuria
Caroline Raphael
Dr R. J. Rathbone
Peter Ratzer
Susan Raven
Peter Rawlings
Charles P. L. Rawson
John Ray
Mr W. Raymond
Trevor Rayne
Martin Rayner
Peter Rea
Maureen Rea
Patrick Reardon
Mr & Mrs R. A. Redhead
Mr T. F. Redman
F. Redmill
Jaine Redmond
Mr Rednall
M. I. Reed
Alec Reed
Dr A. I. Rees
John Reeve
W. Reeves
M. C. Reeves
Mrs R. I. Reeves
David Regan
Sue Reid
Thelma Reid
Miss A. Reid
Mr & Mrs R. Reid
Jane N. Reid
L. E. Reid
Ivan B. Rendall
Hazel Renwick
W. J. Revill
Mr & Mrs Reynold
S. R. C. Reynolds
Mr N. J. Reynolds
Mrs K. L. Reynolds-Jones
David Rhodes
J. O. Rhys
Miss M. Rice
Miss S. P. Richards
Mr G. A. Richards
Mrs L. C. and Mr K. J. Richards
Dr E. H. Richards
N. H. Richardson
George Richardson
C. J. Richardson
Ursula Richardson
E. A. Richardson
M. J. Richardson
Dr R. J. Richardson
Ursula Richley
Dr G. S. Riddell
Carol Riddick
D. J. Riddington
Alan Riddle
Christopher Ridgway
Mrs J. Ridley-Thompson
Mrs A. M. Ridout
Dr Thomas Riebartsch
J. A. Riemer
Steve G. Ries
Danielle Rimmer
Gordon Ringrose
Dr B. Ritson
E. Robarts
Linda Robert
Miss W. Roberts
Michael Roberts
Anne Roberts
Mr H. E. Roberts
Mrs G. R. Roberts
David G. E. Roberts
Mrs C. Roberts
A. C. Roberts
Mr J. P. Roberts
Barbara Roberts
Mrs P. A. Roberts
P. H. W. Roberts
Sheelagh Robertson
Mrs Robertson
N. Roberston
Dr A. John Robertson
Mrs R. G. Robinson
David Robinson and Ruth Hasty
D. H. Robinson
L. F. Robinson
Mrs P. N. Robinson
David Robinson
Sheila Robinson
Brian Robson
Dr G. A. Robson
Mrs B. Robson
A. C. Robson
Miss E. Roche
Mr J. Rochelle
Michael J Roderick
Alan Rodger
I. Rodges
Mr E. Rodrigues
Neil Lloyd Rogall
Sir Frank Rogers
John A. Rogers
Mrs M. L. Rogers
Miss E. L. Rogers
Margaret Rogers
Wayne A. Rohlfs
John Roland
Fiona Rollason
Michael Roller
Susan Rollings
Mr L. A. Rooney
Dr D. B. Roper
David Roper
William Rose and Susan Lawe
Daniel Rose
Mr J. L. Rose FCCA
Gerald B. Rose
Noah Rose
Mrs J. Rose
Mrs DP Rose
H. D and A. L Rose
Anthony Rosen
Margaret Roser
Clive Roslin
Mr Ross
Samantha Ross
Graham Ross
Mr & Mrs Mark Ross
Robert C. Ross-Lewin
Joyce Rosser
Brian D. Roulston
R. H. Rowan
Mrs J. M. Rowe
Michael Rowland
D. A. Rowland
Mr. J. Rowland
J. R. H. Rowland
J. Rowland-Entwistle
David and Diana Rowlands
Mr G. Rowntree
David Rowse
Mr M. L. Royle
Thomas Rozak
P. Rozee
Hilary P. Ruben
J. Rudd
Carol A. Ruddick
Miss M. J. Ruddick
Mr & Mrs M. Rudin
Mr R. J. Ruffell
K. M. Rule
John Rumsey
Dr I. J. Runcie

R. I. Rundle
Dr Noel Russell
Gillian A. Russell
A. Russell
I. Russell-Jarvie
Mr. T. Russen and Miss L. Davies
Tad Rutkowski
Dr Bruce Rutson
Mr J. S. Rutter
Mrs M. J. Ryder
Stephen Ryman
Mr J. H. Sacks
Mr L. Saffron
Mrs A. Sagar
A. J. H. Sale
M. E. Sale
Mrs T. Salisbury
Charles G. Salmon
Ron and Vera Salmon
Mr & Mrs Roy Slater
M. H. Salton
Dr William Salvini
Mrs H. Samain
Victoria Sampson
Mr M. Samuel
D. E. Samuel
Geoffrey J. Samuel
J. E. A. Samuels
Sydney Samuelson
Dr Lisa Sand
Joe Sanders
J. C. Sanderson
Priscilla Sandford
Elizabeth Sandham
Gillian Sandham
V. Sandiford
Dr A. C. E. Sandiland
Dr R. J. Sandry
Mrs D. P. Sands
Mr D. Sandys-Renton
Mr M. Sansam
Q. R. Saoul
Dr Abigail Sargent
David Sarjant
David Satterly
Mr G. Sattinger
Mr & Mrs G. Saunders
M. V. Saunders
Mr J. R. Saunders
M. L. Savage
John W. Savery
Dean Saville
Michael Saward
David de Saxe
J. F. and M. Sayers
Sally Saysell
Anne Scagell
Mr & Mrs P. Scallan
Mrs F. Scarr
B. J. Schafer
Mr. M. Schmittzehe
Theo Schofield
Judith M. Schofield
N. Schofield
Theo P. C. Schofield
Mr & Mrs C. J. Schofield
Michael Schofield
W. E. Scholes
J. M. Schorah
Mr R. Schwarz
Devin Scobie
Margaret Scott
Jen and John Scott
Mr B. Scott
Mr & Mrs J. N. D. Scott
Stella A. Scott
Miss L. H. Scott
Julian Scott
D. A. and Gerda Scott
Mr J. Scott
Mr & Mrs P. Scott
Mrs A. Scott
Mr P. D. Scott
Carolyn Scott
C. G. P. Scott-Malden
Mr J. Scott-Smith
Mrs G. Scovell
Dave Seager
Janet Searle
A. Seaward
John A. Seddon
Mr N. S. Seddon Brown
Mr & Mrs N. G. Sedgwick
Mr & Mrs E. P. & S. A. Seedhouse
Mr G. Segrove
Mr H. J. Seiffer
Dr Leonard M. Selby
Prof. Raman Selden
Paul Sellars
E. Sellars
Mr & Mrs N. Sellers
Mr W. R. Senior
F. B. Seward
Mrs J. Seymour
Mr & Mrs Shamash
Kathryn Shanks
Jean Shapiro
Robin Sharp
Nicholas Sharp
J. E. Sharp
Mrs A. Sharp
John T. L. Sharpe
Dr J. T. R. Sharrock
Vincent Shaw
Dr & Mrs S. A. G. Shaw
Mr V. J. Shaw
Lester W. K. Shaw
Mrs P. F. Sheard
Barry Sheerman
Sylvia Sheinfield
Mr & Mrs Shelmerdine,
Mr N. J. Shepherd
Martin J. Shepherd
Brenda Shepherd
Louise Sheppard
Charles Sheppard
Jenny Sheridan
Padraig Sheridan
Mr F. Sherman
Mr D. A. Sherrell
A. Sherwood
David Shillitoe
R. C. Shilton
Shing Chi Chan
Penelope Jayne Shipton
David Shonfield
Leslie Shore
James Shorrocks
Andrew Short
Douglas Short
Dr & Mrs T. E. Sicks
Mrs A. F. Sics
Vincent Sidworth
Jon Silkin
Dr & Mrs G. M. Siltherland
Harvey Silver
Martin Silver
Dr M. Silverman
Dr & Mrs Silverstone
George H. B. Sim
Robert C Sim
K. H. Simmonds
Hugh J. Simmonds
Betty Simms
Ivor Simon MA
Mr L. J. Simon
C. Simon
Anne Simons
Mr & Mrs D. Simpson
Alan Simpson
Ms L. A. Simpson
D. A. Simpson
Mrs B. Simpson
Dr I. Sims
Mr & Mrs B. Sinclair
Mr R. Sinclair-Taylor
Mrs Edwin Z. Singer
Jaswant Singh
Mrs K. A. Singleton
Mr & Mrs J. B. Sinton
Francesca Skelton
Mr P. E. Skerrett
S. J. Skibicki
Ralph Skilbeck
D. E. Skimmet
Mrs J. Skinner
Patrick Skinner
Marjorie Skipsey
Dr S. Sklar
Agneta Skoglund
Mr D. A. Slade
Dr A. K. B. Slade
Mr D. A. Slade
Duncan Slater
June Slatter
Mr. D. Slee
Mr F. C. Slegg
Alan Sloan
Dr Simon Smail
Richard C. Smail
Mrs S. Smallman
John & Kate Smallwood
Mr B. A. Smart
N. S. L. Smart
Charles Smedley
B. Smedley
A. Smelt
Mrs J. Smith
Mrs D. N. Stuart Smith
Mr & Mrs J. I. Smith
Mrs S. P. D. Smith
Mr G. S. Smith
Mr M. J. Smith
Ms F. M. K. Smith
Wendy Smith
Kenneth E. Smith
R. A. G Smith
Mrs D. Smith
Pamela Smith
Mr D. C. Smith
Robert R. Smith
Gerrilyn Smith
J. W. G. Smith
David G. Smith
Mr C. Smith
Dr J. C. Smith
Mrs C. Smith
Mr R. Smith
Kenneth E. Smith

Cathy Smith
Paula Smith
Malcolm Smith
T. A. Smith
Dave Smith and Bastiaan Jenken
D. Smithers
Roger W. J. Smokcum
L. F. Smyth
Mr & Mrs T. Soane
Mr O. Solivan
Irene Solomon
Dr B. Solomons
Mrs V. Solomons
Dr B. Solomons
Helga T. Somerville
Mrs E. Sones
Mrs F. Southall
David and Sylvia Southern
Kathleen Southon
Mr & Mrs Southon
Mrs W. S. Soutter
Elwyn Soutter
Stephanie Sowerby
J. D. Sparham
Ronald Spark
Mr M. Sparkes
Wg Cdr R. M. Sparkes
Mrs H. J. Sparks
D. H. Sparrow
Dr R. T. Spence
Mr J. Spencely
Martha Smith Spencer
Mary E. Spencer
Mr & Mrs M. Spencer
Mr E. W. Spink
Mr J. F. Spinlove
Nicholas Spruyt
Geoffrey T. Spurrier
D. G. Squires
Miss J. Squires
Mr M. G. Srivalsan
Paul W. Stacey
Sylvia Stagg
Harry Stainton
B. W. Stallard
Mr C. J. Stallard
Dr J. A. Stamford
Dr & Mrs J. A. Stamford
K. J. & M. Standley
Mrs L. Stanford
K. Staniland
S. J. Stanley
P. D. Stannard
Peter Stansbury
Mrs E. Stanton
J. E. Stapleton
Aidan Starkey
Dr M. Starkey
C. P. Statham
Dr & Mrs W. J. Stauble
Mr B. D. Stead
John Stead
Mr & Mrs C. Steane
Mr & Mrs Leslie E. Steele
Dr & Mrs P. Steen
Mr H. W. Steer
Mr & Mrs F. M. Steiner
F. M. Steiner
Dr Paul Steinitz
Carol Stephens
Mrs O. Stephens
T. S. Stephens
Mr G. F. Stephens
Lynda Stephenson
Anthony Stephenson
D & J Stephenson
Philip Stevens
Mr & Mrs A. J. Stevens
John Stevenson
John W. Stewart
Mrs Gordon Stewart
Ian and Jenny Stewart
Aileen M. Stewart
Jan and Robin Stewart
Miss C. Stewart
Captain & Mrs J. S. Stewart
Dr R. H. M. Stewart
R. J. R. Stickland
Joan Stock
Dr Mark Stocker
J. C. M. Stoker
A. C. Stoker
Malcolm Stone
John Stoneborough
Rod Stoneman and Susan Clarke
John Stonier
Dr & Mrs Peter Storey
Stephen Storey
Mr & Mrs D. F. Strachan
M. Strachen
Laurie Stras
Mr J. W. Streek
Mr M. T. Street
Mr F. W. Strevens
Mr & Mrs Stripp
Anthony Strong
Hilary and Malcom Strong
Douglas Stuart
Mrs Peter Stubbs
Mrs J. D. Stubbs
Adriene M. Sturdy
John Storrock
H. Style
D. J. Sumner
Mr R. Sunderland
Michael D. Sutcliffe
Mrs M. L. Sutcliffe
Mr D. J. Sutton
Ms L. Sutton
Clive Sutton
Ms Judith Sutton
Geoffrey Sutton
Lesley Swallow
Mr A W Swallwell
Lindy Swallwell
Ray Sweby
Mr & Mrs H. M. Sweeney
W. B. Swinburne
Mr R. Swindells
A. Swinnerton
Mr C. J. O. Syer
Brenda Symes
Mr & Mrs K. N. Symons
P. J. F. Synge
Mrs H. Tabb
Dr A. J. Taggart
Mr J. Tailyour
Patrick Tailyour
C. Talboys
Mr E. E. Tallis
Vivienne Tan
Dr M. M. Tanaka
A. F. Tanner
Mr & Mrs M. Tarlton
E. R. Tarry
Denis W. Tate
Mr D. W. Tate
Dr P. F. Tatham
Dr P. H. Tattersall
H. T. Tattersall
Mr & Mrs G. Tayar
B. H. Taylor
Wendy Taylor
Mr A. S. Taylor
S. M. R. Taylor
A. Taylor
Mr J. S. Taylor
Mrs A. C. Taylor
Mr T. W. Taylor
A. R. Taylor
Ms L. Taylor
Mr R. J. Taylor
Lt Gen. Sir Allan Taylor MC,KBE
Mr & Mrs N. Taylor
M. Taylor
P. J. Taylor
Mr A. Taylor
Mrs L. Taylor
Mrs J. Taylor
Mr & Mrs Peter Taylor
Jean Taylor
Mr & Mrs Taylor
Mr R. P. Taylor
Mr A. Taylor-Young
Mrs G. Teague
John Parker Teall
P. Teather
Mrs A. Tebbutt
Anne D. Teeman
G. A. F Telford
Mr & Mrs J. Temple
P. Tetley
Mrs K. B. Tew
E. C. Thacker
Mr J. Thoeye
G. T. Thomas
O G Thomas
Mr & Ms Brian Thomas
R. E. Thomas
Mr & Mrs D. Thomas
Alan Thomas
Ms S. Thomas and Ms K. Deane
Dr B. H. Thomas
P. R. and D. Thomas
M. Thomas
Mr V. Thomas
Myfany Thomas
Patricia A. Thomas
B. J. Thomas
Mr & Mrs S. Thomasson
J. Thomerson
B. Thompson
Jacqueline Thompson
Dr R. M. Thompson
Mr J. P. S. Thompson
P. L. F. Thompson
Mrs M. Thompson
B. Thompson
J. R. Thompson
M. E. Thompson
Amanda Thompson
Arabel Thompson
Mr R. Thompson
A. J. Thompson
Mr D. S. Thomson

David Thomson
S. Thomson
Mrs D. A. Thomson
Mr J. D. V. Thomson
Mrs R. Thomson
Mr D. Thornber
Jack Thornley
Mr & Mrs N. Thornton
H. F. Thornton
T. Thornton
Paul Thornton
Mr A. R. Thornton
John L. Thornton
G. N. Thornton
Mr D. Thornton
Peter Thorold
John F. Thorpe
Steven A. Thorpe
Mr & Mrs M. E. Thresh
Peter Throssell
K. Thurstans
George Tierney
Terence Paul Tierney
Floyd Timms
Mr & Mrs M. Titford
Leonard Tivey
Frank Tol
W. G. Tolerton
Cliff Tolley
Neil Tomkinson
Michael Tomlinson
Chris Tomlinson
Mrs R. Tompkins
Mr J. A. E. Tompsett
Nicola Toner
D. Tonkin
J. E. A. Tonkin
Mrs J. Tooley
Kjeu Torkel
Dr C. J. Torrance
T. D. Tosswill
D. and R. Tough
Phillip A. Tour
Mrs J. L. Townend
Dr M. Townend
Mrs W. Towns
A. Townsend
Hillary J. Tradgett
Mr G. Tragen
Mr P. Trenchard-Davies
Mr & Mrs Ian Trewin
M. E. Tribe
R. Trigwell
C. & K. Trinder
John Trotter

Mr & Mrs Tucker
Mr Tuckwell
G. M. Tulip
Mrs M. Turnbull
Paul Turnbull
Mr D. P. Turnbull
Mrs E. Turnbull
Ms C. Turner
Mr N. W. Turner
Pauline Turner
Ms C. Turner
Raymond G. Turner
Simon Turner
Shirley Turner
B. W. B. Turner
Mr & Mrs G. Turner
R. G. Turner
R. K. Turner
Simon Turner & Caroline Bailey
Adrian Turner
Norman Turner
J. S. Turpin
Dr K. Tusiewicz
Curzon Tussaud
Elizabeth Tweddle
Pamela Tydeman
Andy Tye and Sue Hill
Debbie Tyler
Mr I. Tysh
C. J. Ubee
Gail M. Ullman
D. N. Underwood
Mr A. Underwood
Mr R. Underwood
Adrian Underwood
Miss J. P. Urech
Brian Uster
Mr R. Utley
J. Vale
Patricia Valentine
D. Vardy
Mr J. Varley
R. W. Vaughan-Williams
F. Veal
Mark Veit
Dione Venables
Mrs P. Venn
Mrs P. Vereker
Mr & Mrs R. Vernon-Harcourt
Mr & Mrs Villa
D. Vincent
Mr John Vincent
Mr & Mrs Andre Vindevoghel
Mrs A. M. Viney
S. P. Vivian
Mr F. Vogel

M. & N. Vokins
Dr Ashok Vonadker
D. C. Voysey
Mr & Mrs Theodore J. Vreeland
Mr J. F. Waddington
Mrs J. Wade
D. G. Wadsworth
Mark Waghorn
A. C. Wain
David Wainwright
David Waite
Joan Wakeham
Ralph Waley
Mrs V. R. Walker
Mr M. D. Walker
Mrs E. Walker
David Walker
Paul Walker
Michael Walker
Harlan Walker
Mr P. C. Walker
G. Walker
Mr A. K. F. Walker
Mr M. F. Walker
Esme Walker
Mr P. D. Walker
Mrs V. Walker-Dendle
Chris Wall
Gillian Wallace
Mr E. J. Waller
Mr & Mrs W. Waller
Lesley Waller
Mrs M. Waller
Mr & Mrs Ray Waller
D. J. Wallington
Basil Wallwork
P. K. Walsh
Peter and Pam Walshe
Mrs P. R. Walters
Mrs G. Walthoe
N. J. Walton
H. Walton
J. D. Warby
Jane C. Ward
B. Ward
O. M. Ward
Joseph J. Ward
Maj. W. Warden
Mr A. J. Wardrop
Mr & Mrs G. Ware-Owen
John Warner
P. M. Warner
J. A. Warren
Dr Warren

Ms R. M. Warriner
C. M. Warrington
Bruce Wass
Toshio Watanabe
Michael Waterfield
Mr & Mrs John Waterman
L. Waters and P. G. Vanderwent
J. H. Watkins
W. L. G. Watkins
Chrisopher Watkins
Mrs J. Watkiss
Peter Watson
Mr & Mrs Watson
Dr Hugh Watson
Mrs L. Watson
Peter Watson
Mr & Mrs R. A. Watts
Peter Watts
Mr & Mrs Watts
Marisa Way
Sarah Webb
Jean Webb
Mr & Mrs Webberley
Mr & Mrs C. A. L. Weber
Hilary A. Webster
Andrew P. Webster
Mr A. R. Webster
Mr P. Webster
Michael Wedd
Tony Weekes
Mr & Mrs N. R. Weekes
Andy Weeks
Mr A. L. Weil
Mr R. Weirsum
Andrew Welch
J. P. Welch
R. Welch
Ellie Weld
M. A. Wellby
Mrs S. D. Wells
Mrs A. F. Wells
Patrick Wellsbury
A. C. Welsh
G. Wenban
Rosamund Wesson
M. J. West
Mr & Mrs J. A. West
Mr J. F. M. West
Mrs B. A. West
P. A. West
John Westlake
Mr & Mrs Westlake
J. Weston
Mrs D. R. Weston

Mrs M. Weston-Smith
Paul Wharton
E. G. Wheater
C. P. Whipp
Ben Whitaker
Mrs C. C. Whitaker
E. H. Whitaker
G. H. White
J. N. White
Mr & Mrs P. White
Bill & Barbara White
M. W. B. White
Mrs A. W. White
Mr & Mrs Colin White
W. T. White
E. Clifford White
Wendy White
Mr & Mrs R. White
N. H. White
Dr D. M. D. White
Mr P. J. White
J. R. White
Mr & Mrs D. Whitehead
Mr J. Scott Whiteley
Andrew Whiteman
Miss S. I. Whiter & Mr D. J. Buckley
Mr E. V. M. Whiteway
Mr & Mrs Whiting
Mrs G. M. Whitley
Mr & Mrs Whittaker
Mr G. Anthony Whittaker
J. Whittaker
Stephen and Susan Whittle
Mrs L. S. Whitworth
Peter Whyman
Mr A. D. Whyte
Mr W. Whyte
Mrs Wicklam
Brian Wicks
B. M. Wicks
K. A. Wiedersheim
Mrs G. R. Wiffen
M. Michael Wigginton
Ms G. Wight
Lord Wigoder
G. Wilder
William Wildgoose
Jean Wilding
R. C Wiles
M. Wilkie
S. Wilkins
Mrs C. Wilkinson
Mrs V. M. Wilkinson
Hazel Wilkinson
J. G. Wilkinson
Regina C. Wilkinson
Ann Wilks
Carale Wilks
Mr M. Willan
Simon Willbarn
Mr P. Willer
Dr R. F. Willey
Mr A. D. Williams
Mrs O. M. Williams
S. J. Williams
Dr E. Williams
J. R. Williams
Mr D. A. Williams
Mr J. S. Williams
Dr & Mrs G. J. Williams
K. Williams
Dr W. H. Williams
Mr G. L. Williams
Joanne Williams
Jane Williams
Dr Simon Williams
Brian Williams
Dr A. Williams
L. F. Williams
Mr T. P. D. Williams
Mr J. & Mrs R. Williams
Ms S. Williams
John Williams
Joanne Williams
Rona Williams
Alex and Beryl Williams
Mrs E. Williams
Stephen Williamson
A. Williamson
N. M. Williamson
Mr S. Williamson MA
Nigel Williamson
Jonathon Williamson
Simon Willsbourn
Mrs Willson
Kay Willy
Charles Wilson
Mr I. Wilson
C. H. Wilson
Janice Wilson
P. Wilson
Mr T. M. Wilson
Mr & Mrs E. Wilson
Miss K. L. F. Wilson
C. W. Wilson
Dr P. N. Wilson
Peter A. Wilson
David Wilson
J. Wiltshire
A. G Windsor
A. J. Wingate
Mr F. Wingett
Eric Winter and Jean Parker
Mr W. Winter
Alan Wiseman
Mr T. Withers & Miss H. Cox
Margaret Withey
Mr D. A. Witt
Alison Wolf
Mr K. Wolfson
Dr A. G. Wolstenholme
J. M. Womersley
Miss J. F. Wong
Karlten Wong
Mr R. Wood
Mr & Mrs Robert A. Wood
P. G. Wood
Mr A. D. Wood
Miss S. Wood
C. H. Wood
Maureen Wood
Mr & Mrs John Wood
Dr W. G. Wood
Roger Wood
Ms V. Woodbine Parish
Katinka Woodfine
Dr F. Peter Woodford
Nova Wooding
C. A. Woods
J. Woods
Mrs A. A. Woods
K. Woods-Holder
Mrs P. Woodside
Mr C. Woodward
Barbara M. Wooldridge
Vera Woolf
Sir Harry Woolf
Dr A. W. Woolley
Richard Woolrych
Miss E. Wordsworth
D. H. Worgan
Alan Worsdale
Mrs P. Worth
Sue and Julian Worth
Mr & Mrs P. Wraight
Mrs E. M. Wrench
Myron Wright
Mr & Mrs I. Wright
Ken Wright
Alan Wright
Laura Wright
Mrs N. G. Wright
Dr Fiona Wright
Mr & Mrs C. Wright
Mrs P. Wright
Mrs B. M. Wright
Mr A. J. Wright
Dr F. Wright
Mr D. Wurtzel
Richard Wyatt
Richard Wyber
Llinos Wynne
E. J. C. Wynne
Bernary Yates
Paul Yeoman
Ellen Yiu
Dr S. C. B. Yorke
Stewart Yorston
J. Youens ARICS
E. D. Young
Paul H. Young
Percy Young
Mr & Mrs B. Young
Martin Young
P. T. Young
Patrick Young
T. Young
Mr Young
J. M. Younger
Mimi Yournie
Dr Peter Zacharias
Robert Zara
G. B. Zulian

Alphabetical list of entries

Aagrah, Shipley, West Yorkshire
Aagrah, Pudsey, West Yorkshire
Abbey Green, Chester, Cheshire
Abergwynant Hall, Dolgellau, Gwynedd
Adil, Birmingham, West Midlands
Airds Hotel, Port Appin, Strathclyde
Alastair Little, London W1
Alfonso's, Cookham, Berkshire
Al Hamra, London W1
Les Alouettes, Esher, Surrey
Alp-horn, Edinburgh, Lothian
Al San Vincenzo, Cheam, Surrey
Altnaharrie Inn, Ullapool, Highland
Alvaro's, Southend On Sea, Essex
Alverton Manor, Truro, Cornwall
Ana's Bistro, Kenilworth, Warwickshire
Los Andes, Birmingham, West Midlands
Andrew Edmunds, London W1
Angel Inn, Hetton, North Yorkshire
Angelo's, Loughborough, Leicestershire
Ann Fitzgerald's, Mathry, Dyfed
Anna's Place, London N1
Annie's, Swansea, West Glamorgan
Arcadia, Sheffield, South Yorkshire
Ardsheal House, Kentallen, Highland
Arisaig Hotel, Arisaig, Highland
L'Arlequin, London SW8
Armadillo, Liverpool, Merseyside
Armless Dragon, Cardiff, South Glamorgan
Les Artistes Gourmands, Nottingham, Nottinghamshire
Arundell Arms, Lifton, Devon
Ashwick House, Dulverton, Somerset
At the Sign of the Angel, Lacock, Wiltshire
Au Bois St Jean, London NW8
L'Auberge, London SE22
Auberge de Provence, London SW1
Auchterarder House, Auchterarder, Tayside
Auctioneer, Preston, Lancashire
Auntie's, London W1
L'Aventure, London NW8
Aynsome Manor, Cartmel, Cumbria
Ayudhya, Kingston Upon Thames, Surrey
Bahn Thai, London W1
La Baita Da Piero, London E4
Bakestone, Caernarfon, Gwynedd
Bambaya, London N8
Barn, Saintfield, Co Down
Barretts, Glemsford, Suffolk
Basil's Brasserie, Cowbridge, South Glamorgan
La Bastide, London W1
Bay Horse, Ulverston, Cumbria
Bayleaf Tandoori, London N6
Beadles, Birkenhead, Merseyside
Bear Hotel, Crickhowell, Powys
Beau-Rivage, London NW6
Beeches, Standish, Greater Manchester
Bell, Aston Clinton, Buckinghamshire
La Belle Alliance, Blandford Forum, Dorset
La Belle Epoque, Belfast, Co Antrim
La Belle Epoque, Knutsford, Cheshire
Bengal Lancer, London NW5
Beotys, London WC2
Berties Bistro, Elland, West Yorkshire
Le Biarritz, Birmingham, West Midlands
Bibendum, London SW3
Bilbrough Manor, Bilbrough, North Yorkshire
Billy Budd's, Dartmouth, Devon
Bistro 33, Dartmouth, Devon
Bistro Montparnasse, Southsea, Hampshire
Bistro Twenty One, Bristol, Avon
Black Bull, Moulton, North Yorkshire
Black Lion Hotel, Long Melford, Suffolk
Black Swan, Beckingham, Lincolnshire

Blakes Hotel, London SW7
Blinkers French, Manchester, Greater Manchester
Bloom's, London E1
Blostin's, Shepton Mallet, Somerset
Blue Elephant, London SW6
Blue Nile, London W9
Boat Inn, Erbistock, Clwyd
Bobby's, Leicester, Leicestershire
Bodysgallen Hall, Llandudno, Gwynedd
Bombay Bicycle Club, London SW12
Bombay Brasserie, London SW7
Boncompte's, Onchan, Isle Of Man
Le Bonheur, Hampton Wick, London
La Bonne Auberge, South Godstone, Surrey
Bonne Franquette, Egham, Surrey
Bouillabaisse, London SW10
Boulestin, London WC2
Box Tree, Ilkley, West Yorkshire
Boyd's Glass Garden, London W8
Braeval Old Mill, Aberfoyle, Central
La Braseria, Swansea, West Glamorgan
La Brasserie, Cardiff, South Glamorgan
La Brasserie, Morpeth, Northumberland
Brasserie l'Abri, Norwich, Norfolk
Brasted's, Norwich, Norfolk
Breamish House, Powburn, Northumberland
Brewer Street Buttery, London W1
Bridgefield House, Spark Bridge, Cumbria
Brilliant, Southall, London
Brinkley's Champagne Bar, London W1
Britannia Intercontinental Hotel, London W1
Brockencote Hall, Chaddesley Corbett, Hereford & Worcester
Brookdale House, North Huish, Devon
Brown's, Worcester, Hereford & Worcester
Browns, Oxford, Oxfordshire
Browns Hotel, Haddington, Lothian
Bryans, Leeds, West Yorkshire
Buckland-Tout-Saints Hotel, Kingsbridge, Devon
Burrastow House, Walls, Shetland
But'n'Ben, Auchmithie, Tayside
Butchers Arms, Woolhope, Hereford & Worcester
Butley-Orford Oysterage, Orford, Suffolk
Buttercross, Spilsby, Lincolnshire
Buttery, Glasgow, Strathclyde
Byrons, Eastbourne, East Sussex
C'est la Vie, Lytham St Anne's, Lancashire
Caesar's, Llangollen, Clwyd
Café Bistro, London SE3
Café du Marche, London EC1
Café Flo, London NW3
Café Gandolfi, Glasgow, Strathclyde
Café Istanbul, Manchester, Greater Manchester
Café Procope, Newcastle Upon Tyne, Tyne & Wear
Calcot Manor, Tetbury, Gloucestershire
Callow Hall, Ashbourne, Derbyshire
Capital Hotel, London SW3
Le Caprice, London SW1
Carved Angel, Dartmouth, Devon
Le Cassoulet, Cardiff, South Glamorgan
Castle Cottage, Harlech, Gwynedd
Castle Hotel, Taunton, Somerset
Castle Kitchen, Cilgerran, Dyfed
Cavaliers, London SW8
Cedar Restaurant, Evesham, Hereford & Worcester
Ceilidh Place, Ullapool, Highland
Cellar, Anstruther, Fife
Cemlyn, Harlech, Gwynedd
Cezanne, Twickenham, Greater London
Champany Inn, Linlithgow, Lothian
Le Champenois, West Mersea, Essex
Champers, Cardiff, South Glamorgan
Le Champignon Sauvage, Cheltenham, Gloucestershire
Chand, Nottingham, Nottinghamshire
Chandler's, Trefriw, Gwynedd
Chanterelle, London SW7
Chapeltoun House, Stewarton, Strathclyde
Charingworth Manor, Chipping Campden, Gloucestershire
La Chaumière, Cardiff, South Glamorgan
Chedington Court, Chedington, Dorset
Cheevers, Tunbridge Wells, Kent
Chef, London W2
Cherry Orchard, London E2
Cherwell Boathouse, Oxford, Oxfordshire
Chester Grosvenor, Chester, Cheshire
Chez Liline, London N4
Chez Max, Surbiton, Surrey
Chez Moi, London W11
Chez Nous, Plymouth, Devon
Chiang Mai, London W1
Chilka, Brighton, East Sussex
China China, London W1
China City, Cardiff, South Glamorgan
China Palace, Bristol, Avon
Chinon, London W14
Christian's, London W4
Chuen Cheng Ku, London W1

Chung Ying, Birmingham, West Midlands
Chung Ying Garden, Birmingham, West Midlands
Ciboure, London SW1
Clarke's, London W8
Cleeveway House, Bishops Cleeve, Gloucestershire
Cliveden, Taplow, Buckinghamshire
Clos du Roy, Bath, Avon
Cnapan, Newport, Dyfed
Cobbett's, Botley, Hampshire
Cobblers, Llandybie, Dyfed
College Farm, London N3
College Green, Gloucester, Gloucestershire
Collin House, Broadway, Hereford & Worcester
Colony, Weybridge, Surrey
Congham Hall, Grimston, Norfolk
Connaught, London W1
Cook's Delight, Berkhamsted, Hertfordshire
F.Cooke, London E8
Copper Inn, Pangbourne, Berkshire
Cork & Bottle, London WC2
Corney & Barrow, London EC2
Corse Lawn House, Corse Lawn, Gloucestershire
Country Club, Harrow, Greater London
Country Friends, Dorrington, Shropshire
La Coupée, London SE24
Courtyard, Broughton, Lancashire
Crabwall Manor, Mollington, Cheshire
Craigendarroch, Ballater, Grampian
Craigside Manor, Llandudno, Gwynedd
Crinan Hotel, Crinan, Strathclyde
Cringletie House, Peebles, Borders
La Croisette, London SW10
Cromlix House, Kinbuck, Central
Cromwellian, Kirkham, Lancashire
Croque-en-Bouche, Malvern Wells, Hereford & Worcester
Cross, Kingussie, Highland
Crown, Southwold, Suffolk
Crowthers, London SW14
Crust, Bournemouth, Dorset
Crustaceans, Salisbury, Wiltshire
Curry Kuteer, Stafford, Staffordshire
Da Umberto, Ilford, Essex
Danescombe Valley Hotel, Calstock, Cornwall
Daphne, London NW1
Days Of The Raj, Birmingham, West Midlands
Deals, London SW10
Denbigh Arms, Lutterworth, Leicestershire
Diana's Diner, London WC2
Dijonnais, Croydon, Surrey
Dining Room, London SE1
Dordogne, London W4
Dragon's Nest, London W1
Druidstone Hotel, Broad Haven, Dyfed
Drum and Monkey, Harrogate, North Yorkshire
Dukes Hotel, London SW1
Dunain Park, Inverness, Highland
Dundas Arms, Kintbury, Berkshire
Eastern Promise, Grampound, Cornwall
Edwards, Bristol, Avon
Efes Kebab House, London W1
Elgin, London W9
Elham, Liverpool, Merseyside
Elizabethan, Brixham, Devon
Epworth Tap, Epworth, Humberside
L'Escale, Wetherby, West Yorkshire
Eton Wine Bar, Eton, Berkshire
Everest, Cardiff, South Glamorgan
Factor's House, Fort William, Highland
Fairyhill, Reynoldston, West Glamorgan
Far East, Liverpool, Merseyside
Farlam Hall, Brampton, Cumbria
Farmhouse Feast, Roxwell, Essex
Faulkner's, London E8
Feathers Hotel, Woodstock, Oxfordshire
Feldon House, Lower Brailes, Warwickshire
Field Head House, Hawkshead, Cumbria
Fifteen North Parade, Oxford, Oxfordshire
Fifty One Fifty One, London SW3
Fisherman's Lodge, Newcastle Upon Tyne, Tyne & Wear
Fishes', Burnham Market, Norfolk
Fleet Tandoori, London NW3
Flitwick Manor, Flitwick, Bedfordshire
Flora Tea Rooms, Dunwich, Suffolk
Flynn's, Nailsworth, Gloucestershire
Food for Friends, Brighton, East Sussex
Food for Thought, Fowey, Cornwall
Forge, Tickhill, South Yorkshire
Forum Court, London SE25
Fossebridge Inn, Northleach, Gloucestershire
Fountain House, East Bergholt, Essex
Fouter's Bistro, Ayr, Strathclyde
Fowey Brasserie, Fowey, Cornwall
Fox and Goose, Fressingfield, Suffolk
Free Press, Cambridge, Cambridgeshire
French, Altrincham, Greater Manchester
French Cellar, Brighton, East Sussex
French Partridge, Horton, Northamptonshire
Frith's, London W1

Fung Shing, London WC2
Funnywayt'mekalivin, Berwick-upon-Tweed, Northumberland
Gales, Llangollen, Clwyd
Galloping Crayfish, Hungerford, Berkshire
Ganges, Bristol, Avon
Gannets, Newark, Nottinghamshire
Gannets, Aberystwyth, Dyfed
Ganpath, London WC1
Garbo's, London W1
Garden Room, Tisbury, Wiltshire
Gatwick Hilton, Gatwick, West Sussex
Le Gavroche, London W1
Gavvers, London SW1
Gay Hussar, London W1
Gaylord, Manchester, Greater Manchester
General Havelock Inn, Haydon Bridge, Northumberland
George, Stamford, Lincolnshire
George III Hotel, Dolgellau, Gwynedd
George's Brasserie, Canterbury, Kent
Gibbons, Avening, Gloucestershire
Gibsons, Cardiff, South Glamorgan
Gidleigh Park, Chagford, Devon
Gilberts, London SW7
Ginnan, London EC4
Giralda, Pinner, London
Gleddoch House, Langbank, Strathclyde
Golden Cock, Farnley Tyas, West Yorkshire
Good Earth, Esher, Surrey
Good Food, London WC2
Good Friends, London E14
Grafton, London SW4
Grafton Manor, Bromsgrove, Hereford & Worcester
Grahame's Seafare, London W1
La Grande Bouffe, Liverpool, Merseyside
Grange Inn, St Andrews, Fife
Gravetye Manor, Sharpthorne, West Sussex
Great House, Lavenham, Suffolk
Great House, Laleston, Mid Glamorgan
Great Nepalese, London NW1
Great Wall, Newcastle Upon Tyne, Tyne & Wear
Green Apple, Bakewell, Derbyshire
Green Dragon Bistro, Swansea, West Glamorgan
Green Inn, Ballater, Grampian
Green's, London SW1
Greenhead House, Sheffield, South Yorkshire
Greenhouse, Manchester, Greater Manchester
Greens Seafood, Norwich, Norfolk
Grillade, Leeds, West Yorkshire
Grinkle Park Hotel, Easington, Cleveland
Grosvenor Hotel, Rugby, Warwickshire
Guernica, London W1
Halcyon Hotel, Kingfisher Restaurant, London W11
Hambleton Hall, Hambleton, Leicestershire
Handsel's Restaurant, Edinburgh, Lothian
Hanni's, Altrincham, Greater Manchester
Happy Garden, Manchester, Greater Manchester
Happy Gathering, Cardiff, South Glamorgan
Harcourt Arms, Stanton Harcourt, Oxfordshire
Hard Rock Café, London W1
Harding's, North Berwick, Lothian
Harper's, Salisbury, Wiltshire
Harry Ramsden's, Guiseley, West Yorkshire
Harvey's, Bristol, Avon
Harvey's /Troffs, Lincoln, Lincolnshire
Harvey's, London SW17
Heal's, London W1
Helios Fountain, Edinburgh, Lothian
Hendersons, Edinburgh, Lothian
Hendersons, Tiverton, Devon
Henry Wong, Birmingham, West Midlands
Henry's, Birmingham, West Midlands
Herbs, Coventry, West Midlands
L'Hérisson, London SW19
Heskyn Mill, Tideford, Cornwall
Hiders, London SW6
High Moor, Wrightington, Lancashire
Hilaire, London SW7
Hillside Bar, Hillsborough, Co Down
Hintlesham Hall, Hintlesham, Suffolk
Hive on the Quay, Aberaeron, Dyfed
Ho Tung, Birmingham, West Midlands
Ho-Ho, London E18
Hockneys, Croydon, Surrey
Hodgson's, Harrogate, North Yorkshire
Holdsworth House, Halifax, West Yorkshire
Holly Tree, Kentallen, Highland
Homewood Park, Hinton Charterhouse, Avon
Hong Kong, Manchester, Greater Manchester
Honours Mill, Edenbridge, Kent
Hope End, Ledbury, Hereford & Worcester
Hopewell City, Manchester, Greater Manchester
Horn of Plenty, Gulworthy, Devon
Hospitality Inn, Irvine, Strathclyde
Howe Villa, Richmond, North Yorkshire
Hung Toa, London W2
Hungry Monk, Jevington, East Sussex
Hunstrete House, Hunstrete, Avon

Hunters Lodge, Broadway, Hereford & Worcester
Hunts Tor House, Drewsteignton, Devon
Ikeda, London W1
Ikkyu, London W1
L'Incontro, London SW1
India, Folkestone, Kent
Indian Cavalry Club, Edinburgh, Lothian
Indian Ocean, Cardiff, South Glamorgan
Inigo Jones, London WC2
Innsacre Farmhouse Hotel, Shipton Gorge, Dorset
Interlude, London WC2
Inverlochy Castle, Fort William, Highland
Iona, Holywood, Co Down
Isle Of Eriska Hotel, Eriska, Strathclyde
Jade Garden, Newcastle Upon Tyne, Tyne & Wear
Jade Garden, London W1
Jamdani, London W1
Jameson's, Bristol, Avon
Jams, London W1
Jemima's, Haverfordwest, Dyfed
John & Maria's, Pontypridd, Mid Glamorgan
Jule's Cafe, Weobley, Hereford & Worcester
Julius's, London N1
Jumbo Chinese, Leeds, West Yorkshire
Justin De Blank, London W1
Kalamaras, London W2
Kalpna, Edinburgh, Lothian
Kanishka, London W1
Kashmir, Bradford, West Yorkshire
Kathmandu Tandoori, Manchester, Greater Manchester
Keats, London NW3
Kelly's, Edinburgh, Lothian
Kensington Place, London W8
Kenwards, Lewes, East Sussex
Kettners, London W1
KFOG, Lytham St Anne's, Lancashire
Kilfinan Hotel, Kilfinan, Strathclyde
Killiecrankie Hotel, Killiecrankie, Tayside
King's Head, Cuckfield, West Sussex
Kingshead House, Birdlip, Gloucestershire
Kinloch House Hotel, Blairgowrie, Tayside
Kinloch Lodge, Sleat, Isle Of Skye
Kirkstone Foot Country House Hotel, Ambleside, Cumbria
Kirroughtree Hotel, Newton Stewart, Dumfries & Galloway
Knipoch Hotel, Oban, Strathclyde
Knockie Lodge, Whitebridge, Highland
Knockinaam Lodge, Portpatrick, Dumfries & Galloway
Korea House, London W1
Koreana, Manchester, Greater Manchester
Kosmos Taverna, Manchester, Greater Manchester
Kuti's, Southampton, Hampshire
Kwok's Rendezvous, Ipswich, Suffolk
Laburnum House, Wylam, Northumberland
Laden Table, St Keverne, Cornwall
Lai's, Leicester, Leicestershire
Lainston House, Sparsholt, Hampshire
Lake Isle, Uppingham, Leicestershire
Lal Qila, London W1
Lamb Inn, Shipton Under Wychwood, Oxfordshire
Landgate Bistro, Rye, East Sussex
Langan's, Coggeshall, Essex
Langan's Bistro, London W1
Langan's Brasserie, London W1
Langley House Hotel, Langley Marsh, Somerset
Langley Wood, Redlynch, Wiltshire
Lantern, East Molesey, Surrey
Lanterna, Scarborough, North Yorkshire
Last Days of the Empire, London W1
Launceston Place, London W8
Leek's Fish Bar, London SW11
Left Bank, London SW10
Leigh House, Beaconsfield, Buckinghamshire
Leith's, London W11
Lemonia, London NW1
Leo's, Southwell, Nottinghamshire
Lettonie, Bristol, Avon
Liaison, London SW17
Liaison, Solihull, West Midlands
Lichfield's, Richmond, Surrey
Lillibet's, Liversedge, West Yorkshire
Lilly's, London W11
Lime Tree, Manchester, Greater Manchester
Lion's Corner House, Hay On Wye, Powys
Little Barwick House, Barwick, Somerset
Little Byres, Dallington, East Sussex
Little Yang Sing, Manchester, Greater Manchester
Llwynderw Hotel, Llanwrtyd Wells, Powys
Loaves and Fishes, Rockley, Wiltshire
Loch Fyne Oyster Bar, Cairndow, Strathclyde
Lodge, Ottery St Mary, Devon
Lombard Room, King's Norton, West Midlands
Longhouse Buttery, Cullipool, Strathclyde
Longueville Manor, St Saviour, Jersey
Loon Fung, Glasgow, Strathclyde
Loon Fung, Birmingham, West Midlands
Loon Fung, Edinburgh, Lothian
Lou Pescadou, London SW7
Low Greenfield, Buckden, North Yorkshire

Lower Pitt, East Buckland, Devon
Lowiczanka, London W6
Lychgates, Bexhill On Sea, East Sussex
Lygon Arms, Broadway, Hereford & Worcester
Lynton House, Holdenby, Northamptonshire
Lynwood House, Barnstaple, Devon
Ma Cuisine, London SW3
Macduff's, Coleraine, Co Derry
La Madonette, Chipping Norton, Oxfordshire
Maes-y-Neuadd, Talsarnau, Gwynedd
Magno's, London WC2
Magnums Wine Bar, London NW3
Magpie Café, Whitby, North Yorkshire
Maharaja, Birmingham, West Midlands
Malabar, London W8
Mallards, Saint Michael's On Wyre, Lancashire
Mallory Court, Bishops Tachbrook, Warwickshire
Mandalay, London SE10
Mandalay, Leeds, West Yorkshire
Mandarin Kitchen, London W2
Mandeer, London W1
Manleys, Storrington, West Sussex
Le Manoir Aux Quat' Saisons, Great Milton, Oxfordshire
The Manor at Newlands, Guildford, Surrey
Manor Hotel, West Bexington, Dorset
Manor House, Walkington, Humberside
Manzi's, London WC2
Marco's, Norwich, Norfolk
Mark's at Lindhead Cottage, Scarborough, North Yorkshire
Market Restaurant, Manchester, Greater Manchester
Marmion's Brasserie, Melrose, Borders
Maroush I, London W2
Maroush II, London SW3
Marryat Room, Chewton Glen Hotel, New Milton, Hampshire
Martin's, London NW1
Martins, Edinburgh, Lothian
La Mascotte, London NW2
Masons Arms, Branscombe, Devon
Mauro's, Bollington, Cheshire
Maxine's, Midhurst, West Sussex
Maybank Hotel, Aberdovey, Gwynedd
Mayflower, Liverpool, Merseyside
Mayflower, London W1
Mazarin, London SW1
McClements, Twickenham, Greater London
McCoy's Bistro, Staddlebridge, North Yorkshire
Meadowsweet Hotel, Llanrwst, Gwynedd
Melati, London W1
Melissa, Chelmsford, Essex
Le Mesurier, London EC1
Metro Wine Bar, London SW3
Michaels Nook, Grasmere, Cumbria
Michels, Ripley, Surrey
Middlethorpe Hall, York, North Yorkshire
Midsummer House, Cambridge, Cambridgeshire
Mijanou, London SW1
Miller Howe, Windermere, Cumbria
Miller Howe Kaff, Windermere, Cumbria
Mina-Japan, Manchester, Greater Manchester
Minffordd Hotel, Talyllyn, Gwynedd
Ming, London W1
Mister Barretts, Plymouth, Devon
Miyama, London W1
Miyama, London EC4
Mon Plaisir, London WC2
Monkeys, London SW3
Monsieur Frog, London N1
Moon, Kendal, Cumbria
Moon and Sixpence, Bath, Avon
Moonrakers, Alfriston, East Sussex
Moorings, Wells next the Sea, Norfolk
Morefield Motel, Ullapool, Highland
Morels, Haslemere, Surrey
Mortimer's, Bury St Edmunds, Suffolk
Mortimer's On The Quay, Ipswich, Suffolk
Mortons House Hotel, Corfe Castle, Dorset
Moss Nook, Manchester, Greater Manchester
Mr Kuks, Manchester, Greater Manchester
Mr Underhill's, Stonham, Suffolk
Mulberry Room, Torquay, Devon
Mulligan's, Cowbridge, South Glamorgan
Munchy Munchy, Oxford, Oxfordshire
Murrayshall Hotel, Scone, Tayside
Muset, Bristol, Avon
Nansloe, Helston, Cornwall
Nanten Yakitori Bar, London W1
Neal Street Restaurant, London WC2
Neal's Lodge, London SW18
New Emperor, Newcastle Upon Tyne, Tyne & Wear
New Inn, Manaccan, Cornwall
New World, London W1
Nick's, Killinchy, Co Down
Ninety Park Lane, London W1
Ninjin, London W1
Nirmal's Tandoori, Sheffield, South Yorkshire
Noble House, Cardiff, South Glamorgan
Nontas, London NW1
Norfolk Mead Hotel, Coltishall, Norfolk
Normandie, Birtle, Greater Manchester
Northcote Manor, Langho, Lancashire
Number Twelve, Cheltenham, Gloucestershire

Nuthurst Grange, Hockley Heath, West Midlands
Oak Room, Le Meridien Hotel, London W1
Oakes, Stroud, Gloucestershire
Oaksmere, Eye, Suffolk
Oat Cuisine, York, North Yorkshire
Ocean City, Nottingham, Nottinghamshire
October, Glasgow, Strathclyde
Odettes, London NW1
Off the Beeton Track, Cowbridge, South Glamorgan
Office Wine Bar, Tonbridge, Kent
Oh Boy, London SW17
Old Bakehouse, Little Walsingham, Norfolk
Old Bakery, Countesthorpe, Leicestershire
Old Beams, Waterhouses, Staffordshire
Old Coffee Shop, Aberdovey, Gwynedd
Old Deanery, Ripon, North Yorkshire
Old Fire Engine House, Ely, Cambridgeshire
Old Hoops, Saffron Walden, Essex
Old House, Wickham, Hampshire
Old Inn, Drewsteignton, Devon
Old Manor House, Romsey, Hampshire
Old Monastery, Drybridge, Grampian
Old Parsonage, Farrington Gurney, Avon
Old Post Office, Clun, Shropshire
Old Rectory, Campsea Ash, Suffolk
Old Red Lion, Aldborough, Norfolk
Old Station Coffee Shop, Dinas Mawddwy, Gwynedd
Old Thorns, Liphook, Hampshire
Old Vicarage, Witherslack, Cumbria
Old Vicarage, Ridgeway, Derbyshire
Old Vicarage, Worfield, Shropshire
Old Woolhouse, Northleach, Gloucestershire
Olive Tree, Leeds, West Yorkshire
Olivers, Robertsbridge, East Sussex
On the Eighth Day, Manchester, Greater Manchester
One Devonshire Gardens, Glasgow, Strathclyde
One Eleven, Rochdale, Greater Manchester
One Two Three, London W1
Orient, Liverpool, Merseyside
Orso, London WC2
L'Ortolan, Shinfield, Berkshire
Ostlers Close, Cupar, Fife
Otters, London SW6
Le P'tit Normand, London SW18
Palé Hall, Llandderfel, Gwynedd
Panda, Leicester, Leicestershire
Paris House, Woburn, Bedfordshire
Park End, Caldbeck, Cumbria
Parrock Head Farm, Slaidburn, Lancashire
Partners, Okehampton, Devon
Partners 23, Sutton, Surrey
Il Passetto, London WC2
Pattisson's, Lewes, East Sussex
Pearl City, Manchester, Greater Manchester
Pearl Of Siam, London E1
Peat Inn, Peat Inn, Fife
Pebbles, Aylesbury, Buckinghamshire
Peking Duck, Liverpool, Merseyside
Perkins Bar Bistro, Plumtree, Nottinghamshire
Peter Jackson At The Colonial, Glasgow, Strathclyde
Petit Blanc, Oxford, Oxfordshire
La Petite Auberge, Weston Super Mare, Avon
Phoenicia, London W8
Pier at Harwich, Harwich, Essex
Pierre Victoire, Edinburgh, Lothian
Pine Trees, Sway, Hampshire
Pisces, Huddersfield, West Yorkshire
Pizzeria Castello, London SE1
Plaka, Birmingham, West Midlands
Plas Bodegroes, Pwllheli, Gwynedd
Plas Glyn Y Mel, Fishguard, Dyfed
Plough, Clanfield, Oxfordshire
Plumber Manor, Sturminster Newton, Dorset
Plummers, Bedale, North Yorkshire
Polash, Burnham On Crouch, Essex
Pollo, London W1
Polmaily House Hotel, Drumnadrochit, Highland
Pool Court, Pool In Wharfedale, West Yorkshire
Poons, London WC2
Popjoy's, Bath, Avon
Poppies, Brimfield, Hereford & Worcester
Porth Tocyn Hotel, Abersoch, Gwynedd
Porthole Eating House, Bowness On Windermere, Cumbria
Portofino, Kenilworth, Warwickshire
Ports, London SW3
La Potinière, Gullane, Lothian
Potter's Wheel, Walberswick, Suffolk
La Poulbot, London EC2
Le Poussin, Brockenhurst, Hampshire
Priory Hotel, Bath, Avon
Le Provencal, Truro, Cornwall
Provençale, Whitley Bay, Tyne & Wear

Provence, Lymington, Hampshire
Le Quai St Pierre, London W8
Queen's Head, Glanwydden, Gwynedd
Quince & Medlar, Cockermouth, Cumbria
Quincy's, London NW2
Quo Vadis, Coventry, West Midlands
Raffaelli, Edinburgh, Lothian
Raffles, Aldbourne, Wiltshire
Ragam, London W1
Rajdoot, Bristol, Avon
Rajdoot, Birmingham, West Midlands
Rajdoot, London W6
Ram Jam, Stretton, Leicestershire
Ramblers Country House, Corbridge, Northumberland
Ramore, Portrush, Co Antrim
Rani, London N3
Rankins, Sissinghurst, Kent
Rasa Sayang, London NW3
Read's, Esher, Surrey
Read's, Faversham, Kent
Rebato's, London SW8
Red Fort, London W1
Red Sea, London NW6
Redmond's, Cheltenham, Gloucestershire
Reeds, Poughill, Cornwall
Remy's, Torquay, Devon
Renoufs, Rochford, Essex
Restaurant 19, Bradford, West Yorkshire
Restaurant Bosquet, Kenilworth, Warwickshire
Restaurant Lafite, Willerby, Humberside
Restaurant Roger Burdell, Loughborough, Leicestershire
Rêves des Seychelles, London SE7
Rise Of The Raj, Leicester, Leicestershire
Rising Sun, Saint Mawes, Cornwall
La Rive Gauche, London SE1
River Café, London W6
River House, Thornton-le-fylde, Lancashire
River House, Lympstone, Devon
Riverside, Cardiff, South Glamorgan
Riverside, Helford, Cornwall
Riverside Inn, Canonbie, Dumfries & Galloway
Riverside Rooms, King's Lynn, Norfolk
Roadhouse Restaurant, Roade, Northamptonshire
Rocher's, Milford on Sea, Hampshire
Rogano, Glasgow, Strathclyde
Roger's, Windermere, Cumbria
Rookery Hall, Nantwich, Cheshire
Rose and Crown, Wisbech, Cambridgeshire
Röser's, Saint Leonard's, East Sussex
La Rosette, Ballasalla, Isle Of Man
Rothay Manor, Ambleside, Cumbria
Rotisserie, London W12
Royal Oak, Yattendon, Berkshire
Royal Thai Orchids, London SW15
RSJ, London SE1
Rue St Jacques, London W1
La Rueda, London SW4
Rumbles Cottage, Felsted, Essex
Rumwong, Guildford, Surrey
Rupali, Newcastle Upon Tyne, Tyne & Wear
Ryecroft Hotel, Wooler, Northumberland
Ryoma, London W1
Ryton Gardens, Ryton-on-Dunsmore, Warwickshire
Sabras, London NW10
Sachins, Newcastle Upon Tyne, Tyne & Wear
Sagar, Nottingham, Nottinghamshire
Saigon, London W1
St Quentin, London SW3
Salvatore's, Cardiff, South Glamorgan
San Martino, London SW3
Sanam, Manchester, Greater Manchester
Sang Sang, Leeds, West Yorkshire
Sankeys Seafood, Tunbridge Wells, Kent
Santini, London SW1
Savoy Grill, London WC2
Scarista House, Harris, Isle Of Harris
Seafood Restaurant, Great Yarmouth, Norfolk
Seafood Restaurant, Padstow, Cornwall
Seafresh Fish Restaurant, London SW1
Seashell, London NW1
Seaview Hotel, Seaview, Isle Of Wight
Le Select, Poole, Dorset
La Seppia, London W1
Severn Tandoori, Stourport On Severn, Hereford & Worcester
Shamiana, Edinburgh, Lothian
Shao Tao, Cambridge, Cambridgeshire
Shapla Tandoori Restaurant, London SW9
Sharrow Bay, Ullswater, Cumbria
Sheelin, Bellanaleck, Co Fermanagh
Sheila's Cottage, Ambleside, Cumbria
Shepherd's, Stratford Upon Avon, Warwickshire
Sheridans, Moreton In Marsh, Gloucestershire
Sheriff House, Brockdish, Norfolk
Shogun, Nottingham, Nottinghamshire
Si Chuen, London W1
Siam Orchid, Manchester, Greater Manchester
Silver Darling, Aberdeen, Grampian
Simply Nico, London SW1
Singapore Garden Restaurant, London NW6
Singing Chef, Ipswich, Suffolk

Sir Charles Napier Inn, Chinnor, Oxfordshire
Sir Toby's, Stratford Upon Avon, Warwickshire
Skinburness Hotel, Skinburness, Cumbria
Slassor's, Southend On Sea, Essex
Sloans, Birmingham, West Midlands
Soanes, Petworth, West Sussex
Soho Brasserie, London W1
Solo, Goosnargh, Lancashire
Sonny's, London SW13
Sophisticats, Bournemouth, Dorset
Le Soufflé, London W1
South Lodge, Lower Beeding, West Sussex
Spices, London N16
Spindlewood Hotel, Wadhurst, East Sussex
Splinters, Christchurch, Dorset
Sportsman's Arms, Wath in Nidderdale, North Yorkshire
Sree Krishna, London SW17
St Tudno Hotel, Llandudno, Gwynedd
Stane Street Hollow, Pulborough, West Sussex
Stapleford Park, Melton Mowbray, Leicestershire
Starr, Great Dunmow, Essex
Stewart Hotel, Appin, Strathclyde
Stock Hill House, Gillingham, Dorset
Ston Easton Park, Ston Easton, Somerset
Stone Close, Dent, Cumbria
Stone Hall, Wolf's Castle, Dyfed
Strand, Belfast, Co Antrim
Stratfords, Stony Stratford, Buckinghamshire
Stumbles, South Molton, Devon
Summer Isles Hotel, Achiltibuie, Highland
Summer Lodge, Evershot, Dorset
Sundial, Herstmonceux, East Sussex
Sunlaws House, Kelso, Borders
Suntory, London SW1
Supannahong, Bath, Avon
Le Suquet, London SW3
Suruchi, London N1
Sutherlands, London W1
Swan Hotel, Leighton Buzzard, Bedfordshire
Swan Inn, Inkpen, Berkshire
Szechuan House, Edinburgh, Lothian
Tante Claire, London SW3
Tarts, Bath, Avon
Tate Gallery, London SW1
Taychreggan Hotel, Kilchrenan, Strathclyde
Teignworthy Hotel, Chagford, Devon
Thackeray's House, Tunbridge Wells, Kent
Thai House, Cardiff, South Glamorgan
Thai Paradise, Birmingham, West Midlands
That Café, Manchester, Greater Manchester
Theobalds, Ixworth, Suffolk
'36' on the Quay, Emsworth, Hampshire
Thornbury Castle, Thornbury, Avon
Three Chimneys, Dunvegan, Isle Of Skye
Three Chimneys, Biddenden, Kent
Three Cocks Hotel, Three Cocks, Powys
Three Horseshoes, Powerstock, Dorset
Three Lions, Stuckton, Hampshire
Timothys, Perth, Tayside
Tirolerhof, Farnham, Surrey
Tiroran House, Mull, Strathclyde
Topkapi, London W1
Trenchers, Whitby, North Yorkshire
Trillium, Cardiff, South Glamorgan
Les Trois Plats, London SW3
Trotters, Trewellard, Cornwall
Truffles, Bruton, Somerset
Tuk Tuk, London N1
Tullich Lodge, Ballater, Grampian
Tullythwaite House, Underbarrow, Cumbria
Tuo E Mio, Canterbury, Kent
Turnberry Hotel, Turnberry, Strathclyde
Turner's, London SW3
Twenty One, Brighton, East Sussex
Twenty Two, Cambridge, Cambridgeshire
Ty Mawr, Brechfa, Dyfed
Tyddyn Llan, Llandrillo, Clwyd
Ubiquitous Chip, Glasgow, Strathclyde
Umberto Cantina, Edinburgh, Lothian
Undercroft Restaurant, Durham, Co Durham
Uplands, Cartmel, Cumbria
Upper Street Fish Shop, London N1
Upstairs, Cambridge, Cambridgeshire
Verandah Tandoori, Edinburgh, Lothian
Victor's, Darlington, Co Durham
Victorian House, Thornton-cleveleys, Lancashire
Village Bakery, Melmerby, Cumbria
Village Green, Trelleck, Gwent
Village Restaurant, Ramsbottom, Lancashire
Wade & Fryer's, Lytham, Lancashire
Wakaba, London NW3
Wallett's Court, St Margaret's At Cliffe, Kent
Walnut Tree Inn, Llandewi Skirrid, Gwent
Waltons, London SW3
Warehouse Brasserie, Colchester, Essex
Water Margin, Derby, Derbyshire
Water Margin, Leicester, Leicestershire
Waterfront Wine Bar, Edinburgh, Lothian

Waterside Inn, Bray, Berkshire
Weavers, Haworth, West Yorkshire
Weavers Shed, Golcar, West Yorkshire
Well House, Watlington, Oxfordshire
Well House, Liskeard, Cornwall
Western House, Lowick, Northumberland
Wharf, Froghall, Staffordshire
Wheelers, Maldon, Essex
Whipper-In, Oakham, Leicestershire
White Bear, Shipston on Stour, Warwickshire
White Horse Inn, Chilgrove, West Sussex
White House Hotel, Williton, Somerset
White Moss House, Grasmere, Cumbria
White Tower, London W1
Whitechapel Manor, South Molton, Devon
Whitehall, Broxted, Essex
Whiteleaf, Croyde, Devon
Whites, Cricklade, Wiltshire
Wholefood & Vegetarian, Cleveleys, Lancashire
Wickens, Northleach, Gloucestershire
Willow, Croydon, Surrey
Wiltons, London SW1
Wine Bar, Woodbridge, Suffolk
Wine Gallery, London SW10
Wine Gallery, Oxford, Oxfordshire
Wing Ki, Edgware, London
Wings, Colchester, Essex
Winteringham Fields, Winteringham, Humberside
Wolfscastle Country Hotel, Wolf's Castle, Dyfed
Wong Kei, London W1
Woodlands, Ballynahinch, Co Down
Woodlands, Manchester, Greater Manchester
Woodmans Arms Auberge, Hastingleigh, Kent
Woods, Grayshot, Hampshire
Woody And Dutch, Manchester, Greater Manchester
Workhouse, Rhayader, Powys
Y Bistro, Llanberis, Gwynedd
Yang Sing, Manchester, Greater Manchester
Ye Olde Bulls Head Inn, Beaumaris, Gwynedd
Ynyshir Hall, Machynlleth, Powys
Yung's, London W1
Zamoyski's, London NW3
Zazou, London W1
Zen, London SW3
Zen, London W1
Zen, London NW3

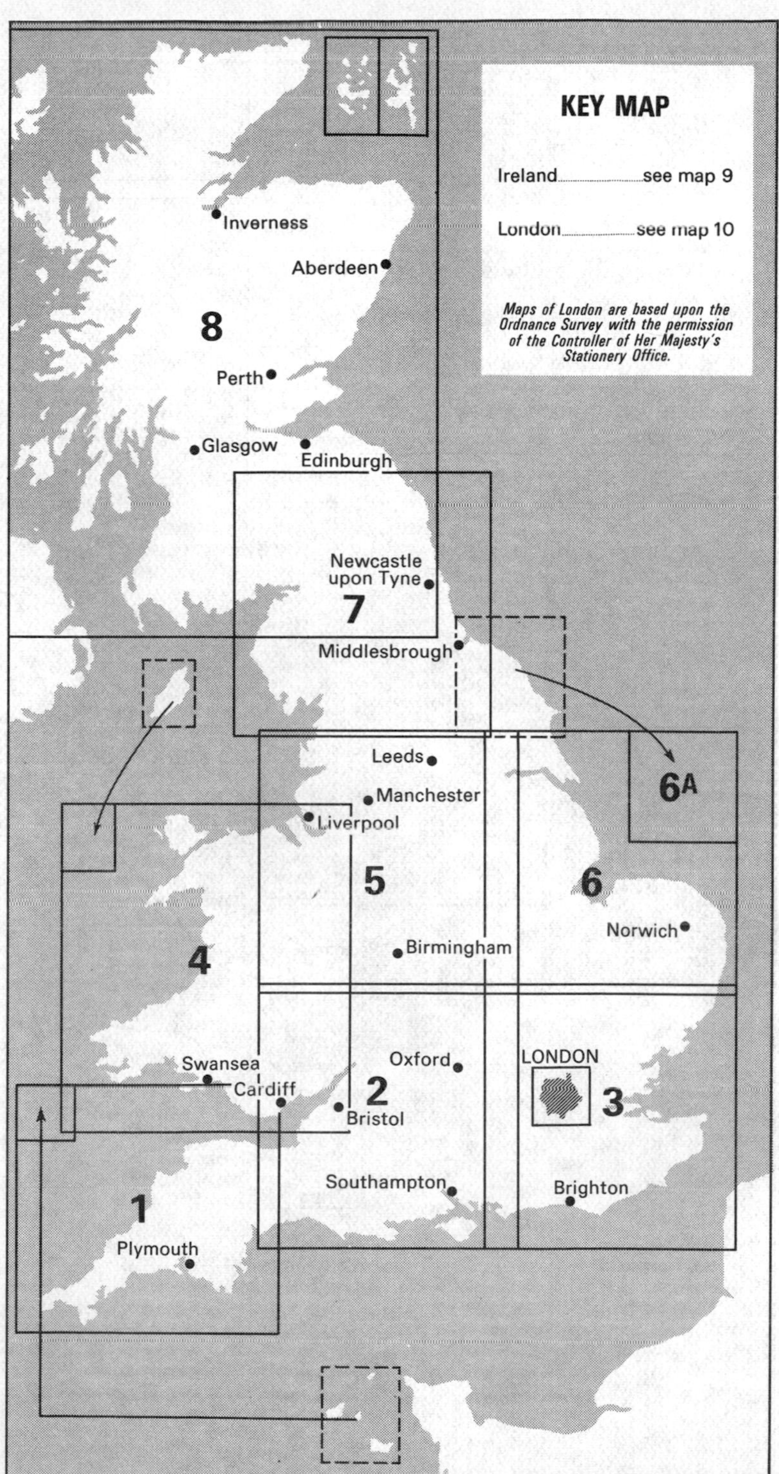
KEY MAP
Ireland..........see map 9
London..........see map 10
Maps of London are based upon the Ordnance Survey with the permission of the Controller of Her Majesty's Stationery Office.
Inverness
Aberdeen
8
Perth
Glasgow
Edinburgh
Newcastle upon Tyne
7
Middlesbrough
Leeds
Manchester
Liverpool
6A
5
6
Norwich
4
Birmingham
Swansea
Oxford
LONDON
Cardiff
2
3
Bristol
Southampton
Brighton
1
Plymouth

Cartographic Services (Cirencester) Ltd

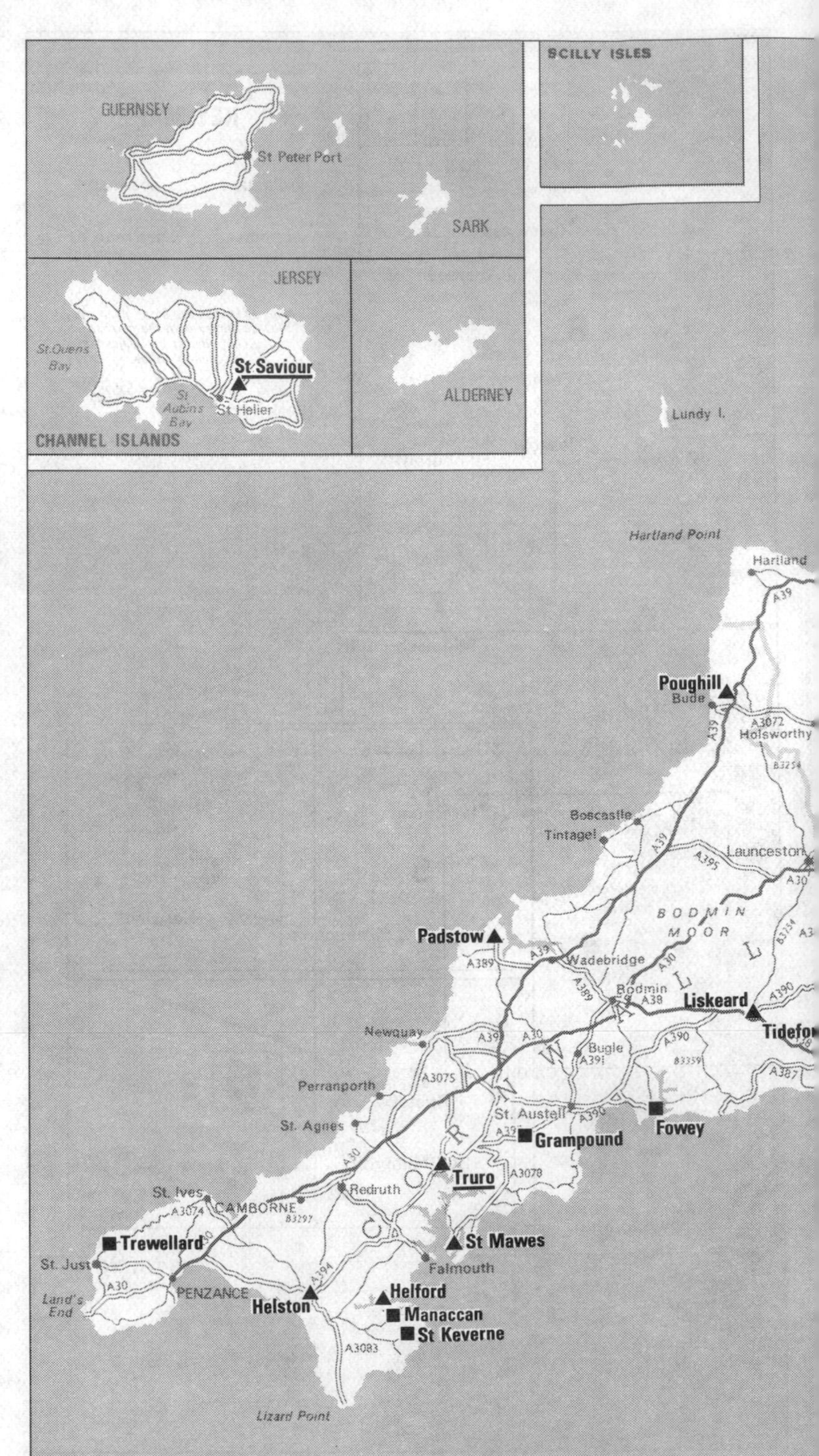

SCILLY ISLES
GUERNSEY
St Peter Port
SARK
JERSEY
St.Ouens Bay
St Saviour
St Aubins Bay
St Helier
ALDERNEY
CHANNEL ISLANDS
Lundy I.
Hartland Point
Hartland
Poughill
Bude
Holsworthy
Boscastle
Tintagel
Launceston
BODMIN MOOR
Padstow
Wadebridge
Bodmin
Liskeard
Newquay
Bugle
Perranporth
St. Agnes
St. Austell
Grampound
Fowey
Truro
St. Ives
CAMBORNE
Redruth
Trewellard
St Mawes
St. Just
Falmouth
PENZANCE
Land's End
Helston
Helford
Manaccan
St Keverne
Lizard Point
CORNWALL

1

DEVON and CORNWALL

CHANNEL ISLANDS

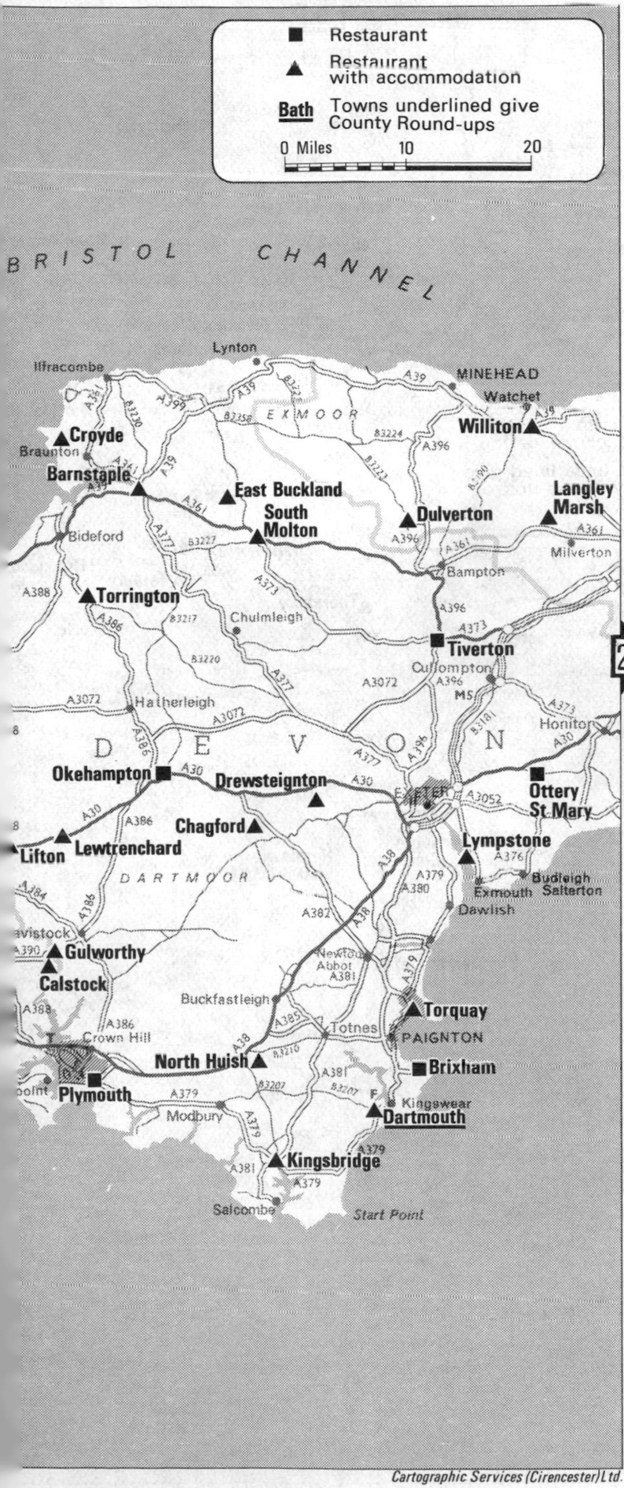

Cartographic Services (Cirencester) Ltd.

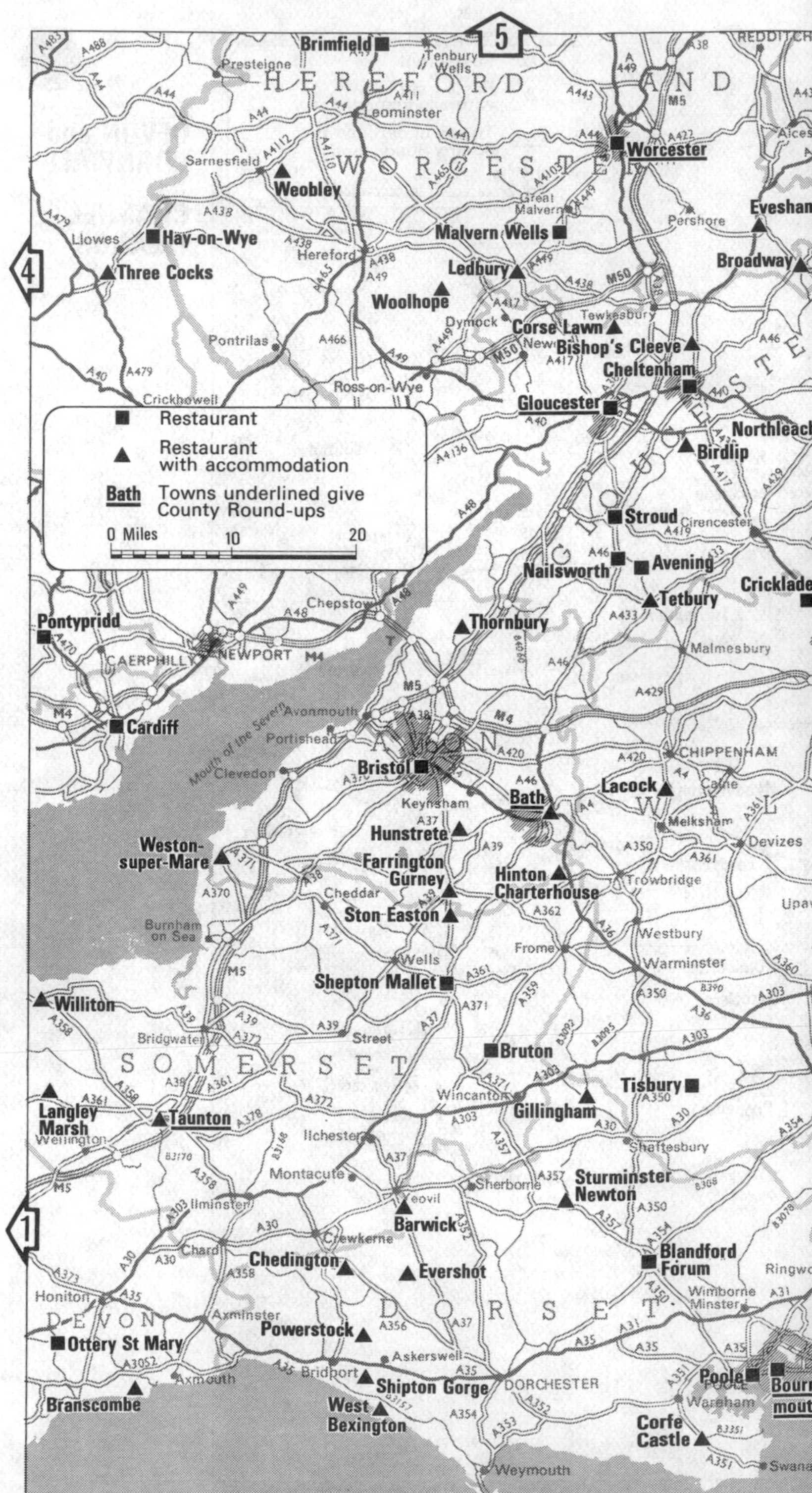

5
4
1
Restaurant
Restaurant with accommodation
Bath
Towns underlined give County Round-ups
0 Miles
10
20
HEREFORD AND WORCESTER
GLOUCESTERSHIRE
AVON
WILTSHIRE
SOMERSET
DORSET
DEVON
Brimfield
Presteigne
Tenbury Wells
Leominster
Sarnesfield
Weobley
Worcester
Evesham
Broadway
Hay-on-Wye
Llowes
Three Cocks
Hereford
Malvern Wells
Great Malvern
Pershore
Ledbury
Woolhope
Tewkesbury
Dymock
Corse Lawn
Bishop's Cleeve
Pontrilas
Ross-on-Wye
Crickhowell
Cheltenham
Gloucester
Northleach
Birdlip
Stroud
Cirencester
Nailsworth
Avening
Tetbury
Cricklade
Chepstow
Pontypridd
Thornbury
CAERPHILLY
NEWPORT
Malmesbury
Cardiff
Avonmouth
Portishead
Mouth of the Severn
Clevedon
Bristol
Keynsham
Bath
CHIPPENHAM
Lacock
Calne
Melksham
Devizes
Hunstrete
Weston-super-Mare
Farrington Gurney
Hinton Charterhouse
Trowbridge
Cheddar
Ston Easton
Burnham on Sea
Westbury
Frome
Wells
Warminster
Shepton Mallet
Williton
Bridgwater
Street
Bruton
Tisbury
Wincanton
Gillingham
Langley Marsh
Wellington
Taunton
Ilchester
Shaftesbury
Montacute
Sherborne
Sturminster Newton
Ilminster
Yeovil
Barwick
Chard
Crewkerne
Blandford Forum
Chedington
Evershot
Ringwood
Honiton
Axminster
Wimborne Minster
Ottery St Mary
Powerstock
Askerswell
Poole
Bournemouth
Axmouth
Bridport
Shipton Gorge
DORCHESTER
Wareham
Branscombe
West Bexington
Corfe Castle
Weymouth
Swanage
Fortuneswell
REDDITCH
Alcester
Upavon
M4
M5
M50

ENGLAND: SOUTH WEST

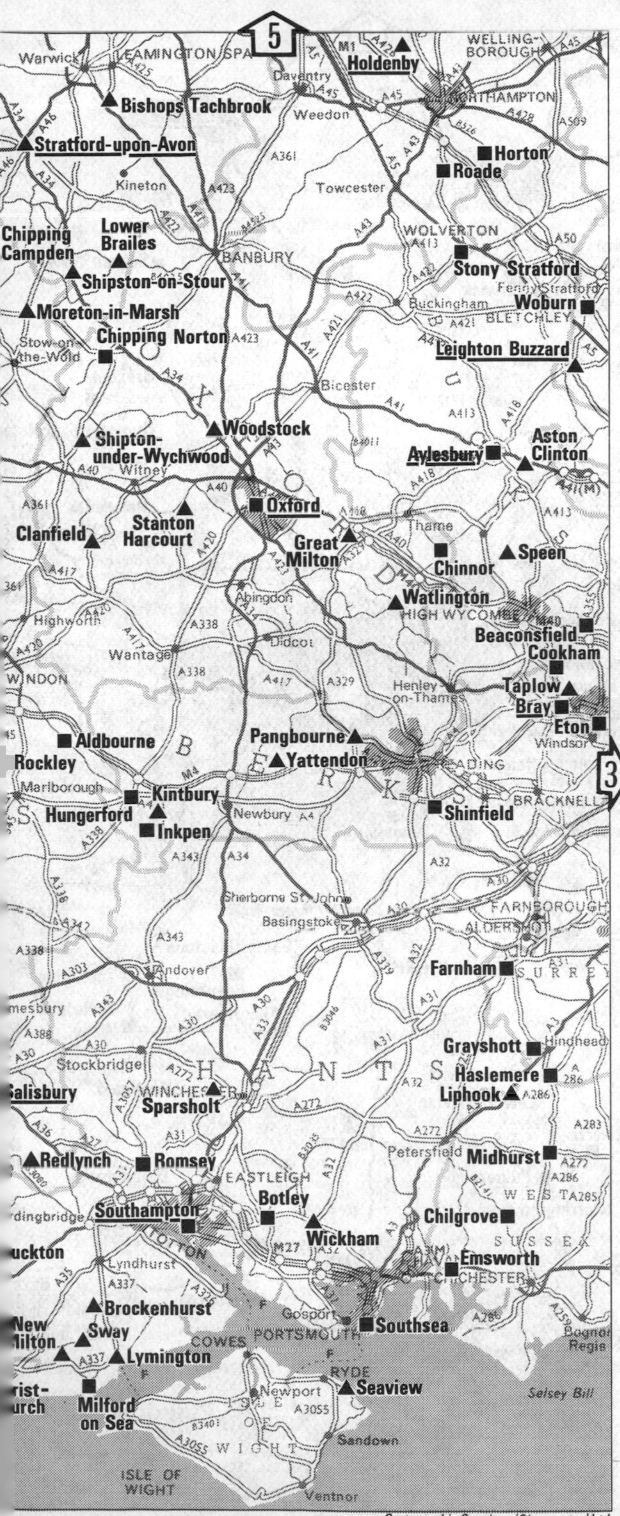

Cartographic Services (Cirencester) Ltd.

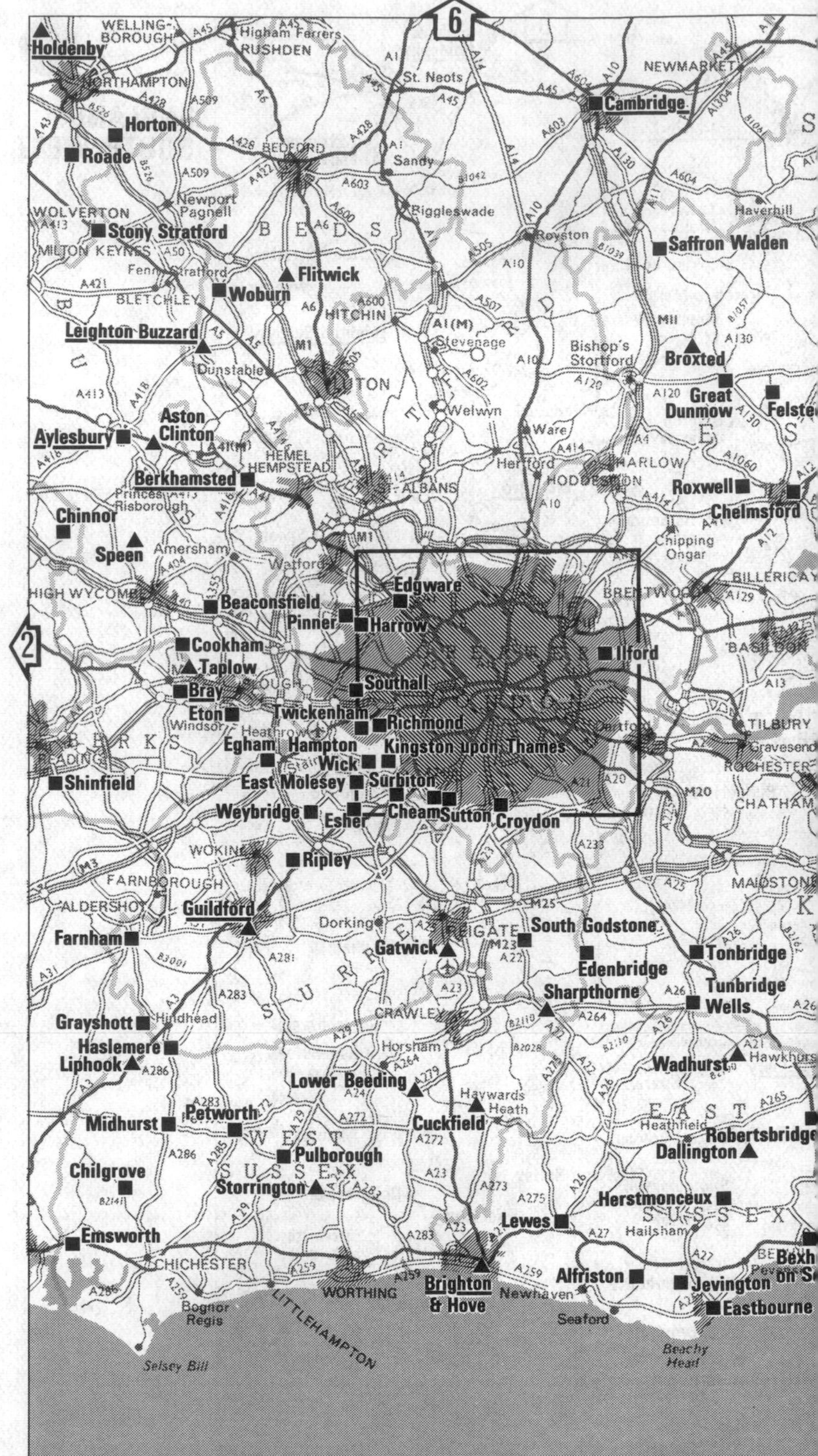

6
2
Holdenby
WELLINGBOROUGH
Higham Ferrers
RUSHDEN
NORTHAMPTON
St. Neots
NEWMARKET
Cambridge
Horton
Roade
BEDFORD
Sandy
Biggleswade
Haverhill
WOLVERTON
Newport Pagnell
Stony Stratford
MILTON KEYNES
B E D S
Royston
Saffron Walden
Fenny Stratford
Flitwick
BLETCHLEY
Woburn
HITCHIN
Leighton Buzzard
Stevenage
Bishop's Stortford
Broxted
Dunstable
LUTON
Great Dunmow
Felste
Welwyn
Aston Clinton
Aylesbury
Ware
HEMEL HEMPSTEAD
Hertford
HARLOW
Berkhamsted
Princes Risborough
ST. ALBANS
HODDESDON
Roxwell
Chelmsford
Chinnor
Speen
Amersham
Chipping Ongar
Watford
Edgware
BILLERICAY
HIGH WYCOMBE
BRENTWOOD
Beaconsfield
Pinner
Harrow
Cookham
Ilford
BASILDON
Taplow
Southall
Bray
Eton
Twickenham
Richmond
Windsor
Heathrow
TILBURY
B E R K S
Egham
Hampton
Kingston upon Thames
Gravesend
READING
Wick
ROCHESTER
Shinfield
East Molesey
Surbiton
CHATHAM
Weybridge
Esher
Cheam
Sutton
Croydon
WOKING
Ripley
FARNBOROUGH
MAIDSTONE
ALDERSHOT
Guildford
Dorking
REIGATE
South Godstone
Farnham
Gatwick
Edenbridge
Tonbridge
Tunbridge Wells
Sharpthorne
CRAWLEY
Grayshott
Hindhead
Haslemere
Liphook
Horsham
Wadhurst
Hawkhurst
Lower Beeding
Haywards Heath
Midhurst
Petworth
Cuckfield
E A S T
Heathfield
Robertsbridge
W E S T
Dallington
Pulborough
Chilgrove
S U S S E X
Storrington
Herstmonceux
Lewes
Hailsham
Emsworth
CHICHESTER
Alfriston
Jevington
Bexhill on Sea
WORTHING
Brighton & Hove
Newhaven
Eastbourne
Bognor Regis
LITTLEHAMPTON
Seaford
Beachy Head
Selsey Bill

ENGLAND: SOUTH EAST

Cartographic Services (Cirencester) Ltd.

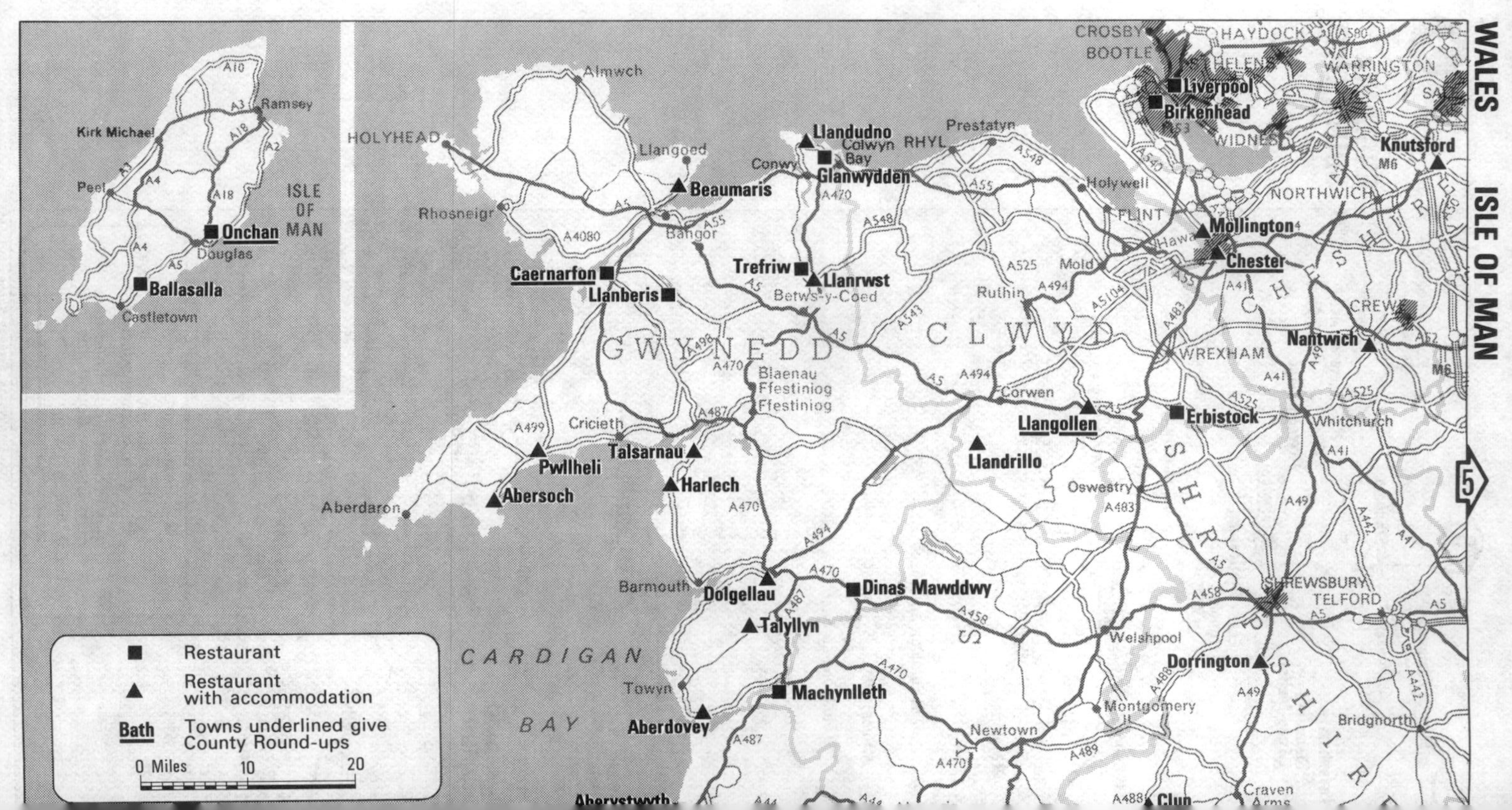
ISLE OF MAN
Ramsey
Kirk Michael
Peel
Onchan
Douglas
Ballasalla
Castletown
HOLYHEAD
Almwch
Llangoed
Rhosneigr
Beaumaris
Bangor
Caernarfon
Llanberis
Llandudno
Colwyn Bay
Conwy
Glanwydden
RHYL
Prestatyn
Holywell
FLINT
Trefriw
Llanrwst
Betws-y-Coed
Mold
Ruthin
CROSBY
BOOTLE
HAYDOCK
WARRINGTON
Liverpool
Birkenhead
WIDNES
NORTHWICH
Knutsford
Mollington
Chester
CREWE
Nantwich
WREXHAM
Whitchurch
Erbistock
GWYNEDD
CLWYD
Blaenau Ffestiniog
Ffestiniog
Corwen
Llangollen
Llandrillo
Oswestry
Cricieth
Talsarnau
Pwllheli
Harlech
Abersoch
Aberdaron
Barmouth
Dolgellau
Dinas Mawddwy
Talyllyn
SHREWSBURY
TELFORD
Welshpool
Dorrington
Towyn
Machynlleth
Aberdovey
Montgomery
Newtown
Bridgnorth
Clun
Craven Arms
CARDIGAN BAY
SHROPSHIRE
Aberystwyth
Restaurant
Restaurant with accommodation
Bath Towns underlined give County Round-ups
0 Miles 10 20

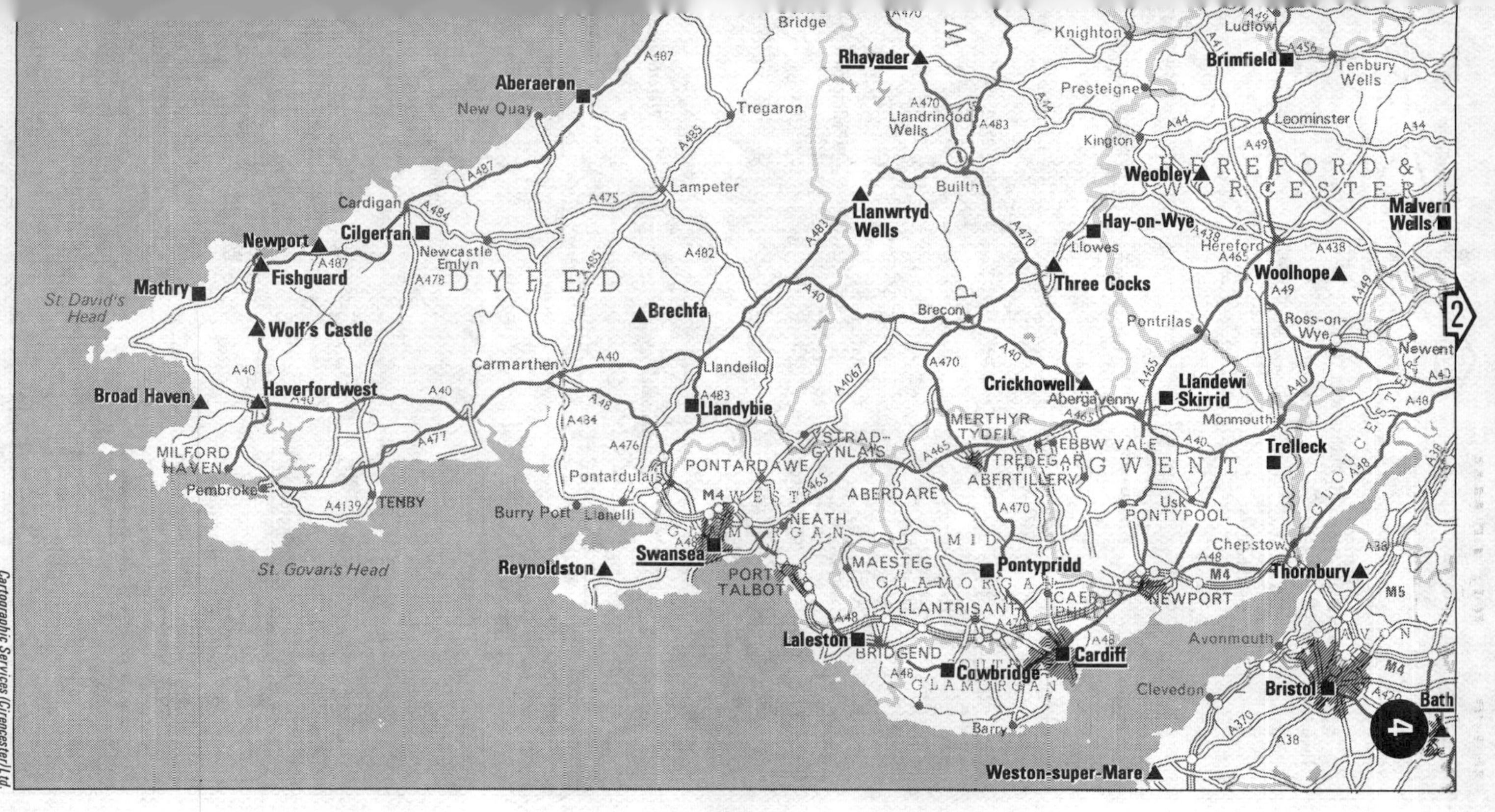

Cartographic Services (Cirencester) Ltd.

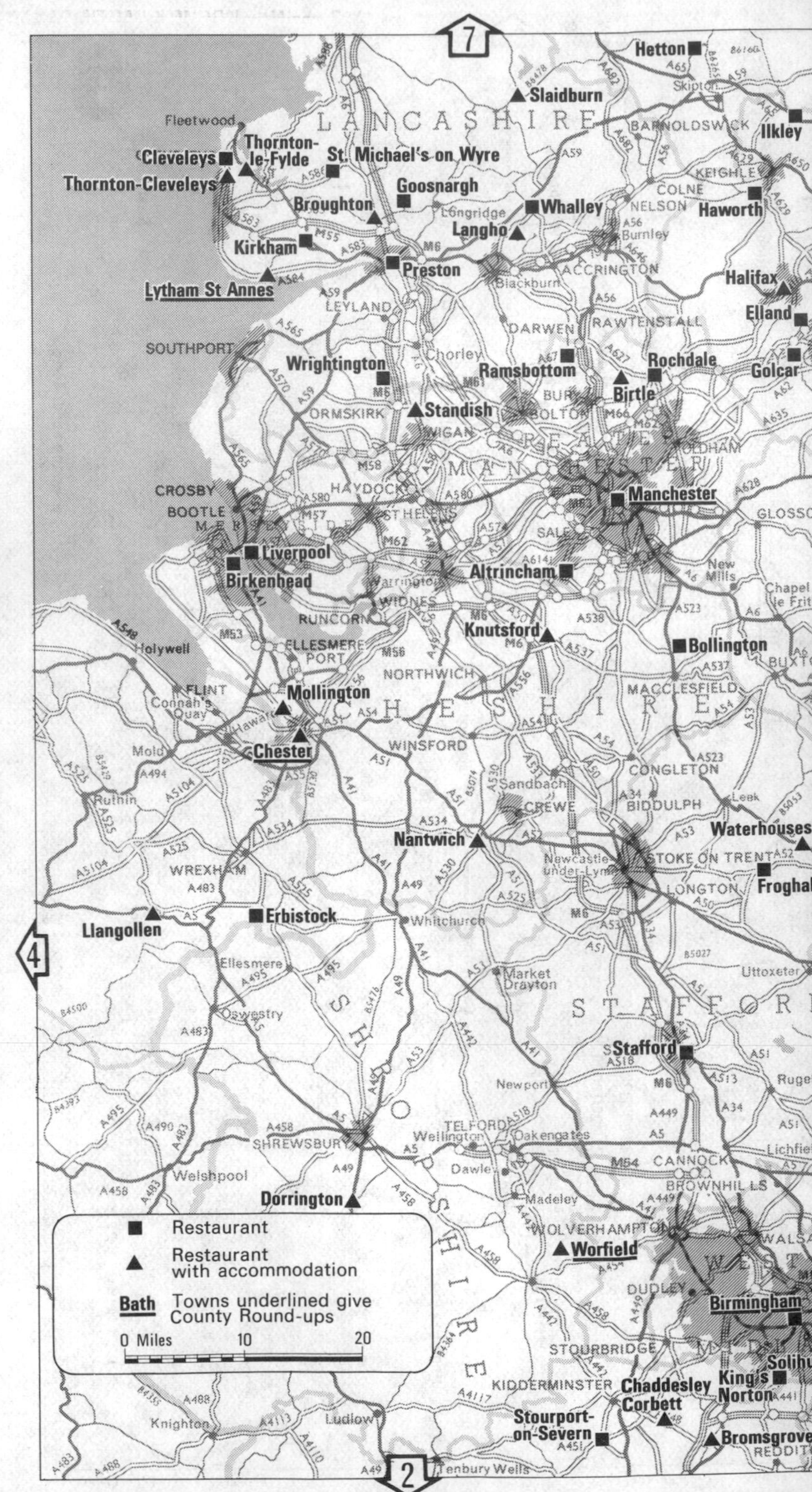

7
4
2
LANCASHIRE
CHESHIRE
STAFFORD
SHROPSHIRE
GREATER MANCHESTER
MERSEYSIDE
Hetton
Slaidburn
Ilkley
Cleveleys
Thornton-le-Fylde
Thornton-Cleveleys
St. Michael's on Wyre
Goosnargh
Broughton
Whalley
Langho
Haworth
Kirkham
Preston
Lytham St Annes
Halifax
Elland
Golcar
Wrightington
Ramsbottom
Rochdale
Birtle
Standish
Manchester
Liverpool
Birkenhead
Altrincham
Knutsford
Bollington
Mollington
Chester
Nantwich
Waterhouses
Froghall
Llangollen
Erbistock
Stafford
Dorrington
Worfield
Birmingham
Solihull
King's Norton
Chaddesley Corbett
Stourport-on-Severn
Bromsgrove
Fleetwood
SOUTHPORT
LEYLAND
ORMSKIRK
WIGAN
CROSBY
BOOTLE
HAYDOCK
ST HELENS
WIDNES
RUNCORN
ELLESMERE PORT
NORTHWICH
WINSFORD
MACCLESFIELD
CONGLETON
BIDDULPH
CREWE
STOKE ON TRENT
LONGTON
WREXHAM
SHREWSBURY
TELFORD
CANNOCK
BROWNHILLS
WOLVERHAMPTON
DUDLEY
STOURBRIDGE
KIDDERMINSTER
Holywell
FLINT
Mold
Ruthin
Oswestry
Welshpool
Knighton
Ludlow
Tenbury Wells
Whitchurch
Market Drayton
Newport
Uttoxeter
Leek
Restaurant
Restaurant with accommodation
Bath
Towns underlined give County Round-ups
0 Miles 10 20

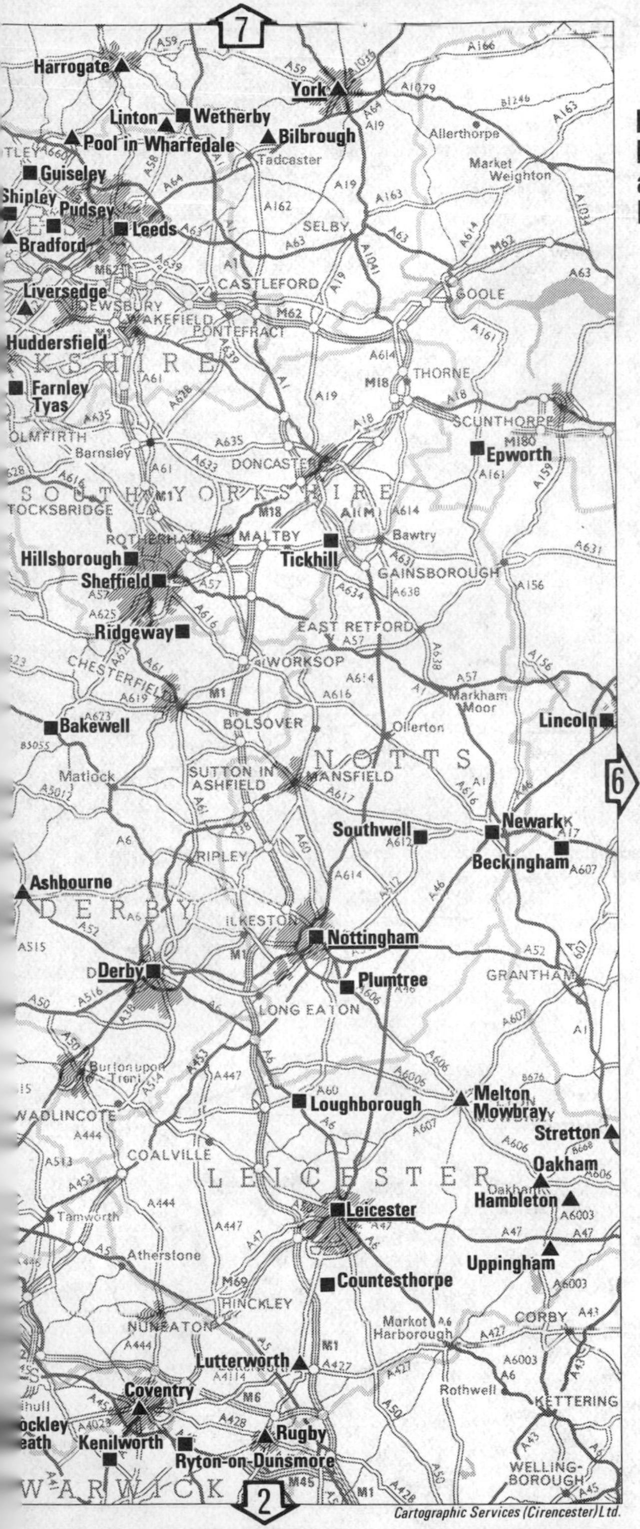

5

ENGLAND: MIDLANDS and NORTH WEST

Cartographic Services (Cirencester) Ltd.

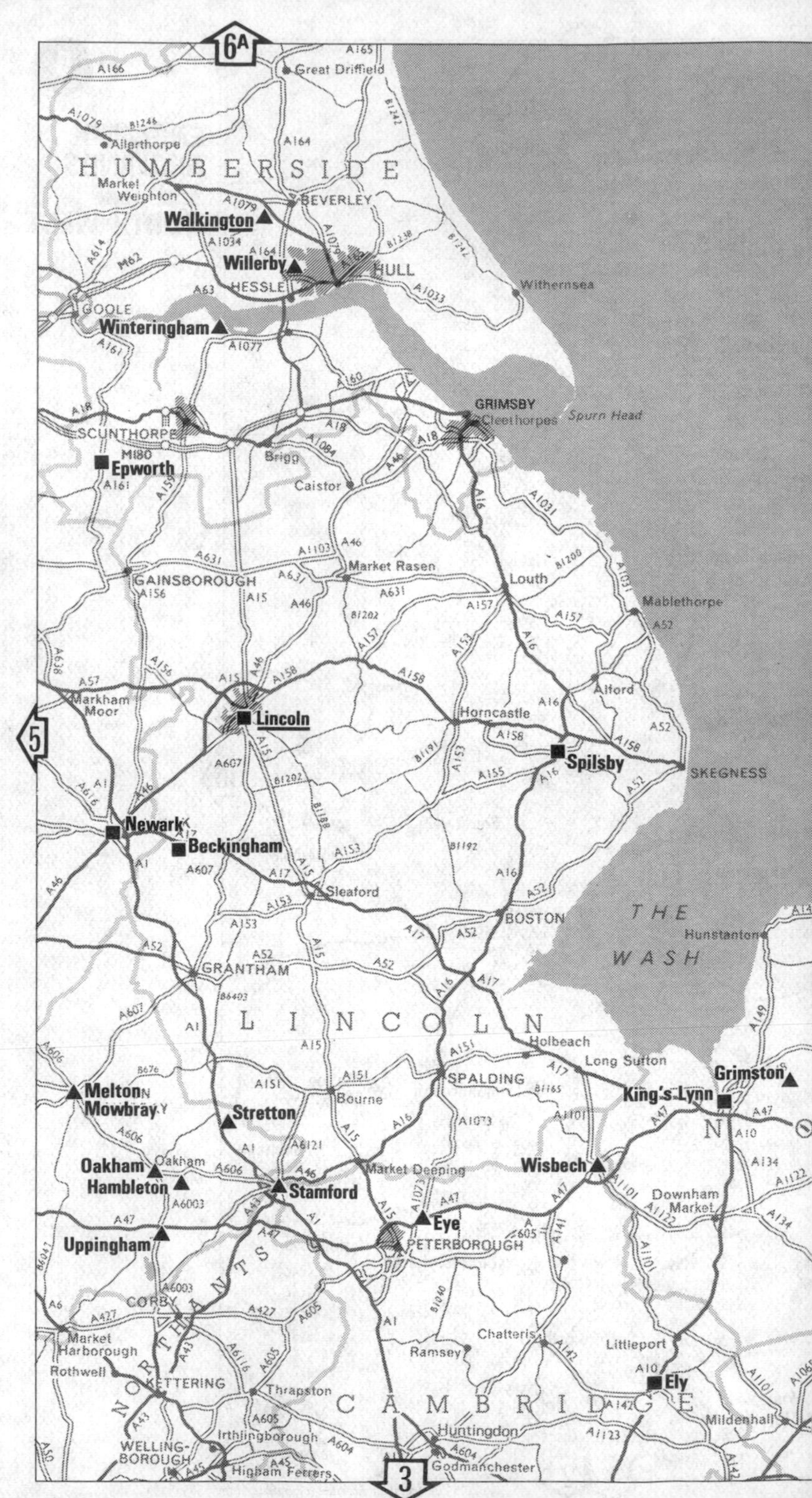

6A
Great Driffield
HUMBERSIDE
Allerthorpe
Market Weighton
BEVERLEY
Walkington
Willerby
HULL
HESSLE
Withernsea
GOOLE
Winteringham
GRIMSBY
Cleethorpes
Spurn Head
SCUNTHORPE
Brigg
Epworth
Caistor
Market Rasen
GAINSBOROUGH
Louth
Mablethorpe
Alford
Markham Moor
5
Lincoln
Horncastle
Spilsby
SKEGNESS
Newark
Beckingham
Sleaford
BOSTON
THE WASH
Hunstanton
GRANTHAM
LINCOLN
Holbeach
Long Sutton
Grimston
SPALDING
King's Lynn
Melton Mowbray
Bourne
Stretton
Oakham
Hambleton
Wisbech
Market Deeping
Stamford
Downham Market
Eye
Uppingham
PETERBOROUGH
NORTHANTS
CORBY
Market Harborough
Chatteris
Ramsey
Littleport
Rothwell
KETTERING
Thrapston
Ely
CAMBRIDGE
Mildenhall
Huntingdon
WELLINGBOROUGH
Irthlingborough
Godmanchester
Higham Ferrers
3

ENGLAND: EAST

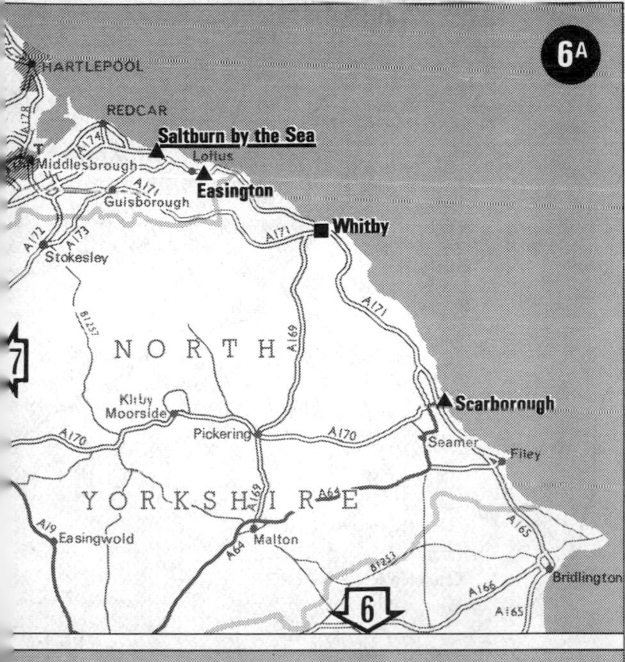

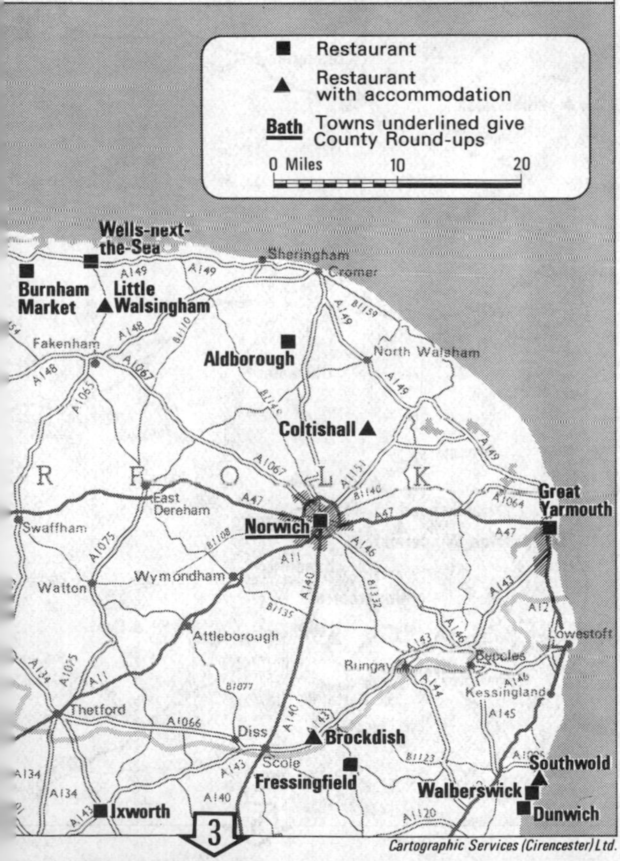

Restaurant

Restaurant with accommodation

Bath Towns underlined give County Round-ups

0 Miles 10 20

Wells-next-the-Sea
Burnham Market
Little Walsingham
Sheringham
Cromer
Fakenham
Aldborough
North Walsham
Coltishall
NORFOLK
East Dereham
Swaffham
Norwich
Great Yarmouth
Wymondham
Watton
Attleborough
Lowestoft
Bungay
Beccles
Kessingland
Thetford
Diss
Brockdish
Scole
Fressingfield
Southwold
Walberswick
Dunwich
Ixworth
3

Cartographic Services (Cirencester) Ltd.

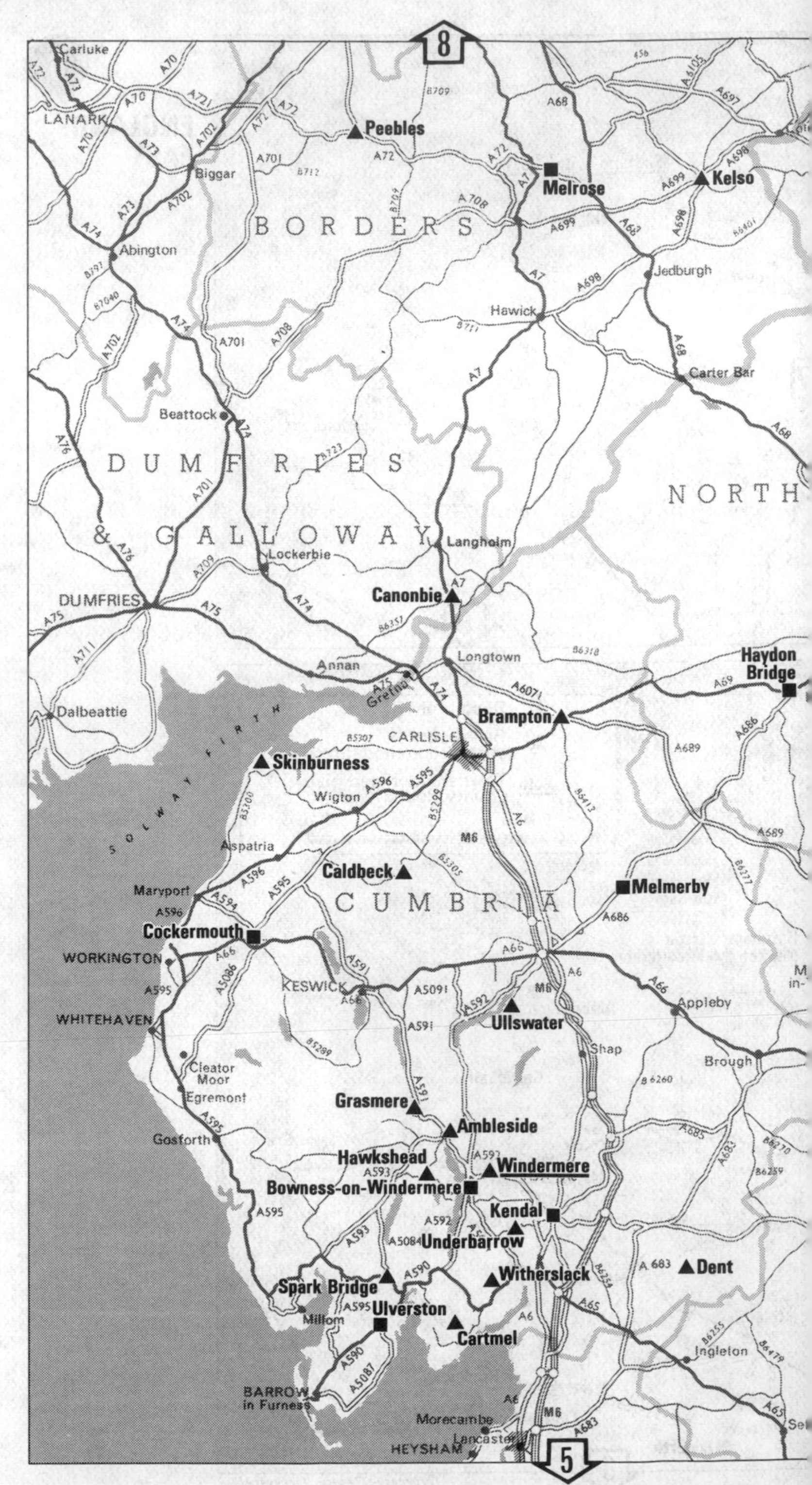

8
Carluke
LANARK
Biggar
Abington
Peebles
Melrose
Kelso
BORDERS
Jedburgh
Hawick
Carter Bar
Beattock
DUMFRIES
& GALLOWAY
NORTH
Lockerbie
Langholm
Canonbie
DUMFRIES
Annan
Gretna
Longtown
Haydon Bridge
Dalbeattie
Brampton
CARLISLE
Skinburness
SOLWAY FIRTH
Wigton
Aspatria
Caldbeck
Melmerby
Maryport
CUMBRIA
Cockermouth
WORKINGTON
KESWICK
Appleby
WHITEHAVEN
Ullswater
Shap
Cleator Moor
Egremont
Brough
Grasmere
Ambleside
Gosforth
Hawkshead
Windermere
Bowness-on-Windermere
Kendal
Underbarrow
Dent
Witherslack
Spark Bridge
Ulverston
Millom
Cartmel
Ingleton
BARROW in Furness
Morecambe
Lancaster
HEYSHAM
5
A70
A73
A72
A721
A702
A701
A74
A708
A7
A68
A697
A6105
A698
A699
A76
A709
A75
A711
A6071
A69
A686
A689
A596
A595
A594
A66
A5086
A591
A5091
A592
A6
M6
A593
A5084
A590
A5087
A65
A683
A685
B6260

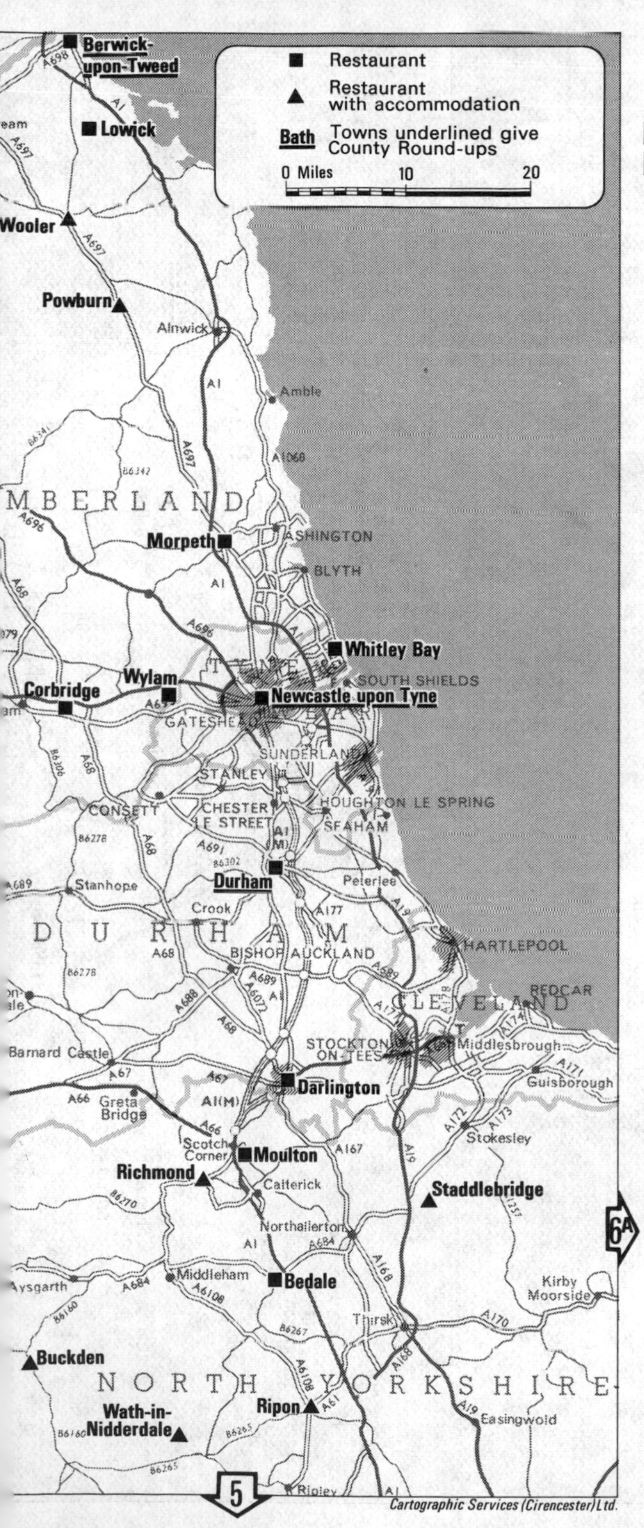

ENGLAND: NORTH

SCOTLAND

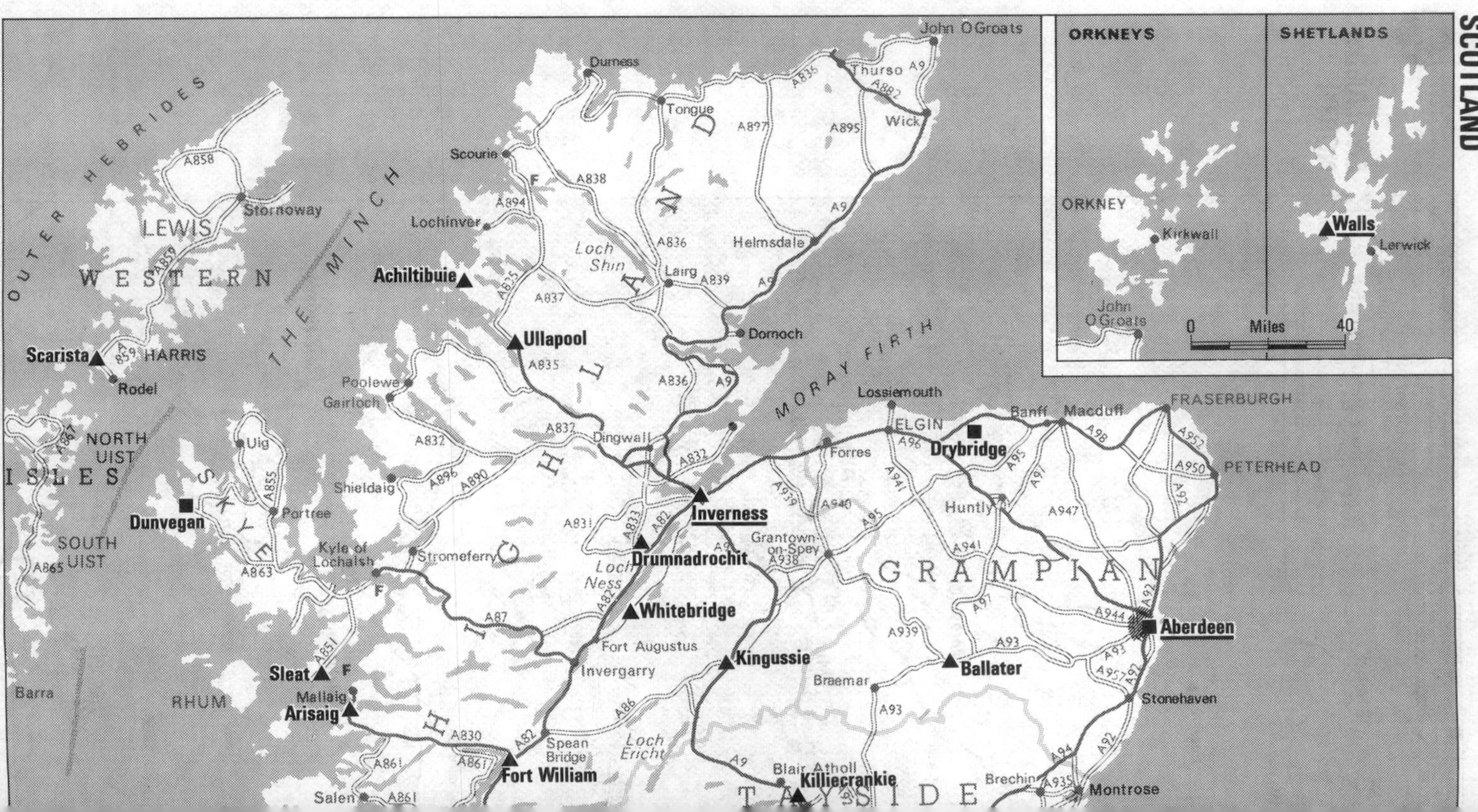

ORKNEYS
SHETLANDS
ORKNEY
Kirkwall
John O Groats
Walls
Lerwick
Miles
0
40
FRASERBURGH
PETERHEAD
Aberdeen
Stonehaven
Montrose
Brechin
Banff
Macduff
Drybridge
Huntly
Ballater
ELGIN
Lossiemouth
Forres
Grantown-on-Spey
Braemar
Blair Atholl
Killiecrankie
Kingussie
Inverness
Drumnadrochit
Whitebridge
Fort Augustus
Invergarry
Loch Ness
Loch Ericht
Spean Bridge
Fort William
Dingwall
Ullapool
Loch Shin
Lairg
Tongue
Durness
Thurso
Wick
Helmsdale
Dornoch
MORAY FIRTH
Scourie
Lochinver
Achiltibuie
Poolewe
Gairloch
Shieldaig
Stromeferry
Kyle of Lochalsh
Mallaig
Arisaig
Sleat
Salen
Portree
Uig
Dunvegan
SKYE
RHUM
THE MINCH
Stornoway
LEWIS
HARRIS
Rodel
Scarista
NORTH UIST
SOUTH UIST
Barra
WESTERN ISLES
OUTER HEBRIDES
HIGHLAND
GRAMPIAN
TAYSIDE

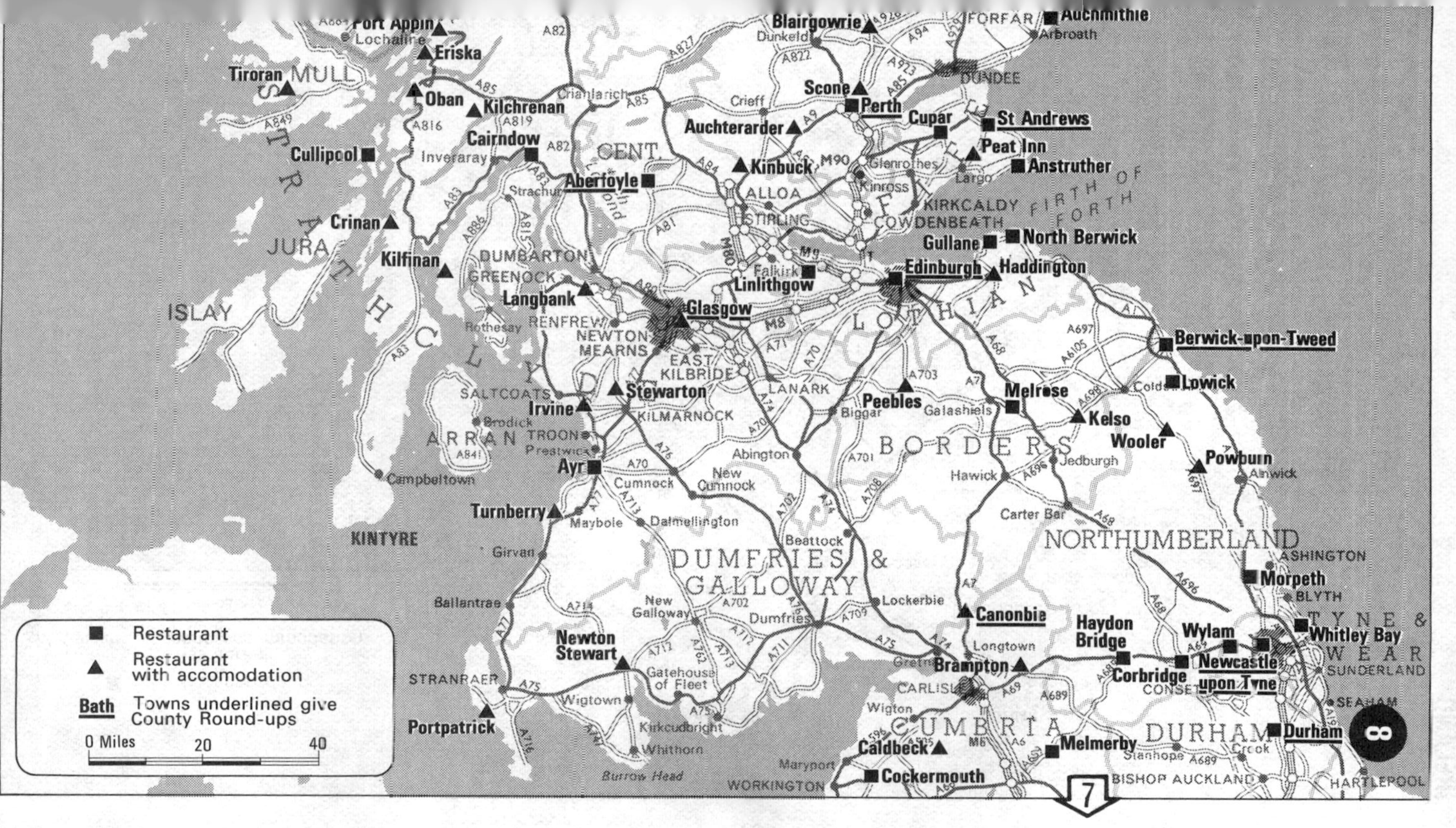
8
Port Appin
Lochaline
Eriska
Tiroran
MULL
Oban
Kilchrenan
Cairndow
Inveraray
Cullipool
Crinan
JURA
Kilfinan
ISLAY
STRATHCLYDE
Crianlarich
CENT.
Aberfoyle
Strachur
DUMBARTON
GREENOCK
Langbank
RENFREW
Rothesay
NEWTON MEARNS
Glasgow
EAST KILBRIDE
SALTCOATS
Stewarton
Irvine
KILMARNOCK
Brodick
ARRAN
TROON
Prestwick
Ayr
Campbeltown
Cumnock
New Cumnock
Turnberry
Maybole
Dalmellington
KINTYRE
Girvan
Ballantrae
New Galloway
Newton Stewart
STRANRAER
Gatehouse of Fleet
Wigtown
Portpatrick
Kirkcudbright
Whithorn
Burrow Head
Blairgowrie
Dunkeld
Crieff
Scone
Perth
Auchterarder
Kinbuck
ALLOA
STIRLING
Falkirk
Linlithgow
Glenrothes
Kinross
FORFAR
Auchmithie
Arbroath
DUNDEE
Cupar
St Andrews
Peat Inn
Anstruther
Largo
FIFE
KIRKCALDY
COWDENBEATH
FIRTH OF FORTH
North Berwick
Gullane
Edinburgh
Haddington
LOTHIAN
LANARK
Peebles
Biggar
Abington
Galashiels
Melrose
Kelso
BORDERS
Hawick
Jedburgh
Carter Bar
Berwick-upon-Tweed
Lowick
Coldstream
Wooler
Powburn
Alnwick
DUMFRIES & GALLOWAY
Beattock
Lockerbie
Dumfries
Canonbie
Longtown
Brampton
CARLISLE
Wigton
CUMBRIA
Caldbeck
Cockermouth
Maryport
WORKINGTON
Melmerby
NORTHUMBERLAND
ASHINGTON
Morpeth
BLYTH
Haydon Bridge
Corbridge
Wylam
Newcastle upon Tyne
Whitley Bay
TYNE & WEAR
SUNDERLAND
SEAHAM
CONSETT
DURHAM
Durham
Stanhope
Crook
BISHOP AUCKLAND
HARTLEPOOL
7
Restaurant
Restaurant with accomodation
Bath Towns underlined give County Round-ups
0 Miles 20 40
Cartographic Services (Cirencester) Ltd.

IRELAND

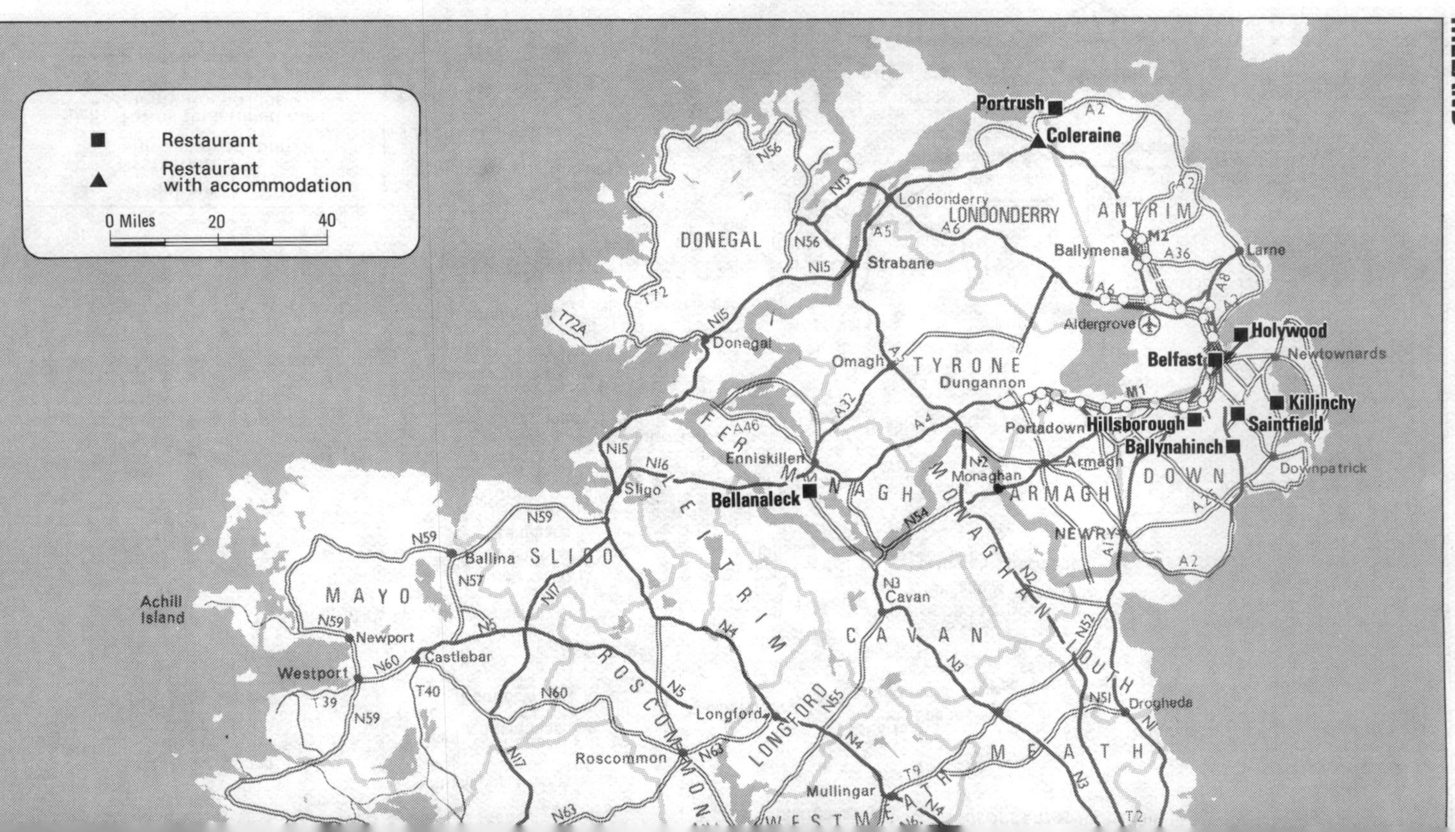

Restaurant
Restaurant with accommodation
0 Miles
20
40
Portrush
Coleraine
Holywood
Killinchy
Saintfield
Belfast
Ballynahinch
Hillsborough
Bellanaleck
Larne
Newtownards
Downpatrick
Ballymena
Aldergrove
Londonderry
Strabane
Omagh
Dungannon
Portadown
Armagh
Monaghan
Newry
Drogheda
Cavan
Enniskillen
Donegal
Sligo
Longford
Mullingar
Roscommon
Ballina
Castlebar
Newport
Westport
Achill Island
ANTRIM
LONDONDERRY
TYRONE
DOWN
ARMAGH
DONEGAL
MONAGHAN
LOUTH
CAVAN
MEATH
LONGFORD
LEITRIM
ROSCOMMON
SLIGO
MAYO

Cartographic Services (Cirencester) Ltd.

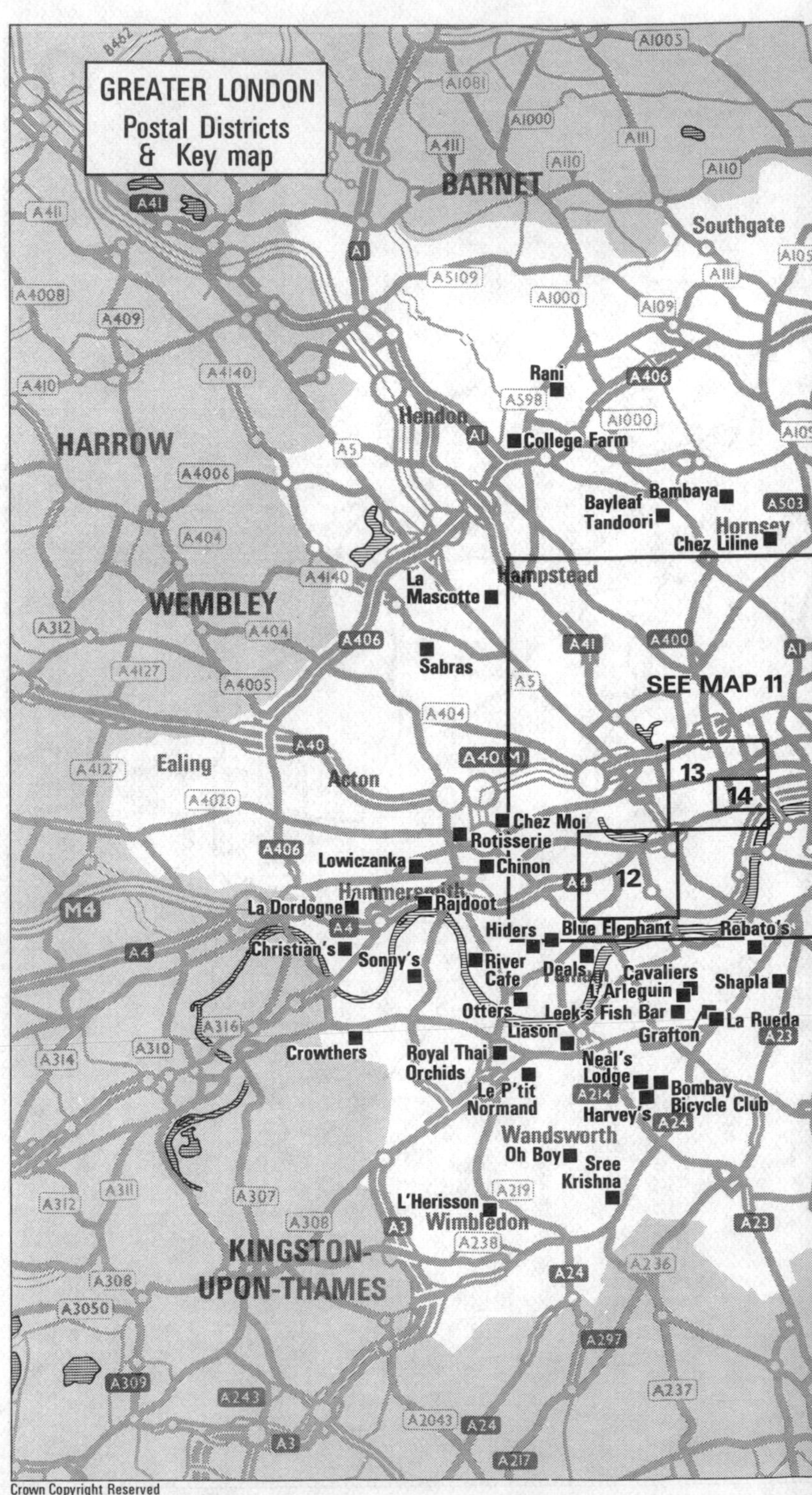
GREATER LONDON
Postal Districts
& Key map
BARNET
Southgate
HARROW
WEMBLEY
Hendon
Rani
College Farm
Bayleaf
Tandoori
Bambaya
Hornsey
Chez Liline
Hampstead
La
Mascotte
Sabras
SEE MAP 11
13
14
12
Ealing
Acton
Chez Moi
Rotisserie
Chinon
Lowiczanka
Hammersmith
La Dordogne
Rajdoot
Christian's
Sonny's
Hiders
Blue Elephant
Rebato's
River
Cafe
Deals
Cavaliers
L'Arlequin
Shapla
Otters
Leek's Fish Bar
La Rueda
Liason
Grafton
Crowthers
Royal Thai
Orchids
Neal's
Lodge
Le P'tit
Normand
Bombay
Bicycle Club
Harvey's
Wandsworth
Oh Boy
Sree
Krishna
L'Herisson
Wimbledon
KINGSTON-
UPON-THAMES

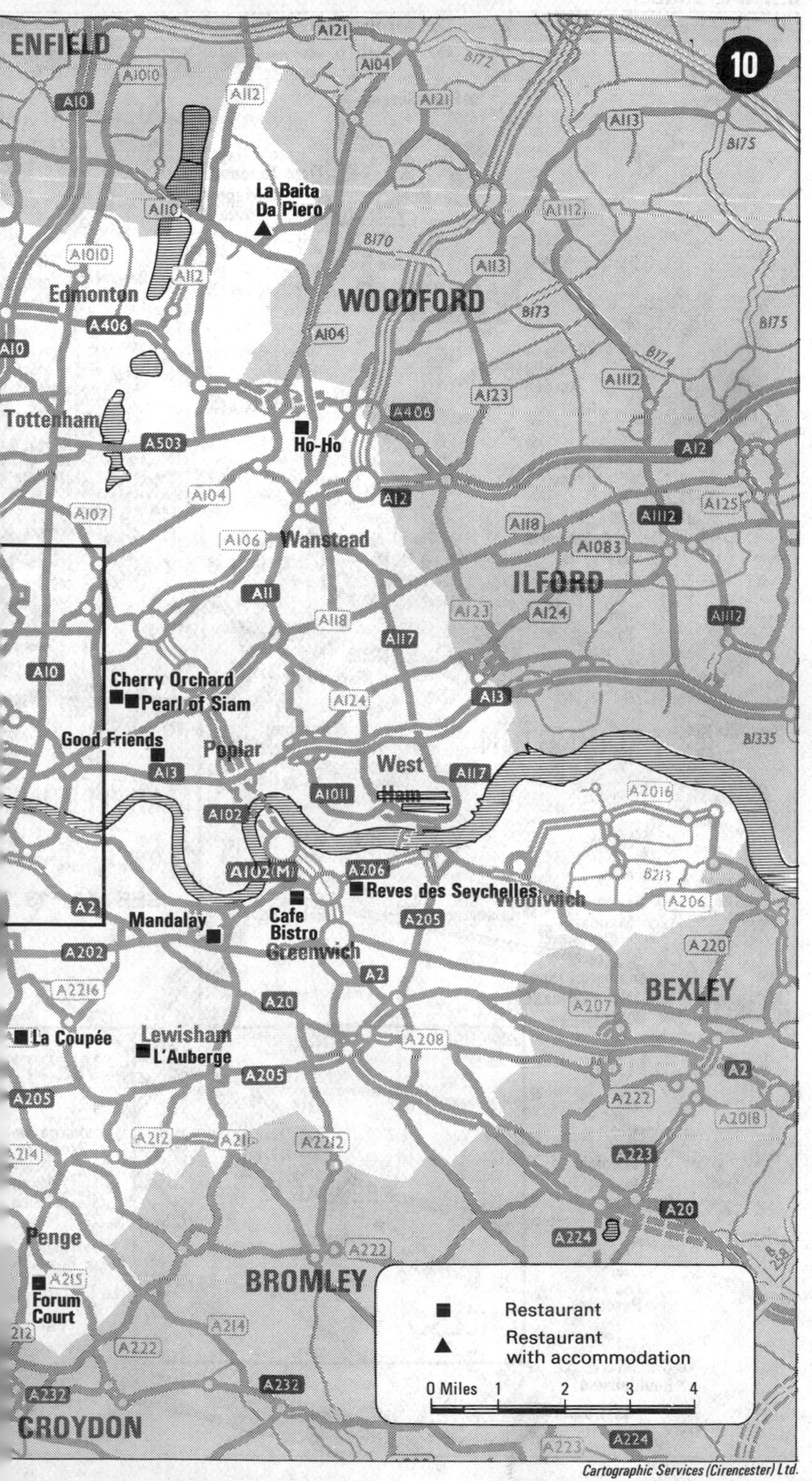

Cartographic Services (Cirencester) Ltd.

Child's Hill
Quincy's
Fortune Green
Hampstead Heath
Rasa Sayang
Keats
Zen W3
Gospel Oak
Fleet Tandoori
Magnums Wine Bar
Zamoyski's
Rosslyn Hill
Cafe Flo
HAMPSTEAD
Wakaba
Bengal Lancer
Kentish Town
Singapore Garden Rest.
Lemonia
Odette's
Primrose Hill
ST. PAN
Daphne
Nontas
Beau-Rivage
Red Sea
L'Aventure
Kilburn
Au Bois St. Jean
Regents Park
Elgin
Maida Vale
Martin's
Kanishka
Seashell
Blue Nile
PADDINGTON
Garbo's
ST. MARYLEBONE
Paddington Sta.
Leith's
Hung Toa
Maroush
Bayswater
Kalamaras
Le Chef
Mandarin Kitchen
SEE MAP 13
Mayfair
Hyde Park
Kensington Place
Lilly's
Boyd's Glass Garden
Malabar
Clarke's
Kingfisher
Kensington Gardens
KENSINGTON
KNIGHTSBRIDGE
WESTM
Auberge de Provence
Phoenicia
Santini
Le Quai St Pierre
SEE MAP 12
Simp
Nico
Ciboure
Seafresh Fish Rest.
Lou Pescadou
Le Mazarin
Pimlico
CHELSEA
La Croisette
Bouillabaise
Left Bank

Cartographic Services (Cirencester) Ltd.

CENTRAL LONDON: South-West

■ Restaurant

▲ Restaurant with accommodation

0 Mile — ¼

Launceston Place

St Quentin

Gilberts

Bombay Brasserie

Bibendum

Hilaire

Les Trois Plats

Chanterelle

Blakes Hotel

Wine Gallery

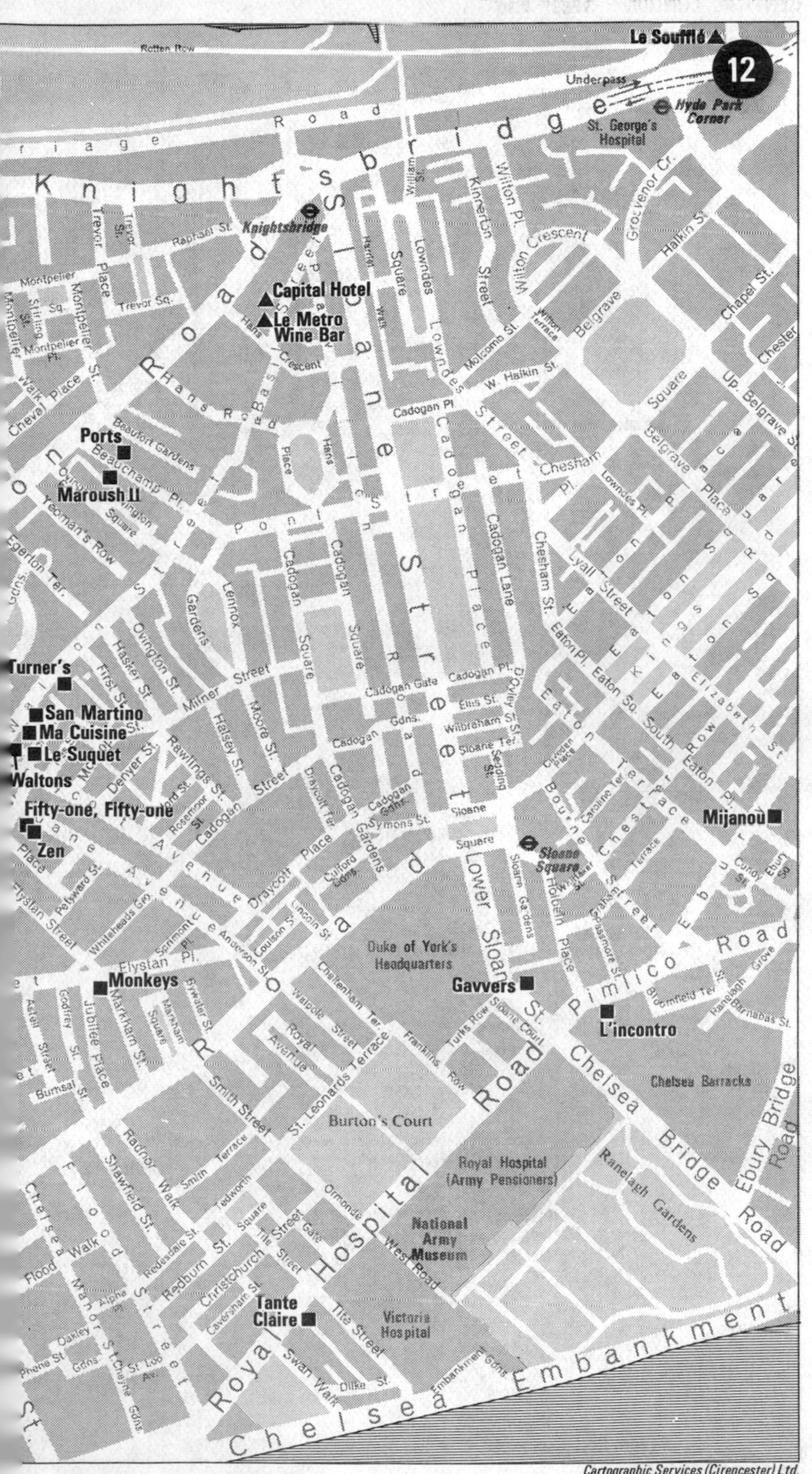

Cartographic Services (Cirencester) Ltd.

CENTRAL LONDON: West End

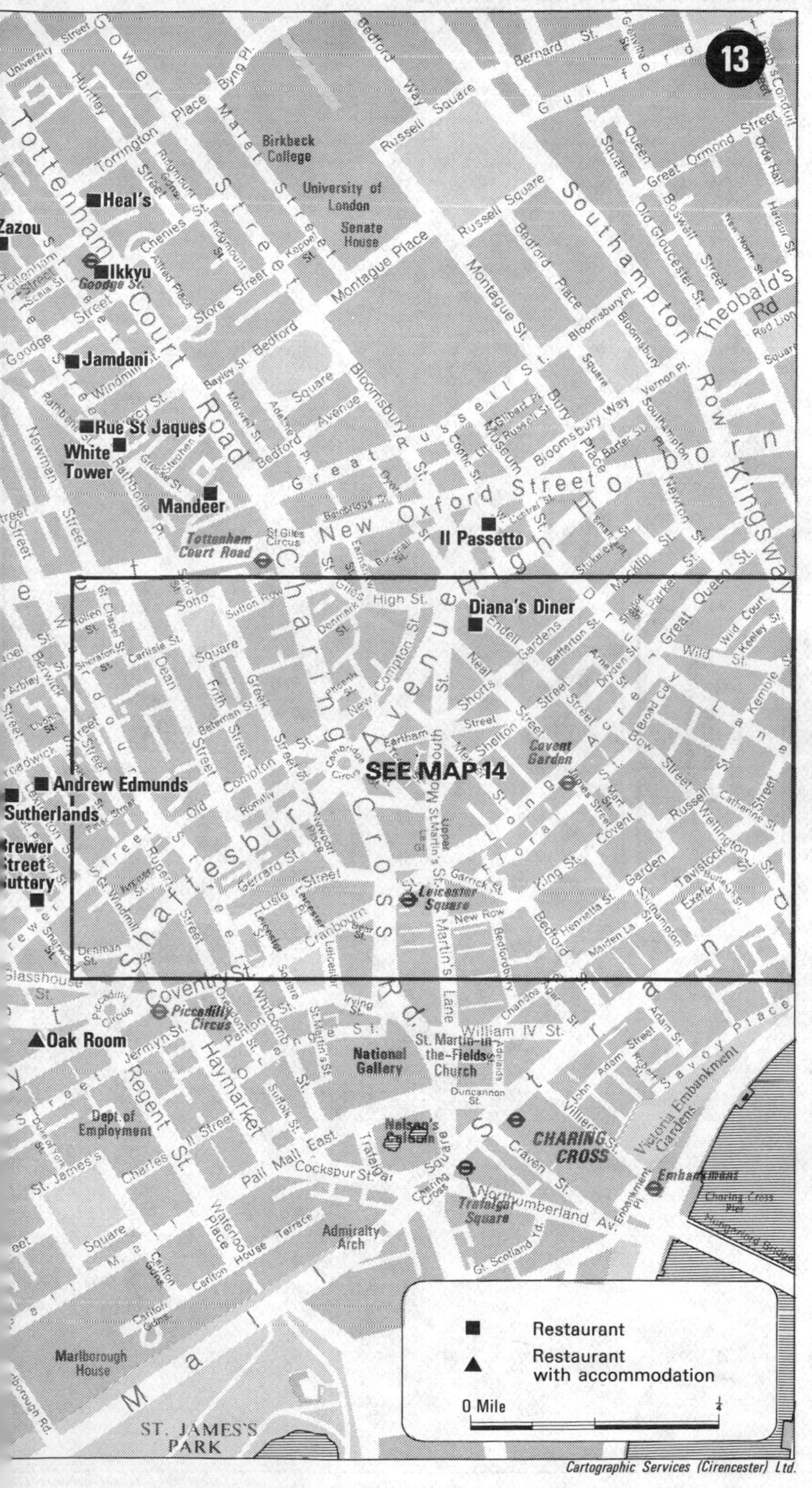

Cartographic Services (Cirencester) Ltd.

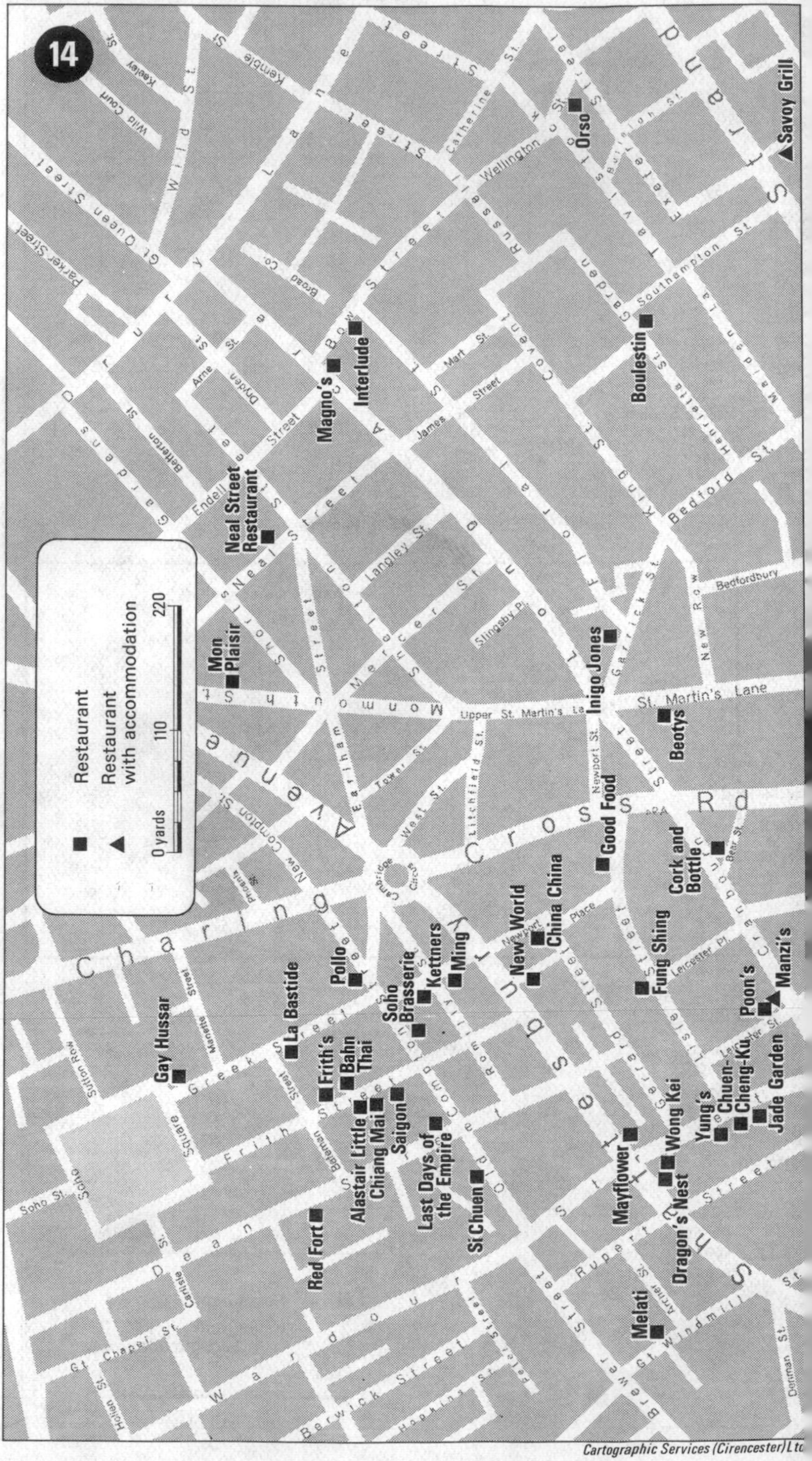

14

■ Restaurant
▲ Restaurant with accommodation

0 yards 110 220

Savoy Grill
Orso
Boulestin
Interlude
Magno's
Neal Street Restaurant
Mon Plaisir
Inigo Jones
Beotys
Good Food
Cork and Bottle
China China
New World
Fung Shing
Manzi's
Poon's
Jade Garden
Cheng-Ku
Chuen-
Yung's
Wong Kei
Dragon's Nest
Mayflower
Melati
Ming
Kettners
Soho Brasserie
Pollo
La Bastide
Gay Hussar
Frith's
Bahn Thai
Alastair Little
Chiang Mai
Saigon
Last Days of the Empire
Si Chuen
Red Fort

Cartographic Services (Cirencester) Ltd

My meal for ___ people cost £ _________ *attach bill where possible*

☐ Please tick if you would like more report forms

I am not connected in any way with management or proprietors.
Name and address (BLOCK CAPITALS)

Signed _________________

Report Form

To the Editor *The Good Food Guide*
FREEPOST, 2 Marylebone Road, London NW1 1YN

From my personal experience the following establishment should/should not be included in the *Guide*.

Telephone____________________

I had lunch/dinner/stayed there on ____________________ 198___

I would rate this establishment _____/20

please continue overleaf

Report Form

To the Editor *The Good Food Guide*
FREEPOST, 2 Marylebone Road, London NW1 1YN

From my personal experience the following establishment should/should not be included in the *Guide*.

____

____

Telephone______________

I had lunch/dinner/stayed there on ______________ 198___

I would rate this establishment _____/20

please continue overleaf

My meal for ____ people cost £ __________ *attach bill where possible*

☐ Please tick if you would like more report forms

I am not connected in any way with management or proprietors.
Name and address (BLOCK CAPITALS)

____

____

Signed ______________________________

Report Form

To the Editor *The Good Food Guide*
FREEPOST, 2 Marylebone Road, London NW1 1YN

From my personal experience the following establishment should/should not be included in the *Guide*.

____

____

Telephone__________________

I had lunch/dinner/stayed there on __________________ 198___

I would rate this establishment ____/20

please continue overleaf

My meal for ____ people cost £ __________ *attach bill where possible*

☐ Please tick if you would like more report forms

I am not connected in any way with management or proprietors.
Name and address (BLOCK CAPITALS)

Signed ____________________